P9-DFZ-734

Table of Problem-Solving Strategies

Note for users of the two-volume edition:
Volume 1 (pp. 1–541) includes chapters 1–16.
Volume 2 (pp. 542–1027) includes chapters 17–30.

Table of Math Relationship Boxes

Brief Contents

Randall D. Knight • Brian Jones • Stuart Field

College Physics: A Strategic Approach, Technology Update
Volume 1

Derived from College Physics: A Strategic Approach, Technology Update, 2/E

Taken from:
College Physics: A Strategic Approach, Technology Update, Second Edition
by Randall D. Knight, Brian Jones, and Stuart Field

Cover Art: Illustration by Melissa Meinhold.

Taken from:

College Physics: A Strategic Approach, Technology Update, Second Edition
by Randall D. Knight, Brian Jones, and Stuart Field
Copyright © 2013, 2010, 2007 by Pearson Education
Published by Pearson
Boston, Massachusetts 02116

This special edition published in cooperation with Pearson Learning Solutions.

Pearson Learning Solutions, 501 Boylston Street, Suite 900, Boston, MA 02116
A Pearson Education Company
www.pearsoned.com

Printed in the United States of America

1 2 3 4 5 6 7 8 9 10 V092 17 16 15 14 13

000200010271773986

CW

ISBN 10: 1-269-35200-8
ISBN 13: 978-1-269-35200-0

About the Authors

Randy Knight has taught introductory physics for 28 years at Ohio State University and California Polytechnic University, where he is currently Professor of Physics and Director of the Minor in Environmental Studies. Randy received a Ph.D. in physics from the University of California, Berkeley and was a post-doctoral fellow at the Harvard-Smithsonian Center for Astrophysics before joining the faculty at Ohio State University. It was at Ohio that he began to learn about the research in physics education that, many years later, led to *Five Easy Lessons: Strategies for Successful Physics Teaching, Physics for Scientists and Engineers: A Strategic Approach,* and now to this book. Randy's research interests are in the field of lasers and spectroscopy. He also directs the environmental studies program at Cal Poly. When he's not in the classroom or in front of a computer, you can find Randy hiking, sea kayaking, playing the piano, or spending time with his wife Sally and their six cats.

Brian Jones has won several teaching awards at Colorado State University during his 20 years teaching in the Department of Physics. His teaching focus in recent years has been the College Physics class, including writing problems for the MCAT exam and helping students review for this test. Brian is also Director of the *Little Shop of Physics,* the Department's engaging and effective hands-on outreach program, which has merited coverage in publications ranging from the *APS News* to *People* magazine. Brian has been invited to give workshops on techniques of science instruction throughout the United States and internationally, including Belize, Chile, Ethiopia, Azerbaijan, Mexico and Slovenia. Previously, he taught at Waterford Kamhlaba United World College in Mbabane, Swaziland, and Kenyon College in Gambier, Ohio. Brian and his wife Carol have dozens of fruit trees and bushes in their yard, including an apple tree that was propagated from a tree in Isaac Newton's garden, and they have traveled and camped in most of the United States.

Stuart Field has been interested in science and technology his whole life. While in school he built telescopes, electronic circuits, and computers. After attending Stanford University, he earned a Ph.D. at the University of Chicago, where he studied the properties of materials at ultralow temperatures. After completing a postdoctoral position at the Massachusetts Institute of Technology, he held a faculty position at the University of Michigan. Currently at Colorado State University, Stuart teaches a variety of physics courses, including algebra-based introductory physics, and was an early and enthusiastic adopter of Knight's *Physics for Scientists and Engineers.* Stuart maintains an active research program in the area of superconductivity. His hobbies include woodworking; enjoying Colorado's great outdoors; and ice hockey, where he plays goalie for a local team.

Preface to the Instructor

In 2006, we published *College Physics: A Strategic Approach,* a new algebra-based physics textbook for students majoring in the biological and life sciences, architecture, natural resources, and other disciplines. As the first such book built from the ground up on research into how students can more effectively learn physics, it quickly gained widespread critical acclaim from professors and students alike. In this second edition, we build on the research-proven instructional techniques introduced in the first edition and the extensive feedback from thousands of users to take student learning even further.

Objectives

Our primary goals in writing *College Physics: A Strategic Approach* have been:

- To provide students with a textbook that's a more manageable size, less encyclopedic in its coverage, and better designed for learning.
- To integrate proven techniques from physics education research into the classroom in a way that accommodates a range of teaching and learning styles.
- To help students develop both quantitative reasoning skills and solid conceptual understanding, with special focus on concepts well documented to cause learning difficulties.
- To help students develop problem-solving skills and confidence in a systematic manner using explicit and consistent tactics and strategies.
- To motivate students by integrating real-world examples relevant to their majors—especially from biology, sports, medicine, the animal world—and that build upon their everyday experiences.
- To utilize proven techniques of visual instruction and design from educational research and cognitive psychology that improve student learning and retention and address a range of learner styles.

A more complete explanation of these goals and the rationale behind them can be found in Randy Knight's paperback book, *Five Easy Lessons: Strategies for Successful Physics Teaching.* Please request a copy from your local Pearson sales representative if it would be of interest to you (ISBN 978-0-805-38702-5).

FIVE EASY LESSONS
Strategies for Successful Physics Teaching

RANDALL D. KNIGHT

What's New to This Edition

Our goal from the beginning has been a textbook combining the best results from physics education research with inspiring photographs and examples connecting physics to the many fields of study of students taking College Physics. In other words, to provide both the motivation needed and the tools required for students to succeed. Our commitment to this goal is undiminished. At the same time, the extensive feedback we've received from scores of instructors and hundreds of students, as well as our own experiences teaching from the book, have led to numerous changes and improvements to the text, figures, and the end-of-chapter problems. These include:

- New illustrated **Chapter Previews** at the start of each chapter provide visual, hierarchical, and non-technical previews proven to help students organize their thinking and improve their understanding of the upcoming material.

- New **Integrated Examples** at the end of each chapter give students additional help in solving general problems not tied to particular sections. Many integrate material from other chapters.
- New **Part Summary Problems** at the end of each of the seven parts of the book test students' abilities to draw on concepts and techniques from multiple chapters. Most of these are MCAT-style passage problems.
- **More streamlined presentations** throughout the text. Based on extensive feedback, we've pared some topics, reconfigured others, and provided a more readable, student-friendly text.
- **Improved and more varied end-of-chapter problems.** Using data from MasteringPhysics, we have reworked the problem sets to enhance clarity, topic coverage, and variety—adding, in particular, more problems based on real-world situations and more problems using ratio reasoning.

At the front of the book, you'll find an illustrated walkthrough of the new media available in this technology update:

- **Nearly 70 PhET simulations** are linked to the Pearson eText and provided in the Study Area of the MasteringPhysics® website (with icons in the print text). These powerful simulations allow students to interact productively with the physics concepts they are learning.
- **Over 100 QR codes throughout the book** allow students to use a mobile phone to instantly watch an interactive video showing a relevant demonstration or problem-solving strategy:
  - **70 Class Videos** present the most interactive parts of co-author Brian Jones' engaging, dynamic lectures, encouraging student viewers to participate by answering questions throughout.

Class Video

  - **30 Video Tutor Solutions** get students warmed up to solve end-of-chapter problems by providing real-world context and reminders of key conceptual ideas within a representative problem that students work through with co-author Brian Jones.
  - **41 Video Tutor Demonstrations feature "pause-and-predict" demonstrations** actively engage the student in understanding the key conceptual ideas underlying the physics principles.
  - **All of these videos also play directly through links within the Pearson eText** as well as the Study Area within MasteringPhysics.
  Please note: Users must download a QR code reader to their mobile phone. Data and roaming charges may also apply.

The more significant textbook content changes include:

- The treatment of Newton's third law in Chapters 4 and 5 has been better focused on the types of problems that students will be asked to solve.
- Angular position and angular velocity are now developed together in Chapter 6, rather then being divided between Chapters 3 and 6. More emphasis has been given to angular position and angular velocity graphs, emphasizing the analogy with the linear position and velocity graphs of Chapter 2.
- The Chapter 10 presentation of work and energy has been streamlined and clarified. The problem-solving strategy for conservation of energy problems now plays a more prominent role.
- Chapter 11, Using Energy, is now more focused on concrete applications of energy use. All discussions of thermal properties have matter have been moved to Chapter 12, which has been reorganized to emphasize the single theme, "What happens to matter when you heat or cool it?"
- The ordering of topics within Chapters 18 and 19 has been revised. Ray tracing and the thin-lens equation are now paired together in Chapter 18; the pinhole camera and color/dispersion have moved to Chapter 19.

■ Chapter 21 has been significantly rewritten to make the difficult idea of electric potential more concrete and usable.

■ The section on household electricity has been moved from Chapter 23 to Chapter 26. Chapter 23 is now better focused on resistors and capacitors while Chapter 26, AC Circuits, has become a more practical chapter with sections on household electricity and electrical safety.

■ Chapters 28–30 on quantum, atomic, and nuclear physics have been significantly streamlined in the hope that more instructors will be able to teach these important topics.

Textbook Organization

College Physics: A Strategic Approach is a 30-chapter text intended for use in a two-semester course. The textbook is divided into seven parts: Part I: *Force and Motion*, Part II: *Conservation Laws*, Part III: *Properties of Matter*, Part IV: *Oscillations and Waves*, Part V: *Optics*, Part VI: *Electricity and Magnetism*, and Part VII: *Modern Physics*.

Part I covers Newton's laws and their applications. The coverage of two fundamental conserved quantities, momentum and energy, is in Part II, for two reasons. First, the way that problems are solved using conservation laws—comparing an *after* situation to a *before* situation—differs fundamentally from the problem-solving strategies used in Newtonian dynamics. Second, the concept of energy has a significance far beyond mechanical (kinetic and potential) energies. In particular, the key idea in thermodynamics is energy, and moving from the study of energy in Part II into thermal physics in Part III allows the uninterrupted development of this important idea.

Optics (Part V) is covered directly after oscillations and waves (Part IV), but *before* electricity and magnetism (Part VI). Further, we treat wave optics before ray optics. Our motivations for this organization are twofold. First, wave optics is largely just an extension of the general ideas of waves; in a more traditional organization, students will have forgotten much of what they learned about waves by the time they get to wave optics. Second, optics as it is presented in introductory physics makes no use of the properties of electromagnetic fields. The documented difficulties that students have with optics are difficulties with waves, not difficulties with electricity and magnetism. There's little reason other than historical tradition to delay optics. However, the optics chapters are easily deferred until after Part VI for instructors who prefer that ordering of topics.

NEW! Split your text the way you split your course! Create a customized textbook by logging on to www.pearsoncustomlibrary.com where you can select the chapters of *College Physics: A Strategic Approach Technology Update* you use in your course. You may also choose a pre-built table of contents for a traditional split of this text (Chapters 1–16 and Chapters 17–30). The choice is yours!

The Student Workbook

A key component of *College Physics: A Strategic Approach* is the accompanying *Student Workbook*. The workbook bridges the gap between textbook and homework problems by providing students the opportunity to learn and practice skills prior to using those skills in quantitative end-of-chapter problems, much as a musician practices technique separately from performance pieces. The workbook exercises, which are keyed to each section of the textbook, focus on developing specific skills, ranging from identifying forces and drawing free-body diagrams to interpreting field diagrams.

The workbook exercises, which are generally qualitative and/or graphical, draw heavily upon the physics education research literature. The exercises deal with issues known to cause student difficulties and employ techniques that have proven to be effective at overcoming those difficulties. The workbook exercises can be used in-class as part of an active-learning teaching strategy, in recitation sections, or as assigned homework. More information about effective use of the *Student Workbook* can be found in the *Instructor's Guide*.

Available versions: Volume 1 (ISBN 978-0-321-59632-1): Chapters 1–16, and Volume 2 (ISBN 978-0-321-59633-8): Chapters 17–30. A package of both volumes is also available (ISBN 978-0-321-59607-9).

Instructor Supplements

NOTE ► For convenience, all of the following instructor supplements (except for the Instructor Resource DVD) can be downloaded from the "Instructor Area," accessed via the left-hand navigation bar of MasteringPhysics (www.masteringphysics.com). ◄

■ The **Instructor Guide for** *College Physics: A Strategic Approach,* a comprehensive and highly acclaimed resource, provides chapter-by-chapter creative ideas and teaching tips for using *College Physics: A Strategic Approach* in your class. In addition, it contains an extensive review of what has been learned from physics education research, and provides guidelines for using active-learning techniques in your classroom. Instructor Guide chapters are provided in Word and PDF formats, and are also found on the *Instructor Resource DVD*.

■ The **Instructor Solutions Manual,** written by Professor Larry Smith, Snow College; Professor Pawan Kahol, Missouri State University; and Professor Marllin Simon, Auburn University, provides *complete* solutions to all the end-of-chapter questions and problems. All solutions follow the Prepare/Solve/Assess problem-solving strategy used in the textbook for quantitative problems, and Reason/Assess strategy for qualitative ones. The solutions are available by chapter in Word and PDF format, and can also be downloaded from the *Instructor Resource Center* (www.pearsonhighered.com/educator).

■ The cross-platform **Instructor Resource DVD** (ISBN 978-0-321-59628-4) provides invaluable and easy-to-use resources for your class, organized by textbook chapter. The contents include a comprehensive library of more than 220 applets from **ActivPhysics OnLine™,** as well as all figures, photos, tables, and summaries from the textbook in JPEG format. In addition, all the Problem-Solving Strategies, Math Relationships Boxes, Tactics Boxes, and Key Equations are provided in editable Word as well as JPEG format. The **Instructor Guide** is also included as editable Word files, along with pdfs of answers to the **Student Workbook** exercises, and **Lecture Outlines (with Classroom Response System "Clicker" Questions)** in PowerPoint.

■ (MP) **MasteringPhysics®** (www.masteringphysics.com) is the most advanced, educationally effective, and widely used physics homework and tutorial system in the world. Eight years in development, it provides instructors with a library of extensively pre-tested end-of-chapter problems and rich, multipart, multistep tutorials that incorporate a wide variety of answer types, wrong answer feedback, individualized help (comprising hints or simpler sub-problems upon request), all driven by the largest metadatabase of student problem-solving in the world. NSF-sponsored published research (and subsequent studies) show that MasteringPhysics has dramatic educational results. MasteringPhysics allows instructors to build wide-ranging homework assignments of just the right difficulty and length and provides them with efficient tools to analyze in unprecedented detail both class trends and the work of any student.

MasteringPhysics routinely provides instant and individualized feedback and guidance to more than 100,000 students every day. A wide range of tools and support make MasteringPhysics fast and easy for instructors and students to learn to use. Extensive class tests show that by the end of their course, an unprecedented 9 out of 10 students recommend MasteringPhysics as their preferred way to study physics and do homework.

In addition to the textbook's end-of-chapter and new end-of-part problems, MasteringPhysics for *College Physics, Second Edition,* also includes author-selected prebuilt assignments, specific tutorials for all the textbook's Problem-Solving Strategies, Tactics Boxes, and Math Relationship boxes, as well as Reading Quizzes and Test Bank questions for each chapter. For the Technology Update of *College Physics,* MasteringPhysics also now has the following functionalities:

■ **Learning Outcomes:** In addition to being able to create their own learning outcomes to associate with questions in an assignment, professors can now select content that is tagged to a large number of publisher-provided learning outcomes. They can also print or export student results based on learning outcomes for their own use or to incorporate into reports for their administration.

■ **Quizzing and Testing Enhancements:** These include options to hide item titles, add password protection, limit access to completed assignments, and to randomize question order in an assignment.

■ **Math Remediation:** Found within selected tutorials, special links provide just-in-time math help and allow students to brush up on the most important mathematical concepts needed to successfully complete assignments.

This new feature links students directly to math review and practice, helping students make the connection between math and physics.

- **Enhanced End-of-Chapter Problems:** A subset of homework problems now offers additional support such as problem-solving strategy hints, relevant math review and practice, links to the eText, and links to the related Video Tutor Solution.

- The **Test Bank**, prepared by Wayne Anderson, contains more than 2,000 high-quality problems, with a range of multiple-choice, true/false, short-answer, and regular homework-type questions. Test files are provided in both TestGen® (an easy-to-use, fully networkable program for creating and editing quizzes and exams) and Word format, and can also be downloaded from www.pearsonhighered.com/educator.

Student Supplements

- The **Student Solutions Manuals Chapters 1–16** (ISBN 978-0-321-59629-1) and **Chapters 17–30** (ISBN 978-0-321-59630-7), written by Professor Larry Smith, Snow College; Professor Pawan Kahol, Missouri State University; and Marllin Simon, Auburn University, provide *detailed* solutions to more than half of the odd-numbered end-of-chapter problems. Following the problem-solving strategy presented in the text, thorough solutions are provided to carefully illustrate both the qualitative (Reason/Assess) and quantitative (Prepare/Solve/Assess) steps in the problem-solving process.

- **MasteringPhysics®** (www.masteringphysics.com) is a homework, tutorial, and assessment system based on years of research into how students work physics problems and precisely where they need help. Studies show that students who use MasteringPhysics significantly increase their scores compared to handwritten homework. MasteringPhyiscs achieves this improvement by providing students with instantaneous feedback specific to their wrong answers, simpler sub-problems upon request when they get stuck, and partial credit for their method(s). This individualized, 24/7 Socratic tutoring is recommended by 9 out of 10 students to their peers as the most effective and time-efficient way to study.

- **Pearson eText** is available through MasteringPhysics, either automatically when MasteringPhysics is packaged with new books, or available as a purchased upgrade online. Allowing students access to the text wherever they have access to the Internet, Pearson eText comprises the full text, including figures that can be enlarged for better viewing. Within eText, students are also able to pop up definitions and terms to help with vocabulary and the reading of the material. Students can also take notes in eText using the annotation feature at the top of each page.

- Over 100 **Video Tutors** play directly through links within the Pearson eText and the Study Area within MasteringPhysics. See page v for more details.

- **Pearson Tutor Services** (www.pearsontutorservices.com) Each student's subscription to MasteringPhysics also contains complimentary access to Pearson Tutor Services, powered by Smarthinking, Inc. By logging in with their MasteringPhysics ID and password, they will be connected to highly qualified e-instructors™ who provide additional, interactive online tutoring on the major concepts of physics. Some restrictions apply; offer subject to change.

Acknowledgments

We have relied upon conversations with and, especially, the written publications of many members of the physics education community. Those who may recognize their influence include Arnold Arons, Uri Ganiel, Fred Goldberg, Ibrahim Halloun, Richard Hake, David Hestenes, Leonard Jossem, Jill Larkin, Priscilla Laws, John Mallinckrodt, Lillian McDermott, Edward "Joe" Redish, Fred Reif, John Rigden, Rachel Scherr, Bruce Sherwood, David Sokoloff, Ronald Thornton, Sheila Tobias, and Alan Van Heuleven.

We are grateful to Larry Smith, Pawan Kahol, and Marllin Simon for the difficult task of writing the *Instructor Solutions Manuals*; to Jim Andrews for coauthoring the Student Workbook (and literally writing out all its answers, with the assistance of Rebecca L. Sobinovsky); to Wayne Anderson, Jim Andrews, Nancy Beverly, David Cole, Karim Diff, Jim Dove, Marty Gelfand, Kathy Harper, Charlie Hibbard, Robert Lutz, Matt Moelter, Kandiah Manivannan, Ken Robinson, and Cindy Schwarz-Rachmilowitz for their contributions to the end-of-chapter questions and problems; to Charlie Hibbard again for helping with the lecture PowerPoints; to Wayne again for helping with the Test Bank questions; and to Steven Vogel for his careful review of the biological content of many chapters and for helpful suggestions.

We especially want to thank our editor Jim Smith, development editor Alice Houston, project editor Martha Steele, production supervisors Nancy Tabor and Camille Herrera, and all the other staff at Pearson Addison-Wesley for their enthusiasm and hard work on this project. Rose Kernan and the team at Nesbitt Graphics, Inc., copy editor Carol Reitz, and photo researcher Eric Schrader get much credit for making this complex project all come together. In addition to the reviewers and classroom testers listed below, who gave invaluable feedback, we are particularly grateful to Jason Harlow for his close scrutiny of every word, symbol, number, and figure.

Randy Knight: I would like to thank my Cal Poly colleagues, especially Matt Moelter, for many valuable conversations and suggestions. I am endlessly grateful to my wife Sally for her love, encouragement, and patience, and to our many cats for nothing in particular other than being cats.

Brian Jones: I would like to thank my fellow AAPT and PIRA members for their insight and ideas, the creative students

and colleagues who are my partners in the Little Shop of Physics, the students in my College Physics classes who help me become a better teacher, and, most of all, my wife Carol, my best friend and gentlest editor, whose love makes the journey worthwhile.

Stuart Field: I would like to thank my wife Julie and my children, Sam and Ellen, for their love, support, and encouragement.

Reviewers and Classroom Testers

Special thanks go to our second edition review panel: Jim Andrews, Taner Edis, Marty Gelfand, Jason Harlow, Charlie Hibbard, Fred Jarka, Gary Morris, and Bruce Schumm.

Susmita Acharya, *Cardinal Stritch University*
Ugur Akgun, *University of Iowa*
Ralph Alexander, *University of Missouri-Rolla*
Donald Anderson, *Ivy Tech*
Steve Anderson, *Montana Tech*
James Andrews, *Youngstown State University*
Charles Ardary, *Edmond Community College*
Charles Bacon, *Ferris State University*
John Barry, *Houston Community College*
David H. Berman, *University of Northern Iowa*
Phillippe Binder, *University of Hawaii-Hilo*
Richard Bone, *Florida International University*
Jeff Bodart, *Chipola College*
James Borgardt, *Juniata College*
Daniela Bortoletto, *Purdue University*
Don Bowen, *Stephen F. Austin State University*
Asa Bradley, *Spokane Falls Community College*
Elena Brewer, *SUNY at Buffalo*
Dieter Brill, *University of Maryland*
Hauke Busch, *Augusta State University*
Kapila Castoldi, *Oakland University*
Michael Cherney, *Creighton University*
Lee Chow, *University of Central Florida*
Song Chung, *William Paterson University*
Alice Churukian, *Concordia College*
Kristi Concannon, *Kings College*
Teman Cooke, *Georgia Perimeter College at Lawrenceville*
Jesse Cude, *Hartnell College*
Melissa H. Dancy, *University of North Carolina at Charlotte*
Loretta Dauwe, *University of Michigan-Flint*
Mark Davenport, *San Antonio College*
Lawrence Day, *Utica College*
Carlos Delgado, *Community College of Southern Nevada*
David Donovan, *Northern Michigan University*
Archana Dubey, *University of Central Florida*
Andrew Duffy, *Boston University*
Taner Edis, *Truman State University*
Ralph Edwards, *Lurleen B. Wallace Community College*

Steve Ellis, *University of Kentucky*
Paula Engelhardt, *Tennessee Technical University*
Davene Eryes, *North Seattle Community College*
Gerard Fasel, *Pepperdine University*
Luciano Fleischfresser, *OSSM Autry Tech*
Cynthia Galovich, *University of Northern Colorado*
Bertram Gamory, *Monroe Community College*
Delena Gatch, *Georgia Southern University*
Martin Gelfand, *Colorado State University*
Terry Golding, *University of North Texas*
Robert Gramer, *Lake City Community College*
William Gregg, *Louisiana State University*
Paul Gresser, *University of Maryland*
Robert Hagood, *Washtenaw Community College*
Jason Harlow, *University of Toronto*
Heath Hatch, *University of Massachusetts*
Carl Hayn, *Santa Clara University*
James Heath, *Austin Community College*
Greg Hood, *Tidewater Community College*
Sebastian Hui, *Florence-Darlington Technical College*
Joey Huston, *Michigan State University*
David Iadevaia, *Pima Community College-East Campus*
Erik Jensen, *Chemeketa Community College*
Todd Kalisik, *Northern Illinois University*
Ju H. Kim, *University of North Dakota*
Armen Kocharian, *California State University Northridge*
J. M. Kowalski, *University of North Texas*
Laird Kramer, *Florida International University*
Chrisopher Kulp, *Eastern Kentucky University*
Richard Kurtz, *Louisiana State University*
Kenneth Lande, *University of Pennsylvania*
Tiffany Landry, *Folsom Lake College*
Todd Leif, *Cloud County Community College*
John Levin, *University of Tennessee-Knoxville*
John Lindberg, *Seattle Pacific University*
Rafael López-Mobilia, *The University of Texas at San Antonio*
Robert W. Lutz, *Drake University*

Lloyd Makorowitz, *SUNY Farmingdale*
Eric Martell, *Millikin University*
Mark Masters, *Indiana University-Purdue*
Denise Meeks, *Pima Community College*
Henry Merrill, *Fox Valley Technical College*
Mike Meyer, *Michigan Technological University*
Karie Meyers, *Pima Community College*
Tobias Moleski, *Nashville State Tech*
April Moore, *North Harris College*
Gary Morris, *Rice University*
Charley Myles, *Texas Tech University*
Meredith Newby, *Clemson University*
David Nice, *Bryn Mawr*
Fred Olness, *Southern Methodist University*
Charles Oliver Overstreet, *San Antonio College*
Paige Ouzts, *Lander University*
Russell Palma, *Minnesota State University-Mankato*
Richard Panek, *Florida Gulf Coast University*
Joshua Phiri, *Florence-Darling Technical College*
Iulia Podariu, *University of Nebraska at Omaha*
David Potter, *Austin Community College*
Promod Pratap, *University of North Carolina-Greensboro*
Michael Pravica, *University of Nevada, Las Vegas*
Earl Prohofsky, *Purdue University*
Marilyn Rands, *Lawrence Technological University*
Andrew Rex, *University of Puget Sound*
Andrew Richter, *Valparaiso University*
Phyliss Salmons, *Embry-Riddle Aeronautical University*
Michael Schaab, *Maine Maritime Academy*
Bruce Schumm, *University of California, Santa Cruz*

Mizuho Schwalm, *University of Minnesota Crookston*
Cindy Schwarz, *Vassar College*
Natalia Semushkhina, *Shippensburg University*
Khazgery (Jerry) Shakov, *Tulane University*
Bart Sheinberg, *Houston Community College*
Marllin Simon, *Auburn University*
Kenneth Smith, *Pennsylvania State University*
Michael Smutko, *Northwestern University*
Jon Son, *Boston University*
Noel Stanton, *Kansas State University*
Donna Stokes, *University of Houston*
Chuck Stone, *North Carolina A&T*
Chun Fu Su, *Mississippi State University*
Jeffrey Sudol, *West Chester University*
William Tireman, *Northern Michigan University*
Negussie Tirfessa, *Manchester Community College*
Rajive Tiwari, *Belmont Abbey College*
Herman Trivilino, *College of the Mainland*
Douglas Tussey, *Pennsylvania State University*
Stephen Van Hook, *Pennsylvania State University*
James Vesenka, *University of New England*
Christos Valiotis, *Antelope Valley College*
Stamatis Vokos, *Seattle Pacific University*
James Wanliss, *Embry-Riddle Aeronautical University*
Henry Weigel, *Arapahoe Community College*
Courtney Willis, *University of Northern Colorado*
Katherine Wu, *University of Tampa*
Ali Yazdi, *Jefferson State Community College*
David Young, *Louisiana State University*
Hsiao-Ling Zhou, *Georgia State University*
Ulrich Zurcher, *Cleveland State University*

Real-World Applications

Applications of biological or medical interest are marked BIO in the list below. MCAT-style Passage Problems are marked BIO below. Other end-of-chapter problems of biological or medical interest are marked BIO in the chapter. "Try It Yourself" experiments are marked TIY.

Studying for and Taking the MCAT Exam

If you are taking the College Physics course, there's a good chance that you are majoring in the biological sciences. There's also a good chance that you are preparing for a career in the health professions, and so might well be required to take the Medical College Admission Test, the MCAT exam.

As this book emphasizes, learning physics isn't just about solving problems; it's about making simplified but realistic models of the world and applying a small number of universal laws to a wide range of situations. The Physical Science portion of the MCAT exam stresses these broader thinking and modeling skills.

Structure of the MCAT Exam

Most of the test consists of a series of passages of technical information followed by a series of questions based on each passage, much like the passage problems at the end of each chapter in this book. Some details:

- **The passages and the questions are *always* integrated.** Understanding the passage and answering the questions will require you to use knowledge from several different areas of physics.
- **Passages will generally be about topics for which you do not have detailed knowledge.** But, if you read carefully, you'll see that the treatment of the passage is based on information you should know well.
- **The test assumes certain background knowledge.** You will need to have facility with central themes and major concepts. You won't need to know the formulas for the energy levels of the particle in a box, but you will need to understand that electrons in atoms exist in quantized energy levels and that shifts from level to level involve the emission and absorption of photons of particular energies.
- **You can't use calculators on the test, so any math that you do will be reasonably simple.** Quickly estimating an answer with ratio reasoning or a knowledge of the scale of physical quantities will be a useful skill.
- **The answers to the questions are all designed to be plausible.** You can't generally weed out the "bad" answers with a quick inspection.
- **The test is given online.** Practicing with MasteringPhysics will help you get used to this format.

Preparing for the Test

Because you have used this book as a tool for learning physics, you should use it as a tool for reviewing for the MCAT exam. Several of the key features of the book will be useful for this, including some that were explicitly designed with the MCAT exam in mind.

As you review the chapters:

- Start with the Chapter Previews, which provide a "big picture" overview of the content. What are the major themes of each chapter? You should be familiar with them, as well as the structure of the content represented by the arrows linking different topics.
- Go through each chapter and review the "Stop to Think" exercises. These are a good way to test your understanding of the key concepts and techniques.
- Each chapter closes with a Passage Problem that is designed to be "MCAT-exam-like." They'll give you good practice with the "read a passage, answer questions" structure of the MCAT exam.

The Passage Problems are a good tool, but the passages usually don't integrate topics that span several chapters—a key feature of the MCAT exam. For integrated passages and problems, turn to the Part Summaries:

- For each Part Summary, read the "One Step Beyond" passage and answer the associated questions.
- After this, read the passages and answer the questions that end each Part Summary section. These passages and associated problems are—by design—very similar to the passages and questions you'll see on the actual MCAT exam.

Taking the Test: Reading the Passage

As you read each passage, you'll need to interpret the information presented and connect it with concepts you are familiar with, translating it into a form that makes sense based on your background.

The next page shows a passage from a recent MCAT exam, with blue annotations highlighting connections you should make as you read.

The section that follows includes MCAT® exam material and is reprinted with permission of the Association of American Medical Colleges (AAMC).

Passage II

When X-rays are produced in an X-ray tube, two types of X-ray spectra are observed: *continuous spectra and line spectra.*

A continuous spectrum is produced by *bremsstrahlung,* the electromagnetic radiation produced when free electrons are accelerated during collisions with ions.

A line spectrum results when an electron having sufficient energy collides with a heavy atom, and an electron in an inner energy level is ejected from the atom. An electron from an outer energy level then fills the vacant inner energy level, resulting in emission of an X-ray photon. For example, if an electron in the $n = 1$ energy level is ejected from an atom, an electron in the $n = 2$ level of the atom can fill the vacancy created in the $n = 1$ level, and a photon with an energy equal to the energy difference between the two levels will be emitted.

A scientist produced both types of spectra using the X-ray tube shown in Figure 1 below.

Figure 1 Heated cathode X-ray tube

The tube contains a heated filament cathode (C), which emits electrons. A power supply (LV) regulates the filament temperature, the electrical current in the tube, and the number of X-rays produced at the anode (A). Another power supply (HV) regulates electron acceleration.

The scientist used an X-ray tube to determine the relationship between X-ray wavelength, λ, and X-ray intensity, I, which is proportional to the number of X-ray photons emitted at λ. The scientist then graphed the results of the experiment, as shown in Figure 2.

Figure 2 X-ray intensity versus wavelength

Translating

You don't know much about x-ray spectra, but look at the details of the passage: Electrons are accelerated by a potential difference. They hit a target and cause electronic excitations that lead to the emission of photons. These are topics you have seen, about which you can reason.

Continuous and line spectra are treated in Chapter 29. A line spectrum results from quantized energy levels that lead to quantum jumps of only certain sizes. For a line spectrum we expect to see high intensities at certain well defined wavelengths.

This is a main theme of Chapters 28 and 29. When an electron jumps from one level to another, the energy of the emitted photon is equal to the energy difference.

Chapters 25 and 28 discuss the operation of an x-ray tube. Electrons accelerated by a high voltage slam into a metal target, emitting x rays, high-energy electromagnetic waves, in the process. The highest energy an x ray can have equals the kinetic energy given to the electron. You don't need to fully understand x-ray tubes to make sense of what is going on. Using an electric field to accelerate charged particles was a major staple of Chapters 20 and 21.

There's a circuit that runs the tube. The "LV" power supply warms the filament so that it emits electrons; the "HV" power supply accelerates the electrons. Since the accelerated electrons are the ones that cause the x rays, it's pretty clear that the HV supply will be the important one.

These peaks are the line spectra. There are two peaks. P_2 corresponds to a longer wavelength than P_1, and so corresponds to a lower frequency and a lower photon energy.

In addition to the two sharp peaks, there is a continuous spectrum. There are no x rays below a certain wavelength—meaning no x rays above a certain energy.

FIGURE MCAT-EXAM.1 Interpreting a passage from a recent version of the MCAT exam.

Taking the Test: Answering the Questions

The passages on the MCAT exam seem complicated at first, but, as we've seen, they are about basic concepts and central themes that you know well. The same is true of the questions; they aren't as difficult as they may seem at first. Read them carefully to see what they are asking then work toward a solution. The practical suggestions below are followed by a detailed overview of the solutions to the problems based on the passage on the previous page.

You Can Answer the Questions in Any Order

The questions test a range of skills and have a range of difficulties. Many questions will involve simple reading comprehension; these are usually quite straightforward. Some require sophisticated reasoning and (slightly) complex mathematical manipulations. Start with the easy ones, ones that you can quickly solve. Save the more complex ones for later, and skip them if time is short. This approach has the added benefit of giving you time to think about different aspects of the problem, gaining in familiarity with it before you tackle the more complex questions.

Take Steps to Simplify or Eliminate Calculations

You won't be allowed to use a calculator on the exam, so any math that you do will be reasonably straightforward. You will very rarely need to complete a calculation—and, given the time constraints, you won't want to. To rapidly converge on a correct answer choice, there are some important "shortcuts" that you can take.

- **Use ratio reasoning.** What's the relationship between the variables involved in a question? You can use this to deduce the answer with only a very simple calculation, as we've seen many times in the book. For instance, suppose you are asked the following question:

  A model rocket is powered by chemical fuel. A student launches a rocket with a small engine containing 1.0 g of combustible fuel. The rocket reaches a speed of 10 m/s. The student then launches the rocket again, using an engine with 4.0 g of fuel. If all other parameters of the launch are kept the same, what final speed would you expect for this second trial?

  This is an energy conversion problem: Chemical energy of the fuel is converted to kinetic energy of the rocket. Kinetic energy is related to the speed by $K = \frac{1}{2} mv^2$. The chemical energy—and thus the kinetic energy—in the second trial is increased by a factor of 4. Since $K \sim v^2$, the speed must increase by a factor of 2, to 20 m/s.

- **Simplify calculations by liberally rounding numbers.** You can round off numbers to make calculations more straightforward. Your final result will probably be close enough to choose the correct answer from the list given. For instance, suppose you are asked the following question:

  A ball moving at 2.0 m/s rolls off edge of table that's 1.2 m high. How far from the edge of the table does the ball land?

  A. 2 m   B. 1.5 m   C. 1 m   D. 0.5 m

We know that the vertical motion of the ball is free fall; so the vertical distance fallen by the ball in a time Δt is $\Delta y = -\frac{1}{2} g t^2$. The time to fall 1.2 m is $\Delta t = \sqrt{2(1.2 \text{ m})/g}$. Rather than complete this calculation, we estimate the results as follows: $\Delta t = \sqrt{2.4/9.8} \approx \sqrt{1/4} = 1/2 = 0.5$ s During this free fall time, the horizontal motion is constant at 2.0 m/s, so we expect the ball to land about 1 m away. Our quick calculation shows us that the correct answer is choice C—no other answer is even close.

- **For calculations using values in scientific notation, compute either the first digits or the exponents, not both.** Look at the answer choices for problem 7 on next page. The answers are only given to one significant digit, which is either a 5, a 2 or a 1. We needn't worry about the exponent or the position of the decimal, or doing a calculation to more than one significant figure. A quick calculation can tell us the correct leading digit, and that's all we need to figure out the result. In other cases, you'll find possible answers with the same leading digit but very different exponents or decimal places. In this case, all you need is a simple order of magnitude estimate to decide on the right result.

- **Where possible, use your knowledge of the expected scale of physical quantities to quickly determine the correct answer.** For instance, suppose a question asks you to find the photon energy for green light of wavelength 550 nm. Visible light has photon energies of about 2 eV, or about 3×10^{-19} J, and that might be enough information to allow you to pick out the correct answer with no calculation.

One Final Tip: Look at the Big Picture

The MCAT exam tests your ability to look at a technical passage about which you have some background knowledge and quickly get a sense of what it is saying, enough to answer questions about it. Keep this big picture in mind:

- **Don't get bogged down in technical details of the particular situation.** Focus on the basic physics.
- **Don't spend too much time on any one question.** If one question is taking too much time, make an educated guess and move on. Rather then spending two minutes working out a detailed calculation, spend this time refining your answers to several more straightforward questions.
- **Don't get confused by details of notation or terminology.** For instance, different people use different symbols for physical variables; in this text we use the symbol K for kinetic energy; others use E_K. Equations might be written slightly differently. Mentally replace these with the forms you are familiar with.

Finally, don't forget the most important aspect of success on the MCAT exam: The best way to prepare for this or any test is simply to understand the subject. As you prepare for the test, focus your energy on reviewing and refining your knowledge of central topics and techniques.

6. In Figure 2, which of the following represents the source of emission peaks P_1 and P_2?

A) Bremsstrahlung

B) Absorption of X-ray photons resulting in electronic excitations in atoms

C) Emission of X-ray photons as a result of electronic transitions in atoms

D) Acceleration of electrons in a magnetic field

7. Based on the tube in Figure 1, to maintain an electron current of 0.005 A and a potential drop of 10^5V between the anode and the cathode, approximately how much power must the tube consume?

A) 5×10^2W

B) 1×10^3W

C) 2×10^5W

D) 2×10^7W

8. The ionization potentials for electrons in the $n = 1$, 2, and 3 energy levels of Pb are $1{,}400 \times 10^{-17}$ J, 240×10^{-17} J, and 48×10^{-17} J, respectively. When an electron in the $n = 2$ level fills a vacancy in the $n = 1$ level, what is the energy of the X-ray that is emitted?

A) 1.92×10^{-15} J

B) 2.40×10^{-15} J

C) 1.16×10^{-14} J

D) 1.40×10^{-14} J

9. According to the passage, bremsstrahlung will NOT be produced by collisions between electrons and:

A) He.

B) He^{2+}.

C) Li^{1+}.

D) protons.

10. In order to increase the maximum kinetic energy of electrons colliding with the anode, the scientist made which of the following changes?

A) The voltage of HV was increased.

B) The voltage of HV was decreased.

C) The voltage of LV was increased.

D) The voltage of LV was decreased.

11. In Figure 2, peaks P_1 and P_2 were produced by events that occurred with unequal probabilities. Which peak was produced by the more probable event?

A) P_1, because the peak has the longer wavelength

B) P_1, because the peak has the lower intensity

C) P_2, because the peak has the longer wavelength

D) P_2, because the peak has the higher intensity

FIGURE MCAT-EXAM.2 Answering the questions for the passage of Figure MCAT-EXAM.1.

Preface to the Student

The most incomprehensible thing about the universe is that it is comprehensible.
—Albert Einstein

(a) Pendulum clock

(b) Gibbon locomotion

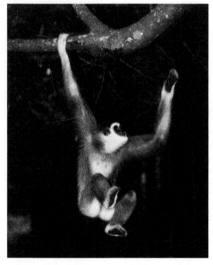

If you are taking a course for which this book is assigned, you probably aren't a physics major or an engineering major. It's likely that you aren't majoring in a physical science. So why are you taking physics?

It's almost certain that you are taking physics because you are majoring in a discipline that requires it. Someone, somewhere, has decided that it's important for you to take this course. And they are right. There is a lot you can learn from physics, even if you don't plan to be a physicist. We regularly hear from doctors, physical therapists, biologists and others that physics was one of the most interesting and valuable courses they took in college.

So, what can you expect to learn in this course? Let's start by talking about what physics is. Physics is a way of thinking about the physical aspects of nature. Physics is not about "facts." It's far more focused on discovering *relationships* between facts and the *patterns* that exist in nature than on learning facts for their own sake. Our emphasis will be on thinking and reasoning. We are going to look for patterns and relationships in nature, develop the logic that relates different ideas, and search for the reasons *why* things happen as they do.

Once we've figured out a pattern, a set of relationships, we'll look at applications to see where this understanding takes us. Let's look at an example. Part (a) of the figure shows an early mechanical clock. The clock uses a *pendulum,* a mass suspended by a thin rod free to pivot about its end, as its timekeeping element. When you study oscillatory motion, you will learn about the motion of a pendulum. You'll learn that the *period* of its motion, the time for one swing, doesn't depend on the amplitude, the size of the swing. This makes a pendulum the ideal centerpiece of a clock.

But there are other systems that look like pendulums too. The gibbon in part (b) of the figure is moving through the trees by swinging from successive handholds. The gibbon's mass is suspended below a point about which it is free to pivot, so the gibbon's motion can be understood as pendulum motion. You can then use your knowledge of pendulums to describe the motion, explaining, for example, why this gibbon is raising its feet as it swings.

Like any subject, physics is best learned by doing. "Doing physics" in this course means solving problems, applying what you have learned to answer questions at the end of the chapter. When you are given a homework assignment, you may find yourself tempted to simply solve the problems by thumbing through the text looking for a formula that seems like it will work. This isn't how to do physics; if it was, whoever required you to take this course wouldn't bother. The folks who designed your major want you to learn to *reason,* not to "plug and chug." Whatever you end up studying or doing for a career, this ability will serve you well. And that's why someone, somewhere, wants you to take physics.

How do you learn to reason in this way? There's no single strategy for studying physics that will work for all students, but we can make some suggestions that will certainly help:

■ **Read each chapter *before* it is discussed in class.** Class attendance is much less effective if you have not prepared. When you first read a chapter, focus on learning new vocabulary, definitions, and notation. You won't understand what's being discussed or how the ideas are being used if you don't know what the terms and symbols mean.

■ **Participate actively in class.** Take notes, ask and answer questions, take part in discussion groups. There is ample scientific evidence that *active participation* is far more effective for learning science than is passive listening.

■ **After class, go back for a careful rereading of the chapter.** In your second reading, pay close attention to the details and the worked examples. Look for the *logic* behind each example, not just at what formula is being used. We have a three-step process by which we solve all of the worked examples in the text. Most chapters have detailed Problem-Solving Strategies to help you see how to apply this procedure to particular topics, and Tactics Boxes that explain specific steps in your analysis.

■ **Apply what you have learned to the homework problems at the end of each chapter.** By following the techniques of the worked examples, applying the tactics and problem-solving strategies, you'll learn how to apply the knowledge you are gaining. In short, you'll learn to reason like a physicist.

■ **Form a study group with two or three classmates.** There's good evidence that students who study regularly with a group do better than the rugged individualists who try to go it alone.

And we have one final suggestion. As you read the book, take part in class, and work through problems, step back every now and then to appreciate the big picture. You are going to study topics that range from motions in the solar system to the electrical signals in the nervous system that let you order your hand to turn the pages of this book. You will learn quantitative methods to calculate things such as how far a car will move as it brakes to a stop and how to build a solenoid for an MRI machine. It's a remarkable breadth of topics and techniques that is based on a very compact set of organizing principles. It's quite remarkable, really, well worthy of your study.

Now, let's get down to work.

Detailed Contents

PART III   Properties of Matter

PART IV   Oscillations and Waves

Force and Motion

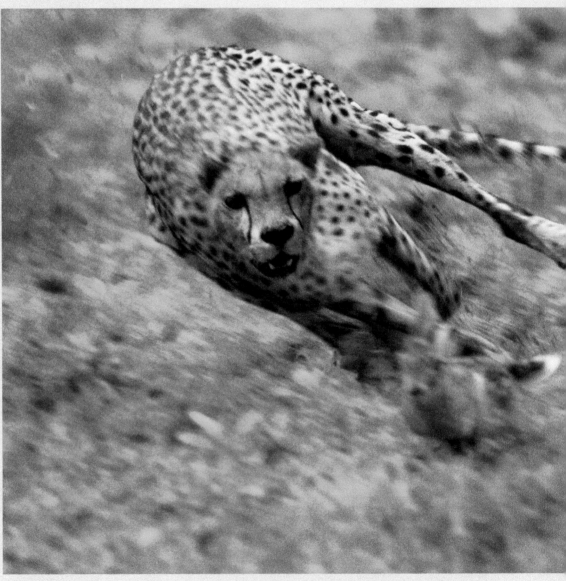

The cheetah is the fastest land animal, able to run at speeds exceeding 60 miles per hour. Nonetheless, the rabbit has an advantage in this chase. It can *change* its motion more quickly and will likely escape. How can you tell, by looking at the picture, that the cheetah is changing its motion?

Why Things Change

Each of the seven parts of this book opens with an overview that gives you a look ahead, a glimpse of where your journey will take you in the next few chapters. It's easy to lose sight of the big picture while you're busy negotiating the terrain of each chapter. In Part I, the big picture is, in a word, *change*.

Simple observations of the world around you show that most things change. Some changes, such as aging, are biological. Others, such as sugar dissolving in your coffee, are chemical. We will look at changes that involve *motion* of one form or another—running and jumping, throwing balls, lifting weights.

There are two big questions we must tackle to study how things change by moving:

- **How do we describe motion?** How should we measure or characterize the motion if we want to analyze it mathematically?
- **How do we explain motion?** Why do objects have the particular motion they do? Why, when you toss a ball upward, does it go up and then come back down rather than keep going up? What are the "laws of nature" that allow us to predict an object's motion?

Two key concepts that will help answer these questions are *force* (the "cause") and *acceleration* (the "effect"). Our basic tools will be three laws of motion elucidated by Isaac Newton. Newton's laws relate force to acceleration, and we will use them to explain and explore a wide range of problems. As we learn to solve problems dealing with motion, we will learn basic techniques that we can apply in all the parts of this book.

Simplifying Models

Reality is extremely complicated. We would never be able to develop a science if we had to keep track of every detail of every situation. Suppose we analyze the tossing of a ball. Is it necessary to analyze the way the atoms in the ball are connected? Do we need to analyze what you ate for breakfast and the biochemistry of how that was translated into muscle power? These are interesting questions, of course. But if our task is to understand the motion of the ball, we need to simplify!

We can do a perfectly fine analysis if we treat the ball as a round solid and your hand as another solid that exerts a force on the ball. This is a *model* of the situation. A model is a simplified description of reality—much as a model airplane is a simplified version of a real airplane—that is used to reduce the complexity of a problem to the point where it can be analyzed and understood.

Model building is a major part of the strategy that we will develop for solving problems in all parts of the book. We will introduce different models in different parts. We will pay close attention to where simplifying assumptions are being made, and why. Learning *how* to simplify a situation is the essence of successful modeling—and successful problem solving.

1 Representing Motion

As this skier moves in a graceful arc through the air, the direction of his motion, and the distance between each of his positions and the next, are constantly changing. What language should we use to describe this motion?

LOOKING AHEAD ▶

The goals of Chapter 1 are to introduce the fundamental concepts of motion and to review the related basic mathematical principles.

The Chapter Preview

Each chapter will start with an overview of the material to come. You should read these chapter previews carefully to get a sense of the content and structure of the chapter.

Arrows will show the connections and flow between different topics in the preview.

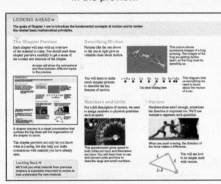

A chapter preview is a visual presentation that outlines the big ideas and the organization of the chapter to come.

The chapter previews not only let you know what is coming, but also help you make connections with material you have already seen.

Looking Back ◀◀

We'll tell you what material from previous chapters is especially important to review to best understand the new material.

Describing Motion

Pictures like the one above or the one at right give us valuable clues about motion.

This picture shows successive images of a frog jumping. The images of the frog are getting farther apart, so the frog must be speeding up.

You will learn to make much simpler pictures to describe the key features of motion.

$t = 0\,s \quad 1\,s \quad 2\,s \quad 3\,s \quad 4\,s \quad 5\,s \quad 6\,s\,7\,s\,8\,s$

Car starts braking here

This diagram tells us everything we need to know about the motion of a car.

Numbers and Units

For a full description of motion, we need to assign numbers to physical quantities such as speed.

This speedometer gives speed in both miles per hour and kilometers per hour. You will learn how to use and convert units and how to describe large and small numbers.

Vectors

Numbers alone aren't enough, sometimes the direction is important too. We'll use **vectors** to represent such quantities.

When you push a swing, the direction of the force makes a difference.

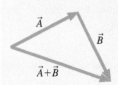

You will see how to do simple math with vectors.

1.1 Motion: A First Look

The concept of motion is a theme that will appear in one form or another throughout this entire book. You have a well-developed intuition about motion, based on your experiences, but you'll see that some of the most important aspects of motion can be rather subtle. We need to develop some tools to help us explain and understand motion, so rather than jumping immediately into a lot of mathematics and calculations, this first chapter focuses on visualizing motion and becoming familiar with the concepts needed to describe a moving object.

One key difference between physics and other sciences is how we set up and solve problems. We'll often use a two-step process to solve motion problems. The first step is to develop a simplified *representation* of the motion so that key elements stand out. For example, the photo of the skier at the start of the chapter allows us to observe his position at many successive times. It is precisely by considering this sort of picture of motion that we will begin our study of this topic. The second step is to analyze the motion with the language of mathematics. The process of putting numbers on nature is often the most challenging aspect of the problems you will solve. In this chapter, we will explore the steps in this process as we introduce the basic concepts of motion.

Types of Motion

As a starting point, let's define **motion** as the change of an object's position or orientation with time. Examples of motion are easy to list. Bicycles, baseballs, cars, airplanes, and rockets are all objects that move. The path along which an object moves, which might be a straight line or might be curved, is called the object's **trajectory**.

FIGURE 1.1 shows four basic types of motion that we will study in this book. In this chapter, we will start with the first type of motion in the figure, motion along a straight line. In later chapters, we will learn about circular motion, which is the motion of an object along a circular path; projectile motion, the motion of an object through the air; and rotational motion, the spinning of an object about an axis.

FIGURE 1.1 Four basic types of motion.

Straight-line motion

Circular motion

Projectile motion

Rotational motion

FIGURE 1.2 Several frames from the
video of a car.

FIGURE 1.3 A motion diagram of the car
shows all the frames simultaneously.

The same amount of time elapses
between each image and the next.

Making a Motion Diagram

An easy way to study motion is to record a video of a moving object with a station-ary camera. A video camera takes images at a fixed rate, typically 30 images every second. Each separate image is called a *frame*. As an example, FIGURE 1.2 shows sev-eral frames from a video of a car going past. Not surprisingly, the car is in a different position in each frame.

NOTE ▶ It's important to keep the camera in a *fixed position* as the object moves by. Don't "pan" it to track the moving object. ◀

Suppose we now edit the video by layering the frames on top of each other and then look at the final result. We end up with the picture in FIGURE 1.3. This composite image, showing an object's positions at several *equally spaced instants of time,* is called a **motion diagram.** As simple as motion diagrams seem, they will turn out to be powerful tools for analyzing motion.

Now let's take our camera out into the world and make some motion diagrams. The following table illustrates how a motion diagram shows important features of different kinds of motion.

Examples of motion diagrams

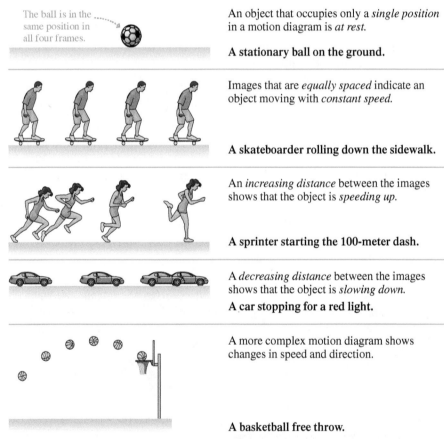

The ball is in the same position in all four frames.

An object that occupies only a *single position* in a motion diagram is *at rest.*

A stationary ball on the ground.

Images that are *equally spaced* indicate an object moving with *constant speed.*

A skateboarder rolling down the sidewalk.

An *increasing distance* between the images shows that the object is *speeding up.*

A sprinter starting the 100-meter dash.

A *decreasing distance* between the images shows that the object is *slowing down.*

A car stopping for a red light.

A more complex motion diagram shows changes in speed and direction.

A basketball free throw.

We have defined several concepts (at rest, constant speed, speeding up, and slow-ing down) in terms of how the moving object appears in a motion diagram. These are called **operational definitions,** meaning that the concepts are defined in terms of a particular procedure or operation performed by the investigator. For example, we could answer the question Is the airplane speeding up? by checking whether or not the images in the plane's motion diagram are getting farther apart. Many of the concepts in physics will be introduced as operational definitions. This reminds us that physics is an experimental science.

STOP TO THINK 1.1 Which car is going faster, A or B? Assume there are equal intervals of time between the frames of both videos.

Car A   Car B

NOTE ► Each chapter in this textbook has several *Stop to Think* questions. These questions are designed to see if you've understood the basic ideas that have just been presented. The answers are given at the end of the chapter, but you should make a serious effort to think about these questions before turning to the answers. If you answer correctly and are sure of your answer rather than just guessing, you can proceed to the next section with confidence. But if you answer incorrectly, it would be wise to reread the preceding sections carefully before proceeding onward. ◄

The Particle Model

For many objects, the motion of the object *as a whole* is not influenced by the details of the object's size and shape. To describe the object's motion, all we really need to keep track of is the motion of a single point: You could imagine looking at the motion of a dot painted on the side of the object.

In fact, for the purposes of analyzing the motion, we can often consider the object *as if* it were just a single point, without size or shape. We can also treat the object *as if* all of its mass were concentrated into this single point. An object that can be represented as a mass at a single point in space is called a **particle.**

If we treat an object as a particle, we can represent the object in each frame of a motion diagram as a simple dot. FIGURE 1.4 shows how much simpler motion diagrams appear when the object is represented as a particle. Note that the dots have been numbered 0, 1, 2, . . . to tell the sequence in which the frames were exposed. These diagrams still convey a complete understanding of the object's motion.

Treating an object as a particle is, of course, a simplification of reality. Such a simplification is called a **model.** Models allow us to focus on the important aspects of a phenomenon by excluding those aspects that play only a minor role. The **particle model** of motion is a simplification in which we treat a moving object as if all of its mass were concentrated at a single point. Using the particle model may allow us to see connections that are very important but that are obscured or lost by examining all the parts of an extended, real object. Consider the motion of the two objects shown in FIGURE 1.5. These two very different objects have exactly the same motion diagram. As we will see, all objects falling under the influence of gravity move in exactly the same manner if no other forces act. The simplification of the particle model has revealed something about the physics that underlies both of these situations.

Not all motions can be reduced to the motion of a single point, as we'll see. But for now, the particle model will be a useful tool in understanding motion.

FIGURE 1.4 Simplifying a motion diagram using the particle model.

(a) Motion diagram of a car stopping

(b) Same motion diagram using the particle model

The same amount of time elapses between each frame and the next.

Numbers show the order in which the frames were taken.

A single dot is used to represent the object.

FIGURE 1.5 The particle model for two falling objects.

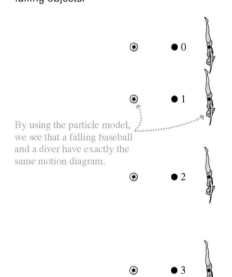

By using the particle model, we see that a falling baseball and a diver have exactly the same motion diagram.

STOP TO THINK 1.2 Three motion diagrams are shown. Which is a dust particle settling to the floor at constant speed, which is a ball dropped from the roof of a building, and which is a descending rocket slowing to make a soft landing on Mars?

A.	B.	C.
0 ●	0 ●	0 ●
1 ●		
2 ●	1 ●	
		1 ●
3 ●	2 ●	2 ●
	3 ●	
4 ●		3 ●
	4 ●	4 ●
5 ●	5 ●	5 ●

1.2 Position and Time: Putting Numbers on Nature

To develop our understanding of motion further, we need to be able to make quantitative measurements: We need to use numbers. As we analyze a motion diagram, it is useful to know where the object is (its *position*) and when the object was at that position (the *time*). We'll start by considering the motion of an object that can move only along a straight line. Examples of this **one-dimensional** or "1-D" motion are a bicyclist moving along the road, a train moving on a long straight track, and an elevator moving up and down a shaft.

Position and Coordinate Systems

FIGURE 1.6 Describing your position.

Suppose you are driving along a long, straight country road, as in FIGURE 1.6, and your friend calls and asks where you are. You might reply that you are 4 miles east of the post office, and your friend would then know just where you were. Your location at a particular instant in time (when your friend phoned) is called your **position.** Notice that to know your position along the road, your friend needed three pieces of information. First, you had to give her a reference point (the post office) from which all distances are to be measured. We call this fixed reference point the **origin.** Second, she needed to know how far you were from that reference point or origin—in this case, 4 miles. Finally, she needed to know which side of the origin you were on: You could be 4 miles to the west of it or 4 miles to the east.

We will need these same three pieces of information in order to specify any object's position along a line. We first choose our origin, from which we measure the position of the object. The position of the origin is arbitrary, and we are free to place it where we like. Usually, however, there are certain points (such as the well-known post office) that are more convenient choices than others.

In order to specify how far our object is from the origin, we lay down an imaginary axis along the line of the object's motion. Like a ruler, this axis is marked off in equally spaced divisions of distance, perhaps in inches, meters, or miles, depending on the problem at hand. We place the zero mark of this ruler at the origin, allowing us to locate the position of our object by reading the ruler mark where the object is.

Finally, we need to be able to specify which side of the origin our object is on. To do this, we imagine the axis extending from one side of the origin with increasing positive markings; on the other side, the axis is marked with increasing *negative* numbers. By reporting the position as either a positive or a negative number, we know on what side of the origin the object is.

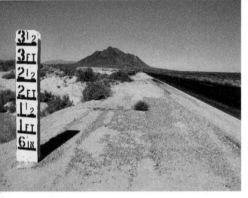

Sometimes measurements have a natural origin. This snow depth gauge has its origin set at road level.

These elements—an origin and an axis marked in both the positive and negative directions—can be used to unambiguously locate the position of an object. We call this a **coordinate system.** We will use coordinate systems throughout this book, and we will soon develop coordinate systems that can be used to describe the positions of objects moving in more complex ways than just along a line. FIGURE 1.7 shows a coordinate system that can be used to locate various objects along the country road discussed earlier.

Although our coordinate system works well for describing the positions of objects located along the axis, our notation is somewhat cumbersome. We need to keep saying things like "the car is at position +4 miles." A better notation, and one that will become particularly important when we study motion in two dimensions, is to use a symbol such as *x* or *y* to represent the position along the axis. Then we can say "the cow is at $x = -5$ miles." The symbol that represents a position along an axis is called a **coordinate.** The introduction of symbols to represent positions (and, later, velocities and accelerations) also allows us to work with these quantities mathematically.

FIGURE 1.7 The coordinate system used to describe objects along a country road.

FIGURE 1.8 below shows how we would set up a coordinate system for a sprinter running a 50-meter race (we use the standard symbol "m" for meters). For horizontal motion like this we usually use the coordinate *x* to represent the position.

FIGURE 1.8 A coordinate system for a 50-meter race.

FIGURE 1.9 Examples of one-dimensional motion.

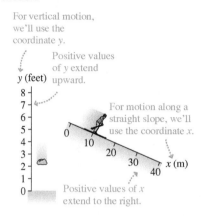

Motion along a straight line need not be horizontal. As shown in FIGURE 1.9, a rock falling vertically downward and a skier skiing down a straight slope are also examples of straight-line or one-dimensional motion.

Time

The pictures in Figure 1.9 show the position of an object at just one instant of time. But a full motion diagram represents how an object moves as time progresses. So far, we have labeled the dots in a motion diagram by the numbers 0, 1, 2, . . . to indicate the order in which the frames were exposed. But to fully describe the motion, we need to indicate the *time,* as read off a clock or a stopwatch, at which each frame of a video was made. This is important, as we can see from the motion diagram of a stopping car in FIGURE 1.10. If the frames were taken 1 second apart, this motion diagram shows a leisurely stop; if 1/10 of a second apart, it represents a screeching halt.

For a complete motion diagram, we thus need to label each frame with its corresponding time (symbol *t*) as read off a clock. But when should we start the clock? Which frame should be labeled *t* = 0? This choice is much like choosing the origin *x* = 0 of a coordinate system: You can pick any arbitrary point in the motion and label it "*t* = 0 seconds." This is simply the instant you decide to start your clock or stopwatch, so it is the origin of your time coordinate. A video frame labeled "*t* = 4 seconds" means it was taken 4 seconds after you started your clock. We typically choose *t* = 0 to represent the "beginning" of a problem, but the object may have been moving before then.

To illustrate, FIGURE 1.11 shows the motion diagram for a car moving at a constant speed and then braking to a halt. Two possible choices for the frame labeled *t* = 0 seconds are shown; our choice depends on what part of the motion we're interested in. Each successive position of the car is then labeled with the clock reading in seconds (abbreviated by the symbol "s").

FIGURE 1.10 Is this a leisurely stop or a screeching halt?

FIGURE 1.11 The motion diagram of a car that travels at constant speed and then brakes to a halt.

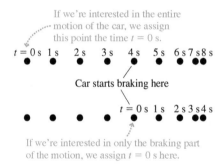

Changes in Position and Displacement

Now that we've seen how to measure position and time, let's return to the problem of motion. To describe motion we'll need to measure the *changes* in position that occur with time. Consider the following:

Sam is standing 50 feet (ft) east of the corner of 12th Street and Vine. He then walks to a second point 150 ft east of Vine. What is Sam's change of position?

FIGURE 1.12 shows Sam's motion on a map. We've placed a coordinate system on the map, using the coordinate *x*. We are free to place the origin of our coordinate system wherever we wish, so we have placed it at the intersection. Sam's initial position is then at x_i = 50 ft. The positive value for x_i tells us that Sam is east of the origin.

FIGURE 1.12 Sam undergoes a displacement Δx from position x_i to position x_f.

The size and the direction of the displacement both matter. Roy Riegels (pursued above by teammate Benny Lom) found this out in dramatic fashion in the 1928 Rose Bowl when he recovered a fumble and ran 69 yards—toward his own team's end zone. An impressive distance, but in the wrong direction!

FIGURE 1.13 A displacement is a signed quantity. Here Δx is a negative number.

A final position to the left of the initial position gives a negative displacement.

FIGURE 1.14 The motion diagram of a bicycle moving to the right at a constant speed.

NOTE ▶ We will label special values of x or y with subscripts. The value at the start of a problem is usually labeled with a subscript "i," for *initial,* and the value at the end is labeled with a subscript "f," for *final.* For cases having several special values, we will usually use subscripts "1," "2," and so on. ◀

Sam's final position is $x_f = 150$ ft, indicating that he is 150 ft east of the origin. You can see that Sam has changed position, and a *change* of position is called a **displacement**. His displacement is the distance labeled Δx in Figure 1.12. The Greek letter delta (Δ) is used in math and science to indicate the *change* in a quantity. Thus Δx indicates a change in the position x.

NOTE ▶ Δx is a *single* symbol. You cannot cancel out or remove the Δ in algebraic operations. ◀

To get from the 50 ft mark to the 150 ft mark, Sam clearly had to walk 100 ft, so the change in his position—his displacement—is 100 ft. We can think about displacement in a more general way, however. **Displacement is the *difference* between a final position x_f and an initial position x_i.** Thus we can write

$$\Delta x = x_f - x_i = 150 \text{ ft} - 50 \text{ ft} = 100 \text{ ft}$$

NOTE ▶ A general principle, used throughout this book, is that the change in any quantity is the final value of the quantity minus its initial value. ◀

Displacement is a *signed quantity;* that is, it can be either positive or negative. If, as shown in FIGURE 1.13, Sam's final position x_f had been at the origin instead of the 150 ft mark, his displacement would have been

$$\Delta x = x_f - x_i = 0 \text{ ft} - 50 \text{ ft} = -50 \text{ ft}$$

The negative sign tells us that he moved to the *left* along the x-axis, or 50 ft *west.*

Change in Time

A displacement is a change in position. In order to quantify motion, we'll need to also consider changes in *time,* which we call **time intervals.** We've seen how we can label each frame of a motion diagram with a specific time, as determined by our stopwatch. FIGURE 1.14 shows the motion diagram of a bicycle moving at a constant speed, with the times of the measured points indicated.

The displacement between the initial position x_i and the final position x_f is

$$\Delta x = x_f - x_i = 120 \text{ ft} - 0 \text{ ft} = 120 \text{ ft}$$

Similarly, we define the time interval between these two points to be

$$\Delta t = t_f - t_i = 6 \text{ s} - 0 \text{ s} = 6 \text{ s}$$

A time interval Δt measures the elapsed time as an object moves from an initial position x_i at time t_i to a final position x_f at time t_f. Note that, unlike Δx, Δt is always positive because t_f is always greater than t_i.

EXAMPLE 1.1 **How long a ride?**

Carol is enjoying a bicycle ride on a country road that runs east-west past a water tower. Define a coordinate system so that increasing x means moving east. At noon, Carol is 3 miles (mi) east of the water tower. A half-hour later, she is 2 mi west of the water tower. What is her displacement during that half-hour?

PREPARE Although it may seem like overkill for such a simple problem, you should start by making a drawing, like the one in FIGURE 1.15, with the x-axis along the road. Distances are measured with respect to the water tower, so it is a natural origin for the

FIGURE 1.15 A drawing of Carol's motion.

coordinate system. Once the coordinate system is established, we can show Carol's initial and final positions and her displacement between the two.

SOLVE We've specified values for Carol's initial and final positions in our drawing. We can thus compute her displacement:

$$\Delta x = x_f - x_i = (-2 \text{ mi}) - (3 \text{ mi}) = -5 \text{ mi}$$

ASSESS Once we've completed the solution to the problem, we need to go back to see if it makes sense. Carol is moving to the west, so we expect her displacement to be negative—and it is. We can see from our drawing in Figure 1.15 that she has moved 5 miles from her starting position, so our answer seems reasonable.

NOTE ▶ All of the numerical examples in the book are worked out with the same three-step process: Prepare, Solve, Assess. It's tempting to cut corners, especially for the simple problems in these early chapters, but you should take the time to do all of these steps now, to practice your problem-solving technique. We'll have more to say about our general problem-solving strategy in Chapter 2. ◀

STOP TO THINK 1.3 Sarah starts at a positive position along the x-axis. She then undergoes a negative displacement. Her final position

A. Is positive.   B. Is negative.   C. Could be either positive or negative.

1.3 Velocity

We all have an intuitive sense of whether something is moving very fast or just cruising slowly along. To make this intuitive idea more precise, let's start by examining the motion diagrams of some objects moving along a straight line at a *constant* speed, objects that are neither speeding up nor slowing down. This motion at a constant speed is called **uniform motion**. As we saw for the skateboarder in Section 1.1, for an object in uniform motion, successive frames of the motion diagram are *equally spaced*. We know now that this means that the object's displacement Δx is the same between successive frames.

To see how an object's displacement between successive frames is related to its speed, consider the motion diagrams of a bicycle and a car, traveling along the same street as shown in FIGURE 1.16. Clearly the car is moving faster than the bicycle: In any 1-second time interval, the car undergoes a displacement $\Delta x = 40$ ft, while the bicycle's displacement is only 20 ft.

The distances traveled in 1 second by the bicycle and the car are a measure of their speeds. The greater the distance traveled by an object in a given time interval, the greater its speed. This idea leads us to define the speed of an object as

$$\text{speed} = \frac{\text{distance traveled in a given time interval}}{\text{time interval}} \tag{1.1}$$

Speed of a moving object

For the bicycle, this equation gives

$$\text{speed} = \frac{20 \text{ ft}}{1 \text{ s}} = 20 \frac{\text{ft}}{\text{s}}$$

while for the car we have

$$\text{speed} = \frac{40 \text{ ft}}{1 \text{ s}} = 40 \frac{\text{ft}}{\text{s}}$$

The speed of the car is twice that of the bicycle, which seems reasonable.

NOTE ▶ The division gives units that are a fraction: ft/s. This is read as "feet per second," just like the more familiar "miles per hour." ◀

FIGURE 1.16 Motion diagrams for a car and a bicycle.

During each second, the car moves twice as far as the bicycle. Hence the car is moving at a greater speed.

FIGURE 1.17 Two bicycles traveling at the same speed, but with different velocities.

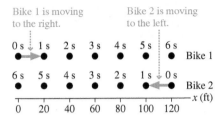

To fully characterize the motion of an object, it is important to specify not only the object's speed but also the *direction* in which it is moving. For example, FIGURE 1.17 shows the motion diagrams of two bicycles traveling at the same speed of 20 ft/s. The two bicycles have the same speed, but something about their motion is different—the *direction* of their motion.

The problem is that the "distance traveled" in Equation 1.1 doesn't capture any information about the direction of travel. But we've seen that the *displacement* of an object does contain this information. We can then introduce a new quantity, the **velocity,** as

$$\text{velocity} = \frac{\text{displacement}}{\text{time interval}} = \frac{\Delta x}{\Delta t} \tag{1.2}$$

Velocity of a moving object

The velocity of bicycle 1 in Figure 1.17, computed using the 1 second time interval between the $t = 2$ s and $t = 3$ s positions, is

$$v = \frac{\Delta x}{\Delta t} = \frac{x_3 - x_2}{3\,\text{s} - 2\,\text{s}} = \frac{60\,\text{ft} - 40\,\text{ft}}{1\,\text{s}} = +20\,\frac{\text{ft}}{\text{s}}$$

while the velocity for bicycle 2, during the same time interval, is

$$v = \frac{\Delta x}{\Delta t} = \frac{x_3 - x_2}{3\,\text{s} - 2\,\text{s}} = \frac{60\,\text{ft} - 80\,\text{ft}}{1\,\text{s}} = -20\,\frac{\text{ft}}{\text{s}}$$

NOTE ▶ We have used x_2 for the position at time $t = 2$ seconds and x_3 for the position at time $t = 3$ seconds. The subscripts serve the same role as before—identifying particular positions—but in this case the positions are identified by the time at which each position is reached. ◀

The two velocities have opposite signs because the bicycles are traveling in opposite directions. **Speed measures only how fast an object moves, but velocity tells us both an object's speed *and its direction.*** A positive velocity indicates motion to the right or, for vertical motion, upward. Similarly, an object moving to the left, or down, has a negative velocity.

NOTE ▶ Learning to distinguish between speed, which is always a positive number, and velocity, which can be either positive or negative, is one of the most important tasks in the analysis of motion. ◀

The velocity as defined by Equation 1.2 is actually what is called the *average* velocity. On average, over each 1 s interval bicycle 1 moves 20 ft, but we don't know if it was moving at exactly the same speed at every moment during this time interval. In Chapter 2, we'll develop the idea of *instantaneous* velocity, the velocity of an object at a particular instant in time. Since our goal in this chapter is to *visualize* motion with motion diagrams, we'll somewhat blur the distinction between average and instantaneous quantities, refining these definitions in Chapter 2, where our goal will be to develop the mathematics of motion.

EXAMPLE 1.2   **Finding the speed of a seabird**

Albatrosses are seabirds that spend most of their lives flying over the ocean looking for food. With a stiff tailwind, an albatross can fly at high speeds. Satellite data on one particularly speedy albatross showed it 60 miles east of its roost at 3:00 PM and then, at 3:20 PM, 86 miles east of its roost. What was its velocity?

PREPARE The statement of the problem provides us with a natural coordinate system: We can measure distances with respect to the roost, with distances to the east as positive. With this coordinate system, the motion of the albatross appears as in FIGURE 1.18. The motion takes place between 3:00 and 3:20, a time interval of 20 minutes, or 0.33 hour.

FIGURE 1.18 The motion of an albatross at sea.

SOLVE We know the initial and final positions, and we know the time interval, so we can calculate the velocity:

$$v = \frac{\Delta x}{\Delta t} = \frac{x_f - x_i}{0.33 \text{ h}} = \frac{26 \text{ mi}}{0.33 \text{ h}} = 79 \text{ mph}$$

ASSESS The velocity is positive, which makes sense because Figure 1.18 shows that the motion is to the right. A speed of 79 mph is certainly fast, but the problem said it was a "particularly speedy" albatross, so our answer seems reasonable. (Indeed, albatrosses have been observed to fly at such speeds in the very fast winds of the Southern Ocean. This problem is based on real observations, as will be our general practice in this book.)

The "Per" in Meters Per Second

The units for speed and velocity are a unit of distance (feet, meters, miles) divided by a unit of time (seconds, hours). Thus we could measure velocity in units of m/s or mph, pronounced "meters *per* second" and "miles *per* hour." The word "per" will often arise in physics when we consider the ratio of two quantities. What do we mean, exactly, by "per"?

If a car moves with a speed of 23 m/s, we mean that it travels 23 meters *for each* 1 second of elapsed time. The word "per" thus associates the number of units in the numerator (23 m) with *one* unit of the denominator (1 s). We'll see many other examples of this idea as the book progresses. You may already know a bit about *density;* you can look up the density of gold and you'll find that it is 19.3 g/cm³ ("grams *per* cubic centimeter"). This means that there are 19.3 grams of gold *for each* 1 cubic centimeter of the metal. Thinking about the word "per" in this way will help you better understand physical quantities whose units are the ratio of two other units.

1.4 A Sense of Scale: Significant Figures, Scientific Notation, and Units

Physics attempts to explain the natural world, from the very small to the exceedingly large. And in order to understand our world, we need to be able to *measure* quantities both minuscule and enormous. A properly reported measurement has three elements. First, we can measure our quantity with only a certain precision. To make this precision clear, we need to make sure that we report our measurement with the correct number of *significant figures.*

Second, writing down the really big and small numbers that often come up in physics can be awkward. To avoid writing all those zeros, scientists use *scientific notation* to express numbers both big and small.

Finally, we need to choose an agreed-upon set of *units* for the quantity. For speed, common units include meters per second and miles per hour. For mass, the kilogram is the most commonly used unit. Every physical quantity that we can measure has an associated set of units.

300 million light years
= 2.8×10^{24} m

120 μm = 1.2×10^{-4} m

From galaxies to cells ... BIO In science, we need to express numbers both very large and very small. The top image is a computer simulation of the structure of the universe. Bright areas represent regions of clustered galaxies. The bottom image is cortical nerve cells. Nerve cells relay signals to each other through a complex web of dendrites. These images, though similar in appearance, differ in scale by a factor of about 2×10^{28}!

FIGURE 1.19 The precision of a measurement depends on the instrument used to make it.

These calipers have a precision of 0.01 mm.

Walter Davis's best long jump on this day was reported as 8.24 m. This implies that the actual length of the jump was between 8.235 m and 8.245 m, a spread of only 0.01 m, which is 1 cm. Does this claimed accuracy seem reasonable?

TRY IT YOURSELF

How tall are you really? If you measure your height in the morning, just after you wake up, and then in the evening, after a full day of activity, you'll find that your evening height is *shorter* by as much as 3/4 inch. Your height decreases over the course of the day as gravity compresses and reshapes your spine. If you give your height as 66 3/16 in, you are claiming more significant figures than are truly warranted; the 3/16 in isn't really reliably known because your height can vary by more than this. Expressing your height to the nearest inch is plenty!

Measurements and Significant Figures

When we measure any quantity, such as the length of a bone or the weight of a specimen, we can do so with only a certain *precision*. The digital calipers in FIGURE 1.19 can make a measurement to within ±0.01 mm, so they have a precision of 0.01 mm. If you made the measurement with a ruler, you probably couldn't do better than about ±1 mm, so the precision of the ruler is about 1 mm. The precision of a measurement can also be affected by the skill or judgment of the person performing the measurement. A stopwatch might have a precision of 0.001 s, but, due to your reaction time, your measurement of the time of a sprinter would be much less precise.

It is important that your measurement be reported in a way that reflects its actual precision. Suppose you use a ruler to measure the length of a particular specimen of a newly discovered species of frog. You judge that you can make this measurement with a precision of about 1 mm, or 0.1 cm. In this case, the frog's length should be reported as, say, 6.2 cm. We interpret this to mean that the actual value falls between 6.15 cm and 6.25 cm and thus rounds to 6.2 cm. Reporting the frog's length as simply 6 cm is saying less than you know; you are withholding information. On the other hand, to report the number as 6.213 cm is wrong. Any person reviewing your work would interpret the number 6.213 cm as meaning that the actual length falls between 6.2125 cm and 6.2135 cm, thus rounding to 6.213 cm. In this case, you are claiming to have knowledge and information that you do not really possess.

The way to state your knowledge precisely is through the proper use of **significant figures.** You can think of a significant figure as a digit that is reliably known. A measurement such as 6.2 cm has *two* significant figures, the 6 and the 2. The next decimal place—the hundredths—is not reliably known and is thus not a significant figure. Similarly, a time measurement of 34.62 s has four significant figures, implying that the 2 in the hundredths place is reliably known.

When we perform a calculation such as adding or multiplying two or more measured numbers, we can't claim more accuracy for the result than was present in the initial measurements. Nine out of ten numbers used in a calculation might be known with a precision of 0.01%, but if the tenth number is poorly known, with a precision of only 10%, then the result of the calculation cannot possibly be more precise than 10%.

Determining the proper number of significant figures is straightforward, but there are a few definite rules to follow. We will often spell out such technical details in what we call a "Tactics Box." A Tactics Box is designed to teach you particular skills and techniques. Each Tactics Box will use the ✐ icon to designate exercises in the *Student Workbook* that you can use to practice these skills.

TACTICS
BOX 1.1   Using significant figures

❶ When you multiply or divide several numbers, or when you take roots, the number of significant figures in the answer should match the number of significant figures of the *least* precisely known number used in the calculation:

Three significant figures

$$3.73 \times 5.7 = 21$$

Two significant figures

Answer should have the *lower* of the two, or two significant figures.

Continued

❷ When you add or subtract several numbers, the number of decimal places in the answer should match the *smallest* number of decimal places of any number used in the calculation:

$$\begin{array}{r} 18.54 \\ +106.6 \\ \hline 125.1 \end{array}$$

— Two decimal places
— One decimal place
Answer should have the *lower* of the two, or one decimal place.

❸ **Exact numbers** have no uncertainty and, when used in calculations, do not change the number of significant figures of measured numbers. Examples of exact numbers are π and the number 2 in the relation $d = 2r$ between a circle's diameter and radius.

There is one notable exception to these rules:

■ It is acceptable to keep one or two extra digits during *intermediate* steps of a calculation. The goal here is to minimize round-off errors in the calculation. But the *final* answer must be reported with the proper number of significant figures.

Exercise 15

EXAMPLE 1.3   **Measuring the velocity of a car**

To measure the velocity of a car, clocks A and B are set up at two points along the road, as shown in FIGURE 1.20. Clock A is precise to 0.01 s, while B is precise to only 0.1 s. The distance between these two clocks is carefully measured to be 124.5 m. The two clocks are automatically started when the car passes a trigger in the road; each clock stops automatically when the car passes that clock. After the car has passed both clocks, clock A is found to read $t_A = 1.22$ s, and clock B to read $t_B = 4.5$ s. The time from the less-precise clock B is correctly reported with fewer significant figures than that from A. What is the velocity of the car, and how should it be reported with the correct number of significant figures?

FIGURE 1.20 Measuring the velocity of a car.

Both clocks start when the car crosses this trigger.

$\Delta x = 124.5$ m

PREPARE To calculate the velocity, we need the displacement Δx and the time interval Δt as the car moves between the two clocks. The displacement is given as $\Delta x = 124.5$ m; we can calculate the time interval as the difference between the two measured times.

SOLVE The time interval is:

This number has one decimal place.   This number has two decimal places.

$$\Delta t = t_B - t_A = (4.5 \text{ s}) - (1.22 \text{ s}) = 3.3 \text{ s}$$

By rule 2 of Tactics Box 1.1, the result should have *one* decimal place.

We can now calculate the velocity with the displacement and the time interval:

The displacement has four significant figures.

$$v = \frac{\Delta x}{\Delta t} = \frac{124.5 \text{ m}}{3.3 \text{ s}} = 38 \text{ m/s}$$

The time interval has two significant figures.   By rule 1 of Tactics Box 1.1, the result should have *two* significant figures.

ASSESS Our final value has two significant figures. Suppose you had been hired to measure the speed of a car this way, and you reported 37.72 m/s. It would be reasonable for someone looking at your result to assume that the measurements you used to arrive at this value were correct to four significant figures and thus that you had measured time to the nearest 0.001 second. Our correct result of 38 m/s has all of the accuracy that you can claim, but no more!

Scientific Notation

It's easy to write down measurements of ordinary-sized objects: Your height might be 1.72 meters, the weight of an apple 0.34 pound. But the radius of a hydrogen atom is 0.000000000053 m, and the distance to the moon is 384000000 m. Keeping track of all those zeros is quite cumbersome.

Beyond requiring you to deal with all the zeros, writing quantities this way makes it unclear how many significant figures are involved. In the distance to the moon given above, how many of those digits are significant? Three? Four? All nine?

Writing numbers using scientific notation avoids both these problems. A value in scientific notation is a number with one digit to the left of the decimal point and zero or more to the right of it, multiplied by a power of ten. This solves the problem of all the zeros and makes the number of significant figures immediately apparent. In scientific notation, writing the distance to the sun as 1.50×10^{11} m implies that three digits are significant; writing it as 1.5×10^{11} m implies that only two digits are.

Even for smaller values, scientific notation can clarify the number of significant figures. Suppose a distance is reported as 1200 m. How many significant figures does this measurement have? It's ambiguous, but using scientific notation can remove any ambiguity. If this distance is known to within 1 m, we can write it as 1.200×10^3 m, showing that all four digits are significant; if it is accurate to only 100 m or so, we can report it as 1.2×10^3 m, indicating two significant figures.

Tactics Box 1.2 shows how to convert a number to scientific notation, and how to correctly indicate the number of significant figures.

TACTICS BOX 1.2 **Using scientific notation**

To convert a number into scientific notation:

❶ For a number greater than 10, move the decimal point to the left until only one digit remains to the left of the decimal point. The remaining number is then multiplied by 10 to a power; this power is given by the number of spaces the decimal point was moved. Here we convert the diameter of the earth to scientific notation:

We move the decimal point until there is only one digit to its left, counting the number of steps.   Since we moved the decimal point 6 steps, the power of ten is 6.

$$6\ 370\ 000 \text{ m} = 6.37 \times 10^6 \text{ m}$$

The number of digits here equals the number of significant figures.

❷ For a number less than 1, move the decimal point to the right until it passes the first digit that isn't a zero. The remaining number is then multiplied by 10 to a negative power; the power is given by the number of spaces the decimal point was moved. For the diameter of a red blood cell we have:

We move the decimal point until it passes the first digit that is not a zero, counting the number of steps.   Since we moved the decimal point 6 steps, the power of ten is −6.

$$0.000\ 007\ 5 \text{ m} = 7.5 \times 10^{-6} \text{ m}$$

The number of digits here equals the number of significant figures.

Exercise 16

Proper use of significant figures is part of the "culture" of science. We will frequently emphasize these "cultural issues" because you must learn to speak the same language as the natives if you wish to communicate effectively! Most students know the rules of significant figures, having learned them in high school, but many fail to apply them. It is important that you understand the reasons for significant figures and that you get in the habit of using them properly.

Units

As we have seen, in order to measure a quantity we need to give it a numerical value. But a measurement is more than just a number—it requires a *unit* to be given. You can't go to the deli and ask for "three quarters of cheese." You need to use a unit—here, one of weight, such as pounds—in addition to the number.

In your daily life, you probably use the English system of units, in which distances are measured in inches, feet, and miles. These units are well adapted for daily life, but they are rarely used in scientific work. Given that science is an international discipline, it is also important to have a system of units that is recognized around the world. For these reasons, scientists use a system of units called *le Système Internationale d'Unités,* commonly referred to as **SI units.** SI units were originally developed by the French in the late 1700s as a way of standardizing and regularizing numbers for commerce and science. We often refer to these as *metric units* because the meter is the basic standard of length.

The three basic SI quantities, shown in Table 1.1, are time, length (or distance), and mass. Other quantities needed to understand motion can be expressed as combinations of these basic units. For example, speed and velocity are expressed in meters per second or m/s. This combination is a ratio of the length unit (the meter) to the time unit (the second).

The importance of units In 1999, the $125 million Mars Climate Orbiter burned up in the Martian atmosphere instead of entering a safe orbit from which it could perform observations. The problem was faulty units! An engineering team had provided critical data on spacecraft performance in English units, but the navigation team assumed these data were in metric units. As a consequence, the navigation team had the spacecraft fly too close to the planet, and it burned up in the atmosphere.

Using Prefixes

We will have many occasions to use lengths, times, and masses that are either much less or much greater than the standards of 1 meter, 1 second, and 1 kilogram. We will do so by using *prefixes* to denote various powers of ten. For instance, the prefix "kilo" (abbreviation k) denotes 10^3, or a factor of 1000. Thus 1 km equals 1000 m, 1 MW equals 10^6 watts, and 1 μV equals 10^{-6} V. Table 1.2 lists the common prefixes that will be used frequently throughout this book. A more extensive list of prefixes is shown inside the cover of the book.

Although prefixes make it easier to talk about quantities, the proper SI units are meters, seconds, and kilograms. Quantities given with prefixed units must be converted to base SI units before any calculations are done. Thus 23.0 cm must be converted to 0.230 m before starting calculations. The exception is the kilogram, which is already the base SI unit.

Unit Conversions

Although SI units are our standard, we cannot entirely forget that the United States still uses English units. Even after repeated exposure to metric units in classes, most of us "think" in English units. Thus it remains important to be able to convert back and forth between SI units and English units. Table 1.3 shows some frequently used conversions that will come in handy.

One effective method of performing unit conversions begins by noticing that since, for example, 1 mi = 1.609 km, the ratio of these two distances—*including their units*—is equal to 1, so that

$$\frac{1 \text{ mi}}{1.609 \text{ km}} = \frac{1.609 \text{ km}}{1 \text{ mi}} = 1$$

A ratio of values equal to 1 is called a **conversion factor.** The following Tactics Box shows how to make a unit conversion.

TABLE 1.1 Common SI units

Quantity	Unit	Abbreviation
time	second	s
length	meter	m
mass	kilogram	kg

TABLE 1.2 Common prefixes

Prefix	Abbreviation	Power of 10
mega-	M	10^6
kilo-	k	10^3
centi-	c	10^{-2}
milli-	m	10^{-3}
micro-	μ	10^{-6}
nano-	n	10^{-9}

TABLE 1.3 Useful unit conversions

1 inch (in) = 2.54 cm
1 foot (ft) = 0.305 m
1 mile (mi) = 1.609 km
1 mile per hour (mph) = 0.447 m/s
1 m = 39.37 in
1 km = 0.621 mi
1 m/s = 2.24 mph

TACTICS
BOX 1.3   **Making a unit conversion**

❶ Start with the quantity you wish to convert.

❷ Multiply by the appropriate conversion factor. Because this conversion factor is equal to 1, multiplying by it does not change the value of the quantity—only its units.

❺ Remember to convert your final answer to the correct number of significant figures!

$$60 \text{ mi} = 60 \text{ mi} \times \frac{1.609 \text{ km}}{1 \text{ mi}} = 96.54 \text{ km} = 97 \text{ km}$$

❸ You can cancel the original unit (here, miles) because it appears in both the numerator and the denominator.

❹ Calculate the answer; it is in the desired units. Remember, 60 mi and 96.54 km are the same distance; they are simply in different units.

Exercise 17

Note that we've rounded the answer to 97 kilometers because the distance we're converting, 60 miles, has only two significant figures.

More complicated conversions can be done with several successive multiplications of conversion factors, as we see in the next example.

EXAMPLE 1.4   **Can a bicycle go that fast?**

In Section 1.3, we calculated the speed of a bicycle to be 20 ft/s. Is this a reasonable speed for a bicycle?

PREPARE In order to determine whether or not this speed is reasonable, we will convert it to more familiar units. For speed, the unit you are most familiar with is likely miles per hour.

SOLVE We first collect the necessary unit conversions:

$$1 \text{ mi} = 5280 \text{ ft} \qquad 1 \text{ hour (1 h)} = 60 \text{ min} \qquad 1 \text{ min} = 60 \text{ s}$$

We then multiply our original value by successive factors of 1 in order to convert the units:

We want to cancel feet here in the numerator . . .

. . . so we multiply by $1 = \dfrac{1 \text{ mi}}{5280 \text{ ft}}$ to get the feet in the denominator.

$$20 \frac{\text{ft}}{\text{s}} = 20 \frac{\text{ft}}{\text{s}} \times \frac{1 \text{ mi}}{5280 \text{ ft}} \times \frac{60 \text{ s}}{1 \text{ min}} \times \frac{60 \text{ min}}{1 \text{ h}} = 14 \frac{\text{mi}}{\text{h}} = 14 \text{ mph}$$

The unwanted units cancel in pairs, as indicated by the colors.

ASSESS Our final result of 14 miles per hour (14 mph) is a very reasonable speed for a bicycle, which gives us confidence in our answer. If we had calculated a speed of 140 miles per hour, we would have suspected that we had made an error because this is quite a bit faster than the average bicyclist can travel!

How many jellybeans are in the jar? Some reasoning about the size of one bean and the size of the jar can give you a one-significant-figure estimate.

Estimation

When scientists and engineers first approach a problem, they may do a quick measurement or calculation to establish the rough physical scale involved. This will help establish the procedures that should be used to make a more accurate measurement—or the estimate may well be all that is needed.

Suppose you see a rock fall off a cliff and would like to know how fast it was going when it hit the ground. By doing a mental comparison with the speeds of familiar objects, such as cars and bicycles, you might judge that the rock was traveling at about 20 mph. This is a one-significant-figure estimate. With some luck, you can probably distinguish 20 mph from either 10 mph or 30 mph, but you certainly cannot distinguish 20 mph from 21 mph just from a visual appearance. A one-significant-figure estimate or calculation, such as this estimate of speed, is called an **order-of-magnitude estimate.** An order-of-magnitude estimate is indicated by the symbol $\sim$, which indicates even less precision than the "approximately equal" symbol $\approx$. You would report your estimate of the speed of the falling rock as $v \sim 20$ mph.

A useful skill is to make reliable order-of-magnitude estimates on the basis of known information, simple reasoning, and common sense. This is a skill that is acquired by practice. Tables 1.4 and 1.5 have information that will be useful for doing estimates.

TABLE 1.4 Some approximate lengths

	Length (m)
Circumference of the earth	4×10^7
Distance from New York to Los Angeles	5×10^6
Distance you can drive in 1 hour	1×10^5
Altitude of jet planes	1×10^4
Distance across a college campus	1000
Length of a football field	100
Length of a classroom	10
Length of your arm	1
Width of a textbook	0.1
Length of your little fingernail	0.01
Diameter of a pencil lead	1×10^{-3}
Thickness of a sheet of paper	1×10^{-4}
Diameter of a dust particle	1×10^{-5}

EXAMPLE 1.5 How fast do you walk?

Estimate how fast you walk, in meters per second.

PREPARE In order to compute speed, we need a distance and a time. If you walked a mile to campus, how long would this take? You'd probably say 30 minutes or so—half an hour. Let's use this rough number in our estimate.

SOLVE Given this estimate, we compute speed as

$$\text{speed} = \frac{\text{distance}}{\text{time}} \sim \frac{1 \text{ mile}}{1/2 \text{ hour}} = 2 \frac{\text{mi}}{\text{h}}$$

But we want the speed in meters per second. Since our calculation is only an estimate, we use an approximate form of the conversion factor from Table 1.3:

$$1 \frac{\text{mi}}{\text{h}} \approx 0.5 \frac{\text{m}}{\text{s}}$$

This gives an approximate walking speed of 1 m/s.

ASSESS Is this a reasonable value? Let's do another estimate. Your stride is probably about 1 yard long—about 1 meter. And you take about one step per second; next time you are walking, you can count and see. So a walking speed of 1 meter per second sounds pretty reasonable.

 PhET: Estimation

TABLE 1.5 Some approximate masses

	Mass (kg)
Large airliner	1×10^5
Small car	1000
Large human	100
Medium-size dog	10
Science textbook	1
Apple	0.1
Pencil	0.01
Raisin	1×10^{-3}
Fly	1×10^{-4}

This sort of estimation is very valuable. We will see many cases in which we need to know an approximate value for a quantity before we start a problem or after we finish a problem, in order to assess our results.

STOP TO THINK 1.4 Rank in order, from the most to the fewest, the number of significant figures in the following numbers. For example, if B has more than C, C has the same number as A, and A has more than D, give your answer as B > C = A > D.

A. 0.43   B. 0.0052   C. 0.430   D. 4.321×10^{-10}

1.5 Vectors and Motion: A First Look

Many physical quantities, such as time, temperature, and weight, can be described completely by a number with a unit. For example, the mass of an object might be 6 kg and its temperature 30° C. When a physical quantity is described by a single number (with a unit), we call it a **scalar quantity.** A scalar can be positive, negative, or zero.

Vectors and scalars

Scalars

Time, temperature and weight are all *scalar* quantities. To specify your weight, the temperature outside, or the current time, you only need a single number.

Vectors

The velocity of the race car is a *vector.* To fully specify a velocity, we need to give its magnitude (e.g., 120 mph) *and* its direction (e.g., west).

The force with which the boy pushes on his friend is another example of a vector. To completely specify this force, we must know not only how hard he pushes (the magnitude) but also in which direction.

The boat's displacement is the straight-line connection from its initial to its final position.

Many other quantities, however, have a directional quality and cannot be described by a single number. To describe the motion of a car, for example, you must specify not only how fast it is moving, but also the *direction* in which it is moving. A **vector quantity** is a quantity that has both a *size* (How far? or How fast?) and a *direction* (Which way?). The size or length of a vector is called its **magnitude.** The magnitude of a vector can be positive or zero, but it cannot be negative.

Some examples of vector and scalar quantities are shown on the left.

We graphically represent a vector as an *arrow,* as illustrated for the velocity and force vectors. The arrow is drawn to point in the direction of the vector quantity, and the *length* of the arrow is proportional to the magnitude of the vector quantity.

When we want to represent a vector quantity with a *symbol,* we need somehow to indicate that the symbol is for a vector rather than for a scalar. We do this by drawing an arrow over the letter that represents the quantity. Thus $\vec{r}$ and $\vec{A}$ are symbols for vectors, whereas r and A, without the arrows, are symbols for scalars. In handwritten work you *must* draw arrows over all symbols that represent vectors. This may seem strange until you get used to it, but it is very important because we will often use both r and $\vec{r}$, or both A and $\vec{A}$, in the same problem, and they mean different things!

NOTE ▶ The arrow over the symbol always points to the right, regardless of which direction the actual vector points. Thus we write $\vec{r}$ or $\vec{A}$, never $\overleftarrow{r}$ or $\overleftarrow{A}$. ◀

Displacement Vectors

For motion along a line, we found in Section 1.2 that the displacement is a quantity that specifies not only how *far* an object moves but also the *direction*—to the left or to the right—that the object moves. Since displacement is a quantity that has both a magnitude (How far?) and a direction, it can be represented by a vector, the **displacement vector.** FIGURE 1.21 shows the displacement vector for Sam's trip that we discussed earlier. We've simply drawn an arrow—the vector—from his initial to his final position and assigned it the symbol $\vec{d}_S$. Because $\vec{d}_S$ has both a magnitude and a direction, it is convenient to write Sam's displacement as $\vec{d}_S = (100 \text{ ft, east})$. The first value in the parentheses is the magnitude of the vector (i.e., the size of the displacement), and the second value specifies its direction.

FIGURE 1.21 Two displacement vectors.

Also shown in Figure 1.21 is the displacement vector $\vec{d}_J$ for Jane, who started on 12th Street and ended up on Vine. As with Sam, we draw her displacement vector as an arrow from her initial to her final position. In this case, $\vec{d}_J = 100$ ft, 30° east of north).

Jane's trip illustrates an important point about displacement vectors. Jane started her trip on 12th Street and ended up on Vine, leading to the displacement vector shown. But to get from her initial to her final position, she needn't have walked along the straight-line path denoted by $\vec{d}_J$. If she walked east along 12th Street to the intersection and then headed north on Vine, her displacement would still be the vector shown. **An object's displacement vector is drawn from the object's initial position to its final position, regardless of the actual path followed between these two points.**

Vector Addition

Let's consider one more trip for the peripatetic Sam. In FIGURE 1.22, he starts at the intersection and walks east 50 ft; then he walks 100 ft to the northeast through a vacant lot. His displacement vectors for the two legs of his trip are labeled $\vec{d}_1$ and $\vec{d}_2$ in the figure.

Sam's trip consists of two legs that can be represented by the two vectors $\vec{d}_1$ and $\vec{d}_2$, but we can represent his trip as a whole, from his initial starting position to his overall final position, with the *net* displacement vector labeled $\vec{d}_{net}$. Sam's net displacement is in a sense the *sum* of the two displacements that made it up, so we can write

$$\vec{d}_{net} = \vec{d}_1 + \vec{d}_2$$

Sam's net displacement thus requires the *addition* of two vectors, but vector addition obeys different rules from the addition of two scalar quantities. The directions of the two vectors, as well as their magnitudes, must be taken into account. Sam's trip suggests that we can add vectors together by putting the "tail" of one vector at the tip of the other. This idea, which is reasonable for displacement vectors, in fact is how *any* two vectors are added. Tactics Box 1.4 shows how to add two vectors $\vec{A}$ and $\vec{B}$.

FIGURE 1.22 Sam undergoes two displacements.

MP **PhET:** Vector Addition

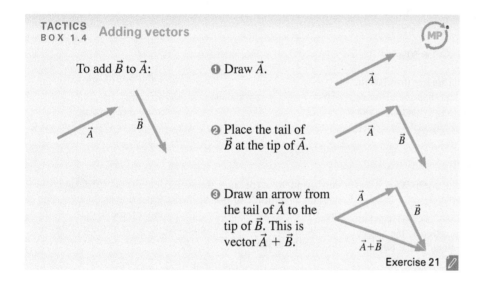

TACTICS BOX 1.4 **Adding vectors**

To add $\vec{B}$ to $\vec{A}$:

❶ Draw $\vec{A}$.

❷ Place the tail of $\vec{B}$ at the tip of $\vec{A}$.

❸ Draw an arrow from the tail of $\vec{A}$ to the tip of $\vec{B}$. This is vector $\vec{A} + \vec{B}$.

Exercise 21

Vectors and Trigonometry

When we need to add displacements or other vectors in more than one dimension, we'll end up computing lengths and angles of triangles. This is the job of trigonometry. Trigonometry will be our primary mathematical tool for vector addition; let's review the basic ideas.

Suppose we have a right triangle with hypotenuse H, angle θ, side opposite the angle O, and side adjacent to the angle A, as shown in FIGURE 1.23. The sine, cosine, and tangent (which we write as "sin," "cos," and "tan") of angle θ are defined as ratios of the sides of the triangle:

$$\sin\theta = \frac{O}{H} \qquad \cos\theta = \frac{A}{H} \qquad \tan\theta = \frac{O}{A} \qquad (1.3)$$

If you know the angle θ and the length of one side, you can use the sine, cosine, or tangent to find the lengths of the other sides. For example, if you know θ and the length A of the adjacent side, you can find the hypotenuse H by rearranging the middle Equation 1.3 to give $H = A/\cos\theta$.

FIGURE 1.23 A right triangle.

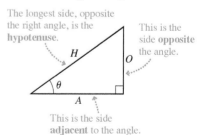

The longest side, opposite the right angle, is the **hypotenuse**.

This is the side **opposite** the angle.

This is the side **adjacent** to the angle.

Conversely, if you know two sides of the triangle, you can find the angle θ by using inverse trigonometric functions:

$$\theta = \sin^{-1}\left(\frac{O}{H}\right) \qquad \theta = \cos^{-1}\left(\frac{A}{H}\right) \qquad \theta = \tan^{-1}\left(\frac{O}{A}\right) \qquad (1.4)$$

We will make regular use of these relationships in the following chapters.

EXAMPLE 1.6   **How far north and east?**

Suppose Alex is navigating using a compass. She starts walking at an angle 60° north of east and walks a total of 100 m. How far north is she from her starting point? How far east?

PREPARE A sketch of Alex's motion is shown in FIGURE 1.24a. We've shown north and east as they would be on a map, and we've noted Alex's displacement as a vector, giving its magnitude and direction. FIGURE 1.24b shows a triangle with this displacement as the hypotenuse. Alex's distance north of her starting point and her distance east of her starting point are the sides of this triangle.

SOLVE The sine and cosine functions are ratios of sides of right triangles, as we saw above. With the 60° angle as noted, the distance north of the starting point is the opposite side of the triangle; the distance east is the adjacent side. Thus:

distance north of start = (100 m) sin (60°) = 87 m

distance east of start = (100 m) cos (60°) = 50 m

ASSESS Both of the distances we calculated are less than 100 m, as they must be, and the distance east is less than the distance north, as our diagram in Figure 1.24b shows it should be. Our

answers seem reasonable. In finding the solution to this problem, we "broke down" the displacement into two different distances, one north and one east. This hints at the idea of the *components* of a vector, something we'll explore in the next chapter.

FIGURE 1.24 An analysis of Alex's motion.

(a)

North

$\vec{d}$ = (100 m, 60° north of east)

60°

East

(b)

The displacement is the hypotenuse of the triangle.

Distance north of start

60°

Distance east of start

EXAMPLE 1.7   **How far away is Anna?**

Anna walks 90 m due east and then 50 m due north. What is her displacement from her starting point?

PREPARE Let's start with the sketch in FIGURE 1.25a. We set up a coordinate system with Anna's original position as the origin, and then we drew her two subsequent motions as the two displacement vectors $\vec{d}_1$ and $\vec{d}_2$.

FIGURE 1.25 Analyzing Anna's motion.

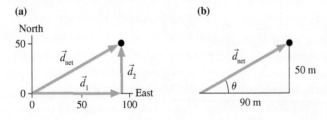

(a)

North

50

$\vec{d}_{net}$

$\vec{d}_1$

$\vec{d}_2$

East

0   50   100

(b)

$\vec{d}_{net}$

θ

90 m

50 m

SOLVE We drew the two vector displacements with the tail of one vector starting at the head of the previous one—exactly what is needed to form a vector sum. The vector $\vec{d}_{net}$ in Figure 1.25a is the vector sum of the successive displacements and thus represents Anna's net displacement from the origin.

Anna's distance from the origin is the length of this vector $\vec{d}_{net}$. FIGURE 1.25b shows that this vector is the hypotenuse of a right triangle with sides 50 m (because Anna walked 50 m

north) and 90 m (because she walked 90 m east). We can compute the magnitude of this vector, her net displacement, using the Pythagorean theorem (the square of the length of the hypotenuse of a triangle is equal to the sum of the squares of the lengths of the sides):

$$d_{net}^2 = (50 \text{ m})^2 + (90 \text{ m})^2$$

$$d_{net} = \sqrt{(50 \text{ m})^2 + (90 \text{ m})^2} = 103 \text{ m} \approx 100 \text{ m}$$

We have rounded off to the appropriate number of significant figures, giving us 100 m for the magnitude of the displacement vector. How about the direction? Figure 1.25b identifies the angle that gives the angle north of east of Anna's displacement. In the right triangle, 50 m is the opposite side and 90 m is the adjacent side, so the angle is given by

$$\theta = \tan^{-1}\left(\frac{50 \text{ m}}{90 \text{ m}}\right) = \tan^{-1}\left(\frac{5}{9}\right) = 29°$$

Putting it all together, we get a net displacement of

$$\vec{d}_{net} = (100 \text{ m}, 29° \text{ north of east})$$

ASSESS We can use our drawing to assess our result. If the two sides of the triangle are 50 m and 90 m, a length of 100 m for the hypotenuse seems about right. The angle is certainly less than 45°, but not too much less, so 29° seems reasonable.

Velocity Vectors

We've seen that a basic quantity describing the motion of an object is its velocity. Velocity is a vector quantity because its specification involves not only how fast an object is moving (its speed) but also the direction in which the object is moving. We thus represent the velocity of an object by a **velocity vector** $\vec{v}$ that points in the direction of the object's motion, and whose magnitude is the object's speed.

FIGURE 1.26a shows the motion diagram of a car accelerating from rest. We've drawn vectors showing the car's displacement between successive positions of the motion diagram. How can we draw the velocity vectors on this diagram? First, note that the direction of the displacement vector is the direction of motion between successive points in the motion diagram. But the velocity of an object also points in the direction of motion, so an object's velocity vector points in the same direction as its displacement vector. Second, we've already noted that the magnitude of the velocity vector—How fast?—is the object's speed. Because higher speeds imply greater displacements in the same time interval, you can see that the length of the velocity vector should be proportional to the length of the displacement vector between successive points on a motion diagram. Consequently, the vectors connecting each dot of a motion diagram to the next, which we previously labeled as displacement vectors, could equally well be identified as velocity vectors. This is shown in FIGURE 1.26b. **From now on, we'll show and label velocity vectors on motion diagrams rather than displacement vectors.**

NOTE ▶ The velocity vectors shown in Figure 1.26b are actually *average* velocity vectors. Because the velocity is steadily increasing, it's a bit less than this average at the start of each time interval, and a bit more at the end. In Chapter 2 we'll refine these ideas as we develop the idea of instantaneous velocity. ◀

FIGURE 1.26 The motion diagram for a car starting from rest.

EXAMPLE 1.8   Drawing a ball's motion diagram

Jake hits a ball at a 60° angle from the horizontal. It is caught by Jim. Draw a motion diagram of the ball that shows velocity vectors rather than displacement vectors.

PREPARE This example is typical of how many problems in science and engineering are worded. The problem does not give a clear statement of where the motion begins or ends. Are we interested in the motion of the ball only during the time it is in the air between Jake and Jim? What about the motion *as* Jake hits it (ball rapidly speeding up) or *as* Jim catches it (ball rapidly slowing down)? Should we include Jim dropping the ball after he catches it? The point is that *you* will often be called on to make a *reasonable interpretation* of a problem statement. In this problem, the details of hitting and catching the ball are complex. The motion of the ball through the air is easier to describe, and it's a motion you might expect to learn about in a physics class. So our *interpretation* is that the motion diagram should start as the ball leaves Jake's bat (ball already moving) and should end the instant it touches Jim's hand (ball still moving). We will model the ball as a particle.

SOLVE With this interpretation in mind, FIGURE 1.27 shows the motion diagram of the ball. Notice how, in contrast to the car of Figure 1.26, the ball is already moving as the motion diagram movie begins. As before, the velocity vectors are shown by connecting the dots with arrows. You can see that the velocity vectors get shorter (ball slowing down), get longer (ball speeding up), and change direction. Each $\vec{v}$ is different, so this is *not* constant-velocity motion.

FIGURE 1.27 The motion diagram of a ball traveling from Jake to Jim.

ASSESS We haven't learned enough to make a detailed analysis of the motion of the ball, but it's still worthwhile to do a quick assessment. Does our diagram make sense? Think about the velocity of the ball—we show it moving upward at the start and downward at the end. This does match what happens when you toss a ball back and forth, so our answer seems reasonable.

$\vec{P}$ and $\vec{Q}$ are two vectors of equal length but different direction. Which vector shows the sum $\vec{P} + \vec{Q}$?

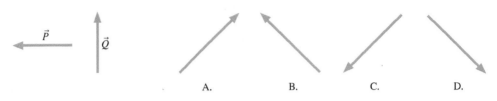

A.   B.   C.   D.

1.6 Where Do We Go from Here?

This first chapter has been an introduction to some of the fundamental ideas about motion and some of the basic techniques that you will use in the rest of the course. You have seen some examples of how to make *models* of a physical situation, thereby focusing in on the essential elements of the situation. You have learned some practical ideas, such as how to convert quantities from one kind of units to another. The rest of this book—and the rest of your course—will extend these themes. You will learn how to model many kinds of physical systems, and learn the technical skills needed to set up and solve problems using these models.

In each chapter of this book, you'll learn both new principles and more tools and techniques. We are starting with motion, but, by the end of the book, you'll have learned about more abstract concepts such as magnetic fields and the structure of the nucleus of the atom. As you proceed, you'll find that each new chapter depends on those that preceded it. The principles and the problem-solving strategies you learned in this chapter will still be needed in Chapter 30.

We'll give you some assistance integrating new ideas with the material of previous chapters. When you start a chapter, the **chapter preview** will let you know which topics are especially important to review. And the last element in each chapter will be an **integrated example** that brings together the principles and techniques you have just learned with those you learned previously. The integrated nature of these examples will also be a helpful reminder that the problems of the real world are similarly complex, and solving such problems requires you to do just this kind of integration.

Our first integrated example is reasonably straightforward because there's not much to integrate yet. The examples in future chapters will be much richer.

◀ Chapter 28 ends with an integrated example that explores the basic physics of magnetic resonance imaging (MRI), explaining how the interaction of magnetic fields with the nuclei of atoms in the body can be used to create an image of the body's interior.

A goose gets its bearings

Migrating geese determine direction using many different tools: by noting local landmarks, by following rivers and roads, and by using the position of the sun in the sky. When the weather is overcast so that they can't use the sun's position to get their bearings, geese may start their day's flight in the wrong direction. FIGURE 1.28 shows the path of a Canada goose that flew in a straight line for some time before making a corrective right-angle turn. One hour after beginning, the goose made a rest stop on a lake due east of its original position.

FIGURE 1.28 Trajectory of a misdirected goose.

a. How much extra distance did the goose travel due to its initial error in flight direction? That is, how much farther did it fly than if it had simply flown directly to its final position on the lake?
b. What was the flight speed of the goose?
c. A typical flight speed for a migrating goose is 80 km/h. Given this, does your result seem reasonable?

PREPARE Figure 1.28 shows the trajectory of the goose, but it's worthwhile to redraw Figure 1.28 and note the displacement from the start to the end of the journey, the shortest distance the goose could have flown. (The examples in the chapter to this point have used professionally rendered drawings, but these are much more careful and detailed than you are likely to make. FIGURE 1.29 shows a drawing that is more typical of what you might actually do when working problems yourself.) Drawing and labeling the displacement between the starting and ending points in Figure 1.29 show that it is the hypotenuse of a right triangle, so we can use our rules for triangles as we look for a solution.

FIGURE 1.29 A typical student sketch shows the motion and the displacement of the goose.

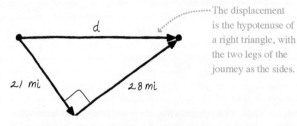

The displacement is the hypotenuse of a right triangle, with the two legs of the journey as the sides.

SOLVE

a. The minimum distance the goose *could* have flown, if it flew straight to the lake, is the hypotenuse of a triangle with sides 21 mi and 28 mi. This straight-line distance is

$$d = \sqrt{(21 \text{ mi})^2 + (28 \text{ mi})^2} = 35 \text{ mi}$$

The actual distance the goose flew is the sum of the distances traveled for the two legs of the journey:

$$\text{distance traveled} = 21 \text{ mi} + 28 \text{ mi} = 49 \text{ mi}$$

The extra distance flown is the difference between the actual distance flown and the straight-line distance—namely, 14 miles.

b. To compute the flight speed, we need to consider the distance that the bird actually flew. The flight speed is the total distance flown divided by the total time of the flight:

$$v = \frac{49 \text{ mi}}{1.0 \text{ h}} = 49 \text{ mi/h}$$

c. To compare our calculated speed with a typical flight speed, we must convert our solution to km/h, rounding off to the correct number of significant digits:

$$49 \, \frac{\text{mi}}{\text{h}} \times \frac{1.61 \text{ km}}{1.00 \text{ mi}} = 79 \, \frac{\text{km}}{\text{h}}$$

A calculator will return many more digits, but the original data had only two significant figures, so we report the final result to this accuracy.

ASSESS In this case, an assessment was built into the solution of the problem. The calculated flight speed matches the expected value for a goose, which gives us confidence that our answer is correct. As a further check, our calculated net displacement of 35 mi seems about right for the hypotenuse of the triangle in Figure 1.29.

SUMMARY

The goals of Chapter 1 have been to introduce the fundamental concepts of motion and to review the related basic mathematical principles.

IMPORTANT CONCEPTS

Motion Diagrams

The particle model represents a moving object as if all its mass were concentrated at a single point. Using this model, we can represent motion with a **motion diagram**, where dots indicate the object's positions at successive times. In a motion diagram, the time interval between successive dots is always the same.

Each dot represents the position of the object. Each position is labeled with the time at which the dot was there.

The time interval between successive positions is the same.

Scalars and Vectors

Scalar quantities have only a magnitude and can be represented by a single number. Temperature, time, and mass are scalars.

A vector is a quantity described by both a magnitude and a direction. Velocity and displacement are vectors.

Velocity vectors can be drawn on a motion diagram by connecting successive points with a vector.

Direction

$\vec{A}$

The length of a vector is proportional to its magnitude.

Velocity vectors span successive points in a motion diagram.

Start

$\vec{v}$

The velocity vectors are getting longer, so the object is speeding up.

Describing Motion

Position locates an object with respect to a chosen coordinate system. It is described by a **coordinate.**

The *coordinate* is the variable used to describe the position.

x (mi)

$-6\ -5\ -4\ -3\ -2\ -1\quad 0\quad 1\quad 2\quad 3\quad 4\quad 5$

This cow is at $x = -5$ miles.   This car is at $x = +4$ miles.

A change in position is called a **displacement.** For motion along a line, a displacement is a signed quantity. The displacement from x_i to x_f is $\Delta x = x_f - x_i$.

Time is measured from a particular instant to which we assign $t = 0$. A **time interval** is the elapsed time between two specific instants t_i and t_f. It is given by $\Delta t = t_f - t_i$.

Velocity is the ratio of the displacement of an object to the time interval during which this displacement occurs:

$$v = \frac{\Delta x}{\Delta t}$$

Units

Every measurement of a quantity must include a unit.

The standard system of units used in science is the SI system. Common SI units include:

- Length: meters (m)
- Time: seconds (s)
- Mass: kilograms (kg)

APPLICATIONS

Working with Numbers

In scientific notation, a number is expressed as a decimal number between 1 and 10 multiplied by a power of ten. In scientific notation, the diameter of the earth is 1.27×10^7 m.

A prefix can be used before a unit to indicate a multiple of 10 or 1/10. Thus we can write the diameter of the earth as 12,700 km, where the k in km denotes 1000.

We can perform a unit conversion to convert the diameter of the earth to a different unit, such as miles. We do so by multiplying by a conversion factor equal to 1, such as 1 = 1 mi/1.61 km.

Significant figures are reliably known digits. The number of significant figures for:

- **Multiplication, division, and powers** is set by the value with the fewest significant figures.
- **Addition and subtraction** is set by the value with the smallest number of decimal places.

An order-of-magnitude estimate is an estimate that has an accuracy of about one significant figure. Such estimates are usually made using rough numbers from everyday experience.

Problem difficulty is labeled as | (straightforward) to |||| (challenging). Problems labeled BIO are of biological or medical interest.

 For homework assigned on MasteringPhysics, go to www.masteringphysics.com

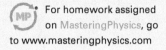 Scan this QR code to launch a Video Tutor Solution that will help you solve problems for this chapter.

QUESTIONS

Conceptual Questions

1. a. Write a paragraph describing the *particle model*. What is it, and why is it important?
   b. Give two examples of situations, different from those described in the text, for which the particle model is appropriate.
   c. Give an example of a situation, different from those described in the text, for which it would be inappropriate.

2. A softball player slides into second base. Use the particle model to draw a motion diagram of the player from the time he begins to slide until he reaches the base. Number the dots in order, starting with zero.

3. A car travels to the left at a steady speed for a few seconds, then brakes for a stop sign. Use the particle model to draw a motion diagram of the car for the entire motion described here. Number the dots in order, starting with zero.

4. A ball is dropped from the roof of a tall building and students in a physics class are asked to sketch a motion diagram for this situation. A student submits the diagram shown in Figure Q1.4. Is the diagram correct? Explain.

   FIGURE Q1.4
   ● 0
   ● 1
   ● 2
   ● 3
   ● 4

5. Write a sentence or two describing the difference between position and displacement. Give one example of each.

6. Give an example of a trip you might take in your car for which the distance traveled as measured on your car's odometer is not equal to the displacement between your initial and final positions.

7. Write a sentence or two describing the difference between speed and velocity. Give one example of each.

8. The motion of a skateboard along a horizontal axis is observed for 5 s. The initial position of the skateboard is negative with respect to a chosen origin, and its velocity throughout the 5 s is also negative. At the end of the observation time, is the skateboard closer to or farther from the origin than initially? Explain.

9. Can the velocity of an object be positive during a time interval in which its position is always negative? Can its velocity be positive during a time interval in which its displacement is negative?

10. Two friends watch a jogger complete a 400 m lap around the track in 100 s. One of the friends states, "The jogger's velocity was 4 m/s during this lap." The second friend objects, saying, "No, the jogger's speed was 4 m/s." Who is correct? Justify your answer.

11. A softball player hits the ball and starts running toward first base. Draw a motion diagram, using the particle model, showing her velocity vectors during the first few seconds of her run.

12. A child is sledding on a smooth, level patch of snow. She encounters a rocky patch and slows to a stop. Draw a motion diagram, using the particle model, showing her velocity vectors.

13. A skydiver jumps out of an airplane. Her speed steadily increases until she deploys her parachute, at which point her speed quickly decreases. She subsequently falls to earth at a constant rate, stopping when she lands on the ground. Draw a motion diagram, using the particle model, that shows her position at successive times and includes velocity vectors.

14. Your roommate drops a tennis ball from a third-story balcony. It hits the sidewalk and bounces as high as the second story. Draw a motion diagram, using the particle model, showing the ball's velocity vectors from the time it is released until it reaches the maximum height on its bounce.

15. A car is driving north at a steady speed. It makes a gradual 90° left turn without losing speed, then continues driving to the west. Draw a motion diagram, using the particle model, showing the car's velocity vectors as seen from a helicopter hovering over the highway.

16. A toy car rolls down a ramp, then across a smooth, horizontal floor. Draw a motion diagram, using the particle model, showing the car's velocity vectors.

17. Estimate the average speed with which you go from home to campus (or another trip you commonly make) via whatever mode of transportation you use most commonly. Give your answer in both mph and m/s. Describe how you arrived at this estimate.

18. Estimate the number of times you sneezed during the past year. Describe how you arrived at this estimate.

19. Density is the ratio of an object's mass to its volume. Would you expect density to be a vector or a scalar quantity? Explain.

Multiple-Choice Questions

20. | A student walks 1.0 mi west and then 1.0 mi north. Afterward, how far is she from her starting point?
    A. 1.0 mi   B. 1.4 mi
    C. 1.6 mi   D. 2.0 mi

21. | Which of the following motions is described by the motion diagram of Figure Q1.21?
    A. An ice skater gliding across the ice.
    B. An airplane braking to a stop after landing.
    C. A car pulling away from a stop sign.
    D. A pool ball bouncing off a cushion and reversing direction.

    FIGURE Q1.21
    0 1 2   3   4   5
    ●● ●   ●   ●   ●

22. | A bird flies 3.0 km due west and then 2.0 km due north. What is the magnitude of the bird's displacement?
    A. 2.0 km   B. 3.0 km
    C. 3.6 km   D. 5.0 km

23. ‖ A bird flies 3.0 km due west and then 2.0 km due north. Another bird flies 2.0 km due west and 3.0 km due north. What is the angle between the net displacement vectors for the two birds?
    A. 23°   B. 34°   C. 56°   D. 90°

24. | A woman walks briskly at 2.00 m/s. How much time will it take her to walk one mile?
    A. 8.30 min   B. 13.4 min   C. 21.7 min   D. 30.0 min

25. | Compute 3.24 m + 0.532 m to the correct number of significant figures.
    A. 3.7 m   B. 3.77 m   C. 3.772 m   D. 3.7720 m

26. | A rectangle has length 3.24 m and height 0.532 m. To the correct number of significant figures, what is its area?
    A. 1.72 m^2 B. 1.723 m^2
    C. 1.7236 m^2 D. 1.72368 m^2

27. | The earth formed 4.57×10^9 years ago. What is this time in seconds?
    A. 1.67×10^{12} s   B. 4.01×10^{13} s
    C. 2.40×10^{15} s   D. 1.44×10^{17} s

28. ‖ An object's average density ρ is defined as the ratio of its mass to its volume: $\rho = M/V$. The earth's mass is 5.94×10^{24} kg, and its volume is 1.08×10^{12} km^3. What is the earth's average density?
    A. 5.50×10^3 kg/m^3 B. 5.50×10^6 kg/m^3
    C. 5.50×10^9 kg/m^3 D. 5.50×10^{12} kg/m^3

PROBLEMS

Section 1.1 Motion: A First Look

1. | You've made a video of a car as it skids to a halt to avoid hitting an object in the road. Use the images from the video to draw a motion diagram of the car from the time the skid begins until the car is stopped.

2. | A man rides a bike along a straight road for 5 min, then has a flat tire. He stops for 5 min to repair the flat, but then realizes he cannot fix it. He continues his journey by walking the rest of the way, which takes him another 10 min. Use the particle model to draw a motion diagram of the man for the entire motion described here. Number the dots in order, starting with zero.

3. | A jogger running east at a steady pace suddenly develops a cramp. He is lucky: A westbound bus is sitting at a bus stop just ahead. He gets on the bus and enjoys a quick ride home. Use the particle model to draw a motion diagram of the jogger for the entire motion described here. Number the dots in order, starting with zero.

Section 1.2 Position and Time: Putting Numbers on Nature

4. | Figure P1.4 shows Sue between her home and the cinema. What is Sue's position x if
    a. Her home is the origin?
    b. The cinema is the origin?

FIGURE P1.4   2 mi   3 mi

5. | Keira starts at position $x = 23$ m along a coordinate axis. She then undergoes a displacement of -45 m. What is her final position?

6. | A car travels along a straight east-west road. A coordinate system is established on the road, with x increasing to the east. The car ends up 14 mi west of the intersection with Mulberry Road. If its displacement was -23 mi, how far from and on which side of Mulberry Road did it start?

7. | Foraging bees often move in straight lines away from and toward their hives. Suppose a bee starts at its hive and flies 500 m due east, then flies 400 m west, then 700 m east. How far is the bee from the hive?

Section 1.3 Velocity

8. | A security guard walks 110 m in one trip around the perimeter of the building. It takes him 240 s to make this trip. What is his speed?

9. ‖ List the following items in order of decreasing speed, from greatest to least: (i) A wind-up toy car that moves 0.15 m in 2.5 s. (ii) A soccer ball that rolls 2.3 m in 0.55 s. (iii) A bicycle that travels 0.60 m in 0.075 s. (iv) A cat that runs 8.0 m in 2.0 s.

10. ‖ Figure P1.10 shows the motion diagram for a horse galloping in one direction along a straight path. Not every dot is labeled, but the dots are at equally spaced instants of time. What is the horse's velocity
    a. During the first ten seconds of its gallop?
    b. During the interval from 30 s to 40 s?
    c. During the interval from 50 s to 70 s?

FIGURE P1.10

11. ‖ It takes Harry 35 s to walk from $x = -12$ m to $x = -47$ m. What is his velocity?

12. | A dog trots from $x = -12$ m to $x = 3$ m in 10 s. What is its velocity?

13. | A ball rolling along a straight line with velocity 0.35 m/s goes from $x = 2.1$ m to $x = 7.3$ m. How much time does this take?

Section 1.4 A Sense of Scale: Significant Figures, Scientific Notation, and Units

14. ‖ Convert the following to SI units:
    a. 9.12 μs   b. 3.42 km
    c. 44 cm/ms   d. 80 km/hour

15. | Convert the following to SI units:
    a. 8.0 in   b. 66 ft/s   c. 60 mph

16. | Convert the following to SI units:
    a. 1.0 hour   b. 1.0 day   c. 1.0 year

17. ‖ List the following three speeds in order, from smallest to largest: 1 mm per μs, 1 km per ks, 1 cm per ms.

18. | How many significant figures does each of the following numbers have?
    a. 6.21   b. 62.1   c. 0.620   d. 0.062
19. | How many significant figures does each of the following numbers have?
    a. 0.621   b. 0.006200
    c. 1.0621   d. 6.21×10^3
20. | Compute the following numbers to 3 significant figures.
    a. 33.3×25.4 b. $33.3 - 25.4$
    c. $\sqrt{33.3}$ d. $333.3 \div 25.4$
21. ‖‖‖ The Empire State Building has a height of 1250 ft. Express this height in meters, giving your result in scientific notation with three significant figures.
22. | Estimate (don't measure!) the length of a typical car. Give your answer in both feet and meters. Briefly describe how you arrived at this estimate.
23. ‖‖ Blades of grass grow from the bottom, so, as growth occurs, BIO the top of the blade moves upward. During the summer, when your lawn is growing quickly, estimate this speed in m/s. Explain how you made this estimate, and express your result in scientific notation.
24. ‖ Estimate the average speed with which the hair on your head BIO grows. Give your answer in both m/s and μm/h. Briefly describe how you arrived at this estimate.
25. ‖ Estimate the average speed at which your fingernails grow, in BIO both m/s and μm/h. Briefly describe how you arrived at this estimate.

Section 1.5 Vectors and Motion: A First Look

26. | Carol and Robin share a house. To get to work, Carol walks north 2.0 km while Robin drives west 7.5 km. How far apart are their workplaces?
27. | Joe and Max shake hands and say goodbye. Joe walks east 0.55 km to a coffee shop, and Max flags a cab and rides north 3.25 km to a bookstore. How far apart are their destinations?
28. ‖ A city has streets laid out in a square grid, with each block 135 m long. If you drive north for three blocks, then west for two blocks, how far are you from your starting point?
29. ‖ A butterfly flies from the top of a tree in the center of a garden to rest on top of a red flower at the garden's edge. The tree is 8.0 m taller than the flower, and the garden is 12 m wide. Determine the magnitude of the butterfly's displacement.
30. ‖‖ A garden has a circular path of radius 50 m. John starts at the easternmost point on this path, then walks counterclockwise around the path until he is at its southernmost point. What is John's displacement? Use the (magnitude, direction) notation for your answer.
31. | Migrating geese tend to travel in straight-line paths at approx- BIO imately constant speed. A goose flies 32 km south, then turns to fly 20 km west. How far is the goose from its original position?
32. ‖‖‖‖ A ball on a porch rolls 60 cm to the porch's edge, drops 40 cm, continues rolling on the grass, and eventually stops 80 cm from the porch's edge. What is the magnitude of the ball's net displacement, in centimeters?
33. ‖ A kicker punts a football from the very center of the field to the sideline 43 yards downfield. What is the net displacement of the ball? (A football field is 53 yards wide.)

General Problems

Problems 34 through 40 are motion problems similar to those you will learn to solve in Chapter 2. For now, simply *interpret* the problem by drawing a motion diagram showing the object's position and its velocity vectors. Do *not* solve these problems or do any mathematics.

34. ‖ In a typical greyhound race, a dog accelerates to a speed of BIO 20 m/s over a distance of 30 m. It then maintains this speed. What would be a greyhound's time in the 100 m dash?
35. ‖ Billy drops a watermelon from the top of a three-story building, 10 m above the sidewalk. How fast is the watermelon going when it hits?
36. ‖ Sam is recklessly driving 60 mph in a 30 mph speed zone when he suddenly sees the police. He steps on the brakes and slows to 30 mph in three seconds, looking nonchalant as he passes the officer. How far does he travel while braking?
37. ‖ A speed skater moving across frictionless ice at 8.0 m/s hits a 5.0-m-wide patch of rough ice. She slows steadily, then continues on at 6.0 m/s. What is her acceleration on the rough ice?
38. ‖ The giant eland, an African antelope, is an exceptional BIO jumper, able to leap 1.5 m off the ground. To jump this high, with what speed must the eland leave the ground?
39. ‖ A ball rolls along a smooth horizontal floor at 10 m/s, then starts up a 20° ramp. How high does it go before rolling back down?
40. ‖ A motorist is traveling at 20 m/s. He is 60 m from a stop light when he sees it turn yellow. His reaction time, before stepping on the brake, is 0.50 s. What steady deceleration while braking will bring him to a stop right at the light?

Problems 41 through 46 show a motion diagram. For each of these problems, write a one or two sentence "story" about a *real object* that has this motion diagram. Your stories should talk about people or objects by name and say what they are doing. Problems 34 through 40 are examples of motion short stories.

41. |

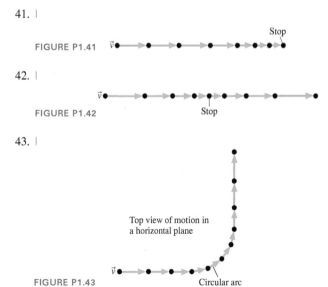

FIGURE P1.41 $\vec{v}$ Stop

42. |

FIGURE P1.42 $\vec{v}$ Stop

43. |

Top view of motion in a horizontal plane

FIGURE P1.43 $\vec{v}$ Circular arc

44. |

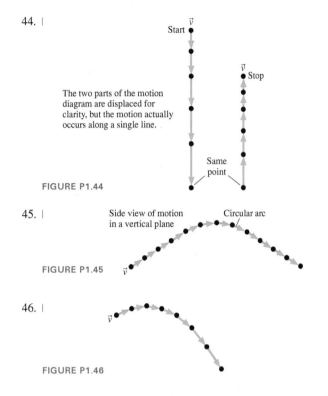

The two parts of the motion diagram are displaced for clarity, but the motion actually occurs along a single line.

FIGURE P1.44

45. |

Side view of motion in a vertical plane

Circular arc

FIGURE P1.45

46. |

FIGURE P1.46

47. ‖‖‖ How many inches does light travel in one nanosecond? The speed of light is 3.0×10^8 m/s.

48. | Joseph watches the roadside mile markers during a long car trip on an interstate highway. He notices that at 10:45 A.M. they are passing a marker labeled 101, and at 11:00 A.M. the car reaches marker 119. What is the car's speed, in mph?

49. ‖ Alberta is going to have dinner at her grandmother's house, but she is running a bit behind schedule. As she gets onto the highway, she knows that she must exit the highway within 45 min if she is not going to arrive late. Her exit is 32 mi away. What is the slowest speed at which she could drive and still arrive in time? Express your answer in miles per hour.

50. ‖ The end of Hubbard Glacier in Alaska advances by an average of 105 feet per year. What is the speed of advance of the glacier in m/s?

51. | The earth completes a circular orbit around the sun in one year. The orbit has a radius of 93,000,000 miles. What is the speed of the earth around the sun in m/s? Report your result using scientific notation.

52. ‖‖ Shannon decides to check the accuracy of her speedometer. She adjusts her speed to read exactly 70 mph on her speedometer and holds this steady, measuring the time between successive mile markers separated by exactly 1.00 mile. If she measures a time of 54 s, is her speedometer accurate? If not, is the speed it shows too high or too low?

53. ‖ Motor neurons in mammals transmit signals from the brain to
BIO skeletal muscles at approximately 25 m/s. Estimate how much time in ms (10^{-3} s) it will take for a signal to get from your brain to your hand.

54. ‖ Satellite data taken several times per hour on a particular
BIO albatross showed travel of 1200 km over a time of 1.4 days.
   a. Given these data, what was the bird's average speed in mph?
   b. Data on the bird's position were recorded only intermittently. Explain how this means that the bird's actual average speed was higher than what you calculated in part a.

55. | Your brain communicates with your body using *nerve*
BIO *impulses,* electrical signals propagated along axons. Axons come in two varieties: insulated axons with a sheath made of myelin, and uninsulated axons with no such sheath. Myelinated (sheathed) axons conduct nerve impulses much faster than unmyelinated (unsheathed) axons. The impulse speed depends on the diameter of the axons and the sheath, but a typical myelinated axon transmits nerve impulses at a speed of about 25 m/s, much faster than the typical 2.0 m/s for an unmyelinated axon. Figure P1.55 shows three equal-length nerve fibers consisting of eight axons in a row. Nerve impulses enter at the left side simultaneously and travel to the right.
   a. Draw motion diagrams for the nerve impulses traveling along fibers A, B, and C.
   b. Which nerve impulse arrives at the right side first?
   c. Which will be last?

Unmyelinated fiber A:

Individual
Partly myelinated fiber B: axons

Fully myelinated fiber C:

FIGURE P1.55

56. ‖ The bacterium *Escherichia coli* (or *E. coli*) is a single-celled
BIO organism that lives in the gut of healthy humans and animals. Its body shape can be modeled as a 2-μm-long cylinder with a 1 μm diameter, and it has a mass of 1×10^{-12} g. Its chromosome consists of a single double-stranded chain of DNA 700 times longer than its body length. The bacterium moves at a constant speed of 20 μm/s, though not always in the same direction. Answer the following questions about *E. coli* using SI units (unless specifically requested otherwise) and correct significant figures.
   a. What is its length?
   b. Diameter?
   c. Mass?
   d. What is the length of its DNA, in millimeters?
   e. If the organism were to move along a straight path, how many meters would it travel in one day?

57. ‖ The bacterium *Escherichia*
BIO *coli* (or *E. coli*) is a single-celled organism that lives in the gut of healthy humans and animals. When grown in a uniform medium rich in salts and amino acids, it swims along zig-zag paths at a constant speed. Figure P1.57 shows the positions of an *E. coli* as it moves from point A to point

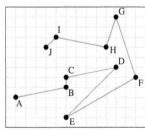

FIGURE P1.57

J. Each segment of the motion can be identified by two letters, such as segment BC. During which segments, if any, does the bacterium have the same
   a. Displacement?   b. Speed?   c. Velocity?

58. ▮ In 2003, the population of the United States was 291 million people. The per-capita income was $31,459. What was the total income of everyone in the United States? Express your answer in scientific notation, with the correct number of significant figures.

59. ▮ The sun is 30° above the horizon. It makes a 52-m-long shadow of a tall tree. How high is the tree?

60. ▮ A large passenger aircraft accelerates down the runway for a distance of 3000 m before leaving the ground. It then climbs at a steady 3.0° angle. After the plane has traveled 3000 m along this new trajectory, (a) how high is it, and (b) how far horizontally is it, from its initial position?

61. ▮ Starting from its nest, an eagle flies at constant speed for 3.0 min due east, then 4.0 min due north. From there the eagle flies directly to its nest at the same speed. How long is the eagle in the air?

62. ▮ John walks 1.00 km north, then turns right and walks 1.00 km east. His speed is 1.50 m/s during the entire stroll.
   a. What is the magnitude of his displacement, from beginning to end?
   b. If Jane starts at the same time and place as John, but walks in a straight line to the endpoint of John's stroll, at what speed should she walk to arrive at the endpoint just when John does?

Passage Problems

Growth Speed

The images of trees in Figure P1.63 come from a catalog advertising fast-growing trees. If we mark the position of the top of the tree in the successive years, as shown in the graph in the figure, we obtain a motion diagram much like ones we have seen for other kinds of motion. The motion isn't steady, of course. In some months the tree grows rapidly; in other months, quite slowly. We can see, though, that the average speed of growth is fairly constant for the first few years.

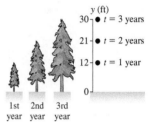

FIGURE P1.63

63. ▮ What is the tree's speed of growth, in feet per year, from $t = 1$ yr to $t = 3$ yr?
   A. 12 ft/yr   B. 9 ft/yr   C. 6 ft/yr   D. 3 ft/yr

64. ▮ What is this speed in m/s?
   A. 9×10^{-8} m/s   B. 3×10^{-9} m/s
   C. 5×10^{-6} m/s   D. 2×10^{-6} m/s

65. ▮ At the end of year 3, a rope is tied to the very top of the tree to steady it. This rope is staked into the ground 15 feet away from the tree. What angle does the rope make with the ground?
   A. 63°   B. 60°   C. 30°   D. 27°

STOP TO THINK ANSWERS

Stop to Think 1.1: B. The images of B are farther apart, so B travels a greater distance than does A during the same intervals of time.

Stop to Think 1.2: A. Dropped ball. **B.** Dust particle. **C.** Descending rocket.

Stop to Think 1.3: C. Depending on her initial positive position and how far she moves in the negative direction, she could end up on either side of the origin.

Stop to Think 1.4: D > C > B = A.

Stop to Think 1.5: B. The vector sum is found by placing the tail of one vector at the head of the other.

2 Motion in One Dimension

A horse can run at 35 mph, much faster than a human. And yet, surprisingly, a man can win a race against a horse if the length of the course is right. When, and how, can a man outrun a horse?

LOOKING AHEAD ▶

The goal of Chapter 2 is to describe and analyze linear motion.

Describing Motion

We began discussing motion in Chapter 1. In Chapter 2, you'll learn more ways to represent motion. You will also learn general strategies for solving problems.

Motion diagrams and graphs are key parts of the problem-solving strategies that we will develop in this chapter.

> **Looking Back ◀◀**
> 1.5 Velocity vectors and motion diagrams

Position

Position is defined in terms of a coordinate system and units of our choosing.

A game of football is really about motion in one dimension with a well-defined coordinate system.

> **Looking Back ◀◀**
> 1.2 Position and displacement

Velocity

Velocity is the rate of change of position.

A small change in position during an interval of time means a small velocity; a larger change means a larger velocity.

> **Looking Back ◀◀**
> 1.3 Velocity

Acceleration

Acceleration is the rate of change of velocity.

A cheetah is capable of a rapid change in velocity—that is a large acceleration. We'll see how to solve problems of changing velocity by using the concept of acceleration.

Analyzing Motion

Once you know how to describe motion, you'll be ready to do some analysis.

The main engines of a Saturn V fire for $2\frac{1}{2}$ minutes. How high will the rocket be and how fast will it be going when the engines shut off?

Constant Velocity

One important case we will consider is motion in a straight line at a constant velocity— uniform motion.

Each minute, the ship moves the same distance in the same direction.

Constant Acceleration

Another special case is motion with constant acceleration.

We think of acceleration as "speeding up," but braking to a stop involves a change in velocity—an acceleration—as well.

Free Fall

Free fall is a special case of constant acceleration.

Once the coin leaves your hand, it's in free fall, and its motion is similar to that of a falling ball or a jumping gazelle.

2.1 Describing Motion

The modern name for the mathematical description of motion, without regard to causes, is **kinematics.** The term comes from the Greek word *kinema,* meaning "movement." You know this word through its English variation *cinema*—motion pictures! This chapter will focus on the kinematics of motion in one dimension, motion along a straight line.

 PhET: Moving Man

Representing Position

As we saw in Chapter 1, kinematic variables such as position and velocity are measured with respect to a coordinate system, an axis that *you* impose on a system. We will use an *x*-axis to analyze both horizontal motion and motion on a ramp; a *y*-axis will be used for vertical motion. We will adopt the convention that the positive end of an *x*-axis is to the right and the positive end of a *y*-axis is up. This convention is illustrated in FIGURE 2.1.

Now, let's look at a practical problem of the sort that we first saw in Chapter 1. FIGURE 2.2 is a motion diagram, made at 1 frame per minute, of a straightforward situation: A student walking to school. She is moving horizontally, so we use the variable *x* to describe her motion. We have set the origin of the coordinate system, $x = 0$, at her starting position, and we measure her position in meters. We have included velocity vectors connecting successive positions on the motion diagram, as we saw we could do in Chapter 1. The motion diagram shows that she leaves home at a time we choose to call $t = 0$ min, and then makes steady progress for a while. Beginning at $t = 3$ min there is a period in which the distance traveled during each time interval becomes shorter—perhaps she slowed down to speak with a friend. Then, at $t = 6$ min, the distances traveled within each interval are longer—perhaps, realizing she is running late, she begins walking more quickly.

FIGURE 2.1 Sign conventions for position.

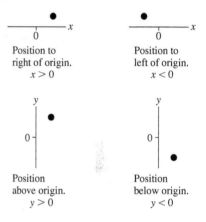

Position to right of origin. $x > 0$

Position to left of origin. $x < 0$

Position above origin. $y > 0$

Position below origin. $y < 0$

FIGURE 2.2 The motion diagram of a student walking to school and a coordinate axis for making measurements.

Every dot in the motion diagram of Figure 2.2 represents the student's position at a particular time. For example, the student is at position $x = 120$ m at $t = 2$ min. Table 2.1 lists her position for every point in the motion diagram.

The motion diagram of Figure 2.2 is one way to represent the student's motion. Presenting the data as in Table 2.1 is a second way to represent this motion. A third way to represent the motion is to make a graph. FIGURE 2.3 is a graph of the positions of the student at different times; we say it is a graph of *x* versus *t* for the student. We have merely taken the data from the table and plotted these particular points on the graph.

NOTE ▶ A graph of "*a* versus *b*" means that *a* is graphed on the vertical axis and *b* on the horizontal axis. ◀

We can flesh out the graph of Figure 2.3, though. Common sense tells us that the student was *somewhere specific* at all times: There was never a time when she failed to have a well-defined position, nor could she occupy two positions at one time. (As reasonable as this belief appears to be, we'll see that it's not entirely accurate when we get to quantum physics!) We also can assume that, from the start to the end of her motion, the student moved *continuously* through all intervening points of space, so

TABLE 2.1 Measured positions of a student walking to school

Time t (min)	Position x (m)	Time t (min)	Position x (m)
0	0	5	220
1	60	6	240
2	120	7	340
3	180	8	440
4	200	9	540

FIGURE 2.3 A graph of the student's motion.

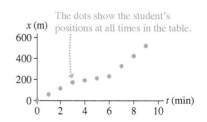

The dots show the student's positions at all times in the table.

FIGURE 2.4 Extending the graph of Figure 2.3 to a position-versus-time graph.

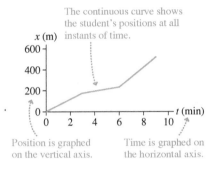

The continuous curve shows the student's positions at all instants of time.

Position is graphed on the vertical axis.

Time is graphed on the horizontal axis.

we can represent her motion as a continuous curve that passes through the measured points, as shown in FIGURE 2.4. Such a continuous curve that shows an object's position as a function of time is called a **position-versus-time graph** or, sometimes, just a *position graph*.

NOTE ▶ A graph is *not* a "picture" of the motion. The student is walking along a straight line, but the graph itself is not a straight line. Further, we've graphed her position on the vertical axis even though her motion is horizontal. A graph is an *abstract representation* of motion. We will place significant emphasis on the process of interpreting graphs, and many of the exercises and problems will give you a chance to practice these skills. ◀

CONCEPTUAL EXAMPLE 2.1   Interpreting a car's position-versus-time graph

The graph in FIGURE 2.5 represents the motion of a car along a straight road. Describe (in words) the motion of the car.

FIGURE 2.5 Position-versus-time graph for the car.

FIGURE 2.6 Looking at the position-versus-time graph in detail.

1. At $t = 0$ min, the car is 10 km to the right of the origin.

2. The value of x decreases for 30 min, indicating that the car is moving to the left.

5. The car reaches the origin at $t = 80$ min.

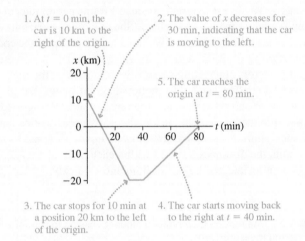

3. The car stops for 10 min at a position 20 km to the left of the origin.

4. The car starts moving back to the right at $t = 40$ min.

REASON The vertical axis in Figure 2.5 is labeled "x (km)"; position is measured in kilometers. Our convention for motion along the x-axis given in Figure 2.1 tells us that x increases as the car moves to the right and x decreases as the car moves to the left. The graph thus shows that the car travels to the left for 30 minutes, stops for 10 minutes, then travels to the right for 40 minutes. It ends up 10 km to the left of where it began. FIGURE 2.6 gives a full explanation of the reasoning.

ASSESS   The car travels to the left for 30 minutes and to the right for 40 minutes. Nonetheless, it ends up to the left of where it started. This means that the car was moving faster when it was moving to the left than when it was moving to the right. We can deduce this fact from the graph as well, as we will see in the next section.

Representing Velocity

FIGURE 2.7 Sign conventions for velocity.

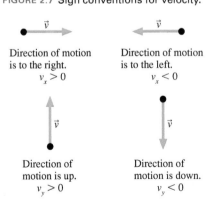

Direction of motion is to the right.
$v_x > 0$

Direction of motion is to the left.
$v_x < 0$

Direction of motion is up.
$v_y > 0$

Direction of motion is down.
$v_y < 0$

Velocity is a vector; it has both a magnitude and a direction. When we draw a velocity vector on a diagram, we use an arrow labeled with the symbol $\vec{v}$ to represent the magnitude and the direction. For motion in one dimension, vectors are restricted to point only "forward" or "backward" for horizontal motion (or "up" or "down" for vertical motion). This restriction lets us simplify our notation for vectors in one dimension. When we solve problems for motion along an x-axis, we will represent velocity with the symbol v_x. v_x will be positive or negative, corresponding to motion to the right or the left, as shown in FIGURE 2.7. For motion along a y-axis, we will use the symbol v_y to represent the velocity; the sign conventions are also illustrated in Figure 2.7. We will use the symbol v, with no subscript, to represent the speed of an object. **Speed is the *magnitude* of the velocity vector** and is always positive.

For motion along a line, the definition of velocity from Chapter 1 can be written as

$$v_x = \frac{\Delta x}{\Delta t} \tag{2.1}$$

This agrees with the sign conventions in Figure 2.7. If Δx is positive, x is increasing, the object is moving to the right, and Equation 2.1 gives a positive value for velocity. If Δx is negative, x is decreasing, the object is moving to the left, and Equation 2.1 gives a negative value for velocity.

Equation 2.1 is the first of many kinematic equations we'll see in this chapter. We'll often specify equations in terms of the coordinate x, but if the motion is vertical, in which case we use the coordinate y, the equations can be easily adapted. For example, Equation 2.1 for motion along a vertical axis becomes

$$v_y = \frac{\Delta y}{\Delta t} \qquad (2.2)$$

From Position to Velocity

Let's take another look at the motion diagram of the student walking to school. As we see in FIGURE 2.8, where we have repeated the motion diagram of Figure 2.2, her motion has three clearly defined phases. In each phase her speed is constant (because the velocity vectors have the same length) but the speed varies from phase to phase.

FIGURE 2.8 Revisiting the motion diagram of the student walking to school.

Her motion has three different phases; similarly, the position-versus-time graph redrawn in FIGURE 2.9a has three clearly defined segments with three different slopes. Looking at the different segments of the graph, we can see that there's a relationship between her speed and the slope of the graph: **A faster speed corresponds to a steeper slope.**

FIGURE 2.9 Revisiting the graph of the motion of the student walking to school.

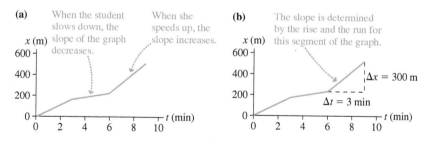

The correspondence is actually deeper than this. Let's look at the slope of the third segment of the position-versus-time graph, as shown in FIGURE 2.9b. The slope of a graph is defined as the ratio of the "rise," the vertical change, to the "run," the horizontal change. For the segment of the graph shown, the slope is:

$$\text{slope of graph} = \frac{\text{rise}}{\text{run}} = \frac{\Delta x}{\Delta t}$$

This ratio has a physical meaning—it's the velocity, exactly as we defined it in Equation 2.1. We've shown this correspondence for one particular graph, but it is a

Time lines BIO This section of the trunk of a pine tree shows the light bands of spring growth and the dark bands of summer and fall growth in successive years. If you focus on the spacing of successive dark bands, you can think of this picture as a motion diagram for the tree, representing its growth in diameter. The years of rapid growth (large distance between dark bands) during wet years and slow growth (small distance between dark bands) during years of drought are readily apparent.

PhET: Equation Grapher

FIGURE 2.10 Deducing the velocity-versus-time graph from the position-versus-time graph.

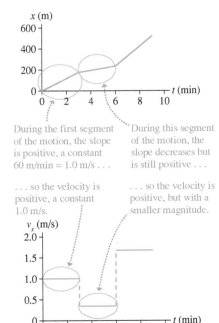

During the first segment of the motion, the slope is positive, a constant 60 m/min = 1.0 m/s . . .

. . . so the velocity is positive, a constant 1.0 m/s.

During this segment of the motion, the slope decreases but is still positive . . .

. . . so the velocity is positive, but with a smaller magnitude.

general principle: **The slope of an object's position-versus-time graph is the object's velocity at that point in the motion.** This principle also holds for negative slopes, which correspond to negative velocities. We can associate the slope of a position-versus-time graph, a *geometrical* quantity, with velocity, a *physical* quantity. This is an important aspect of interpreting position-versus-time graphs, as outlined in Tactics Box 2.1.

TACTICS BOX 2.1 Interpreting position-versus-time graphs

Information about motion can be obtained from position-versus-time graphs as follows:

❶ Determine an object's *position* at time t by reading the graph at that instant of time.

❷ Determine the object's *velocity* at time t by finding the slope of the position graph at that point. Steeper slopes correspond to faster speeds.

❸ Determine the *direction of motion* by noting the sign of the slope. Positive slopes correspond to positive velocities and, hence, to motion to the right (or up). Negative slopes correspond to negative velocities and, hence, to motion to the left (or down).

Exercises 2,3

NOTE ▶ The slope is a ratio of intervals, $\Delta x/\Delta t$, not a ratio of coordinates; that is, the slope is *not* simply x/t. ◀

NOTE ▶ We are distinguishing between the actual slope and the *physically meaningful* slope. If you were to use a ruler to measure the rise and the run of the graph, you could compute the actual slope of the line as drawn on the page. That is not the slope we are referring to when we equate the velocity with the slope of the line. Instead, we find the *physically meaningful* slope by measuring the rise and run using the scales along the axes. The "rise" Δx is some number of meters; the "run" Δt is some number of seconds. The physically meaningful rise and run include units, and the ratio of these units gives the units of the slope. ◀

We can now use the approach of Tactics Box 2.1 to analyze the student's position-versus-time graph that we saw in Figure 2.4. We can determine her velocity during the first phase of her motion by measuring the slope of the line:

$$v_x = \text{slope} = \frac{\Delta x}{\Delta t} = \frac{180 \text{ m}}{3 \text{ min}} = 60\frac{\text{m}}{\text{min}} \times \frac{1 \text{ min}}{60 \text{ s}} = 1.0 \text{ m/s}$$

In completing this calculation, we've converted to more usual units for speed, m/s. During this phase of the motion, her velocity is constant, so a graph of velocity versus time appears as a horizontal line at 1.0 m/s, as shown in FIGURE 2.10. We can do similar calculations to show that her velocity during the second phase of her motion (i.e., the slope of the position graph) is +0.33 m/s, and then increases to +1.7 m/s during the final phase. We combine all of this information to create the **velocity-versus-time graph** shown in Figure 2.10.

An inspection of the velocity-versus-time graph shows that it matches our understanding of the student's motion: There are three phases of the motion, each with constant speed. In each phase, the velocity is positive because she is always moving to the right. The second phase is slow (low velocity) and the third phase fast (high velocity.) All of this can be clearly seen on the velocity-versus-time graph, which is yet another way to represent her motion.

NOTE ▶ The velocity-versus-time graph in Figure 2.10 includes vertical segments in which the velocity changes instantaneously. Such rapid changes are an idealization; it actually takes a small amount of time to change velocity. ◀

EXAMPLE 2.2 **Analyzing a car's position graph**

FIGURE 2.11 gives the position-versus-time graph of a car.

a. Draw the car's velocity-versus-time graph.
b. Describe the car's motion in words.

FIGURE 2.11 The position-versus-time graph of a car.

PREPARE Figure 2.11 is a graphical representation of the motion. The car's position-versus-time graph is a sequence of three straight lines. Each of these straight lines represents uniform motion at a constant velocity. We can determine the car's velocity during each interval of time by measuring the slope of the line.

SOLVE

a. From $t = 0$ s to $t = 2$ s ($\Delta t = 2$ s) the car's displacement is $\Delta x = -4$ m $- 0$ m $= -4$ m. The velocity during this interval is

$$v_x = \frac{\Delta x}{\Delta t} = \frac{-4 \text{ m}}{2 \text{ s}} = -2 \text{ m/s}$$

The car's position does not change from $t = 2$ s to $t = 4$ s ($\Delta x = 0$ m), so $v_x = 0$ m/s. Finally, the displacement

between $t = 4$ s and $t = 6$ s ($\Delta t = 2$ s) is $\Delta x = 10$ m. Thus the velocity during this interval is

$$v_x = \frac{10 \text{ m}}{2 \text{ s}} = 5 \text{ m/s}$$

These velocities are represented graphically in FIGURE 2.12.

FIGURE 2.12 The velocity-versus-time graph for the car.

b. The velocity-versus-time graph of Figure 2.12 shows the motion in a way that we can describe in a straightforward manner: The car backs up for 2 s at 2 m/s, sits at rest for 2 s, then drives forward at 5 m/s for 2 s.

ASSESS Notice that the velocity graph and the position graph look completely different. They should! The value of the velocity graph at any instant of time equals the *slope* of the position graph. Since the position graph is made up of segments of constant slope, the velocity graph should be made up of segments of constant *value*, as it is. This gives us confidence that the graph we have drawn is correct.

From Velocity to Position

We've now seen how to move between different representations of uniform motion. There's one last issue to address: If you have a graph of velocity versus time, how can you determine the position graph?

Suppose you leave a lecture hall and begin walking toward your next class, which is down the hall to the west. You then realize that you left your textbook (which you always bring to class with you!) at your seat. You turn around and run back to the lecture hall to retrieve it. A velocity-versus-time graph for this motion appears as the top graph in FIGURE 2.13. There are two clear phases to the motion: walking away from class (velocity +1.0 m/s) and running back (velocity −3.0 m/s.) How can we deduce your position-versus-time graph?

As before, we can analyze the graph segment by segment. This process is shown in Figure 2.13, in which the upper velocity-versus-time graph is used to deduce the lower position-versus-time graph. For each of the two segments of the motion, the sign of the velocity tells us whether the slope of the graph is positive or negative; the magnitude of the velocity tells how steep the slope is. The final result makes sense; it shows 15 seconds of slowly increasing position (walking away) and then 5 seconds of rapidly decreasing position (running back.) And you end up back where you started.

There's one important detail that we didn't talk about in the preceding paragraph: How did we know that the position graph started at $x = 0$ m? The velocity graph tells us the *slope* of the position graph, but it doesn't tell us where the position graph should start. Although you're free to select any point you choose as the origin of the coordinate system, here it seems reasonable to set $x = 0$ m at your starting point in the lecture hall; as you walk away, your position increases.

FIGURE 2.13 Deducing a position graph from a velocity-versus-time graph.

As you move away, your velocity is +1.0 m/s . . .   As you return, your velocity is −3.0 m/s . . .

. . . so the slope of your position graph is +1.0 m/s.   . . . so the slope of your position graph is −3.0 m/s.

Which position-versus-time graph best describes the motion diagram at left?

A. B. C. D.

2.2 Uniform Motion

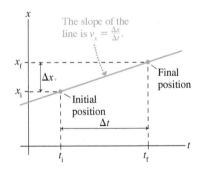

A ship on a constant heading at a steady speed is a practical example of uniform motion.

If you drive your car on a straight road at a perfectly steady 60 miles per hour (mph), you will cover 60 mi during the first hour, another 60 mi during the second hour, yet another 60 mi during the third hour, and so on. This is an example of what we call *uniform motion*. **Straight-line motion in which equal displacements occur during any successive equal-time intervals is called uniform motion** or constant-velocity motion.

> NOTE ▶ The qualifier "any" is important. If during each hour you drive 120 mph for 30 min and stop for 30 min, you will cover 60 mi during each successive 1 hour interval. But you will *not* have equal displacements during successive 30 min intervals, so this motion is not uniform. Your constant 60 mph driving is uniform motion because you will find equal displacements no matter how you choose your successive time intervals. ◀

FIGURE 2.14 shows a motion diagram and a graph for an object in uniform motion. Notice that the position-versus-time graph for uniform motion is a straight line. This follows from the requirement that all values of Δx corresponding to the same value of Δt be equal. In fact, an alternative definition of uniform motion is: **An object's motion is uniform if and only if its position-versus-time graph is a straight line.**

FIGURE 2.14 Motion diagram and position-versus-time graph for uniform motion.

Uniform motion

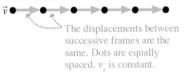

The displacements between successive frames are the same. Dots are equally spaced. v_x is constant.

The position-versus-time graph is a straight line. The slope of the line is v_x.

Equal displacements

Equations of Uniform Motion

An object is in uniform motion along the *x*-axis with the linear position-versus-time graph shown in **FIGURE 2.15**. Recall from Chapter 1 that we denote the object's initial position as x_i at time t_i. The term "initial" refers to the starting point of our analysis or the starting point in a problem. The object may or may not have been in motion prior to t_i. We use the term "final" for the ending point of our analysis or the ending point of a problem, and denote the object's final position x_f at the time t_f. As we've seen, the object's velocity v_x along the *x*-axis can be determined by finding the slope of the graph:

$$v_x = \frac{\text{rise}}{\text{run}} = \frac{\Delta x}{\Delta t} = \frac{x_f - x_i}{t_f - t_i} \tag{2.3}$$

Equation 2.3 can be rearranged to give

$$x_f = x_i + v_x \,\Delta t \tag{2.4}$$

Position equation for an object in uniform motion (v_x is constant)

FIGURE 2.15 Position-versus-time graph for an object in uniform motion.

The slope of the line is $v_x = \frac{\Delta x}{\Delta t}$.

where $\Delta t = t_f - t_i$ is the interval of time in which the object moves from position x_i to position x_f. Equation 2.4 applies to any time interval Δt during which the velocity is constant. We can also write this in terms of the object's displacement, $\Delta x = x_f - x_i$:

$$\Delta x = v_x \,\Delta t \tag{2.5}$$

The velocity of an object in uniform motion tells us the amount by which its position changes during each second. An object with a velocity of 20 m/s *changes* its position by 20 m during every second of motion: by 20 m during the first second of its motion, by another 20 m during the next second, and so on. We say that position is changing at the *rate* of 20 m/s. If the object starts at $x_i = 10$ m, it will be at $x = 30$ m after 1 s of motion and at $x = 50$ m after 2 s of motion. Thinking of velocity like this will help you develop an intuitive understanding of the connection between velocity and position.

Physics may seem densely populated with equations, but most equations follow a few basic forms. The mathematical form of Equation 2.5 is a type that we will see again: The displacement Δx is *proportional* to the time interval Δt.

NOTE ▶ The important features of a proportional relationship are described below. In this text, the first time we use a particular mathematical form we will provide such an overview. In future chapters, when we see other examples of this type of relationship, we will refer back to this overview. ◀

Proportional relationships

We say that y is **proportional** to x if they are related by an equation of this form:

$$y = Cx$$

y is proportional to x

We call C the **proportionality constant**. A graph of y versus x is a straight line that passes through the origin.

When we double x, y doubles as well.

SCALING If x has the initial value x_1, then y has the initial value $y_1 = Cx_1$. Changing x from x_1 to x_2 changes y from y_1 to y_2. The ratio of y_2 to y_1 is

$$\frac{y_2}{y_1} = \frac{Cx_2}{Cx_1} = \frac{x_2}{x_1}$$

The ratio of y_2 to y_1 is exactly the same as the ratio of x_2 to x_1. If y is proportional to x, which is often written $y \propto x$, then x and y change by the same factor:

- If you double x, you double y.
- If you decrease x by a factor of 3, you decrease y by a factor of 3.

If two variables have a proportional relationship, we can draw important conclusions from ratios without knowing the value of the proportionality constant C. We can often solve problems in a very straightforward manner by looking at such ratios. This is an important skill called *ratio reasoning*.

Exercise 11

Mathematical Forms These three figures show graphs of a mathematical equation, the kinetic energy of a moving object versus its speed, and the potential energy of a spring versus the displacement of the end of the spring. All three graphs have the same overall appearance. The three expressions differ in their variables, but all three equations have the same **mathematical form**. There are only a handful of different mathematical forms that we'll use in this text. As we meet each form for the first time, we will give an overview. When you see it again, we'll insert an icon that refers back to the overview so that you can remind yourself of the key details.

EXAMPLE 2.3 **If a train leaves Cleveland at 2:00 . . .**

A train is moving due west at a constant speed. A passenger notes that it takes 10 minutes to travel 12 km. How long will it take the train to travel 60 km?

PREPARE For an object in uniform motion, Equation 2.5 shows that the distance traveled Δx is proportional to the time interval Δt, so this is a good problem to solve using ratio reasoning.

SOLVE We are comparing two cases: the time to travel 12 km and the time to travel 60 km. Because Δx is proportional to Δt, the ratio of the times will be equal to the ratio of the distances. The ratio of the distances is

$$\frac{\Delta x_2}{\Delta x_1} = \frac{60 \text{ km}}{12 \text{ km}} = 5$$

Continued

This is equal to the ratio of the times:

$$\frac{\Delta t_2}{\Delta t_1} = 5$$

$$\Delta t_2 = \text{time to travel 60 km} = 5\Delta t_1 = 5 \times (10 \text{ min}) = 50 \text{ min}$$

It takes 10 minutes to travel 12 km; it will take 50 minutes—5 times as long—to travel 60 km.

ASSESS For an object in steady motion, it makes sense that 5 times the distance requires 5 times the time. We can see that using ratio reasoning is a straightforward way to solve this problem. We don't need to know the proportionality constant (in this case, the velocity); we just used ratios of distances and times.

From Velocity to Position, One More Time

We've seen that we can deduce an object's velocity by measuring the slope of its position graph. Conversely, if we have a velocity graph, we can say something about position—not by looking at the slope of the graph, but by looking at what we call the *area under the graph.* Let's look at an example.

Suppose a car is in uniform motion at 12 m/s. How far does it travel—that is, what is its displacement—during the time interval between $t = 1.0$ s and $t = 3.0$ s?

Equation 2.5, $\Delta x = v_x \Delta t$, describes the displacement mathematically; for a graphical interpretation, consider the graph of velocity versus time in FIGURE 2.16. In the figure, we've shaded a rectangle whose height is the velocity v_x and whose base is the time interval Δt. The area of this rectangle is $v_x \Delta t$. Looking at Equation 2.5, we see that this quantity is also equal to the displacement of the car. The area of this rectangle is the area between the axis and the line representing the velocity; we call it the "area under the graph." We see that the **displacement Δx is equal to the area under the velocity graph during interval Δt.**

Whether we use Equation 2.5 or the area under the graph to compute the displacement, we get the same result:

$$\Delta x = v_x \Delta t = (12 \text{ m/s})(2.0 \text{ s}) = 24 \text{ m}$$

Although we've shown that the displacement is the area under the graph only for uniform motion, where the velocity is constant, we'll soon see that this result applies to any one-dimensional motion.

NOTE ▶ Wait a minute! The displacement $\Delta x = x_f - x_i$ is a length. How can a length equal an area? Recall that earlier, when we found that the velocity is the slope of the position graph, we made a distinction between the *actual* slope and the *physically meaningful* slope? The same distinction applies here. The velocity graph does indeed bound a certain area on the page. That is the actual area, but it is *not* the area to which we are referring. Once again, we need to measure the quantities we are using, v_x and Δt, by referring to the scales on the axes. Δt is some number of seconds, while v_x is some number of meters per second. When these are multiplied together, the *physically meaningful* area has units of meters, appropriate for a displacement. ◀

FIGURE 2.16 Displacement is the area under a velocity-versus-time graph.

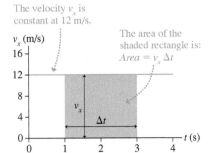

STOP TO THINK 2.2 Four objects move with the velocity-versus-time graphs shown. Which object has the largest displacement between $t = 0$ s and $t = 2$ s?

2.3 Instantaneous Velocity

The objects we've studied so far have moved with a constant, unchanging velocity or, like the car in Example 2.1, changed abruptly from one constant velocity to another. This is not very realistic. Real moving objects speed up and slow down, *changing* their velocity. As an extreme example, think about a drag racer. In a typical race, the car begins at rest but, 1 second later, is moving at over 25 miles per hour!

For one-dimensional motion, an object changing its velocity is either speeding up or slowing down. When you drive your car, as you speed up or slow down—changing your velocity—a glance at your speedometer tells you how fast you're going *at that instant.* An object's velocity—a speed *and* a direction—at a specific *instant* of time *t* is called the object's **instantaneous velocity.**

But what does it mean to have a velocity "at an instant"? An instantaneous velocity of magnitude 60 mph means that the rate at which your car's position is changing—at that exact instant—is such that it would travel a distance of 60 miles in 1 hour *if* it continued at that rate without change. Said another way, if *just for an instant* your car matches the velocity of another car driving at a steady 60 mph, then your instantaneous velocity is 60 mph. **From now on, the word "velocity" will always mean instantaneous velocity.**

For uniform motion, we found that an object's position-versus-time graph is a straight line and the object's velocity is the slope of that line. In contrast, FIGURE 2.17 shows that the position-versus-time graph for a drag racer is a *curved* line. The displacement Δx during equal intervals of time gets greater as the car speeds up. Even so, we can use the slope of the position graph to measure the car's velocity. We can say that

instantaneous velocity v_x at time t = slope of position graph at time t (2.6)

But how do we determine the slope of a curved line at a particular point? The following table gives the necessary details.

A drag racer moves with rapidly changing velocity.

FIGURE 2.17 Position-versus-time graph for a drag racer.

Finding the instantaneous velocity

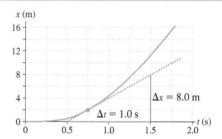

If the velocity changes, the position graph is a curved line. But we can still compute a slope by considering a small segment of the graph. Let's look at the motion in a very small time interval right around $t = 0.75$ s. This is highlighted with a circle, and we show a close-up in the next graph, at right.

Now that we have magnified a small part of the position graph, we see that the graph in this small part appears to have a constant slope. It is always possible to make the graph appear as a straight line by choosing a small enough time interval. We can find the slope of the line by calculating the rise over run, just as before:

$$v_x = \frac{1.6 \text{ m}}{0.20 \text{ s}} = 8.0 \text{ m/s}$$

This is the slope of the graph at $t = 0.75$ s and thus the velocity at this instant of time.

Graphically, the slope of the curve at a particular point is the same as the slope of a straight line drawn *tangent* to the curve at that point. **The slope of the tangent line is the instantaneous velocity at that instant of time.**

Calculating rise over run for the tangent line, we get

$$v_x = \frac{8.0 \text{ m}}{1.0 \text{ s}} = 8.0 \text{ m/s}$$

This is the same value we obtained from considering the close-up view.

CONCEPTUAL EXAMPLE 2.4   **Analyzing an elevator's position graph**

FIGURE 2.18 shows the position-versus-time graph of an elevator.

a. Sketch an approximate velocity-versus-time graph.
b. At which point or points is the elevator moving the fastest?
c. Is the elevator ever at rest? If so, at which point or points?

FIGURE 2.18 The position-versus-time graph for an elevator.

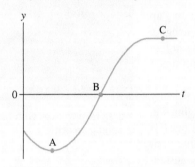

REASON a. Notice that the position graph shows y versus t, rather than x versus t, indicating that the motion is vertical rather than horizontal. Our analysis of one-dimensional motion has made no assumptions about the direction of motion, so it applies equally well to both horizontal and vertical motion. As we just found, the velocity at a particular instant of time is the slope of a tangent line to the position-versus-time graph at that time. We can move point-by-point along the position-versus-time graph, noting the slope of the tangent at each point. This will give us the velocity at that point.

Initially, to the left of point A, the slope is negative and thus the velocity is negative (i.e., the elevator is moving downward). But the slope decreases as the curve flattens out, and by the time the graph gets to point A, the slope is zero. The slope then increases to a maximum value at point B, decreases back to zero a little before point C, and remains at zero thereafter. This reasoning process is outlined in FIGURE 2.19a, and FIGURE 2.19b shows the approximate velocity-versus-time graph that results.

The other questions were answered during the construction of the graph:

b. The elevator moves the fastest at point B where the slope of the position graph is the steepest.

FIGURE 2.19 Finding a velocity graph from a position graph.

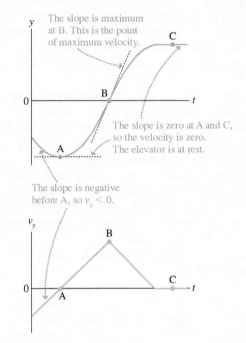

c. A particle at rest has $v_y = 0$. Graphically, this occurs at points where the tangent line to the position-versus-time graph is horizontal and thus has zero slope. Figure 2.19 shows that the slope is zero at points A and C. At point A, the velocity is only instantaneously zero as the particle reverses direction from downward motion (negative velocity) to upward motion (positive velocity). At point C, the elevator has actually stopped and remains at rest.

ASSESS The best way to check our work is to look at different segments of the motion and see if the velocity and position graphs match. Until point A, y is decreasing. The elevator is going down, so the velocity should be negative, which our graph shows. Between points A and C, y is increasing, so the velocity should be positive, which is also a feature of our graph. The steepest slope is at point B, so this should be the high point of our velocity graph, as it is.

For uniform motion we showed that the displacement Δx is the area under the velocity-versus-time graph during time interval Δt. We can generalize this idea to the case of an object whose velocity varies. FIGURE 2.20a on the next page is the velocity-versus-time graph for an object whose velocity changes with time. Suppose we know the object's position to be x_i at an initial time t_i. Our goal is to find its position x_f at a later time t_f.

Because we know how to handle constant velocities, let's *approximate* the velocity function of Figure 2.20a as a series of constant-velocity steps of width Δt as shown in FIGURE 2.21b. The velocity during each step is constant (uniform motion), so we can calculate the displacement during each step as the area of the rectangle under the curve. The total displacement of the object between t_i and t_f can be found as the sum of all the individual displacements during each of the constant-velocity steps. We can see in Figure 2.20b that the total displacement is approximately equal to the area under the graph, even in the case where the velocity varies. Although the approximation shown in the figure is rather rough, with only nine steps, we can imagine that it could be made as accurate as desired by having more and more ever-narrower steps.

FIGURE 2.20 Approximating a velocity-versus-time graph with a series of constant-velocity steps.

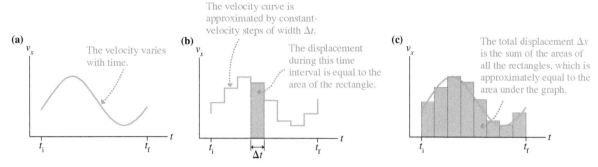

Consequently, an object's displacement is related to its velocity by

$$x_f - x_i = \Delta x = \text{area under the velocity graph } v_x \text{ between } t_i \text{ and } t_f \quad (2.7)$$

EXAMPLE 2.5 **The displacement during a rapid start**

FIGURE 2.21 shows the velocity-versus-time graph of a car pulling away from a stop. How far does the car move during the first 3.0 s?

PREPARE Figure 2.21 is a graphical representation of the motion. The question How far? indicates that we need to find a displacement Δx rather than a position x. According to Equation 2.7, the car's displacement $\Delta x = x_f - x_i$ between $t = 0$ s and $t = 3$ s is the area under the curve from $t = 0$ s to $t = 3$ s.

FIGURE 2.21 Velocity-versus-time graph for the car of Example 2.5.

SOLVE The curve in this case is an angled line, so the area is that of a triangle:

$$\Delta x = \text{area of triangle between } t = 0 \text{ s and } t = 3 \text{ s}$$

$$= \tfrac{1}{2} \times \text{base} \times \text{height} = \tfrac{1}{2} \times 3 \text{ s} \times 12 \text{ m/s} = 18 \text{ m}$$

The car moves 18 m during the first 3 seconds as its velocity changes from 0 to 12 m/s.

ASSESS The physically meaningful area is a product of s and m/s, so Δx has the proper units of m. Let's check the numbers to see if they make physical sense. The final velocity, 12 m/s, is about 25 mph. Pulling away from a stop, you might expect to reach this speed in about 3 s—at least if you have a reasonably sporty vehicle! If the car had moved at a constant 12 m/s (the final velocity) during these 3 s, the distance would be 36 m. The actual distance traveled during the 3 s is 18 m—half of 36 m. This makes sense, as the velocity was 0 m/s at the start of the problem and increased steadily to 12 m/s.

STOP TO THINK 2.3 Which velocity-versus-time graph goes with the position-versus-time graph on the left?

2.4 Acceleration

The goal of this chapter is to describe motion. We've seen that velocity describes the rate at which an object changes position. We need one more motion concept to complete the description, one that will describe an object whose velocity is changing.

As an example, let's look at a frequently quoted measurement of car performance, the time it takes the car to go from 0 to 60 mph. Table 2.2 shows this time for two different cars.

Let's look at motion diagrams for the Porsche and the Volkswagen in FIGURE 2.22. We can see two important facts about the motion. First, the lengths of the velocity vectors are increasing, showing that the speeds are increasing. Second, the velocity vectors for the Porsche are increasing in length more rapidly than those of the VW. The quantity we seek is one that measures how rapidly an object's velocity vectors change in length.

TABLE 2.2 Performance data for vehicles

Vehicle	Time to go from 0 to 60 mph
1997 Porsche 911 Turbo S	3.6 s
1973 Volkswagen Super Beetle Convertible	24 s

FIGURE 2.22 Motion diagrams for the Porsche and Volkswagen.

When we wanted to measure changes in position, the ratio $\Delta x/\Delta t$ was useful. This ratio, which we defined as the velocity, is the *rate of change of position*. Similarly, we can measure how rapidly an object's velocity changes with the ratio $\Delta v_x/\Delta t$. Given our experience with velocity, we can say a couple of things about this new ratio:

■ The ratio $\Delta v_x/\Delta t$ is the *rate of change of velocity*.
■ The ratio $\Delta v_x/\Delta t$ is the *slope of a velocity-versus-time graph*.

We will define this ratio as the **acceleration,** for which we use the symbol a_x:

$$a_x = \frac{\Delta v_x}{\Delta t} \tag{2.8}$$

Definition of acceleration as the rate of change of velocity

Similarly, $a_y = \Delta v_y/\Delta t$ for vertical motion.

As an example, let's calculate the acceleration for the Porsche and the Volkswagen. For both, the initial velocity $(v_x)_i$ is zero and the final velocity $(v_x)_f$ is 60 mph. Thus the *change* in velocity is $\Delta v_x = 60$ mph. In m/s, our SI unit of velocity, $\Delta v_x = 27$ m/s.

Now we can use Equation 2.8 to compute acceleration. Let's start with the Porsche, which speeds up to 27 m/s in $\Delta t = 3.6$ s:

$$a_{\text{Porsche}x} = \frac{\Delta v_x}{\Delta t} = \frac{27 \text{ m/s}}{3.6 \text{ s}} = 7.5 \frac{\text{m/s}}{\text{s}}$$

Here's the meaning of this final figure: Every second, the Porsche's velocity changes by 7.5 m/s. In the first second of motion, the Porsche's velocity increases by 7.5 m/s; in the next second, it increases by another 7.5 m/s, and so on. After 1 second, the velocity is 7.5 m/s; after 2 seconds, it is 15 m/s. This increase continues as long as the Porsche has this acceleration. We thus interpret the units as 7.5 meters per second, per second—7.5 (m/s)/s.

The Volkswagen's acceleration is

$$a_{\text{VW}x} = \frac{\Delta v_x}{\Delta t} = \frac{27 \text{ m/s}}{24 \text{ s}} = 1.1 \frac{\text{m/s}}{\text{s}}$$

Cushion kinematics When a car hits an obstacle head-on, the damage to the car and its occupants can be reduced by making the acceleration as small as possible. As we can see from Equation 2.8, acceleration can be reduced by making the *time* for a change in velocity as long as possible. This is the purpose of the yellow crash cushion barrels you may have seen in work zones on highways—to lengthen the time of a collision with a barrier.

Class Video

In each second, the Volkswagen changes its speed by 1.1 m/s. This is only 1/7 the acceleration of the Porsche! The reasons the Porsche is capable of greater acceleration has to do with what *causes* the motion. We will explore the reasons for acceleration in Chapter 4. For now, we will simply note that the Porsche is capable of much greater acceleration, something you would have suspected.

NOTE ▶ It is customary to abbreviate the acceleration units (m/s)/s as m/s². For example, we'll write that the Volkswagen has an acceleration of 1.1 m/s². When you use this notation, keep in mind the *meaning* of the notation as "(meters per second) per second." ◀

TABLE 2.3 Velocity data for the Volkswagen and the Porsche

Time (s)	Velocity of VW (m/s)	Velocity of Porsche (m/s)
0	0	0
1	1.1	7.5
2	2.2	15.0
3	3.3	22.5
4	4.4	30.0

Representing Acceleration

Let's use the values we have computed for acceleration to make a table of velocities for the Porsche and the Volkswagen we considered earlier. Table 2.3 uses the idea that the VW's velocity increases by 1.1 m/s every second while the Porsche's velocity increases by 7.5 m/s every second. The data in Table 2.3 are the basis for the velocity-versus-time graphs in FIGURE 2.23. As you can see, an object undergoing constant acceleration has a straight–line velocity graph.

The slope of either of these lines—the rise over run—is $\Delta v_x/\Delta t$. Comparing this with Equation 2.8, we see that the equation for the slope is the same as that for the acceleration. That is, **an object's acceleration is the slope of its velocity-versus-time graph:**

$$\text{acceleration } a_x \text{ at time } t = \text{slope of velocity graph at time } t \qquad (2.9)$$

The VW has a smaller acceleration, so its velocity graph has a smaller slope.

FIGURE 2.23 Velocity-versus-time graphs for the two cars.

CONCEPTUAL EXAMPLE 2.6 Analyzing a car's velocity graph

FIGURE 2.24a is a graph of velocity versus time for a car. Sketch a graph of the car's acceleration versus time.

REASON The graph can be divided into three sections:

- An initial segment, in which the velocity increases at a steady rate.
- A middle segment, in which the velocity is constant.
- A final segment, in which the velocity decreases at a steady rate.

In each section, the acceleration is the slope of the velocity-versus-time graph. Thus the initial segment has constant, positive acceleration, the middle segment has zero acceleration, and the

final segment has constant, *negative* acceleration. The acceleration graph appears in FIGURE 2.24b.

ASSESS This process is analogous to finding a velocity graph from the slope of a position graph. The middle segment having zero acceleration does *not* mean that the velocity is zero. The velocity is constant, which means it is *not changing* and thus the car is not accelerating. The car does accelerate during the initial and final segments. The magnitude of the acceleration is a measure of how quickly the velocity is changing. How about the sign? This is an issue we will address in the next section.

FIGURE 2.24 Finding an acceleration graph from a velocity graph.

FIGURE 2.25 Determining the sign of the
acceleration.

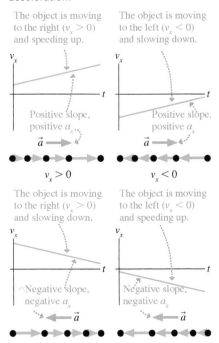

The Sign of the Acceleration

It's a natural tendency to think that a positive value of a_x or a_y describes an object that is speeding up while a negative value describes an object that is slowing down (decelerating). Unfortunately, this simple interpretation *does not work.*

Because an object can move right or left (or, equivalently, up and down) while either speeding up or slowing down, there are four situations to consider. FIGURE 2.25 shows a motion diagram and a velocity graph for each of these situations. As we've seen, an object's acceleration is the slope of its velocity graph, so a positive slope implies a positive acceleration and a negative slope implies a negative acceleration.

Acceleration, like velocity, is really a vector quantity, a concept that we will explore more fully in Chapter 3. Figure 2.25 shows the acceleration vectors for the four situations. The acceleration vector points in the same direction as the velocity vector $\vec{v}$ for an object that is speeding up and opposite to $\vec{v}$ for an object that is slowing down.

An object that speeds up as it moves to the right (positive v_x) has a positive acceleration, but an object that speeds up as it moves to the left (negative v_x) has a negative acceleration. Whether or not an object that is slowing down has a negative acceleration depends on whether the object is moving to the right or to the left. This is admittedly a bit more complex than thinking that negative acceleration always means slowing down, but our definition of acceleration as the slope of the velocity graph forces us to pay careful attention to the sign of the acceleration.

FIGURE 2.26 The red dots show the positions of the top of the Saturn V rocket at equally spaced intervals of time during liftoff.

STOP TO THINK 2.4   A particle moves with the velocity-versus-time graph shown here. At which labeled point is the magnitude of the acceleration the greatest?

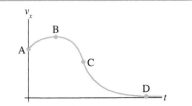

2.5 Motion with Constant Acceleration

For uniform motion—motion with constant velocity—we found in Equation 2.3 a simple relationship between position and time. It's no surprise that there are also simple relationships that connect the various kinematic variables in constant-acceleration motion. We will start with a concrete example, the launch of a Saturn V rocket like the one that carried the Apollo astronauts to the moon in the 1960s and 1970s. FIGURE 2.26 shows one frame from a video of a rocket lifting off the launch pad. The red dots show the positions of the top of the rocket at equally spaced intervals of time in earlier frames of the video. This is a motion diagram for the rocket, and we can see that the velocity is increasing. The graph of velocity versus time in FIGURE 2.27 shows that the velocity is increasing at a fairly constant rate. We can approximate the rocket's motion as constant acceleration.

We can use the slope of the graph in Figure 2.27 to determine the acceleration of the rocket:

$$a_y = \frac{\Delta v_y}{\Delta t} = \frac{27 \text{ m/s}}{1.5 \text{ s}} = 18 \text{ m/s}^2$$

This acceleration is more than double the acceleration of the Porsche, and it goes on for quite a long time—the first phase of the launch lasts over 2 minutes! How fast is the rocket moving at the end of this acceleration, and how far has it traveled? To answer questions like these, we first need to work out some basic kinematic formulas for motion with constant acceleration.

FIGURE 2.27 A graph of the rocket's velocity versus time.

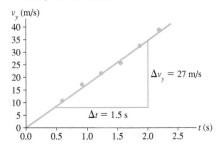

▶ **Solar sailing** A rocket achieves a high speed by having a very high acceleration. A different approach is represented by a solar sail. A spacecraft with a solar sail accelerates due to the pressure of sunlight from the sun on a large, mirrored surface. The acceleration is minuscule, but it can continue for a long, long time. After an acceleration period of a few *years,* the spacecraft will reach a respectable speed!

Constant-Acceleration Equations

Consider an object whose acceleration a_x remains constant during the time interval $\Delta t = t_f - t_i$. At the beginning of this interval, the object has initial velocity $(v_x)_i$ and initial position x_i. Note that t_i is often zero, but it need not be. FIGURE 2.28a shows the acceleration-versus-time graph. It is a horizontal line between t_i and t_f, indicating a *constant* acceleration.

The object's velocity is changing because the object is accelerating. We can use the acceleration to find $(v_x)_f$ at a later time t_f. We defined acceleration as

$$a_x = \frac{\Delta v_x}{\Delta t} = \frac{(v_x)_f - (v_x)_i}{\Delta t} \tag{2.10}$$

which is rearranged to give

$$(v_x)_f = (v_x)_i + a_x \, \Delta t \tag{2.11}$$

Velocity equation for an object with constant acceleration

NOTE ▶ We have expressed this equation for motion along the *x*-axis, but it is a general result that will apply to any axis. ◀

The velocity-versus-time graph for this constant-acceleration motion, shown in FIGURE 2.28b, is a straight line with value $(v_x)_i$ at time t_i and with slope a_x.

We would also like to know the object's position x_f at time t_f. As you learned earlier, the displacement Δx during a time interval Δt is the area under the velocity-versus-time graph. The shaded area in Figure 2.28b can be subdivided into a rectangle of area $(v_x)_i \, \Delta t$ and a triangle of area $\frac{1}{2}(a_x \, \Delta t)(\Delta t) = \frac{1}{2}a_x(\Delta t)^2$. Adding these gives

$$x_f = x_i + (v_x)_i \, \Delta t + \tfrac{1}{2}a_x(\Delta t)^2 \tag{2.12}$$

Position equation for an object with constant acceleration

where $\Delta t = t_f - t_i$ is the elapsed time. The fact that the time interval Δt appears in the equation as $(\Delta t)^2$ causes the position-versus-time graph for constant-acceleration motion to have a parabolic shape. For the rocket launch of Figure 2.26, a graph of the position of the top of the rocket versus time appears as in FIGURE 2.29.

Equations 2.11 and 2.12 are two of the basic kinematic equations for motion with constant acceleration. They allow us to predict an object's position and velocity at a future instant of time. We need one more equation to complete our set, a direct relationship between displacement and velocity. To derive this relationship, we first use Equation 2.11 to write $\Delta t = ((v_x)_f - (v_x)_i)/a_x$. We can substitute this into Equation 2.12 to obtain

$$(v_x)_f^2 = (v_x)_i^2 + 2a_x \, \Delta x \tag{2.13}$$

Relating velocity and displacement for constant-acceleration motion

In Equation 2.13 $\Delta x = x_f - x_i$ is the *displacement* (not the distance!). Notice that Equation 2.13 does not require knowing the time interval Δt. This is an important equation in problems where you're not given information about times. Equations 2.11, 2.12, and 2.13 are the key equations for motion with constant acceleration. These results are summarized in Table 2.4.

FIGURE 2.28 Acceleration and velocity graphs for motion with constant acceleration.

(a) Acceleration

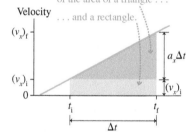

The displacement Δx is the area under this curve: the sum of the area of a triangle . . .

(b) Velocity . . . and a rectangle.

FIGURE 2.29 Position-versus-time graph for the Saturn V rocket launch.

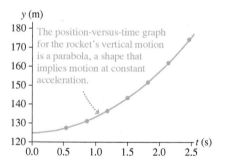

The position-versus-time graph for the rocket's vertical motion is a parabola, a shape that implies motion at constant acceleration.

TABLE 2.4 Kinematic equations for motion with constant acceleration

$(v_x)_f = (v_x)_i + a_x \, \Delta t$

$x_f = x_i + (v_x)_i \, \Delta t + \tfrac{1}{2}a_x(\Delta t)^2$

$(v_x)_f^2 = (v_x)_i^2 + 2a_x \, \Delta x$

Coming to a stop

As you drive in your car at 15 m/s (just a bit under 35 mph), you see a child's ball roll into the street ahead of you. You hit the brakes and stop as quickly as you can. In this case, you come to rest in 1.5 s. How far does your car travel as you brake to a stop?

PREPARE   The problem statement gives us a description of motion in words. To help us visualize the situation, **FIGURE 2.30** illustrates the key features of the motion with a motion diagram and a velocity graph. The graph is based on the car slowing from 15 m/s to 0 m/s in 1.5 s.

SOLVE   We've assumed that your car is moving to the right, so its initial velocity is $(v_x)_i = +15$ m/s. After you come to rest, your final velocity is $(v_x)_f = 0$ m/s. The acceleration is given by Equation 2.10:

$$a_x = \frac{\Delta v_x}{\Delta t} = \frac{(v_x)_f - (v_x)_i}{\Delta t} = \frac{0 \text{ m/s} - 15 \text{ m/s}}{1.5 \text{ s}} = -10 \text{ m/s}^2$$

An acceleration of -10 m/s^2 (really -10 m/s per second) means the car slows by 10 m/s every second.

Now that we know the acceleration, we can compute the distance that the car moves as it comes to rest using Equation 2.12:

$$x_f - x_i = (v_x)_i \Delta t + \tfrac{1}{2} a_x (\Delta t)^2$$
$$= (15 \text{ m/s})(1.5 \text{ s}) + \tfrac{1}{2}(-10 \text{ m/s}^2)(1.5 \text{ s})^2 = 11 \text{ m}$$

ASSESS   11 m is a little over 35 feet. That's a reasonable distance for a quick stop while traveling at about 35 mph. The purpose of the Assess step is not to prove that your solution is correct but to use common sense to recognize answers that are clearly wrong. Had you made a calculation error and ended up with an answer of 1.1 m—less than 4 feet—a moment's reflection should indicate that this couldn't possibly be correct.

FIGURE 2.30 Motion diagram and velocity graph for a car coming to a stop.

We'll assume that the car moves to the right.

The velocity vectors get shorter, so the acceleration vector points to the left.

$\vec{a}$

$\vec{v}$

v_x (m/s)

As the car brakes, its velocity steadily decreases.

At 1.5 s, the car has come to rest.

15

10

5

0

0   0.5   1.0   1.5 t (s)

Graphs will be an important component of our problem solutions, so we want to consider the types of graphs we are likely to encounter in more detail. **FIGURE 2.31** is a graphical comparison of motion with constant velocity (uniform motion) and motion with constant acceleration. Notice that uniform motion is really a special case of constant-acceleration motion in which the acceleration happens to be zero.

FIGURE 2.31 Motion with constant velocity and constant acceleration. These graphs assume $x_i = 0$, $(v_x)_i > 0$, and (for constant acceleration) $a_x > 0$.

(a) Motion at constant velocity

(b) Motion at constant acceleration

a_x

Zero

0

t

a_x Horizontal line

0

t

The acceleration is constant.

v_x Horizontal line

$(v_x)_i$

t

The velocity is constant.

v_x Straight line

$(v_x)_i$

t

The slope is a_x.

x

Straight line

x_i

t

The slope is v_x.

x

Parabola

x_i

t

For motion at constant acceleration, a graph of position versus time is a *parabola*. This is a new mathematical form, one that we will see again. If $(v_x)_i = 0$, the second equation in Table 2.4 is simply

$$\Delta x = \tfrac{1}{2}a_x(\Delta t)^2 \qquad\qquad (2.14)$$

Δx depends on the *square* of Δt; we call this a *quadratic relationship*.

✏ Quadratic relationships

Two quantities are said to have a **quadratic relationship** if y is proportional to the square of x. We write the mathematical relationship as

$$y = Ax^2$$

y is proportional to x^2

The graph of a quadratic relationship is a parabola.

Doubling x causes y to change by a factor of 4.

SCALING If x has the initial value x_1, then y has the initial value $y_1 = A(x_1)^2$. Changing x from x_1 to x_2 changes y from y_1 to y_2. The ratio of y_2 to y_1 is

$$\frac{y_2}{y_1} = \frac{A(x_2)^2}{A(x_1)^2} = \left(\frac{x_2}{x_1}\right)^2$$

The ratio of y_2 to y_1 is the square of the ratio of x_2 to x_1. If y is a quadratic function of x, a change in x by some factor changes y by the square of that factor:

- If you increase x by a factor of 2, you increase y by a factor of $2^2 = 4$.
- If you decrease x by a factor of 3, you decrease y by a factor of $3^2 = 9$.

Generally, we can say that:
Changing x by a factor of c changes y by a factor of c^2.

Exercise 19 ✏

Getting up to speed BIO A bird must have a minimum speed to fly. Generally, the larger the bird, the faster the takeoff speed. Small birds can get moving fast enough to fly with a vigorous jump, but larger birds may need a running start. This swan must accelerate for a long distance in order to achieve the high speed it needs to fly, so it makes a frenzied dash across the frozen surface of a pond. Swans require a long, clear stretch of water or land to become airborne. Airplanes require an even faster takeoff speed and thus an even longer runway, as we will see.

EXAMPLE 2.8 **Displacement of a drag racer**

A drag racer, starting from rest, travels 6.0 m in 1.0 s. Suppose the car continues this acceleration for an additional 4.0 s. How far from the starting line will the car be?

PREPARE We assume that the acceleration is constant, so the displacement will follow Equation 2.14. This is a *quadratic relationship,* so the displacement will scale as the square of the time.

SOLVE After 1.0 s, the car has traveled 6.0 m; after another 4.0 s, a total of 5.0 s will have elapsed. The time has increased by a factor of 5, so the displacement will increase by a factor of 5^2, or 25. The total displacement is

$$\Delta x = 25(6.0 \text{ m}) = 150 \text{ m}$$

ASSESS This is a big distance in a short time, but drag racing is a fast sport, so our answer makes sense.

STOP TO THINK 2.5 A cyclist is at rest at a traffic light. When the light turns green, he begins accelerating at 1.2 m/s². How many seconds after the light turns green does he reach his cruising speed of 6.0 m/s?

A. 1.0 s   B. 2.0 s   C. 3.0 s   D. 4.0 s   E. 5.0 s

Dinner at a distance BIO A chameleon's tongue is a powerful tool for catching prey. Certain species can extend the tongue to a distance of over 1 ft in less than 0.1 s! A study of the kinematics of the motion of the chameleon tongue, using techniques like those in this chapter, reveals that the tongue has a period of rapid acceleration followed by a period of constant velocity. This knowledge is a very valuable clue in the analysis of the evolutionary relationships between chameleons and other animals.

Building a complex structure requires careful planning. The architect's visualization and drawings have to be complete before the detailed procedures of construction get under way. The same is true for solving problems in physics.

2.6 Solving One-Dimensional Motion Problems

The big challenge when solving a physics problem is to translate the words into symbols that can be manipulated, calculated, and graphed. This translation from words to symbols is the heart of problem solving in physics. Ambiguous words and phrases must be clarified, the imprecise must be made precise, and you must arrive at an understanding of exactly what the question is asking.

In this section we will explore some general problem-solving strategies that we will use throughout the text, applying them to problems of motion along a line.

A Problem-Solving Strategy

The first step in solving a seemingly complicated problem is to break it down into a series of smaller steps. In worked examples in the text, we use a problem-solving strategy that consists of three steps: *prepare*, *solve*, and *assess*. Each of these steps has important elements that you should follow when you solve problems on your own.

 Problem-Solving Strategy

PREPARE The Prepare step of a solution is where you identify important elements of the problem and collect information you will need to solve it. It's tempting to jump right to the Solve step, but a skilled problem solver will spend the most time on this step, the preparation. Preparation includes:

- **Drawing a picture.** In many cases, this is the most important part of a problem. The picture lets you model the problem and identify the important elements. As you add information to your picture, the outline of the solution will take shape. For the problems in this chapter, a picture could be a motion diagram or a graph—or perhaps both.
- **Collecting necessary information.** The problem's statement may give you some values of variables. Other important information may be implied or must be looked up in a table. Gather everything you need to solve the problem and compile it in a list.
- **Doing preliminary calculations.** There are a few calculations, such as unit conversions, that are best done in advance of the main part of the solution.

SOLVE The Solve step of a solution is where you actually do the mathematics or reasoning necessary to arrive at the answer needed. This is the part of the problem-solving strategy that you likely think of when you think of "solving problems." But don't make the mistake of starting here! The Prepare step will help you be certain you understand the problem before you start putting numbers in equations.

ASSESS The Assess step of your solution is very important. When you have an answer, you should check to see whether it makes sense. Ask yourself:

- **Does my solution answer the question that was asked?** Make sure you have addressed all parts of the question and clearly written down your solutions.
- **Does my answer have the correct units and number of significant figures?**
- **Does the value I computed make physical sense?** In this book all calculations use physically reasonable numbers. You will not be given a problem to solve in which the final velocity of a bicycle is 100 miles per hour! If your answer seems unreasonable, go back and check your work.
- **Can I estimate what the answer should be to check my solution?**
- **Does my final solution make sense in the context of the material I am learning?**

The Pictorial Representation

Many physics problems, including 1-D motion problems, often have several variables and other pieces of information to keep track of. The best way to tackle such problems is to draw a picture, as we noted when we introduced a general problem-solving strategy. But what kind of picture should you draw?

In this section, we will begin to draw **pictorial representations** as an aid to solving problems. A pictorial representation shows all of the important details that we need to keep track of and will be very important in solving motion problems.

TACTICS BOX 2.2   Drawing a pictorial representation

❶ **Sketch the situation.** Not just any sketch: Show the object at the *beginning* of the motion, at the *end*, and at any point where the character of the motion changes. Very simple drawings are adequate.
❷ **Establish a coordinate system.** Select your axes and origin to match the motion.
❸ **Define symbols.** Use the sketch to define symbols representing quantities such as position, velocity, acceleration, and time. *Every* variable used later in the mathematical solution should be defined on the sketch.

We will generally combine the pictorial representation with a **list of values**, which will include:

■ *Known information.* Make a table of the quantities whose values you can determine from the problem statement or that you can find quickly with simple geometry or unit conversions.
■ *Desired unknowns.* What quantity or quantities will allow you to answer the question?

Exercise 21 ✎

EXAMPLE 2.9   Drawing a pictorial representation

Complete a pictorial representation and a list of values for the following problem: A rocket sled accelerates at 50 m/s² for 5 s. What are the total distance traveled and the final velocity?

PREPARE FIGURE 2.32a shows a pictorial representation as drawn by an artist in the style of the figures in this book. This is

FIGURE 2.32 Constructing a pictorial representation and a list of values.

(a) Artist's version
Pictorial representation

List of values

Known
$x_i = 0$ m
$(v_x)_i = 0$ m/s
$t_i = 0$ s
$a_x = 50$ m/s²
$t_f = 5$ s

Find
$x_f, (v_x)_f$

(b) Student sketch

certainly neater and more artistic than the sketches you will make when solving problems yourself! FIGURE 2.32b shows a sketch like one you might actually do. It's less formal, but it contains all of the important information you need to solve the problem.

NOTE ▶ Throughout this book we will illustrate select examples with actual hand-drawn figures so that you have them to refer to as you work on your own pictures for homework and practice. ◀

Let's look at how these pictures were constructed. The motion has a clear beginning and end; these are the points sketched. A coordinate system has been chosen with the origin at the starting point. The quantities x, v_x, and t are needed at both points, so these have been defined on the sketch and distinguished by subscripts. The acceleration is associated with an interval between these points. Values for two of these quantities are given in the problem statement. Others, such as $x_i = 0$ m and $t_i = 0$ s, are inferred from our choice of coordinate system. The value $(v_x)_i = 0$ m/s is part of our *interpretation* of the problem. Finally, we identify x_f and $(v_x)_f$ as the quantities that will answer the question. We now understand quite a bit about the problem and would be ready to start a quantitative analysis.

ASSESS We didn't *solve* the problem; that was not our purpose. Constructing a pictorial representation and a list of values is part of a systematic approach to interpreting a problem and getting ready for a mathematical solution.

The Visual Overview

The pictorial representation and the list of values are a very good complement to the motion diagram and other ways of looking at a problem that we have seen. As we translate a problem into a form we can solve, we will combine these elements into what we will term a **visual overview.** The visual overview will consist of some or all of the following elements:

- A *motion diagram.* A good strategy for solving a motion problem is to start by drawing a motion diagram.
- A *pictorial representation*, as defined above.
- A *graphical representation.* For motion problems, it is often quite useful to include a graph of position and/or velocity.
- A *list of values.* This list should sum up all of the important values in the problem.

Future chapters will add other elements to this visual overview of the physics.

EXAMPLE 2.10   **Kinematics of a rocket launch**

A Saturn V rocket is launched straight up with a constant acceleration of 18 m/s². After 150 s, how fast is the rocket moving and how far has it traveled?

PREPARE FIGURE 2.33 shows a visual overview of the rocket launch that includes a motion diagram, a pictorial representation, and a list of values. The visual overview shows the whole problem in a nutshell. The motion diagram illustrates the motion of the rocket. The pictorial representation (produced according to Tactics Box 2.2) shows axes, identifies the important points of the motion, and defines variables. Finally, we have included a list of values that gives the known and unknown quantities. In the visual overview we have taken the statement of the problem in words and made it much more precise; it contains everything you need to know about the problem.

SOLVE Our first task is to find the final velocity. Our list of values includes the initial velocity, the acceleration, and the time

interval, so we can use the first kinematic equation of Table 2.4 to find the final velocity:

$$(v_y)_f = (v_y)_i + a_y \, \Delta t = 0 \text{ m/s} + (18 \text{ m/s}^2)(150 \text{ s})$$
$$= 2700 \text{ m/s}$$

The distance traveled is found using the second equation in Table 2.4:

$$y_f = y_i + (v_y)_i \, \Delta t + \tfrac{1}{2} a_y (\Delta t)^2$$
$$= 0 \text{ m} + (0 \text{ m/s})(150 \text{ s}) + \tfrac{1}{2}(18 \text{ m/s}^2)(150 \text{ s})^2$$
$$= 2.0 \times 10^5 \text{ m} = 200 \text{ km}$$

ASSESS The acceleration is very large, and it goes on for a long time, so the large final velocity and large distance traveled seem reasonable.

FIGURE 2.33 Visual overview of the rocket launch.

Motion diagram

$\vec{v}$

$\vec{a}$

The motion diagram for the rocket shows the full range of the motion.

Pictorial representation

y

$y_f, (v_y)_f, t_f$

$\vec{a}$

0 $y_i, (v_y)_i, t_i$

The pictorial representation identifies the two important points of the motion, the start and the end, and shows that the rocket accelerates between them.

List of values

Known
$$y_i = 0 \text{ m}$$
$$(v_y)_i = 0 \text{ m/s}$$
$$t_i = 0 \text{ s}$$
$$a_y = 18 \text{ m/s}^2$$
$$t_f = 150 \text{ s}$$

Find
$$(v_y)_f \text{ and } y_f$$

The list of values makes everything concrete. We define the start of the problem to be at time 0 s, when the rocket has a position of 0 m and a velocity of 0 m/s. The end of the problem is at time 150 s. We are to find the position and velocity at this time.

Problem-Solving Strategy for Motion with Constant Acceleration

Earlier in this section, we introduced a general problem-solving strategy. Now we will adapt this general strategy to solving problems of motion with constant acceleration. We will introduce such specific problem-solving strategies in future chapters as well.

PROBLEM-SOLVING
STRATEGY 2.1   Motion with constant acceleration

PREPARE Draw a visual overview of the problem. This should include a motion diagram, a pictorial representation, and a list of values; a graphical representation may be useful for certain problems.

SOLVE The mathematical solution is based on the three equations in Table 2.4.

- Though the equations are phrased in terms of the variable x, it's customary to use y for motion in the vertical direction.
- Use the equation that best matches what you know and what you need to find. For example, if you know acceleration and time and are looking for a change in velocity, the first equation is the best one to use.
- Uniform motion with constant velocity has $a = 0$.

ASSESS Is your result believable? Does it have proper units? Does it make sense?

Exercise 25

EXAMPLE 2.11   Calculating the minimum length of a runway

A fully loaded Boeing 747 with all engines at full thrust accelerates at 2.6 m/s². Its minimum takeoff speed is 70 m/s. How much time will the plane take to reach its takeoff speed? What minimum length of runway does the plane require for takeoff?

PREPARE The visual overview of FIGURE 2.34 summarizes the important details of the problem. We set x_i and t_i equal to zero at the starting point of the motion, when the plane is at rest and the acceleration begins. The final point of the motion is when the plane achieves the necessary takeoff speed of 70 m/s. The plane is accelerating to the right, so we will compute the time for the plane to reach a velocity of 70 m/s and the position of the plane at this time, giving us the minimum length of the runway.

FIGURE 2.34 Visual overview for an accelerating plane.

SOLVE First we solve for the time required for the plane to reach takeoff speed. We can use the first equation in Table 2.4 to compute this time:

$$(v_x)_f = (v_x)_i + a_x \Delta t$$

$$70 \text{ m/s} = 0 \text{ m/s} + (2.6 \text{ m/s}^2) \Delta t$$

$$\Delta t = \frac{70 \text{ m/s}}{2.6 \text{ m/s}^2} = 26.9 \text{ s}$$

We keep an extra significant figure here because we will use this result in the next step of the calculation.

Given the time that the plane takes to reach takeoff speed, we can compute the position of the plane when it reaches this speed using the second equation in Table 2.4:

$$x_f = x_i + (v_x)_i \Delta t + \tfrac{1}{2} a_x (\Delta t)^2$$
$$= 0 \text{ m} + (0 \text{ m/s})(26.9 \text{ s}) + \tfrac{1}{2}(2.6 \text{ m/s}^2)(26.9 \text{ s})^2$$
$$= 940 \text{ m}$$

Our final answers are thus that the plane will take 27 s to reach takeoff speed, with a minimum runway length of 940 m.

ASSESS Think about the last time you flew; 27 s seems like a reasonable time for a plane to accelerate on takeoff. Actual runway lengths at major airports are 3000 m or more, a few times greater than the minimum length, because they have to allow for emergency stops during an aborted takeoff. (If we had calculated a distance far greater than 3000 m, we would know we had done something wrong!)

EXAMPLE 2.12   Finding the braking distance

A car is traveling at a speed of 30 m/s, a typical highway speed, on wet pavement. The driver sees an obstacle ahead and decides to stop. From this instant, it takes him 0.75 s to begin applying the brakes. Once the brakes are applied, the car experiences an acceleration of −6.0 m/s². How far does the car travel from the instant the driver notices the obstacle until stopping?

PREPARE This problem is more involved than previous problems we have solved, so we will take more care with the visual overview in FIGURE 2.35. In addition to a motion diagram and a pictorial representation, we include a graphical representation. Notice that there are two different phases of the motion: a constant-velocity phase before braking begins, and a steady slowing

Continued

FIGURE 2.35 Visual overview for a car braking to a stop.

down once the brakes are applied. We will need to do two different calculations, one for each phase. Consequently, we've used numerical subscripts rather than a simple i and f.

SOLVE From t_1 to t_2 the velocity stays constant at 30 m/s. This is uniform motion, so the position at time t_2 is computed using Equation 2.4:

$$x_2 = x_1 + (v_x)_1(t_2 - t_1) = 0 \text{ m} + (30 \text{ m/s})(0.75 \text{ s})$$
$$= 22.5 \text{ m}$$

At t_2, the velocity begins to decrease at a steady -6.0 m/s² until the car comes to rest at t_3. This time interval can be computed using the first equation in Table 2.4, $(v_x)_3 = (v_x)_2 + a_x \Delta t$:

$$\Delta t = t_3 - t_2 = \frac{(v_x)_3 - (v_x)_2}{a_x} = \frac{0 \text{ m/s} - 30 \text{ m/s}}{-6.0 \text{ m/s}^2} = 5.0 \text{ s}$$

The position at time t_3 is computed using the second equation in Table 2.4; we take point 2 as the initial point and point 3 as the final point for this phase of the motion and use $\Delta t = t_3 - t_2$:

$$x_3 = x_2 + (v_x)_2 \Delta t + \tfrac{1}{2}a_x(\Delta t)^2$$
$$= 22.5 \text{ m} + (30 \text{ m/s})(5.0 \text{ s}) + \tfrac{1}{2}(-6.0 \text{ m/s}^2)(5.0 \text{ s})^2$$
$$= 98 \text{ m}$$

x_3 is the position of the car at the end of the problem—and so the car travels 98 m before coming to rest.

ASSESS The numbers for the reaction time and the acceleration on wet pavement are reasonable ones for an alert driver in a car with good tires. The final distance is quite large—it is more than the length of a football field.

ActivPhysics: 1.7, 1.10

2.7 Free Fall

A particularly important example of constant acceleration is the motion of an object moving under the influence of gravity only, and no other forces. This motion is called **free fall**. Strictly speaking, free fall occurs only in a vacuum, where there is no air resistance. But if you drop a hammer, air resistance is nearly negligible, so we'll make only a very slight error in treating it *as if* it were in free fall. If you drop a feather, air resistance is *not* negligible, and we can't make this approximation. Motion with air resistance is a problem we will study in Chapter 5. Until then, we will restrict our attention to situations in which air resistance can be ignored, and we will make the reasonable assumption that falling objects are in free fall.

As part of his early studies of motion, Galileo did the first careful experiments on free fall and made the surprising observation that two objects of different weight dropped from the same height will, if air resistance can be neglected, hit the ground at the same time and with the same speed. In fact—as Galileo surmised, and as a famous demonstration on the moon showed—in a vacuum, where there is no air resistance, this holds true for *any* two objects.

Galileo's discovery about free fall means that **any two objects in free fall, regardless of their mass, have the same acceleration.** This is an especially important conclusion. FIGURE 2.36a shows the motion diagram of an object that was released from rest and falls freely. The motion diagram and graph would be identical for a falling baseball or a falling boulder! FIGURE 2.36b shows the object's velocity graph. As we can see, the velocity changes at a steady rate. The slope of the velocity-versus-time graph is the free-fall acceleration $a_{\text{free fall}}$.

Instead of dropping the object, suppose we throw it upward. What happens then? You know that the object will move up and that its speed will decrease as it rises.

"Looks like Mr. Galileo was correct ..." was the comment made by Apollo 15 astronaut David Scott, who dropped a hammer and a feather on the moon. The objects were dropped from the same height at the same time and hit the ground simultaneously—something that would not happen in the atmosphere of the earth!

FIGURE 2.36 Motion of an object in free fall.

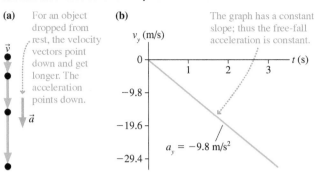

(a) For an object dropped from rest, the velocity vectors point down and get longer. The acceleration points down.

$\vec{v}$
$\vec{a}$

(b)

The graph has a constant slope; thus the free-fall acceleration is constant.

v_y (m/s)

t (s)

$a_y = -9.8$ m/s²

(c) If the object is initially moving up, the velocity vectors point up but get shorter. The acceleration still points down.

$\vec{v}$
$\vec{a}$

Class Video

This is illustrated in the motion diagram of FIGURE 2.36c, which shows a surprising result: Even though the object is moving up, its acceleration still points down. In fact, **the free-fall acceleration always points down,** no matter what direction an object is moving.

NOTE ▶ Despite the name, free fall is not restricted to objects that are literally falling. Any object moving under the influence of gravity only, and no other forces, is in free fall. This includes objects falling straight down, objects that have been tossed or shot straight up, objects in projectile motion (such as a passed football), and, as we will see, satellites in orbit. In this chapter we consider only objects that move up and down along a vertical line; projectile motion will be studied in Chapter 3. ◀

The free-fall acceleration is always in the same direction, and on earth, it always has approximately the same magnitude. Careful measurements show that the value of the free-fall acceleration varies slightly at different places on the earth, but for the calculations in this book we will use the the following average value:

$$\vec{a}_{\text{free fall}} = (9.80 \text{ m/s}^2, \text{ vertically downward}) \qquad (2.15)$$

Standard value for the acceleration of an object in free fall

The magnitude of the **free-fall acceleration** has the special symbol g:

$$g = 9.80 \text{ m/s}^2$$

We will generally work with two significant figures and so will use $g = 9.8$ m/s².

Several points about free fall are worthy of note:

- g, by definition, is *always* positive. **There will never be a problem that uses a negative value for g.**
- The velocity graph in Figure 2.36b has a negative slope. Even though a falling object speeds up, it has *negative* acceleration. Alternatively, notice that the acceleration vector $\vec{a}_{\text{free fall}}$ points down. Thus g is *not* the object's acceleration, simply the magnitude of the acceleration. The one-dimensional acceleration is

$$a_y = a_{\text{free fall}} = -g$$

It is a_y that is negative, not g.

- Because free fall is motion with constant acceleration, we can use the kinematic equations of Table 2.4 with the acceleration being due to gravity, $a_y = -g$.
- g is not called "gravity." Gravity is a force, not an acceleration. g is the *free-fall acceleration.*
- $g = 9.80$ m/s² only on earth. Other planets have different values of g. You will learn in Chapter 6 how to determine g for other planets.

Some of the children are moving up and some are moving down, but all are in free fall—and so are accelerating downward at 9.8 m/s².

TRY IT YOURSELF

A reaction time challenge Hold a $1 (or larger!) bill by an upper corner. Have a friend prepare to grasp a lower corner, putting her fingers *near but not touching* the bill. Tell her to try to catch the bill when you drop it by simply closing her fingers without moving her hand downward—and that if she can catch it, she can keep it. Don't worry; the bill's free fall will keep your money safe. In the few tenths of a second that it takes your friend to react, free fall will take the bill beyond her grasp.

■ We will sometimes compute acceleration in units of g. An acceleration of 9.8 m/s² is an acceleration of $1g$; an acceleration of 19.6 m/s² is $2g$. Generally, we can compute

$$\text{acceleration (in units of } g) = \frac{\text{acceleration (in units of m/s}^2)}{9.8 \text{ m/s}^2} \qquad (2.16)$$

This allows us to express accelerations in units that have a definite physical reference.

EXAMPLE 2.13   **Analyzing a rock's fall**

A heavy rock is dropped from rest at the top of a cliff and falls 100 m before hitting the ground. How long does the rock take to fall to the ground, and what is its velocity when it hits?

PREPARE **FIGURE 2.37** shows a visual overview with all necessary data. We have placed the origin at the ground, which makes $y_i = 100$ m.

FIGURE 2.37 Visual overview of a falling rock.

SOLVE Free fall is motion with the specific constant acceleration $a_y = -g$. The first question involves a relation between time and distance, a relation expressed by the second equation in Table 2.4. Using $(v_y)_i = 0$ m/s and $t_i = 0$ s, we find

$$y_f = y_i + (v_y)_i \, \Delta t + \tfrac{1}{2} a_y \, \Delta t^2 = y_i - \tfrac{1}{2} g \, \Delta t^2 = y_i - \tfrac{1}{2} g t_f^2$$

We can now solve for t_f:

$$t_f = \sqrt{\frac{2(y_i - y_f)}{g}} = \sqrt{\frac{2(100 \text{ m} - 0 \text{ m})}{9.80 \text{ m/s}^2}} = 4.52 \text{ s}$$

Now that we know the fall time, we can use the first kinematic equation to find $(v_y)_f$:

$$(v_y)_f = (v_y)_i - g \, \Delta t = -g t_f = -(9.80 \text{ m/s}^2)(4.52 \text{ s})$$
$$= -44.3 \text{ m/s}$$

ASSESS Are the answers reasonable? Well, 100 m is about 300 feet, which is about the height of a 30-floor building. How long does it take something to fall 30 floors? Four or five seconds seems pretty reasonable. How fast would it be going at the bottom? Using an approximate version of our conversion factor 1 m/s ≈ 2 mph, we find that 44.3 m/s ≈ 90 mph. That also seems like a pretty reasonable speed for something that has fallen 30 floors. Suppose we had made a mistake. If we misplaced a decimal point we could have calculated a speed of 443 m/s, or about 900 mph! This is clearly *not* reasonable. If we had misplaced the decimal point in the other direction, we would have calculated a speed of 4.3 m/s ≈ 9 mph. This is another unreasonable result, because this is slower than a typical bicycling speed.

CONCEPTUAL EXAMPLE 2.14   **Analyzing the motion of a ball tossed upward**

Draw a motion diagram and a velocity-versus-time graph for a ball tossed straight up in the air from the point that it leaves the hand until just before it is caught.

REASON You know what the motion of the ball looks like: The ball goes up, and then it comes back down again. This complicates the drawing of a motion diagram a bit, as the ball retraces its route as it falls. A literal motion diagram would show the upward motion and downward motion on top of each other, leading to confusion. We can avoid this difficulty by horizontally separating the upward motion and downward motion diagrams. This will not affect our conclusions because it does not change any of the vectors. The motion diagram and velocity-versus-time graph appear as in **FIGURE 2.38** on the next page.

ASSESS The highest point in the ball's motion, where it reverses direction, is called a *turning point*. What are the velocity and the acceleration at this point? We can see from the motion diagram that the velocity vectors are pointing upward but getting shorter

as the ball approaches the top. As it starts to fall, the velocity vectors are pointing downward and getting longer. There must be a moment—just an instant as $\vec{v}$ switches from pointing up to pointing down—when the velocity is zero. Indeed, the ball's velocity *is* zero for an instant at the precise top of the motion! We can also see on the velocity graph that there is one instant of time when $v_y = 0$. This is the turning point.

But what about the acceleration at the top? Many people expect the acceleration to be zero at the highest point. But recall that the velocity at the top point is changing—from up to down. If the velocity is changing, there *must* be an acceleration. The slope of the velocity graph at the instant when $v_y = 0$—that is, at the highest point—is no different than at any other point in the motion. The ball is still in free fall with acceleration $a_y = -g$!

Another way to think about this is to note that zero acceleration would mean no change of velocity. When the ball reached zero velocity at the top, it would hang there and not fall if the acceleration were also zero!

FIGURE 2.38 Motion diagram and velocity graph of a ball tossed straight up in the air.

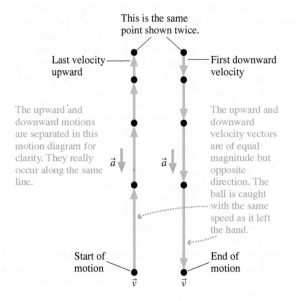

This is the same point shown twice.

Last velocity upward

First downward velocity

The upward and downward motions are separated in this motion diagram for clarity. They really occur along the same line.

$\vec{a}$ $\vec{a}$

The upward and downward velocity vectors are of equal magnitude but opposite direction. The ball is caught with the same speed as it left the hand.

Start of motion

End of motion

$\vec{v}$ $\vec{v}$

The ball starts with a positive (upward) velocity that steadily decreases.

When the ball reaches its highest point, its velocity is instantaneously zero. This is the turning point of the motion.

Now the ball is moving downward. The velocity is negative.

v_y

t

$a_y = -9.8 \text{ m/s}^2$

During the entire motion, the acceleration is that of free fall. The slope of the velocity graph is constant and negative.

EXAMPLE 2.15   **Finding the height of a leap**

A springbok is an antelope found in southern Africa that gets its name from its remarkable jumping ability. When a springbok is startled, it will leap straight up into the air—a maneuver called a "pronk." A springbok goes into a crouch to perform a pronk. It then extends its legs forcefully, accelerating at 35 m/s² for 0.70 m as its legs straighten. Legs fully extended, it leaves the ground and rises into the air.

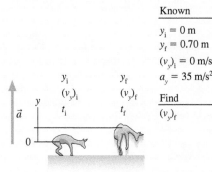

a. At what speed does the springbok leave the ground?
b. How high does it go?

PREPARE We begin with the visual overview shown in FIGURE 2.39, where we've identified two different phases of the motion: the springbok pushing off the ground and the springbok rising into the air. We'll treat these as two separate problems that we solve in turn. We will "re-use" the variables y_i, y_f, $(v_y)_i$, and $(v_y)_f$ for the two phases of the motion.

For the first part of our solution, in Figure 2.39a we choose the origin of the y-axis at the position of the springbok deep in the crouch. The final position is the top extent of the push, at the instant the springbok leaves the ground. We want to find the velocity at this position because that's how fast the springbok is moving as it leaves the ground. Figure 2.39b essentially starts over—we have defined a new vertical axis with its origin at the ground, so the highest point of the springbok's motion is a

FIGURE 2.39 A visual overview of the springbok's leap.

(a) Pushing off the ground

y_i y_f
$(v_y)_i$ $(v_y)_f$
t_i t_f

$\vec{a}$ y

0

Known
$y_i = 0$ m
$y_f = 0.70$ m
$(v_y)_i = 0$ m/s
$a_y = 35$ m/s²

Find
$(v_y)_f$

(b) Rising into the air

y

$y_f, (v_y)_f, t_f$

$\vec{a}$

$\vec{v}$

0   $y_i, (v_y)_i, t_i$

Known
$y_i = 0$ m
$(v_y)_i$ is equal to $(v_y)_f$ from part a
$(v_y)_f = 0$ m/s
$a_y = -9.8$ m/s²

Find
y_f

Continued

distance above the ground. The table of values shows the key piece of information for this second part of the problem: The initial velocity for part b is the final velocity from part a.

After the springbok leaves the ground, this is a free-fall problem because the springbok is moving under the influence of gravity only. We want to know the height of the leap, so we are looking for the height at the top point of the motion. This is a turning point of the motion, with the instantaneous velocity equal to zero. Thus y_f, the height of the leap, is the springbok's position at the instant $(v_y)_f = 0$.

SOLVE a. For the first phase, pushing off the ground, we have information about displacement, initial velocity, and acceleration, but we don't know anything about the time interval. The third equation in Table 2.4 is perfect for this type of situation. We can rearrange it to solve for the velocity with which the springbok lifts off the ground:

$$(v_y)_f^2 = v_i^2 + 2a_y\Delta y = (0 \text{ m/s})^2 + 2(35 \text{ m/s}^2)(0.70 \text{ m}) = 49 \text{ m}^2/\text{s}^2$$

$$(v_y)_f = \sqrt{49 \text{ m}^2/\text{s}^2} = 7.0 \text{ m/s}$$

The springbok leaves the ground with a speed of 7.0 m/s.

b. Now we are ready for the second phase of the motion, the vertical motion after leaving the ground. The third equation in Table 2.4 is again appropriate because again we don't know the time. Because $y_i = 0$, the springbok's displacement is $\Delta y = y_f - y_i = y_f$, the height of the vertical leap. From part a, the initial velocity is $(v_y)_i = 7.0$ m/s, and the final velocity is $(v_y)_f = 0$. This is free-fall motion, with $a_y = -g$; thus

$$(v_y)_f^2 = 0 = (v_y)_i^2 - 2g\Delta y = (v_y)_i^2 - 2gy_f$$

which gives

$$(v_y)_i^2 = 2gy_f$$

Solving for y_f, we get a jump height of

$$y_f = \frac{(7.0 \text{ m/s})^2}{2(9.8 \text{ m/s}^2)} = 2.5 \text{ m}$$

ASSESS 2.5 m is a remarkable leap—a bit over 8 ft—but these animals are known for their jumping ability, so this seems reasonable.

FIGURE 2.40 Velocity-versus-time and position-versus-time graphs for a sprint between a man and a horse.

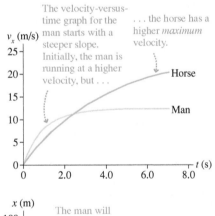

The velocity-versus-time graph for the man starts with a steeper slope.
Initially, the man is running at a higher velocity, but . . .

. . . the horse has a higher *maximum* velocity.

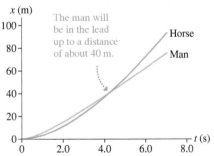

The man will be in the lead up to a distance of about 40 m.

The caption accompanying the photo at the start of the chapter asked a question about animals and their athletic abilities: Who is the winner in a race between a horse and a man? The surprising answer is "It depends." Specifically, the winner depends on the length of the race.

Some animals are capable of high speed; others are capable of great acceleration. Horses can run much faster than humans, but, when starting from rest, humans are capable of much greater initial acceleration. FIGURE 2.40 shows velocity and position graphs for an elite male sprinter and a thoroughbred racehorse. The horse's maximum velocity is about twice that of the man, but the man's initial acceleration—the slope of the velocity graph at early times—is about twice that of the horse. As the second graph shows, a man could win a *very* short race. For a longer race, the horse's higher maximum velocity will put it in the lead; the men's world-record time for the mile is a bit under 4 min, but a horse can easily run this distance in less than 2 min.

For a race of many miles, another factor comes into play: energy. A very long race is less about velocity and acceleration than about endurance—the ability to continue expending energy for a long time. In such endurance trials, humans often win. We will explore such energy issues in Chapter 11.

STOP TO THINK 2.6 A volcano ejects a chunk of rock straight up at a velocity of $v_y = 30$ m/s. Ignoring air resistance, what will be the velocity v_y of the rock when it falls back into the volcano's crater?

A. > 30 m/s   B. 30 m/s   C. 0 m/s   D. -30 m/s   E. < -30 m/s

Speed versus endurance

Cheetahs have the highest top speed of any land animal, but they usually fail in their attempts to catch their prey because their endurance is limited. They can maintain their maximum speed of 30 m/s for only about 15 s before they need to stop.

Thomson's gazelles, their preferred prey, have a lower top speed than cheetahs, but they can maintain this speed for a few minutes. When a cheetah goes after a gazelle, success or failure is a simple matter of kinematics: Is the cheetah's high speed enough to allow it to reach its prey before the cheetah runs out of steam? The following problem uses realistic data for such a chase.

A cheetah has spotted a gazelle. The cheetah leaps into action, reaching its top speed of 30 m/s in a few seconds. At this instant, the gazelle, 160 m from the running cheetah, notices the danger and heads directly away. The gazelle accelerates at 4.5 m/s² for 6.0 s, then continues running at a constant speed. After reaching its maximum speed, the cheetah can continue running for only 15 s. Does the cheetah catch the gazelle, or does the gazelle escape?

PREPARE The example asks, "Does the cheetah catch the gazelle?" Our most challenging task is to translate these words into a graphical and mathematical problem that we can solve using the techniques of the chapter.

There are two related problems: the motion of the cheetah and the motion of the gazelle, for which we'll use the subscripts "C" and "G". Let's take our starting time, $t_1 = 0$ s, as the instant that the gazelle notices the cheetah and begins to run. We'll take the position of the cheetah at this instant as the origin of our coordinate system, so $x_{1C} = 0$ m and $x_{1G} = 160$ m—the gazelle is 160 m away when it notices the cheetah. We've used this information to draw the visual overview in FIGURE 2.41, which includes motion diagrams and velocity graphs for the cheetah and the gazelle. The visual overview sums up everything we know about the problem.

With a clear picture of the situation, we can now rephrase the problem this way: Compute the position of the cheetah and the position of the gazelle at $t_3 = 15$ s, the time when the cheetah needs to break off the chase. If $x_{3G} \geq x_{3C}$, then the gazelle stays out in front and escapes. If $x_{3G} < x_{3C}$, the cheetah wins the race—and gets its dinner.

SOLVE The cheetah is in uniform motion for the entire duration of the problem, so we can use Equation 2.4 to solve for its position at $t_3 = 15$ s:

$$x_{3C} = x_{1C} + (v_x)_{1C}\Delta t = 0 \text{ m} + (30 \text{ m/s})(15 \text{ s}) = 450 \text{ m}$$

The gazelle's motion has two phases: one of constant acceleration and then one of constant velocity. We can solve for the position and the velocity at t_2, the end of the first phase, using the first two equations in Table 2.4. Let's find the velocity first:

$$(v_x)_{2G} = (v_x)_{1G} + (a_x)_G\Delta t = 0 \text{ m/s} + (4.5 \text{ m/s}^2)(6.0 \text{ s}) = 27 \text{ m/s}$$

The gazelle's position at t_2 is:

Δt is the time for this phase of the motion, $t_2 - t_1 = 6.0$ s.

$$x_{2G} = x_{1G} + (v_x)_{1G}\Delta t + \tfrac{1}{2}(a_x)_G(\Delta t)^2$$
$$= 160 \text{ m} + 0 + \tfrac{1}{2}(4.5 \text{ m/s}^2)(6.0 \text{ s})^2 = 240 \text{ m}$$

The gazelle has a head start; it begins at $x_{1G} = 160$ m.

From t_2 to t_3 the gazelle moves at a constant speed, so we can use the uniform motion equation, Equation 2.4, to find its final position:

The gazelle begins this phase of the motion at $x_{2G} = 240$ m.   *Δt for this phase of the motion is $t_3 - t_2 = 9.0$ s.*

$$x_{3G} = x_{2G} + (v_x)_{2G}\Delta t = 240 \text{ m} + (27 \text{ m/s})(9.0 \text{ s}) = 480 \text{ m}$$

x_{3C} is 450 m; x_{3G} is 480 m. The gazelle is 30 m ahead of the cheetah when the cheetah has to break off the chase, so the gazelle escapes.

ASSESS Does our solution make sense? Let's look at the final result. The numbers in the problem statement are realistic, so we expect our results to mirror real life. The speed for the gazelle is close to that of the cheetah, which seems reasonable for two animals known for their speed. And the result is the most common occurrence—the chase is close, but the gazelle gets away.

FIGURE 2.41 Visual overview for the cheetah and for the gazelle.

SUMMARY

The goal of Chapter 2 has been to describe and analyze linear motion.

GENERAL STRATEGIES

Problem-Solving Strategy

Our general problem-solving strategy has three parts:

PREPARE Set up the problem:

- Draw a picture.
- Collect necessary information.
- Do preliminary calculations.

SOLVE Do the necessary mathematics or reasoning.

ASSESS Check your answer to see if it is complete in all details and makes physical sense.

Visual Overview

A visual overview consists of several pieces that completely specify a problem. This may include any or all of the elements below:

Motion diagram	Pictorial representation	Graphical representation	List of values

IMPORTANT CONCEPTS

Velocity is the rate of change of position:

$$v_x = \frac{\Delta x}{\Delta t}$$

Acceleration is the rate of change of velocity:

$$a_x = \frac{\Delta v_x}{\Delta t}$$

The units of acceleration are m/s^2.

An object is speeding up if v_x and a_x have the same sign, slowing down if they have opposite signs.

A position-versus-time graph plots position on the vertical axis against time on the horizontal axis.

A velocity-versus-time graph plots velocity on the vertical axis against time on the horizontal axis.

APPLICATIONS

Uniform motion

An object in uniform motion has a constant velocity. Its velocity graph is a horizontal line; its position graph is linear.

Kinematic equation for uniform motion:

$$x_f = x_i + v_x \, \Delta t$$

Uniform motion is a special case of constant-acceleration motion, with $a_x = 0$.

Motion with constant acceleration

An object with constant acceleration has a constantly changing velocity. Its velocity graph is linear; its position graph is a parabola.

Kinematic equations for motion with constant acceleration:

$$(v_x)_f = (v_x)_i + a_x \, \Delta t$$

$$x_f = x_i + (v_x)_i \, \Delta t + \tfrac{1}{2} a_x (\Delta t)^2$$

$$(v_x)_f^2 = (v_x)_i^2 + 2 a_x \, \Delta x$$

Free fall

Free fall is a special case of constant-acceleration motion; the acceleration has magnitude $g = 9.80 \, m/s^2$ and is always directed vertically downward whether an object is moving up or down.

Problem difficulty is labeled as I (straightforward) to IIIII (challenging). Problems labeled INT integrate significant material from earlier chapters; BIO are of biological or medical interest.

For homework assigned on MasteringPhysics, go to www.masteringphysics.com

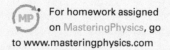

Scan this QR code to launch a **Video Tutor Solution** that will help you solve problems for this chapter.

QUESTIONS

Conceptual Questions

1. A person gets in an elevator on the ground floor and rides it to the top floor of a building. Sketch a velocity-versus-time graph for this motion.

2. a. Give an example of a vertical motion with a positive velocity and a negative acceleration.
   b. Give an example of a vertical motion with a negative velocity and a negative acceleration.

3. Sketch a velocity-versus-time graph for a rock that is thrown straight upward, from the instant it leaves the hand until the instant it hits the ground.

4. You are driving down the road at a constant speed. Another car going a bit faster catches up with you and passes you. Draw a position graph for both vehicles on the same set of axes, and note the point on the graph where the other vehicle passes you.

5. A car is traveling north. Can its acceleration vector ever point south? Explain.

6. BIO Certain animals are capable of running at great speeds; other animals are capable of tremendous accelerations. Speculate on which would be more beneficial to a predator—large maximum speed or large acceleration.

7. A ball is thrown straight up into the air. At each of the following instants, is the ball's acceleration a_y equal to g, $-g$, 0, $< g$, or $> g$?
   a. Just after leaving your hand?
   b. At the very top (maximum height)?
   c. Just before hitting the ground?

8. A rock is *thrown* (not dropped) straight down from a bridge into the river below.
   a. Immediately after being released, is the magnitude of the rock's acceleration greater than g, less than g, or equal to g? Explain.
   b. Immediately before hitting the water, is the magnitude of the the rock's acceleration greater than g, less than g, or equal to g? Explain.

9. Figure Q2.9 shows an object's position-versus-time graph. The letters A to E correspond to various segments of the motion in which the graph has constant slope.

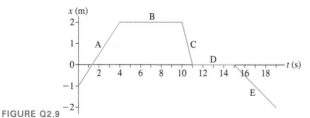

FIGURE Q2.9

   a. Write a realistic motion short story for an object that would have this position graph.
   b. In which segment(s) is the object at rest?

   c. In which segment(s) is the object moving to the right?
   d. Is the speed of the object during segment C greater than, equal to, or less than its speed during segment E? Explain.

10. Figure Q2.10 shows the position graph for an object moving along the horizontal axis.
    a. Write a realistic motion short story for an object that would have this position graph.
    b. Draw the corresponding velocity graph.

FIGURE Q2.10

11. Figure Q2.11 shows the position-versus-time graphs for two objects, A and B, that are moving along the same axis.
    a. At the instant $t = 1$ s, is the speed of A greater than, less than, or equal to the speed of B? Explain.
    b. Do objects A and B ever have the *same* speed? If so, at what time or times? Explain.

    FIGURE Q2.11

12. Figure Q2.12 shows a position-versus-time graph. At which lettered point or points is the object
    a. Moving the fastest?
    b. Moving to the left?
    c. Speeding up?
    d. Slowing down?
    e. Turning around?

    FIGURE Q2.12

13. Figure Q2.13 is the velocity-versus-time graph for an object moving along the x-axis.
    a. During which segment(s) is the velocity constant?
    b. During which segment(s) is the object speeding up?
    c. During which segment(s) is the object slowing down?
    d. During which segment(s) is the object standing still?
    e. During which segment(s) is the object moving to the right?

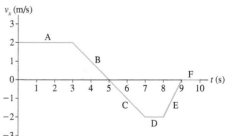

FIGURE Q2.13

14. A car traveling at velocity v takes distance d to stop after the brakes are applied. What is the stopping distance if the car is initially traveling at velocity $2v$? Assume that the acceleration due to the braking is the same in both cases.

Multiple-Choice Questions

15. | Figure Q2.15 shows the position graph of a car traveling on a straight road. At which labeled instant is the speed of the car greatest?

16. | Figure Q2.16 shows the position graph of a car traveling on a straight road. The velocity at instant 1 is _____ and the velocity at instant 2 is _____.
    A. positive, negative
    B. positive, positive
    C. negative, negative
    D. negative, zero
    E. positive, zero

FIGURE Q2.15

FIGURE Q2.16

17. | Figure Q2.17 shows an object's position-versus-time graph. What is the velocity of the object at $t = 6$ s?
    A. 0.67 m/s
    B. 0.83 m/s
    C. 3.3 m/s
    D. 4.2 m/s
    E. 25 m/s

FIGURE Q2.17

18. | The following options describe the motion of four cars A–D. Which car has the largest acceleration?
    A. Goes from 0 m/s to 10 m/s in 5.0 s
    B. Goes from 0 m/s to 5.0 m/s in 2.0 s
    C. Goes from 0 m/s to 20 m/s in 7.0 s
    D. Goes from 0 m/s to 3.0 m/s in 1.0 s

19. | A car is traveling at $v_x = 20$ m/s. The driver applies the brakes, and the car slows with $a_x = -4.0$ m/s². What is the stopping distance?
    A. 5.0 m
    B. 25 m
    C. 40 m
    D. 50 m

20. ‖ Velocity-versus-time graphs for three drag racers are shown in Figure Q2.20. At $t = 5.0$ s, which car has traveled the furthest?
    A. Andy
    B. Betty
    C. Carl
    D. All have traveled the same distance

FIGURE Q2.20

21. | Which of the three drag racers in Question 20 had the greatest acceleration at $t = 0$ s?
    A. Andy
    B. Betty
    C. Carl
    D. All had the same acceleration

22. ‖ Ball 1 is thrown straight up in the air and, at the same instant, ball 2 is released from rest and allowed to fall. Which velocity graph in Figure Q2.22 best represents the motion of the two balls?

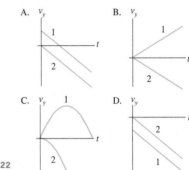

FIGURE Q2.22

23. ‖ Figure Q2.23 shows a motion diagram with the clock reading (in seconds) shown at each position. From $t = 9$ s to $t = 15$ s the object is at the same position. After that, it returns along the same track. The positions of the dots for $t \geq 16$ s are offset for clarity. Which graph best represents the object's *velocity?*

FIGURE Q2.23

24. ‖ A car can go from 0 to 60 mph in 7.0 s. Assuming that it could maintain the same acceleration at higher speeds, how long would it take the car to go from 0 to 120 mph?
    A. 10 s
    B. 14 s
    C. 21 s
    D. 28 s

25. ‖ A car can go from 0 to 60 mph in 12 s. A second car is capable of twice the acceleration of the first car. Assuming that it could maintain the same acceleration at higher speeds, how much time will this second car take to go from 0 to 120 mph?
    A. 12 s
    B. 9.0 s
    C. 6.0 s
    D. 3.0 s

PROBLEMS

Section 2.1 Describing Motion

1. ‖ Figure P2.1 shows a motion diagram of a car traveling down a street. The camera took one frame every second. A distance scale is provided.
   a. Measure the *x*-value of the car at each dot. Place your data in a table, similar to Table 2.1, showing each position and the instant of time at which it occurred.
   b. Make a graph of *x* versus *t*, using the data in your table. Because you have data only at certain instants of time, your graph should consist of dots that are not connected together.

FIGURE P2.1

2. | For each motion diagram in Figure P2.2, determine the sign (positive or negative) of the position and the velocity.

FIGURE P2.2

3. | Write a short description of the motion of a real object for which Figure P2.3 would be a realistic position-versus-time graph.

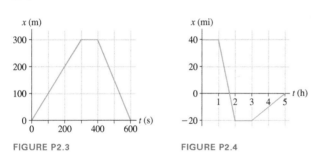

FIGURE P2.3   FIGURE P2.4

4. | Write a short description of the motion of a real object for which Figure P2.4 would be a realistic position-versus-time graph.

5. ‖ The position graph of Figure P2.5 shows a dog slowly sneaking up on a squirrel, then putting on a burst of speed.
   a. For how many seconds does the dog move at the slower speed?
   b. Draw the dog's velocity-versus-time graph. Include a numerical scale on both axes.

FIGURE P2.5

6. ‖ The position graph of Figure P2.6 represents the motion of a ball being rolled back and forth by two children.
   a. At what positions are the two children sitting?
   b. Draw the ball's velocity-versus-time graph. Include a numerical scale on both axes.

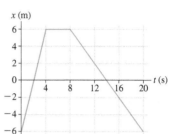

FIGURE P2.6

7. ‖ A rural mail carrier is driving slowly, putting mail in mailboxes near the road. He overshoots one mailbox, stops, shifts into reverse, and then backs up until he is at the right spot. The velocity graph of Figure P2.7 represents his motion.
   a. Draw the mail carrier's position-versus-time graph. Assume that *x* = 0 m at *t* = 0 s.
   b. What is the position of the mailbox?

FIGURE P2.7   FIGURE P2.8

8. ‖ For the velocity-versus-time graph of Figure P2.8:
   a. Draw the corresponding position-versus-time graph. Assume that *x* = 0 m at *t* = 0 s.
   b. What is the object's position at *t* = 12 s?
   c. Describe a moving object that could have these graphs.

9. ‖ A bicyclist has the position-versus-time graph shown in Figure P2.9. What is the bicyclist's velocity at *t* = 10 s, at *t* = 25 s, and at *t* = 35 s?

FIGURE P2.9

Section 2.2 Uniform Motion

10. | In college softball, the distance from the pitcher's mound to the batter is 43 feet. If the ball leaves the bat at 100 mph, how much time elapses between the hit and the ball reaching the pitcher?

11. ‖ Alan leaves Los Angeles at 8:00 A.M. to drive to San Francisco, 400 mi away. He travels at a steady 50 mph. Beth leaves Los Angeles at 9:00 A.M. and drives a steady 60 mph.
    a. Who gets to San Francisco first?
    b. How long does the first to arrive have to wait for the second?

12. ‖ Richard is driving home to visit his parents. 125 mi of the trip are on the interstate highway where the speed limit is 65 mph. Normally Richard drives at the speed limit, but today he is running late and decides to take his chances by driving at 70 mph. How many minutes does he save?

13. ‖‖ In a 5.00 km race, one runner runs at a steady 12.0 km/h and another runs at 14.5 km/h. How long does the faster runner have to wait at the finish line to see the slower runner cross?

14. ‖‖‖ In an 8.00 km race, one runner runs at a steady 11.0 km/h and another runs at 14.0 km/h. How far from the finish line is the slower runner when the faster runner finishes the race?

15. ‖ A car moves with constant velocity along a straight road. Its position is $x_1 = 0$ m at $t_1 = 0$ s and is $x_2 = 30$ m at $t_2 = 3.0$ s. Answer the following by considering ratios, without computing the car's velocity.
    a. What is the car's position at $t = 1.5$ s?
    b. What will be its position at $t = 9.0$ s?

16. ‖ While running a marathon, a long-distance runner uses a stopwatch to time herself over a distance of 100 m. She finds that she runs this distance in 18 s. Answer the following by considering ratios, without computing her velocity.
    a. If she maintains her speed, how much time will it take her to run the next 400 m?
    b. How long will it take her to run a mile at this speed?

Section 2.3 Instantaneous Velocity

17. ‖ Figure P2.17 shows the position graph of a particle.
    a. Draw the particle's velocity graph for the interval $0 \text{ s} \le t \le 4$ s.
    b. Does this particle have a turning point or points? If so, at what time or times?

FIGURE P2.17

18. ‖ A somewhat idealized graph of the speed of the blood in the ascending aorta during one beat of the heart appears as in Figure P2.18.
    a. Approximately how far, in cm, does the blood move during one beat?
    b. Assume similar data for the motion of the blood in your aorta. Estimate how many beats of the heart it will it take the blood to get from your heart to your brain.

BIO

FIGURE P2.18

19. ‖‖ A car starts from $x_i = 10$ m at $t_i = 0$ s and moves with the velocity graph shown in Figure P2.19.
    a. What is the object's position at $t = 2$ s, 3 s, and 4 s?
    b. Does this car ever change direction? If so, at what time?

FIGURE P2.19

20. ‖ Figure P2.20 shows a graph of actual position-versus-time data for a particular type of drag racer known as a "funny car."
    a. Estimate the car's velocity at 2.0 s.
    b. Estimate the car's velocity at 4.0 s.

FIGURE P2.20

Section 2.4 Acceleration

21. ‖ Figure P2.21 shows the velocity graph of a bicycle. Draw the bicycle's acceleration graph for the interval $0 \text{ s} \le t \le 4$ s. Give both axes an appropriate numerical scale.

FIGURE P2.21   FIGURE P2.22

22. ‖‖‖ Figure P2.22 shows the velocity graph of a train that starts from the origin at $t = 0$ s.
    a. Draw position and acceleration graphs for the train.
    b. Find the acceleration of the train at $t = 3.0$ s.

23. ‖ For each motion diagram shown earlier in Figure P2.2, determine the sign (positive or negative) of the acceleration.

24. ‖ Figure P2.18 showed data for the speed of blood in the aorta. Determine the magnitude of the acceleration for both phases, speeding up and slowing down.

BIO

25. ‖ Figure P2.25 is a somewhat simplified velocity graph for Olympic sprinter Carl Lewis starting a 100 m dash. Estimate his acceleration during each of the intervals A, B, and C.

FIGURE P2.25

Section 2.5 Motion with Constant Acceleration

26. ‖ A Thomson's gazelle can reach a speed of 13 m/s in 3.0 s. A lion can reach a speed of 9.5 m/s in 1.0 s. A trout can reach a speed of 2.8 m/s in 0.12 s. Which animal has the largest acceleration?

BIO

27. ‖ When striking, the pike, a
BIO predatory fish, can accelerate
from rest to a speed of 4.0 m/s
in 0.11 s.
    a. What is the acceleration of
    the pike during this strike?
    b. How far does the pike move
    during this strike?

28. ‖ a. What constant acceleration, in SI units, must a car have to
    go from zero to 60 mph in 10 s?
    b. What fraction of g is this?
    c. How far has the car traveled when it reaches 60 mph?
    Give your answer both in SI units and in feet.

29. ‖ Light-rail passenger trains that provide transportation within
    and between cities are capable of modest accelerations. The
    magnitude of the maximum acceleration is typically 1.3 m/s²,
    but the driver will usually maintain a constant acceleration that
    is less than the maximum. A train travels through a congested
    part of town at 5.0 m/s. Once free of this area, it speeds up to 12
    m/s in 8.0 s. At the edge of town, the driver again accelerates,
    with the same acceleration, for another 16 s to reach a higher
    cruising speed. What is the final speed?

30. ‖ A speed skater moving across frictionless ice at 8.0 m/s hits a
    5.0-m-wide patch of rough ice. She slows steadily, then contin-
    ues on at 6.0 m/s. What is her acceleration on the rough ice?

31. ‖ A small propeller airplane can comfortably achieve a high
    enough speed to take off on a runway that is 1/4 mile long. A large,
    fully loaded passenger jet has about the same acceleration from
    rest, but it needs to achieve twice the speed to take off. What is the
    minimum runway length that will serve? **Hint:** You can solve this
    problem using ratios without having any additional information.

32. ‖ Figure P2.32 shows a veloc-
    ity-versus-time graph for a par-
    ticle moving along the x-axis.
    At $t = 0$ s, assume that $x = 0$ m.
    a. What are the particle's posi-
    tion, velocity, and accelera-
    tion at $t = 1.0$ s?
    b. What are the particle's posi-
    tion, velocity, and accelera-
    tion at $t = 3.0$ s?

v_x (m/s)

FIGURE P2.32

Section 2.6 Solving One-Dimensional Motion Problems

33. ‖ A driver has a reaction time of 0.50 s, and the maximum
    deceleration of her car is 6.0 m/s². She is driving at 20 m/s
    when suddenly she sees an obstacle in the road 50 m in front of
    her. Can she stop the car in time to avoid a collision?

34. ‖ Chameleons catch insects with their tongues, which they can
BIO rapidly extend to great lengths. In a typical strike, the chameleon's
    tongue accelerates at a remarkable 250 m/s² for 20 ms, then
    travels at constant speed for another 30 ms. During this total
    time of 50 ms, 1/20 of a second, how far does the tongue reach?

35. ‖ You're driving down the highway late one night at 20 m/s
    when a deer steps onto the road 35 m in front of you. Your reac-
    tion time before stepping on the brakes is 0.50 s, and the maxi-
    mum deceleration of your car is 10 m/s².
    a. How much distance is between you and the deer when you
    come to a stop?
    b. What is the maximum speed you could have and still not hit
    the deer?

36. ‖ A light-rail train going from one station to the next on a
    straight section of track accelerates from rest at 1.1 m/s² for 20 s.
    It then proceeds at constant speed for 1100 m before slowing
    down at 2.2 m/s² until it stops at the station.
    a. What is the distance between the stations?
    b. How much time does it take the train to go between the
    stations?

37. ‖ A simple model for a person running the 100 m dash is to
    assume the sprinter runs with constant acceleration until
    reaching top speed, then maintains that speed through the finish
    line. If a sprinter reaches his top speed of 11.2 m/s in 2.14 s,
    what will be his total time?

Section 2.7 Free Fall

38. ‖ Ball bearings can be made by letting spherical drops of
    molten metal fall inside a tall tower—called a *shot tower*—and
    solidify as they fall.
    a. If a bearing needs 4.0 s to solidify enough for impact, how
    high must the tower be?
    b. What is the bearing's impact velocity?

39. ‖ In the chapter, we saw that a person's reaction time is gener-
BIO ally not quick enough to allow the person to catch a dollar bill
    dropped between the fingers. If a typical reaction time in this
    case is 0.25 s, how long would a bill need to be for a person to
    have a good chance of catching it?

40. ‖ A ball is thrown vertically upward with a speed of 19.6 m/s.
    a. What are the ball's velocity and height after 1.00, 2.00, 3.00,
    and 4.00 s?
    b. Draw the ball's velocity-versus-time graph. Give both axes
    an appropriate numerical scale.

41. ‖ A student at the top of a building of height h throws ball A
    straight upward with speed v_0 and throws ball B straight down-
    ward with the same initial speed.
    a. Compare the balls' accelerations, both direction and magni-
    tude, immediately after they leave her hand. Is one accelera-
    tion larger than the other? Or are the magnitudes equal?
    b. Compare the final speeds of the balls as they reach the
    ground. Is one larger than the other? Or are they equal?

42. ‖ Excellent human jumpers can leap straight up to a height of
    110 cm off the ground. To reach this height, with what speed
    would a person need to leave the ground?

43. ‖ A football is kicked straight up into the air; it hits the ground
    5.2 s later.
    a. What was the greatest height reached by the ball? Assume it
    is kicked from ground level.
    b. With what speed did it leave the kicker's foot?

44. ‖‖ In an action movie, the villain is rescued from the ocean by
    grabbing onto the ladder hanging from a helicopter. He is so
    intent on gripping the ladder that he lets go of his briefcase of
    counterfeit money when he is 130 m above the water. If the
    briefcase hits the water 6.0 s later, what was the speed at which
    the helicopter was ascending?

45. ‖‖ A rock climber stands on top of a 50-m-high cliff overhang-
    ing a pool of water. He throws two stones vertically downward
    1.0 s apart and observes that they cause a single splash. The ini-
    tial speed of the first stone was 2.0 m/s.
    a. How long after the release of the first stone does the second
    stone hit the water?
    b. What was the initial speed of the second stone?
    c. What is the speed of each stone as they hit the water?

General Problems

46. ||| Actual velocity data for a lion pursuing prey are shown in
BIO Figure P2.46. Estimate:
   a. The initial acceleration of the lion.
   b. The acceleration of the lion at 2 s and at 4 s.
   c. The distance traveled by the lion between 0 s and 8 s.

FIGURE P2.46

Problems 47 and 48 concern *nerve impulses*, electrical signals propagated along nerve fibers consisting of many *axons* (fiberlike extensions of nerve cells) connected end-to-end. Axons come in two varieties: insulated axons with a sheath made of myelin, and uninsulated axons with

FIGURE P2.47

no such sheath. Myelinated (sheathed) axons conduct nerve impulses much faster than unmyelinated (unsheathed) axons. The impulse speed depends on the diameter of the axons and the sheath, but a typical myelinated axon transmits nerve impulses at a speed of about 25 m/s, much faster than the typical 2.0 m/s for an unmyelinated axon. Figure P2.47 shows small portions of three nerve fibers consisting of axons of equal size. Two-thirds of the axons in fiber B are myelinated.

47. | Suppose nerve impulses simultaneously enter the left side of
BIO the nerve fibers sketched in Figure P2.47, then propagate to the right. Draw qualitatively accurate position and velocity graphs for the nerve impulses in all three cases. A nerve fiber is made up of many axons, but show the propagation of the impulses only over the six axons shown here.

48. | Suppose that the nerve fibers in Figure P2.47 connect a fin-
BIO ger to your brain, a distance of 1.2 m.
   a. What are the travel times of a nerve impulse from finger to brain along fibers A and C?
   b. For fiber B, 2/3 of the length is composed of myelinated axons, 1/3 unmyelinated axons. Compute the travel time for a nerve impulse on this fiber.
   c. When you touch a hot stove with your finger, the sensation of pain must reach your brain as a nerve signal along a nerve fiber before your muscles can react. Which of the three fibers gives you the best protection against a burn? Are any of these fibers unsuitable for transmitting urgent sensory information?

49. || A truck driver has a shipment of apples to deliver to a destination 440 miles away. The trip usually takes him 8 hours. Today he finds himself daydreaming and realizes 120 miles into his trip that he is running 15 minutes later than his usual pace at this point. At what speed must he drive for the remainder of the trip to complete the trip in the usual amount of time?

50. || When you sneeze, the air in your lungs accelerates from rest
BIO to approximately 150 km/h in about 0.50 seconds.
   a. What is the acceleration of the air in m/s^2?
   b. What is this acceleration, in units of g?

51. || Figure P2.51 shows the motion diagram, made at two frames of film per second, of a ball rolling along a track. The track has a 3.0-m-long sticky section.

FIGURE P2.51

   a. Use the scale to determine the positions of the center of the ball. Place your data in a table, similar to Table 2.1, showing each position and the instant of time at which it occurred.
   b. Make a graph of x versus t for the ball. Because you have data only at certain instants of time, your graph should consist of dots that are not connected together.
   c. What is the *change* in the ball's position from $t = 0$ s to $t = 1.0$ s?
   d. What is the *change* in the ball's position from $t = 2.0$ s to $t = 4.0$ s?
   e. What is the ball's velocity before reaching the sticky section?
   f. What is the ball's velocity after passing the sticky section?
   g. Determine the ball's acceleration on the sticky section of the track.

52. || Julie drives 100 mi to Grandmother's house. On the way to Grandmother's, Julie drives half the *distance* at 40 mph and half the distance at 60 mph. On her return trip, she drives half the *time* at 40 mph and half the time at 60 mph.
   a. How long does it take Julie to complete the trip to Grandmother's house?
   b. How long does the return trip take?

53. || The takeoff speed for an Airbus A320 jetliner is 80 m/s. Velocity data measured during takeoff are as shown in the table.
   a. What is the takeoff speed in miles per hour?
   b. What is the jetliner's acceleration during takeoff?
   c. At what time do the wheels leave the ground?
   d. For safety reasons, in case of an aborted takeoff, the runway must be three times the takeoff distance. Can an A320 take off safely on a 2.5-mi-long runway?

t(s)	v_x(m/s)
0	0
10	23
20	46
30	69

54. |||| Does a real automobile have constant acceleration? Measured data for a Porsche 944 Turbo at maximum acceleration are as shown in the table.
   a. Convert the velocities to m/s, then make a graph of velocity versus time. Based on your graph, is the acceleration constant? Explain.
   b. Draw a smooth curve through the points on your graph, then use your graph to *estimate* the car's acceleration at 2.0 s and 8.0 s. Give your answer in SI units. **Hint:** Remember that acceleration is the slope of the velocity graph.

t(s)	v_x(mph)
0	0
2	28
4	46
6	60
8	70
10	78

55. ‖ People hoping to travel to other worlds are faced with huge challenges. One of the biggest is the time required for a journey. The nearest star is 4.1×10^{16} m away. Suppose you had a spacecraft that could accelerate at $1.0g$ for half a year, then continue at a constant speed. (This is far beyond what can be achieved with any known technology.) How long would it take you to reach the nearest star to earth?

56. ‖ You are driving to the grocery store at 20 m/s. You are 110 m from an intersection when the traffic light turns red. Assume that your reaction time is 0.70 s and that your car brakes with constant acceleration.
    a. How far are you from the intersection when you begin to apply the brakes?
    b. What acceleration will bring you to rest right at the intersection?
    c. How long does it take you to stop?

57. ‖ When you blink your eye, the upper lid goes from rest with your
BIO eye open to completely covering your eye in a time of 0.024 s.
    a. Estimate the distance that the top lid of your eye moves during a blink.
    b. What is the acceleration of your eyelid? Assume it to be constant.
    c. What is your upper eyelid's final speed as it hits the bottom eyelid?

58. ‖ A bush baby, an African
BIO primate, is capable of leaping vertically to the remarkable height of 2.3 m. To jump this high, the bush baby accelerates over a distance of 0.16 m while rapidly extending its legs. The acceleration during the jump is approximately constant. What is the acceleration in m/s^2 and in g's?

59. ‖ When jumping, a flea reaches a takeoff speed of 1.0 m/s over
BIO a distance of 0.50 mm.
    a. What is the flea's acceleration during the jump phase?
    b. How long does the acceleration phase last?
    c. If the flea jumps straight up, how high will it go? (Ignore air resistance for this problem; in reality, air resistance plays a large role, and the flea will not reach this height.)

60. ‖ Certain insects can achieve
BIO seemingly impossible accelerations while jumping. The click beetle accelerates at an astonishing $400g$ over a distance of 0.60 cm as it rapidly bends its thorax, making the "click" that gives it its name.
    a. Assuming the beetle jumps straight up, at what speed does it leave the ground?
    b. How much time is required for the beetle to reach this speed?
    c. Ignoring air resistance, how high would it go?

61. ‖ Divers compete by diving into a 3.0-m-deep pool from a platform 10 m above the water. What is the magnitude of the minimum acceleration in the water needed to keep a diver from hitting the bottom of the pool? Assume the acceleration is constant.

62. ‖ A student standing on the ground throws a ball straight up. The ball leaves the student's hand with a speed of 15 m/s when the hand is 2.0 m above the ground. How long is the ball in the air before it hits the ground? (The student moves her hand out of the way.)

63. ‖ A rock is tossed straight up with a speed of 20 m/s. When it returns, it falls into a hole 10 m deep.
    a. What is the rock's velocity as it hits the bottom of the hole?
    b. How long is the rock in the air, from the instant it is released until it hits the bottom of the hole?

64. ‖ A 200 kg weather rocket is loaded with 100 kg of fuel and fired straight up. It accelerates upward at 30.0 m/s^2 for 30.0 s, then runs out of fuel. Ignore any air resistance effects.
    a. What is the rocket's maximum altitude?
    b. How long is the rocket in the air?
    c. Draw a velocity-versus-time graph for the rocket from liftoff until it hits the ground.

65. ‖ A juggler throws a ball straight up into the air with a speed of 10 m/s. With what speed would she need to throw a second ball half a second later, starting from the same position as the first, in order to hit the first ball at the top of its trajectory?

66. ‖ A hotel elevator ascends 200 m with a maximum speed of 5.0 m/s. Its acceleration and deceleration both have a magnitude of 1.0 m/s^2.
    a. How far does the elevator move while accelerating to full speed from rest?
    b. How long does it take to make the complete trip from bottom to top?

67. ‖ A car starts from rest at a stop sign. It accelerates at 2.0 m/s^2 for 6.0 seconds, coasts for 2.0 s, and then slows down at a rate of 1.5 m/s^2 for the next stop sign. How far apart are the stop signs?

68. ‖ A toy train is pushed forward and released at $x_i = 2.0$ m with a speed of 2.0 m/s. It rolls at a steady speed for 2.0 s, then one wheel begins to stick. The train comes to a stop 6.0 m from the point at which it was released. What is the train's acceleration after its wheel begins to stick?

69. ‖ Heather and Jerry are standing on a bridge 50 m above a river. Heather throws a rock straight down with a speed of 20 m/s. Jerry, at exactly the same instant of time, throws a rock straight up with the same speed. Ignore air resistance.
    a. How much time elapses between the first splash and the second splash?
    b. Which rock has the faster speed as it hits the water?

70. ‖ A motorist is driving at 20 m/s when she sees that a traffic light 200 m ahead has just turned red. She knows that this light stays red for 15 s, and she wants to reach the light just as it turns green again. It takes her 1.0 s to step on the brakes and begin slowing at a constant deceleration. What is her speed as she reaches the light at the instant it turns green?

71. ‖ A "rocket car" is launched along a long straight track at $t = 0$ s. It moves with constant acceleration $a_1 = 2.0$ m/s^2. At $t = 2.0$ s, a second car is launched along a parallel track, from the same starting point, with constant acceleration $a_2 = 8.0$ m/s^2.
    a. At what time does the second car catch up with the first one?
    b. How far have the cars traveled when the second passes the first?

72. ‖ A Porsche challenges a Honda to a 400 m race. Because the Porsche's acceleration of 3.5 m/s^2 is larger than the Honda's 3.0 m/s^2, the Honda gets a 50-m head start. Assume, somewhat unrealistically, that both cars can maintain these accelerations the entire distance. Who wins, and by how much time?

73. ▐▌▌▌▌ The minimum stopping distance for a car traveling at a speed of 30 m/s is 60 m, including the distance traveled during the driver's reaction time of 0.50 s.
   a. What is the minimum stopping distance for the same car traveling at a speed of 40 m/s?
   b. Draw a position-versus-time graph for the motion of the car in part a. Assume the car is at $x_i = 0$ m when the driver first sees the emergency situation ahead that calls for a rapid halt.

74. ▐▌▌▌▌ A rocket is launched straight up with constant acceleration. Four seconds after liftoff, a bolt falls off the side of the rocket. The bolt hits the ground 6.0 s later. What was the rocket's acceleration?

Passage Problems

Free Fall on Different Worlds

Objects in free fall on the earth have acceleration $a_y = -9.8$ m/s^2. On the moon, free-fall acceleration is approximately 1/6 of the acceleration on earth. This changes the scale of problems involving free fall. For instance, suppose you jump straight upward, leaving the ground with velocity v_i and then steadily slowing until reaching zero velocity at your highest point. Because your initial velocity is determined mostly by the strength of your leg muscles, we can assume your initial velocity would be the same on the moon. But considering the final equation in Table 2.4 we can see that, with a smaller free-fall acceleration, your maximum height would be greater. The following questions ask you to think about how certain athletic feats might be performed in this reduced-gravity environment.

75. | If an astronaut can jump straight up to a height of 0.50 m on earth, how high could he jump on the moon?
   A. 1.2 m   B. 3.0 m   C. 3.6 m   D. 18 m

76. | On the earth, an astronaut can safely jump to the ground from a height of 1.0 m; her velocity when reaching the ground is slow enough to not cause injury. From what height could the astronaut safely jump to the ground on the moon?
   A. 2.4 m   B. 6.0 m   C. 7.2 m   D. 36 m

77. | On the earth, an astronaut throws a ball straight upward; it stays in the air for a total time of 3.0 s before reaching the ground again. If a ball were to be thrown upward with the same initial speed on the moon, how much time would pass before it hit the ground?
   A. 7.3 s   B. 18 s   C. 44 s   D. 108 s

STOP TO THINK ANSWERS

Stop to Think 2.1: D. The motion consists of two constant-velocity phases; the second one has a greater velocity. The correct graph has two straight-line segments, with the second one having a steeper slope.

Stop to Think 2.2: B. The displacement is the area under a velocity-versus-time curve. In all four cases, the graph is a straight line, so the area under the curve is a rectangle. The area is the product of the length times the height, so the largest displacement belongs to the graph with the largest product of the length (the time interval, in s) times the height (the velocity, in m/s).

Stop to Think 2.3: C. Consider the slope of the position-versus-time graph; it starts out positive and constant, then decreases to zero. Thus the velocity graph must start with a constant positive value, then decrease to zero.

Stop to Think 2.4: C. Acceleration is the slope of the velocity-versus-time graph. The largest magnitude of the slope is at point C.

Stop to Think 2.5: E. An acceleration of 1.2 m/s^2 corresponds to an increase of 1.2 m/s every second. At this rate, the cruising speed of 6.0 m/s will be reached after 5.0 s.

Stop to Think 2.6: D. The final velocity will have the same *magnitude* as the initial velocity, but the velocity is negative because the rock will be moving downward.

3 Vectors and Motion in Two Dimensions

Once the leopard jumps, its trajectory is fixed by the initial speed and angle of the jump. How can we work out where the leopard will land?

LOOKING AHEAD ▶

The goals of Chapter 3 are to learn more about vectors and to use vectors as a tool to analyze motion in two dimensions.

Tools for Describing Motion

In the last chapter, we discussed motion along a line. In this chapter, we'll look at motion in which the direction changes. We'll need new tools.

Types of Motion

There are a few basic types of motion that we'll consider. In each case there is an acceleration due to a change in speed or direction—or both.

> **Looking Back ◀◀**
> 1.1–1.2 Basic motion concepts

Vectors

We use vectors to describe quantities, like velocity, for which both the magnitude and direction are important.

Vectors specify a direction as well as a magnitude.

> **Looking Back ◀◀**
> 1.5 Vectors

Motion on a Ramp

Gravity causes the motion, but it's not straight down—it's at an angle.

A speed skier is accelerating down a ramp. How fast is he moving at the end of his run?

> **Looking Back ◀◀**
> 2.5 Motion with constant acceleration

Vector Math

Our basic kinematic variables are vectors. Working with them means learning how to work with vectors.

You'll learn how to add, subtract, and perform other mathematical operations on vectors.

Projectile Motion

Objects launched through the air follow a parabolic path. Water going over the falls, the leaping salmon, footballs, and jumping leopards all follow similar paths.

The salmon is moving horizontally and vertically—as do all objects undergoing projectile motion.

> **Looking Back ◀◀**
> 2.7 Free fall

Vector Components

We make measurements in a coordinate system. How do vectors fit in?

You'll learn how to find the components of vectors and how to add and subtract vectors using components.

Circular Motion

Motion in a circle at a constant speed involves acceleration, but not the constant acceleration you studied in Chapter 2.

The riders are moving at a constant speed but with an ever-changing direction. It is the changing direction that causes the acceleration and makes the ride fun.

3.1 Using Vectors

FIGURE 3.1 The velocity vector $\vec{v}$ has both a magnitude and a direction.

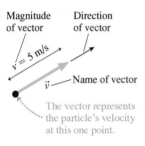

In the previous chapter, we solved many problems in which an object moved in a straight-line path. In this chapter, we will look at particles that take curving paths—motion in two dimensions. Because the direction of motion will be so important, we need to develop an appropriate mathematical language to describe it—the language of vectors.

We introduced the concept of a vector in Chapter 1, and in the next few sections we will develop that concept into a useful and powerful tool. We will practice using vectors by analyzing a problem of motion in one dimension (that of motion on a ramp) and by studying the interesting notion of relative velocity. We will then be ready to analyze the two-dimensional motion of projectiles and of objects moving in a circle.

Recall from Chapter 1 that a vector is a quantity with both a size (magnitude) and a direction. FIGURE 3.1 shows how to represent a particle's velocity as a vector $\vec{v}$. The particle's speed at this point is 5 m/s *and* it is moving in the direction indicated by the arrow. The magnitude of a vector is represented by the letter without an arrow. In this case, the particle's speed—the magnitude of the velocity vector $\vec{v}$—is $v = 5$ m/s. The magnitude of a vector, a *scalar* quantity, cannot be a negative number.

FIGURE 3.2 Displacement vectors.

(a)

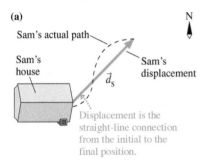

> **NOTE** ► Although the vector arrow is drawn across the page, from its tail to its tip, this arrow does *not* indicate that the vector "stretches" across this distance. Instead, the arrow tells us the value of the vector quantity only at the one point where the tail of the vector is placed. ◄

We found in Chapter 1 that the displacement of an object is a vector drawn from its initial position to its position at some later time. Because displacement is an easy concept to think about, we can use it to introduce some of the properties of vectors. However, **all the properties we will discuss in this chapter (addition, subtraction, multiplication, components) apply to all types of vectors, not just to displacement.**

Suppose that Sam, our old friend from Chapter 1, starts from his front door, walks across the street, and ends up 200 ft to the northeast of where he started. Sam's displacement, which we will label $\vec{d}_S$, is shown in FIGURE 3.2a. The displacement vector is a straight-line connection from his initial to his final position, not necessarily his actual path. The dashed line indicates a possible route Sam might have taken, but his displacement is the vector $\vec{d}_S$.

(b)

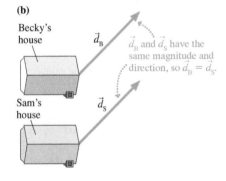

To describe a vector we must specify both its magnitude and its direction. We can write Sam's displacement as

$$\vec{d}_S = (200 \text{ ft, northeast})$$

where the first number specifies the magnitude and the second item gives the direction. The magnitude of Sam's displacement is $d_S = 200$ ft, the distance between his initial and final points.

Sam's next-door neighbor Becky also walks 200 ft to the northeast, starting from her own front door. Becky's displacement $\vec{d}_B = (200 \text{ ft, northeast})$ has the same magnitude and direction as Sam's displacement $\vec{d}_S$. Because vectors are defined by their magnitude and direction, **two vectors are equal if they have the same magnitude and direction.** This is true regardless of the individual starting points of the vectors. Thus the two displacements in FIGURE 3.2b are equal to each other, and we can write $\vec{d}_B = \vec{d}_S$.

Vector Addition

As we saw in Chapter 1, we can combine successive displacements by vector addition. Let's review and extend this concept. FIGURE 3.3 shows the displacement of a hiker who starts at point P and ends at point S. She first hikes 4 miles to the east, then 3 miles to the north. The first leg of the hike is described by the displacement vector $\vec{A} = (4 \text{ mi, east})$. The second leg of the hike has displacement $\vec{B} = (3 \text{ mi, north})$. By definition, a vector from her initial position P to her final position S is also a displacement. This is vector $\vec{C}$ on the figure. $\vec{C}$ is the *net displacement* because it describes the net result of the hiker's having first displacement $\vec{A}$, then displacement $\vec{B}$.

FIGURE 3.3 The net displacement $\vec{C}$ resulting from two displacements $\vec{A}$ and $\vec{B}$.

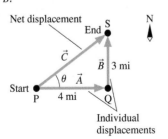

The word "net" implies addition. The net displacement $\vec{C}$ is an initial displacement $\vec{A}$ *plus* a second displacement $\vec{B}$, or

(MP) **PhET:** Vector Addition

$$\vec{C} = \vec{A} + \vec{B} \qquad (3.1)$$

The sum of two vectors is called the **resultant vector.** Vector addition is commutative: $\vec{A} + \vec{B} = \vec{B} + \vec{A}$. You can add vectors in any order you wish.

Look back at Tactics Box 1.4 on page 19 to review the three-step procedure for adding two vectors. This tip-to-tail method for adding vectors, which is used to find $\vec{C} = \vec{A} + \vec{B}$ in Figure 3.3, is called *graphical addition.* Any two vectors of the same type—two velocity vectors or two force vectors—can be added in exactly the same way.

When two vectors are to be added, it is often convenient to draw them with their tails together, as shown in FIGURE 3.4a. To evaluate $\vec{D} + \vec{E}$, you could move vector $\vec{E}$ over to where its tail is on the tip of $\vec{D}$, then use the tip-to-tail rule of graphical addition. This gives vector $\vec{F} = \vec{D} + \vec{E}$ in FIGURE 3.4b. Alternatively, FIGURE 3.4c shows that the vector sum $\vec{D} + \vec{E}$ can be found as the diagonal of the parallelogram defined by $\vec{D}$ and $\vec{E}$. This method is called the *parallelogram rule* of vector addition.

FIGURE 3.4 Two vectors can be added using the tip-to-tail rule or the parallelogram rule.

(a)

$\vec{E}$

$\vec{D}$

What is $\vec{D} + \vec{E}$?

(b)

$\vec{F} = \vec{D} + \vec{E}$

$\vec{E}$

$\vec{D}$

Tip-to-tail rule:
Slide the tail of $\vec{E}$ to the tip of $\vec{D}$.

(c)

$\vec{E}$ $\vec{F} = \vec{D} + \vec{E}$

$\vec{D}$

Parallelogram rule:
Find the diagonal of the parallelogram formed by $\vec{D}$ and $\vec{E}$.

Vector addition is easily extended to more than two vectors. FIGURE 3.5 shows the path of a hiker moving from initial position 0 to position 1, then position 2, then position 3, and finally arriving at position 4. These four segments are described by displacement vectors $\vec{d}_1$, $\vec{d}_2$, $\vec{d}_3$, and $\vec{d}_4$. The hiker's *net* displacement, an arrow from position 0 to position 4, is the vector $\vec{d}_{net}$. In this case,

$$\vec{d}_{net} = \vec{d}_1 + \vec{d}_2 + \vec{d}_3 + \vec{d}_4 \qquad (3.2)$$

The vector sum is found by using the tip-to-tail method three times in succession.

Multiplication by a Scalar

The hiker in Figure 3.3 started with displacement $\vec{A}_1 = (4 \text{ mi, east})$. Suppose a second hiker walks twice as far to the east. The second hiker's displacement will then certainly be $\vec{A}_2 = (8 \text{ mi, east})$. The words "twice as" indicate a multiplication, so we can say

$$\vec{A}_2 = 2\vec{A}_1$$

Multiplying a vector by a positive scalar gives another vector of *different magnitude* but pointing in the *same direction*.

Let the vector $\vec{A}$ be specified as a magnitude A and a direction θ_A; that is, $\vec{A} = (A, \theta_A)$. Now let $\vec{B} = c\vec{A}$, where c is a positive scalar constant. Then

$$\vec{B} = c\vec{A} \text{ means that } (B, \theta_B) = (cA, \theta_A) \qquad (3.3)$$

The vector is stretched or compressed by the factor c (i.e., vector $\vec{B}$ has magnitude $B = cA$), but $\vec{B}$ points in the same direction as $\vec{A}$. This is illustrated in FIGURE 3.6.

Suppose we multiply $\vec{A}$ by zero. Using Equation 3.3, we get

$$0 \cdot \vec{A} = \vec{0} = (0 \text{ m, direction undefined}) \qquad (3.4)$$

The product is a vector having zero length or magnitude. This vector is known as the **zero vector,** denoted $\vec{0}$. The direction of the zero vector is irrelevant; you cannot describe the direction of an arrow of zero length!

FIGURE 3.5 The net displacement after four individual displacements.

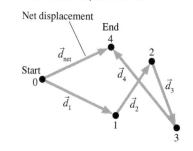

Net displacement

End
4

$\vec{d}_{net}$

Start
0

$\vec{d}_1$

$\vec{d}_2$

$\vec{d}_3$

$\vec{d}_4$

2

1

3

FIGURE 3.6 Multiplication of a vector by a positive scalar.

The length of $\vec{B}$ is "stretched" by the factor c; that is, $B = cA$.

$\vec{B} = c\vec{A}$

$\vec{A}$

θ_A

$\theta_B = \theta_A$

$\vec{B}$ points in the same direction as $\vec{A}$.

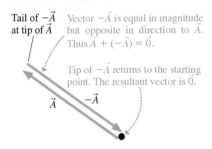

FIGURE 3.7 Vector $-\vec{A}$.

Tail of $-\vec{A}$ at tip of $\vec{A}$

Vector $-\vec{A}$ is equal in magnitude but opposite in direction to $\vec{A}$. Thus $\vec{A} + (-\vec{A}) = \vec{0}$.

Tip of $-\vec{A}$ returns to the starting point. The resultant vector is $\vec{0}$.

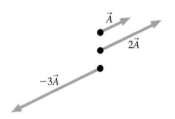

FIGURE 3.8 Vectors $\vec{A}$, $2\vec{A}$, and $-3\vec{A}$.

What happens if we multiply a vector by a negative number? Equation 3.3 does not apply if $c < 0$ because vector $\vec{B}$ cannot have a negative magnitude. Consider the vector $-\vec{A}$, which is equivalent to multiplying $\vec{A}$ by -1. Because

$$\vec{A} + (-\vec{A}) = \vec{0} \tag{3.5}$$

The vector $-\vec{A}$ must be such that, when it is added to $\vec{A}$, the resultant is the zero vector $\vec{0}$. In other words, the *tip* of $-\vec{A}$ must return to the *tail* of $\vec{A}$, as shown in FIGURE 3.7. This will be true only if $-\vec{A}$ is equal in magnitude to $\vec{A}$ but opposite in direction. Thus we can conclude that

$$-\vec{A} = (A, \text{ direction opposite } \vec{A}) \tag{3.6}$$

Multiplying a vector by -1 reverses its direction without changing its length.

As an example, FIGURE 3.8 shows vectors $\vec{A}$, $2\vec{A}$, and $-3\vec{A}$. Multiplication by 2 doubles the length of the vector but does not change its direction. Multiplication by -3 stretches the length by a factor of 3 *and* reverses the direction.

Vector Subtraction

How might we *subtract* vector $\vec{B}$ from vector $\vec{A}$ to form the vector $\vec{A} - \vec{B}$? With numbers, subtraction is the same as the addition of a negative number. That is, $5 - 3$ is the same as $5 + (-3)$. Similarly, $\vec{A} - \vec{B} = \vec{A} + (-\vec{B})$. We can use the rules for vector addition and the fact that $-\vec{B}$ is a vector opposite in direction to $\vec{B}$ to form rules for vector subtraction.

TACTICS BOX 3.1 Subtracting vectors

To subtract $\vec{B}$ from $\vec{A}$:

❶ Draw $\vec{A}$.

❷ Place the tail of $-\vec{B}$ at the tip of $\vec{A}$.

❸ Draw an arrow from the tail of $\vec{A}$ to the tip of $-\vec{B}$. This is vector $\vec{A} - \vec{B}$.

Exercises 5–8

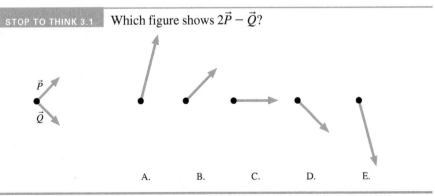

STOP TO THINK 3.1 Which figure shows $2\vec{P} - \vec{Q}$?

A.   B.   C.   D.   E.

3.2 Using Vectors on Motion Diagrams

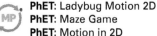
PhET: Ladybug Motion 2D
PhET: Maze Game
PhET: Motion in 2D

In Chapter 2, we defined velocity for one-dimensional motion as an object's displacement—the change in position—divided by the time interval in which the change occurs:

$$v_x = \frac{\Delta x}{\Delta t} = \frac{x_f - x_i}{\Delta t}$$

In two dimensions, an object's displacement is a vector. Suppose an object undergoes displacement $\vec{d}$ during the time interval Δt. Let's define an object's velocity *vector* to be

$$\vec{v} = \frac{\vec{d}}{\Delta t} = \left(\frac{d}{\Delta t}, \text{ same direction as } \vec{d} \right) \qquad (3.7)$$

Definition of velocity in two or more dimensions

Notice that we've multiplied a vector by a scalar: The velocity vector is simply the displacement vector multiplied by the scalar $1/\Delta t$. Consequently, as we found in Chapter 1, **the velocity vector points in the direction of the displacement.** As a result, we can use the dot-to-dot vectors on a motion diagram to visualize the velocity.

NOTE ▶ Strictly speaking, the velocity defined in Equation 3.7 is the *average* velocity for the time interval Δt. This is adequate for using motion diagrams to visualize motion. As we did in Chapter 2, when we make Δt very small, we get an *instantaneous* velocity we can use in performing some calculations. ◀

EXAMPLE 3.1   **Finding the velocity of an airplane**

A small plane is 100 km due east of Denver. After 1 hour of flying at a constant speed in the same direction, it is 200 km due north of Denver. What is the plane's velocity?

PREPARE The initial and final positions of the plane are shown in FIGURE 3.9; the displacement $\vec{d}$ is the vector that points from the initial to the final position.

FIGURE 3.9 Displacement vector for an airplane.

SOLVE The length of the displacement vector is the hypotenuse of a right triangle:

$$d = \sqrt{(100 \text{ km})^2 + (200 \text{ km})^2} = 224 \text{ km}$$

The direction of the displacement vector is described by the angle θ in Figure 3.9. From trigonometry, this angle is

$$\theta = \tan^{-1}\left(\frac{200 \text{ km}}{100 \text{ km}} \right) = \tan^{-1}(2.00) = 63.4°$$

Thus the plane's displacement vector is

$$\vec{d} = (224 \text{ km}, 63.4° \text{ north of west})$$

Because the plane undergoes this displacement during 1 hour, its velocity is

$$\vec{v} = \left(\frac{d}{\Delta t}, \text{ same direction as } \vec{d} \right) = \left(\frac{224 \text{ km}}{1 \text{ h}}, 63.4° \text{ north of west} \right)$$
$$= (224 \text{ km/h}, 63.4° \text{ north of west})$$

ASSESS The plane's *speed* is the magnitude of the velocity, $v = 224$ km/h. This is approximately 140 mph, which is a reasonable speed for a small plane.

Lunging versus veering BIO The top photo shows a barracuda, a type of fish that catches prey with a rapid linear acceleration, a quick change in speed. The barracuda's body shape is optimized for such a straight-line strike. The butterfly fish in the bottom photo has a very different appearance. It can't rapidly change its speed, but its body shape lets it quickly change its direction. Once the barracuda gets up to speed, it can't change its direction very easily, so the butterfly fish can, by employing this other type of acceleration, avoid capture.

We defined an object's acceleration in one dimension as $a_x = \Delta v_x/\Delta t$. In two dimensions, we need to use a vector to describe acceleration. The vector definition of acceleration is a straightforward extension of the one-dimensional version:

$$\vec{a} = \frac{\vec{v}_f - \vec{v}_i}{t_f - t_i} = \frac{\Delta \vec{v}}{\Delta t} \tag{3.8}$$

Definition of acceleration in two or more dimensions

There is an acceleration whenever there is a *change* in velocity. Because velocity is a vector, it can change in either or both of two possible ways:

1. The magnitude can change, indicating a change in speed.
2. The direction of motion can change.

In Chapter 2 we saw how to compute an acceleration vector for the first case, in which an object speeds up or slows down while moving in a straight line. In this chapter we will examine the second case, in which an object changes its direction of motion.

Suppose an object has an initial velocity $\vec{v}_i$ at time t_i and later, at time t_f, has velocity $\vec{v}_f$. The fact that the velocity *changes* tells us the object undergoes an acceleration during the time interval $\Delta t = t_f - t_i$. We see from Equation 3.8 that the acceleration points in the same direction as the vector $\Delta \vec{v}$. This vector is the change in the velocity $\Delta \vec{v} = \vec{v}_f - \vec{v}_i$, so to know which way the acceleration vector points, we have to perform the vector subtraction $\vec{v}_f - \vec{v}_i$. Tactics Box 3.1 showed how to perform vector subtraction. Tactics Box 3.2 shows how to use vector subtraction to find the acceleration vector.

TACTICS
BOX 3.2   **Finding the acceleration vector**   (MP)

To find the acceleration between velocity $\vec{v}_i$ and velocity $\vec{v}_f$:

❶ Draw the velocity vector $\vec{v}_f$.

❷ Draw $-\vec{v}_i$ at the tip of $\vec{v}_f$.

❸ Draw $\Delta \vec{v} = \vec{v}_f - \vec{v}_i$
$= \vec{v}_f + (-\vec{v}_i)$
This is the direction of $\vec{a}$.

❹ Return to the original motion diagram. Draw a vector at the middle point in the direction of $\Delta \vec{v}$; label it $\vec{a}$. This is the average acceleration at the midpoint between $\vec{v}_i$ and $\vec{v}_f$.

Exercises 11,12

Now that we know how to determine acceleration vectors, we can make a complete motion diagram with dots showing the position of the object, average velocity vectors found by connecting the dots with arrows, and acceleration vectors found using Tactics Box 3.2. Note that there is *one* acceleration vector linking each *two* velocity vectors, and $\vec{a}$ is drawn at the dot between the two velocity vectors it links. Let's look at two examples, one with changing speed and one with changing direction.

EXAMPLE 3.2 **Drawing the acceleration for a Mars descent**

A spacecraft slows as it safely descends to the surface of Mars. Draw a complete motion diagram for the last few seconds of the descent.

PREPARE FIGURE 3.10 shows two versions of a motion diagram: a professionally drawn version like you generally find in this text and a simpler version similar to what you might draw for a homework assignment. As the spacecraft slows in its descent, the dots get closer together and the velocity vectors get shorter.

SOLVE The inset in Figure 3.10 shows how Tactics Box 3.2 is used to determine the acceleration at one point. All the other acceleration vectors will be similar, because for each pair of velocity vectors the earlier one is longer than the later one.

ASSESS As the spacecraft slows, the acceleration vectors and velocity vectors point in opposite directions, consistent with what we learned about the sign of the acceleration in Chapter 2.

FIGURE 3.10 Motion diagram for a descending spacecraft.

EXAMPLE 3.3 **Drawing the acceleration for a Ferris wheel ride**

Anne rides a Ferris wheel at an amusement park. Draw a complete motion diagram for Anne's ride.

PREPARE FIGURE 3.11 shows 10 points of the motion during one complete revolution of the Ferris wheel. A person riding a Ferris wheel moves in a circle at a constant speed,

FIGURE 3.11 Motion diagram for Anne on a Ferris wheel.

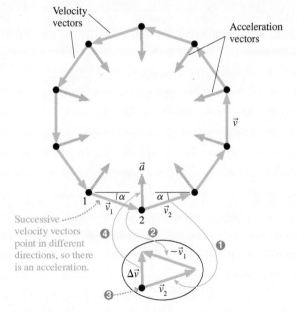

Continued

so we've shown equal distances between successive dots. As before, the velocity vectors are found by connecting each dot to the next. Note that the velocity vectors are *straight lines,* not curves.

We see that all the velocity vectors have the same length, but each has a different *direction,* and that means Anne is accelerating. This is not a "speeding up" or "slowing down" acceleration, but is, instead, a "change of direction" acceleration.

SOLVE The inset to Figure 3.11 shows how to use the steps of Tactics Box 3.2 to find the acceleration at one particular position, at the bottom of the circle. Vector $\vec{v}_1$ is the velocity vector that leads into this dot, while $\vec{v}_2$ moves away from it. From the circular geometry of the main figure, the two angles marked α are equal. Thus we see that $\vec{v}_2$ and $-\vec{v}_1$ form an isosceles triangle and vector $\Delta\vec{v} = \vec{v}_2 - \vec{v}_1$ is exactly vertical, toward the center of the circle. If we did a similar calculation for each point of the motion, we'd find a similar result: In each case, the acceleration points toward the center of the circle.

ASSESS The speed is constant but the direction is changing, so there is an acceleration, as we expect.

No matter which dot you select on the motion diagram of Figure 3.11, the velocities change in such a way that the acceleration vector $\vec{a}$ points directly toward the center of the circle. An acceleration vector that always points toward the center of a circle is called a *centripetal acceleration.* We will have much more to say about centripetal acceleration later in this chapter.

3.3 Coordinate Systems and Vector Components

In the past two sections, we have seen how to add and subtract vectors graphically, using these operations to deduce important details of motion. But the graphical combination of vectors is not an especially good way to find quantitative results. In this section we will introduce a *coordinate description* of vectors that will be the basis for doing vector calculations.

Coordinate Systems

As we saw in Chapter 1, the world does not come with a coordinate system attached to it. A coordinate system is an artificially imposed grid that you place on a problem in order to make quantitative measurements. The right choice of coordinate system will make a problem easier to solve. We will generally use **Cartesian coordinates,** the familiar rectangular grid with perpendicular axes, as illustrated in FIGURE 3.12.

Archaeologists establish a coordinate system so that they can precisely determine the positions of objects they excavate.

FIGURE 3.12 A Cartesian coordinate system.

Coordinate axes have a positive end and a negative end, separated by zero at the origin where the two axes cross. When you draw a coordinate system, it is important to label the axes. This is done by placing *x* and *y* labels at the *positive* ends of the axes, as in Figure 3.12. The purpose of the labels is twofold:

- To identify which axis is which.
- To identify the positive ends of the axes.

This will be important when you need to determine whether the quantities in a problem should be assigned positive or negative values.

Component Vectors

FIGURE 3.13 shows a vector $\vec{A}$ and an xy-coordinate system that we've chosen. Once the directions of the axes are known, we can define two new vectors *parallel to the axes* that we call the **component vectors** of $\vec{A}$. Vector $\vec{A}_x$, called the *x-component vector*, is the projection of $\vec{A}$ along the x-axis. Vector $\vec{A}_y$, the *y-component vector*, is the projection of $\vec{A}$ along the y-axis. Notice that the component vectors are perpendicular to each other.

You can see, using the parallelogram rule, that $\vec{A}$ is the vector sum of the two component vectors:

$$\vec{A} = \vec{A}_x + \vec{A}_y \qquad (3.9)$$

In essence, we have "broken" vector $\vec{A}$ into two perpendicular vectors that are parallel to the coordinate axes. We say that we have **decomposed** or **resolved** vector $\vec{A}$ into its component vectors.

> **NOTE** ▶ It is not necessary for the tail of $\vec{A}$ to be at the origin. All we need to know is the *orientation* of the coordinate system so that we can draw $\vec{A}_x$ and $\vec{A}_y$ parallel to the axes. ◀

Components

You learned in Chapter 2 to give the one-dimensional kinematic variable v_x a positive sign if the velocity vector $\vec{v}$ points toward the positive end of the x-axis and a negative sign if $\vec{v}$ points in the negative x-direction. The basis of this rule is that is the x-component of We need to extend this idea to vectors in general.

Suppose we have a vector $\vec{A}$ that has been decomposed into component vectors $\vec{A}_x$ and $\vec{A}_y$ parallel to the coordinate axes. We can describe each component vector with a single number (a scalar) called the **component**. The *x-component* and *y-component* of vector $\vec{A}$, denoted A_x and A_y, are determined as follows:

TACTICS BOX 3.3 Determining the components of a vector

❶ The absolute value $|A_x|$ of the x-component A_x is the magnitude of the component vector $\vec{A}_x$.
❷ The *sign* of A_x is positive if $\vec{A}_x$ points in the positive x-direction, negative if $\vec{A}_x$ points in the negative x-direction.
❸ The y-component A_y is determined similarly.

Exercises 16–18 🖉

In other words, the component A_x tells us two things: how big $\vec{A}_x$ is and which end of the axis $\vec{A}_x$ points toward. FIGURE 3.14 shows three examples of determining the components of a vector.

> **NOTE** ▶ $\vec{A}_x$ and $\vec{A}_y$ are *component vectors;* they have a magnitude and a direction. A_x and A_y are simply *components*. The components A_x and A_y are scalars—just numbers (with units) that can be positive or negative. ◀

Much of physics is expressed in the language of vectors. We will frequently need to decompose a vector into its components or to "reassemble" a vector from its components, moving back and forth between the graphical and the component representations of a vector.

Let's start with the problem of decomposing a vector into its x- and y-components. FIGURE 3.15a on the next page shows a vector $\vec{A}$ at an angle θ above horizontal. It is *essential* to use a picture or diagram such as this to define the angle you are using to describe a vector's direction. $\vec{A}$ points to the right and up, so Tactics Box 3.3 tells us that the components A_x and A_y are both positive.

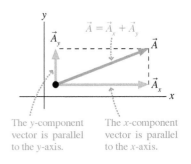

FIGURE 3.13 Component vectors $\vec{A}_x$ and $\vec{A}_y$ are drawn parallel to the coordinate axes such that $\vec{A} = \vec{A}_x + \vec{A}_y$.

The y-component vector is parallel to the y-axis.

The x-component vector is parallel to the x-axis.

FIGURE 3.14 Determining the components of a vector.

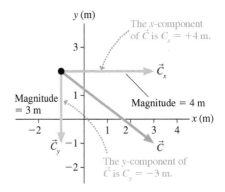

FIGURE 3.15 Breaking a vector into components.

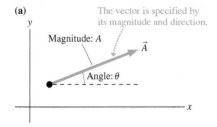

(a)

FIGURE 3.16 Specifying a vector from its components.

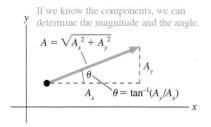

FIGURE 3.17 Relationships for a vector with a negative component.

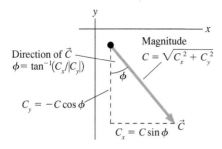

We can find the components using trigonometry, as illustrated in FIGURE 3.15b. For this case, we find that

$$A_x = A \cos \theta$$
$$A_y = A \sin \theta \qquad (3.10)$$

where A is the magnitude, or length, of $\vec{A}$. These equations convert the length and angle description of vector $\vec{A}$ into the vector's components, but they are correct *only* if θ is measured from horizontal.

Alternatively, if we are given the components of a vector, we can determine the length and angle of the vector from the x- and y-components, as shown in FIGURE 3.16. Because A in Figure 3.16 is the hypotenuse of a right triangle, its length is given by the Pythagorean theorem:

$$A = \sqrt{A_x^2 + A_y^2} \qquad (3.11)$$

Similarly, the tangent of angle θ is the ratio of the opposite side to the adjacent side, so

$$\theta = \tan^{-1}\left(\frac{A_y}{A_x}\right) \qquad (3.12)$$

Equations 3.11 and 3.12 can be thought of as the "inverse" of Equations 3.10.

How do things change if the vector isn't pointing to the right and up—that is, if one of the components is negative? FIGURE 3.17 shows vector $\vec{C}$ pointing to the right and down. In this case, the component vector $\vec{C}_y$ is pointing *down,* in the negative y-direction, so the y-component C_y is a *negative* number. The angle ϕ is drawn measured from the y-axis, so the components of $\vec{C}$ are

$$C_x = C \sin \phi$$
$$C_y = -C \cos \phi \qquad (3.13)$$

The roles of sine and cosine are reversed from those in Equations 3.10 because the angle ϕ is measured with respect to vertical, not horizontal.

NOTE ▶ Whether the x- and y-components use the sine or cosine depends on how you define the vector's angle. As noted above, you *must* draw a diagram to define the angle that you use, and you must be sure to refer to the diagram when computing components. Don't use Equations 3.10 or 3.13 as general rules—they aren't! They appear as they do because of how we defined the angles. ◀

Next, let's look at the "inverse" problem for this case: determining the length and direction of the vector given the components. The signs of the components don't matter for determining the length; the Pythagorean theorem always works to find the length or magnitude of a vector because the squares eliminate any concerns over the signs. The length of the vector in Figure 3.17 is simply

$$C = \sqrt{C_x^2 + C_y^2} \qquad (3.14)$$

When we determine the direction of the vector from its components, we must consider the signs of the components. Finding the angle of vector $\vec{C}$ in Figure 3.17 requires the length of C_y *without* the minus sign, so vector $\vec{C}$ has direction

$$\phi = \tan^{-1}\left(\frac{C_x}{|C_y|}\right) \qquad (3.15)$$

Notice that the roles of x and y differ from those in Equation 3.12.

EXAMPLE 3.4   Finding the components of an acceleration vector

Find the x- and y-components of the acceleration vector $\vec{a}$ shown in FIGURE 3.18.

FIGURE 3.18 Acceleration vector $\vec{a}$ of Example 3.4.

FIGURE 3.19 The components of the acceleration vector.

PREPARE It's important to *draw* the vectors. Making a sketch is crucial to setting up this problem. FIGURE 3.19 shows the original vector $\vec{a}$ decomposed into component vectors parallel to the axes.

SOLVE The acceleration vector $\vec{a} = (6.0 \text{ m/s}^2, 30°$ below the negative x-axis) points to the left (negative x-direction) and down (negative y-direction), so the components a_x and a_y are both negative:

$$a_x = -a\cos 30° = -(6.0 \text{ m/s}^2)\cos 30° = -5.2 \text{ m/s}^2$$
$$a_y = -a\sin 30° = -(6.0 \text{ m/s}^2)\sin 30° = -3.0 \text{ m/s}^2$$

ASSESS The magnitude of the y-component is less than that of the x-component, as seems to be the case in Figure 3.19, a good check on our work. The units of a_x and a_y are the same as the units of vector $\vec{a}$. Notice that we had to insert the minus signs manually by observing that the vector points down and to the left.

STOP TO THINK 3.2   What are the x- and y-components C_x and C_y of vector $\vec{C}$?

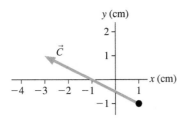

Working with Components

We've seen how to add vectors graphically, but there's an easier way: using components. To illustrate, let's look at the vector sum $\vec{C} = \vec{A} + \vec{B}$ for the vectors shown in FIGURE 3.20. You can see that the component vectors of $\vec{C}$ are the sums of the component vectors of $\vec{A}$ and $\vec{B}$. The same is true of the components: $C_x = A_x + B_x$ and $C_y = A_y + B_y$.

In general, if $\vec{D} = \vec{A} + \vec{B} + \vec{C} + \cdots$, then the x- and y-components of the resultant vector $\vec{D}$ are

$$D_x = A_x + B_x + C_x + \cdots$$
$$D_y = A_y + B_y + C_y + \cdots$$

(3.16)

This method of vector addition is called *algebraic addition*.

FIGURE 3.20 Using components to add vectors.

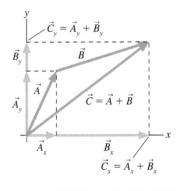

EXAMPLE 3.5   Using algebraic addition to find a bird's displacement

A bird flies 100 m due east from a tree, then 200 m northwest (that is, 45° north of west). What is the bird's net displacement?

PREPARE FIGURE 3.21a on the next page shows the displacement vectors $\vec{A} = (100 \text{ m}, \text{east})$ and $\vec{B} = (200 \text{ m}, \text{northwest})$ and also the net displacement $\vec{C}$. We draw vectors tip-to-tail if we are going to add them graphically, but it's usually easier to draw them all from the origin if we are going to use algebraic addition. FIGURE 3.21b redraws the vectors with their tails together.

Continued

FIGURE 3.21 Finding the net displacement.

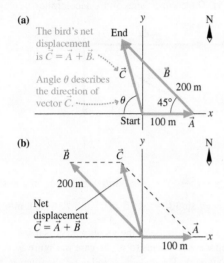

(a)

(b)

SOLVE To add the vectors algebraically we must know their components. From the figure these are seen to be

$$A_x = 100 \text{ m}$$

$$A_y = 0 \text{ m}$$

$$B_x = -(200 \text{ m}) \cos 45° = -141 \text{ m}$$

$$B_y = (200 \text{ m}) \sin 45° = 141 \text{ m}$$

We learned *from the figure* that $\vec{B}$ has a negative x-component. Adding $\vec{A}$ and $\vec{B}$ by components gives

$$C_x = A_x + B_x = 100 \text{ m} - 141 \text{ m} = -41 \text{ m}$$

$$C_y = A_y + B_y = 0 \text{ m} + 141 \text{ m} = 141 \text{ m}$$

The magnitude of the net displacement $\vec{C}$ is

$$C = \sqrt{C_x^2 + C_y^2} = \sqrt{(-41 \text{ m})^2 + (141 \text{ m})^2} = 147 \text{ m}$$

The angle θ, as defined in Figure 3.21, is

$$\theta = \tan^{-1}\left(\frac{C_y}{|C_x|}\right) = \tan^{-1}\left(\frac{141 \text{ m}}{41 \text{ m}}\right) = 74°$$

Thus the bird's net displacement is $\vec{C} = (147 \text{ m}, 74°$ north of west).

ASSESS The final values of C_x and C_y match what we would expect from the sketch in Figure 3.21. The geometric addition was a valuable check on the answer we found by algebraic addition.

When you look at a trail map for a hike in a mountainous region, it will give the length of a trail *and* the elevation gain—an important variable! The elevation gain is simply d_y, the vertical component of the displacement for the hike.

Vector subtraction and the multiplication of a vector by a scalar are also easily performed using components. To find $\vec{D} = \vec{P} - \vec{Q}$ we would compute

$$D_x = P_x - Q_x$$
$$D_y = P_y - Q_y \tag{3.17}$$

Similarly, $\vec{T} = c\vec{S}$ is

$$T_x = cS_x$$
$$T_y = cS_y \tag{3.18}$$

The next few chapters will make frequent use of *vector equations*. For example, you will learn that the equation to calculate the net force on a car skidding to a stop is

$$\vec{F} = \vec{n} + \vec{w} + \vec{f} \tag{3.19}$$

Equation 3.19 is really just a shorthand way of writing the two simultaneous equations:

$$F_x = n_x + w_x + f_x$$
$$F_y = n_y + w_y + f_y \tag{3.20}$$

In other words, a vector equation is interpreted as meaning: Equate the x-components on both sides of the equals sign, then equate the y-components. Vector notation allows us to write these two equations in a more compact form.

FIGURE 3.22 A coordinate system with tilted axes.

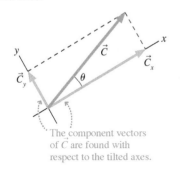

The component vectors of $\vec{C}$ are found with respect to the tilted axes.

Tilted Axes

Although we are used to having the x-axis horizontal, there is no requirement that it has to be that way. In Chapter 1, we saw that for motion on a slope, it is often most convenient to put the x-axis along the slope. When we add the y-axis, this gives us a tilted coordinate system such as that shown in **FIGURE 3.22**.

Finding components with tilted axes is no harder than what we have done so far. Vector $\vec{C}$ in Figure 3.22 can be decomposed into component vectors $\vec{C}_x$ and $\vec{C}_y$, with $C_x = C\cos\theta$ and $C_y = C\sin\theta$.

STOP TO THINK 3.3   Angle ϕ that specifies the direction of $\vec{C}$ is computed as

A. $\tan^{-1}(C_x/C_y)$.

B. $\tan^{-1}(C_x/|C_y|)$.

C. $\tan^{-1}(|C_x|/|C_y|)$.

D. $\tan^{-1}(C_y/C_x)$.

E. $\tan^{-1}(C_y/|C_x|)$.

F. $\tan^{-1}(|C_y|/|C_x|)$.

3.4 Motion on a Ramp

In this section, we will examine the problem of motion on a ramp or incline. There are three reasons to look at this problem. First, it will provide good practice at using vectors to analyze motion. Second, it is a simple problem for which we can find an exact solution. Third, this seemingly abstract problem has real and important applications.

We begin with a constant-velocity example to give us some practice with vectors and components before moving on to the more general case of accelerated motion.

Class Video

EXAMPLE 3.6   **Finding the height gained on a slope**

A car drives up a steep 10° slope at a constant speed of 15 m/s. After 10 s, how much height has the car gained?

PREPARE FIGURE 3.23 is a visual overview, with x- and y-axes defined. The velocity vector $\vec{v}$ points up the slope. We are interested in the vertical motion of the car, so we decompose $\vec{v}$ into component vectors $\vec{v}_x$ and $\vec{v}_y$ as shown.

FIGURE 3.23 Visual overview of a car moving up a slope.

Known
$x_i = y_i = 0$ m
$t_i = 0$ s, $t_f = 10$ s
$v = 15$ m/s
$\theta = 10°$

Find
Δy

SOLVE The velocity component we need is v_y; this describes the vertical motion of the car. Using the rules for finding components outlined above, we find

$$v_y = v\sin\theta = (15 \text{ m/s})\sin(10°) = 2.6 \text{ m/s}$$

Because the velocity is constant, the car's vertical displacement (i.e., the height gained) during 10 s is

$$\Delta y = v_y\,\Delta t = (2.6 \text{ m/s})(10 \text{ s}) = 26 \text{ m}$$

ASSESS The car is traveling at a pretty good clip—15 m/s is a bit faster than 30 mph—up a steep slope, so it should climb a respectable height in 10 s. 26 m, or about 80 ft, seems reasonable.

Accelerated Motion on a Ramp

FIGURE 3.24a on the next page shows a crate sliding down a frictionless (i.e., smooth) ramp tilted at angle θ. The crate accelerates due to the action of gravity, but it is *constrained* to accelerate parallel to the surface. What is the acceleration?

A motion diagram for the crate is drawn in FIGURE 3.24b. There is an acceleration because the velocity is changing, with both the acceleration and velocity vectors parallel to the ramp. We can take advantage of the properties of vectors to find the crate's acceleration. To do so, FIGURE 3.24c sets up a coordinate system with the x-axis along the ramp and the y-axis perpendicular. All motion will be along the x-axis.

FIGURE 3.24 Acceleration on an inclined plane.

(a)

Angle of incline θ

(b)

$\vec{v}$ $\vec{a}$

θ

(c)

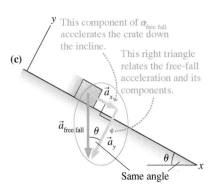

y This component of $\vec{a}_{\text{free fall}}$ accelerates the crate down the incline.

This right triangle relates the free-fall acceleration and its components.

$\vec{a}_x$

$\vec{a}_{\text{free fall}}$ θ $\vec{a}_y$

θ x

Same angle

Video Tutor Demonstration

If the incline suddenly vanished, the object would have a free-fall acceleration $\vec{a}_{\text{free fall}}$ straight down. As Figure 3.24c shows, this acceleration vector can be decomposed into two component vectors: a vector $\vec{a}_x$ that is *parallel* to the incline and a vector $\vec{a}_y$ that is *perpendicular* to the incline. The vector addition rules studied earlier in this chapter tell us that $\vec{a}_{\text{free fall}} = \vec{a}_x + \vec{a}_y$.

The motion diagram shows that the object's actual acceleration $\vec{a}_x$ is parallel to the incline. The surface of the incline somehow "blocks" the other component of the acceleration $\vec{a}_y$, through a process we will examine in Chapter 5, but $\vec{a}_x$ is unhindered. It is this component of $\vec{a}_{\text{free fall}}$, parallel to the incline, that accelerates the object.

We can use trigonometry to work out the magnitude of this acceleration. Figure 3.24c shows that the three vectors $\vec{a}_{\text{free fall}}$, $\vec{a}_y$, and $\vec{a}_x$ form a right triangle with angle θ as shown; this angle is the same as the angle of the incline. By definition, the magnitude of $\vec{a}_{\text{free fall}}$ is g. This vector is the hypotenuse of the right triangle. The vector we are interested in, $\vec{a}_x$, is opposite angle θ. Thus the value of the acceleration along a frictionless slope is

$$a_x = \pm g \sin\theta \qquad (3.21)$$

NOTE ▶ The correct sign depends on the direction in which the ramp is tilted. The acceleration in Figure 3.24 is $+g\sin\theta$, but upcoming examples will show situations in which the acceleration is $-g\sin\theta$. ◀

Let's look at Equation 3.21 to verify that it makes sense. A good way to do this is to consider some **limiting cases** in which the angle is at one end of its range. In these cases, the physics is clear and we can check our result. Let's look at two such possibilities:

1. Suppose the plane is perfectly horizontal, with $\theta = 0°$. If you place an object on a horizontal surface, you expect it to stay at rest with no acceleration. Equation 3.21 gives $a_x = 0$ when $\theta = 0°$, in agreement with our expectations.
2. Now suppose you tilt the plane until it becomes vertical, with $\theta = 90°$. You know what happens—the object will be in free fall, parallel to the vertical surface. Equation 3.21 gives $a_x = g$ when $\theta = 90°$, again in agreement with our expectations.

NOTE ▶ Checking your answer by looking at such limiting cases is a very good way to see if your answer makes sense. We will often do this in the Assess step of a solution. ◀

◀ **Extreme physics** A speed skier, on wide skis with little friction, wearing an aerodynamic helmet and crouched low to minimize air resistance, moves in a straight line down a steep slope—pretty much like an object sliding down a frictionless ramp. There is a maximum speed that a skier could possibly achieve at the end of the slope. Course designers set the starting point to keep this maximum speed within reasonable (for this sport!) limits.

EXAMPLE 3.7   **Maximum possible speed for a skier**

The Willamette Pass ski area in Oregon was the site of the 1993 U.S. National Speed Skiing Competition. The skiers started from rest and then accelerated down a stretch of the mountain with a reasonably constant slope, aiming for the highest possible speed at the end of this run. During this acceleration phase, the skiers traveled 360 m while dropping a vertical distance of 170 m. What is the fastest speed a skier could achieve at the end of this run? How much time would this fastest run take?

PREPARE We begin with the visual overview in FIGURE 3.25. The motion diagram shows the acceleration of the skier and the pictorial representation gives an overview of the problem including the dimensions of the slope. As before, we put the x-axis along the slope.

FIGURE 3.25 Visual overview of a skier accelerating down a slope.

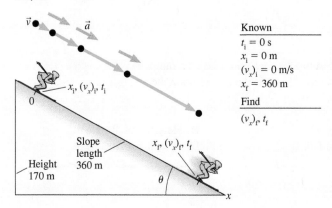

Known
$t_i = 0$ s
$x_i = 0$ m
$(v_x)_i = 0$ m/s
$x_f = 360$ m

Find
$(v_x)_f, t_f$

SOLVE The fastest possible run would be one without any friction or air resistance, meaning the acceleration down the slope is given by Equation 3.21. The acceleration is in the positive x-direction, so we use the positive sign. What is the angle in Equation 3.21? Figure 3.25 shows that the 360-m-long slope is the hypotenuse of a triangle of height 170 m, so we use trigonometry to find

$$\sin\theta = \frac{170 \text{ m}}{360 \text{ m}}$$

which gives $\theta = \sin^{-1}(170/360) = 28°$. Equation 3.21 then gives

$$a_x = +g\sin\theta = (9.8 \text{ m/s}^2)(\sin 28°) = 4.6 \text{ m/s}^2$$

For linear motion with constant acceleration, we can use the third of the kinematic equations in Table 2.4: $(v_x)_f^2 = (v_x)_i^2 + 2a_x \Delta x$. The initial velocity $(v_x)_i$ is zero; thus:

This is the distance along the slope, the length of the run.

$$(v_x)_f = \sqrt{2a_x\Delta x} = \sqrt{2(4.6 \text{ m/s}^2)(360 \text{ m})} = 58 \text{ m/s}$$

This is the fastest that any skier could hope to be moving at the end of the run. Any friction or air resistance would decrease this speed. Because the acceleration is constant and the initial velocity $(v_x)_i$ is zero, the time of the fastest-possible run is

$$\Delta t = \frac{(v_x)_f}{a_x} = \frac{58 \text{ m/s}}{4.6 \text{ m/s}^2} = 13 \text{ s}$$

A speed skiing event is a quick affair!

ASSESS The final speed we calculated is 58 m/s, which is about 130 mph, reasonable because we expect a high speed for this sport. In the competition noted, the actual winning speed was 111 mph, not much slower than the result we calculated. Obviously, the efforts to minimize friction and air resistance are working!

Skis on snow have very little friction, but there are other ways to reduce the friction between surfaces. For instance, a roller coaster car rolls along a track on low-friction wheels. No drive force is applied to the cars after they are released at the top of the first hill: the speed changes due to gravity alone. The cars speed up as they go down hills and slow down as they climb.

EXAMPLE 3.8 **Speed of a roller coaster**

A classic wooden coaster has cars that go down a big first hill, gaining speed. The cars then ascend a second hill with a slope of 30°. If the cars are going 25 m/s at the bottom and it takes them 2.0 s to climb this hill, how fast are they going at the top?

PREPARE We start with the visual overview in FIGURE 3.26, which includes a motion diagram, a pictorial representation, and a list of values. We've done this with a sketch such as you might draw for your homework. Notice how the motion diagram of Figure 3.26 differs from that of the previous example: The velocity decreases as the car moves up the hill, so the acceleration vector is opposite the direction of the velocity vector. The motion is along the x-axis, as before, but the acceleration vector points in the negative x-direction, so the component a_x is negative. In the motion diagram, notice that we drew only a single acceleration vector—a reasonable shortcut because we know that the acceleration is constant. One vector can represent the acceleration for the entire motion.

FIGURE 3.26 The coaster's speed decreases as it goes up the hill.

Known
$x_i = 0$ m
$(v_x)_i = 25$ m/s
$t_i = 0$ s
$t_f = 2.0$ s
$\theta = 30°$

Find
$(v_x)_f$

Continued

SOLVE To determine the final speed, we need to know the acceleration. We will assume that there is no friction or air resistance, so the magnitude of the roller coaster's acceleration is given by Equation 3.21 using the minus sign, as noted:

$$a_x = -g\sin\theta = -(9.8 \text{ m/s}^2)\sin 30° = -4.9 \text{ m/s}^2$$

The speed at the top of the hill can then be computed using our kinematic equation for velocity:

$$(v_x)_f = (v_x)_i + a_x\,\Delta t = 25 \text{ m/s} + (-4.9 \text{ m/s}^2)(2.0 \text{ s}) = 15 \text{ m/s}$$

ASSESS The speed is less at the top of the hill than at the bottom, as it should be, but the coaster is still moving at a pretty good clip at the top—almost 35 mph. This seems reasonable; a fast ride is a fun ride.

STOP TO THINK 3.4   A block of ice slides down a ramp. For which height and base length is the acceleration the greatest?

A. Height 4 m, base 12 m   B. Height 3 m, base 6 m
C. Height 2 m, base 5 m   D. Height 1 m, base 3 m

3.5 Relative Motion

FIGURE 3.27 Amy, Bill, and Carlos each measure the velocity of the runner. The velocities are shown relative to Amy.

You've now dealt many times with problems that say something like "A car travels at 30 m/s" or "A plane travels at 300 m/s." But, as we will see, we may need to be a bit more specific.

In FIGURE 3.27, Amy, Bill, and Carlos are watching a runner. According to Amy, the runner's velocity is $v_x = 5$ m/s. But to Bill, who's riding alongside, the runner is lifting his legs up and down but going neither forward nor backward relative to Bill. As far as Bill is concerned, the runner's velocity is $v_x = 0$ m/s. Carlos sees the runner receding in his rearview mirror, in the *negative x*-direction, getting 10 m farther away from him every second. According to Carlos, the runner's velocity is $v_x = -10$ m/s. Which is the runner's *true* velocity?

Velocity is not a concept that can be true or false. The runner's velocity *relative to Amy* is 5 m/s; that is, his velocity is 5 m/s in a coordinate system attached to Amy and in which Amy is at rest. The runner's velocity relative to Bill is 0 m/s, and the velocity relative to Carlos is -10 m/s. These are all valid descriptions of the runner's motion.

Relative Velocity

Suppose we know that the runner's velocity relative to Amy is 5 m/s; we will call this velocity $(v_x)_{RA}$. The second subscript "RA" means "**R**unner relative to **A**my." We also know that the velocity of **C**arlos relative to **A**my is 15 m/s; we write this as $(v_x)_{CA} = 15$ m/s. It is equally valid to compute Amy's velocity relative to Carlos. From Carlos's point of view, Amy is moving to the left at 15 m/s; we write Amy's velocity relative to Carlos as $(v_x)_{AC} = -15$ m/s; note that $(v_x)_{AC} = -(v_x)_{CA}$.

Given the runner's velocity relative to Amy and Amy's velocity relative to Carlos, we can compute the runner's velocity relative to Carlos by combining the two velocities we know. The subscripts as we have defined them are our guide for this combination:

$$(v_x)_{RC} = (v_x)_{RA} + (v_x)_{AC} \tag{3.22}$$

The "A" appears on the right of the first expression and on the left of the second; when we combine these velocities, we "cancel" the A to get $(v_x)_{RC}$.

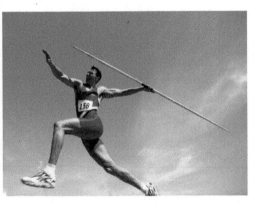

Throwing for the gold An athlete throwing the javelin does so while running. It's harder to throw the javelin on the run, but there's a very good reason to do so. The distance of the throw will be determined by the velocity of the javelin with respect to the ground—which is the sum of the velocity of the throw plus the velocity of the athlete. A faster run means a longer throw.

Generally, you can add two relative velocities in this manner, by "canceling" subscripts as in Equation 3.22. In Chapter 27, when we learn about relativity, we will have a more rigorous scheme for computing relative velocities, but this technique will serve our purposes at present.

EXAMPLE 3.9 Speed of a seabird

Researchers doing satellite tracking of albatrosses in the Southern Ocean observed a bird maintaining sustained flight speeds of 35 m/s—nearly 80 mph! This seems surprisingly fast until you realize that this particular bird was flying with the wind, which was moving at 23 m/s. What was the bird's airspeed—its speed relative to the air? This is a truer measure of its flight speed.

PREPARE FIGURE 3.28 shows the wind and the albatross moving to the right, so all velocities will be positive. We've shown the

FIGURE 3.28 Relative velocities for the albatross and the wind for Example 3.9.

Known
$(v_x)_{bw} = 35$ m/s
$(v_x)_{aw} = 23$ m/s

Find
$(v_x)_{ba}$

velocity $(v_x)_{bw}$ of the **bird** with respect to the **water**, which is the measured flight speed, and the velocity $(v_x)_{aw}$ of the **air** with respect to the **water**, which is the known wind speed. We want to find the bird's airspeed—the speed of the **bird** with respect to the **air**.

SOLVE We need the subscript for the water to "cancel," so, according to Equation 3.22, we write

$$(v_x)_{ba} = (v_x)_{bw} + (v_x)_{wa}$$

The term $(v_x)_{wa}$, is the opposite of the second of our known values, so we use $(v_x)_{wa} = -(v_x)_{aw} = -23$ m/s to find

$$(v_x)_{ba} = (35 \text{ m/s}) + (-23 \text{ m/s}) = 12 \text{ m/s}$$

ASSESS 12 m/s—about 25 mph—is a reasonable airspeed for a bird. And it's slower than the observed flight speed, which makes sense because the bird is flying with the wind.

This technique for finding relative velocities also works for two-dimensional situations, as we see in the next example. Relative motion in two dimensions is another good exercise in working with vectors.

EXAMPLE 3.10 Finding the ground speed of an airplane

Cleveland is approximately 300 miles east of Chicago. A plane leaves Chicago flying due east at 500 mph. The pilot forgot to check the weather and doesn't know that the wind is blowing to the south at 100 mph. What is the plane's velocity relative to the ground?

PREPARE FIGURE 3.29 is a visual overview of the situation. We are given the speed of the **plane** relative to the **air** ($\vec{v}_{pa}$) and the

FIGURE 3.29 The wind causes a plane flying due east in the air to move to the southeast relative to the ground.

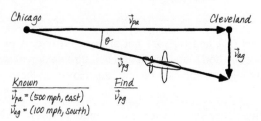

Known
$\vec{v}_{pa} = (500 \text{ mph, east})$
$\vec{v}_{ag} = (100 \text{ mph, south})$

Find
$\vec{v}_{pg}$

speed of the **air** relative to the **ground** ($\vec{v}_{ag}$); the speed of the **plane** relative to the **ground** will be the vector sum of these velocities:

$$\vec{v}_{pg} = \vec{v}_{pa} + \vec{v}_{ag}$$

This vector sum is shown in Figure 3.29.

SOLVE The plane's speed relative to the ground is the hypotenuse of the right triangle in Figure 3.29; thus:

$$v_{pg} = \sqrt{v_{pa}^2 + v_{ag}^2} = \sqrt{(500 \text{ mph})^2 + (100 \text{ mph})^2} = 510 \text{ mph}$$

The plane's direction can be specified by the angle θ measured from due east:

$$\theta = \tan^{-1}\left(\frac{100 \text{ mph}}{500 \text{ mph}}\right) = \tan^{-1}(0.20) = 11°$$

The velocity of the plane relative to the ground is thus

$$\vec{v}_{pg} = (510 \text{ mph}, 11° \text{ south of east})$$

ASSESS The good news is that the wind is making the plane move a bit faster relative to the ground; the bad news is that the wind is making the plane move in the wrong direction!

(a)

(b)

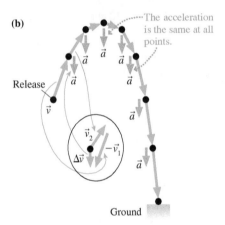

3.6 Motion in Two Dimensions: Projectile Motion

Balls flying through the air, long jumpers, and cars doing stunt jumps are all examples of the two-dimensional motion that we call *projectile motion*. Projectile motion is an extension to two dimensions of the free-fall motion we studied in Chapter 2. A **projectile is an object that moves in two dimensions under the influence of gravity and nothing else.** Although real objects are also influenced by air resistance, the effect of air resistance is small for reasonably dense objects moving at modest speeds, so we can ignore it for the cases we consider in this chapter. As long as we can neglect air resistance, any projectile will follow the same type of path: a trajectory with the mathematical form of a parabola. Because the form of the motion will always be the same, the strategies we develop to solve one projectile problem can be applied to others as well.

FIGURE 3.30a shows the parabolic arc of a ball tossed into the air; the camera has captured its position at equal intervals of time. In FIGURE 3.30b we show the motion diagram for this toss, with velocity vectors connecting the points. The acceleration vector points in the same direction as the change in velocity $\Delta\vec{v}$, which we can compute using the techniques of Tactics Box 3.2. You can see that the acceleration vector points straight down; a careful analysis would show that it has magnitude 9.80 m/s^2. Consequently, the acceleration of a projectile is the same as the acceleration of an object falling straight down—namely, the free-fall acceleration:

$$\vec{a}_{\text{free fall}} = (9.80 \text{ m/s}^2, \text{ straight down})$$

Because the free-fall acceleration is the same for all objects, it is no wonder that the shape of the trajectory—a parabola—is the same as well.

As the projectile moves, the free-fall acceleration will change the vertical component of the velocity, but there will be no change to the horizontal component of the velocity. Therefore, the vertical and horizontal components of the acceleration are

$$a_x = 0 \text{ m/s}^2$$
$$a_y = -g = -9.80 \text{ m/s}^2 \tag{3.23}$$

The vertical component of acceleration a_y for all projectile motion is just the familiar $-g$ of free fall, while the horizontal component a_x is zero.

Analyzing Projectile Motion

Suppose you toss a basketball down the court, as shown in FIGURE 3.31. To study this projectile motion, we've established a coordinate system with the x-axis horizontal and the y-axis vertical. The start of a projectile's motion is called the *launch,* and the angle θ of the initial velocity $\vec{v}_i$ above the horizontal (i.e., above the x-axis) is the **launch angle.** As you learned in Section 3.3, the initial velocity vector $\vec{v}_i$ can be expressed in terms of the x- and y-components $(v_x)_i$ and $(v_y)_i$. You can see from the figure that

$$(v_x)_i = v_i \cos\theta$$
$$(v_y)_i = v_i \sin\theta \tag{3.24}$$

where v_i is the initial speed.

NOTE ▶ The components $(v_x)_i$ and $(v_y)_i$ are not always positive. A projectile launched at an angle *below* the horizontal (such as a ball thrown downward from the roof of a building) has *negative* values for θ and $(v_y)_i$. However, the *speed* v_i is always positive. ◀

To see how the acceleration determines the subsequent motion, FIGURE 3.32 shows a projectile launched at a speed of 22.0 m/s at an angle of 63° from the horizontal.

FIGURE 3.31 The launch and motion of a projectile.

Video Tutor Demonstration

In Figure 3.32a, the initial velocity vector is broken into its horizontal and vertical components. In Figure 3.32b, the velocity vector and its component vectors are shown every subsequent 1.0 s. Because there is no horizontal acceleration ($a_x = 0$), the value of v_x never changes. In contrast, v_y decreases by 9.8 m/s every second. This is what it *means* to accelerate at $a_y = -9.8$ m/s^2 = $(-9.8$ m/s) per second. Nothing *pushes* the projectile along the curve. Instead, the downward acceleration changes the velocity vector as shown, causing it to increase downward as the motion proceeds. At the end of the motion, when the ball is at the same height as it started, v_y is -19.6 m/s, the negative of its initial value. **The ball finishes its motion moving downward at the same speed as it started moving upward,** just as we saw in the case of one-dimensional free fall in Chapter 2.

You can see from Figure 3.32 that **projectile motion is made up of two independent motions: uniform motion at constant velocity in the horizontal direction and free-fall motion in the vertical direction.** In Chapter 2, we saw kinematic equations for constant-velocity and constant-acceleration motion. We can adapt these general equations to this current case: The horizontal motion is constant-velocity motion at $(v_x)_i$; the vertical motion is constant-acceleration motion with initial velocity $(v_y)_i$ and an acceleration of $a_y = -g$.

$$x_f = x_i + (v_x)_i \, \Delta t \qquad y_f = y_i + (v_y)_i \, \Delta t - \tfrac{1}{2}g(\Delta t)^2$$

$$(v_x)_f = (v_x)_i = \text{constant} \qquad (v_y)_f = (v_y)_i - g \, \Delta t \tag{3.25}$$

Equations of motion for the parabolic trajectory of a projectile

A close look at these equations reveals a surprising fact: **The horizontal and vertical components of projectile motion are independent of each other.** The initial horizontal velocity has *no* influence over the vertical motion, and vice versa. This independence of the horizontal and vertical motions is illustrated in FIGURE 3.33, which shows a strobe photograph of two balls, one shot horizontally and the other released from rest at the same instant. The *vertical* motions of the two balls are identical, and they hit the floor simultaneously. Neither ball has any initial motion in the vertical direction, so both fall distance h in the same amount of time.

Let's extend these ideas to consider a "classic" problem in physics:

A hungry hunter in the jungle wants to shoot down a coconut that is hanging from the branch of a tree. He aims the gun directly at the coconut, but as luck would have it the coconut falls from the branch at the exact instant the hunter pulls the trigger. Does the bullet hit the coconut?

FIGURE 3.34 shows a useful way to analyze this problem. Figure 3.34a shows the trajectory of a projectile. Without gravity, a projectile would follow a

FIGURE 3.32 The velocity and acceleration vectors of a projectile.

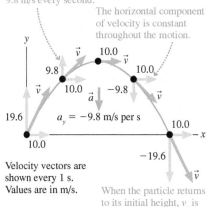

(a)

(b)

Velocity vectors are shown every 1 s. Values are in m/s.

When the particle returns to its initial height, v_y is opposite its initial value.

FIGURE 3.33 A projectile launched horizontally falls in the same time as a projectile that is released from rest.

FIGURE 3.34 A projectile follows a parabolic trajectory because it "falls" a distance $\tfrac{1}{2}gt^2$ below a straight-line trajectory.

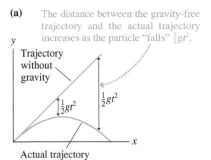

(a) The distance between the gravity-free trajectory and the actual trajectory increases as the particle "falls" $\tfrac{1}{2}gt^2$.

Trajectory without gravity

$\tfrac{1}{2}gt^2$

$\tfrac{1}{2}gt^2$

Actual trajectory

(b)

Trajectory without gravity

$\tfrac{1}{2}gt^2$

Actual trajectory of bullet

A game of catch in a moving vehicle
While riding in a car moving at a constant speed, toss a ball or a coin into the air. You can easily catch it! The ball and you continue to move forward at a constant speed during the ball's up-and-down vertical motion. The vertical motion is completely independent of, and unaffected by, the horizontal motion. From the point of view of a person watching you drive by, the ball's motion would be a parabolic arc.

straight line. Because of gravity, the particle at time t has "fallen" a distance $\frac{1}{2}gt^2$ below this line. The separation grows as $\frac{1}{2}gt^2$, giving the trajectory its parabolic shape. Figure 3.34b applies this reasoning to the bullet and coconut. Although the bullet travels very fast, it follows a slightly curved trajectory, not a straight line. Had the coconut stayed on the tree, the bullet would have curved under its target because gravity causes it to fall a distance $\frac{1}{2}gt^2$ below the straight line. But $\frac{1}{2}gt^2$ is also the distance the coconut falls while the bullet is in flight. Thus, as Figure 3.34b shows, the bullet and the coconut fall the same distance and meet at the same point!

STOP TO THINK 3.5   A 100 g ball rolls off a table and lands 2 m from the base of the table. A 200 g ball rolls off the same table with the same speed. How far does it land from the base of the table?

A. <1 m.   B. 1 m.
C. Between 1 m and 2 m.   D. 2 m.
E. Between 2 m and 4 m.   F. 4 m.

3.7 Projectile Motion: Solving Problems

Now that we have a good idea of how projectile motion works, we can use that knowledge to solve some true two-dimensional motion problems.

EXAMPLE 3.11   **Planning a Hollywood stunt**

To get the shots of cars flying through the air in movies, it is sometimes necessary to drive a car off a cliff and film it. Suppose a stunt man drives a car off a 10-m-high cliff at a speed of 20 m/s How far does the car land from the base of the cliff?

PREPARE We start with a visual overview of the situation in FIGURE 3.35. Note that we have chosen to put the origin of the coordinate system at the base of the cliff. We assume that the car is moving horizontally as it leaves the cliff. In this case, the x- and y-components of the initial velocity are

$$(v_x)_i = v_i = 20 \text{ m/s}$$

$$(v_y)_i = 0 \text{ m/s}$$

FIGURE 3.35 Visual overview for Example 3.11.

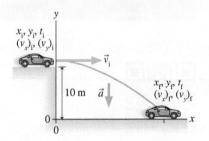

Known
$x_i = 0$ m
$(v_y)_i = 0$ m/s
$t_i = 0$ s
$y_i = 10$ m, $y_f = 0$ m
$(v_x)_i = v_i = 20$ m/s
$a_x = 0$ m/s^2
$a_y = -g$

Find
x_f

SOLVE Each point on the trajectory has x- and y-components of position, velocity, and acceleration but only *one* value of time. The time needed to move horizontally to the final position x_f is the *same* time needed to fall 10 m vertically. **Although the horizontal and vertical motions are independent, they are both**

related to the time t. This is a critical observation for solving projectile motion problems. We will call the time interval between the car leaving the cliff and landing on the ground Δt. In this problem, we'll analyze the vertical motion first. We can solve the vertical-motion equations for the time interval Δt. We'll then use that value of Δt in the equation for the horizontal motion.

The vertical motion is just free fall. The initial vertical velocity is zero; the car falls from $y_i = 10$ m to $y_f = 0$ m. We can analyze this motion using the vertical-position equation from Equations 3.25:

$$y_f = y_i + (v_y)_i \, \Delta t - \frac{1}{2}g(\Delta t)^2$$

$$0 \text{ m} = 10 \text{ m} + (0 \text{ m/s})(\Delta t) - \frac{1}{2}(9.8 \text{ m/s}^2)(\Delta t)^2$$

Rearranging the terms and then solving for Δt give

$$-10 \text{ m} = -\frac{1}{2}(9.8 \text{ m/s}^2)(\Delta t)^2$$

$$\Delta t = \sqrt{\frac{2(10 \text{ m})}{9.8 \text{ m/s}^2}} = 1.43 \text{ s}$$

Now that we have the time, we can use the horizontal-position equation from Equations 3.25 to find out where the car lands:

$$x_f = x_i + (v_x)_i \, \Delta t$$

$$x_f = 0 \text{ m} + (20 \text{ m/s})(1.43 \text{ s}) = 29 \text{ m}$$

ASSESS The cliff height is $h \approx 33$ ft and the initial horizontal velocity is $(v_x)_i \approx 40$ mph. At this speed, a car moves faster than 60 feet per second, so traveling $x_f = 29$ m ≈ 95 ft before hitting the ground seems quite reasonable.

The approach of Example 3.11 is a general one. We can condense the relevant details into a problem-solving strategy.

PROBLEM-SOLVING STRATEGY 3.1   Projectile motion problems

PREPARE   There are a number of steps that you should go through in setting up the solution to a projectile motion problem:

■ Make simplifying assumptions. Whether the projectile is a car or a basketball, the motion will be the same.
■ Draw a visual overview including a pictorial representation showing the beginning and ending points of the motion.
■ Establish a coordinate system with the *x*-axis horizontal and the *y*-axis vertical. In this case, you know that the horizontal acceleration will be zero and the vertical acceleration will be free fall: $a_x = 0$ and $a_y = -g$.
■ Define symbols and write down a list of known values. Identify what the problem is trying to find.

SOLVE   There are two sets of kinematic equations for projectile motion, one for the horizontal component and one for the vertical:

Horizontal	Vertical
$x_f = x_i + (v_x)_i \, \Delta t$	$y_f = y_i + (v_y)_i \, \Delta t - \frac{1}{2} g (\Delta t)^2$
$(v_x)_f = (v_x)_i = \text{constant}$	$(v_y)_f = (v_y)_i - g \, \Delta t$

Δt **is the same for the horizontal and vertical components of the motion.** Find Δt by solving for the vertical or the horizontal component of the motion; then use that value to complete the solution for the other component.

ASSESS   Check that your result has the correct units, is reasonable, and answers the question.

Galileo was the first person to make a serious study of projectile motion, deducing the independence of the horizontal and vertical components. This page from his notes shows his analysis of a projectile launched horizontally. In his day, this topic was cutting-edge science; now it is in Chapter 3 of a 30-chapter book!

 ActivPhysics: 3.1, 3.2, 3.3, 3.4, 3.5, 3.6, 3.7
PhET: Projectile Motion

EXAMPLE 3.12   **Checking the feasibility of a Hollywood stunt**

The main characters in the movie *Speed* are on a bus that has been booby-trapped to explode if its speed drops below 50 mph. But there is a problem ahead: A 50 ft section of a freeway overpass is missing. They decide to jump the bus over the gap. The road leading up to the break has an angle of about 5°. A view of the speedometer just before the jump shows that the bus is traveling at 67 mph. The movie bus makes the jump and survives. Is this realistic, or movie fiction?

PREPARE   We begin by converting speed and distance to SI units. The initial speed is $v_i = 30$ m/s and the size of the gap is $L = 15$ m. Next, following the problem-solving strategy, we make a sketch, the visual overview shown in FIGURE 3.36, and a list of

FIGURE 3.36 Visual overview of the bus jumping the gap.

values. In choosing our axes, we've placed the origin at the point where the bus starts its jump. The initial velocity vector is tilted 5° above horizontal, so the components of the initial velocity are

$$(v_x)_i = v_i \cos \theta = (30 \text{ m/s})(\cos 5°) = 30 \text{ m/s}$$
$$(v_y)_i = v_i \sin \theta = (30 \text{ m/s})(\sin 5°) = 2.6 \text{ m/s}$$

How do we specify the "end" of the problem? By setting $y_f = 0$ m, we'll solve for the horizontal distance x_f at which the bus returns to its initial height. If x_f exceeds 50 ft, the bus successfully clears the gap. We have optimistically drawn our diagram as if the bus makes the jump, but . . .

SOLVE   Problem-Solving Strategy 3.1 suggests using one component of the motion to solve for Δt. We will begin with the vertical motion. The kinematic equation for the vertical position is

$$y_f = y_i + (v_y)_i \, \Delta t - \frac{1}{2} g (\Delta t)^2$$

We know that $y_f = y_i = 0$ m. If we factor out Δt, the position equation becomes

$$0 = \Delta t \left((v_y)_i - \frac{1}{2} g \, \Delta t \right)$$

One solution to this equation is $\Delta t = 0$ s. This is a legitimate solution, but it corresponds to the instant when $y = 0$ at the beginning

Continued

of the trajectory. We want the second solution, for $y = 0$ at the end of the trajectory, which is when

$$0 = (v_y)_i - \tfrac{1}{2} g \, \Delta t = (2.6 \text{ m/s}) - \tfrac{1}{2}(9.8 \text{ m/s}^2) \, \Delta t$$

which gives

$$\Delta t = \frac{2 \times (2.6 \text{ m/s})}{9.8 \text{ m/s}^2} = 0.53 \text{ s}$$

During the 0.53 s that the bus is moving vertically it is also moving horizontally. The final horizontal position of the bus is $x_f = x_i + (v_x)_i \, \Delta t$, or

$$x_f = 0 \text{ m} + (30 \text{ m/s})(0.53 \text{ s}) = 16 \text{ m}$$

This is how far the bus has traveled horizontally when it returns to its original height. 16 m is a bit more than the width of the gap, so a bus coming off a 5° ramp at the noted speed would make it—just barely!

ASSESS We can do a quick check on our math by noting that the bus takes off and lands at the same height. This means, as we saw in Figure 3.32b, that the y-velocity at the landing should be the negative of its initial value. We can use the velocity equation for the vertical component of the motion to compute the final value and see that the final velocity value is as we predict:

$$(v_y)_f = (v_y)_i - g \, \Delta t$$

$$= (2.6 \text{ m/s}) - (9.8 \text{ m/s}^2)(0.53 \text{ s}) = -2.6 \text{ m/s}$$

During the filming of the movie, the filmmakers really did jump a bus over a gap in an overpass! The actual jump was a bit more complicated than our example because a real bus, being an extended object rather than a particle, will start rotating as the front end comes off the ramp. The actual stunt jump used an extra ramp to give a boost to the front end of the bus. Nonetheless, our example shows that the filmmakers did their homework and devised a situation in which the physics was correct.

The Range of a Projectile

When the quarterback throws a football down the field, how far will it go? What will be the **range** for this particular projectile motion, the horizontal distance traveled?

Example 3.12 was a range problem—for a given speed and a given angle, we wanted to know how far the bus would go. The speed and the angle are the two variables that determine the range. A higher speed means a greater range, of course. But how does angle figure in?

FIGURE 3.37 shows the trajectory that a projectile launched at 100 m/s will follow for different launch angles. At very small or very large angles, the range is quite small. If you throw a ball at a 75° angle, it will do a great deal of up-and-down motion, but it won't achieve much horizontal travel. If you throw a ball at a 15° angle, the ball won't be in the air long enough to go very far. These cases both have the same range, as Figure 3.37 shows.

If the angle is too small or too large, the range is shorter than it could be. The "just right" case that gives the maximum range when landing at the same elevation as the launch is a launch angle of 45°, as Figure 3.37 shows.

If that's true, why does a long jumper take off at an angle that is so much less than 45°, as shown in FIGURE 3.38? One reason is that he changes the position of his legs as he jumps—he doesn't really land at the same height as that from which he took off, which changes things a bit. But there's a more important reason. In Figure 3.37 we looked at the range of projectiles that were launched at the *same speed* to see that a 45° angle gave the longest range. But the biomechanics of running and jumping don't allow you to keep the same launch speed as you increase the angle of your jump. Any increase in your launch angle comes at the sacrifice of speed, so the situation of Figure 3.37 doesn't apply. The optimum angle for jumping is less than 45° because your faster jump speed outweighs the effect of a smaller jump angle.

For other projectiles, such as golf balls and baseballs, the optimal angle is less than 45° for a different reason: air resistance. Up to this point we've ignored air resistance, but for small objects traveling at high speeds, air resistance is critical. Aerodynamic forces come into play, causing the projectile's trajectory to deviate from a parabola. The maximum range for a golf ball comes at an angle much less than 45°, as you no doubt know if you have ever played golf.

Video Tutor Demonstration

FIGURE 3.37 Trajectories of a projectile for different launch angles, assuming air resistance can be neglected.

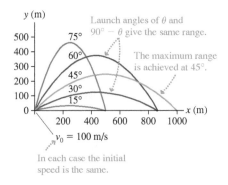

Launch angles of θ and $90° - \theta$ give the same range.

The maximum range is achieved at 45°.

y (m)

75°
60°
45°
30°
15°

x (m)

200   400   600   800   1000

$v_0 = 100$ m/s

In each case the initial speed is the same.

FIGURE 3.38 The trajectory of a long jumper.

▶ **Physics of fielding** BIO The batter hits a high fly ball, and the fielder makes a graceful arc to the exact spot where it lands, catching it on the run. He didn't estimate velocity and calculate the ball's trajectory, so how did he do it? The key is that the fielder is in constant motion. He monitors the relative motion of the ball as he runs and makes adjustments in his velocity to keep the ball at a constant angle with respect to him. By doing this, he'll be at the right spot when the ball lands. He doesn't know where the ball will land—just how to be there when it does!

3.8 Motion in Two Dimensions: Circular Motion

The 32 cars on the London Eye Ferris wheel move at a constant speed of about 0.5 m/s in a vertical circle of radius 65 m. The cars may move at a constant speed, but they do *not* move with constant velocity. Velocity is a vector that depends on both an object's speed *and* its direction of motion, and the direction of circular motion is constantly changing. This is the hallmark of **uniform circular motion**: constant speed, but continuously changing direction. We will introduce some basic ideas about circular motion in this section, then return to treat it in considerably more detail in Chapter 6. For now, we will consider only objects that move around a circular trajectory at constant speed.

Period, Frequency, and Speed

The time interval it takes an object to go around a circle one time, completing one revolution (abbreviated rev), is called the **period** of the motion. Period is represented by the symbol T.

Rather than specify the time for one revolution, we can specify circular motion by its **frequency,** the number of revolutions per second, for which we use the symbol f. An object with a period of one-half second completes 2 revolutions each second. Similarly, an object can make 10 revolutions in 1 s if its period is one-tenth of a second. This shows that frequency is the inverse of the period:

$$f = \frac{1}{T} \tag{3.26}$$

Although frequency is often expressed as "revolutions per second," *revolutions* are not true units but merely the counting of events. Thus the SI unit of frequency is simply inverse seconds, or s^{-1}. Frequency may also be given in revolutions per minute (rpm) or another time interval, but these usually need to be converted to s^{-1} before doing calculations.

FIGURE 3.39 shows an object moving at a constant speed in a circular path of radius R. We know the time for one revolution—one period T—and we know the distance traveled, so we can write an equation relating the period, the radius, and the speed:

$$v = \frac{2\pi R}{T} \tag{3.27}$$

Given Equation 3.26 relating frequency and period, we can also write this equation as

$$v = 2\pi f R \tag{3.28}$$

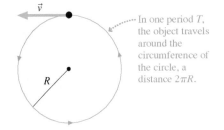

The London Eye Ferris wheel.

FIGURE 3.39 Relating frequency and speed.

In one period T, the object travels around the circumference of the circle, a distance $2\pi R$.

EXAMPLE 3.13 **Spinning some tunes**

An audio CD has a diameter of 120 mm and spins at up to 540 rpm. When a CD is spinning at its maximum rate, how much time is required for one revolution? If a speck of dust rides on the outside edge of the disk, how fast is it moving?

PREPARE Before we get started, we need to do some unit conversions. The diameter of a CD is given as 120 mm, which is 0.12 m. The radius is 0.060 m. The frequency is given in rpm; we need to convert this to s^{-1}:

$$f = 540 \, \frac{\text{rev}}{\text{min}} \times \frac{1 \text{ min}}{60 \text{ s}} = 9.0 \, \frac{\text{rev}}{\text{s}} = 9.0 \text{ s}^{-1}$$

Continued

SOLVE The time for one revolution is the period; this is given by Equation 3.26:

$$T = \frac{1}{f} = \frac{1}{9.0 \text{ s}^{-1}} = 0.11 \text{ s}$$

The dust speck is moving in a circle of radius 0.12 m at a frequency of 9.0 s⁻¹. We can use Equation 3.28 to find the speed:

$$v = 2\pi f R = 2\pi(9.0 \text{ s}^{-1})(0.060 \text{ m}) = 3.4 \text{ m/s}$$

ASSESS If you've watched a CD spin, you know that it takes much less than a second to go around, so the value for the period seems reasonable. The speed we calculate for the dust speck is nearly 8 mph, but for a point on the edge of the CD to go around so many times in a second, it must be moving pretty fast.

Acceleration in Circular Motion

It may seem strange to think that an object moving with constant speed can be accelerating, but that's exactly what an object in uniform circular motion is doing. It is accelerating because its velocity is changing as its direction of motion changes. What is the acceleration in this case? We saw in Example 3.3 that for circular motion at a constant speed, **the acceleration vector $\vec{a}$ points toward the center of the circle.** This is an idea that is worth reviewing. As you can see in FIGURE 3.40, the velocity is always tangent to the circle, so $\vec{v}$ and $\vec{a}$ are perpendicular to each other at all points on the circle.

An acceleration that always points directly toward the center of a circle is called a **centripetal acceleration.** The word "centripetal" comes from a Greek root meaning "center seeking."

NOTE ▶ Centripetal acceleration is not a new type of acceleration; all we are doing is *naming* an acceleration that corresponds to a particular type of motion. The magnitude of the centripetal acceleration is constant because each successive $\Delta\vec{v}$ in the motion diagram has the same length. ◀

To complete our description of circular motion, we need to find a quantitative relationship between the magnitude of the acceleration a and the speed v. Let's return to the case of the Ferris wheel. During a time Δt in which a car on the Ferris wheel moves around the circle from point 1 to point 2, the car moves through an angle θ and undergoes a displacement $\vec{d}$, as shown in FIGURE 3.41a. We've chosen a relatively large angle θ for our drawing so that angular relationships can be clearly seen, but for a small angle the displacement is essentially identical to the actual distance traveled, and we'll make this approximation.

FIGURE 3.41b shows how the velocity changes as the car moves, and FIGURE 3.41c shows the vector calculation of the change in velocity. The triangle we use to make this calculation is geometrically *similar* to the one that shows the displacement, as

FIGURE 3.40 The velocity and acceleration vectors for circular motion.

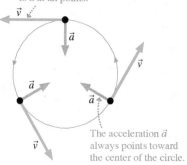

The velocity $\vec{v}$ is always tangent to the circle and perpendicular to $\vec{a}$ at all points.

The acceleration $\vec{a}$ always points toward the center of the circle.

PhET: Motion in 2D
PhET: Ladybug Revolution

Class Video

FIGURE 3.41 Changing position and velocity for an object in circular motion.

(a)

As the car moves from point 1 to point 2, the displacement is $\vec{d}$.

(b)

The magnitude of the velocity is constant, but the direction changes.

(c) The change in velocity is a vector pointing toward the center of the circle.

$$\Delta\vec{v} = \vec{v}_2 - \vec{v}_1$$

These triangles are similar.

This triangle is the same as in part a, but rotated.

Figure 3.41c shows. This is a key piece of information: You'll remember from geometry that similar triangles have equal ratios of their sides, so we can write

$$\frac{\Delta v}{v} = \frac{d}{r} \tag{3.29}$$

where Δv is the magnitude of the velocity-change vector $\Delta \vec{v}$. We've used the unsubscripted speed v for the length of a side of the first triangle because it is the same for velocities $\vec{v}_1$ and $\vec{v}_2$.

Now we're ready to compute the acceleration. The displacement is just the speed v times the time interval Δt, so we can write

$$d = v\Delta t$$

We can substitute this for d in Equation 3.29 to obtain

$$\frac{\Delta v}{v} = \frac{v\Delta t}{r}$$

which we can rearrange like so:

$$\frac{\Delta v}{\Delta t} = \frac{v^2}{r}$$

We recognize the left-hand side of the equation as the acceleration, so this becomes

$$a = \frac{v^2}{r}$$

Combining this magnitude with the direction we noted above, we can write the centripetal acceleration as

$$\vec{a} = \left(\frac{v^2}{r}, \text{ toward center of circle} \right) \tag{3.30}$$

Centripetal acceleration of object moving in a circle of radius r at speed v

QUADRATIC

(MP) **ActivPhysics:** 4.1

CONCEPTUAL EXAMPLE 3.14 **Acceleration on a swing**

A child is riding a playground swing. The swing rotates in a circle around a central point where the rope or chain for the swing is attached. The speed isn't changing at the lowest point of the motion, but the direction is—this is circular motion, with an acceleration directed upward, as shown in FIGURE 3.42. More acceleration will mean a more exciting ride. What change could the child make to increase the acceleration she experiences?

FIGURE 3.42 A child at the lowest point of motion on a swing.

REASON The acceleration the child experiences is the "changing direction" acceleration of circular motion, given by Equation 3.30. The acceleration depends on the speed and the radius of the circle. The radius of the circle is determined by the length of the chain or rope, so the only easy way to change the acceleration is to change the speed, which she could do by swinging higher. Because the acceleration is proportional to the square of the speed, doubling the speed means a fourfold increase in the acceleration.

ASSESS If you have ever ridden a swing, you know that the acceleration you experience is greater the faster you go—so our answer makes sense.

EXAMPLE 3.15   **Finding the acceleration of a Ferris wheel**

A typical carnival Ferris wheel has a radius of 9.0 m and rotates 6.0 times per minute. What magnitude acceleration do the riders experience?

PREPARE The cars on a Ferris wheel move in a circle at constant speed; the acceleration the riders experience is a centripetal acceleration.

SOLVE In order to use Equation 3.30 to compute an acceleration, we need to know the speed v of a rider on the Ferris wheel. The wheel rotates 6.0 times per minute; therefore, the time for one

rotation (i.e., the period) is 10 s. We can use Equation 3.27 to find the speed:

$$v = \frac{2\pi R}{T} = \frac{(2\pi)(9.0 \text{ m})}{10 \text{ s}} = 5.7 \text{ m/s}$$

Knowing the speed, we can use Equation 3.30 to find the magnitude of the acceleration:

$$a = \frac{v^2}{r} = \frac{(5.7 \text{ m/s})^2}{9.0 \text{ m}} = 3.6 \text{ m/s}^2$$

ASSESS This is about 1/3 of the free-fall acceleration; the acceleration, in units of g, is $0.37g$. This is enough to notice, but not enough to be scary! Our answer seems reasonable.

What Comes Next: Forces

So far we have been studying motion without saying too much about what actually *causes* motion. Kinematics, the mathematical description of motion, is a good place to start because motion is very visible and very familiar. And in our study of motion we have introduced many of the basic tools, such as vectors, that we will use in the rest of the book.

But now it's time to look at what causes motion: forces. By learning about forces, which you will do in the next several chapters, you will be able to explore a much wider range of problems in much more depth. As an example, think about the picture of a roller coaster with an inverted loop. How is it that riders can go through the loop and not fall out of their seats? This is just one of the problems that you will study once you know a bit about forces and the connection between forces and motion.

◄ **Amusement park kinematics** Acceleration is fun—at least that's what the designer of this roller coaster seems to think! The coaster has ramps that give linear acceleration, parabolic segments in which the coaster follows a projectile path with a free-fall acceleration, and circular arcs in which the centripetal acceleration is greater than g. All of this acceleration means there are forces on the riders—and the coaster must be carefully designed so that these forces are well within safe limits.

STOP TO THINK 3.6   Which of the following particles has the greatest centripetal acceleration?

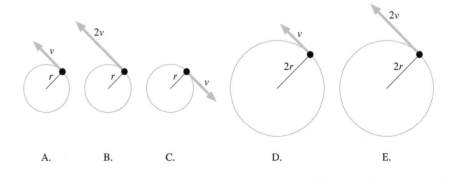

A.   B.   C.   D.   E.

World-record jumpers

Frogs, with their long, strong legs, are excellent jumpers. And thanks to the good folks of Calaveras County, California, who have a jumping frog contest every year in honor of a Mark Twain story, we have very good data as to just how far a determined frog can jump. The current record holder is Rosie the Ribeter, a bullfrog who made a leap of 6.5 m from a standing start. This compares favorably with the world record for a human, which is a mere 3.7 m.

Typical data for a serious leap by a bullfrog look like this: The frog goes into a crouch, then rapidly extends its legs by 15 cm as it pushes off, leaving the ground at an angle of 30° to the horizontal. It's in the air for 0.68 s before landing at the same height from which it took off. Given this leap, what is the acceleration while the frog is pushing off? How far does the frog jump?

PREPARE The problem really has two parts: the leap through the air and the acceleration required to produce this leap. We'll need to analyze the leap—the projectile motion—first, which will give us the frog's launch speed and the distance of the jump. Once we know the velocity with which the frog leaves the ground, we can calculate its acceleration while pushing off the ground. Let's start with a visual overview of the two parts, as shown in FIGURE 3.43. Notice that the second part of the problem uses a different x-axis, tilted as we did earlier for motion on a ramp.

SOLVE The "flying through the air" part of Figure 3.43a is projectile motion. The frog lifts off at a 30° angle with a speed v_i; the x- and y-components of the initial velocity are

$$(v_x)_i = v_i \cos (30°)$$
$$(v_y)_i = v_i \sin (30°)$$

The vertical motion can be analyzed as we did in Example 3.12. The kinematic equation is

$$y_f = y_i + (v_y)_i \Delta t + \tfrac{1}{2} a_y (\Delta t)^2$$

We know that $y_f = y_i = 0$, so this reduces to

$$(v_y)_i = -\tfrac{1}{2} a_y \Delta t = -\tfrac{1}{2}(-9.8 \text{ m/s}^2)(0.68 \text{ s}) = 3.3 \text{ m/s}$$

We know the y-component of the velocity and the angle, so we can find the magnitude of the velocity and the x-component:

$$v_i = \frac{(v_y)_i}{\sin 30°} = \frac{3.3 \text{ m/s}}{\sin 30°} = 6.6 \text{ m/s}$$

$$(v_x)_i = v_i \cos 30° = (6.6 \text{ m/s}) \cos 30° = 5.7 \text{ m/s}$$

The horizontal motion is uniform motion, so the frog's horizontal position when it returns to the ground is

$$x_f = x_i + (v_x)_i \Delta t = 0 + (5.7 \text{ m/s})(0.68 \text{ s}) = 3.9 \text{ m}$$

This is the length of the jump.

Now that we know how fast the frog is going when it leaves the ground, we can calculate the acceleration necessary to produce this jump—the "pushing off the ground" part of Figure 3.43b. We've drawn the x-axis along the direction of motion, as we did for problems of motion on a ramp. We know the displacement Δx of the jump but not the time, so we can use the third equation in Table 2.4:

$$(v_x)_f^2 = (v_x)_i^2 + 2a_x \Delta x$$

The initial velocity is zero, the final velocity is $(v_x)_f = 6.6$ m/s, and the displacement is the 15 cm (or 0.15 m) stretch of the legs during the jump. Thus the frog's acceleration while pushing off is

$$a_x = \frac{(v_x)_f^2}{2\Delta x} = \frac{(6.6 \text{ m/s})^2}{2(0.15 \text{ m})} = 150 \text{ m/s}^2$$

ASSESS A 3.9 m jump is more than a human can achieve, but it's less than the record for a frog, so the final result for the distance seems reasonable. Such a long jump must require a large acceleration during the pushing-off phase, which is what we found.

FIGURE 3.43 A visual overview for the leap of a frog.

SUMMARY

The goals of Chapter 3 have been to learn more about vectors and to use vectors as a tool to analyze motion in two dimensions.

GENERAL PRINCIPLES

Projectile Motion

A projectile is an object that moves through the air under the influence of gravity and nothing else.

The path of the motion is a parabola.

The motion consists of two pieces:

1. Vertical motion with free-fall acceleration, $a_y = -g$.

2. Horizontal motion with constant velocity.

Kinematic equations:

$$x_f = x_i + (v_x)_i\, \Delta t$$

$$(v_x)_f = (v_x)_i = \text{constant}$$

$$y_f = y_i + (v_y)_i\, \Delta t - \tfrac{1}{2}g(\Delta t)^2$$

$$(v_y)_f = (v_y)_i - g\, \Delta t$$

Circular Motion

For an object moving in a circle at a constant speed:

- The period T is the time for one rotation.
- The frequency $f = 1/T$ is the number of revolutions per second.
- The velocity is tangent to the circular path.
- The acceleration points toward the center of the circle and has magnitude

$$a = \frac{v^2}{r}$$

Centripetal acceleration

IMPORTANT CONCEPTS

Vectors and Components

A vector can be decomposed into x- and y-**components**.

The magnitude and direction of a vector can be expressed in terms of its components.

The sign of the components depends on the direction of the vector:

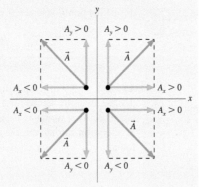

The Acceleration Vector

We define the acceleration vector as

$$\vec{a} = \frac{\vec{v}_f - \vec{v}_i}{t_f - t_i} = \frac{\Delta \vec{v}}{\Delta t}$$

We find the acceleration vector on a motion diagram as follows:

Dots show positions at equal time intervals.

Velocity vectors go dot to dot.

The acceleration vector points in the direction of $\Delta \vec{v}$.

The difference in the velocity vectors is found by adding the negative of $\vec{v}_i$ to $\vec{v}_f$.

APPLICATIONS

Relative motion

Velocities can be expressed relative to an observer. We can add relative velocities to convert to another observer's point of view.

c = car, r = runner, g = ground

The speed of the car with respect to the runner is:

$$(v_x)_{cr} = (v_x)_{cg} + (v_x)_{gr}$$

Motion on a ramp

An object sliding down a ramp will accelerate parallel to the ramp:

$$a_x = \pm g\sin\theta$$

The correct sign depends on the direction in which the ramp is tilted.

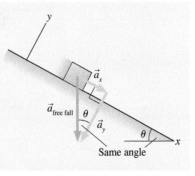

Same angle

Problem difficulty is labeled as ‖ (straightforward) to ‖‖‖ (challenging). Problems labeled ‖‖ integrate significant material from earlier chapters; BIO are of biological or medical interest.

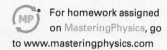 For homework assigned on MasteringPhysics, go to www.masteringphysics.com

 Scan this QR code to launch a Video Tutor Solution that will help you solve problems for this chapter.

QUESTIONS

Conceptual Questions

1. a. Can a vector have nonzero magnitude if a component is zero? If no, why not? If yes, give an example.
   b. Can a vector have zero magnitude and a nonzero component? If no, why not? If yes, give an example.
2. Is it possible to add a scalar to a vector? If so, demonstrate. If not, explain why not.
3. Suppose two vectors have unequal magnitudes. Can their sum be $\vec{0}$? Explain.
4. Suppose $\vec{C} = \vec{A} + \vec{B}$
   a. Under what circumstances does $C = A + B$?
   b. Could $C = A - B$? If so, how? If not, why not?
5. For a projectile, which of the following quantities are constant during the flight: x, y, v_x, v_y, v, a_x, a_y? Which of the quantities are zero throughout the flight?
6. A baseball player throws a ball at a 40° angle to the ground. The ball lands on the ground some distance away.
   a. Is there any point on the trajectory where $\vec{v}$ and $\vec{a}$ are parallel to each other? If so, where?
   b. Is there any point where $\vec{v}$ and $\vec{a}$ are perpendicular to each other? If so, where?
7. An athlete performing the long jump tries to achieve the maximum distance from the point of takeoff to the first point of touching the ground. After the jump, rather than land upright, she extends her legs forward as in the photo. How does this affect the time in the air? How does this give the jumper a longer range?
8. A person trying to throw a ball as far as possible will run forward during the throw. Explain why this increases the distance of the throw.
9. A passenger on a jet airplane claims to be able to walk at a speed in excess of 500 mph. Can this be true? Explain.
10. If you go to a ski area, you'll likely find that the beginner's slope has the smallest angle. Use the concept of acceleration on a ramp to explain why this is so.
11. In an amusement-park ride, cars rolling along at high speed suddenly head up a long, straight ramp. They roll up the ramp, reverse direction at the highest point, then roll backward back down the ramp. In each of the following segments of the motion, are the cars accelerating, or is their acceleration zero? If accelerating, which way does their acceleration vector point?
    a. As the cars roll up the ramp.
    b. At the highest point on the ramp.
    c. As the cars roll back down the ramp.

12. There are competitions in which pilots fly small planes low over the ground and drop weights, trying to hit a target. A pilot flying low and slow drops a weight; it takes 2.0 s to hit the ground, during which it travels a horizontal distance of 100 m. Now the pilot does a run at the same height but twice the speed. How much time does it take the weight to hit the ground? How far does it travel before it lands?
13. A cyclist goes around a level, circular track at constant speed. Do you agree or disagree with the following statement: "Because the cyclist's speed is constant, her acceleration is zero." Explain.
14. You are driving your car in a circular path on level ground at a constant speed of 20 mph. At the instant you are driving north, and turning left, are you accelerating? If so, toward what point of the compass (N, S, E, W) does your acceleration vector point? If not, why not?
15. An airplane has been directed to fly in a clockwise circle, as seen from above, at constant speed until another plane has landed. When the plane is going north, is it accelerating? If so, in what direction does the acceleration vector point? If not, why not?
16. When you go around a corner in your car, your car follows a path that is a segment of a circle. To turn safely, you should keep your car's acceleration below some safe upper limit. If you want to make a "tighter" turn—that is, turn in a circle with a smaller radius—how should you adjust your speed? Explain.

Multiple-Choice Questions

17. ‖ Which combination of the vectors shown in Figure Q3.17 has the largest magnitude?

    A. $\vec{A} + \vec{B} + \vec{C}$
    B. $\vec{B} + \vec{A} - \vec{C}$
    C. $\vec{A} - \vec{B} + \vec{C}$
    D. $\vec{C} - \vec{A} - \vec{C}$

    FIGURE Q3.17

18. ‖ Two vectors appear as in Figure Q3.18. Which combination points directly to the left?

    A. $\vec{P} + \vec{Q}$
    B. $\vec{P} - \vec{Q}$
    C. $\vec{Q} - \vec{P}$
    D. $-\vec{Q} - \vec{P}$

    FIGURE Q3.18

19. ‖ The gas pedal in a car is sometimes referred to as "the accelerator." Which other controls on the vehicle can be used to produce acceleration?
    A. The brakes.
    B. The steering wheel.
    C. The gear shift.
    D. All of the above.

20. | A car travels at constant speed along the curved path shown from above in Figure Q3.20. Five possible vectors are also shown in the figure; the letter E represents the zero vector. Which vector best represents
    a. The car's *velocity* at position 1?
    b. The car's *acceleration* at point 1?
    c. The car's *velocity* at position 2?
    d. The car's *acceleration* at point 2?
    e. The car's *velocity* at position 3?
    f. The car's *acceleration* at point 3?

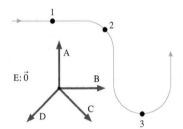

FIGURE Q3.20

21. | A ball is fired from a cannon at point 1 and follows the trajectory shown in Figure Q3.21. Air resistance may be neglected. Five possible vectors are also shown in the figure; the letter E represents the zero vector. Which vector best represents
    a. The ball's *velocity* at position 2?
    b. The ball's *acceleration* at point 2?
    c. The ball's *velocity* at position 3?
    d. The ball's *acceleration* at point 3?

FIGURE Q3.21

22. | A ball thrown at an initial angle of 37.0° and initial velocity of 23.0 m/s reaches a maximum height h, as shown in Figure Q3.22. With what initial speed must a ball be thrown *straight up* to reach the same maximum height h?
    A. 13.8 m/s   B. 17.3 m/s
    C. 18.4 m/s   D. 23.0 m/s

FIGURE Q3.22

23. | A cannon, elevated at 40° is fired at a wall 300 m away on level ground, as shown in Figure Q3.23. The initial speed of the cannonball is 89 m/s

FIGURE Q3.23

a. How long does it take for the ball to hit the wall?
    A. 1.3 s   B. 3.3 s   C. 4.4 s
    D. 6.8 s   E. 7.2 s
b. At what height h does the ball hit the wall?
    A. 39 m   B. 47 m   C. 74 m
    D. 160 m   E. 210 m

24. | A car drives horizontally off a 73-m-high cliff at a speed of 27 m/s. Ignore air resistance.
    a. How long will it take the car to hit the ground?
        A. 2.0 s   B. 3.2 s   C. 3.9 s
        D. 4.9 s   E. 5.0 s
    b. How far from the base of the cliff will the car hit?
        A. 74 m   B. 88 m   C. 100 m
        D. 170 m   E. 280 m

25. | A football is kicked at an angle of 30° with a speed of 20 m/s. To the nearest second, how long will the ball stay in the air?
    A. 1 s   B. 2 s   C. 3 s   D. 4 s

26. | A football is kicked at an angle of 30° with a speed of 20 m/s. To the nearest 5 m, how far will the ball travel?
    A. 15 m   B. 25 m   C. 35 m   D. 45 m

27. | Riders on a Ferris wheel move in a circle with a speed of 4.0 m/s. As they go around, they experience a centripetal acceleration of 2.0 m/s². What is the diameter of this particular Ferris wheel?
    A. 4.0 m   B. 6.0 m   C. 8.0 m
    D. 16 m   E. 24 m

PROBLEMS

Section 3.1 Using Vectors

1. ‖ Trace the vectors in Figure P3.1 onto your paper. Then use graphical methods to draw the vectors (a) $\vec{A} + \vec{B}$ and (b) $\vec{A} - \vec{B}$.

FIGURE P3.1

2. ‖‖ Trace the vectors in Figure P3.2 onto your paper. Then use graphical methods to draw the vectors (a) $\vec{A} + \vec{B}$ and (b) $\vec{A} - \vec{B}$.

FIGURE P3.2

Section 3.2 Using Vectors on Motion Diagrams

3. | A car goes around a corner in a circular arc at constant speed. Draw a motion diagram including positions, velocity vectors, and acceleration vectors.

4. | a. Is the object's average speed between points 1 and 2 greater than, less than, or equal to its average speed between points 0 and 1? Explain how you can tell.
    b. Find the average acceleration vector at point 1 of the three-point motion diagram in Figure P3.4.

FIGURE P3.4

5. ▥ Figure 3.11 showed the motion diagram for Anne as she rode a Ferris wheel that was turning at a constant speed. The inset to the figure showed how to find the acceleration vector at the lowest point in her motion. Use a similar analysis to find Anne's acceleration vector at the 12 o'clock, 4 o'clock, and 8 o'clock positions of the motion diagram. Use a ruler so that your analysis is accurate.

Section 3.3 Coordinate Systems and Vector Components

6. ▯ A position vector with magnitude 10 m points to the right and up. Its *x*-component is 6.0 m. What is the value of its *y*-component?

7. ▥ A velocity vector 40° above the positive *x*-axis has a *y*-component of 10 m/s. What is the value of its *x*-component?

8. ▯ Jack and Jill ran up the hill at 3.0 m/s. The horizontal component of Jill's velocity vector was 2.5 m/s.
   a. What was the angle of the hill?
   b. What was the vertical component of Jill's velocity?

9. ▯ A cannon tilted upward at 30° fires a cannonball with a speed of 100 m/s. At that instant, what is the component of the cannonball's velocity parallel to the ground?

10. ▯ a. What are the *x*- and *y*-components of vector $\vec{E}$ of Figure P3.10 in terms of the angle θ and the magnitude E?
    b. For the same vector, what are the *x*- and *y*-components in terms of the angle ϕ and the magnitude E?

FIGURE P3.10

11. ▯ Draw each of the following vectors, then find its *x*- and *y*-components.
    a. $\vec{d} = (100 \text{ m}, 45° \text{ below } +x\text{-axis})$
    b. $\vec{v} = (300 \text{ m/s}, 20° \text{ above } +x\text{-axis})$
    c. $\vec{a} = (5.0 \text{ m/s}^2, -y\text{-direction})$

12. ▯ Draw each of the following vectors, then find its *x*- and *y*-components.
    a. $\vec{d} = (2.0 \text{ km}, 30° \text{ left of } +y\text{-axis})$
    b. $\vec{v} = (5.0 \text{ cm/s}, -x\text{-direction})$
    c. $\vec{a} = (10 \text{ m/s}^2, 40° \text{ left of } -y\text{-axis})$

13. ▯ Each of the following vectors is given in terms of its *x*- and *y*-components. Draw the vector, label an angle that specifies the vector's direction, then find the vector's magnitude and direction.
    a. $v_x = 20 \text{ m/s}, v_y = 40 \text{ m/s}$
    b. $a_x = 2.0 \text{ m/s}^2, a_y = -6.0 \text{ m/s}^2$

14. ▯ Each of the following vectors is given in terms of its *x*- and *y*-components. Draw the vector, label an angle that specifies the vector's direction, then find the vector's magnitude and direction.
    a. $v_x = 10 \text{ m/s}, v_y = 30 \text{ m/s}$
    b. $a_x = 20 \text{ m/s}^2, a_y = 10 \text{ m/s}^2$

15. ▥ While visiting England, you decide to take a jog and find yourself in the neighborhood shown on the map in Figure P3.15. What is your displacement after running 2.0 km on Strawberry Fields, 1.0 km on Penny Lane, and 4.0 km on Abbey Road?

FIGURE P3.15

Section 3.4 Motion on a Ramp

16. ▥ You begin sliding down a 15° ski slope. Ignoring friction and air resistance, how fast will you be moving after 10 s?

17. ▥ A car traveling at 30 m/s runs out of gas while traveling up a 5.0° slope. How far will it coast before starting to roll back down?

18. ▯ In the Soapbox Derby, young participants build non-motorized cars with very low-friction wheels. Cars race by rolling down a hill. The track at Akron's Derby Downs, where the national championship is held, begins with a 55-ft-long section tilted 13° below horizontal.

    a. What is the maximum possible acceleration of a car moving down this stretch of track?
    b. If a car starts from rest and undergoes this acceleration for the full 55 ft, what is its final speed in m/s?

19. ▥ A piano has been pushed to the top of the ramp at the back of a moving van. The workers think it is safe, but as they walk away, it begins to roll down the ramp. If the back of the truck is 1.0 m above the ground and the ramp is inclined at 20°, how much time do the workers have to get to the piano before it reaches the bottom of the ramp?

20. ▯ Starting from rest, several toy cars roll down ramps of differing lengths and angles. Rank them according to their speed at the bottom of the ramp, from slowest to fastest. Car A goes down a 10 m ramp inclined at 15°, car B goes down a 10 m ramp inclined at 20°, car C goes down an 8.0 m ramp inclined at 20°, and car D goes down a 12 m ramp inclined at 12°.

Section 3.5 Relative Motion

21. ▯ Anita is running to the right at 5 m/s, as shown in Figure P3.21. Balls 1 and 2 are thrown toward her at 10 m/s by friends standing on the ground. According to Anita, what is the speed of each ball?

FIGURE P3.21

22. ▯ Anita is running to the right at 5 m/s, as shown in Figure P3.22. Balls 1 and 2 are thrown toward her by friends standing on the ground. According to Anita, both balls are approaching her at 10 m/s. According to her friends, with what speeds were the balls thrown?

FIGURE P3.22

23. ▥ A boat takes 3.0 h to travel 30 km down a river, then 5.0 h to return. How fast is the river flowing?

24. ▥ Two children who are bored while waiting for their flight at the airport decide to race from one end of the 20-m-long moving sidewalk to the other and back. Phillippe runs on the sidewalk at 2.0 m/s (relative to the sidewalk). Renee runs on the floor at 2.0 m/s. The sidewalk moves at 1.5 m/s relative to the floor. Both make the turn instantly with no loss of speed.
    a. Who wins the race?
    b. By how much time does the winner win?

25. ▥ A skydiver deploys his parachute when he is 1000 m directly above his desired landing spot. He then falls through the air at a steady 5.0 m/s. There is a breeze blowing to the west at 2.0 m/s.
    a. At what angle with respect to vertical does he fall?
    b. By what distance will he miss his desired landing spot?

Section 3.6 Motion in Two Dimensions: Projectile Motion

Section 3.7 Projectile Motion: Solving Problems

26. ▥ An object is launched with an initial velocity of 50.0 m/s at a launch angle of 36.9° above the horizontal.
    a. Make a table showing values of x, y, v_x, v_y, and the speed v every 1 s from $t = 0$ s to $t = 6$ s.
    b. Plot a graph of the object's trajectory during the first 6 s of motion.

27. ▥ A ball is thrown horizontally from a 20-m-high building with a speed of 5.0 m/s.
    a. Make a sketch of the ball's trajectory.
    b. Draw a graph of v_x, the horizontal velocity, as a function of time. Include units on both axes.
    c. Draw a graph of v_y, the vertical velocity, as a function of time. Include units on both axes.
    d. How far from the base of the building does the ball hit the ground?

28. ▥ A ball with a horizontal speed of 1.25 m/s rolls off a bench 1.00 m above the floor.
    a. How long will it take the ball to hit the floor?
    b. How far from a point on the floor directly below the edge of the bench will the ball land?

29. ▥ King Arthur's knights use a catapult to launch a rock from their vantage point on top of the castle wall, 12 m above the moat. The rock is launched at a speed of 25 m/s and an angle of 30° above the horizontal. How far from the castle wall does the launched rock hit the ground?

30. ▥ Two spheres are launched horizontally from a 1.0-m-high table. Sphere A is launched with an initial speed of 5.0 m/s. Sphere B is launched with an initial speed of 2.5 m/s.
    a. What are the times for each sphere to hit the floor?
    b. What are the distances that each travels from the edge of the table?

31. ▥ A rifle is aimed horizontally at a target 50 m away. The bullet hits the target 2.0 cm below the aim point.
    a. What was the bullet's flight time?
    b. What was the bullet's speed as it left the barrel?

32. ▥ A gray kangaroo can bound across a flat stretch of ground
BIO with each jump carrying it 10 m from the takeoff point. If the kangaroo leaves the ground at a 20° angle, what are its (a) take-off speed and (b) horizontal speed?

33. ▥ On the Apollo 14 mission to the moon, astronaut Alan Shepard hit a golf ball with a golf club improvised from a tool. The free-fall acceleration on the moon is 1/6 of its value on earth. Suppose he hit the ball with a speed of 25 m/s at an angle 30° above the horizontal.
    a. How long was the ball in flight?
    b. How far did it travel?
    c. Ignoring air resistance, how much farther would it travel on the moon than on earth?

Section 3.8 Motion in Two Dimensions: Circular Motion

34. ▮ An old-fashioned LP record rotates at $33\frac{1}{3}$ rpm.
    a. What is its frequency, in rev/s?
    b. What is its period, in seconds?

35. ▮ A typical hard disk in a computer spins at 5400 rpm.
    a. What is the frequency, in rev/s?
    b. What is the period, in seconds?

36. ▮ Racing greyhounds are capable of rounding corners at very
BIO high speeds. A typical greyhound track has turns that are 45-m-diameter semicircles. A greyhound can run around these turns at a constant speed of 15 m/s. What is its acceleration in m/s² and in units of g?

37. ▥ A CD-ROM drive in a computer spins the 12-cm-diameter disks at 10,000 rpm.
    a. What are the disk's period (in s) and frequency (in rev/s)?
    b. What would be the speed of a speck of dust on the outside edge of this disk?
    c. What is the acceleration in units of g that this speck of dust experiences?

38. ▥ To withstand "g-forces" of up to 10 g's, caused by suddenly
BIO pulling out of a steep dive, fighter jet pilots train on a "human centrifuge." 10 g's is an acceleration of 98 m/s². If the length of the centrifuge arm is 12 m, at what speed is the rider moving when she experiences 10 g's?

39. ▥ A particle rotates in a circle with centripetal acceleration $a = 8.0$ m/s². What is a if
    a. The radius is doubled without changing the particle's speed?
    b. The speed is doubled without changing the circle's radius?

40. ▥ Entrance and exit ramps for freeways are often circular stretches of road. As you go around one at a constant speed, you will experience a constant acceleration. Suppose you drive through an entrance ramp at a modest speed and your acceleration is 3.0 m/s². What will be the acceleration if you double your speed?

41. ▥ A peregrine falcon in a tight, circular turn can attain a cen-
BIO tripetal acceleration 1.5 times the free-fall acceleration. If the falcon is flying at 20 m/s, what is the radius of the turn?

General Problems

42. ▮ Suppose $\vec{C} = \vec{A} + \vec{B}$ where vector $\vec{A}$ has components $A_x = 5$, $A_y = 2$ and vector $\vec{B}$ has components $B_x = -3$, $B_y = -5$.
    a. What are the x- and y-components of vector $\vec{C}$?
    b. Draw a coordinate system and on it show vectors $\vec{A}$, $\vec{B}$, and $\vec{C}$.
    c. What are the magnitude and direction of vector $\vec{C}$?

43. | Suppose $\vec{D} = \vec{A} - \vec{B}$ where vector $\vec{A}$ has components $A_x = 5$, $A_y = 2$ and vector $\vec{B}$ has components $B_x = -3$, $B_y = -5$.

   a. What are the x- and y-components of vector $\vec{D}$?
   b. Draw a coordinate system and on it show vectors $\vec{A}$, $\vec{B}$, and $\vec{D}$.
   c. What are the magnitude and direction of vector $\vec{D}$?

44. ‖ Suppose $\vec{E} = 2\vec{A} + 3\vec{B}$ where vector $\vec{A}$ has components $A_x = 5$, $A_y = 2$ and vector $\vec{B}$ has components $B_x = -3$, $B_y = -5$.

   a. What are the x- and y-components of vector $\vec{E}$?
   b. Draw a coordinate system and on it show vectors $\vec{A}$, $\vec{B}$, and $\vec{E}$.
   c. What are the magnitude and direction of vector $\vec{E}$?

45. ‖ For the three vectors shown in Figure P3.45, the vector sum $\vec{D} = \vec{A} + \vec{B} + \vec{C}$ has components $D_x = 2$ and $D_y = 0$.

   a. What are the x- and y-components of vector $\vec{B}$?
   b. Write $\vec{B}$ as a magnitude and a direction.

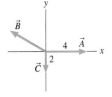

FIGURE P3.45

46. ‖ Let $\vec{A} = (3.0 \text{ m}, 20° \text{ south of east})$, $\vec{B} = (2.0 \text{ m, north})$, and $\vec{C} = (5.0 \text{ m}, 70° \text{ south of west})$.

   a. Draw and label $\vec{A}$, $\vec{B}$, and $\vec{C}$ with their tails at the origin. Use a coordinate system with the x-axis to the east.
   b. Write the x- and y-components of vectors $\vec{A}$, $\vec{B}$, and $\vec{C}$.
   c. Find the magnitude and the direction of $\vec{D} = \vec{A} + \vec{B} + \vec{C}$.

47. ‖ A typical set of stairs is angled at 38°. You climb a set of stairs at a speed of 3.5 m/s.

   a. How much height will you gain in 2.0 s?
   b. How much horizontal distance will you cover in 2.0 s?

48. ‖ The minute hand on a watch is 2.0 cm long. What is the displacement vector of the tip of the minute hand

   a. From 8:00 to 8:20 A.M.?
   b. From 8:00 to 9:00 A.M.?

49. ‖‖ A field mouse trying to escape a hawk runs east for 5.0 m, darts southeast for 3.0 m, then drops 1.0 m down a hole into its burrow. What is the magnitude of the net displacement of the mouse?

50. ‖ A pilot in a small plane encounters shifting winds. He flies 26.0 km northeast, then 45.0 km due north. From this point, he flies an additional distance in an unknown direction, only to find himself at a small airstrip that his map shows to be 70.0 km directly north of his starting point. What were the length and direction of the third leg of his trip?

51. ‖ A small plane is 100 km south of the equator. The plane is flying at 150 km/h at a heading of 30° to the west of north. In how many minutes will the plane cross the equator?

52. ‖ The bacterium *Escherichia coli* (or *E. coli*) is a single-
BIO celled organism that lives in the gut of healthy humans and animals. When grown in a uniform medium rich in salts and amino acids, these bacteria swim along zig-zag paths at a constant speed of 20 μm/s. Figure P3.52 shows the trajectory of an *E. coli* as it moves from point A to point E. Each segment of the motion can be identified by two letters, such as segment BC.

   a. For each of the four segments in the bacterium's trajectory, calculate the x- and y-components of its displacement and of its velocity.
   b. Calculate both the total distance traveled and the magnitude of the net displacement for the entire motion.
   c. What are the magnitude and the direction of the bacterium's average velocity for the entire trip?

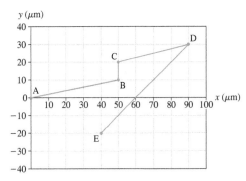

FIGURE P3.52

53. ‖‖ A skier is gliding along at 3.0 m/s on horizontal, frictionless snow. He suddenly starts down a 10° incline. His speed at the bottom is 15 m/s.

   a. What is the length of the incline?
   b. How long does it take him to reach the bottom?

54. ‖‖ A block slides along the frictionless track shown in Figure P3.54 with an initial speed of 5.0 m/s. Assume it turns all the corners smoothly, with no loss of speed.

FIGURE P3.54

   a. What is the block's speed as it goes over the top?
   b. What is its speed when it reaches the level track on the right side?
   c. By what percentage does the block's final speed differ from its initial speed? Is this surprising?

55. ‖‖ One game at the amusement park has you push a puck up a long, frictionless ramp. You win a stuffed animal if the puck, at its highest point, comes to within 10 cm of the end of the ramp without going off. You give the puck a push, releasing it with a speed of 5.0 m/s when it is 8.5 m from the end of the ramp. The puck's speed after traveling 3.0 m is 4.0 m/s. Are you a winner?

56. ‖‖ When the moving sidewalk at the airport is broken, as it often seems to be, it takes you 50 s to walk from your gate to the baggage claim. When it is working and you stand on the moving sidewalk the entire way, without walking, it takes 75 s to travel the same distance. How long will it take you to travel from the gate to baggage claim if you walk while riding on the moving sidewalk?

57. ‖‖ Ships A and B leave port together. For the next two hours, ship A travels at 20 mph in a direction 30° west of north while ship B travels 20° east of north at 25 mph.

   a. What is the distance between the two ships two hours after they depart?
   b. What is the speed of ship A as seen by ship B?

58. ‖ Mary needs to row her boat across a 100-m-wide river that is flowing to the east at a speed of 1.0 m/s. Mary can row the boat with a speed of 2.0 m/s relative to the water.

   a. If Mary rows straight north, how far downstream will she land?
   b. Draw a picture showing Mary's displacement due to rowing, her displacement due to the river's motion, and her net displacement.

59. ‖ A flock of ducks is trying to migrate south for the winter, but they keep being blown off course by a wind blowing from the west at 12 m/s. A wise elder duck finally realizes that the solution is to fly at an angle to the wind. If the ducks can fly at 16 m/s relative to the air, in what direction should they head in order to move directly south?

60. ||| A kayaker needs to paddle north across a 100-m-wide harbor. The tide is going out, creating a tidal current flowing east at 2.0 m/s. The kayaker can paddle with a speed of 3.0 m/s.
    a. In which direction should he paddle in order to travel straight across the harbor?
    b. How long will it take him to cross?

61. |||| A plane has an airspeed of 200 mph. The pilot wishes to reach a destination 600 mi due east, but a wind is blowing at 50 mph in the direction 30° north of east.
    a. In what direction must the pilot head the plane in order to reach her destination?
    b. How long will the trip take?

62. ||| The Gulf Stream off the east coast of the United States can flow at a rapid 3.6 m/s to the north. A ship in this current has a cruising speed of 10 m/s. The captain would like to reach land at a point due west from the current position.
    a. In what direction with respect to the water should the ship sail?
    b. At this heading, what is the ship's speed with respect to land?

63. || A physics student on Planet Exidor throws a ball, and it follows the parabolic trajectory shown in Figure P3.63. The ball's position is shown at 1.0 s intervals until $t = 3.0$ s. At $t = 1.0$ s, the ball's velocity has components $v_x = 2.0$ m/s, $v_y = 2.0$ m/s.

FIGURE P3.63

    a. Determine the x- and y-components of the ball's velocity at $t = 0.0$ s, 2.0 s, and 3.0 s.
    b. What is the value of g on Planet Exidor?
    c. What was the ball's launch angle?

64. ||| A ball thrown horizontally at 25 m/s travels a horizontal distance of 50 m before hitting the ground. From what height was the ball thrown?

65. ||| In 1780, in what is now referred
BIO to as "Brady's Leap," Captain Sam Brady of the U.S. Continental Army escaped certain death from his enemies by running over the edge of the cliff above Ohio's Cuyahoga River, which is confined at that spot to a gorge. He landed safely on the far side of the river. It was reported that he leapt 22 ft across while falling 20 ft.

FIGURE P3.65

    a. Representing the distance jumped as L and the vertical drop as h, as shown in Figure P3.65, derive an expression for the minimum speed v he would need to make his leap if he ran straight off the cliff.
    b. Evaluate your expression for a 22 ft jump with a 20 ft drop to the other side.
    c. Is it reasonable that a person could make this leap? Use the fact that the world record for the 100 m dash is approximately 10 s to estimate the maximum speed such a runner would have.

66. ||| The longest recorded pass in an NFL game traveled 83 yards in the air from the quarterback to the receiver. Assuming that the pass was thrown at the optimal 45° angle, what was the speed at which the ball left the quarterback's hand?

67. ||| A spring-loaded gun, fired vertically, shoots a marble 6.0 m straight up in the air. What is the marble's range if it is fired horizontally from 1.5 m above the ground?

68. || In a shot-put event, an athlete throws the shot with an initial speed of 12.0 m/s at a 40.0° angle from the horizontal. The shot leaves her hand at a height of 1.80 m above the ground.
    a. How far does the shot travel?
    b. Repeat the calculation of part (a) for angles 42.5°, 45.0°, and 47.5°. Put all your results, including 40.0°, in a table. At what angle of release does she throw the farthest?

69. ||| A tennis player hits a ball 2.0 m above the ground. The ball leaves his racquet with a speed of 20 m/s at an angle 5.0° above the horizontal. The horizontal distance to the net is 7.0 m, and the net is 1.0 m high. Does the ball clear the net? If so, by how much? If not, by how much does it miss?

70. |||| Water at the top of Horseshoe Falls (part of Niagara Falls) is moving horizontally at 9.0 m/s as it goes off the edge and plunges 53 m to the pool below. If you ignore air resistance, at what angle is the falling water moving as it enters the pool?

71. ||| Figure 3.37 shows that the range of a projectile launched at a 60° angle has the same range as a projectile launched at a 30° angle—but they won't be in the air for the same amount of time. Suppose a projectile launched at a 30° angle is in the air for 2.0 s. How long will the projectile be in the air if it is launched with the same speed at a 60° angle?

72. || A supply plane needs to drop a package of food to scientists working on a glacier in Greenland. The plane flies 100 m above the glacier at a speed of 150 m/s. How far short of the target should it drop the package?

73. ||| A child slides down a frictionless 3.0-m-long playground slide tilted upward at an angle of 40°. At the end of the slide, there is an additional section that curves so that the child is launched off the end of the slide horizontally.
    a. How fast is the child moving at the bottom of the slide?
    b. If the end of the slide is 0.40 m above the ground, how far from the end does she land?

74. ||| A sports car is advertised to be able to "reach 60 mph in 5 sec-
INT onds flat, corner at 0.85g, and stop from 70 mph in only 168 feet."
    a. In which of those three situations is the magnitude of the car's acceleration the largest? In which is it the smallest?
    b. At 60 mph, what is the smallest turning radius that this car can navigate?

75. || A Ford Mustang can accelerate from 0 to 60 mph in a time of
INT 5.6 s. A Mini Cooper isn't capable of such a rapid start, but it can turn in a very small circle 34 ft in diameter. How fast would you need to drive the Mini Cooper in this tight circle to match the magnitude of the Mustang's acceleration?

76. || The "Screaming Swing" is a carnival ride that is—not surprisingly—a giant swing. It's actually two swings moving in opposite directions. At the bottom of its arc, riders are moving at 30 m/s with respect to the ground in a 50-m-diameter circle.
    a. What is the acceleration, in m/s² and in units of g, that riders experience?
    b. At the bottom of the ride, as they pass each other, how fast do the riders move with respect to each other?

77. || On an otherwise straight stretch of road near Moffat, Colorado, the road suddenly turns. This bend in the road is a segment of a circle with radius 110 m. Drivers are cautioned to slow down to 40 mph as they navigate the curve.
    a. If you heed the sign and slow to 40 mph, what will be your acceleration going around the curve at this constant speed? Give your answer in m/s² and in units of g.
    b. At what speed would your acceleration be double that at the recommended speed?

Passage Problems

Riding the Water Slide

A rider on a water slide goes through three different kinds of motion, as illustrated in Figure P3.78. Use the data and details from the figure to answer the following questions.

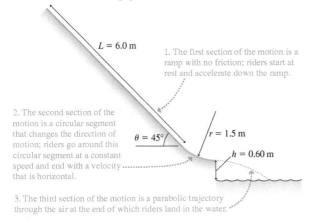

1. The first section of the motion is a ramp with no friction; riders start at rest and accelerate down the ramp.

$L = 6.0$ m

2. The second section of the motion is a circular segment that changes the direction of motion; riders go around this circular segment at a constant speed and end with a velocity that is horizontal.

$\theta = 45°$

$r = 1.5$ m

$h = 0.60$ m

3. The third section of the motion is a parabolic trajectory through the air at the end of which riders land in the water.

FIGURE P3.78

78. | At the end of the first section of the motion, riders are moving at what approximate speed?
    A. 3 m/s   B. 6 m/s   C. 9 m/s   D. 12 m/s

79. | Suppose the acceleration during the second section of the motion is too large to be comfortable for riders. What change could be made to decrease the acceleration during this section?
    A. Reduce the radius of the circular segment.
    B. Increase the radius of the circular segment.
    C. Increase the angle of the ramp.
    D. Increase the length of the ramp.

80. | What is the vertical component of the velocity of a rider as he or she hits the water?
    A. 2.4 m/s   B. 3.4 m/s   C. 5.2 m/s   D. 9.1 m/s

81. | Suppose the designers of the water slide want to adjust the height h above the water so that riders land twice as far away from the bottom of the slide. What would be the necessary height above the water?
    A. 1.2 m   B. 1.8 m   C. 2.4 m   D. 3.0 m

82. | During which section of the motion is the magnitude of the acceleration experienced by a rider the greatest?
    A. The first.   B. The second.
    C. The third.   D. It is the same in all sections.

STOP TO THINK ANSWERS

Stop to Think 3.1: A. The graphical construction of $2\vec{P} - \vec{Q}$ is shown at right.

Stop to Think 3.2: From the axes on the graph, we can see that the x- and y-components are −4 cm and +2 cm, respectively.

$2\vec{P} - \vec{Q}$

$-\vec{Q}$

$2\vec{P}$

Stop to Think 3.3: C. Vector $\vec{C}$ points to the left and down, so both C_x and C_y are negative. C_x is in the numerator because it is the side opposite ϕ.

Stop to Think 3.4: B. The angle of the slope is greatest in this case, leading to the greatest acceleration.

Stop to Think 3.5: D. Mass does not appear in the kinematic equations, so the mass has no effect; the balls will follow the same path.

Stop to Think 3.6: B. The magnitude of the acceleration is v^2/r. Acceleration is largest for the combination of highest speed and smallest radius.

4 Forces and Newton's Laws of Motion

These ice boats sail across the ice at great speeds. What gets the boats moving in the first place? What keeps them moving once they're going?

LOOKING AHEAD ▶

The goal of Chapter 4 is to establish a connection between force and motion.

What Causes Motion?

Galileo was the first to realize that objects in *uniform motion* require no "cause" for their motion. Only *changes* in motion—accelerations—require a cause: a *force*.

What is a Force?

We'll understand force by first examining the properties common to all forces, then by studying a number of forces we'll encounter often.

Forces are a *push* or a *pull*, act on an *object*, and have an identifiable *agent*. Forces are *vectors*.

Looking Back ◀◀
1.5 Vectors and motion

Newton's Third Law

When two objects interact, each exerts a force on the other. Newton's third law tells us that these two forces point in *opposite* directions but have the *same* magnitudes.

The force of the hammer on the nail has the same magnitude as the force of the nail on the hammer.

Some Important Forces

It's important to understand the characteristics of a number of important forces. Some of the forces you'll learn about in this chapter are . . .

Weight
The force of gravity acting on an object.

Spring force
The force exerted by a stretched or compressed spring.

Normal force
A force that a surface exerts on an object.

Newton's Second Law

Newton's second law tells us what forces *do* when applied to an object. We'll find that forces act to *accelerate* objects. We will use Newton's second law throughout this textbook to solve a wide variety of physics problems.

An object's acceleration vector is in the same direction as the net force acting on the object.

Looking Back ◀◀
2.4 Acceleration

Looking Back ◀◀
3.2–3.3 Vectors and coordinate systems

Identifying and Representing Forces

One of the most important skills you'll learn in this chapter is to properly identify the forces that act on an object. Then you'll learn to organize these forces in a *free-body diagram*.

Tension $\vec{T}$

Weight $\vec{w}$

Other than the weight force, all forces acting on an object come from other objects that *touch* it.

We can represent all the forces acting on an object in a free-body diagram.

4.1 What Causes Motion?

The ice boats shown in the chapter-opening photo fly across the frozen lake at some 60 mph. We could use kinematics to describe the boats' motion with pictures, graphs, and equations. Kinematics provides a language to describe *how* something moves, but tells us nothing about *why* the boats accelerate briskly before reaching their top speed. For the more fundamental task of understanding the *cause* of motion, we turn our attention to **dynamics.** Dynamics joins with kinematics to form **mechanics,** the general science of motion. We study dynamics qualitatively in this chapter, then develop it quantitatively in the next four chapters.

As we remarked in Chapter 1, Aristotle (384–322 BC) and his contemporaries in the world of ancient Greece were very interested in motion. One question they asked was: What is the "natural state" of an object if left to itself? It does not take an expensive research program to see that every moving object on earth, if left to itself, eventually comes to rest. You must push a shopping cart to keep it rolling, but when you stop pushing, the cart soon comes to rest; a boulder bounds downhill and then tumbles to a halt. Having observed many such examples himself, Aristotle concluded that the natural state of an earthly object is to be *at rest*. An object at rest requires no explanation; it is doing precisely what comes naturally to it. We'll soon see, however, that this simple viewpoint is *incomplete*.

Aristotle further pondered moving objects. A moving object is *not* in its natural state and thus requires an explanation: Why is this object moving? What keeps it going and prevents it from being in its natural state? When a puck is sliding across the ice, what keeps it going? Why does an arrow fly through the air once it is no longer being pushed by the bowstring? Although these questions seem like reasonable ones to pose, it was Galileo who first showed that the questions being asked were, in fact, the wrong ones.

Galileo reopened the question of the "natural state" of objects. He suggested focusing on the *idealized case* in which resistance to the motion (e.g., friction or air resistance) is zero. He performed many experiments to study motion. Let's imagine a modern experiment of this kind, as shown in FIGURE 4.1.

The rocks in this rockslide quickly came to rest. Is this the "natural state" of objects?

FIGURE 4.1 Sleds sliding on increasingly smooth surfaces.

(a) Smooth snow

On smooth snow, the sled soon comes to rest.

(b) Slick ice

On slick ice, the sled slides farther.

(c) Frictionless surface

If friction could be reduced to zero, the sled would *never* stop.

▶ **Interstellar coasting** A nearly perfect example of Newton's first law is the pair of Voyager space probes launched in 1977. Both spacecraft long ago ran out of fuel and are now coasting through the frictionless vacuum of space. Although not entirely free of influence from the sun's gravity, they are now so far from the sun and other stars that gravitational influences are very nearly zero. Thus, according to the first law, they will continue at their current speed of about 40,000 miles per hour essentially forever. Billions of years from now, long after our solar system is dead, the Voyagers will still be drifting through the stars.

Getting the ketchup out The ketchup stuck at the bottom of the bottle is initially at rest. If you hit the bottom of the bottle, the bottle suddenly moves down, taking the ketchup on the bottom of the bottle with it, so that the ketchup just stays stuck to the bottom. But if instead you hit *up* on the bottle, as shown, you force the bottle rapidly upward. By the first law, the ketchup that was stuck to the bottom stays at rest, so it separates from the upward-moving bottle: The ketchup has moved forward with respect to the bottle!

FIGURE 4.2 Newton's first law tells us: Wear your seatbelts!

At the instant of impact, the car and driver are moving at the same speed.

The car slows as it hits, but the driver continues at the same speed . . .

. . . until he hits the now-stationary dashboard. Ouch!

Tyler slides down a hill on his sled, then out onto a horizontal patch of smooth snow, which is shown in Figure 4.1a. Even if the snow is quite smooth, the friction between the sled and the snow will soon cause the sled to come to rest. What if Tyler slides down the hill onto some very slick ice, as in Figure 4.1b? This gives very low friction, and the sled could slide for quite a distance before stopping. Galileo's genius was to imagine the case where *all* sources of friction, air resistance, and other retarding influences were removed, as for the sled in Figure 4.1c sliding on idealized *frictionless* ice. We can imagine in that case that the sled, once started in its motion, would continue in its motion *forever,* moving in a straight line with no loss of speed. In other words, **the natural state of an object—its behavior if free of external influences—is** *uniform motion* **with constant velocity!** Further, "at rest" has no special significance in Galileo's view of motion; it is simply uniform motion that happens to have a velocity of zero. This implies that an object at rest, in the absence of external influences, will remain at rest forever.

Galileo's ideas were completely counter to those of the ancient Greeks. We no longer need to explain why a sled continues to slide across the ice; that motion is its "natural" state. What needs explanation, in this new viewpoint, is why objects *don't* continue in uniform motion. Why does a sliding puck eventually slow to a stop? Why does a stone, thrown upward, slow and eventually fall back down? Galileo's new viewpoint was that the stone and the puck are *not* free of "influences": The stone is somehow pulled toward the earth, and some sort of retarding influence acted to slow the sled down. Today, we call such influences that lead to deviations from uniform motion **forces.**

Galileo's experiments were limited to motion along horizontal surfaces. It was left to Newton to generalize Galileo's conclusions, and today we call this generalization Newton's first law of motion.

> **Newton's first law** Consider an object with no force acting on it. If it is at rest, it will remain at rest; if it is moving, it will continue to move in a straight line at a constant speed.

As an important application of Newton's first law, consider the crash test of FIGURE 4.2. As the car contacts the wall, the wall exerts a force on the car and it begins to slow. But the wall is a force on the *car,* not on the dummy. In accordance with Newton's first law, the unbelted dummy continues to move straight ahead at his original speed. Only when he collides violently with the dashboard of the stopped car is there a force acting to halt the dummy's uniform motion. If he had been wearing a seatbelt, the influence (i.e., the force) of the seatbelt would have slowed the dummy at the much lower rate at which the car slows down. We'll study the forces of collisions in detail in Chapter 10.

4.2 Force

Newton's first law tells us that an object in motion subject to no forces will continue to move in a straight line forever. But this law does not explain in any detail exactly what a force *is.* Unfortunately, there is no simple one-sentence definition of force. The concept of force is best introduced by looking at examples of some common forces and considering the basic properties shared by all forces. This will be our task in the next two sections. Let's begin by examining the properties that all forces have in common, as presented in the table on the next page.

What is a force?

A force is a push or a pull.

Our commonsense idea of a **force** is that it is a *push* or a *pull*. We will refine this idea as we go along, but it is an adequate starting point. Notice our careful choice of words: We refer to "*a* force" rather than simply "force." We want to think of a force as a very specific *action,* so that we can talk about a single force or perhaps about two or three individual forces that we can clearly distinguish—hence the concrete idea of "a force" acting on an object.

A force acts on an object.

Implicit in our concept of force is that **a force acts on an object.** In other words, pushes and pulls are applied *to* something—an object. From the object's perspective, it has a force *exerted* on it. Forces do not exist in isolation from the object that experiences them.

A force requires an agent.

Every force has an **agent,** something that acts or pushes or pulls; that is, a force has a specific, identifiable *cause.* As you throw a ball, it is your hand, while in contact with the ball, that is the agent or the cause of the force exerted on the ball. *If* a force is being exerted on an object, you must be able to identify a specific cause (i.e., the agent) of that force. Conversely, a force is not exerted on an object *unless* you can identify a specific cause or agent. Note that an agent can be an inert object such as a tabletop or a wall. Such agents are the cause of many common forces.

A force is a vector.

If you push an object, you can push either gently or very hard. Similarly, you can push either left or right, up or down. To quantify a push, we need to specify both a magnitude *and* a direction. It should thus come as no surprise that a force is a vector quantity. The general symbol for a force is the vector symbol $\vec{F}$. The size or strength of such a force is its magnitude F.

A force can be either a contact force . . .

There are two basic classes of forces, depending on whether the agent touches the object or not. **Contact forces** are forces that act on an object by touching it at a point of contact. The bat must touch the ball to hit it. A string must be tied to an object to pull it. The majority of forces that we will examine are contact forces.

. . . or a long-range force.

Long-range forces are forces that act on an object without physical contact. Magnetism is an example of a long-range force. You have undoubtedly held a magnet over a paper clip and seen the paper clip leap up to the magnet. A coffee cup released from your hand is pulled to the earth by the long-range force of gravity.

Let's summarize these ideas as our definition of force:

- A force is a push or a pull on an object.
- A force is a vector. It has both a magnitude and a direction.
- A force requires an agent. Something does the pushing or pulling. The agent can be an inert object such as a tabletop or a wall.
- A force is either a contact force or a long-range force. Gravity is the only long-range force we will deal with until much later in the book.

There's one more important aspect of forces. If you push against a door (the object) to close it, the door pushes back against your hand (the agent). If a tow rope pulls on a car (the object), the car pulls back on the rope (the agent). In general, if an agent exerts a force on an object, the object exerts a force on the agent. We really need to think of a force as an *interaction* between two objects. Although the interaction perspective is a more exact way to view forces, it adds complications that we would like to avoid for now. Our approach will be to start by focusing on how a single object responds to forces exerted on it. Later in this chapter, we'll return to the larger issue of how two or more objects interact with each other.

Force Vectors

We can use a simple diagram to visualize how forces are exerted on objects. Because we are using the particle model, in which objects are treated as points, the process of drawing a force vector is straightforward. Here is how it goes:

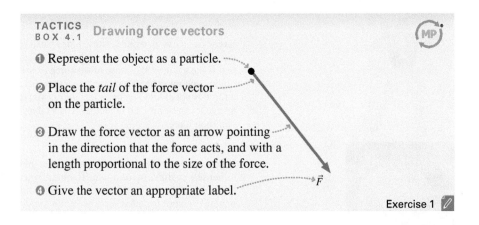

TACTICS BOX 4.1   Drawing force vectors

❶ Represent the object as a particle.

❷ Place the *tail* of the force vector on the particle.

❸ Draw the force vector as an arrow pointing in the direction that the force acts, and with a length proportional to the size of the force.

❹ Give the vector an appropriate label.

$\vec{F}$

Exercise 1

Step 2 may seem contrary to what a "push" should do (it may look as if the force arrow is *pulling* the object rather than *pushing* it), but recall that moving a vector does not change it as long as the length and angle do not change. The vector $\vec{F}$ is the same regardless of whether the tail or the tip is placed on the particle. Our reason for using the tail will become clear when we consider how to combine several forces.

FIGURE 4.3 shows three examples of force vectors. One is a pull, one a push, and one a long-range force, but in all three the *tail* of the force vector is placed on the particle representing the object.

FIGURE 4.3 Three force vectors.

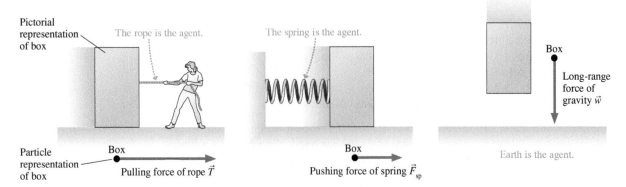

Combining Forces

FIGURE 4.4a shows a top view of a box being pulled by two ropes, each exerting a force on the box. How will the box respond? Experimentally, we find that when several forces $\vec{F}_1, \vec{F}_2, \vec{F}_3, \ldots$ are exerted on an object, they combine to form a **net force** that is the *vector* sum of all the forces:

$$\vec{F}_{\text{net}} = \vec{F}_1 + \vec{F}_2 + \vec{F}_3 + \cdots \tag{4.1}$$

That is, the single force $\vec{F}_{\text{net}}$ causes the exact same motion of the object as the combination of original forces $\vec{F}_1, \vec{F}_2, \vec{F}_3, \ldots$. Mathematically, this summation is called a *superposition* of forces. The net force is sometimes called the *resultant force*. FIGURE 4.4b shows the net force on the box.

> **NOTE** ▶ It is important to realize that the net force $\vec{F}_{\text{net}}$ is not a new force acting *in addition* to the original forces $\vec{F}_1, \vec{F}_2, \vec{F}_3, \ldots$. Instead, we should think of the original forces being *replaced* by $\vec{F}_{\text{net}}$. ◀

FIGURE 4.4 Two forces applied to a box.

(a)

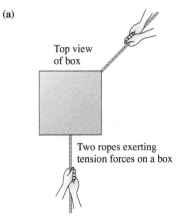

Top view of box

Two ropes exerting tension forces on a box

(b)

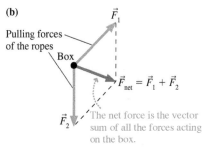

Pulling forces of the ropes

Box

$\vec{F}_{\text{net}} = \vec{F}_1 + \vec{F}_2$

The net force is the vector sum of all the forces acting on the box.

STOP TO THINK 4.1 Two of the three forces exerted on an object are shown. The net force points directly to the left. Which is the missing third force?

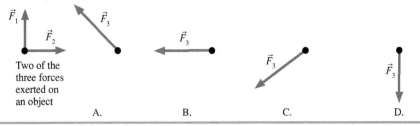

Two of the three forces exerted on an object

A.　　B.　　C.　　D.

4.3 A Short Catalog of Forces

There are many forces we will deal with over and over. This section will introduce you to some of them and to the symbols we use to represent them.

Weight

A falling rock is pulled toward the earth by the long-range force of gravity. Gravity is what keeps you in your chair, keeps the planets in their orbits around the sun, and shapes the large-scale structure of the universe. We'll have a thorough look at gravity in Chapter 6. For now we'll concentrate on objects on or near the surface of the earth (or other planet).

The gravitational pull of the earth on an object on or near the surface of the earth is called **weight.** The symbol for weight is $\vec{w}$. Weight is the only long-range force we will encounter in the next few chapters. The agent for the weight force is the *entire earth* pulling on an object. The weight force is in some ways the simplest force we'll study. As FIGURE 4.5 shows, **an object's weight vector always points vertically downward,** no matter how the object is moving.

> **NOTE** ▶ We often refer to "the weight" of an object. This is an informal expression for w, the magnitude of the weight force exerted on the object. Note that **weight is not the same thing as mass.** We will briefly examine mass later in the chapter and explore the connection between weight and mass in Chapter 5. ◀

FIGURE 4.5 Weight always points vertically downward.

Free fall, moving up

Free fall, moving down

Projectile motion

$\vec{w}$

Rolling　　At rest

Springs come in many forms. When deflected, they push or pull with a spring force.

Spring Force

Springs exert one of the most basic contact forces. A spring can either push (when compressed) or pull (when stretched). FIGURE 4.6 shows the **spring force.** In both cases, pushing and pulling, the tail of the force vector is placed on the particle in the force diagram. There is no special symbol for a spring force, so we simply use a subscript label: $\vec{F}_{sp}$.

FIGURE 4.6 The spring force is parallel to the spring.

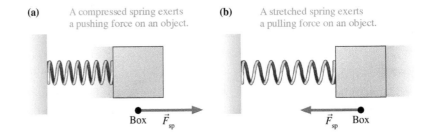

(a) A compressed spring exerts a pushing force on an object.

(b) A stretched spring exerts a pulling force on an object.

Box $\vec{F}_{sp}$

$\vec{F}_{sp}$ Box

Although you may think of a spring as a metal coil that can be stretched or compressed, this is only one type of spring. Hold a ruler, or any other thin piece of wood or metal, by the ends and bend it slightly. It flexes. When you let go, it "springs" back to its original shape. This is just as much a spring as is a metal coil.

Tension Force

FIGURE 4.7 Tension is parallel to the rope.

The rope exerts a tension force on the sled.

Sled $\vec{T}$

When a string or rope or wire pulls on an object, it exerts a contact force that we call the **tension force,** represented by $\vec{T}$. **The direction of the tension force is always in the direction of the string or rope,** as you can see in FIGURE 4.7. When we speak of "the tension" in a string, this is an informal expression for T, the size or magnitude of the tension force. Note that the tension force can only *pull* in the direction of the string; if you try to *push* with a string, it will go slack and be unable to exert a force.

We can think about the tension force using a microscopic picture. If you were to use a very powerful microscope to look inside a rope, you would "see" that it is made of *atoms* joined together by *molecular bonds.* Molecular bonds are not rigid connections between the atoms. They are more accurately thought of as tiny *springs* holding the atoms together, as in FIGURE 4.8. Pulling on the ends of a string or rope stretches the molecular springs ever so slightly. The tension within a rope and the tension force experienced by an object at the end of the rope are really the net spring force exerted by billions and billions of microscopic springs.

This atomic-level view of tension introduces a new idea: a microscopic **atomic model** for understanding the behavior and properties of **macroscopic** (i.e., containing many atoms) objects. We will frequently use atomic models to obtain a deeper understanding of our observations.

The atomic model of tension also helps to explain one of the basic properties of ropes and strings. When you pull on a rope tied to a heavy box, the rope in turn exerts a tension force on the box. If you pull harder, the tension force on the box becomes greater. How does the box "know" that you are pulling harder on the other end of the rope? According to our atomic model, when you pull harder on the rope, its microscopic springs stretch a bit more, increasing the spring force they exert on each other—and on the box they're attached to.

FIGURE 4.8 An atomic model of tension.

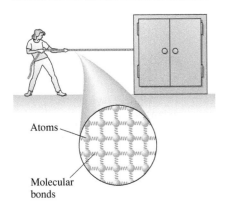

Atoms

Molecular bonds

Normal Force

If you sit on a bed, the springs in the mattress compress and, as a consequence of the compression, exert an upward force on you. Stiffer springs would show less compression but would still exert an upward force. The compression of extremely stiff springs might be measurable only by sensitive instruments. Nonetheless, the springs would compress ever so slightly and exert an upward spring force on you.

FIGURE 4.9 shows a book resting on top of a sturdy table. The table may not visibly flex or sag, but—just as you do to the bed—the book compresses the molecular springs in the table. The compression is very small, but it is not zero. As a consequence, the compressed molecular springs *push upward* on the book. We say that "the table" exerts the upward force, but it is important to understand that the pushing is *really* done by molecular springs. Similarly, an object resting on the ground compresses the molecular springs holding the ground together and, as a consequence, the ground pushes up on the object.

We can extend this idea. Suppose you place your hand on a wall and lean against it, as shown in FIGURE 4.10. Does the wall exert a force on your hand? As you lean, you compress the molecular springs in the wall and, as a consequence, they push outward *against* your hand. So the answer is Yes, the wall does exert a force on you. It's not hard to see this if you examine your hand as you lean: You can see that your hand is slightly deformed, and becomes more so the harder you lean. This deformation is direct evidence of the force that the wall exerts on your hand. Consider also what would happen if the wall suddenly vanished. Without the wall there to push against you, you would topple forward.

The force the table surface exerts is vertical, while the force the wall exerts is horizontal. In all cases, the force exerted on an object that is pressing against a surface is in a direction *perpendicular* to the surface. Mathematicians refer to a line that is perpendicular to a surface as being *normal* to the surface. In keeping with this terminology, we define the **normal force** as the force exerted by a surface (the agent) against an object that is pressing against the surface. The symbol for the normal force is $\vec{n}$.

We're not using the word "normal" to imply that the force is an "ordinary" force or to distinguish it from an "abnormal force." A surface exerts a force *perpendicular* (i.e., normal) to itself as the molecular springs press *outward*. FIGURE 4.11 shows an object on an inclined surface, a common situation. Notice how the normal force $\vec{n}$ is perpendicular to the surface.

The normal force is a very real force arising from the very real compression of molecular bonds. It is in essence just a spring force, but one exerted by a vast number of microscopic springs acting at once. The normal force is responsible for the "solidness" of solids. It is what prevents you from passing right through the chair you are sitting in and what causes the pain and the lump if you bang your head into a door. Your head can then tell you that the force exerted on it by the door was very real!

Friction

You've certainly observed that a rolling or sliding object, if not pushed or propelled, slows down and eventually stops. You've probably discovered that you can slide better across a sheet of ice than across asphalt. And you also know that most objects stay in place on a table without sliding off even if the table is tilted a bit. The force responsible for these sorts of behavior is **friction.** The symbol for friction is $\vec{f}$.

Friction, like the normal force, is exerted by a surface. Unlike the normal force, however, **the frictional force is always *parallel* to the surface,** not perpendicular to it. (In many cases, a surface will exert *both* a normal and a frictional force.) On a microscopic level, friction arises as atoms from the object and atoms on the surface run into each other. The rougher the surface is, the more these atoms are forced into close proximity and, as a result, the larger the friction force. We will develop a

FIGURE 4.9 An atomic model of the force exerted by a table.

The compressed molecular springs push upward on the object.

Atoms

Molecular bonds

FIGURE 4.10 The wall pushes outward against your hand.

The compressed molecular springs in the wall press outward against her hand.

FIGURE 4.11 The normal force is perpendicular to the surface.

$\vec{n}$

Skier

The surface pushes outward against the bottom of the skis. The force is perpendicular to the surface.

simple model of friction in the next chapter that will be sufficient for our needs. For now, it is useful to distinguish between two kinds of friction:

■ *Kinetic friction,* denoted $\vec{f}_k$, acts as an object slides across a surface. Kinetic friction is a force that always "opposes the motion," meaning that the friction force $\vec{f}_k$ on a sliding object points in the direction opposite the direction of the object's motion.

■ *Static friction,* denoted $\vec{f}_s$, is the force that keeps an object "stuck" on a surface and prevents its motion relative to the surface. Finding the direction of $\vec{f}_s$ is a little trickier than finding it for $\vec{f}_k$. Static friction points opposite the direction in which the object *would* move if there were no friction. That is, it points in the direction necessary to *prevent* motion.

FIGURE 4.12 shows examples of kinetic and static friction.

FIGURE 4.12 Kinetic and static friction are parallel to the surface.

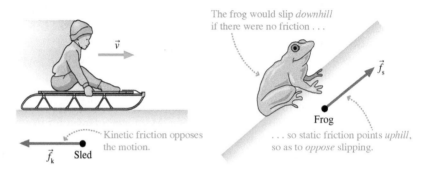

Drag

Friction at a surface is one example of a *resistive force,* a force that opposes or resists motion. Resistive forces are also experienced by objects moving through *fluids*—gases (like air) and liquids (like water). This kind of resistive force—the force of a fluid on a moving object—is called **drag** and is symbolized as $\vec{D}$. Like kinetic friction, **drag points opposite the direction of motion.** FIGURE 4.13 shows an example of drag.

Drag can be a large force for objects moving at high speeds or in dense fluids. Hold your arm out the window as you ride in a car and feel how hard the air pushes against your arm; note also how the air resistance against your arm increases rapidly as the car's speed increases. Drop a lightweight bead into a beaker of water and watch how slowly it settles to the bottom. The drag force of the water on the bead is significant.

On the other hand, for objects that are heavy and compact, moving in air, and with a speed that is not too great, the drag force of air resistance is fairly small. To keep things as simple as possible, **you can neglect air resistance in all problems unless a problem explicitly asks you to include it.** The error introduced into calculations by this approximation is generally pretty small.

FIGURE 4.13 Air resistance is an example of drag.

Air resistance is a significant force on falling leaves. It points opposite the direction of motion.

Thrust

A jet airplane obviously has a force that propels it forward; likewise for the rocket in FIGURE 4.14. This force, called **thrust,** occurs when a jet or rocket engine expels gas molecules at high speed. Thrust is a contact force, with the exhaust gas being the agent that pushes on the engine. The process by which thrust is generated is rather subtle and requires an appreciation of Newton's third law, introduced later in this

FIGURE 4.14 The thrust force on a rocket is opposite the direction of the expelled gases.

Thrust force is exerted on a rocket by exhaust gases.

chapter. For now, we need only consider that **thrust is a force opposite the direction in which the exhaust gas is expelled.** There's no special symbol for thrust, so we will call it $\vec{F}_{\text{thrust}}$.

Electric and Magnetic Forces

Electricity and magnetism, like gravity, exert long-range forces. The forces of electricity and magnetism act on charged particles. We will study electric and magnetic forces in detail in Part VI of this book. For now, it is worth noting that the forces holding molecules together—the molecular bonds—are not actually tiny springs. Atoms and molecules are made of charged particles—electrons and protons—and what we call a molecular bond is really an electric force between these particles. So when we say that the normal force and the tension force are due to "molecular springs," or that friction is due to atoms running into each other, what we're really saying is that these forces, at the most fundamental level, are actually electric forces between the charged particles in the atoms.

It's a drag At the high speeds attained by racing cyclists, air drag can become very significant. The world record for the longest distance traveled in one hour on an ordinary bicycle is 56.38 km, set by Chris Boardman in 1996. But a bicycle with an aerodynamic shell has a much lower drag force, allowing it to attain significantly higher speeds. The bike shown here was pedaled 84.22 km in one hour by Sam Whittingham in 2004, for an amazing average speed of 52.3 mph!

4.4 Identifying Forces

Force and motion problems generally have two basic steps:

1. Identify all of the forces acting on an object.
2. Use Newton's laws and kinematics to determine the motion.

Understanding the first step is the primary goal of this chapter. We'll turn our attention to step 2 in the next chapter.

A typical physics problem describes an object that is being pushed and pulled in various directions. Some forces are given explicitly, while others are only implied. In order to proceed, it is necessary to determine all the forces that act on the object. It is also necessary to avoid including forces that do not really exist. Now that you have learned the properties of forces and seen a catalog of typical forces, we can develop a step-by-step method for identifying each force in a problem. A list of the most common forces we'll come across in the next few chapters is given in Table 4.1.

TABLE 4.1 Common forces and their notation

Force	Notation
General force	$\vec{F}$
Weight	$\vec{w}$
Spring force	$\vec{F}_{\text{sp}}$
Tension	$\vec{T}$
Normal force	$\vec{n}$
Static friction	$\vec{f}_{\text{s}}$
Kinetic friction	$\vec{f}_{\text{k}}$
Drag	$\vec{D}$
Thrust	$\vec{F}_{\text{thrust}}$

TACTICS
BOX 4.2 Identifying forces

❶ **Identify the object of interest.** This is the object whose motion you wish to study.

❷ **Draw a picture of the situation.** Show the object of interest and all other objects—such as ropes, springs, and surfaces—that touch it.

❸ **Draw a closed curve around the object.** Only the object of interest is inside the curve; everything else is outside.

❹ **Locate every point on the boundary of this curve where other objects touch the object of interest.** These are the points where *contact forces* are exerted on the object.

❺ **Name and label each contact force acting on the object.** There is at least one force at each point of contact; there may be more than one. When necessary, use subscripts to distinguish forces of the same type.

❻ **Name and label each long-range force acting on the object.** For now, the only long-range force is weight.

Exercises 4–8

Class Video

CONCEPTUAL EXAMPLE 4.1   **Identifying forces on a bungee jumper**

A bungee jumper has leapt off a bridge and is nearing the bottom of her fall. What forces are being exerted on the bungee jumper?

REASON   **FIGURE 4.15** Forces on a bungee jumper.

❶ Identify the object of interest. Here the object is the bungee jumper.

❷ Draw a picture of the situation.

❸ Draw a closed curve around the object.

❹ Locate the points where other objects touch the object of interest. Here the only point of contact is where the cord attaches to her ankles.

❺ Name and label each contact force. The force exerted by the cord is a tension force.

❻ Name and label long-range forces. Weight is the only one.

CONCEPTUAL EXAMPLE 4.2   **Identifying forces on a skier**

A skier is being towed up a snow-covered hill by a tow rope. What forces are being exerted on the skier?

REASON   **FIGURE 4.16** Forces on a skier.

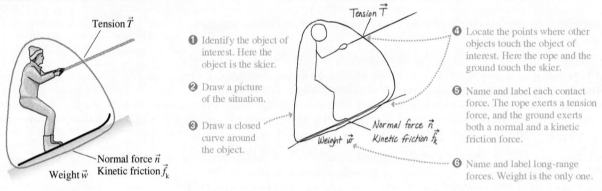

❶ Identify the object of interest. Here the object is the skier.

❷ Draw a picture of the situation.

❸ Draw a closed curve around the object.

❹ Locate the points where other objects touch the object of interest. Here the rope and the ground touch the skier.

❺ Name and label each contact force. The rope exerts a tension force, and the ground exerts both a normal and a kinetic friction force.

❻ Name and label long-range forces. Weight is the only one.

NOTE ▶ You might have expected two friction forces and two normal forces in Example 4.2, one on each ski. Keep in mind, however, that we're working within the particle model, which represents the skier by a single point. A particle has only one contact with the ground, so there is a single normal force and a single friction force. The particle model is valid if we want to analyze the motion of the skier as a whole, but we would have to go beyond the particle model to find out what happens to each ski. ◀

CONCEPTUAL EXAMPLE 4.3   **Identifying forces on a rocket**

A rocket is being launched to place a new satellite in orbit. Air resistance is not negligible. What forces are being exerted on the rocket?

REASON

FIGURE 4.17 Forces on a rocket.

STOP TO THINK 4.2 You've just kicked a rock, and it is now sliding across the ground about 2 meters in front of you. Which of these are forces acting on the rock? List all that apply.

A. Gravity, acting downward   B. The normal force, acting upward
C. The force of the kick, acting in the direction of motion
D. Friction, acting opposite the direction of motion
E. Air resistance, acting opposite the direction of motion

4.5 What Do Forces Do?

The fundamental question is: How does an object move when a force is exerted on it? The only way to answer this question is to do experiments. To do experiments, however, we need a way to reproduce the same force again and again, and we need a standard object so that our experiments are repeatable.

FIGURE 4.18 shows how you can use your fingers to stretch a rubber band to a certain length—say, 10 centimeters—that you can measure with a ruler. We'll call this the *standard length.* You know that a stretched rubber band exerts a force because your fingers *feel* the pull. Furthermore, this is a reproducible force. The rubber band exerts the same force every time you stretch it to the standard length. We'll call the magnitude of this force the *standard force F.* Not surprisingly, two identical rubber bands, each stretched to the standard length, exert twice the force of one rubber band; three rubber bands exert three times the force; and so on.

We'll also need several identical standard objects to which the force will be applied. As we learned in Chapter 1, the SI unit of mass is the kilogram (kg). The kilogram is defined in terms of a particular metal block kept in a vault in Paris. For our standard objects, we will make ourselves several identical copies, each with, by definition, a mass of 1 kg. At this point, you can think of mass as the "quantity of matter" in an object. This idea will suffice for now, but by the end of this section, we'll be able to give a more precise meaning to the concept of mass.

Now we're ready to start the virtual experiment. First, place one of the 1 kg blocks on a frictionless surface. (In a real experiment, we can nearly eliminate friction by floating the block on a cushion of air.) Second, attach a rubber band to the block and stretch the band to the standard length. Then the block experiences the same force *F* as your finger did. As the block starts to move, in order to keep the pulling force constant you must *move your hand* in just the right way to keep the length of the rubber band—and thus the force—*constant.* FIGURE 4.19 shows the experiment being carried out. Once the motion is complete, you can use motion diagrams and kinematics to analyze the block's motion.

FIGURE 4.18 **A reproducible force.**

One rubber band
stretched the standard
length exerts the
standard force *F*.

Two rubber bands
stretched the standard
length exert twice
the standard force.

FIGURE 4.19 **Measuring the motion of a 1 kg block that is pulled with a constant force.**

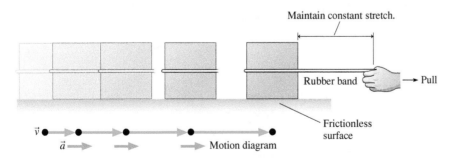

The motion diagram in Figure 4.19 shows that the velocity vectors are getting longer, so the velocity is increasing: The block is *accelerating.* Furthermore, a close inspection of the motion diagram shows that the acceleration vectors are all the same length. This is the first important finding of this experiment: **An object pulled with**

FIGURE 4.20 Graph of acceleration versus force.

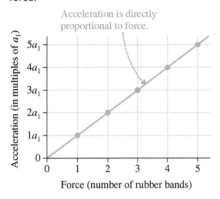

FIGURE 4.21 Graph of acceleration versus number of blocks.

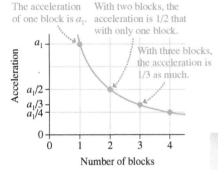

a constant force moves with a constant acceleration. This finding could not have been anticipated in advance. It's conceivable that the object would speed up for a while and then move with a steady speed. Or that it would continue to speed up, but that the *rate* of increase, the acceleration, would steadily decline. But these descriptions do not match what happens. Instead, the object continues *with a constant acceleration* for as long as you pull it with a constant force. We'll call this constant acceleration of *one* block pulled by *one* band a_1.

What happens if you increase the force by using several rubber bands? To find out, use two rubber bands. Stretch both to the standard length to double the force to $2F$, then measure the acceleration. Measure the acceleration due to three rubber bands, then four, and so on. FIGURE 4.20 is a graph of the results. Force is the independent variable, the one you can control, so we've placed force on the horizontal axis to make an acceleration-versus-force graph. The graph reveals our second important finding: **Acceleration is directly proportional to force.**

The final question for our virtual experiment is: How does the acceleration of an object depend on the mass of the object, the "quantity of matter" that it contains? To find out, we'll glue two of our 1 kg blocks together, so that we have a block with twice as much matter as a 1 kg block—that is, a 2 kg block. Now apply the same force—a single rubber band—as you applied to the single 1 kg block. FIGURE 4.21 shows that the acceleration is *one-half* as great as that of the single block. If we glue three blocks together, making a 3 kg object, we find that the acceleration is only *one-third* of the 1 kg block's acceleration. In general, we find that the acceleration is proportional to the *inverse* of the mass of the object. So our third important result is: **Acceleration is *inversely proportional* to an object's mass.**

Inversely proportional relationships

Two quantities are said to be **inversely proportional** to each other if one quantity is proportional to the *inverse* of the other. Mathematically, this means that

$$y = \frac{A}{x}$$

y is inversely proportional to *x*

Here, A is a proportionality constant. This relationship is sometimes written as $y \propto 1/x$.

SCALING
- If you double x, you halve y.
- If you triple x, y is reduced by a factor of 3.
- If you halve x, y doubles.
- If you reduce x by a factor of 3, y becomes 3 times as large.

RATIOS For any two values of x—say, x_1 and x_2—we have

$$y_1 = \frac{A}{x_1} \quad \text{and} \quad y_2 = \frac{A}{x_2}$$

Dividing the y_1 equation by the y_2 equation, we find

$$\frac{y_1}{y_2} = \frac{A/x_1}{A/x_2} = \frac{A}{x_1} \frac{x_2}{A} = \frac{x_2}{x_1}$$

That is, the ratio of y-values is the inverse of the ratio of the corresponding values of x.

LIMITS
- As x gets very large, y approaches zero.
- As x approaches zero, y gets very large.

Exercise 10

Our original idea of mass was that it was a measure of the "quantity of matter" that an object contains. Now we see that a more precise way of defining the mass of an object is in terms of its *acceleration*. You're familiar with this idea: It's much harder to get your car rolling by pushing it than to get your bicycle rolling; it's harder to stop a heavily loaded grocery cart than to stop a skateboard. This tendency to resist a change in velocity (i.e., to resist speeding up or slowing down) is called **inertia.** Thus we can say that more massive objects have more inertia.

These considerations allow us to unambiguously determine the mass of an object by measuring its acceleration, as the next example shows.

Feel the difference Because of its high sugar content, a can of regular soda has a mass about 4% greater than that of a can of diet soda. If you try to judge which can is more massive by simply holding one in each hand, this small difference is almost impossible to detect. If you *move* the cans up and down, however, the difference becomes subtly but noticeably apparent: People evidently are more sensitive to how the mass of each can resists acceleration than they are to the cans' weights alone.

EXAMPLE 4.4 **Finding the mass of an unknown block**

When a rubber band is stretched to pull on a 1.0 kg block with a constant force, the acceleration of the block is measured to be 3.0 m/s². When a block with an unknown mass is pulled with the same rubber band, using the same force, its acceleration is 5.0 m/s². What is the mass of the unknown block?

PREPARE Each block's acceleration is inversely proportional to its mass.

SOLVE We can use the result of the Inversely Proportional Relationships box to write

$$\frac{3.0 \text{ m/s}^2}{5.0 \text{ m/s}^2} = \frac{m}{1.0 \text{ kg}}$$

or

$$m = \frac{3.0 \text{ m/s}^2}{5.0 \text{ m/s}^2}(1.0 \text{ kg}) = 0.60 \text{ kg}$$

ASSESS With the same force applied, the unknown block had a *larger* acceleration than the 1.0 kg block. It makes sense, then, that its mass—its resistance to acceleration—is *less* than 1.0 kg.

STOP TO THINK 4.3 Two rubber bands stretched to the standard length cause an object to accelerate at 2 m/s². Suppose another object with twice the mass is pulled by four rubber bands stretched to the standard length. What is the acceleration of this second object?

A. 1 m/s²   B. 2 m/s²   C. 4 m/s²   D. 8 m/s²   E. 16 m/s²

4.6 Newton's Second Law

We can now summarize the results of our experiments. We've seen that **a force causes an object to accelerate. The acceleration *a* is directly proportional to the force *F* and inversely proportional to the mass *m*.** We can express both these relationships in equation form as

$$a = \frac{F}{m} \tag{4.2}$$

Note that if we double the size of the force *F*, the acceleration *a* will double, as we found experimentally. And if we triple the mass *m*, the acceleration will be only one-third as great, again agreeing with experiment.

Equation 4.2 tells us the magnitude of an object's acceleration in terms of its mass and the force applied. But our experiments also had another important finding: The *direction* of the acceleration was the same as the direction of the force. We can express this fact by writing Equation 4.2 in *vector* form as

$$\vec{a} = \frac{\vec{F}}{m} \tag{4.3}$$

Finally, our experiment was limited to looking at an object's response to a *single* applied force acting in a single direction. Realistically, an object is likely to be subjected to several distinct forces $\vec{F}_1, \vec{F}_2, \vec{F}_3, \ldots$ that may point in different directions. What happens then? Experiments show that the acceleration of the object is determined by the *net force* acting on it. Recall from Figure 4.4 and Equation 4.1 that the net force is the *vector sum* of all forces acting on the object. So if several forces are acting, we use the *net* force in Equation 4.4.

Newton was the first to recognize these connections between force and motion. This relationship is known today as Newton's second law.

> **Newton's second law** An object of mass m subjected to forces $\vec{F}_1, \vec{F}_2, \vec{F}_3, \ldots$ will undergo an acceleration $\vec{a}$ given by
>
> $$\vec{a} = \frac{\vec{F}_{net}}{m} \qquad (4.4)$$
>
>
>
> where the net force $\vec{F}_{net} = \vec{F}_1 + \vec{F}_2 + \vec{F}_3 + \cdots$ is the vector sum of all forces acting on the object. **The acceleration vector $\vec{a}$ points in the same direction as the net force vector $\vec{F}_{net}$.**

We'll use Newton's second law in Chapter 5 to solve many kinds of motion problems; for the moment, however, the critical idea is that an object accelerates in the direction of the net force acting on it.

The significance of Newton's second law cannot be overstated. There was no reason to suspect that there should be any simple relationship between force and acceleration. Yet a simple but exceedingly powerful equation relates the two. Newton's work, preceded to some extent by Galileo's, marks the beginning of a highly successful period in the history of science during which it was learned that the behavior of physical objects can often be described and predicted by mathematical relationships. While some relationships are found to apply only in special circumstances, others seem to have universal applicability. Those equations that appear to apply at all times and under all conditions have come to be called "laws of nature." Newton's second law is a law of nature; you will meet others as we go through this book.

We can rewrite Newton's second law in the form

$$\vec{F}_{net} = m\vec{a} \qquad (4.5)$$

which is how you'll see it presented in many textbooks and how, in practice, we'll often use the second law. Equations 4.4 and 4.5 are mathematically equivalent, but Equation 4.4 better describes the central idea of Newtonian mechanics: A force applied to an object causes the object to accelerate.

An unfair advantage? Race car driver Danica Patrick was the subject of controversial comments by other drivers who thought her small mass of 45 kg gave her an advantage over heavier drivers; the next-lightest driver's mass was 61 kg. Because every driver's car must have the same mass, Patrick's overall racing mass was lower than any other driver's. Because a car's acceleration is inversely proportional to its mass, her car could be expected to have a slightly greater acceleration.

NOTE ▶ When several forces act on an object, be careful not to think that the strongest force "overcomes" the others to determine the motion on its own. It is $\vec{F}_{net}$, the sum of *all* the forces, that determines the acceleration $\vec{a}$. ◀

CONCEPTUAL EXAMPLE 4.5   **Acceleration of a wind-blown basketball**

A basketball is released from rest in a stiff breeze directed to the right. In what direction does the ball accelerate?

REASON As shown in **FIGURE 4.22a**, two forces are acting on the ball: its weight $\vec{w}$ directed downward and a wind force $\vec{F}_{wind}$ pushing the ball to the right. Newton's second law tells us that the direction of the acceleration is the same as the direction of the net force $\vec{F}_{net}$. In **FIGURE 4.22b** we find $\vec{F}_{net}$ by graphical vector addition of $\vec{w}$ and $\vec{F}_{wind}$. We see that $\vec{F}_{net}$ and therefore $\vec{a}$ point down and to the right.

FIGURE 4.22 A basketball falling in a strong breeze.

(a) The force of the wind is to the right.

$\vec{F}_{wind}$

The weight force points down.

$\vec{w}$

(b) The acceleration is in the direction of $\vec{F}_{net}$.

$\vec{a}$

$\vec{F}_{net}$

Units of Force

Because $\vec{F}_{net} = m\vec{a}$, the unit of force must be mass units multiplied by acceleration units. We've previously specified the SI unit of mass as the kilogram. We can now define the basic unit of force as "the force that causes a 1 kg mass to accelerate at 1 m/s²." From Newton's second law, this force is

$$1 \text{ basic unit of force} = (1 \text{ kg}) \times (1 \text{ m/s}^2) = 1 \frac{\text{kg} \cdot \text{m}}{\text{s}^2}$$

This basic unit of force is called a *newton:* One **newton** is the force that causes a 1 kg mass to accelerate at 1 m/s². The abbreviation for newton is N. Mathematically, $1 \text{ N} = 1 \text{ kg} \cdot \text{m/s}^2$.

The newton is a *secondary unit,* meaning that it is defined in terms of the *primary units* of kilograms, meters, and seconds. We will introduce other secondary units as needed.

It is important to develop a feeling for what the size of forces should be. Table 4.2 lists some typical forces. As you can see, "typical" forces on "typical" objects are likely to be in the range 0.01–10,000 N. Forces less than 0.01 N are too small to consider unless you are dealing with very small objects. Forces greater than 10,000 N would make sense only if applied to very massive objects.

The unit of force in the English system is the *pound* (abbreviated lb). Although the definition of the pound has varied throughout history, it is now defined in terms of the newton:

$$1 \text{ pound} = 1 \text{ lb} = 4.45 \text{ N}$$

You very likely associate pounds with kilograms rather than with newtons. Everyday language often confuses the ideas of mass and weight, but we're going to need to make a clear distinction between them. We'll have more to say about this in the next chapter.

TABLE 4.2 Approximate magnitude of some typical forces

Force	Approximate magnitude (newtons)
Weight of a U.S. nickel	0.05
Weight of a 1-pound object	5
Weight of a 110-pound person	500
Propulsion force of a car	5000
Thrust force of a rocket motor	5,000,000

EXAMPLE 4.6 **Pulling an airplane**

In 2000, a team of 60 British police officers set a world record by pulling a Boeing 747, with a mass of 205,000 kg, a distance of 100 m in 53.3 s. Estimate the force with which each officer pulled on the plane.

PREPARE If we assume that the plane undergoes a constant acceleration, we can use kinematics to find the magnitude of that acceleration. Then we can use Newton's second law to find the force applied to the airplane. FIGURE 4.23 shows the visual overview of the airplane.

FIGURE 4.23 Visual overview of the airplane accelerating.

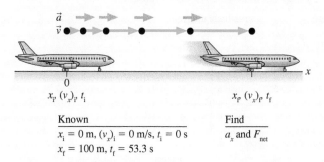

SOLVE Because we know the net displacement of the plane and the time it took to move, we can use the kinematic equation

$$x_f = x_i + (v_x)_i \, \Delta t + \tfrac{1}{2} a_x \, (\Delta t)^2$$

to find the airplane's acceleration a_x. Using the known values $x_i = 0$ m and $(v_x)_i = 0$ m/s, we can solve for the acceleration:

$$a_x = \frac{2x_f}{(\Delta t)^2} = \frac{2(100 \text{ m})}{(53.3 \text{ s})^2} = 0.0704 \text{ m/s}^2$$

Now we apply Newton's second law. The net force is

$$F_{net} = ma_x = (205,000 \text{ kg})(0.0704 \text{ m/s}^2) = 1.44 \times 10^4 \text{ N}$$

This is the force applied by all 60 men. Each man thus applies about 1/60th of this force, or around 240 N.

ASSESS Converting this force to pounds, we have

$$F = 240 \text{ N} \times \frac{1 \text{ lb}}{4.45 \text{ N}} = 54 \text{ lb}$$

Our answer is suspiciously low. Burly policemen can certainly apply a force greater than 54 lb. The fact that our calculation ended with a force that appears too small suggests we've overlooked something. In fact, we have. We've neglected the rolling friction of the plane's tires. We'll learn how to deal with friction in the next chapter, where we'll find that, because of the opposing friction force, the men have to pull harder than our estimate, in which we've ignored friction.

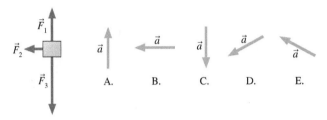

STOP TO THINK 4.4 Three forces act on an object. In which direction does the object accelerate?

4.7 Free-Body Diagrams

PhET: Forces in 1D
PhET: The Ramp

Having discussed at length what is and is not a force, and what forces do to an object, we are ready to assemble our knowledge about force and motion into a single diagram called a **free-body diagram.** A free-body diagram represents the object as a particle and shows *all* of the forces acting on the object. Learning how to draw a correct free-body diagram is a very important skill, one that in the next chapter will become a critical part of our strategy for solving motion problems. For now, let's concentrate on the basic skill of constructing a correct free-body diagram.

**TACTICS
BOX 4.3**   Drawing a free-body diagram

❶ **Identify all forces acting on the object.** This step was described in Tactics Box 4.2.
❷ **Draw a coordinate system.** Use the axes defined in your pictorial representation (Tactics Box 2.2). If those axes are tilted, for motion along an incline, then the axes of the free-body diagram should be similarly tilted.
❸ **Represent the object as a dot at the origin of the coordinate axes.** This is the particle model.
❹ **Draw vectors representing each of the identified forces.** This was described in Tactics Box 4.1. Be sure to label each force vector.
❺ **Draw and label the *net force* vector $\vec{F}_{net}$.** Draw this vector beside the diagram, not on the particle. Then check that $\vec{F}_{net}$ points in the same direction as the acceleration vector $\vec{a}$ on your motion diagram. Or, if appropriate, write $\vec{F}_{net} = \vec{0}$.

Exercises 17–22

EXAMPLE 4.7   **Forces on an upward-accelerating elevator**

An elevator, suspended by a cable, speeds up as it moves upward from the ground floor. Draw a free-body diagram of the elevator.

PREPARE FIGURE 4.24 illustrates the steps listed in Tactics Box 4.3.

FIGURE 4.24 Free-body diagram of an elevator accelerating upward.

ASSESS The coordinate axes, with a vertical y-axis, are the ones we use in a pictorial representation of the motion. The elevator is accelerating upward, so $\vec{F}_{net}$ must point upward. For this to be true, the magnitude of $\vec{T}$ must be greater than the magnitude of $\vec{w}$. The diagram has been drawn accordingly.

EXAMPLE 4.8 Forces on a rocket-propelled ice block

Bobby straps a small model rocket to a block of ice and shoots it across the smooth surface of a frozen lake. Friction is negligible. Draw a visual overview—a motion diagram, force identification diagram, and free-body diagram—of the block of ice.

PREPARE We treat the block of ice as a particle. The visual overview consists of a motion diagram to determine $\vec{a}$, a force identification picture, and a free-body diagram. The statement of the situation tells us that friction is negligible. We can draw these three pictures using Problem-Solving Strategy 1.1 for the motion diagram, Tactics Box 4.2 to identify the forces, and Tactics Box

4.3 to draw the free-body diagrams. These pictures are shown in FIGURE 4.25.

ASSESS The motion diagram tells us that the acceleration is in the positive x-direction. According to the rules of vector addition, this can be true only if the upward-pointing $\vec{n}$ and the downward-pointing $\vec{w}$ are equal in magnitude and thus cancel each other. The vectors have been drawn accordingly, and this leaves the net force vector pointing toward the right, in agreement with $\vec{a}$ from the motion diagram.

FIGURE 4.25 Visual overview for a block of ice shooting across a frictionless frozen lake.

EXAMPLE 4.9 Forces on a towed skier

A tow rope pulls a skier up a snow-covered hill at a constant speed. Draw a full visual overview of the skier.

PREPARE This is Example 4.2 again with the additional information that the skier is moving at a constant speed. If we were doing a kinematics problem, the pictorial representation would

use a tilted coordinate system with the x-axis parallel to the slope, so we use these same tilted coordinate axes for the free-body diagram. The motion diagram, force identification diagram, and free-body diagram are shown in FIGURE 4.26.

FIGURE 4.26 Visual overview for a skier being towed at a constant speed.

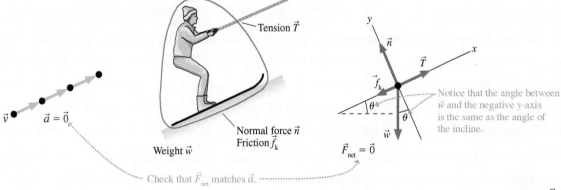

Continued

ASSESS We have shown $\vec{T}$ pulling parallel to the slope and $\vec{f}_k$, which opposes the direction of motion, pointing down the slope. The normal force $\vec{n}$ is perpendicular to the surface and thus along the y-axis. Finally, and this is important, the weight $\vec{w}$ is *vertically* downward, *not* along the negative y-axis.

The skier moves in a straight line with constant speed, so $\vec{a} = \vec{0}$. Newton's second law then tells us that $\vec{F}_{net} = m\vec{a} = \vec{0}$. Thus we have drawn the vectors such that the forces add to zero. We'll learn more about how to do this in Chapter 5.

Free-body diagrams will be our major tool for the next several chapters. Careful practice with the workbook exercises and homework in this chapter will pay immediate benefits in the next chapter. Indeed, it is not too much to assert that a problem is more than half solved when you correctly complete the free-body diagram.

> **STOP TO THINK 4.5** An elevator suspended by a cable is moving upward and slowing to a stop. Which free-body diagram is correct?

FIGURE 4.27 The hammer and the nail are a system of interacting objects.

FIGURE 4.28 The hammer and nail each exert a force on the other.

The hammer exerts a force on the nail . . .

. . . but the *nail* also exerts a force on the *hammer*.

4.8 Newton's Third Law

Thus far, we've focused on the motion of a single particle responding to well-defined forces exerted by other objects, or to long-range forces. A skier sliding downhill, for instance, is subject to frictional and normal forces from the slope, and the pull of gravity on his body. Once we have identified these forces, we can use Newton's second law to calculate the acceleration, and hence the overall motion, of the skier.

But motion in the real world often involves two or more objects *interacting* with each other. Consider the hammer and nail in FIGURE 4.27. As the hammer hits the nail, the nail pushes back on the hammer. A bat and a ball, your foot and a soccer ball, and the earth–moon system are other examples of interacting objects.

Newton's second law is not sufficient to explain what happens when two or more objects interact. It does not explain how the force of the hammer on the nail is related to the force of the nail on the hammer. In this section we will introduce another law of physics, Newton's *third* law, that describes how two objects interact with each other.

Interacting Objects

Think about the hammer and nail in Figure 4.27. As FIGURE 4.28 shows, the hammer certainly exerts a force on the nail as it drives the nail forward. At the same time, the nail exerts a force on the hammer. If you are not sure that it does, imagine hitting the nail with a glass hammer. It's the force of the nail on the hammer that would cause the glass to shatter.

Indeed, if you stop to think about it, any time that object A pushes or pulls on object B, object B pushes or pulls back on object A. As you push on a filing cabinet to move it, the cabinet pushes back on you. (If you pushed forward without the cabinet pushing back, you would fall forward in the same way you do if someone suddenly opens a door you're leaning against.) Your chair pushes upward on you (the normal force that keeps you from falling) while, at the same time, you push down on the chair, compressing the cushion. These are examples of what we call an *interaction*. An **interaction** is the mutual influence of two objects on each other.

These examples illustrate a key aspect of interactions: The forces involved in an interaction between two objects always occur as a *pair*. To be more specific, if object A exerts a force $\vec{F}_{\text{A on B}}$ on object B, then object B exerts a force $\vec{F}_{\text{B on A}}$ on object A. This pair of forces, shown in FIGURE 4.29, is called an **action/reaction pair.** Two objects interact by exerting an action/reaction pair of forces on each other. Notice the very explicit subscripts on the force vectors. The first letter is the *agent*—the source of the force—and the second letter is the *object* on which the force acts. $\vec{F}_{\text{A on B}}$ is thus the force exerted *by* A *on* B.

NOTE ▶ The name "action/reaction pair" is somewhat misleading. The forces occur simultaneously, and we cannot say which is the "action" and which the "reaction." Neither is there any implication about cause and effect; the action does not cause the reaction. **An action/reaction pair of forces exists as a pair, or not at all.** For action/reaction pairs, the labels are the key: Force $\vec{F}_{\text{A on B}}$ is paired with force $\vec{F}_{\text{B on A}}$. ◀

Reasoning with Newton's Third Law

We've discovered that two objects always interact via an action/reaction pair of forces. Newton was the first to recognize how the two members of an action/reaction pair of forces are related to each other. Today we know this as Newton's third law:

Newton's third law Every force occurs as one member of an action/reaction pair of forces.

- The two members of an action/reaction pair act on two *different* objects.
- The two members of an action/reaction pair point in *opposite* directions and are *equal in magnitude*.

Newton's third law is often stated: "For every action there is an equal but opposite reaction." While this is a catchy phrase, it lacks the preciseness of our preferred version. In particular, it fails to capture an essential feature of the two members of an action/reaction pair—that each acts on a *different* object. This is shown in FIGURE 4.30, where a hammer hitting a nail exerts a force $\vec{F}_{\text{hammer on nail}}$ on the nail; by the third law, the nail must exert a force $\vec{F}_{\text{nail on hammer}}$ to complete the action/reaction pair.

Figure 4.30 also illustrates that these two forces point in *opposite directions*. This feature of the third law is also in accord with our experience. If the hammer hits the nail with a force directed to the right, the force of the nail on the hammer is directed to the left; if the force of my chair on me pushes up, the force of me on the chair pushes down.

Finally, Figure 4.30 shows that, according to Newton's third law, the two members of an action/reaction pair have *equal* magnitudes, so that $F_{\text{hammer on nail}} = F_{\text{nail on hammer}}$. This is something new, and it is by no means obvious. Indeed, this statement causes students the most trouble when applying the third law because it seems so counter to our intuition, as the following example shows.

FIGURE 4.29 An action/reaction pair of forces.

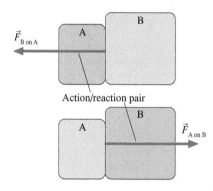

Action/reaction pair

FIGURE 4.30 Newton's third law.

Each force in an action/reaction pair acts on a *different* object.

This is a force on the hammer.

This is a force on the nail.

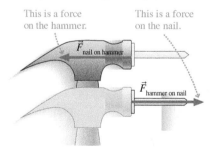

The members of the pair point in *opposite directions*, but are of *equal magnitude*.

Video Tutor Demonstration

Revenge of the target We normally think of the damage that the force of a bullet inflicts on its target. But according to Newton's third law, the target exerts an equal force on the bullet. The photo shows the damage sustained by bullets fired at 1600, 1800, and 2000 ft/s, after impacting a test target. The appearance of the bullet before firing is shown at the left.

CONCEPTUAL EXAMPLE 4.10   **The bug versus the windshield**

During the collision between a bug and the windshield of a fast-moving truck, which force has greater magnitude: the force of the windshield on the bug or the force of the bug on the windshield?

REASON   The third law tells us that the magnitude of the force of the windshield on the bug must be *equal* to that of the bug on the windshield! How can this be, when the bug is so small compared to the truck? The source of puzzlement in problems like this is that Newton's third law equates the size of the *forces* acting on the two objects, not their *accelerations*. The acceleration of each object depends not only on the force applied to it, but also, according to Newton's second law, on its mass. The bug and the truck do in fact feel forces of equal strength from the other, but the bug, with its very small mass, undergoes an extreme acceleration from this force while the acceleration of the heavy truck is negligible.

ASSESS   It is important to separate the *effects* of the forces (the accelerations) from the causes (the forces themselves). Because two interacting objects can have very different masses, their accelerations can be very different even though the interaction forces are of the same strength.

FIGURE 4.31 Examples of propulsion.

(a) The person pushes backward against the surface. The surface pushes forward on the person.

$\vec{f}_{\text{surface on person}}$

$\vec{f}_{\text{person on surface}}$

Action/reaction pair

(b) The tire pushes backward against the road. The road pushes forward on the tire.

$\vec{f}_{\text{road on tire}}$

$\vec{f}_{\text{tire on road}}$

Action/reaction pair

FIGURE 4.32 When the driver hits the gas, the force of the track on the tire is so great that the tire deforms.

$\vec{F}_{\text{road on tire}}$

You can *see* that the force of the road on the tire points forward by the way it twists the rubber of the tire.

We'll return to Newton's third law in Chapter 5, where we'll use it to solve problems involving two or more interacting objects.

Propulsion

A sprinter accelerates out of the blocks. Because he's accelerating, there must be a force on him in the forward direction. For a system with an internal source of energy, a force that drives the system is a force of **propulsion.** Propulsion is an important feature not only of walking or running but also of the forward motion of cars, jets, and rockets. Propulsion is somewhat counterintuitive, so it is worth a closer look.

If you tried to walk across a frictionless floor, your foot would slip and slide *backward.* In order for you to walk, the floor needs to have friction so that your foot *sticks* to the floor as you straighten your leg, moving your body forward. The friction that prevents slipping is *static* friction. Static friction, you will recall, acts in the direction that prevents slipping, so the static friction force $\vec{f}_{\text{S on P}}$ (for Surface on Person) has to point in the *forward* direction to prevent your foot from slipping backward. As shown in FIGURE 4.31a, it is this forward-directed static friction force that propels you forward! The force of your foot on the floor, $\vec{f}_{\text{P on S}}$, is the other half of the action/reaction pair, and it points in the opposite direction as you push backward against the floor.

Similarly, the car in FIGURE 4.31b uses static friction to propel itself. The car uses its motor to turn the tires, causing the tires to push backward against the road ($\vec{f}_{\text{tire on road}}$). The road surface responds by pushing the car forward ($\vec{f}_{\text{road on tire}}$). This force of the road on the tire can be seen in photos of drag racers, where the forces are very great (FIGURE 4.32). Again, the forces involved are *static* friction forces. The tire is rolling, but the bottom of the tire, where it contacts the road, is instantaneously at rest. If it weren't, you would leave one giant skid mark as you drove and would burn off the tread within a few miles.

Rocket motors are somewhat different because they are not pushing *against* anything external. That's why rocket propulsion works in the vacuum of space. Instead, the rocket engine pushes hot, expanding gases out of the back of the rocket, as shown in FIGURE 4.33. In response, the exhaust gases push the rocket forward with the force we've called *thrust*.

Now we've assembled all the pieces we need in order to start solving problems in dynamics. We have seen what forces are and how to identify them, and we've learned how forces cause objects to accelerate according to Newton's second law. We've also found how Newton's third law governs the interaction forces between two objects. Our goal in the next several chapters is to apply Newton's laws to a variety of problems involving straight-line and circular motion.

FIGURE 4.33 Rocket propulsion.

The rocket pushes the hot gases backward. The gases push the rocket forward.

$\vec{F}_{\text{gases on rocket}}$

Action/reaction pair

$\vec{F}_{\text{rocket on gases}}$

STOP TO THINK 4.6 A small car is pushing a larger truck that has a dead battery. The mass of the truck is greater than the mass of the car. Which of the following statements is true?

A. The car exerts a force on the truck, but the truck doesn't exert a force on the car.
B. The car exerts a larger force on the truck than the truck exerts on the car.
C. The car exerts the same amount of force on the truck as the truck exerts on the car.
D. The truck exerts a larger force on the car than the car exerts on the truck.
E. The truck exerts a force on the car, but the car doesn't exert a force on the truck.

INTEGRATED EXAMPLE 4.11 | **Pulling an excursion train**

An engine slows as it pulls two cars of an excursion train up a mountain. Draw a visual overview (motion diagram, a force identification diagram, and free-body diagram) for the car just behind the engine. Ignore friction.

PREPARE Because the train is slowing down, the motion diagram consists of a series of particle positions that become closer together at successive times; the corresponding velocity vectors become shorter and shorter. To identify the forces acting on the car we use the steps of Tactics Box 4.2. Finally, we can draw a free-body diagram using Tactics Box 4.3.

SOLVE Finding the forces acting on car 1 can be tricky. The engine exerts a forward force $\vec{F}_{\text{engine on 1}}$ on car 1 where the engine touches the front of car 1. At its back, car 1 touches car 2, so car 2

must also exert a force on car 1. The direction of this force can be understood from Newton's third law. Car 1 exerts an uphill force on car 2 in order to pull it up the mountain. Thus, by Newton's third law, car 2 must exert an oppositely directed *downhill* force on car 1. This is the force we label $\vec{F}_{\text{2 on 1}}$. The three diagrams that make up the full visual overview are shown in FIGURE 4.34.

ASSESS Correctly preparing the three diagrams illustrated in this example is critical for solving problems using Newton's laws. The motion diagram allows you to determine the direction of the acceleration and hence of $\vec{F}_{\text{net}}$. Using the force identification diagram, you will correctly identify all the forces acting on the object and, just as important, not add any extraneous forces. And by properly drawing these force vectors in a free-body diagram, you'll be ready for the quantitative application of Newton's laws that is the focus of Chapter 5.

FIGURE 4.34 Visual overview for a slowing train car being pulled up a mountain.

Motion diagram	**Force identification** (Numbered steps from Tactics Box 4.2)	**Free-body diagram** (Numbered steps from Tactics Box 4.3)
	❶ The object of interest is car 1.	❶ Identify all forces (already done).
	❷ Draw a picture.	❷ Draw a coordinate system. Because the motion here is along an incline, we tilt our *x*-axis to match.
	❸ Draw a closed curve around the object.	❸ Represent the object as a dot at the origin.
	❹ Locate the points where the object touches other objects.	❹ Draw vectors representing each identified force.
	❺ Name and label each contact force.	❺ Draw the net force vector. Check that it points in the same direction as $\vec{a}$.
	❻ Weight is the only long-range force.	

Because the train is slowing down, its acceleration vector points in the direction opposite its motion.

Car 1

Car 2

$\vec{F}_{\text{engine on 1}}$ ❹❺

❹❺ Normal force $\vec{n}$

❹❺ $\vec{F}_{\text{2 on 1}}$

❻ Weight $\vec{w}$

y

$\vec{n}$ ❹

$\vec{F}_{\text{2 on 1}}$ ❸ ❹ x ❷

$\vec{F}_{\text{engine on 1}}$ ❹

$\vec{w}$ ❹

$\vec{F}_{\text{net}}$ ❺

SUMMARY

The goal of Chapter 4 has been to establish a connection between force and motion.

GENERAL PRINCIPLES

Newton's First Law

Consider an object with no force acting on it. If it is at rest, it will remain at rest. If it is in motion, then it will continue to move in a straight line at a constant speed.

$$\vec{F} = \vec{0}$$
$$\vec{a} = \vec{0}$$

The first law tells us that no "cause" is needed for motion. Uniform motion is the "natural state" of an object.

Newton's Second Law

An object with mass m will undergo acceleration

$$\vec{a} = \frac{\vec{F}_{\text{net}}}{m}$$

where the net force $\vec{F}_{\text{net}} = \vec{F}_1 + \vec{F}_2 + \vec{F}_3 + \cdots$ is the vector sum of all the individual forces acting on the object.

The second law tells us that a net force causes an object to accelerate. This is the connection between force and motion. The acceleration points in the direction of $\vec{F}_{\text{net}}$.

Newton's Third Law

Every force occurs as one member of an **action/reaction** pair of forces. The two members of an action/reaction pair:

• act on two *different* objects.

• point in opposite directions and are equal in magnitude:

$$\vec{F}_{\text{A on B}} = -\vec{F}_{\text{B on A}}$$

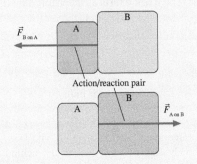

Action/reaction pair

IMPORTANT CONCEPTS

Force is a push or pull on an object.

• Force is a vector, with a magnitude and a direction.

• A force requires an agent.

• A force is either a contact force or a long-range force.

The SI unit of force is the **newton** (N). A 1 N force will cause a 1 kg mass to accelerate at 1 m/s^2.

Net force is the vector sum of all the forces acting on an object.

$$\vec{F}_{\text{net}} = \vec{F}_1 + \vec{F}_2 + \vec{F}_3$$

Mass is the property of an object that determines its resistance to acceleration.

If the same force is applied to objects A and B, then the ratio of their accelerations is related to the ratio of their masses as

$$\frac{a_{\text{A}}}{a_{\text{B}}} = \frac{m_{\text{B}}}{m_{\text{A}}}$$

The mass of objects can be determined in terms of their accelerations.

APPLICATIONS

Identifying Forces

Forces are identified by locating the points where other objects touch the object of interest. These are points where contact forces are exerted. In addition, objects feel a long-range weight force.

Thrust force $\vec{F}_{\text{thrust}}$

Weight $\vec{w}$ Normal force $\vec{n}$

Free-Body Diagrams

A free-body diagram represents the object as a particle at the origin of a coordinate system. Force vectors are drawn with their tails on the particle. The net force vector is drawn beside the diagram.

Problem difficulty is labeled as | (straightforward) to |||| (challenging). Problems labeled INT integrate significant material from earlier chapters; BIO are of biological or medical interest.

 For homework assigned on MasteringPhysics, go to www.masteringphysics.com

 Scan this QR code to launch a **Video Tutor Solution** that will help you solve problems for this chapter.

QUESTIONS

Conceptual Questions

1. A hockey puck slides along the surface of the ice. If friction and air resistance are negligible, what force is required to keep the puck moving?

2. If an object is not moving, does that mean that there are no forces acting on it? Explain.

3. An object moves in a straight line at a constant speed. Is it true that there must be no forces of any kind acting on this object? Explain.

4. A ball sits near the front of a child's wagon. As she pulls on the wagon and it begins to move forward, the ball rolls toward the back of the wagon. Explain why the ball rolls in this direction.

5. If you know all of the forces acting on a moving object, can you tell in which direction the object is moving? If the answer is Yes, explain how. If the answer is No, give an example.

6. Three arrows are shot horizontally. They have left the bow and are traveling parallel to the ground as shown in Figure Q4.6. Air resistance is negligible. Rank in order, from largest to smallest, the magnitudes of the *horizontal* forces F_1, F_2, and F_3 acting on the arrows. Some may be equal. State your reasoning.

FIGURE Q4.6

7. A carpenter wishes to tighten the heavy head of his hammer onto its light handle. Which method shown in Figure Q4.7 will better tighten the head? Explain.

8. BIO Internal injuries in vehicular accidents may be due to what is called the "third collision." The first collision is the vehicle hitting the external object. The second collision is the person hitting

FIGURE Q4.7

something on the inside of the car, such as the dashboard or windshield. This may cause external lacerations. The third collision, possibly the most damaging to the body, is when organs, such as the heart or brain, hit the ribcage, skull, or other confines of the body, bruising the tissues on the leading edge and tearing the organ from its supporting structures on the trailing edge.
   a. Why is there a third collision? In other words, why are the organs still moving after the second collision?
   b. If the vehicle was traveling at 60 mph before the first collision, would the organs be traveling more than, equal to, or less than 60 mph just before the third collision?

9. a. Give an example of the motion of an object in which the frictional force on the object is directed opposite to the motion.
   b. Give an example of the motion of an object in which the frictional force on the object is in the same direction as the motion.

10. Suppose you are an astronaut in deep space, far from any source of gravity. You have two objects that look identical, but one has a large mass and the other a small mass. How can you tell the difference between the two?

11. Jonathan accelerates away from a stop sign. His eight-year-old daughter sits in the passenger seat. On whom does the back of the seat exert a greater force?

12. The weight of a box sitting on the floor points directly down. The normal force of the floor on the box points directly up. Need these two forces have the same magnitude? Explain.

13. A ball weighs 2.0 N when placed on a scale. It is then thrown straight up. What is its weight at the very top of its motion? Explain.

14. Josh and Taylor, standing face-to-face on frictionless ice, push off each other, causing each to slide backward. Josh is much bigger than Taylor. After the push, which of the two is moving faster?

15. A person sits on a sloped hillside. Is it ever possible to have the static friction force on this person point down the hill? Explain.

16. BIO Walking without slipping requires a static friction force between your feet (or footwear) and the floor. As described in this chapter, the force on your foot as you push off the floor is forward while the force exerted by your foot on the floor is backward. But what about your *other* foot, the one moved during a stride? What is the direction of the force on that foot as it comes into contact with the floor? Explain.

17. Figure 4.31b showed a situation in which the force of the road on the car's tire points forward. In other situations, the force points backward. Give an example of such a situation.

18. Alyssa pushes to the right on a filing cabinet; the friction force from the floor pushes on it to the left. Because the cabinet doesn't move, these forces have the same magnitude. Do they form an action/reaction pair? Explain.

19. A very smart three-year-old child is given a wagon for her birthday. She refuses to use it. "After all," she says, "Newton's third law says that no matter how hard I pull, the wagon will exert an equal but opposite force on me. So I will never be able to get it to move forward." What would you say to her in reply?

20. Will hanging a magnet in front of an iron cart, as shown in Figure Q4.20, make it go? Explain why or why not.

FIGURE Q4.20

Multiple-Choice Questions

21. | Figure Q4.21 shows the view looking down onto a frictionless sheet of ice. A puck, tied with a string to point P, slides on the surface of the ice in the circular path shown. If the string suddenly snaps when the puck is in the position shown, which path best represents the puck's subsequent motion?

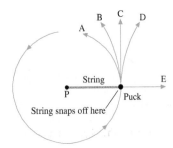

FIGURE Q4.21

22. | A block has acceleration a when pulled by a string. If two identical blocks are glued together and pulled with twice the original force, their acceleration will be
    A. $(1/4)a$ B. $(1/2)a$
    C. a D. $2a$
    E. $4a$

23. | A 5.0 kg block has an acceleration of 0.20 m/s² when a force is exerted on it. A second block has an acceleration of 0.10 m/s² when subject to the same force. What is the mass of the second block?
    A. 10 kg   B. 5.0 kg   C. 2.5 kg   D. 7.5 kg

24. | Tennis balls experience a large drag force. A tennis ball is hit so that it goes straight up and then comes back down. The direction of the drag force is
    A. Always up.
    B. Up and then down.
    C. Always down.
    D. Down and then up.

25. | A person gives a box a shove so that it slides up a ramp, then reverses its motion and slides down. The direction of the force of friction is
    A. Always down the ramp.
    B. Up the ramp and then down the ramp.
    C. Always down the ramp.
    D. Down the ramp and then up the ramp.

26. | A person is pushing horizontally on a box with a constant force, causing it to slide across the floor with a constant speed. If the person suddenly stops pushing on the box, the box will
    A. Immediately come to a stop.
    B. Continue moving at a constant speed for a while, then gradually slow down to a stop.
    C. Immediately change to a slower but constant speed.
    D. Immediately begin slowing down and eventually stop.

27. | Rachel is pushing a box across the floor while Jon, at the same time, is hoping to stop the box by pushing in the opposite direction. There is friction between the box and floor. If the box is moving at constant speed, then the magnitude of Rachel's pushing force is
    A. Greater than the magnitude of Jon's force.
    B. Equal to the magnitude of Jon's force.
    C. Less than the magnitude of Jon's force.
    D. The question can't be answered without knowing how large the friction force is.

28. || Dave pushes his four-year-old son Thomas across the snow on a sled. As Dave pushes, Thomas speeds up. Which statement is true?
    A. The force of Dave on Thomas is larger than the force of Thomas on Dave.
    B. The force of Thomas on Dave is larger than the force of Dave on Thomas.
    C. Both forces have the same magnitude.
    D. It depends on how hard Dave pushes on Thomas.

29. | Figure Q4.29 shows block A sitting on top of block B. A constant force $\vec{F}$ is exerted on block B, causing block B to accelerate to the right. Block A rides on block B without slipping. Which statement is true?
    A. Block B exerts a friction force on block A, directed to the left.
    B. Block B exerts a friction force on block A, directed to the right.
    C. Block B does not exert a friction force on block A.

FIGURE Q4.29

PROBLEMS

Section 4.1 What Causes Motion?

1. | Whiplash injuries during an automobile accident are caused
BIO by the inertia of the head. If someone is wearing a seatbelt, her body will tend to move with the car seat. However, her head is free to move until the neck restrains it, causing damage to the neck. Brain damage can also occur.

   Figure P4.1 shows two sequences of head and neck motion for a passenger in an auto accident. One corresponds to a head-on collision, the other to a rear-end collision. Which is which? Explain.

FIGURE P4.1

2. | An automobile has a head-on
BIO collision. A passenger in the car
experiences a compression injury
to the brain. Is this injury most
likely to be in the front or rear
portion of the brain? Explain.

3. | In a head-on collision, an infant
is much safer in a child safety seat
when the seat is installed facing
the rear of the car. Explain.

Section 4.2 Force

Problems 4 through 6 show two forces acting on an object at rest.
Redraw the diagram, then add a third force that will allow the object
to remain at rest. Label the new force $\vec{F}_3$.

4. ‖   5. ‖   6. ‖

FIGURE P4.4   FIGURE P4.5   FIGURE P4.6

Section 4.3 A Short Catalog of Forces

Section 4.4 Identifying Forces

7. ‖ A mountain climber is hanging from a rope in the middle of a
crevasse. The rope is vertical. Identify the forces on the mountain climber.

8. ‖ A circus clown hangs from one end of a large spring. The
other end is anchored to the ceiling. Identify the forces on the
clown.

9. ‖‖ A baseball player is sliding into second base. Identify the
forces on the baseball player.

10. ‖‖‖ A jet plane is speeding down the runway during takeoff. Air
resistance is not negligible. Identify the forces on the jet.

11. | A skier is sliding down a 15° slope. Friction is not negligible.
Identify the forces on the skier.

12. ‖ A tennis ball is flying horizontally across the net. Air resistance is not negligible. Identify the forces on the ball.

Section 4.5 What Do Forces Do?

13. ‖‖ Figure P4.13 shows an acceleration-versus-force graph for
three objects pulled by rubber bands. The mass of object 2 is
0.20 kg. What are the masses of objects 1 and 3? Explain your
reasoning.

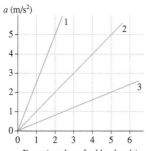

FIGURE P4.13   Force (number of rubber bands)

14. | A constant force applied to object A causes it to accelerate at
5 m/s². The same force applied to object B causes an acceleration
of 3 m/s². Applied to object C, it causes an acceleration of 8 m/s².
   a. Which object has the largest mass?
   b. Which object has the smallest mass?
   c. What is the ratio of mass A to mass B (m_A/m_B)?

15. | Two rubber bands pulling on an object cause it to accelerate
at 1.2 m/s².
   a. What will be the object's acceleration if it is pulled by four
rubber bands?
   b. What will be the acceleration of two of these objects glued
together if they are pulled by two rubber bands?

16. | A constant force is applied to an object, causing the object to
accelerate at 10 m/s². What will the acceleration be if
   a. The force is halved?
   b. The object's mass is halved?
   c. The force and the object's mass are both halved?
   d. The force is halved and the object's mass is doubled?

17. | A constant force is applied to an object, causing the object to
accelerate at 8.0 m/s². What will the acceleration be if
   a. The force is doubled?
   b. The object's mass is doubled?
   c. The force and the object's mass are both doubled?
   d. The force is doubled and the object's mass is halved?

18. ‖‖ A man pulling an empty wagon causes it to accelerate at
1.4 m/s². What will the acceleration be if he pulls with the same
force when the wagon contains a child whose mass is three
times that of the wagon?

19. | A car has a maximum acceleration of 5.0 m/s². What will the
maximum acceleration be if the car is towing another car of the
same mass?

Section 4.6 Newton's Second Law

20. ‖ Figure P4.20 shows an acceleration-versus-force graph for a
500 g object. Redraw this graph and add appropriate acceleration values on the vertical scale.

FIGURE P4.20

21. | Figure P4.21 shows an object's acceleration-versus-force
graph. What is the object's mass?

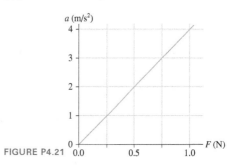

FIGURE P4.21

22. ‖ Two children fight over a 200 g stuffed bear. The 25 kg boy pulls to the right with a 15 N force and the 20 kg girl pulls to the left with a 17 N force. Ignore all other forces on the bear (such as its weight).
    a. At this instant, can you say what the velocity of the bear is? If so, what are the magnitude and direction of the velocity?
    b. At this instant, can you say what the acceleration of the bear is? If so, what are the magnitude and direction of the acceleration?

23. ‖ A 1500 kg car is traveling along a straight road at 20 m/s.
    Ⓝ Two seconds later its speed is 21 m/s. What is the magnitude of the net force acting on the car during this time?

24. ‖ Very small forces can have tremendous effects on the motion of very small objects. Consider a single electron, with a mass of 9.1×10^{-31} kg, subject to a single force equal to the weight of a penny, 2.5×10^{-2} N. What is the acceleration of the electron?

25. ‖ The motion of a very massive object is hardly affected by what would seem to be a substantial force. Consider a super-tanker, with a mass of 3.0×10^8 kg. If it is pushed by a rocket motor (see Table 4.2) and is subject to no other forces, what will be the magnitude of its acceleration?

Section 4.7 Free-Body Diagrams

Problems 26 through 28 show a free-body diagram. For each, (a) Redraw the free-body diagram and (b) Write a short description of a real object for which this is the correct free-body diagram. Use Examples 4.3, 4.4, and 4.5 as models of what a description should be like.

26. │

FIGURE P4.26

27. │

FIGURE P4.27

28. │

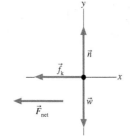

FIGURE P4.28

Problems 29 through 35 describe a situation. For each, identify all forces acting on the object and draw a free-body diagram of the object.

29. ‖ Your car is sitting in the parking lot.
30. ‖ Your car is accelerating from a stop.
31. ‖ Your car is slowing to a stop from a high speed.
32. ‖ Your physics textbook is sliding across the table.
33. ‖ An ascending elevator, hanging from a cable, is coming to a stop.
34. ‖ A skier slides down a slope at a constant speed.
35. ‖‖ You hold a picture motionless against a wall by pressing on it, as shown in Figure P4.35.

FIGURE P4.35

Section 4.8 Newton's Third Law

36. ‖ A weightlifter stands up from a squatting position while holding a heavy barbell across his shoulders. Identify all the action/reaction pairs of forces between the weight lifter and the barbell.

37. ‖ Three ice skaters, numbered 1, 2, and 3, stand in a line, each with her hands on the shoulders of the skater in front. Skater 3, at the rear, pushes on skater 2. Identify all the action/reaction pairs of forces between the three skaters. Draw a free-body diagram for skater 2, in the middle. Assume the ice is frictionless.

38. │ A girl stands on a sofa. Identify all the action/reaction pairs of forces between the girl and the sofa.

General Problems

39. │ Redraw the motion diagram
    Ⓝ shown in Figure P4.39, then draw a vector beside it to show the direction of the net force acting on the object. Explain your reasoning.
40. │ Redraw the motion diagram
    Ⓝ shown in Figure P4.40, then draw a vector beside it to show the direction of the net force acting on the object. Explain your reasoning.
41. │ Redraw the motion diagram
    Ⓝ shown in Figure P4.41, then draw a vector beside it to show the direction of the net force acting on the object. Explain your reasoning.

FIGURE P4.39   FIGURE P4.40

FIGURE P4.41   FIGURE P4.42

42. │ Redraw the motion diagram shown in Figure P4.42, then
    Ⓝ draw a vector beside it to show the direction of the net force acting on the object. Explain your reasoning.

Problems 43 through 49 show a free-body diagram. For each:

a. Redraw the diagram.
b. Identify the direction of the acceleration vector $\vec{a}$ and show it as a vector next to your diagram. Or, if appropriate, write $\vec{a} = \vec{0}$.
c. Write a short description of a real object for which this is the correct free-body diagram. Use Examples 4.7, 4.8, and 4.9 as models of what a description should be like.

43. |

FIGURE P4.43

44. |

FIGURE P4.44

45. |

FIGURE P4.45

46. |

FIGURE P4.46

47. |

FIGURE P4.47

48. |

FIGURE P4.48

49. |

FIGURE P4.49

50. ‖‖ A student draws the flawed free-body diagram shown in Figure P4.50 to represent the forces acting on a car traveling at constant speed on a level road. Identify the errors in the diagram, then draw a correct free-body diagram for this situation.

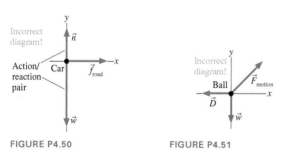

FIGURE P4.50

FIGURE P4.51

51. ‖ A student draws the flawed free-body diagram shown in Figure P4.51 to represent the forces acting on a golf ball that is traveling upward and to the right a very short time after being hit off the tee. Air resistance is assumed to be relevant. Identify the errors in the diagram, then draw a correct free-body diagram for this situation.

Problems 52 through 63 describe a situation. For each, draw a motion diagram, a force identification diagram, and a free-body diagram.

52. ‖ An elevator, suspended by a single cable, has just left the tenth floor and is speeding up as it descends toward the ground floor.

53. ‖‖ A rocket is being launched straight up. Air resistance is not negligible.

54. ‖‖ A jet plane is speeding down the runway during takeoff. Air resistance is not negligible.

55. ‖ You've slammed on the brakes and your car is skidding to a stop while going down a 20° hill.

56. ‖ A skier is going down a 20° slope. A *horizontal* headwind is blowing in the skier's face. Friction is small, but not zero.

57. ‖ A bale of hay sits on the bed of a trailer. The trailer is starting to accelerate forward, and the bale is slipping toward the back of the trailer.

58. ‖ A Styrofoam ball has just been shot straight up. Air resistance is not negligible.

59. ‖‖ A spring-loaded gun shoots a plastic ball. The trigger has just been pulled and the ball is starting to move down the barrel. The barrel is horizontal.

60. ‖ A person on a bridge throws a rock straight down toward the water. The rock has just been released.

61. ‖‖ A gymnast has just landed on a trampoline. She's still moving downward as the trampoline stretches.

62. ‖‖ A heavy box is in the back of a truck. The truck is accelerating to the right. Apply your analysis to the box.

63. ‖ A bag of groceries is on the back seat of your car as you stop for a stop light. The bag does not slide. Apply your analysis to the bag.

64. ‖ A rubber ball bounces. We'd like to understand *how* the ball bounces.

   a. A rubber ball has been dropped and is bouncing off the floor. Draw a motion diagram of the ball during the brief time interval that it is in contact with the floor. Show 4 or 5 frames as the ball compresses, then another 4 or 5 frames as it expands. What is the direction of $\vec{a}$ during each of these parts of the motion?

   b. Draw a picture of the ball in contact with the floor and identify all forces acting on the ball.

   c. Draw a free-body diagram of the ball during its contact with the ground. Is there a net force acting on the ball? If so, in which direction?

   d. During contact, is the force of the ground on the ball larger, smaller, or equal to the weight of the ball? Use your answers to parts a–c to explain your reasoning.

65. ‖ If a car stops suddenly, you feel "thrown forward." We'd like to understand what happens to the passengers as a car stops. Imagine yourself sitting on a *very* slippery bench inside a car. This bench has no friction, no seat back, and there's nothing for you to hold on to.

   a. Draw a picture and identify all of the forces acting on you as the car travels in a straight line at a perfectly steady speed on level ground.

   b. Draw your free-body diagram. Is there a net force on you? If so, in which direction?

   c. Repeat parts a and b with the car slowing down.

   d. Describe what happens to you as the car slows down.

   e. Use Newton's laws to explain why you seem to be "thrown forward" as the car stops. Is there really a force pushing you forward?

66. ⦀ The fastest pitched baseball was clocked at 46 m/s. If the
BIO   pitcher exerted his force (assumed to be horizontal and constant)
      over a distance of 1.0 m, and a baseball has a mass of 145 g,
      a. Draw a free-body diagram of the ball during the pitch.
      b. What force did the pitcher exert on the ball during this
         record-setting pitch?
      c. Estimate the force in part b as a fraction of the pitcher's
         weight.
67. | The froghopper, champion leaper of the insect world, can
BIO   jump straight up at 4.0 m/s. The jump itself lasts a mere 1.0 ms
      before the insect is clear of the ground.
      a. Draw a free-body diagram of this mighty leaper while the
         jump is taking place.
      b. While the jump is taking place, is the force that the ground
         exerts on the froghopper greater than, less than, or equal to
         the insect's weight? Explain.
68. ⦀ A beach ball is thrown straight up, and some time later it
      lands on the sand. Is the magnitude of the net force on the ball
      greatest when it is going up or when it is on the way down? Or
      is it the same in both cases? Explain. Air resistance should not
      be neglected for a large, light object.

Passage Problems

A Simple Solution for a Stuck Car

If your car is stuck in the mud and you don't have a winch to pull it
out, you can use a piece of rope and a tree to do the trick. First, you
tie one end of the rope to your car and the other to a tree, then pull as
hard as you can on the middle of the rope, as shown in Figure
P4.69a. This technique applies a force to the car much larger than the
force that you can apply directly. To see why the car experiences
such a large force, look at the forces acting on the center point of the
rope, as shown in Figure P4.69b. The sum of the forces is zero, thus
the tension is much greater than the force you apply. It is this tension
force that acts on the car and, with luck, pulls it free.

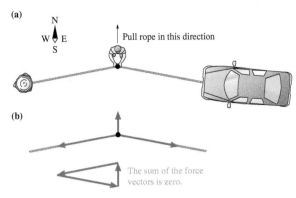

(a)

Pull rope in this direction

(b)

The sum of the force
vectors is zero.

FIGURE P4.69

69. | The sum of the three forces acting on the center point of the
      rope is assumed to be zero because
      A. This point has a very small mass.
      B. Tension forces in a rope always cancel.
      C. This point is not accelerating.
      D. The angle of deflection is very small.
70. | When you are pulling on the rope as shown, what is the
      approximate direction of the tension force on the tree?
      A. North   B. South   C. East   D. West
71. | Assume that you are pulling on the rope but the car is not
      moving. What is the approximate direction of the force of the
      mud on the car?
      A. North   B. South   C. East   D. West
72. | Suppose your efforts work, and the car begins to move for-
      ward out of the mud. As it does so, the force of the car on the
      rope is
      A. Zero.
      B. Less than the force of the rope on the car.
      C. Equal to the force of the rope on the car.
      D. Greater than the force of the rope on the car.

STOP TO THINK ANSWERS

Stop to Think 4.1: C.

$\vec{F}_1$
$\vec{F}_2$
$\vec{F}_3$
— y-component of $\vec{F}_3$
cancels y-component of $\vec{F}_1$.

x-component of $\vec{F}_3$ is to
the left and larger than
the x-component of $\vec{F}_2$.

Stop to Think 4.2: A, B, and D. Friction and the normal force are
the only contact forces. Nothing is touching the rock to provide a
"force of the kick." We've agreed to ignore air resistance unless a
problem specifically calls for it.

Stop to Think 4.3: B. Acceleration is proportional to force, so doubling the number of rubber bands doubles the acceleration of the
original object from 2 m/s² to 4 m/s². But acceleration is also
inversely proportional to mass. Doubling the mass cuts the acceleration in half, back to 2 m/s².

Stop to Think 4.4: D

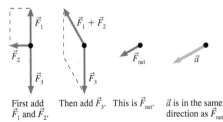

$\vec{F}_1$
$\vec{F}_2$
$\vec{F}_3$
First add
$\vec{F}_1$ and $\vec{F}_2$.

$\vec{F}_1 + \vec{F}_2$
$\vec{F}_3$
Then add $\vec{F}_3$. This is $\vec{F}_{net}$.

$\vec{F}_{net}$

$\vec{a}$
$\vec{a}$ is in the same
direction as $\vec{F}_{net}$.

Stop to Think 4.5: C. The acceleration vector points downward as
the elevator slows. $\vec{F}_{net}$ points in the same direction as $\vec{a}$, so $\vec{F}_{net}$ also
points downward. This will be true if the tension is less than the
weight: $T < w$.

Stop to Think 4.6: C. Newton's third law says that the force of A on
B is *equal* and opposite to the force of B on A. This is always true. The
mass of the objects isn't relevant.

5 Applying Newton's Laws

Why does this sky surfer fall at a constant speed? And why does he suddenly slow down when his parachute opens?

LOOKING AHEAD ▶

The goal of Chapter 5 is to learn how to solve problems about motion along a straight line.

Equilibrium Problems

An object at rest or moving at a constant velocity has zero acceleration. According to Newton's second law, this means that the net force on it must also be zero.

This boulder is in *static equilibrium:* It remains at rest.

A ski lift, moving at a constant velocity, is in *dynamic equilibrium.*

Looking Back ◀◀
4.4, 4.7 Identifying forces, free-body diagrams
4.6 Newton's second law

Interacting Objects

When two objects interact with each other, each exerts a force on the other. By Newton's third law, these forces are equal in magnitude but oppositely directed.

The barge pushes back on the tug just as hard as the tug pushes on the barge. Newton's third law will help you understand the motion of objects that are in contact with each other.

A common way for two objects to interact is with ropes or strings under tension. You'll learn how to solve problems involving tension and how pulleys act to change the direction of the tension force.

Applying Newton's Second Law

In this chapter, you'll learn how to use Newton's second law in component form to solve a variety of problems in mechanics.

What are the blocks' accelerations?

Friction, tension, gravity, and the pulley all act in this problem. You'll learn explicit strategies to solve problems like this.

3 kg

1 kg

Looking Back ◀◀
2.5, 2.7 Constant acceleration and free fall
3.2–3.3 Vectors and components

Forces and Newton's Second Law

Chapter 4 introduced several important forces. Now you'll need to understand these forces in more detail, so that you can use them in Newton's second law. For example, you'll learn . . .

. . . that **mass and weight are not the same thing.** However, you'll find that there is a simple relationship between the two.

. . . a simple model for friction that provides a reasonably accurate description of how static and kinetic friction behave.

Static friction adjusts its magnitude as needed to keep the sofa from slipping.

Kinetic (sliding) friction does not depend on an object's speed.

This astronaut on the moon weighs only 1/6 of what he does on earth. His *mass*, however, is the same on both the moon and the earth.

This human tower is in equilibrium because the net force on each man is zero.

5.1 Equilibrium

Chapter 4 introduced Newton's three laws of motion. Now, in Chapter 5, we want to use these laws to solve force and motion problems. This chapter focuses on objects that are at rest or that move in a straight line, such as runners, bicycles, cars, planes, and rockets. Circular motion and rotational motion will be treated in Chapters 6 and 7.

The simplest applications of Newton's second law, $\vec{F}_{net} = m\vec{a}$, are those for which the acceleration $\vec{a}$ is *zero*. In such cases, the net force acting on the object must be zero as well. One way an object can have $\vec{a} = \vec{0}$ is to be at rest. An object that remains at rest is said to be in **static equilibrium**. A second way for an object to have $\vec{a} = \vec{0}$ is to move in a straight line at a constant speed. Such an object is in **dynamic equilibrium**. The key property of both these cases of **equilibrium** is that the net force acting on the object is $\vec{F}_{net} = \vec{0}$.

To use Newton's laws, we have to identify all the forces acting on an object and then evaluate $\vec{F}_{net}$. Recall that $\vec{F}_{net}$ is the vector sum

$$\vec{F}_{net} = \vec{F}_1 + \vec{F}_2 + \vec{F}_3 + \cdots$$

where $\vec{F}_1$, $\vec{F}_2$, and so on are the individual forces, such as tension or friction, acting on the object. We found in Chapter 3 that vector sums can be evaluated in terms of the x- and y-components of the vectors; that is, the x-component of the net force is $(F_{net})_x = F_{1x} + F_{2x} + F_{3x} + \cdots$. If we restrict ourselves to problems where all the forces are in the xy-plane, then the equilibrium requirement $\vec{F}_{net} = \vec{a} = \vec{0}$ is a shorthand way of writing two simultaneous equations:

$$(F_{net})_x = F_{1x} + F_{2x} + F_{3x} + \cdots = 0$$
$$(F_{net})_y = F_{1y} + F_{2y} + F_{3y} + \cdots = 0$$

Recall from your math classes that the Greek letter Σ (sigma) stands for "the sum of." It will be convenient to abbreviate the sum of the x-components of all forces as

$$F_{1x} + F_{2x} + F_{3x} + \cdots = \sum F_x$$

With this notation, Newton's second law for an object in equilibrium, with $\vec{a} = \vec{0}$, can be written as the two equations

$$\sum F_x = ma_x = 0 \quad \text{and} \quad \sum F_y = ma_y = 0 \qquad (5.1)$$

In equilibrium, the sums of the x- and y-components of the force are zero

Although this may look a bit forbidding, we'll soon see how to use a free-body diagram of the forces to help evaluate these sums.

When an object is in equilibrium, we are usually interested in finding the forces that keep it in equilibrium. Newton's second law is the basis for a strategy for solving equilibrium problems.

PROBLEM-SOLVING
STRATEGY 5.1   **Equilibrium problems**

PREPARE First check that the object is in equilibrium: Does $\vec{a} = \vec{0}$?

- An object at rest is in static equilibrium.
- An object moving at a constant velocity is in dynamic equilibrium.

Then identify all forces acting on the object and show them on a free-body diagram. Determine which forces you know and which you need to solve for.

Continued

SOLVE An object in equilibrium must satisfy Newton's second law for the case where $\vec{a} = \vec{0}$. In component form, the requirement is

$$\sum F_x = ma_x = 0 \quad \text{and} \quad \sum F_y = ma_y = 0$$

You can find the force components that go into these sums directly from your free-body diagram. From these two equations, solve for the unknown forces in the problem.

ASSESS Check that your result has the correct units, is reasonable, and answers the question.

Static Equilibrium

EXAMPLE 5.1 **Forces supporting an orangutan**

An orangutan weighing 500 N hangs from a vertical vine. What is the tension in the vine?

PREPARE The orangutan is at rest, so it is in static equilibrium. The net force on it must then be zero. FIGURE 5.1 first identifies the forces acting on the orangutan: the upward force of the tension in the vine and the downward, long-range force of gravity. These forces are then shown on a free-body diagram, where it's noted that equilibrium requires $\vec{F}_{net} = \vec{0}$.

FIGURE 5.1 The forces on an orangutan.

SOLVE Neither force has an x-component, so we need to examine only the y-components of the forces. In this case, the y-component of Newton's second law is

$$\sum F_y = T_y + w_y = ma_y = 0$$

You might have been tempted to write $T_y - w_y$ because the weight force points down. But remember that T_y and w_y are *components* of vectors, and can thus be positive (for a vector such as $\vec{T}$ that points up) or negative (for a vector such as $\vec{w}$ that points down). The fact that $\vec{w}$ points down is taken into account when we *evaluate* the components—that is, when we write them in terms of the *magnitudes* T and w of the vectors $\vec{T}$ and $\vec{w}$.

Because the tension vector $\vec{T}$ points straight up, in the positive y-direction, its y-component is $T_y = T$. Because the weight vector $\vec{w}$ points straight down, in the negative y-direction, its y-component is $w_y = -w$. This is where the signs enter. With these components, Newton's second law becomes

$$T - w = 0$$

This equation is easily solved for the tension in the vine:

$$T = w = 500 \text{ N}$$

ASSESS It's not surprising that the tension in the vine equals the weight of the orangutan. However, we'll soon see that this is *not* the case if the object is accelerating.

EXAMPLE 5.2 **Readying a wrecking ball**

A wrecking ball weighing 2500 N hangs from a cable. Prior to swinging, it is pulled back to a 20° angle by a second, horizontal cable. What is the tension in the horizontal cable?

PREPARE Because the ball is not moving, it hangs in static equilibrium, with $\vec{a} = \vec{0}$, until it is released. In FIGURE 5.2, we start by identifying all the forces acting on the ball: a tension force from each cable and the ball's weight. We've used different symbols $\vec{T}_1$ and $\vec{T}_2$ for the two different tension forces. We then construct a free-body diagram for these three forces, noting that $\vec{F}_{net} = m\vec{a} = \vec{0}$. We're looking for the magnitude T_1 of the tension force $\vec{T}_1$ in the horizontal cable.

FIGURE 5.2 Visual overview of a wrecking ball just before release.

Continued

SOLVE The requirement of equilibrium is $\vec{F}_{net} = m\vec{a} = \vec{0}$. In component form, we have the two equations:

$$\sum F_x = T_{1x} + T_{2x} + w_x = ma_x = 0$$

$$\sum F_y = T_{1y} + T_{2y} + w_y = ma_y = 0$$

As always, we *add* the force components together. Now we're ready to write the components of each force vector in terms of the magnitudes and directions of those vectors. We learned how to do this in Section 3.3 of Chapter 3. With practice you'll learn to read the components directly off the free-body diagram, but to begin it's worthwhile to organize the components into a table.

Force	Name of x-component	Value of x-component	Name of y-component	Value of y-component
$\vec{T}_1$	T_{1x}	$-T_1$	T_{1y}	0
$\vec{T}_2$	T_{2x}	$T_2\sin\theta$	T_{2y}	$T_2\cos\theta$
$\vec{w}$	w_x	0	w_y	$-w$

We see from the free-body diagram that $\vec{T}_1$ points along the negative x-axis, so $T_{1x} = -T_1$ and $T_{1y} = 0$. We need to be careful with our trigonometry as we find the components of $\vec{T}_2$. Remembering that the side adjacent to the angle is related to the cosine,

we see that the vertical (y) component of $\vec{T}_2$ is $T_2\cos\theta$. Similarly, the horizontal (x) component is $T_2\sin\theta$. The weight vector points straight down, so its y-component is $-w$. Notice that negative signs enter as we evaluate the components of the vectors, *not* when we write Newton's second law. This is a critical aspect of solving force and motion problems. With these components, Newton's second law now becomes

$$-T_1 + T_2\sin\theta + 0 = 0 \quad \text{and} \quad 0 + T_2\cos\theta - w = 0$$

We can rewrite these equations as

$$T_2\sin\theta = T_1 \quad \text{and} \quad T_2\cos\theta = w$$

These are two simultaneous equations with two unknowns: T_1 and T_2. To eliminate T_2 from the two equations, we solve the second equation for T_2, giving $T_2 = w/\cos\theta$. Then we insert this expression for T_2 into the first equation to get

$$T_1 = \frac{w}{\cos\theta}\sin\theta = \frac{\sin\theta}{\cos\theta}w = w\tan\theta = (2500\text{ N})\tan 20° = 910\text{ N}$$

where we made use of the fact that $\tan\theta = \sin\theta/\cos\theta$.

ASSESS It seems reasonable that to pull the ball back to this modest angle, a force substantially less than the ball's weight will be required.

CONCEPTUAL EXAMPLE 5.3   **Forces in static equilibrium**

A rod is free to slide on a frictionless sheet of ice. One end of the rod is lifted by a string. If the rod is at rest, which diagram in FIGURE 5.3 shows the correct angle of the string?

FIGURE 5.3 Which is the correct angle of the string?

(a)   (b)   (c)

Frictionless surface

REASON If the rod is to hang motionless, it must be in static equilibrium with $\sum F_x = ma_x = 0$ and $\sum F_y = ma_y = 0$. FIGURE 5.4 shows free-body diagrams for the three string orientations. Remember that tension always acts along the direction of the string and that the weight force always points straight down. The

FIGURE 5.4 Free-body diagrams for three angles of the string.

(a)   (b)   (c)

ice pushes up with a normal force perpendicular to the surface, but frictionless ice cannot exert any horizontal force. If the string is angled, we see that its horizontal component exerts a net force on the rod. Only in case b, where the tension and the string are vertical, can the net force be zero.

ASSESS If friction were present, the rod could in fact hang as in cases a or c. But without friction, the rods in these cases would slide until they came to rest as in case b.

Dynamic Equilibrium

EXAMPLE 5.4   **Tension in towing a car**

A car with a mass of 1500 kg is being towed at a steady speed by a rope held at a 20° angle. A friction force of 320 N opposes the car's motion. What is the tension in the rope?

PREPARE The car is moving in a straight line at a constant speed ($\vec{a} = \vec{0}$) so it is in dynamic equilibrium and must have

$\vec{F}_{net} = m\vec{a} = \vec{0}$. FIGURE 5.5 shows three contact forces acting on the car—the tension force $\vec{T}$, friction $\vec{f}$, and the normal force $\vec{n}$—and the long-range force of gravity $\vec{w}$. These four forces are shown on the free-body diagram.

FIGURE 5.5 Visual overview of a car being towed.

SOLVE This is still an equilibrium problem, even though the car is moving, so our problem-solving procedure is unchanged. With four forces, the requirement of equilibrium is

$$\sum F_x = n_x + T_x + f_x + w_x = ma_x = 0$$

$$\sum F_y = n_y + T_y + f_y + w_y = ma_y = 0$$

We can again determine the horizontal and vertical components of the forces by "reading" the free-body diagram. The results are shown in the table.

Force	Name of x-component	Value of x-component	Name of y-component	Value of y-component
$\vec{n}$	n_x	0	n_y	n
$\vec{T}$	T_x	$T\cos\theta$	T_y	$T\sin\theta$
$\vec{f}$	f_x	$-f$	f_y	0
$\vec{w}$	w_x	0	w_y	$-w$

With these components, Newton's second law becomes

$$T\cos\theta - f = 0$$

$$n + T\sin\theta - w = 0$$

The first equation can be used to solve for the tension in the rope:

$$T = \frac{f}{\cos\theta} = \frac{320\ \text{N}}{\cos 20°} = 340\ \text{N}$$

to two significant figures. It turned out that we did not need the y-component equation in this problem. We would need it if we wanted to find the normal force $\vec{n}$.

ASSESS Had we pulled the car with a horizontal rope, the tension would need to exactly balance the friction force of 320 N. Because we are pulling at an angle, however, part of the tension in the rope pulls *up* on the car instead of in the forward direction. Thus we need a little more tension in the rope when it's at an angle.

5.2 Dynamics and Newton's Second Law

Newton's second law is the essential link between force and motion. The essence of Newtonian mechanics can be expressed in two steps:

- The forces acting on an object determine its acceleration $\vec{a} = \vec{F}_{net}/m$.
- The object's motion can be found by using $\vec{a}$ in the equations of kinematics.

We want to develop a strategy to solve a variety of problems in mechanics, but first we need to write the second law in terms of its components. To do so, let's first rewrite Newton's second law in the form

$$\vec{F}_{net} = \vec{F}_1 + \vec{F}_2 + \vec{F}_3 + \cdots = m\vec{a}$$

where $\vec{F}_1, \vec{F}_2, \vec{F}_3$, and so on are the forces acting on an object. To write the second law in component form merely requires that we use the x- and y-components of the acceleration. Thus Newton's second law, $\vec{F}_{net} = m\vec{a}$, is

$$\sum F_x = ma_x \quad \text{and} \quad \sum F_y = ma_y \qquad (5.2)$$

Newton's second law in component form

The first equation says that **the component of the acceleration in the x-direction is determined by the sum of the x-components of the forces acting on the object.** A similar statement applies to the y-direction.

There are two basic types of problems in mechanics. In the first, you use information about forces to find an object's acceleration, then use kinematics to determine the object's motion. In the second, you use information about the object's motion to determine its acceleration, then solve for unknown forces. Either way, the two equations of Equation 5.2 are the link between force and motion, and they form the basis of a problem-solving strategy. The primary goal of this chapter is to illustrate the use of this strategy.

PROBLEM-SOLVING
STRATEGY 5.2   Dynamics problems

PREPARE   Sketch a visual overview consisting of:

- A list of values that identifies known quantities and what the problem is trying to find.
- A force identification diagram to help you identify all the forces acting on the object.
- A free-body diagram that shows all the forces acting on the object.

If you'll need to use kinematics to find velocities or positions, you'll also need to sketch:

- A motion diagram to determine the direction of the acceleration.
- A pictorial representation that establishes a coordinate system, shows important points in the motion, and defines symbols.

It's OK to go back and forth between these steps as you visualize the situation.

SOLVE   Write Newton's second law in component form as

$$\sum F_x = ma_x \qquad \text{and} \qquad \sum F_y = ma_y$$

You can find the components of the forces directly from your free-body diagram. Depending on the problem, either:

- Solve for the acceleration, then use kinematics to find velocities and positions.
- Use kinematics to determine the acceleration, then solve for unknown forces.

ASSESS   Check that your result has the correct units, is reasonable, and answers the question.

Exercise 24

EXAMPLE 5.5   **Putting a golf ball**

A golfer putts a 46 g ball with a speed of 3.0 m/s. Friction exerts a 0.020 N retarding force on the ball, slowing it down. Will her putt reach the hole, 10 m away?

PREPARE   FIGURE 5.6 is a visual overview of the problem. We've collected the known information, drawn a sketch, and identified what we want to find. The motion diagram shows that the ball is slowing down as it rolls to the right, so the acceleration vector points to the left. Next, we identify the forces acting on the ball and show them on a free-body diagram. Note that the net force points to the left, as it must because the acceleration points to the left.

FIGURE 5.6 Visual overview of a golf putt.

Known
$x_i = 0$ m $f = 0.020$ N
$(v_x)_i = 3.0$ m/s $m = 0.046$ kg
$(v_x)_f = 0$ m/s

Find
x_f

SOLVE Newton's second law in component form is

$$\sum F_x = n_x + f_x + w_x = 0 - f + 0 = ma_x$$

$$\sum F_y = n_y + f_y + w_y = n + 0 - w = ma_y = 0$$

We've written the equations as sums, as we did with equilibrium problems, then "read" the values of the force components from the free-body diagram. The components are simple enough in this problem that we don't really need to show them in a table. It is particularly important to notice that we set $a_y = 0$ in the second equation. This is because the ball does not move in the y-direction, so it can't have any acceleration in the y-direction. This will be an important step in many problems.

The first equation is $-f = ma_x$, from which we find

$$a_x = -\frac{f}{m} = \frac{-(0.020 \text{ N})}{0.046 \text{ kg}} = -0.43 \text{ m/s}^2$$

The negative sign shows that the acceleration is directed to the left, as expected.

Now that we know the acceleration, we can use kinematics to find how far the ball will roll before stopping. We don't have any information about the time it takes for the ball to stop, so we'll use the kinematic equation $(v_x)_f^2 = (v_x)_i^2 + 2a_x(x_f - x_i)$. This gives

$$x_f = x_i + \frac{(v_x)_f^2 - (v_x)_i^2}{2a_x} = 0 \text{ m} + \frac{(0 \text{ m/s})^2 - (3.0 \text{ m/s})^2}{2(-0.43 \text{ m/s}^2)} = 10.5 \text{ m}$$

If her aim is true, the ball will just make it into the hole.

ASSESS It seems reasonable that a ball putted on grass with an initial speed of 3 m/s—about jogging speed—would travel roughly 10 m.

EXAMPLE 5.6 **Finding a rocket cruiser's acceleration**

A rocket cruiser with a mass of 2200 kg and weighing 5000 N is flying horizontally over the surface of a distant planet. At its present speed, a 3000 N drag force acts on the cruiser. The cruiser's engines can be tilted so as to provide a thrust angled up or down. The pilot turns the thrust up to 14,000 N while pivoting the engines to continue flying horizontally. What is the cruiser's acceleration?

PREPARE FIGURE 5.7 is a visual overview in which we've listed the known information, identified the forces on the cruiser, and drawn a free-body diagram. (Because kinematics is not needed to find the acceleration, we don't need a pictorial diagram.) As discussed in Chapter 4, the thrust force points *opposite* the direction of the rocket exhaust, which we've shown at angle θ. The thrust must have an upward vertical component to balance the weight force; otherwise, the cruiser would fall. To continue flying horizontally requires the net force to be directed forward.

SOLVE Newton's second law in component form is

$$\sum F_x = (F_{\text{thrust}})_x + D_x + w_x = ma_x$$

$$\sum F_y = (F_{\text{thrust}})_y + D_y + w_y = ma_y$$

From the free-body diagram, we see that $(F_{\text{thrust}})_x = F_{\text{thrust}}\cos\theta$, $(F_{\text{thrust}})_y = F_{\text{thrust}}\sin\theta$, $D_x = -D$, $D_y = 0$, $w_x = 0$, and $w_y = -w$. We know that a_y must be zero because the cruiser is to accelerate *horizontally*. Thus the second law becomes

$$F_{\text{thrust}}\cos\theta - D = ma_x$$

$$F_{\text{thrust}}\sin\theta - w = 0$$

The first of these equations contains a_x, the quantity we want to find, but we can't solve for a_x without knowing what θ is. Fortunately, we can use the second equation to find θ, then use this value of θ in the first equation to find a_x.
The second equation gives

$$\sin\theta = \frac{w}{F_{\text{thrust}}} = \frac{5000 \text{ N}}{14,000 \text{ N}} = 0.357$$

$$\theta = \sin^{-1}(0.357) = 20.9°$$

Now we can use this value in the first equation to get

$$a_x = \frac{1}{m}(F_{\text{thrust}}\cos\theta - D)$$
$$= \frac{1}{2200 \text{ kg}}[(14,000 \text{ N})\cos(20.9°) - 3000 \text{ N}] = 4.6 \text{ m/s}^2$$

ASSESS An important key to solving this problem was to use the information that the cruiser accelerates only in the horizontal direction. Mathematically, this means that $a_y = 0$. Because the thrust is much greater than the weight, we need only a modest downward component of the thrust to cancel the weight and let the cruiser accelerate horizontally. So our engine tilt seems reasonable.

FIGURE 5.7 Visual overview of a rocket cruiser.

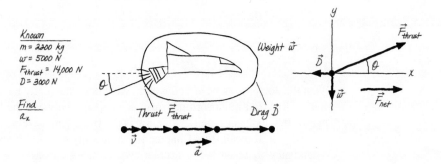

EXAMPLE 5.7 Towing a car with acceleration

A car with a mass of 1500 kg is being towed by a rope held at a 20° angle. A friction force of 320 N opposes the car's motion. What is the tension in the rope if the car goes from rest to 12 m/s in 10 s?

PREPARE You should recognize that this problem is almost identical to Example 5.4. The difference is that the car is now accelerating, so it is no longer in equilibrium. This means, as shown in FIGURE 5.8, that the net force is not zero. We've already identified all the forces in Example 5.4.

SOLVE Newton's second law in component form is

$$\sum F_x = n_x + T_x + f_x + w_x = ma_x$$
$$\sum F_y = n_y + T_y + f_y + w_y = ma_y = 0$$

We've again used the fact that $a_y = 0$ for motion that is purely along the x-axis. The components of the forces were worked out in Example 5.4. With that information, Newton's second law in component form is

$$T\cos\theta - f = ma_x$$
$$n + T\sin\theta - w = 0$$

Because the car speeds up from rest to 12 m/s in 10 s, we can use kinematics to find the acceleration:

$$a_x = \frac{\Delta v_x}{\Delta t} = \frac{(v_x)_f - (v_x)_i}{t_f - t_i} = \frac{(12\ \text{m/s}) - (0\ \text{m/s})}{(10\ \text{s}) - (0\ \text{s})} = 1.2\ \text{m/s}^2$$

We can now use the first Newton's-law equation above to solve for the tension. We have

$$T = \frac{ma_x + f}{\cos\theta} = \frac{(1500\ \text{kg})(1.2\ \text{m/s}^2) + 320\ \text{N}}{\cos 20°} = 2300\ \text{N}$$

ASSESS The tension is substantially more than the 340 N found in Example 5.4. It takes a much more force to accelerate the car than to keep it rolling at a constant speed.

FIGURE 5.8 Visual overview of a car being towed.

Known

$x_i = 0$ m
$(v_x)_i = 0$ m/s
$t_i = 0$ s, $\theta = 20°$
$m = 1500$ kg
$f = 320$ N
$(v_x)_f = 12$ m/s
$t_f = 10$ s

Find
T

These first examples have shown all the details of our problem-solving strategy. Our purpose has been to demonstrate how the strategy is put into practice. Future examples will be briefer, but the basic *procedure* will remain the same.

STOP TO THINK 5.1 A Martian lander is approaching the surface. It is slowing its descent by firing its rocket motor. Which is the correct free-body diagram for the lander?

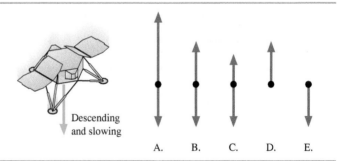

5.3 Mass and Weight

When the doctor asks what you weigh, what does she really mean? We do not make much distinction in our ordinary use of language between the terms "weight" and "mass," but in physics their distinction is of critical importance.

Mass, you'll recall from Chapter 4, is a quantity that describes an object's inertia, its tendency to resist being accelerated. Loosely speaking, it also describes the amount of matter in an object. Mass, measured in kilograms, is an intrinsic property of an object; it has the same value wherever the object may be and whatever forces might be acting on it.

Weight, on the other hand, is a *force*. Specifically, it is the gravitational force exerted on an object by a planet. Weight is a vector, not a scalar, and the vector's direction is always straight down. Weight is measured in newtons.

Mass and weight are not the same thing, but they are related. We can use Galileo's discovery about free fall to make the connection. FIGURE 5.9 shows the free-body diagram of an object in free fall. The *only* force acting on this object is its weight $\vec{w}$ the downward pull of gravity. Newton's second law for this object is

$$\vec{F}_{net} = \vec{w} = m\vec{a} \qquad (5.3)$$

Recall Galileo's discovery that *any* object in free fall, regardless of its mass, has the same acceleration:

$$\vec{a}_{freefall} = (g, \text{downward}) \qquad (5.4)$$

where $g = 9.80 \text{ m/s}^2$ is the free-fall acceleration at the earth's surface. So a_y in Equation 5.3 is equal to $-g$, and we have $-w = -mg$, or

$$w = mg \qquad (5.5)$$

The magnitude of the weight force, which we call simply "the weight," is directly proportional to the mass, with g as the constant of proportionality. Thus, for example, the weight of a 3.6 kg book is $w = (3.6 \text{ kg})(9.8 \text{ m/s}^2) = 35$ N.

> NOTE ▶ Although we derived the relationship between mass and weight for an object in free fall, the weight of an object is *independent* of its state of motion. Equation 5.5 holds for an object at rest on a table, sliding horizontally, or moving in any other way. ◀

Because an object's weight depends on g, and the value of g varies from planet to planet, weight is not a fixed, constant property of an object. The value of g at the surface of the moon is about one-sixth its earthly value, so an object on the moon would have only one-sixth its weight on earth. The object's weight on Jupiter would be greater than its weight on earth. Its mass, however, would be the same. The amount of matter has not changed, only the gravitational force exerted on that matter.

So, when the doctor asks what you weigh, she really wants to know your *mass*. That's the amount of matter in your body. You can't really "lose weight" by going to the moon, even though you would weigh less there!

Measuring Mass and Weight

A *pan balance,* shown in FIGURE 5.10, is a device for measuring *mass.* You may have used a pan balance to "weigh" chemicals in a chemistry lab. An unknown mass is placed in one pan, then known masses are added to the other until the pans balance. Gravity pulls down on both sides, effectively *comparing* the masses, and the unknown mass equals the sum of the known masses that balance it. Although a pan balance requires gravity in order to function, it does not depend on the value of g. Consequently, the pan balance would give the same result on another planet.

A *spring scale* measures weight, not mass. A spring scale can be understood on the basis of Newton's second law. The object being weighed compresses the springs, as shown in FIGURE 5.11 on the following page, which then push up with force $\vec{F}_{sp}$. But because the object is at rest, in static equilibrium, the net force on it must be zero. Thus the upward spring force must exactly balance the downward weight force:

$$F_{sp} = w = mg \qquad (5.6)$$

The *reading* of a spring scale is F_{sp}, the magnitude of the force that the spring is exerting. If the object is in equilibrium, then F_{sp} is exactly equal to the object's weight w. The scale does not "know" the weight of the object. All it can do is measure how much its spring is stretched or compressed. On a different planet, with a

FIGURE 5.9 The free-body diagram of an object in free fall.

On the moon, astronaut John Young jumps 2 feet straight up, despite his spacesuit that weighs 370 pounds on earth. On the moon, where $g = 1.6 \text{ m/s}^2$, he and his suit together weighed only 90 pounds.

FIGURE 5.10 A pan balance measures mass.

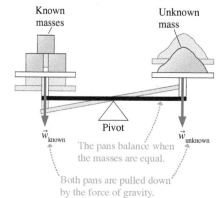

FIGURE 5.11 A spring scale measures weight.

different value for g, the expansion or compression of the spring would be different and the scale's reading would be different.

The unit of force in the English system is the *pound*. We noted in Chapter 4 that the pound is defined as 1 lb = 4.45 N. An object whose weight $w = mg$ is 4.45 N has a mass

$$m = \frac{w}{g} = \frac{4.45 \text{ N}}{9.80 \text{ m/s}^2} = 0.454 \text{ kg} = 454 \text{ g}$$

You may have learned in previous science classes that "1 pound = 454 grams" or, equivalently, "1 kg = 2.2 lb." Strictly speaking, these well-known "conversion factors" are not true. They are comparing a weight (pounds) to a mass (kilograms). The correct statement is: "A mass of 1 kg has a weight on *earth* of 2.2 pounds." On another planet, the weight of a 1 kg mass would be something other than 2.2 pounds.

EXAMPLE 5.8 **Masses of people**

What is the mass, in kilograms, of a 90 pound gymnast, a 160 pound professor, and a 240 pound football player?

SOLVE We must convert their weights into newtons; then we can find their masses from $m = w/g$:

$$w_{\text{gymnast}} = 90 \text{ lb} \times \frac{4.45 \text{ N}}{1 \text{ lb}} = 400 \text{ N} \qquad m_{\text{gymnast}} = \frac{w_{\text{gymnast}}}{g} = \frac{400 \text{ N}}{9.80 \text{ m/s}^2} = 41 \text{ kg}$$

$$w_{\text{prof}} = 160 \text{ lb} \times \frac{4.45 \text{ N}}{1 \text{ lb}} = 710 \text{ N} \qquad m_{\text{prof}} = \frac{w_{\text{prof}}}{g} = \frac{710 \text{ N}}{9.80 \text{ m/s}^2} = 72 \text{ kg}$$

$$w_{\text{football}} = 240 \text{ lb} \times \frac{4.45 \text{ N}}{1 \text{ lb}} = 1070 \text{ N} \qquad m_{\text{football}} = \frac{w_{\text{football}}}{g} = \frac{1070 \text{ N}}{9.80 \text{ m/s}^2} = 110 \text{ kg}$$

ASSESS It's worth remembering that a *typical* adult has a mass in the range of 60 to 80 kg.

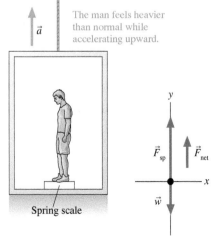

This popular amusement park ride shoots you straight up with an acceleration of $4g$. As a result, you feel five times as heavy as usual.

FIGURE 5.12 A man weighing himself in an accelerating elevator.

The man feels heavier than normal while accelerating upward.

Spring scale

Apparent Weight

The weight of an object is the force of gravity on that object. You may never have thought about it, but gravity is not a force that you can feel or sense directly. Your *sensation* of weight—how heavy you *feel*—is due to *contact forces* pressing against you. Surfaces touch you and activate nerve endings in your skin. As you read this, your sensation of weight is due to the normal force exerted on you by the chair in which you are sitting. When you stand, you feel the contact force of the floor pushing against your feet.

When you stand on a scale, the contact force is the upward spring force F_{sp} acting on your feet. If you and the scale are in equilibrium, with $\vec{a} = \vec{0}$, this spring force and thus the scale reading are equal to your weight.

What would happen, however, if you stood on a scale while *accelerating* upward in an elevator? What would the scale read then? Recall the sensations you feel while being accelerated. You feel "heavy" when an elevator suddenly accelerates upward, and you feel lighter than normal as the upward-moving elevator brakes to a halt. Your true weight $w = mg$ has not changed during these events, but your *sensation* of your weight has.

To investigate this, imagine a man weighing himself by standing on a spring scale in an elevator as it accelerates upward. What does the scale read? As FIGURE 5.12 shows, the only forces acting on the man are the upward spring force of the scale and the downward weight force. Because the man now has an acceleration $\vec{a}$, according to Newton's second law there must be a net force acting on the man in the direction of $\vec{a}$.

Looking at the free-body diagram in Figure 5.12, we see that the y-component of Newton's second law is

$$\sum F_y = (F_{sp})_y + w_y = F_{sp} - w = ma_y \qquad (5.7)$$

where m is the man's mass. Solving Equation 5.7 for F_{sp} gives

$$F_{sp} = w + ma_y \qquad (5.8)$$

If the elevator is either at rest or moving with constant velocity, then $a_y = 0$ and the man is in equilibrium. In that case, $F_{sp} = w$ and the scale correctly reads his weight. But if $a_y \neq 0$, the scale's reading is *not* the man's true weight. If the elevator is accelerating upward, then $a_y = +a$, and Equation 5.8 reads $F_{sp} = w + a$. Thus $F_{sp} > w$ and the man *feels* heavier than normal. If the elevator is accelerating downward, the acceleration vector $\vec{a}$ points downward and $a_y = -a$. Thus $F_{sp} < w$ and the man feels lighter.

Let's define a person's **apparent weight** w_{app} as the magnitude of the contact force that supports him; in this case, this is the spring force F_{sp}. From Equation 5.8, the apparent weight is

$$w_{app} = w + ma_y = mg + ma_y = m(g + a_y) \qquad (5.9)$$

Thus, when the man accelerates upward, his apparent weight is greater than his true weight; when accelerating downward, his apparent weight is less than his true weight.

An object doesn't have to be on a scale for its apparent weight to differ from its true weight. An object's apparent weight is the magnitude of the contact force supporting it. It makes no difference whether this is the spring force of the scale or simply the normal force of the floor.

The idea of apparent weight has important applications. Astronauts are nearly crushed by their apparent weight during a rocket launch when a is much greater than g. Much of the thrill of amusement park rides, such as roller coasters, comes from rapid changes in your apparent weight.

TRY IT YOURSELF

Physics students can't jump The next time you ride up in an elevator, try jumping in the air just as the elevator starts to rise. You'll feel like you can hardly get off the ground. This is because with $a_y > 0$ your apparent weight is *greater* than your actual weight; for an elevator with a large acceleration it's like trying to jump while carrying an extra 20 pounds. What will happen if you jump as the elevator slows at the top?

EXAMPLE 5.9 **Apparent weight in an elevator**

Anjay's mass is 70 kg. He's standing on a scale in an elevator. As the elevator stops, the scale reads 750 N. Had the elevator been moving up or down? If the elevator had been moving at 5.0 m/s, how long does it take to stop?

PREPARE The scale reading as he stops is his apparent weight, so $w_{app} = 750$ N. Because we know his mass m, we can use Equation 5.9 to find the elevator's acceleration a_y. Then we can use kinematics to find the time it takes to stop the elevator.

SOLVE From Equation 5.9 we have $w_{app} = m(g + a_y)$, so that

$$a_y = \frac{w_{app}}{m} - g = \frac{750 \text{ N}}{70 \text{ kg}} - 9.80 \text{ m/s}^2 = 0.91 \text{ m/s}^2$$

This is a *positive* acceleration. If the elevator is stopping with a positive acceleration, it must have been moving *down,* with a negative velocity.

To find the stopping time, we can use the kinematic equation

$$(v_y)_f = (v_y)_i + a_y \, \Delta t$$

to get

$$\Delta t = \frac{(v_y)_f - (v_y)_i}{a_y} = \frac{(0 \text{ m/s}) - (-5.0 \text{ m/s})}{0.91 \text{ m/s}^2} = 5.5 \text{ s}$$

Notice that we used -5.0 m/s as the initial velocity because the elevator was moving down before it stopped.

ASSESS Anjay's true weight is $mg = (70 \text{ kg})(9.8 \text{ m/s}^2) = 670$ N. Thus his apparent weight is *greater* than his true weight. You have no doubt experienced this sensation in an elevator that is stopping as it reaches the ground floor. If it had stopped while going up, you'd feel *lighter* than your true weight.

Weightlessness

One last issue before leaving this topic: Suppose the elevator cable breaks and the elevator, along with the man and his scale, plunges straight down in free fall! What will the scale read? The acceleration in free fall is $a_y = -g$. When this acceleration is used in Equation 5.9, we find that $w_{app} = 0$! In other words, the man has *no sensation* of weight.

A weightless experience You probably wouldn't want to experience weightlessness in a falling elevator. But, as we learned in Chapter 3, objects undergoing projectile motion are in free fall as well. The special plane shown flies in the same parabolic trajectory as would a projectile with no air resistance. Objects inside, such as these passengers, are then moving along a perfect free-fall trajectory. Just as for the man in the elevator, they then float with respect to the plane's interior. Such flights can last up to 30 seconds.

Think about this carefully. Suppose, as the elevator falls, the man inside releases a ball from his hand. In the absence of air resistance, as Galileo discovered, both the man and the ball would fall at the same rate. From the man's perspective, the ball would appear to "float" beside him. Similarly, the scale would float beneath him and not press against his feet. He is what we call *weightless*.

Surprisingly, "weightless" does *not* mean "no weight." An object that is **weightless** has no *apparent* weight. The distinction is significant. The man's weight is still *mg* because gravity is still pulling down on him, but he has no *sensation* of weight as he free falls. The term "weightless" is a very poor one, likely to cause confusion because it implies that objects have no weight. As we see, that is not the case.

But isn't this exactly what happens to astronauts orbiting the earth? You've seen films of astronauts and various objects floating inside the Space Shuttle. If an astronaut tries to stand on a scale, it does not exert any force against her feet and reads zero. She is said to be weightless. But if the criterion to be weightless is to be in free fall, and if astronauts orbiting the earth are weightless, does this mean that they are in free fall? This is a very interesting question to which we shall return in Chapter 6.

STOP TO THINK 5.2 You're bouncing up and down on a trampoline. At the very highest point of your motion, your apparent weight is

A. More than your true weight.
B. Less than your true weight.
C. Equal to your true weight.
D. Zero.

5.4 Normal Forces

In Chapter 4 we saw that an object at rest on a table is subject to an upward force due to the table. This force is called the *normal force* because it is always directed normal, or perpendicular, to the surface of contact. As we saw, the normal force has its origin in the atomic "springs" that make up the surface. The harder the object bears down on the surface, the more these springs are compressed and the harder they push back. Thus the normal force *adjusts* itself so that the object stays on the surface without penetrating it. This fact is key in solving for the normal force.

EXAMPLE 5.10 **Normal force on a pressed book**

A 1.2 kg book lies on a table. The book is pressed down from above with a force of 15 N. What is the normal force acting on the book from the table below?

PREPARE The book is not moving and is thus in static equilibrium. We need to identify the forces acting on the book, and prepare a free-body diagram showing these forces. These steps are illustrated in FIGURE 5.13.

FIGURE 5.13 Finding the normal force on a book pressed from above.

SOLVE Because the book is in static equilibrium, the net force on it must be zero. The only forces acting are in the y-direction, so Newton's second law

$$\sum F_y = n_y + w_y + F_y = n - w - F = ma_y = 0$$

We learned in the last section that the weight force is $w = mg$. The weight of the book is thus

$$w = mg = (1.2 \text{ kg})(9.8 \text{ m/s}^2) = 12 \text{ N}$$

With this information, we see that the normal force exerted by the table is

$$n = F + w = 15 \text{ N} + 12 \text{ N} = 27 \text{ N}$$

ASSESS The magnitude of the normal force is *larger* than the weight of the book. From the table's perspective, the extra force from the hand pushes the book further into the atomic springs of the table. These springs then push back harder, giving a normal force that is greater than the weight of the book.

A common situation is an object on a ramp or incline. If friction is neglected, there are only two forces acting on the object: gravity and the normal force. However, we need to carefully work out the components of these two forces in order to solve dynamics problems. FIGURE 5.14a shows how. Be sure you avoid the two common errors shown in FIGURE 5.14b.

FIGURE 5.14 The forces on an object on an incline.

(a) Analyzing forces on an incline

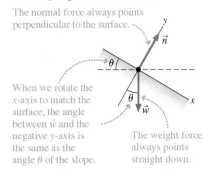

The normal force always points perpendicular to the surface.

When we rotate the x-axis to match the surface, the angle between $\vec{w}$ and the negative y-axis is the same as the angle θ of the slope.

The weight force always points straight down.

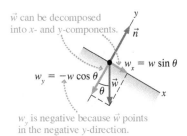

$\vec{w}$ can be decomposed into x- and y-components.

$w_x = w \sin\theta$

$w_y = -w \cos\theta$

w_y is negative because $\vec{w}$ points in the negative y-direction.

(b) Two common mistakes to avoid

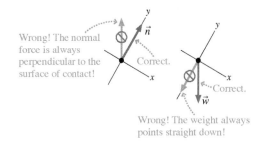

Wrong! The normal force is always perpendicular to the surface of contact!

Correct.

Correct.

Wrong! The weight always points straight down!

EXAMPLE 5.11 **Acceleration of a downhill skier**

A skier slides down a steep slope of 27° on ideal, frictionless snow. What is his acceleration?

PREPARE FIGURE 5.15 is a visual overview. We choose a coordinate system tilted so that the x-axis points down the slope. This greatly simplifies the analysis, because with this choice $a_y = 0$ (the skier does not move in the y-direction at all). The free-body diagram is based on the information in Figure 5.14.

FIGURE 5.15 Visual overview of a downhill skier.

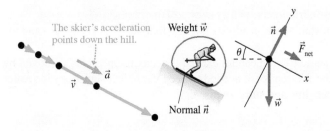

The skier's acceleration points down the hill.

Weight $\vec{w}$

Normal $\vec{n}$

SOLVE We can now use Newton's second law in component form to find the skier's acceleration:

$$\sum F_x = w_x + n_x = ma_x$$
$$\sum F_y = w_y + n_y = ma_y$$

Because $\vec{n}$ points directly in the positive y-direction, $n_y = n$ and $n_x = 0$. Figure 5.14a showed the important fact that the angle between $\vec{w}$ and the negative y-axis is the *same* as the slope angle θ. With this information, the components of $\vec{w}$ are $w_x = w \sin\theta = mg \sin\theta$ and $w_y = -w \cos\theta = -mg \cos\theta$, where we used the fact that $w = mg$. With these components in hand, Newton's second law becomes

$$\sum F_x = w_x + n_x = mg \sin\theta = ma_x$$
$$\sum F_y = w_y + n_y = -mg \cos\theta + n = ma_y = 0$$

In the second equation we used the fact that $a_y = 0$. The m cancels in the first of these equations, leaving us with

$$a_x = g \sin\theta$$

This is the expression for acceleration on a frictionless surface that we presented, without proof, in Chapter 3. Now we've justified our earlier assertion. We can use this to calculate the skier's acceleration:

$$a_x = g \sin\theta = (9.8 \text{ m/s}^2) \sin(27°) = 4.4 \text{ m/s}^2$$

ASSESS Our result shows that when $\theta = 0$, so that the slope is horizontal, the skier's acceleration is zero, as it should be. Further, when $\theta = 90°$ (a vertical slope), his acceleration is g, which makes sense because he's in free fall when $\theta = 90°$. Notice that the mass canceled out, so we didn't need to know the skier's mass.

5.5 Friction

In everyday life, friction is everywhere. Friction is absolutely essential for many things we do. Without friction you could not walk, drive, or even sit down (you would slide right off the chair!). It is sometimes useful to think about idealized frictionless situations, but it is equally necessary to understand a real world where friction is present. Although friction is a complicated force, many aspects of friction can be described with a simple model.

Class Video

FIGURE 5.16 Static friction keeps an object from slipping.

(a) Force identification

Pushing force $\vec{F}_{push}$

Weight $\vec{w}$

Normal $\vec{n}$ Friction $\vec{f}_s$

(b) Free-body diagram

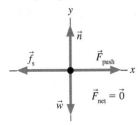

FIGURE 5.17 Static friction acts in *response* to an applied force.

(a) Pushing gently: friction pushes back gently.

$\vec{f}_s$ balances $\vec{F}_{push}$ and the box does not move.

(b) Pushing harder: friction pushes back harder.

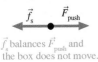

$\vec{f}_s$ grows as $\vec{F}_{push}$ increases, but the two still cancel and the box remains at rest.

(c) Pushing harder still: $\vec{f}_s$ is now pushing back as hard as it can.

$f_{s\,max}$

Now the magnitude of f_s has reached its maximum value $f_{s\,max}$. If $\vec{F}_{push}$ gets any bigger, the forces will *not* cancel and the box will start to accelerate.

TABLE 5.1 Coefficients of friction

Materials	Static μ_s	Kinetic μ_k	Rolling μ_r
Rubber on concrete	1.00	0.80	0.02
Steel on steel (dry)	0.80	0.60	0.002
Steel on steel (lubricated)	0.10	0.05	
Wood on wood	0.50	0.20	
Wood on snow	0.12	0.06	
Ice on ice	0.10	0.03	

Static Friction

Chapter 4 defined static friction $\vec{f}_s$ as the force that a surface exerts on an object to keep it from slipping across that surface. Consider the woman pushing on the box in **FIGURE 5.16a**. Because the box is not moving with respect to the floor, the woman's push to the right must be balanced by a static friction force $\vec{f}_s$ pointing to the left. This is the general rule for finding the *direction* of $\vec{f}_s$: Decide which way the object *would* move if there were no friction. The static friction force $\vec{f}_s$ then points in the opposite direction, to prevent motion relative to the surface.

Determining the *magnitude* of $\vec{f}_s$ is a bit trickier. Because the box is at rest, it's in static equilibrium. From the free-body diagram of **FIGURE 5.16b**, this means that the static friction force must exactly balance the pushing force, so that $f_s = F_{push}$. As shown in **FIGURES 5.17a** and **5.17b**, the harder the woman pushes, the harder the friction force from the floor pushes back. If she reduces her pushing force, the friction force will automatically be reduced to match. Static friction acts in *response* to an applied force.

But there's clearly a limit to how big $\vec{f}_s$ can get. If she pushes hard enough, the box will slip and start to move across the floor. In other words, the static friction force has a *maximum* possible magnitude $f_{s\,max}$, as illustrated in **FIGURE 5.17c**. Experiments with friction (first done by Leonardo da Vinci) show that $f_{s\,max}$ is proportional to the magnitude of the normal force between the surface and the object; that is,

$$f_{s\,max} = \mu_s n \qquad (5.10)$$

where μ_s is called the **coefficient of static friction.** The coefficient is a number that depends on the materials from which the object and the surface are made. The higher the coefficient of static friction, the greater the "stickiness" between the object and the surface, and the harder it is to make the object slip. Table 5.1 lists some approximate values of coefficients of friction.

NOTE ▶ Equation 5.10 does *not* say $f_s = \mu_s n$. The value of f_s depends on the force or forces that static friction has to balance to keep the object from moving. It can have any value from zero up to, but not exceeding, $\mu_s n$. ◀

So our rules for static friction are:

- The direction of static friction is such as to oppose motion.
- The magnitude f_s of static friction adjusts itself so that the net force is zero and the object doesn't move.
- The magnitude of static friction cannot exceed the maximum value $f_{s\,max}$ given by Equation 5.10. If the friction force needed to keep the object stationary is greater than $f_{s\,max}$, the object slips and starts to move.

Kinetic Friction

Once the box starts to slide, as in **FIGURE 5.18**, the static friction force is replaced by a kinetic (or sliding) friction force $\vec{f}_k$. Kinetic friction is in some ways simpler than static friction: The direction of $\vec{f}_k$ is always opposite the direction in which an object

FIGURE 5.18 The kinetic friction force is *opposite* the direction of motion.

The kinetic friction force is the same no matter how fast the object slides.

slides across the surface, and experiments show that kinetic friction, unlike static friction, has a nearly *constant* magnitude, given by

$$f_k = \mu_k n \tag{5.11}$$

where μ_k is called the **coefficient of kinetic friction**. Equation 5.11 also shows that kinetic friction, like static friction, is proportional to the magnitude of the normal force n. Notice that **the magnitude of the kinetic friction force does not depend on how fast the object is sliding.**

Table 5.1 includes approximate values of μ_k. You can see that $\mu_k < \mu_s$, which explains why it is easier to keep a box moving than it was to start it moving.

Rolling Friction

If you slam on the brakes hard enough, your car tires slide against the road surface and leave skid marks. This is kinetic friction because the tire and the road are *sliding* against each other. A wheel *rolling* on a surface also experiences friction, but not kinetic friction: The portion of the wheel that contacts the surface is stationary with respect to the surface, not sliding. The photo in FIGURE 5.19 was taken with a stationary camera. Note how the part of the wheel touching the ground is not blurred, indicating that this part of the wheel is not moving with respect to the ground.

Textbooks draw wheels as circles, but no wheel is perfectly round. The weight of the wheel, and of any object supported by the wheel, causes the bottom of the wheel to flatten where it touches the surface, as FIGURE 5.20 shows. As a wheel rolls forward, the leading part of the tire must become deformed. This requires that the road push *backward* on the tire. In this way the road causes a backward force, even without slipping between the tire and the road.

The force of this *rolling friction* can be calculated in terms of a **coefficient of rolling friction** μ_r:

$$f_r = \mu_r n \tag{5.12}$$

with the *direction* of the force opposing the direction of motion. Thus rolling friction acts very much like kinetic friction, but values of μ_r (see Table 5.1) are much lower than values of μ_k. This is why it is easier to roll an object on wheels than to slide it.

FIGURE 5.19 The bottom of the wheel is stationary.

FIGURE 5.20 Rolling friction is due to deformation of a wheel.

The wheel flattens where it touches the road.

Soon, this part of the tire will be flattened. To flatten it, the road must push *back* on the tire.

STOP TO THINK 5.3 Rank in order, from largest to smallest, the size of the friction forces $\vec{f}_A$ to $\vec{f}_E$ in the five different situations (one or more friction forces could be zero). The box and the floor are made of the same materials in all situations.

| At rest | On the verge of slipping | Speeding up $\vec{a}$ | Constant speed $\vec{a} = \vec{0}$ | Slowing down $\vec{a}$ |

No push $\vec{f}_A$ A.

Push $\vec{f}_B$ B.

Push $\vec{f}_C$ C.

Push $\vec{f}_D$ D.

Push $\vec{f}_E$ E.

Working with Friction Forces

These ideas can be summarized in a *model* of friction:

ActivPhysics: 2.5, 2.6
PhET: Forces in 1D
PhET: Friction
PhET: The Ramp

Static: $\vec{f}_s = $ (magnitude $\leq f_{s\,max} = \mu_s n$,
            direction as necessary to prevent motion)

Kinetic: $\vec{f}_k = (\mu_k n$, direction opposite the motion)

Rolling: $\vec{f}_r = (\mu_r n$, direction opposite the motion)

$$(5.13)$$

p.37
PROPORTIONAL

Here "motion" means "motion relative to the surface." The maximum value of static friction $f_{s\,max} = \mu_s n$ occurs at the point where the object slips and begins to move. Note that only one kind of friction force at a time can act on an object.

NOTE ▶ Equations 5.13 are a "model" of friction, not a "law" of friction. These equations provide a reasonably accurate, but not perfect, description of how friction forces act. They are a simplification of reality that works reasonably well, which is what we mean by a "model." They are not a "law of nature" on a level with Newton's laws. ◀

Optimized braking If you slam on your brakes, your wheels will lock up and you'll go into a skid. Then it is the *kinetic* friction force between the road and your tires that slows your car to a halt. If, however, you apply the brakes such that you don't quite skid and your tires continue to roll, the force stopping you is the *static* friction force between the road and your tires. This is a better way to brake, because the maximum static friction force is always greater than the kinetic friction force. *Antilock braking systems* (ABS) automatically do this for you when you slam on the brakes, stopping you in the shortest possible distance.

TACTICS BOX 5.1 Working with friction forces

❶ If the object is *not moving* relative to the surface it's in contact with, then the friction force is **static friction**. Draw a free-body diagram of the object. The *direction* of the friction force is such as to oppose sliding of the object relative to the surface. Then use Problem-Solving Strategy 5.1 to solve for f_s. If f_s is greater than $f_{s\,max} = \mu_s n$, then static friction cannot hold the object in place. The assumption that the object is at rest is not valid, and you need to redo the problem using kinetic friction.
❷ If the object is *sliding* relative to the surface, then **kinetic friction** is acting. From Newton's second law, find the normal force n. Equation 5.13 then gives the magnitude and direction of the friction force.
❸ If the object is *rolling* along the surface, then **rolling friction** is acting. From Newton's second law, find the normal force n. Equation 5.13 then gives the magnitude and direction of the friction force.

Exercises 20, 21

EXAMPLE 5.12 **Finding the force to push a box**

Carol pushes a 10.0 kg wood box across a wood floor at a steady speed of 2.0 m/s. How much force does Carol exert on the box?

PREPARE Let's assume the box slides to the right. In this case, a kinetic friction force $\vec{f}_k$, opposes the motion by pointing to the left. In **FIGURE 5.21** we identify the forces acting on the box and construct a free-body diagram.

FIGURE 5.21 Forces on a box being pushed across a floor.

SOLVE The box is moving at a constant speed, so it is in dynamic equilibrium with $\vec{F}_{net} = \vec{0}$. This means that the x- and y-components of the net force must be zero:

$$\sum F_x = n_x + w_x + F_x + (f_k)_x = 0 + 0 + F - f_k = 0$$
$$\sum F_y = n_y + w_y + F_y + (f_k)_y = n - w + 0 + 0 = 0$$

In the first equation, the x-component of $\vec{f}_k$ is equal to $-f_k$ because $\vec{f}_k$ is directed to the left. Similarly, $w_y = -w$ because the weight force points down.

From the first equation, we see that Carol's pushing force is $F = f_k$. To evaluate this, we need f_k. Here we can use our model for kinetic friction:

$$f_k = \mu_k n$$

Because the friction is wood sliding on wood, we can use Table 5.1 to find $\mu_k = 0.20$. Further, we can use the second Newton's-law equation to find that the normal force is $n = w = mg$. Thus

$$F = f_k = \mu_k n = \mu_k mg$$
$$= (0.20)(10.0 \text{ kg})(9.80 \text{ m/s}^2) = 20 \text{ N}$$

This is the force that Carol needs to apply to the box to keep it moving at a steady speed.

ASSESS The speed of 2.0 m/s with which Carol pushes the box does not enter into the answer. This is because our model of kinetic friction does not depend on the speed of the sliding object.

To push or pull a lawn roller?

A lawn roller is a heavy cylinder used to flatten a bumpy lawn, as shown in FIGURE 5.22. Is it easier to push or pull such a roller? Which is more effective for flattening the lawn: pushing or pulling? Assume that the pushing or pulling force is directed along the handle of the roller.

FIGURE 5.22 Pushing and pulling a lawn roller.

REASON FIGURE 5.23 shows free-body diagrams for the two cases. We assume that the roller is pushed at a constant speed so that it is in dynamic equilibrium with $\vec{F}_{net} = \vec{0}$. Because the roller does not move in the y-direction, the y-component of the net force must be zero. According to our model, the magnitude f_r of rolling friction is proportional to the magnitude n of the normal force. If we *push* on the roller, our pushing force $\vec{F}$ will have a downward y-component. To compensate for this, the normal force must increase and, because $f_r = \mu_r n$, the rolling friction will increase as well. This makes the roller harder to move. If we *pull* on the roller, the now upward y-component of $\vec{F}$ will lead to a

reduced value of n and hence of f_r. Thus the roller is easier to pull than to push.

FIGURE 5.23 Free-body diagrams for the lawn roller.

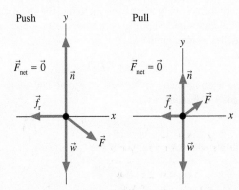

However, the purpose of the roller is to flatten the soil. If the normal force $\vec{n}$ of the ground on the roller is greater, then by Newton's third law the force of the roller on the ground will be greater as well. So for smoothing your lawn, it's better to push.

ASSESS You've probably experienced this effect while using an upright vacuum cleaner. The vacuum is harder to push on the forward stroke than when drawing it back.

How to dump a file cabinet

A 50.0 kg steel file cabinet is in the back of a dump truck. The truck's bed, also made of steel, is slowly tilted. What is the magnitude of the static friction force on the cabinet when the bed is tilted 20°? At what angle will the file cabinet begin to slide?

PREPARE We'll use our model of static friction. The file cabinet will slip when the static friction force reaches its maximum possible value $f_{s\,max}$. FIGURE 5.24 shows the visual overview when the truck bed is tilted at angle θ. We can make the analysis easier if we tilt the coordinate system to match the bed of the truck. To prevent the file cabinet from slipping, the static friction force must point *up* the slope.

SOLVE Before it slips, the file cabinet is in static equilibrium. Newton's second law gives

$$\sum F_x = n_x + w_x + (f_s)_x = 0$$
$$\sum F_y = n_y + w_y + (f_s)_y = 0$$

From the free-body diagram we see that f_s has only a negative x-component and that n has only a positive y-component. We also have $w_x = w\sin\theta$ and $w_y = -w\cos\theta$. Thus the second law becomes

$$\sum F_x = w\sin\theta - f_s = mg\sin\theta - f_s = 0$$
$$\sum F_y = n - w\cos\theta = n - mg\cos\theta = 0$$

FIGURE 5.24 Visual overview of a file cabinet in a tilted dump truck.

Known
$\mu_s = 0.80$ $m = 50.0$ kg
$\mu_k = 0.60$
Find
f_s when $\theta = 20°$
θ at which cabinet slips

Normal $\vec{n}$
Friction $\vec{f_s}$ Weight $\vec{w}$

Continued

The x-component equation allows us to determine the magnitude of the static friction force when $\theta = 20°$:

$$f_s = mg \sin\theta = (50.0 \text{ kg})(9.80 \text{ m/s}^2) \sin 20° = 168 \text{ N}$$

This value does not require that we know μ_s. The coefficient of static friction enters only when we want to find the angle at which the file cabinet slips. Slipping occurs when the static friction force reaches its maximum value:

$$f_s = f_{s\,max} = \mu_s n$$

From the y-component of Newton's second law we see that $n = mg \cos\theta$. Consequently,

$$f_{s\,max} = \mu_s mg \cos\theta$$

The x-component of the second law gave

$$f_s = mg \sin\theta$$

Setting $f_s = f_{s\,max}$ then gives

$$mg \sin\theta = \mu_s mg \cos\theta$$

The mg in both terms cancels, and we find

$$\frac{\sin\theta}{\cos\theta} = \tan\theta = \mu_s$$

$$\theta = \tan^{-1}\mu_s = \tan^{-1}(0.80) = 39°$$

ASSESS Steel doesn't slide all that well on unlubricated steel, so a fairly large angle is not surprising. The answer seems reasonable. It is worth noting that $n = mg \cos\theta$ in this example. A common error is to use simply $n = mg$. Be sure to evaluate the normal force within the context of each particular problem.

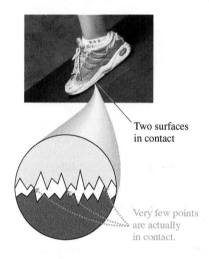

FIGURE 5.25 A microscopic view of friction.

Two surfaces in contact

Very few points are actually in contact.

Causes of Friction

It is worth a brief pause to look at the *causes* of friction. All surfaces, even those quite smooth to the touch, are very rough on a microscopic scale. When two objects are placed in contact, they do not make a smooth fit. Instead, as **FIGURE 5.25** shows, the high points on one surface become jammed against the high points on the other surface, while the low points are not in contact at all. Only a very small fraction (typically 10^{-4}) of the surface area is in actual contact. The amount of contact depends on how hard the surfaces are pushed together, which is why friction forces are proportional to n.

For an object to slip, you must push it hard enough to overcome the forces exerted at these contact points. Once the two surfaces are sliding against each other, their high points undergo constant collisions, deformations, and even brief bonding that lead to the resistive force of kinetic friction.

5.6 Drag

The air exerts a drag force on objects as they move through it. You experience drag forces every day as you jog, bicycle, ski, or drive your car. The drag force $\vec{D}$:

- Is opposite in direction to the velocity $\vec{v}$.
- Increases in magnitude as the object's speed increases.

At relatively low speeds, the drag force in air is small and can usually be neglected, but drag plays an important role as speeds increase. Fortunately, we can use a fairly simple *model* of drag if the following three conditions are met:

- The object's size (diameter) is between a few millimeters and a few meters.
- The object's speed is less than a few hundred meters per second.
- The object is moving through the air near the earth's surface.

These conditions are usually satisfied for balls, people, cars, and many other objects in our everyday experience. Under these conditions, the drag force can be written:

$$\vec{D} = \left(\tfrac{1}{2}C_D\rho Av^2, \text{ direction opposite the motion}\right) \quad (5.14)$$

Drag force on an object of cross-section area A moving at speed v

D

p.47

v

QUADRATIC

Here, ρ is the density of air ($\rho = 1.22$ kg/m^3 at sea level), A is the cross-section area of the object (in m^2), and the **drag coefficient** C_D depends on the details of the object's shape. However, the value of C_D for everyday moving objects is roughly 1/2, so a good approximation to the drag force is

$$D \approx \tfrac{1}{4}\rho A v^2 \qquad (5.15)$$

This is the expression for the magnitude of the drag force that we'll use in this chapter.

The size of the drag force in air is proportional to the *square* of the object's speed: If the speed doubles, the drag increases by a factor of 4. This model of drag fails for objects that are very small (such as dust particles) or very fast (such as jet planes) or that move in other media (such as water).

FIGURE 5.26 shows that the area A in Equation 5.14 is the cross section of the object as it "faces into the wind." It's interesting to note that the magnitude of the drag force depends on the object's *size and shape* but not on its *mass*. This has important consequences for the motion of falling objects.

FIGURE 5.26 How to calculate the cross-section area A.

A is the cross-section area of the cyclist as seen from the front. This area is approximated by the rectangle shown, with area $A = h \times w$.

The cross-section area of a sphere is a circle: For this soccer ball, $A = \pi r^2$.

Terminal Speed

Just after an object is released from rest, its speed is low and the drag force is small (as shown in FIGURE 5.27a). Because the net force is nearly equal to the weight, the object will fall with an acceleration only a little less than g. As it falls farther, its speed and hence the drag force increase. Now the net force is smaller, so the acceleration is smaller (as shown in FIGURE 5.27b). It's still speeding up, but at a lower *rate*. Eventually the speed will increase to a point such that the magnitude of the drag force *equals* the weight (as shown in FIGURE 5.27c). The net force and hence the acceleration at this speed are then *zero,* and the object falls with a *constant* speed. The speed at which the exact balance between the upward drag force and the downward weight force causes an object to fall without acceleration is called the **terminal speed** v_{term}. **Once an object has reached terminal speed, it will continue falling at that speed until it hits the ground.**

It's straightforward to compute the terminal speed. It is the speed, by definition, at which $D = w$ or, equivalently, $\tfrac{1}{4}\rho A v^2 = mg$. This speed is then

$$v_{\text{term}} \approx \sqrt{\dfrac{4mg}{\rho A}} \qquad (5.16)$$

This equation shows that a more massive object has a greater terminal speed than a less massive object of equal size. A 10-cm-diameter lead ball, with a mass of 6 kg, has a terminal speed of 150 m/s, while a 10-cm-diameter Styrofoam ball, with a mass of 50 g, has a terminal speed of only 14 m/s.

FIGURE 5.27 A falling object eventually reaches terminal speed.

(a) At low speeds, D is small and the ball falls with $a \approx g$.

(b) As v increases, so does D. The net force and hence a get smaller.

(c) Eventually, v reaches a value such that $D = w$. Then the net force is zero and the ball falls at a constant speed.

EXAMPLE 5.15 **Terminal speeds of a skydiver and a mouse**

A skydiver and his pet mouse jump from a plane. Estimate their terminal speeds.

PREPARE To use Equation 5.16 we need to estimate the mass m and cross-section area A of both man and mouse. FIGURE 5.28 shows how. A typical skydiver might be 1.8 m long and 0.4 m wide ($A = 0.72$ m^2) with a mass of 75 kg, while a mouse has a mass of perhaps 20 g (0.020 kg) and is 7 cm long and 3 cm wide ($A = 0.07$ m $\times$ 0.03 m = 0.0021 m^2).

FIGURE 5.28 The cross-section areas of a skydiver and a mouse.

SOLVE We can use Equation 5.16 to find that for the skydiver

$$v_{\text{term}} \approx \sqrt{\frac{4mg}{\rho A}} = \sqrt{\frac{4(75 \text{ kg})(9.8 \text{ m/s}^2)}{(1.22 \text{ kg/m}^3)(0.72 \text{ m}^2)}} = 58 \text{ m/s}$$

This is roughly 130 mph. A higher speed can be reached by falling feet first or head first, which reduces the area A. Fortunately the skydiver can open his parachute, greatly increasing A. This brings his terminal speed down to a safe value.

For the mouse we have

$$v_{\text{term}} \approx \sqrt{\frac{4mg}{\rho A}} = \sqrt{\frac{4(0.020 \text{ kg})(9.8 \text{ m/s}^2)}{(1.22 \text{ kg/m}^2)(0.0021 \text{ m}^2)}} = 17 \text{ m/s}$$

The mouse has no parachute—nor does he need one! A mouse's terminal speed is slow enough that he can fall from any height, even out of an airplane, and survive. Cats, too, have relatively low terminal speeds. In a study of cats that fell from high rises, over 90% survived—including one that fell 45 stories!

ASSESS The mouse survives the fall not only because of its lower terminal speed. The smaller an animal's body, the proportionally more robust it is. Further, a small animal's low mass and terminal speed mean that it has a very small *kinetic energy*, an idea we'll study in Chapter 10.

Although we've focused our analysis on falling objects, the same ideas apply to objects moving horizontally. If an object is thrown or shot horizontally, $\vec{D}$ causes the object to slow down. An airplane reaches its maximum speed, which is analogous to the terminal speed, when the drag is equal to and opposite the thrust: $D = F_{\text{thrust}}$. The net force is then zero and the plane cannot go any faster.

We will continue to neglect drag unless a problem specifically calls for drag to be considered.

STOP TO THINK 5.4 The terminal speed of a Styrofoam ball is 15 m/s. Suppose a Styrofoam ball is shot straight down with an initial speed of 30 m/s. Which velocity graph is correct?

5.7 Interacting Objects

ActivPhysics: 2.7, 2.8, 2.9

Up to this point we have studied the dynamics of a single object subject to forces exerted on it by other objects. In Example 5.11, for instance, the box was acted upon by friction, normal, weight, and pushing forces that came from the floor, the earth, and the person pushing. As we've seen, such problems can be solved by an application of Newton's second law after all the forces have been identified.

But in Chapter 4 we found that real-world motion often involves two or more objects interacting with each other. We further found that forces always come in action/reaction *pairs* that are related by Newton's third law. To remind you, Newton's third law states:

- Every force occurs as one member of an action/reaction pair of forces. The two members of the pair always act on *different* objects.
- The two members of an action/reaction pair point in *opposite* directions and are *equal* in magnitude.

Our goal in this section is to learn how to apply the second *and* third laws to interacting objects.

Objects in Contact

One common way that two objects interact is via direct contact forces between them. Consider, for example, the two blocks being pushed across a frictionless table in FIGURE 5.29. To analyze block A's motion, we need to identify all the forces acting on it and then draw its free-body diagram. We repeat the same steps to analyze the motion of block B. However, the forces on A and B are *not* independent: Forces $\vec{F}_{\text{B on A}}$ acting on block A and $\vec{F}_{\text{A on B}}$ acting on block B are an action/reaction pair and thus have the same magnitude. Furthermore, because the two blocks are in contact, their *accelerations* must be the same, so that $a_{Ax} = a_{Bx} = a_x$. Because the accelerations of both blocks are equal, we can drop the subscripts A and B and call both accelerations a_x.

These observations suggest that we can't solve for the motion of one block without considering the motion of the other. The following revised version of our basic Problem-Solving Strategy 5.2 that was developed earlier in this chapter shows how to do this.

FIGURE 5.29 Two boxes moving together have the same acceleration.

PROBLEM-SOLVING
STRATEGY 5.3 **Objects-in-contact problems**

PREPARE Identify those objects whose motion you wish to study. Make simplifying assumptions.

Prepare a visual overview:

- Make a sketch of the situation. Define symbols and identify what the problem is trying to find. You may want to give each object its own coordinate system.
- Draw each object separately and prepare a *separate* force identification diagram for each object.
- Identify the action/reaction pairs of forces. If object A acts on object B with force $\vec{F}_{\text{A on B}}$, then identify the force $\vec{F}_{\text{B on A}}$ that B exerts on A.
- Draw a *separate* free-body diagram for each object. Use subscript labels to distinguish forces, such as $\vec{n}$ and $\vec{w}$, that act independently on more than one object.

SOLVE Use Newton's second and third laws:

- Write Newton's second law in component form for each object. Find the force components from the free-body diagrams.
- Equate the magnitudes of the two forces in each action/reaction pair.
- Determine how the accelerations of the objects are related to each other. Objects in contact will have the *same* acceleration; Section 5.8 shows how accelerations are related for objects connected by ropes or strings.
- Solve for the unknown forces or acceleration.

ASSESS Check that your result has the correct units, is reasonable, and answers the question.

NOTE ▶ Two steps are especially important when drawing the free-body diagrams. First, draw a *separate* diagram for each object. They need not have the same coordinate system. Second, show only the forces acting *on* that object. The force $\vec{F}_{\text{AonB}}$ goes on the free-body diagram of object B, but $\vec{F}_{\text{BonA}}$ goes on the diagram of object A. The two members of an action/reaction pair *always* appear on two different free-body diagrams—*never* on the same diagram. ◀

You might be puzzled that the Solve step calls for the use of the third law to equate just the *magnitudes* of action/reaction forces. What about the "opposite in direction" part of the third law? You have already used it! Your free-body diagrams should show the two members of an action/reaction pair to be opposite in direction, and that information will have been utilized in writing the second-law equations. Because the directional information has already been used, all that is left is the magnitude information.

EXAMPLE 5.16   **Pushing two blocks**

FIGURE 5.30 shows a 5.0 kg block A being pushed with a 3.0 N force. In front of this block is a 10 kg block B; the two blocks move together. What force does block A exert on block B?

FIGURE 5.30 Two blocks are pushed by a hand.

Frictionless surface

5.0 kg 10 kg

PREPARE The visual overview of **FIGURE 5.31** lists the known information and identifies F_{AonB} as what we're trying to find. Then, following the steps of Problem-Solving Strategy 5.3, we've drawn *separate* force identification diagrams and *separate* free-body diagrams for the two blocks. Both blocks have a weight force and a normal force, so we've used subscripts A and B to distinguish between them.

The force $\vec{F}_{\text{AonB}}$ is the contact force that block A exerts on B; it forms an action/reaction pair with the force $\vec{F}_{\text{BonA}}$ that block B exerts on A. Notice that force $\vec{F}_{\text{AonB}}$ is drawn acting on block B; it is the force *of* A *on* B. **Force vectors are always drawn on the free-body diagram of the object that *experiences* the force,** not the object exerting the force. Because action/reaction pairs act in opposite directions, force $\vec{F}_{\text{BonA}}$ pushes backward on block A and appears on A's free-body diagram.

SOLVE We begin by writing Newton's second law in component form for each block. Because the motion is only in the *x*-direction, we need only the *x*-component of the second law. For block A,

$$\sum F_x = (F_{\text{H}})_x + (F_{\text{BonA}})_x = m_{\text{A}}a_{\text{Ax}}$$

The force components can be "read" from the free-body diagram, where we see $\vec{F}_{\text{H}}$ pointing to the right and $\vec{F}_{\text{BonA}}$ pointing to the left. Thus

$$F_{\text{H}} - F_{\text{BonA}} = m_{\text{A}}a_{\text{Ax}}$$

For B, we have

$$\sum F_x = (F_{\text{AonB}})_x = F_{\text{AonB}} = m_{\text{B}}a_{\text{Bx}}$$

We have two additional pieces of information: First, Newton's third law tells us that $F_{\text{BonA}} = F_{\text{AonB}}$. Second, the boxes are in contact and must have the same acceleration a_x: that is, $a_{\text{Ax}} = a_{\text{Bx}} = a_x$. With this information, the two *x*-component equations become

$$F_{\text{H}} - F_{\text{AonB}} = m_{\text{A}}a_x$$

$$F_{\text{AonB}} = m_{\text{B}}a_x$$

Our goal is to find F_{AonB}, so we need to eliminate the unknown acceleration a_x. From the first equation, $a_x = F_{\text{AonB}}/m_{\text{B}}$. Substituting this into the second equation gives

$$F_{\text{H}} - F_{\text{AonB}} = \frac{m_{\text{A}}}{m_{\text{B}}}F_{\text{AonB}}$$

This can be solved for the force of block A on block B, giving

$$F_{\text{AonB}} = \frac{F_{\text{H}}}{1 + m_{\text{A}}/m_{\text{B}}} = \frac{3.0\ \text{N}}{1 + (5.0\ \text{kg})/(10\ \text{kg})} = \frac{3.0\ \text{N}}{1.5} = 2.0\ \text{N}$$

ASSESS Force F_{H} accelerates both blocks, a total mass of 15 kg, but force F_{AonB} on B accelerates only block B, with a mass of 10 kg. Thus it makes sense that $F_{\text{AonB}} < F_{\text{H}}$.

FIGURE 5.31 A visual overview of the two blocks.

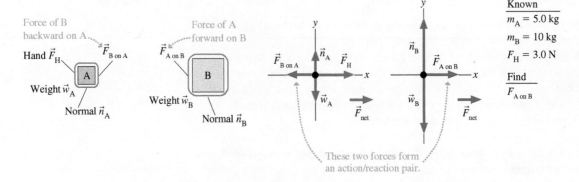

Force of B backward on A

Hand $\vec{F}_{\text{H}}$ $\vec{F}_{\text{BonA}}$

A

Weight $\vec{w}_{\text{A}}$

Normal $\vec{n}_{\text{A}}$

Force of A forward on B

$\vec{F}_{\text{AonB}}$

B

Weight $\vec{w}_{\text{B}}$

Normal $\vec{n}_{\text{B}}$

$\vec{F}_{\text{BonA}}$ $\vec{n}_{\text{A}}$ $\vec{F}_{\text{H}}$

$\vec{w}_{\text{A}}$ $\vec{F}_{\text{net}}$

$\vec{n}_{\text{B}}$ $\vec{F}_{\text{AonB}}$

$\vec{w}_{\text{B}}$ $\vec{F}_{\text{net}}$

These two forces form an action/reaction pair.

Known
$m_{\text{A}} = 5.0\ \text{kg}$
$m_{\text{B}} = 10\ \text{kg}$
$F_{\text{H}} = 3.0\ \text{N}$

Find
F_{AonB}

STOP TO THINK 5.5   Boxes P and Q are sliding to the right across a frictionless table. The hand H is slowing them down. The mass of P is larger than the mass of Q. Rank in order, from largest to smallest, the *horizontal* forces on P, Q, and H.

A. $F_{\text{Q on H}} = F_{\text{H on Q}} = F_{\text{P on Q}} = F_{\text{Q on P}}$

B. $F_{\text{Q on H}} = F_{\text{H on Q}} > F_{\text{P on Q}} = F_{\text{Q on P}}$

C. $F_{\text{Q on H}} = F_{\text{H on Q}} < F_{\text{P on Q}} = F_{\text{Q on P}}$

D. $F_{\text{H on Q}} = F_{\text{H on P}} > F_{\text{P on Q}}$

5.8 Ropes and Pulleys

Many objects are connected by strings, ropes, cables, and so on. In single-particle dynamics, we defined *tension* as the force exerted on an object by a rope or string. We can learn several important facts about ropes and tension by considering the box being pulled by a rope in FIGURE 5.32; the rope in turn is being pulled by a hand that exerts a force $\vec{F}$ on the rope.

The box is pulled by the rope, so the box's free-body diagram shows a tension force $\vec{T}$. The *rope* is subject to two horizontal forces: the force $\vec{F}$ of the hand on the rope, and the force $\vec{F}_{\text{box on rope}}$ with which the box pulls back on the rope. $\vec{T}$ and $\vec{F}_{\text{box on rope}}$ form an action/reaction pair, so their magnitudes are equal: $F_{\text{box on rope}} = T$. Newton's second law *for the rope* is thus

$$\sum F_x = F - F_{\text{box on rope}} = F - T = m_{\text{rope}} a_x \qquad (5.17)$$

where m_{rope} is the rope's mass.

In many problems, the mass of a string or rope is significantly less than the mass of the objects it pulls on. In that case, it's reasonable to make the approximation—called the **massless string approximation**—that $m_{\text{rope}} = 0$. If $m_{\text{rope}} = 0$, then the right side of Equation 5.17 is zero and so $T = F$. In other words, **the tension in a massless string or rope equals the magnitude of the force pulling on the end of the string or rope.** As a result:

■ A massless string or rope "transmits" a force undiminished from one end to the other: If you pull on one end of a rope with force F, the other end of the rope pulls on what it's attached to with a force of the same magnitude F.

■ The tension in a massless string or rope is the same from one end to the other.

FIGURE 5.32 **A box being pulled by a rope.**

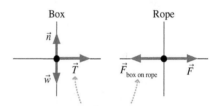

The tension $\vec{T}$ is the force that the rope exerts on the box. Thus $\vec{T}$ and $\vec{F}_{\text{box on rope}}$ are an action/reaction pair and have the same magnitude.

MP **ActivPhysics: 2.10, 2.11**

CONCEPTUAL EXAMPLE 5.17   **Pulling a rope**

FIGURE 5.33a shows a student pulling horizontally with a 100 N force on a rope that is attached to a wall. In FIGURE 5.33b, two students in a tug-of-war pull on opposite ends of a rope with 100 N each. Is the tension in the second rope larger, smaller, or the same as that in the first?

FIGURE 5.33 **Pulling on a rope. Which produces a larger tension?**

(a)   **(b)**

REASON Surely pulling on a rope from both ends causes more tension than pulling on one end. Right? Before jumping to

conclusions, let's analyze the situation carefully. We found above that the force pulling on the end of a rope—here, the 100 N force exerted by the student—and the tension in the rope have the same magnitude. Thus, the tension in rope 1 is 100 N, the force with which the student pulls on the rope.

To find the tension in the second rope, consider the force that the *wall* exerts on the *first* rope. The first rope is in equilibrium, so the 100 N force exerted by the student must be balanced by a 100 N force on the rope from the wall. The first rope is being pulled from *both* ends by a 100 N force—the exact same situation as for the second rope, pulled by the students. A rope doesn't care whether it's being pulled on by a wall or by a person, so the tension in the second rope is the *same* as that in the first, or 100 N.

ASSESS This example reinforces what we just learned about ropes: A rope pulls on the objects at each of its ends with a force equal in magnitude to the tension, and the external force applied to each end of the rope and the rope's tension have equal magnitude.

FIGURE 5.34 An ideal pulley changes the direction in which a tension force acts, but not its magnitude.

Pulleys

Strings and ropes often pass over pulleys. FIGURE 5.34 shows a simple situation in which block B drags block A across a table as it falls. As the string moves, static friction between the string and the pulley causes the pulley to turn. If we assume that

- The string *and* the pulley are both massless, and
- There is no friction where the pulley turns on its axle,

then no net force is needed to accelerate the string or turn the pulley. In this case, **the tension in a massless string is unchanged by passing over a massless, frictionless pulley.** We'll assume such an ideal pulley for problems in this chapter. Later, when we study rotational motion in Chapter 8, we'll consider the effect of the pulley's mass.

In some situations we are interested in the force exerted on the pulley by the rope. Even though the pulley in FIGURE 5.35 is frictionless, the tension force still pulls on the pulley. Because the rope is under tension on *both* sides of the pulley, the pulley is subject to *two* tension forces, one from each side of the rope. The net force on the pulley due to the rope is then the vector sum of these two tension forces, both of which have the same magnitude, equal to the rope's tension.

We can collect all these observations about ropes, pulleys, and tension into a Tactics Box. We'll use these three rules extensively in solving problems with ropes, strings, and pulleys.

FIGURE 5.35 Tension forces on a pulley.

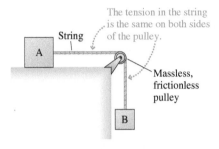

The two tension forces have the *same* magnitude.

TACTICS BOX 5.2 **Working with ropes and pulleys**

For massless ropes or strings and massless, frictionless pulleys:

- If a force pulls on one end of a rope, the tension in the rope equals the magnitude of the pulling force.
- If two objects are connected by a rope, the tension is the same at both ends.
- If the rope passes over a pulley, the tension in the rope is unaffected.

Exercises 29–32

EXAMPLE 5.18 **Placing a leg in traction**

For serious fractures of the leg, the leg may need to have a stretching force applied to it to keep contracting leg muscles from forcing the broken bones together too hard. This is often done using *traction*, an arrangement of a rope, a weight, and pulleys as shown in FIGURE 5.36. The rope must make the same angle θ on

FIGURE 5.36 A leg in traction.

4.2 kg

both sides of the pulley so that the net force of the rope on the pulley is horizontally to the right, but θ can be adjusted to control the amount of traction. The doctor has specified 50 N of traction for this patient, with a 4.2 kg hanging mass. What is the proper angle θ?

PREPARE The pulley attached to the patient's leg is in static equilibrium, so the net force on it must be zero. FIGURE 5.37 shows a free-body diagram for the pulley, which we'll assume to be frictionless. Forces $\vec{T}_1$ and $\vec{T}_2$ are the tension forces of the rope as it

FIGURE 5.37 Free-body diagram for the pulley.

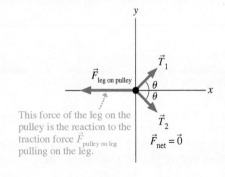

pulls on the pulley. These forces are equal in magnitude for a frictionless pulley, and their combined pull is to the right. This force is balanced by the force $\vec{F}_{\text{leg on pulley}}$ of the patient's leg pulling to the left. The traction force $\vec{F}_{\text{pulley on leg}}$ forms an action/reaction pair with $\vec{F}_{\text{leg on pulley}}$, so 50 N of traction means that $\vec{F}_{\text{leg on pulley}}$ also has a magnitude of 50 N.

SOLVE Two important properties of ropes, given in Tactics Box 5.2, are that (1) the tension equals the magnitude of the force pulling on its end and (2) the tension is the same throughout the rope. Thus, if a hanging mass m pulls on the rope with its weight mg, the tension along the entire rope is $T = mg$. For a 4.2 kg hanging mass, the tension is then $T = mg = 41$ N.

The pulley, in equilibrium, must satisfy Newton's second law for the case where $\vec{a} = \vec{0}$. Thus

$$\sum F_x = T_{1x} + T_{2x} + (F_{\text{leg on pulley}})_x = ma_x = 0$$

The tension forces both have the same magnitude T, and both are at angle θ from horizontal. The x-component of the leg force is negative because it's directed to the left. Then Newton's law becomes

$$2T\cos\theta - F_{\text{leg on pulley}} = 0$$

so that

$$\cos\theta = \frac{F_{\text{leg on pulley}}}{2T} = \frac{50 \text{ N}}{82 \text{ N}} = 0.61$$

$$\theta = \cos^{-1}(0.61) = 52°$$

ASSESS The traction force would approach $2mg = 82$ N if angle θ approached zero because the two tensions would pull in parallel. Conversely, the traction force would approach 0 N if θ approached 90°. Because the desired traction force is roughly halfway between 0 N and 82 N, an angle near 45° is reasonable.

EXAMPLE 5.19 **Lifting a stage set**

A 200 kg set used in a play is stored in the loft above the stage. The rope holding the set passes up and over a pulley, then is tied backstage. The director tells a 100 kg stagehand to lower the set. When he unties the rope, the set falls and the unfortunate man is hoisted into the loft. What is the stagehand's acceleration?

PREPARE FIGURE 5.38 shows the visual overview. The objects of interest are the stagehand M and the set S, for which we've drawn separate free-body diagrams. Assume a massless rope and a massless, frictionless pulley. Tension forces $\vec{T}_S$ and $\vec{T}_M$ are due to a massless rope going over an ideal pulley, so their magnitudes are the same.

FIGURE 5.38 Visual overview for the stagehand and set.

Since the rope is massless and the pulley ideal, the magnitudes of these two tensions are the same.

Known
$m_M = 100$ kg
$m_S = 200$ kg

Find
a_{My}

SOLVE From the two free-body diagrams, we can write Newton's second law in component form. For the man we have

$$\sum F_{My} = T_M - w_M = T_M - m_M g = m_M a_{My}$$

For the set we have

$$\sum F_{Sy} = T_S - w_S = T_S - m_S g = m_S a_{Sy}$$

Only the y-equations are needed. Because the stagehand and the set are connected by a rope, the upward distance traveled by one is the *same* as the downward distance traveled by the other. Thus the *magnitudes* of their accelerations must be the same, but, as Figure 5.38 shows, their *directions* are opposite. We can express this mathematically as $a_{Sy} = -a_{My}$. We also know that the two tension forces have equal magnitudes, which we'll call T. Inserting this information into the above equations gives

$$T - m_M g = m_M a_{My}$$

$$T - m_S g = -m_S a_{My}$$

These are simultaneous equations in the two unknowns T and a_{My}. We can solve for T in the first equation to get

$$T = m_M a_{My} + m_M g$$

Inserting this value of T into the second equation then gives

$$m_M a_{My} + m_M g - m_S g = -m_S a_{My}$$

which we can rewrite as

$$(m_S - m_M)g = (m_S + m_M)a_{My}$$

Finally, we can solve for the hapless stagehand's acceleration:

$$a_{My} = \frac{m_S - m_M}{m_S + m_M} g = \left(\frac{100 \text{ kg}}{300 \text{ kg}}\right) \times 9.80 \text{ m/s}^2 = 3.3 \text{ m/s}^2$$

This is also the acceleration with which the set falls. If the rope's tension was needed, we could now find it from $T = m_M a_{My} + m_M g$.

ASSESS If the stagehand weren't holding on, the set would fall with free-fall acceleration g. The stagehand acts as a *counterweight* to reduce the acceleration.

EXAMPLE 5.20 **A not-so-clever bank robbery**

Bank robbers have pushed a 1000 kg safe to a second-story floor-to-ceiling window. They plan to break the window, then lower the safe 3.0 m to their truck. Not being too clever, they stack up 500 kg of furniture, tie a rope between the safe and the furniture, and place the rope over a pulley. Then they push the safe out the window. What is the safe's speed when it hits the truck? The coefficient of kinetic friction between the furniture and the floor is 0.50.

PREPARE The visual overview in FIGURE 5.39 establishes a coordinate system and defines the symbols that will be needed to calculate the safe's motion. The objects of interest are the safe S and the furniture F, which we will model as particles. We will assume a massless rope and a massless, frictionless pulley; the tension is then the same everywhere in the rope.

SOLVE We can write Newton's second law directly from the free-body diagrams. For the furniture,

$$\sum F_{Fx} = T_F - f_k = T - f_k = m_F a_{Fx}$$

$$\sum F_{Fy} = n - w_F = n - m_F g = 0$$

And for the safe,

$$\sum F_{Sy} = T_S - w_S = T - m_S g = m_S a_{Sy}$$

The safe and the furniture are tied together, so their accelerations have the same magnitude. But as the furniture slides to the right with positive acceleration a_{Fx}, the safe falls in the negative y-direction, so its acceleration a_{Sy} is negative; we can express this mathematically as $a_{Fx} = -a_{Sy}$. We also have made use of the fact that $T_S = T_F = T$. We have one additional piece of information, the model of kinetic friction:

$$f_k = \mu_k n = \mu_k m_F g$$

where we used the y-equation of the furniture to deduce that $n = m_F g$. Substitute this result for f_k into the x-equation of the furniture, then rewrite the furniture's x-equation and the safe's y-equation:

$$T - \mu_k m_F g = -m_F a_{Sy}$$

$$T - m_S g = m_S a_{Sy}$$

We have succeeded in reducing our knowledge to two simultaneous equations in the two unknowns a_{Sy} and T. We subtract the second equation from the first to eliminate T:

$$(m_S - \mu_k m_F)g = -(m_S + m_F)a_{Sy}$$

Finally, we can solve for the safe's acceleration:

$$a_{Sy} = -\left(\frac{m_S - \mu_k m_F}{m_S + m_F}\right)g$$

$$= -\frac{1000 \text{ kg} - 0.5(500 \text{ kg})}{1000 \text{ kg} + 500 \text{ kg}} \times 9.80 \text{ m/s}^2 = -4.9 \text{ m/s}^2$$

Now we need to calculate the kinematics of the falling safe. Because the time of the fall is not known or needed, we can use

$$(v_y)_f^2 = (v_y)_i^2 + 2a_{Sy}\,\Delta y = 0 + 2a_{Sy}(y_f - y_i) = -2a_{Sy}y_i$$

$$(v_y)_f = \sqrt{-2a_{Sy}y_i} = \sqrt{-2(-4.9 \text{ m/s}^2)(3.0 \text{ m})} = 5.4 \text{ m/s}$$

The value of $(v_y)_f$ is negative, but we only needed to find the speed, so we took the absolute value. It seems unlikely that the truck will survive the impact of the 1000 kg safe!

FIGURE 5.39 Visual overview of the furniture and falling safe.

Newton's three laws form the cornerstone of the science of mechanics. These laws allowed scientists to understand many diverse phenomena, from the motion of a raindrop to the orbits of the planets. These laws were so precise at predicting motion that they went unchallenged for well over two hundred years. At the beginning of the twentieth century, however, it began to be apparent that the laws of mechanics and the laws of electricity and magnetism were somehow inconsistent. Bringing these two apparently disconnected theories into harmony required the genius of a young patent clerk named Albert Einstein. In doing so, he shook the foundations not only of Newtonian mechanics but also of our very notions of space and time. We will continue to develop Newtonian mechanics for the next few chapters because of its tremendous importance to the physics of everyday life. But it's worth keeping in the back of your mind that Newton's laws aren't the ultimate statement about motion. Later in this textbook we'll reexamine motion and mechanics from the perspective of Einstein's theory of relativity.

STOP TO THINK 5.6   All three 50 kg blocks are at rest. Is the tension in rope 2 greater than, less than, or equal to the tension in rope 1?

INTEGRATED EXAMPLE 5.21   **Stopping distances**

A 1500 kg car is traveling at a speed of 30 m/s when the driver slams on the brakes and skids to a halt. Determine the stopping distance if the car is traveling up a 10° slope, down a 10° slope, or on a level road.

PREPARE We'll represent the car as a particle and we'll use the model of kinetic friction. We want to solve the problem only once, not three separate times, so we'll leave the slope angle θ unspecified until the end.

FIGURE 5.40 shows the visual overview. We've shown the car sliding uphill, but these representations work equally well for a level or downhill slide if we let θ be zero or negative, respectively. We've used a tilted coordinate system so that the motion is along the x-axis. The car *skids* to a halt, so we've taken the coefficient of *kinetic* friction for rubber on concrete from Table 5.1.

SOLVE Newton's second law and the model of kinetic friction are

$$\sum F_x = n_x + w_x + (f_k)_x$$
$$= 0 - mg\sin\theta - f_k = ma_x$$
$$\sum F_y = n_y + w_y + (f_k)_y$$
$$= n - mg\cos\theta + 0 = ma_y = 0$$

We've written these equations by "reading" the motion diagram and the free-body diagram. Notice that both components of the weight vector $\vec{w}$ are negative. $a_y = 0$ because the motion is entirely along the x-axis.

The second equation gives $n = mg\cos\theta$. Using this in the friction model, we find $f_k = \mu_k mg\cos\theta$. Inserting this result back into the first equation then gives

$$ma_x = -mg\sin\theta - \mu_k mg\cos\theta$$
$$= -mg(\sin\theta + \mu_k\cos\theta)$$
$$a_x = -g(\sin\theta + \mu_k\cos\theta)$$

This is a constant acceleration. Constant-acceleration kinematics gives

$$(v_x)_f^2 = 0 = (v_x)_i^2 + 2a_x(x_f - x_i) = (v_x)_i^2 + 2a_x x_f$$

which we can solve for the stopping distance x_f:

$$x_f = -\frac{(v_x)_i^2}{2a_x} = \frac{(v_x)_i^2}{2g(\sin\theta + \mu_k\cos\theta)}$$

Notice how the minus sign in the expression for a_x canceled the minus sign in the expression for x_f. Evaluating our result at the three different angles gives the stopping distances:

$$x_f = \begin{cases} 48\text{ m} & \theta = 10° & \text{uphill} \\ 57\text{ m} & \theta = 0° & \text{level} \\ 75\text{ m} & \theta = -10° & \text{downhill} \end{cases}$$

The implications are clear about the danger of driving downhill too fast!

ASSESS 30 m/s ≈ 60 mph and 57 m ≈ 180 feet on a level surface. These are similar to the stopping distances you learned when you got your driver's license, so the results seem reasonable. Additional confirmation comes from noting that the expression for a_x becomes $-g\sin\theta$ if $\mu_k = 0$. This is what you learned in Chapter 3 for the acceleration on a frictionless inclined plane.

FIGURE 5.40 Visual overview for a skidding car.

This representation works for a downhill slide if we let θ be negative.

Stops

Normal $\vec{n}$
Weight $\vec{w}$ Friction $\vec{f_k}$

Known
$x_i = 0\text{ m}, t_i = 0\text{ s}$ $(v_x)_i = 30\text{ m/s}$
$m = 1500\text{ kg}$ $(v_x)_f = 0\text{ m/s}$
$\mu_k = 0.80$
$\theta = -10°, 0, 10$

Find
$\Delta x = x_f - x_i = x_f$

SUMMARY

The goal of Chapter 5 has been to learn how to solve problems about motion in a straight line.

GENERAL STRATEGY

All examples in this chapter follow a three-part strategy. You'll become a better problem solver if you adhere to it as you do the homework problems. The *Dynamics Worksheets* in the *Student Workbook* will help you structure your work in this way.

Equilibrium Problems

Object at rest or moving at constant velocity.

PREPARE Make simplifying assumptions.

• Check that the object is either at rest or moving with constant velocity ($\vec{a} = \vec{0}$).

• Identify forces and show them on a free-body diagram.

SOLVE Use Newton's second law in component form:

$$\sum F_x = ma_x = 0$$
$$\sum F_y = ma_y = 0$$

"Read" the components from the free-body diagram.

ASSESS Is your result reasonable?

Dynamics Problems

Object accelerating.

PREPARE Make simplifying assumptions. Make a **visual overview:**

• Sketch a pictorial representation.

• Identify known quantities and what the problem is trying to find.

• Identify all forces and show them on a free-body diagram.

SOLVE Use Newton's second law in component form:

$$\sum F_x = ma_x \text{ and } \sum F_y = ma_y$$

"Read" the components of the vectors from the free-body diagram. If needed, use kinematics to find positions and velocities.

ASSESS Is your result reasonable?

Objects in Contact

Two or more objects interacting.

PREPARE Make a **visual overview:**

• Sketch a pictorial representation.

• Identify all forces acting on *each* object.

• Identify action/reaction pairs of forces acting on objects in the system.

• Draw a *separate* free-body diagram for each object.

SOLVE Write Newton's second law for each object. Use Newton's third law to equate the magnitudes of action/reaction pairs. Determine how the accelerations of the objects are related to each other.

ASSESS Is your result reasonable?

IMPORTANT CONCEPTS

Specific information about three important forces:

Weight $\vec{w} = (mg, \text{downward})$

Friction $\vec{f}_s = (0 \text{ to } \mu_s n, \text{direction as necessary to prevent motion})$

$\vec{f}_k = (\mu_k n, \text{direction opposite the motion})$

$\vec{f}_r = (\mu_r n, \text{direction opposite the motion})$

Drag $\vec{D} \approx (\frac{1}{4}\rho A v^2, \text{direction opposite the motion})$ for motion in air

Newton's laws are vector expressions. You must write them out by components:

$$(F_{net})_x = \sum F_x = ma_x$$
$$(F_{net})_y = \sum F_y = ma_y$$

For equilibrium problems, $a_x = 0$ and $a_y = 0$.

APPLICATIONS

Apparent weight is the magnitude of the contact force supporting an object. It is what a scale would read, and it is your sensation of weight:

$$w_{app} = m(g + a_y)$$

Apparent weight equals your true weight $w = mg$ only when $a_y = 0$.

A falling object reaches **terminal speed**

$$v_{term} \approx \sqrt{\frac{4mg}{\rho A}}$$

Terminal speed is reached when the drag force exactly balances the weight force: $\vec{a} = \vec{0}$.

Strings and pulleys

• A string or rope pulls what it's connected to with a force equal to its tension.

• The tension in a rope is equal to the force pulling on the rope.

• The tension in a massless rope is the same at all points in the rope.

• Tension does not change when a rope passes over a massless, frictionless pulley.

$F_{\text{rope on wall}}$ = tension

$F_{\text{hand on rope}}$ = tension

Problem difficulty is labeled as | (straightforward) to ||||
(challenging). Problems labeled ✎ can be done
on a Workbook Dynamics Worksheet; NT integrate
significant material from earlier chapters;
BIO are of biological or medical interest.

For homework assigned
on MasteringPhysics, go
to www.masteringphysics.com

Scan this QR code to launch
a **Video Tutor Solution** that
will help you solve problems
for this chapter.

QUESTIONS

Conceptual Questions

1. An object is subject to two forces that do not point in opposite directions. Is it possible to choose their magnitudes so that the object is in equilibrium? Explain.

2. Are the objects described here in static equilibrium, dynamic equilibrium, or not in equilibrium at all?
   a. A girder is lifted at constant speed by a crane.
   b. A girder is lowered by a crane. It is slowing down.
   c. You're straining to hold a 200 lb barbell over your head.
   d. A jet plane has reached its cruising speed and altitude.
   e. A rock is falling into the Grand Canyon.
   f. A box in the back of a truck doesn't slide as the truck stops.

3. What forces are acting on you right now? What net force is acting on you right now?

4. Decide whether each of the following is true or false. Give a reason!
   a. The mass of an object depends on its location.
   b. The weight of an object depends on its location.
   c. Mass and weight describe the same thing in different units.

5. An astronaut takes his bathroom scale to the moon and then stands on it. Is the reading of the scale his true weight? Explain.

6. A light block of mass m and a heavy block of mass M are attached to the ends of a rope. A student holds the heavier block and lets the lighter block hang below it, as shown in Figure Q5.6. Then she lets go. Air resistance can be neglected.
   a. What is the tension in the rope while the blocks are falling, before either hits the ground?
   b. Would your answer be different if she had been holding the lighter block initially?

FIGURE Q5.6

7. Four balls are thrown straight up. Figure Q5.7 is a "snapshot" showing their velocities. They have the same size but different mass. Air resistance is negligible. Rank in order, from largest to smallest, the magnitudes of the net forces, F_{net1}, F_{net2}, F_{net3}, F_{net4}, acting on the balls. Some may be equal. Give your answer in the form A > B = C > D, and state your reasoning.

FIGURE Q5.7

8. Suppose you attempt to pour out 100 g of salt, using a pan balance for measurements, while in an elevator that is accelerating upward. Will the quantity of salt be too much, too little, or the correct amount? Explain.

9. a. Can the normal force on an object be directed horizontally? If not, why not? If so, provide an example.
   b. Can the normal force on an object be directed downward? If not, why not? If so, provide an example.

10. A ball is thrown straight up. Taking the drag force of air into account, does it take longer for the ball to travel to the top of its motion or for it to fall back down again?

11. Three objects move through the air as shown in Figure Q5.11. Rank in order, from largest to smallest, the three drag forces D_1, D_2, and D_3. Some may be equal. Give your answer in the form A > B = C and state your reasoning.

FIGURE Q5.11

12. A skydiver is falling at her terminal speed. Right after she opens her parachute, which has a very large area, what is the direction of the net force on her?

13. Raindrops can fall at different speeds; some fall quite quickly, others quite slowly. Why might this be true?

14. An airplane moves through the air at a constant speed. The jet engine's thrust applies a force in the direction of motion. Reducing thrust will cause the plane to fly at a slower—but still constant—speed. Explain why this is so.

15. Is it possible for an object to travel in air faster than its terminal speed? If not, why not? If so, explain how this might happen.

For Questions 16 through 19, determine the tension in the rope at the point indicated with a dot.

- All objects are at rest.
- The strings and pulleys are massless, and the pulleys are frictionless.

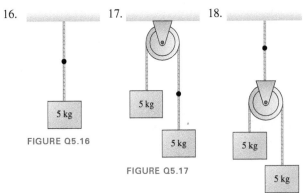

16.

FIGURE Q5.16

17.

FIGURE Q5.17

18.

FIGURE Q5.18

19.

FIGURE Q5.19

20. The floor is frictionless. In which direction is the kinetic friction force on block 1 in Figure Q5.20? On block 2? Explain.

FIGURE Q5.20

Multiple-Choice Questions

21. ‖ The wood block in Figure Q5.21 is at rest on a wood ramp. In which direction is the static friction force on block 1?
    A. Up the slope.
    B. Down the slope.
    C. The friction force is zero.
    D. There's not enough information to tell.

22. ‖ A 2.0 kg ball is suspended by two light strings as shown in Figure Q5.22. What is the tension T in the angled string?
    A. 9.5 N   B. 15 N   C. 20 N
    D. 26 N   E. 30 N

FIGURE Q5.22

23. | While standing in a low tunnel, you raise your arms and push against the ceiling with a force of 100 N. Your mass is 70 kg.
    a. What force does the ceiling exert on you?
       A. 10 N   B. 100 N   C. 690 N
       D. 790 N   E. 980 N
    b. What force does the floor exert on you?
       A. 10 N   B. 100 N   C. 690 N
       D. 790 N   E. 980 N

24. | A 5.0 kg dog sits on the floor of an elevator that is accelerating *downward* at 1.20 m/s².
    a. What is the magnitude of the normal force of the elevator floor on the dog?
       A. 34 N   B. 43 N   C. 49 N
       D. 55 N   E. 74 N
    b. What is the magnitude of the force of the dog on the elevator floor?
       A. 4.2 N   B. 49 N   C. 55 N
       D. 43 N   E. 74 N

25. | A 3.0 kg puck slides due east on a horizontal frictionless surface at a constant speed of 4.5 m/s. Then a force of magnitude 6.0 N, directed due north, is applied for 1.5 s. Afterward,
    a. What is the northward component of the puck's velocity?
       A. 0.50 m/s   B. 2.0 m/s   C. 3.0 m/s
       D. 4.0 m/s   E. 4.5 m/s
    b. What is the speed of the puck?
       A. 4.9 m/s   B. 5.4 m/s   C. 6.2 m/s
       D. 7.5 m/s   E. 11 m/s

26. | A rocket in space, initially at rest, fires its main engines at a constant thrust. As it burns fuel, the mass of the rocket decreases. Which of the graphs in Figure Q5.26 best represents the velocity of the rocket as a function of time?

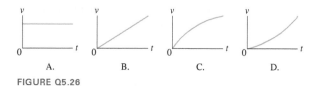

FIGURE Q5.26

27. | Eric has a mass of 60 kg. He is standing on a scale in an elevator that is accelerating downward at 1.7 m/s². What is the approximate reading on the scale?
    A. 0 N   B. 400 N   C. 500 N   D. 600 N

28. | The two blocks in Figure Q5.28 are at rest on frictionless surfaces. What must be the mass of the right block in order that the two blocks remain stationary?
    A. 4.9 kg   B. 6.1 kg   C. 7.9 kg
    D. 9.8 kg   E. 12 kg

FIGURE Q5.28

29. | A football player at practice pushes a 60 kg blocking sled across the field at a constant speed. The coefficient of kinetic friction between the grass and the sled is 0.30. How much force must he apply to the sled?
    A. 18 N   B. 60 N   C. 180 N   D. 600 N

30. | Two football players are pushing a 60 kg blocking sled across the field at a constant speed of 2.0 m/s. The coefficient of kinetic friction between the grass and the sled is 0.30. Once they stop pushing, how far will the sled slide before coming to rest?
    A. 0.20 m   B. 0.68 m   C. 1.0 m   D. 6.6 m

31. ‖ Land Rover ads used to claim that their vehicles could climb a slope of 45°. For this to be possible, what must be the minimum coefficient of static friction between the vehicle's tires and the road?
    A. 0.5   B. 0.7   C. 0.9   D. 1.0

32. ‖ A truck is traveling at 30 m/s on a slippery road. The driver slams on the brakes and the truck starts to skid. If the coefficient of kinetic friction between the tires and the road is 0.20, how far will the truck skid before stopping?
    A. 230 m   B. 300 m   C. 450 m   D. 680 m

PROBLEMS

Section 5.1 Equilibrium

1. | The three ropes in Figure P5.1 are tied to a small, very light ring. Two of the ropes are anchored to walls at right angles, and the third rope pulls as shown. What are T_1 and T_2, the magnitudes of the tension forces in the first two ropes?

FIGURE P5.1   FIGURE P5.2

2. ||| The three ropes in Figure P5.2 are tied to a small, very light ring. Two of these ropes are anchored to walls at right angles with the tensions shown in the figure. What are the magnitude and direction of the tension $\vec{T}_3$ in the third rope?

3. |||| A 20 kg loudspeaker is suspended 2.0 m below the ceiling by two cables that are each 30° from vertical. What is the tension in the cables?

4. || A 1000 kg steel beam is supported by the two ropes shown in Figure P5.4. Each rope can support a maximum sustained tension of 5600 N. Do the ropes break?

FIGURE P5.4

5. | A cable is used to raise a 25 kg urn from an underwater archeological site. There is a 25 N drag force from the water as the urn is raised at a constant speed. What is the tension in the cable?

6. |||| When you bend your knee, the quadriceps muscle is stretched. This increases the tension in the quadriceps tendon attached to your kneecap (patella), which, in turn, increases the tension in the patella tendon that attaches your kneecap to your lower leg bone (tibia). Simultaneously, the end of your upper leg bone (femur) pushes outward on the patella. Figure P5.6 shows how these parts of a knee joint are arranged. What size force does the femur exert on the kneecap if the tendons are oriented as in the figure and the tension in each tendon is 60 N?

FIGURE P5.6

7. || The two angled ropes used to support the crate in Figure P5.7 can withstand a maximum tension of 1500 N before they break. What is the largest mass the ropes can support?

FIGURE P5.7

Section 5.2 Dynamics and Newton's Second Law

8. || A force with x-component F_x acts on a 500 g object as it moves along the x-axis. The object's acceleration graph (a_x versus t) is shown in Figure P5.8. Draw a graph of F_x versus t.

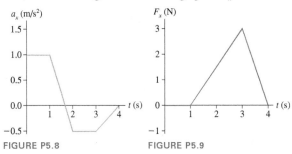

FIGURE P5.8   FIGURE P5.9

9. || A force with x-component F_x acts on a 2.0 kg object as it moves along the x-axis. A graph of F_x versus t is shown in Figure P5.9. Draw an acceleration graph (a_x versus t) for this object.

10. | A force with x-component F_x acts on a 500 g object as it moves along the x-axis. A graph of F_x versus t is shown in Figure P5.10. Draw an acceleration graph (a_x versus t) for this object.

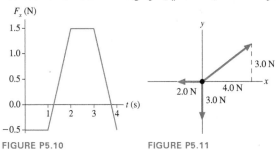

FIGURE P5.10   FIGURE P5.11

11. || The forces in Figure P5.11 are acting on a 2.0 kg object. Find the values of a_x and a_y, the x- and y-components of the object's acceleration.

12. | The forces in Figure P5.12 are acting on a 2.0 kg object. Find the values of a_x and a_y, the x- and y-components of the object's acceleration.

FIGURE P5.12

13. | A horizontal rope is tied to a 50 kg box on frictionless ice. What is the tension in the rope if
    a. The box is at rest?
    b. The box moves at a steady 5.0 m/s?
    c. The box has $v_x = 5.0$ m/s and $a_x = 5.0$ m/s²?

14. |||| A crate pushed along the floor with velocity $\vec{v}_i$ slides a distance d after the pushing force is removed.
    a. If the mass of the crate is doubled but the initial velocity is not changed, what distance does the crate slide before stopping? Explain.
    b. If the initial velocity of the crate is doubled to $2\vec{v}_i$ but the mass is not changed, what distance does the crate slide before stopping? Explain.

15. || In a head-on collision, a car stops in 0.10 s from a speed of 14 m/s. The driver has a mass of 70 kg, and is, fortunately, tightly strapped into his seat. What force is applied to the driver by his seat belt during that fraction of a second?

Section 5.3 Mass and Weight

16. | An astronaut's weight on earth is 800 N. What is his weight on Mars, where $g = 3.76$ m/s²?

17. | A woman has a mass of 55.0 kg.
   a. What is her weight on earth?
   b. What are her mass and her weight on the moon, where $g = 1.62$ m/s²?

18. ||| A box with a 75 kg passenger inside is launched straight up into the air by a giant rubber band. After the box has left the rubber band but is still moving *upward,*
   a. What is the passenger's true weight?
   b. What is the passenger's apparent weight?

19. || a. How much force does an 80 kg astronaut exert on his chair while sitting at rest on the launch pad?
   b. How much force does the astronaut exert on his chair while accelerating straight up at 10 m/s²?

20. | It takes the elevator in a skyscraper 4.0 s to reach its cruising speed of 10 m/s. A 60 kg passenger gets aboard on the ground floor. What is the passenger's apparent weight
   a. Before the elevator starts moving?
   b. While the elevator is speeding up?
   c. After the elevator reaches its cruising speed?

21. || Zach, whose mass is 80 kg, is in an elevator descending at 10 m/s. The elevator takes 3.0 s to brake to a stop at the first floor.
   a. What is Zach's apparent weight before the elevator starts braking?
   b. What is Zach's apparent weight while the elevator is braking?

22. ||| Figure P5.22 shows the velocity graph of a 75 kg passenger in an elevator. What is the passenger's apparent weight at $t = 1.0$ s? At 5.0 s? At 9.0 s?

FIGURE P5.22

Section 5.4 Normal Forces

23. || a. A 0.60 kg bullfrog is sitting at rest on a level log. How large is the normal force of the log on the bullfrog?
   b. A second 0.60 kg bullfrog is on a log tilted 30° above horizontal. How large is the normal force of the log on this bullfrog?

24. ||| A 23 kg child goes down a straight slide inclined 38° above horizontal. The child is acted on by his weight, the normal force from the slide, and kinetic friction.
   a. Draw a free-body diagram of the child.
   b. How large is the normal force of the slide on the child?

Section 5.5 Friction

25. ||| Bonnie and Clyde are sliding a 300 kg bank safe across the floor to their getaway car. The safe slides with a constant speed if Clyde pushes from behind with 385 N of force while Bonnie pulls forward on a rope with 350 N of force. What is the safe's coefficient of kinetic friction on the bank floor?

26. ||| A 4000 kg truck is parked on a 15° slope. How big is the friction force on the truck?

27. ||| A 1000 kg car traveling at a speed of 40 m/s skids to a halt on wet concrete where $\mu_k = 0.60$. How long are the skid marks?

28. | A stubborn 120 kg mule sits down and refuses to move. To drag the mule to the barn, the exasperated farmer ties a rope around the mule and pulls with his maximum force of 800 N.

The coefficients of friction between the mule and the ground are $\mu_s = 0.80$ and $\mu_k = 0.50$. Is the farmer able to move the mule?

29. ||| A 10 kg crate is placed on a horizontal conveyor belt. The materials are such that $\mu_s = 0.50$ and $\mu_k = 0.30$.
   a. Draw a free-body diagram showing all the forces on the crate if the conveyer belt runs at constant speed.
   b. Draw a free-body diagram showing all the forces on the crate if the conveyer belt is speeding up.
   c. What is the maximum acceleration the belt can have without the crate slipping?
   d. If acceleration of the belt exceeds the value determined in part c, what is the acceleration of the crate?

30. || What is the minimum downward force on the box in Figure P5.30 that will keep it from slipping? The coefficients of static and kinetic friction between the box and the floor are 0.35 and 0.25, respectively.

FIGURE P5.30

Section 5.6 Drag

31. || What is the drag force on a 1.6-m-wide, 1.4-m-high car traveling at
   a. 10 m/s (≈22 mph)?   b. 30 m/s (≈65 mph)?

32. ||| A 22-cm-diameter bowling ball has a terminal speed of 77 m/s. What is the ball's mass?

33. |||| A 75 kg skydiver can be modeled as a rectangular "box" with dimensions 20 cm × 40 cm × 1.8 m. What is his terminal speed if he falls feet first?

Section 5.7 Interacting Objects

34. ||| A 1000 kg car pushes a 2000 kg truck that has a dead battery. When the driver steps on the accelerator, the drive wheels of the car push backward against the ground with a force of 4500 N.
   a. What is the magnitude of the force of the car on the truck?
   b. What is the magnitude of the force of the truck on the car?

35. |||| Blocks with masses of 1.0 kg, 2.0 kg, and 3.0 kg are lined up in a row on a frictionless table. All three are pushed forward by a 12 N force applied to the 1.0 kg block. How much force does the 2.0 kg block exert on (a) the 3.0 kg block and (b) the 1.0 kg block?

Section 5.8 Ropes and Pulleys

36. ||| What is the tension in the rope of Figure P5.36?

37. || A 2.0-m-long, 500 g rope pulls a 10 kg block of ice across a horizontal, frictionless surface. The block accelerates at 2.0 m/s². How much force pulls forward on (a) the block of ice, (b) the rope?

FIGURE P5.36

38. || Figure P5.38 shows two 1.00 kg blocks connected by a rope. A second rope hangs beneath the lower block. Both ropes have a mass of 250 g. The entire assembly is accelerated upward at 3.00 m/s² by force $\vec{F}$.
   a. What is F?
   b. What is the tension at the top end of rope 1?
   c. What is the tension at the bottom end of rope 1?
   d. What is the tension at the top end of rope 2?

FIGURE P5.38

39. ‖ Each of 100 identical blocks sitting on a frictionless surface is connected to the next block by a massless string. The first block is pulled with a force of 100 N.
    a. What is the tension in the string connecting block 100 to block 99?
    b. What is the tension in the string connecting block 50 to block 51?

40. ‖ Two blocks on a frictionless table, A and B, are connected by a massless string. When block A is pulled with a certain force, dragging block B, the tension in the string is 24 N. When block B is pulled by the same force, dragging block A, the tension is 18 N. What is the ratio m_A/m_B of the blocks' masses?

General Problems

41. ‖‖ A 500 kg piano is being lowered into position by a crane while two people steady it with ropes pulling to the sides. Bob's rope pulls to the left, 15° below horizontal, with 500 N of tension. Ellen's rope pulls toward the right, 25° below horizontal.
    a. What tension must Ellen maintain in her rope to keep the piano descending vertically at constant speed?
    b. What is the tension in the vertical main cable supporting the piano?

42. ‖ Dana has a sports medal suspended by a long ribbon from her rearview mirror. As she accelerates onto the highway, she notices that the medal is hanging at an angle of 10° from the vertical.
    a. Does the medal lean toward or away from the windshield? Explain.
    b. What is her acceleration?

43. ‖ Figure P5.43 shows the velocity graph of a 2.0 kg object as it moves along the x-axis. What is the net force acting on this object at $t = 1$ s? At 4 s? At 7 s?

FIGURE P5.43

FIGURE P5.44

44. ‖ Figure P5.44 shows the net force acting on a 2.0 kg object as it moves along the x-axis. The object is at rest at the origin at $t = 0$ s. What are its acceleration and velocity at $t = 6.0$ s?

45. ‖ A 50 kg box hangs from a rope. What is the tension in the rope if
    a. The box is at rest?
    b. The box has $v_y = 5.0$ m/s and is speeding up at 5.0 m/s²?

46. ‖ A 50 kg box hangs from a rope. What is the tension in the rope if
    a. The box moves up at a steady 5.0 m/s?
    b. The box has $v_y = 5.0$ m/s and is slowing down at 5.0 m/s²?

47. ‖ Your forehead can withstand a force of about 6.0 kN before fracturing, while your cheekbone can only withstand about 1.3 kN.
    BIO a. If a 140 g baseball strikes your head at 30 m/s and stops in 0.0015 s, what is the magnitude of the ball's acceleration?
    b. What is the magnitude of the force that stops the baseball?
    c. What force does the baseball apply to your head? Explain.
    d. Are you in danger of a fracture if the ball hits you in the forehead? In the cheek?

48. ‖‖ Seat belts and air bags save lives by reducing the forces exerted on the driver and passengers in an automobile collision. BIO Cars are designed with a "crumple zone" in the front of the car.

In the event of an impact, the passenger compartment decelerates over a distance of about 1 m as the front of the car crumples. An occupant restrained by seat belts and air bags decelerates with the car. By contrast, an unrestrained occupant keeps moving forward with no loss of speed (Newton's first law!) until hitting the dashboard or windshield, as we saw in Figure 4.2. These are unyielding surfaces, and the unfortunate occupant then decelerates over a distance of only about 5 mm.
    a. A 60 kg person is in a head-on collision. The car's speed at impact is 15 m/s. Estimate the net force on the person if he or she is wearing a seat belt and if the air bag deploys.
    b. Estimate the net force that ultimately stops the person if he or she is not restrained by a seat belt or air bag.
    c. How do these two forces compare to the person's weight?

49. ‖‖‖ Bob, who has a mass of 75 kg, can throw a 500 g rock with a speed of 30 m/s. The distance through which his hand moves as he INT accelerates the rock forward from rest until he releases it is 1.0 m.
    a. What constant force must Bob exert on the rock to throw it with this speed?
    b. If Bob is standing on frictionless ice, what is his recoil speed after releasing the rock?

50. ‖‖‖ An 80 kg spacewalking astronaut pushes off a 640 kg satellite, exerting a 100 N force for the 0.50 s it takes him to INT straighten his arms. How far apart are the astronaut and the satellite after 1.0 min?

51. ‖ What thrust does a 200 g model rocket need in order to have a vertical acceleration of 10.0 m/s²
    a. On earth?
    b. On the moon, where $g = 1.62$ m/s²?

52. ‖‖‖ A 20,000 kg rocket has a rocket motor that generates 3.0×10^5 N of thrust.
    a. What is the rocket's initial upward acceleration?
    b. At an altitude of 5.0 km the rocket's acceleration has increased to 6.0 m/s². What mass of fuel has it burned?

53. ‖‖ You've always wondered about the acceleration of the elevators in the 101-story-tall Empire State Building. One day, while visiting New York, you take your bathroom scales into the elevator and stand on them. The scales read 150 lb as the door closes. The reading varies between 120 lb and 170 lb as the elevator travels 101 floors.
    a. What is the magnitude of the acceleration as the elevator starts upward?
    b. What is the magnitude of the acceleration as the elevator brakes to a stop?

54. ‖‖‖ A 23 kg child goes down a straight slide inclined 38° above horizontal. The child is acted on by his weight, the normal force from the slide, kinetic friction, and a horizontal rope exerting a 30 N force as shown in Figure P5.54. How large is the normal force of the slide on the child?

FIGURE P5.54

55. ‖ Josh starts his sled at the top of a 3.0-m-high hill that has a constant slope of 25°. After reaching the bottom, he slides across a horizontal patch of snow. The hill is frictionless, but INT the coefficient of kinetic friction between his sled and the snow is 0.05. How far from the base of the hill does he end up?

56. ‖ A wood block, after being given a starting push, slides down a wood ramp at a constant speed. What is the angle of the ramp above horizontal?

57. ‖ Researchers often use *force plates* to measure the forces
BIO that people exert against the floor during movement. A force
INT plate works like a bathroom scale, but it keeps a record of how
the reading changes with time. Figure P5.57 shows the data
from a force plate as a woman jumps straight up and then
lands.
   a. What was the vertical component of her acceleration during
   push-off?
   b. What was the vertical component of her acceleration while
   in the air?
   c. What was the vertical component of her acceleration during
   the landing?
   d. What was her speed as her feet left the force plate?
   e. How high did she jump?

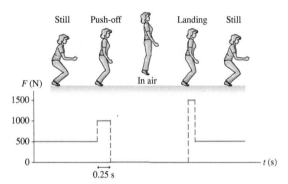

FIGURE P5.57

58. ‖‖‖ A 77 kg sprinter is running the 100 m dash. At one instant,
BIO early in the race, his acceleration is 4.7 m/s².
   a. What *total* force does the track surface exert on the sprinter?
   Assume his acceleration is parallel to the ground. Give
   your answer as a magnitude and an angle with respect to
   the horizontal.
   b. This force is applied to one foot (the other foot is in the air),
   which for a fraction of a second is stationary with respect to
   the track surface. Because the foot is stationary, the net force
   on it must be zero. Thus the force of the lower leg bone on
   the foot is equal but opposite to the force of the track on the
   foot. If the lower leg bone is 60° from horizontal, what are
   the components of the leg's force on the foot in the directions parallel and perpendicular to the leg? (Force components perpendicular to the leg can cause dislocation of the
   ankle joint.)

59. ‖‖‖ Sam, whose mass is 75 kg, takes off across level snow on his
jet-powered skis. The skis have a thrust of 200 N and a coefficient of kinetic friction on snow of 0.10. Unfortunately, the skis
run out of fuel after only 10 s.
   a. What is Sam's top speed?
   b. How far has Sam traveled when he finally coasts to a
   stop?

60. ‖‖‖ A person with compromised pinch
strength in his fingers can only exert a nor-
BIO mal force of 6.0 N to either side of a pinch-
held object, such as the book shown in
Figure P5.60. What is the heaviest book he
can hold onto vertically before it slips out of
his fingers? The coefficient of static friction
of the surface between the fingers and the
book cover is 0.80.

FIGURE P5.60

61. ‖‖‖ A 1.0 kg wood block is pressed against a
vertical wood wall by a 12 N force as shown
in Figure P5.61. If the block is initially at
rest, will it move upward, move downward,
or stay at rest?

FIGURE P5.61

62. ‖‖‖ A 50,000 kg locomotive, with steel
wheels, is traveling at 10 m/s on steel rails
when its engine and brakes both fail. How far will the locomotive roll before it comes to a stop?

63. ‖ An Airbus A320 jetliner has a takeoff mass of 75,000 kg. It
reaches its takeoff speed of 82 m/s (180 mph) in 35 s. What is
the thrust of the engines? You can neglect air resistance but not
rolling friction.

64. ‖‖‖‖ A 2.0 kg wood block is launched up a wooden ramp that is
inclined at a 35° angle. The block's initial speed is 10 m/s.
   a. What vertical height does the block reach above its starting
   point?
   b. What speed does it have when it slides back down to its
   starting point?

65. ‖‖‖ Two blocks are at rest
on a frictionless incline,
as shown in Figure P5.65.
What are the tensions in
the two strings?

FIGURE P5.65

66. ‖ Two identical blocks
are stacked one on top
of the other. The bottom
block is free to slide on a frictionless surface. The coefficient
of static friction between the blocks is 0.35. What is the maximum horizontal force that can be applied to the lower block
without the upper block slipping?

67. ‖‖‖ A wood block is sliding up a wood ramp. If the ramp is very
steep, the block will reverse direction at its highest point and
slide back down. If the ramp is shallow, the block will stop
when it reaches its highest point. What is the smallest ramp
angle, measured from the horizontal, for which the block will
slide back down?

68. ‖‖‖‖ The fastest recorded skydive was by an Air Force officer
who jumped from a helium balloon at an elevation of
103,000 ft, three times higher than airliners fly. Because the
density of air is so low at these altitudes, he reached a speed
of 614 mph at an elevation of 90,000 ft, then gradually
slowed as the air became more dense. Assume that he fell in
the spread-eagle position of Example 5.15 and that his low-
altitude terminal speed is 125 mph. Use this information to
determine the density of air at 90,000 ft.

69. ‖‖‖‖ A 2.7 g Ping-Pong ball has a diameter of 4.0 cm.
   a. The ball is shot straight up at twice its terminal speed. What
   is its initial acceleration?
   b. The ball is shot straight down at twice its terminal speed.
   What is its initial acceleration?

70. ‖‖‖‖ Two blocks are connected by a string as in Figure P5.70.
What is the upper block's acceleration if the coefficient of
kinetic friction between the block and the table is 0.20?

FIGURE P5.70   FIGURE P5.71

71. ⦀ The 10 kg block in Figure P5.71 slides down a frictionless ramp. What is its acceleration?

72. ‖ A 2.0 kg wood block is pulled along a wood floor at a steady speed. A second wood block, with mass 3.0 kg, is attached to the first by a horizontal string. What is the magnitude of the force pulling on the first block?

73. ⦀ A magician pulls a tablecloth out from under some dishes. How far do the dishes move during the 0.25 s it takes to pull out the tablecloth? The coefficient of kinetic friction between the cloth and the dishes is $\mu_k = 0.12$.

74. ‖ The 100 kg block in Figure P5.74 takes 6.0 s to reach the floor after being released from rest. What is the mass of the block on the left?

FIGURE P5.74

Problems 75 and 76 show free-body diagrams. For each,

a. Write a realistic dynamics problem for which this is the correct free-body diagram. Your problem should ask a question that can be answered with a value of position or velocity (such as "How far?" or "How fast?"), and should give sufficient information to allow a solution.

b. Solve your problem!

75. |

76. ⦀

FIGURE P5.75   FIGURE P5.76

In Problems 77 through 79 you are given the dynamics equations that are used to solve a problem. For each of these, you are to

a. Write a realistic problem for which these are the correct equations.

b. Draw the free-body diagram and the pictorial representation for your problem.

c. Finish the solution of the problem.

77. ‖ $-0.80n = (1500 \text{ kg})a_x$
    $n - (1500 \text{ kg})(9.8 \text{ m/s}^2) = 0$

78. ‖ $T - 0.2n - (20 \text{ kg})(9.8 \text{ m/s}^2)\sin 20° = (20 \text{ kg})(2.0 \text{ m/s}^2)$
    $n - (20 \text{ kg})(9.8 \text{ m/s}^2)\cos 20° = 0$

79. ‖ $(100 \text{ N})\cos 30° - f_k = (20 \text{ kg})a_x$
    $n + (100 \text{ N})\sin 30° - (20 \text{ kg})(9.8 \text{ m/s}^2) = 0$
    $f_k = 0.20n$

Passage Problems

Sliding on the Ice

In the winter sport of curling, players give a 20 kg stone a push across a sheet of ice. The stone moves approximately 40 m before coming to rest. The final position of the stone, in principle, only depends on the initial speed at which it is launched and the force of friction between the ice and the stone, but team members can use brooms to sweep the ice in front of the stone to adjust its speed and trajectory a bit; they must do this without touching the stone. Judicious sweeping can lengthen the travel of the stone by 3 m.

80. | A curler pushes a stone to a speed of 3.0 m/s over a time of 2.0 s. Ignoring the force of friction, how much force must the curler apply to the stone to bring it up to speed?
    A. 3.0 N   B. 15 N   C. 30 N   D. 150 N

81. | The sweepers in a curling competition adjust the trajectory of the stone by
    A. Decreasing the coefficient of friction between the stone and the ice.
    B. Increasing the coefficient of friction between the stone and the ice.
    C. Changing friction from kinetic to static.
    D. Changing friction from static to kinetic.

82. | Suppose the stone is launched with a speed of 3 m/s and travels 40 m before coming to rest. What is the *approximate* magnitude of the friction force on the stone?
    A. 0 N   B. 2 N   C. 20 N   D. 200 N

83. | Suppose the stone's mass is increased to 40 kg, but it is launched at the same 3 m/s. Which one of the following is true?
    A. The stone would now travel a longer distance before coming to rest.
    B. The stone would now travel a shorter distance before coming to rest.
    C. The coefficient of friction would now be greater.
    D. The force of friction would now be greater.

STOP TO THINK ANSWERS

Stop to Think 5.1: A. The lander is descending and slowing. The acceleration vector points upward, and so $\vec{F}_{net}$ points upward. This can be true only if the thrust has a larger magnitude than the weight.

Stop to Think 5.2: D. When you are in the air, there is *no* contact force supporting you, so your apparent weight is zero: You are weightless.

Stop to Think 5.3: $f_B > f_C = f_D = f_E > f_A$. Situations C, D, and E are all kinetic friction, which does not depend on either velocity or acceleration. Kinetic friction is less than the maximum static friction that is exerted in B. $f_A = 0$ because no friction is needed to keep the object at rest.

Stop to Think 5.4: D. The ball is shot *down* at 30 m/s, so $v_{0y} = -30$ m/s. This exceeds the terminal speed, so the upward drag force is *greater* than the downward weight force. Thus the ball *slows down* even though it is "falling." It will slow until $v_y = -15$ m/s, the terminal velocity, then maintain that velocity.

Stop to Think 5.5: B. $F_{Q\,on\,H} = F_{H\,on\,Q}$ and $F_{P\,on\,Q} = F_{Q\,on\,P}$ because these are action/reaction pairs. Box Q is slowing down and therefore must have a net force to the left. So from Newton's second law we also know that $F_{H\,on\,Q} > F_{P\,on\,Q}$.

Stop to Think 5.6: Equal to. Each block is hanging in equilibrium, with no net force, so the upward tension force is mg.

6 Circular Motion, Orbits, and Gravity

Motorcyclists in the "Globe of Death" ride their bikes on the inside of a spherical steel frame, seeming to defy gravity as they ride up the sides and upside down over the top. What prevents them from falling?

LOOKING AHEAD ▶

The goal of Chapter 6 is to learn about motion in a circle, including orbital motion under the influence of a gravitational force.

Uniform Circular Motion

A particle moving in a circle at a constant speed undergoes **uniform circular motion**. In this chapter you'll learn how to describe a particle's motion in terms of its *angular* position and *angular* velocity.

We'll also review the important idea that a particle moving in a circle has an acceleration directed toward the center of the circle.

> **Looking Back ◀◀**
> 2.2 Uniform motion
> 3.8 Circular motion

The acceleration points toward the center of the circle.

Dynamics of Uniform Circular Motion

Because a particle moving in a circle has an acceleration that points toward the center of the circle, there must be a net force toward the center to cause this acceleration.

> **Looking Back ◀◀**
> 5.2 Using Newton's second law

The net force on the girl is directed toward the center of the circle.

The normal force of the track and the car's weight combine to provide a net force toward the circle's center.

Apparent Forces in Circular Motion

An object moving in a circle appears to experience a force that "flings" it outward. You'll learn that these apparent forces are not real forces, but are in fact a consequence of Newton's first law.

> **Looking Back ◀◀**
> 5.3 Weight and apparent weight

What holds these riders in this carnival ride against the wall?

Newton's Law of Gravity

Newton discovered the law that governs gravity. You'll learn how it applies to an apple falling to earth or a rock falling on the moon, and how this law governs the motions of the moon, the planets, and even distant galaxies.

Newton's great insight was that the law of gravity described not only falling objects but also the orbits of the moon and planets.

Even the structure of distant galaxies is determined by Newton's law of gravity.

Gravity and Orbits

If an object moves fast enough, it can orbit the earth, the sun, or another planet.

An orbit can be thought of as projectile motion where the ground curves away just as fast as the object falls.

The space station appears weightless, but gravity still acts strongly on it; only its *apparent weight* is zero.

6.1 Uniform Circular Motion

We began our study of circular motion in Section 3.8. There, we learned how to describe the circular motion of a particle in terms of its period and frequency. We also learned that a particle moving in a circle has an acceleration—even if the particle's speed is constant—because the *direction* of its velocity is constantly changing.

In this chapter, we'll study the simplest kind of circular motion, in which a particle moves at a *constant* speed around its circular path. FIGURE 6.1 shows a particle undergoing this uniform circular motion. The particle might be a satellite moving in an orbit, a ball on the end of a string, or even just a dot painted on the side of a wheel. Regardless of what the particle represents, its velocity vector is always tangent to the circular path. The particle's speed v is constant, so the vector's length stays constant as the particle moves around the circle.

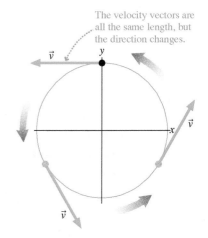

FIGURE 6.1 A particle in uniform circular motion.

The velocity vectors are all the same length, but the direction changes.

Angular Position

In order to describe the position of a particle as it moves around the circle, it is convenient to use the angle θ from the positive x-axis. This is shown in FIGURE 6.2. Because the particle travels in a circle with a fixed radius r, specifying θ completely locates the position of the particle. Thus we call angle θ the **angular position** of the particle.

We define θ to be positive when measured *counterclockwise* from the positive x-axis. An angle measured *clockwise* from the positive x-axis has a negative value. "Clockwise" and "counterclockwise" in circular motion are analogous, respectively, to "left of the origin" and "right of the origin" in linear motion, which we associated with negative and positive values of x.

Rather than measure angles in degrees, mathematicians and scientists usually measure angle θ in the angular unit of *radians*. In Figure 6.2, we also show the **arc length** s, the distance that the particle has traveled along its circular path. We define the particle's angle θ in **radians** in terms of this arc length and the radius of the circle:

$$\theta \text{ (radians)} = \frac{s}{r} \tag{6.1}$$

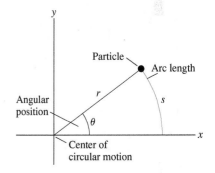

FIGURE 6.2 A particle's angular position is described by angle θ.

This is a sensible definition of an angle: The farther the particle has traveled around the circle (i.e., the greater s is), the larger the angle θ in radians. The radian, abbreviated rad, is the SI unit of angle. An angle of 1 rad has an arc length s exactly equal to the radius r. An important consequence of Equation 6.1 is that the arc length spanning the angle θ is

$$s = r\theta \tag{6.2}$$

NOTE ▶ Equation 6.2 is valid only if θ is measured in radians, not degrees. This very simple relationship between angle and arc length is one of the primary motivations for using radians. ◀

When a particle travels all the way around the circle—completing one *revolution,* abbreviated rev—the arc length it travels is the circle's circumference $2\pi r$. Thus the angle of a full circle is

$$\theta_{\text{full circle}} = \frac{s}{r} = \frac{2\pi r}{r} = 2\pi \text{ rad}$$

We can use this fact to define conversion factors among revolutions, radians, and degrees:

$$1 \text{ rev} = 360° = 2\pi \text{ rad}$$

$$1 \text{ rad} = 1 \text{ rad} \times \frac{360°}{2\pi \text{ rad}} = 57.3°$$

We will often specify angles in degrees, but keep in mind that the SI unit is the radian. You can visualize angles in radians by remembering that 1 rad is just about 60°.

Angular Displacement and Angular Velocity

For the *linear* motion you studied in Chapters 1 and 2, a particle with a larger velocity undergoes a greater displacement in each second than one with a smaller velocity, as FIGURE 6.3a shows. FIGURE 6.3b shows two particles undergoing uniform *circular* motion. The particle on the left is moving slowly around the circle; it has gone only one-quarter of the way around after 5 seconds. The particle on the right is moving much faster around the circle, covering half of the circle in the same 5 seconds. You can see that the particle to the right undergoes twice the **angular displacement** $\Delta\theta$ during each interval as the particle to the left. Its **angular velocity,** the angular displacement through which the particle moves each second, is twice as large.

FIGURE 6.3 Comparing uniform linear and circular motion.

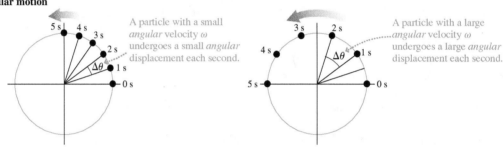

(a) Uniform linear motion

A particle with a small velocity v undergoes a small displacement each second.

A particle with a large velocity v undergoes a large displacement each second.

(b) Uniform circular motion

A particle with a small *angular* velocity ω undergoes a small *angular* displacement each second.

A particle with a large *angular* velocity ω undergoes a large *angular* displacement each second.

In analogy with linear motion, where $v_x = \Delta x/\Delta t$, we thus define the angular velocity as

$$\omega = \frac{\text{angular displacement}}{\text{time interval}} = \frac{\Delta\theta}{\Delta t} \qquad (6.3)$$

Angular velocity of a particle in uniform circular motion

The symbol ω is a lowercase Greek omega, *not* an ordinary w. The SI unit of angular velocity is rad/s.

Figure 6.3a shows that the displacement Δx of a particle in uniform linear motion changes by the same amount each second. Similarly, as Figure 6.3b shows, the *angular* displacement $\Delta\theta$ of a particle in uniform *circular* motion changes by the same amount each second. This means that **the angular velocity $\omega = \Delta\theta/\Delta t$ is constant for a particle moving with uniform circular motion.**

EXAMPLE 6.1 **Comparing angular velocities**

Find the angular velocities of the two particles in Figure 6.3b.

PREPARE For uniform circular motion, we can use any angular displacement $\Delta\theta$, as long as we use the corresponding time interval Δt. For each particle, we'll choose the angular displacement corresponding to the motion from $t = 0$ s to $t = 5$ s.

SOLVE The particle on the left travels one-quarter of a full circle during the 5 s time interval. We learned earlier that a full circle corresponds to an angle of 2π rad, so the angular displacement for this particle is $\Delta\theta = (2\pi \text{ rad})/4 = \pi/2$ rad. Thus its angular velocity is

$$\omega = \frac{\Delta\theta}{\Delta t} = \frac{\pi/2 \text{ rad}}{5 \text{ s}} = 0.31 \text{ rad/s}$$

The particle on the right travels halfway around the circle, or π rad, in the 5 s interval. Its angular velocity is

$$\omega = \frac{\Delta\theta}{\Delta t} = \frac{\pi \text{ rad}}{5 \text{ s}} = 0.63 \text{ rad/s}$$

ASSESS The angular velocity of the particle on the right is 0.63 rad/s, meaning that the particle travels through an angle of 0.63 rad each second. Because 1 rad $\approx$ 60°, 0.63 rad is roughly 35°. In Figure 6.3b, the particle on the right appears to move through an angle of about this size during each 1 s time interval, so our answer is reasonable.

Angular velocity, like the velocity v_x of one-dimensional motion, can be positive or negative. The signs for ω noted in FIGURE 6.4 are based on the convention that angles are positive when measured counterclockwise from the positive x-axis.

We've already noted how circular motion is analogous to linear motion, with angular variables replacing linear variables. Thus much of what you learned about linear kinematics and dynamics carries over to circular motion. For example, Equation 2.4 gave us a formula for computing a linear displacement during a time interval:

$$x_f - x_i = \Delta x = v_x \, \Delta t$$

You can see from Equation 6.3 that we can write a similar equation for the angular displacement:

$$\theta_f - \theta_i = \Delta\theta = \omega \, \Delta t \tag{6.4}$$

Angular displacement for uniform circular motion

For linear motion, we use the term *speed v* when we are not concerned with the direction of motion, *velocity* v_x when we are. For circular motion, we define the **angular speed** to be the absolute value of the angular velocity, so that it's a positive quantity irrespective of the particle's direction of rotation. Although potentially confusing, it is customary to use the symbol ω for angular speed *and* for angular velocity. If the direction of rotation is not important, we will interpret ω to mean angular speed. In kinematic equations, such as Equation 6.4, ω is always the angular velocity, and you need to use a negative value for clockwise rotation.

FIGURE 6.4 Positive and negative angular velocities.

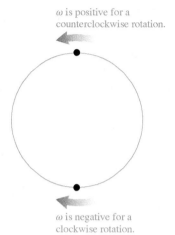

ω is positive for a counterclockwise rotation.

ω is negative for a clockwise rotation.

EXAMPLE 6.2 **Kinematics at the roulette wheel**

A small steel ball rolls counterclockwise around the inside of a 30.0-cm-diameter roulette wheel. The ball completes exactly 2 rev in 1.20 s.

a. What is the ball's angular velocity?
b. What is the ball's angular position at $t = 2.00$ s? Assume $\theta_i = 0$.

PREPARE Treat the ball as a particle in uniform circular motion.

SOLVE

a. The ball's angular velocity is $\omega = \Delta\theta/\Delta t$. We know that the ball completes 2 revolutions in 1.20 s, and that each revolution corresponds to an angular displacement $\Delta\theta = 2\pi$ rad. Thus

$$\omega = \frac{2(2\pi \text{ rad})}{1.20 \text{ s}} = 10.5 \text{ rad/s}$$

Because the rotation direction is counterclockwise, the angular velocity is positive.

b. The ball moves with constant angular velocity, so its angular position is given by Equation 6.4. Thus the ball's angular position at $t = 2.00$ s is

$$\theta_f = \theta_i + \omega \, \Delta t = 0 \text{ rad} + (10.5 \text{ rad/s})(2.00 \text{ s}) = 21.0 \text{ rad}$$

If we're interested in where the ball is in the wheel at $t = 2.00$ s, we can write its angular position as an integer multiple of 2π (representing the number of complete revolutions the ball has made) plus a remainder:

$$\theta_f = 21.0 \text{ rad} = 3.34 \times 2\pi \text{ rad}$$
$$= 3 \times 2\pi \text{ rad} + 0.34 \times 2\pi \text{ rad}$$
$$= 3 \times 2\pi \text{ rad} + 2.1 \text{ rad}$$

In other words, at $t = 2.00$ s, the ball has completed 3 rev and is 2.1 rad = 120° into its fourth revolution. An observer would say that the ball's angular position is $\theta = 120°$.

ASSESS Since the ball completes 2 revolutions in 1.20 s, it seems reasonable that it completes 3.34 revolutions in 2.00 s.

The angular speed ω is closely related to the period T and the frequency f of the motion. If a particle in uniform circular motion moves around a circle once, which by definition takes time T, its angular displacement is $\Delta\theta = 2\pi$ rad. The angular speed is thus

$$\omega = \frac{2\pi \text{ rad}}{T} \tag{6.5}$$

◀ **Why do clocks go clockwise?** In the northern hemisphere, the rotation of the earth causes the sun to follow a circular arc through the southern sky, rising in the east and setting in the west. For millennia, humans have marked passing time by noting the position of shadows cast by the sun, which sweep in an arc from west to east—eventually leading to the development of the sundial, the first practical timekeeping device. In the northern hemisphere, sundials point north, and the shadow sweeps around the dial from left to right. Early clockmakers used the same convention, which is how it came to be clockwise.

We can also write the angular speed in terms of the frequency $f = 1/T$:

$$\omega = (2\pi \text{ rad})f \tag{6.6}$$

where f must be in rev/s. For example, a particle in circular motion with frequency 10 rev/s would have angular speed $\omega = 20\pi \text{ rad/s} = 62.8 \text{ rad/s}$.

EXAMPLE 6.3 | **Rotations in a car engine**

The crankshaft in your car engine is turning at 3000 rpm. What is the shaft's angular velocity?

PREPARE We'll need to convert rpm to rev/s; then we can use Equation 6.6.

SOLVE We convert rpm to rev/s by

$$\left(3000 \frac{\text{rev}}{\text{min}}\right)\left(\frac{1 \text{ min}}{60 \text{ s}}\right) = 50 \text{ rev/s}$$

Thus the crankshaft's angular velocity is

$$\omega = (2\pi \text{ rad})f = (2\pi \text{ rad})(50 \text{ rev/s}) = 314 \text{ rad/s}$$

FIGURE 6.5 Angular position for the ball on the roulette wheel.

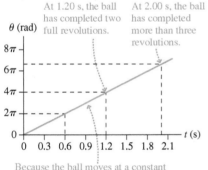

At 1.20 s, the ball has completed two full revolutions.

At 2.00 s, the ball has completed more than three revolutions.

Because the ball moves at a constant angular velocity, a graph of the angular position versus time is a straight line.

Angular-Position and Angular-Velocity Graphs

For the one-dimensional motion you studied in Chapter 3, we found that position- and velocity-versus-time graphs were important and useful representations of motion. We can use the same kinds of graphs to represent angular motion. Let's begin by considering the motion of the roulette ball of Example 6.2. We found that it had angular velocity $\omega = 10.5 \text{ rad/s}$, meaning that its angular *position* changed by +10.5 rad every second. This is exactly analogous to the one-dimensional motion problem of a car driving in a straight line with a velocity of 10.5 m/s, so that its position increases by 10.5 m each second. Using this analogy, we can construct the **angular position-versus-time graph** for the roulette ball shown in FIGURE 6.5.

The angular velocity is given by $\omega = \Delta\theta/\Delta t$. Graphically, this is the *slope* of the angular position-versus-time graph, just as the ordinary velocity is the slope of the position-versus-time graph. Thus we can create an **angular velocity-versus-time graph** by finding the slope of the corresponding angular position-versus-time graph.

EXAMPLE 6.4 | **Graphing a bike ride**

Jake rides his bicycle home from campus. FIGURE 6.6 is the angular position-versus-time graph for a small rock stuck in the tread of his tire. First, draw the rock's angular velocity-versus-time graph, using rpm on the vertical axis. Then interpret the graphs with a story about Jake's ride.

PREPARE Angular velocity ω is the slope of the angular position-versus-time graph.

SOLVE We can see that $\omega = 0 \text{ rad/s}$ during the first and last 30 s of Jake's ride because the horizontal segments of the graph have zero slope. Between $t = 30 \text{ s}$ and $t = 150 \text{ s}$, an interval of 120 s,

FIGURE 6.6 Angular position-versus-time graph for Jake's bike ride.

the rock's angular velocity (the slope of the angular position-versus-time graph) is

$$\omega = \text{slope} = \frac{2500 \text{ rad} - 0 \text{ rad}}{120 \text{ s}} = 20.8 \text{ rad/s}$$

We need to convert this to rpm:

$$\omega = \left(\frac{20.8 \text{ rad}}{1 \text{ s}}\right)\left(\frac{1 \text{ rev}}{2\pi \text{ rad}}\right)\left(\frac{60 \text{ s}}{1 \text{ min}}\right) = 200 \text{ rpm}$$

These values have been used to draw the angular velocity-versus-time graph of FIGURE 6.7. It looks like Jake waited 30 s for the light to change, then pedaled so that the bike wheel turned at a constant angular velocity of 200 rpm. 2.0 min later, he quickly braked to a stop for another 30-s-long red light.

FIGURE 6.7 Angular velocity-versus-time graph for Jake's bike ride.

ASSESS At 200 rpm for 2 minutes, the wheel would turn roughly 400 times or, at ≈6 rad/rev, through about 2400 rad. Our answer seems reasonable.

STOP TO THINK 6.1 Which particle has angular position $5\pi/2$?

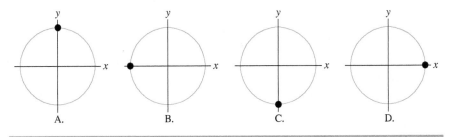

A. B. C. D.

6.2 Speed, Velocity, and Acceleration in Uniform Circular Motion

The preceding section described uniform circular motion in terms of angular variables. In Chapter 3, we introduced a description of uniform circular motion in terms of velocity and acceleration vectors. We will now unite these two different descriptions, which will enable us to consider a much wider range of problems.

 PhET: Ladybug Motion 2D
PhET: Ladybug Revolution

Speed

In Chapter 3, we found that the speed of a particle moving with frequency f around a circular path of radius r is $v = 2\pi f r$. If we combine this result with Equation 6.5 for the angular speed, we find that speed v and angular speed ω are related by

$$v = \omega r \tag{6.7}$$

Relationship between speed and angular speed

NOTE ▶ In Equation 6.7, ω **must be in units of rad/s.** If you are given a frequency in rev/s or rpm, you should convert it to an angular speed in rad/s. ◀

EXAMPLE 6.5 **Finding the speed at two points on a CD**

The diameter of an audio compact disc is 12.0 cm. When the disc is spinning at its maximum rate of 540 rpm, what is the speed of a point (a) at a distance 3.0 cm from the center and (b) at the outside edge of the disc, 6.0 cm from the center?

PREPARE Consider two points A and B on the rotating compact disc in FIGURE 6.8. During one period T, the disc rotates once, and both points rotate through the same angle, 2π rad. Thus the angular speed, $\omega = 2\pi/T$, is the same for these two points; in fact, it is the same for all points on the disc. But as they go around one time, the two points move different *distances;* the outer point B goes around a larger circle. The two points thus have different *speeds.* We can solve this problem by first finding the angular speed of the disc and then computing the speeds at the two points.

FIGURE 6.8 The rotation of an audio compact disc.

SOLVE We first convert the frequency of the disc from rpm to rev/s:

$$f = \left(540\,\frac{\text{rev}}{\text{min}}\right) \times \left(\frac{1\,\text{min}}{60\,\text{s}}\right) = 9.00\,\text{rev/s}$$

We can compute the angular speed using Equation 6.6:

$$\omega = (2\pi\,\text{rad})(9.00\,\text{rev/s}) = 56.5\,\text{rad/s}$$

We can now use Equation 6.7 to compute the speeds of points on the disc. At point A, $r = 3.0$ cm $= 0.030$ m, so the speed is

$$v_B = \omega r = (56.5\,\text{rad/s})(0.030\,\text{m}) = 1.7\,\text{m/s}$$

At point B, $r = 6.0$ cm $= 0.060$ m, so the speed at the outside edge is

$$v_B = \omega r = (56.5\,\text{rad/s})(0.060\,\text{m}) = 3.4\,\text{m/s}$$

ASSESS The speeds are a few meters per second, which seems reasonable. The point farther from the center is moving at a higher speed, as we expected.

Velocity and Acceleration

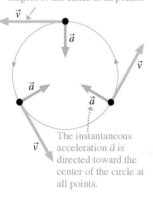
FIGURE 6.9 Velocity and acceleration for uniform circular motion.

The instantaneous velocity $\vec{v}$ is tangent to the circle at all points.

The instantaneous acceleration $\vec{a}$ is directed toward the center of the circle at all points.

Although the *speed* of a particle in uniform circular motion is constant, its *velocity* is not constant because the *direction* of the motion is always changing. As you learned in Chapter 3, and as FIGURE 6.9 reminds you, there is an acceleration at every point in the motion, with the acceleration vector $\vec{a}$ pointing toward the center of the circle. We called this the *centripetal acceleration,* and we showed that for uniform circular motion the acceleration was given by $a = v^2/r$. Because $v = \omega r$, we can also write this relationship in terms of the angular speed:

$$a = \frac{v^2}{r} = \omega^2 r \qquad (6.8)$$

Centripetal acceleration for uniform circular motion

QUADRATIC

Acceleration depends on speed, but also distance from the center of the circle.

Who has the larger acceleration?

Two children are riding in circles on a merry-go-round, as shown in FIGURE 6.10. Which child experiences the larger acceleration?

FIGURE 6.10 Top view of a merry-go-round.

Jacob Emma

REASON As Example 6.2 showed, all points on the merry-go-round move at the same angular speed. The second expression for the acceleration in Equation 6.8 tells us that $a = \omega^2 r$. As the two children are moving with the same angular speed, Emma, with a larger value of r, experiences a larger acceleration.

ASSESS In Example 6.5, we saw that points farther from the center move at a higher speed. This would imply a higher acceleration as well, so our answer makes sense.

| EXAMPLE 6.7 | Finding the period of a carnival ride |

In the Quasar carnival ride, passengers travel in a horizontal 5.0-m-radius circle. For safe operation, the maximum sustained acceleration that riders may experience is 20 m/s², approximately twice the free-fall acceleration. What is the period of the ride when it is being operated at the maximum acceleration?

FIGURE 6.11 Visual overview for the Quasar carnival ride.

Known
$r = 5.0$ m
$a = 20$ m/s²
Find
T

PREPARE We will assume that the cars on the ride are in uniform circular motion. The visual overview of FIGURE 6.11 shows a top view of the motion of the ride.

SOLVE The angular speed can be computed from the acceleration by rearranging Equation 6.8:

$$\omega = \sqrt{\frac{a}{r}} = \sqrt{\frac{20 \text{ m/s}^2}{5.0 \text{ m}}} = 2.0 \text{ rad/s}$$

At this angular speed, the period is $T = 2\pi/\omega = 3.1$ s.

ASSESS One rotation in just over 3 seconds seems reasonable for a pretty zippy carnival ride. The period for this particular ride is actually 3.7 s, so it runs a bit slower than the maximum safe speed.

STOP TO THINK 6.2   Rank in order, from largest to smallest, the centripetal accelerations of particles A to D.

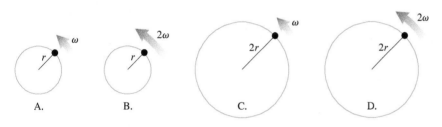

A.   B.   C.   D.

6.3 Dynamics of Uniform Circular Motion

Riders traveling around on a circular carnival ride are accelerating, as we have just seen. Consequently, according to Newton's second law, the riders must have a net *force* acting on them. In this section, we'll look at the forces that cause uniform circular motion.

We've already determined the acceleration of a particle in uniform circular motion—the centripetal acceleration of Equation 6.8. Newton's second law tells us what the net force must be to cause this acceleration:

$$\vec{F}_{\text{net}} = m\vec{a} = \left(\frac{mv^2}{r} = m\omega^2 r, \text{ toward center of circle} \right) \quad (6.9)$$

Net force producing the centripetal acceleration of uniform circular motion

In other words, **a particle of mass m moving at constant speed v around a circle of radius r must always have a net force of magnitude $mv^2/r = m\omega^2 r$ pointing toward the center of the circle,** as in FIGURE 6.12. It is this net force that causes the centripetal acceleration of circular motion. Without such a net force, the particle would move off in a straight line tangent to the circle.

The force described by Equation 6.9 is not a *new* kind of force. The net force will be due to one or more of our familiar forces, such as tension, friction, or the normal

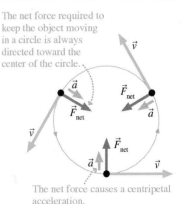

Hurling the heavy hammer This man is throwing a hammer that weighs over 30 pounds as far as he can by spinning the hammer around in a circle and then letting go. While he holds the handle, the hammer follows a circular path. He must provide a very large force directed toward the center of the circle to produce the centripetal acceleration, as you can see by how he is leaning away from the hammer. When he lets go, there is no longer a force directed toward the center, and the hammer will stop going in a circle and fly across the field.

FIGURE 6.12 Net force for circular motion.

The net force required to keep the object moving in a circle is always directed toward the center of the circle.

The net force causes a centripetal acceleration.

force. Equation 6.9 simply tells us how the net force needs to act—how strongly and in which direction—to cause the particle to move with speed v in a circle of radius r.

In each example of circular motion that we will consider in this chapter, a physical force or a combination of forces directed toward the center produces the necessary acceleration. In some cases, the circular motion and the force are obvious, as in the hammer throw. Other cases are more subtle. For instance, for a car following a circular path on a level road, the necessary force is provided by the friction force between the tires and the road.

CONCEPTUAL EXAMPLE 6.8   Forces on a car

A car drives through a circularly shaped valley at a constant speed. At the very bottom of the valley, is the normal force of the road on the car greater than, less than, or equal to the car's weight?

REASON FIGURE 6.13 shows a visual overview of the situation. The car is accelerating, even though it is moving at a constant speed, because its direction is changing. When the car is at the bottom of the valley, the center of its circular path is directly above it and so its acceleration vector points straight up. The free-body diagram of Figure 6.13 identifies the only two forces acting on the car as the normal force, pointing upward, and its weight, pointing downward. Which is larger: n or w?

Because $\vec{a}$ points upward, by Newton's second law there must be a net force on the car that also points upward. In order for this to be the case, the free-body diagram shows that the magnitude of the normal force must be *greater* than the weight.

FIGURE 6.13 Visual overview for the car in the valley.

ASSESS You have probably experienced this situation. As you drive through a dip in the road, you feel "heavier" than normal. As discussed in Section 5.3, this is because your apparent weight—the normal force that supports you—is greater than your true weight.

Solving Circular Dynamics Problems

We have one basic equation for circular dynamics problems, Equation 6.9, which is just a version of Newton's second law. The techniques for solving circular dynamics problems are thus quite similar to those we have used for solving other Newton's second-law problems.

PROBLEM-SOLVING STRATEGY 6.1   Circular dynamics problems

PREPARE Begin your visual overview with a pictorial representation in which you sketch the motion, define symbols, define axes, and identify what the problem is trying to find. There are two common situations:

- If the motion is in a horizontal plane, like a tabletop, draw the free-body diagram with the circle viewed edge-on, the x-axis pointing toward the center of the circle, and the y-axis perpendicular to the plane of the circle.
- If the motion is in a vertical plane, like a Ferris wheel, draw the free-body diagram with the circle viewed face-on, the x-axis pointing toward the center of the circle, and the y-axis tangent to the circle.

SOLVE Newton's second law for uniform circular motion, $\vec{F}_{net} = (mv^2/r,$ toward center of circle), is a vector equation. Some forces act in the plane of the circle, some act perpendicular to the circle, and some may have components in both directions. In the coordinate system described above, with the x-axis pointing toward the center of the circle, Newton's second law is

$$\sum F_x = \frac{mv^2}{r} = m\omega^2 r \quad \text{and} \quad \sum F_y = 0$$

Continued

That is, the net force toward the center of the circle has magnitude $mv^2/r = m\omega^2 r$ while the net force perpendicular to the circle is zero. The components of the forces are found directly from the free-body diagram. Depending on the problem, either:

■ Use the net force to determine the speed v, then use circular kinematics to find frequencies or angular velocities.
■ Use circular kinematics to determine the speed v, then solve for unknown forces.

ASSESS Make sure your net force points toward the center of the circle. Check that your result has the correct units, is reasonable, and answers the question.

Exercise 13

| EXAMPLE 6.9 | Analyzing the motion of a cart |

An energetic father places his 20 kg child on a 5.0 kg cart to which a 2.0-m-long rope is attached. He then holds the end of the rope and spins the cart and child around in a circle, keeping the rope parallel to the ground. If the tension in the rope is 100 N, how much time does it take for the cart to make one rotation?

PREPARE We proceed according to the steps of Problem-Solving Strategy 6.1. FIGURE 6.14 shows a visual overview of the problem. The main reason for the pictorial representation on the left is to illustrate the relevant geometry and to define the symbols that will be used. A circular dynamics problem usually does not have starting and ending points like a projectile problem, so subscripts such as x_i or y_f are usually not needed. Here we need to define the cart's speed v and the radius r of the circle.

The object moving in the circle is the cart plus the child, a total mass of 25 kg; the free-body diagram shows the forces. Because the motion is in a horizontal plane, Problem-Solving Strategy 6.1 tells us to draw the free-body diagram looking at the edge of the circle, with the x-axis pointing toward the center of the circle and the y-axis perpendicular to the plane of the circle. Three forces are acting on the cart: the weight force $\vec{w}$, the normal force of the ground $\vec{n}$, and the tension force of the rope $\vec{T}$.

Notice that there are two quantities for which we use the symbol T: the tension and the period. We will include additional information when necessary to distinguish the two.

SOLVE There is no net force in the y-direction, perpendicular to the circle, so $\vec{w}$ and $\vec{n}$ must be equal and opposite. There is a net force in the x-direction, toward the center of the circle, as there must be to cause the centripetal acceleration of circular motion. Only the tension force has an x-component, so Newton's second law is

$$\sum F_x = T = \frac{mv^2}{r}$$

We know the mass, the radius of the circle, and the tension, so we can solve for v:

$$v = \sqrt{\frac{Tr}{m}} = \sqrt{\frac{(100 \text{ N})(2.0 \text{ m})}{25 \text{ kg}}} = 2.83 \text{ m/s}$$

From this, we can compute the period with a slight rearrangement of Equation 3.27:

$$T = \frac{2\pi r}{v} = \frac{(2\pi)(2.0 \text{ m})}{2.83 \text{ m/s}} = 4.4 \text{ s}$$

ASSESS The speed is about 3 m/s. Because 1 m/s ≈ 2 mph, the child is going about 6 mph. A trip around the circle in just over 4 s at a speed of about 6 mph sounds reasonable; it's a fast ride, but not so fast as to be scary!

FIGURE 6.14 A visual overview of the cart spinning in a circle.

The pictorial representation shows a top view.   The free-body diagram shows an edge-on view.

Known
$m = 25 \text{ kg}$
$r = 2.0 \text{ m}$
Tension $T = 100 \text{ N}$

Find
Period T in seconds

Cart r Dad

$\vec{v}$

$\vec{n}$ $\vec{F}_{net}$

$\vec{T}$ x

$\vec{w}$

This is the plane of the motion.

EXAMPLE 6.10   **Finding the maximum speed to turn a corner**

What is the maximum speed with which a 1500 kg car can make a turn around a curve of radius 20 m on a level (unbanked) road without sliding? (This radius turn is about what you might expect at a major intersection in a city.)

PREPARE We start with the visual overview in FIGURE 6.15. The car moves along a circular arc at a constant speed—uniform circular motion—for the quarter-circle necessary to complete the turn. The motion before and after the turn is not relevant to the problem. The more interesting issue is *how* a car turns a corner. What force or forces can we identify that cause the direction of the velocity vector to change? Imagine you are driving a car on a frictionless road, such as a very icy road. You would not be able to turn a corner. Turning the steering wheel would be of no use; the car would slide straight ahead, in accordance with both Newton's first law and the experience of anyone who has ever driven on ice! So it must be *friction* that causes the car to turn.

The top view of the tire in Figure 6.15 shows the force on one of the car's tires as it turns a corner. If the road surface were frictionless, the tire would slide straight ahead. The force that prevents an object from sliding across a surface is *static friction*. Static friction $\vec{f}_s$ pushes *sideways* on the tire, toward the center of the circle. How do we know the direction is sideways? If $\vec{f}_s$ had a component either parallel to $\vec{v}$ or opposite $\vec{v}$, it would cause the car to speed up or slow down. Because the car changes direction but not speed, static friction must be perpendicular to $\vec{v}$. Thus $\vec{f}_s$ causes the centripetal acceleration of circular motion around the curve. With this in mind, the free-body diagram, drawn from behind the car, shows the static friction force pointing toward the center of the circle. Because the motion is in a horizontal plane, we've again chosen an *x*-axis toward the center of the circle and a *y*-axis perpendicular to the plane of motion.

SOLVE The only force in the *x*-direction, toward the center of the circle, is static friction. Newton's second law along the *x*-axis is

$$\sum F_x = f_s = \frac{mv^2}{r}$$

The only difference between this example and the preceding one is that the tension force toward the center has been replaced by a static friction force toward the center.

Newton's second law in the *y*-direction is

$$\sum F_y = n - w = ma_y = 0$$

so that $n = w = mg$.

The net force toward the center of the circle is the force of static friction. Recall from Equation 5.10 in Chapter 5 that static friction has a maximum possible value:

$$f_{s\,max} = \mu_s n = \mu_s mg$$

Because the static friction force has a maximum value, there will be a maximum speed at which a car can turn without sliding. This speed is reached when the static friction force reaches its maximum value $f_{s\,max} = \mu_s mg$. If the car enters the curve at a speed higher than the maximum, static friction cannot provide the necessary centripetal acceleration and the car will slide.

Thus the maximum speed occurs at the maximum value of the force of static friction, or when

$$f_{s\,max} = \frac{mv_{max}^2}{r}$$

Using the known value of $f_{s\,max}$, we find

$$\frac{mv_{max}^2}{r} = f_{s\,max} = \mu_s mg$$

Rearranging, we get

$$v_{max}^2 = \mu_s g r$$

For rubber tires on pavement, we find from Table 5.1 that $\mu_s = 1.0$. We then have

$$v_{max} = \sqrt{\mu_s g r} = \sqrt{(1.0)(9.8 \text{ m/s}^2)(20 \text{ m})} = 14 \text{ m/s}$$

ASSESS 14 m/s ≈ 30 mph, which seems like a reasonable upper limit for the speed at which a car can go around a curve without sliding. There are two other things to note about the solution:

- The car's mass canceled out. The maximum speed *does not* depend on the mass of the vehicle, though this may seem surprising.
- The final expression for v_{max} *does* depend on the coefficient of friction and the radius of the turn. v_{max} decreases if μ is less (a slipperier road) or if *r* is smaller (a tighter turn). Both make sense.

FIGURE 6.15 Visual overview of a car turning a corner.

Known
m = 1500 kg
r = 20 m
μ_s = 1.0
Find
v_{max}

This force prevents the tire from slipping sideways.

Top view of car   Top view of tire   Rear view of car

Because v_{max} depends on μ_s and because μ_s depends on road conditions, the maximum safe speed through turns can vary dramatically. Wet or icy roads lower the value of μ_s and thus lower the maximum speed of turns. A car that easily handles a curve in dry weather can suddenly slide out of control when the pavement is wet. Icy conditions are even worse. If you lower the value of the coefficient of friction in Example 6.10 from 1.0 (dry pavement) to 0.1 (icy pavement), the maximum speed for the turn goes down to 4.4 m/s—about 10 mph!

Race cars turn corners at much higher speeds than normal passenger vehicles. One design modification of the *cars* to allow this is the addition of wings, as on the car in FIGURE 6.16. The wings provide an additional force pushing the car *down* onto the pavement by deflecting air upward. This extra downward force increases the normal force, thus increasing the maximum static friction force and making faster turns possible.

There are also design modifications of the *track* to allow race cars to take corners at high speeds. If the track is banked by raising the outside edge of curved sections, the normal force can provide some of the force necessary to produce the centripetal acceleration, as we will see in the next example. The curves on racetracks may be quite sharply banked. Curves on ordinary highways are often banked as well, though at more modest angles suiting the lower speeds.

FIGURE 6.16 Wings on an Indy racer.

A banked turn on a racetrack.

EXAMPLE 6.11 Finding speed on a banked turn

A curve on a racetrack of radius 70 m is banked at a 15° angle. At what speed can a car take this curve without assistance from friction?

PREPARE After drawing the pictorial representation in FIGURE 6.17, we use the force identification diagram to find that, given that there is no friction acting, the only two forces are the normal force and the car's weight. We can then construct the free-body diagram, making sure that we draw the normal force perpendicular to the road's surface.

Even though the car is tilted, it is still moving in a *horizontal* circle. Thus, following Problem-Solving Strategy 6.1, we choose

FIGURE 6.17 Visual overview for the car on a banked turn.

the *x*-axis to be horizontal and pointing toward the center of the circle.

SOLVE Without friction, $n_x = n\sin\theta$ is the only component of force toward the center of the circle. It is this inward component of the normal force on the car that causes it to turn the corner. Newton's second law is

$$\sum F_x = n\sin\theta = \frac{mv^2}{r}$$

$$\sum F_y = n\cos\theta - w = 0$$

where θ is the angle at which the road is banked, and we've assumed that the car is traveling at the correct speed v. From the *y*-equation,

$$n = \frac{w}{\cos\theta} = \frac{mg}{\cos\theta}$$

Substituting this into the *x*-equation and solving for v give

$$\left(\frac{mg}{\cos\theta}\right)\sin\theta = mg\tan\theta = \frac{mv^2}{r}$$

$$v = \sqrt{rg\tan\theta} = 14 \text{ m/s}$$

ASSESS This is $\approx$30 mph, a reasonable speed. Only at this exact speed can the turn be negotiated without reliance on friction forces.

Maximum Walking Speed

Humans and other two-legged animals have two basic gaits: walking and running. At slow speeds, you walk. When you need to go faster, you run. Why don't you just walk faster? There is an upper limit to the speed of walking, and this limit is set by the physics of circular motion.

FIGURE 6.18 Analysis of a walking stride.

(a) Walking stride During each stride, her hip undergoes circular motion.

The radius of the circular motion is the length of the leg from the foot to the hip.

The circular motion requires a force directed toward the center of the circle.

(b) Forces in the stride Side view (same as photo)

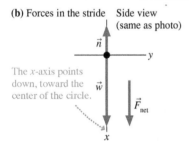

The x-axis points down, toward the center of the circle.

Think about the motion of your body as you take a walking stride. You put one foot forward, then push off with your rear foot. Your body pivots over your front foot, and you bring your rear foot forward to take the next stride. As you can see in FIGURE 6.18a, the path that your body takes during this stride is the arc of a circle. **In a walking gait, your body is in circular motion as you pivot on your forward foot.**

A force toward the center of the circle is required for this circular motion, as shown in Figure 6.18. FIGURE 6.18b shows the forces acting on the woman's body during the midpoint of the stride: her weight, directed down, and the normal force of the ground, directed up. Newton's second law for the x-axis is

$$\sum F_x = w - n = \frac{mv^2}{r}$$

Because of her circular motion, the net force must point toward the center of the circle, or, in this case, down. In order for the net force to point down, the normal force must be *less* than her weight. Your body tries to "lift off" as it pivots over your foot, decreasing the normal force exerted on you by the ground. The normal force becomes smaller as you walk faster, but n cannot be less than zero. Thus the maximum possible walking speed v_{max} occurs when $n = 0$. Setting $n = 0$ in Newton's second law gives

$$w = mg = \frac{mv_{max}^2}{r}$$

Thus

$$v_{max} = \sqrt{gr} \tag{6.10}$$

The maximum possible walking speed is limited by r, the length of the leg, and g, the free-fall acceleration. This formula is a good approximation of the maximum walking speed for humans and other animals. The maximum walking speed is higher for animals with longer legs. Giraffes, with their very long legs, can walk at high speeds. Animals such as mice with very short legs have such a low maximum walking speed that they rarely use this gait. Mice generally run to get from one place to another.

For humans, the length of the leg is approximately 0.7 m, so we calculate a maximum speed of

$$v_{max} \approx 2.6 \text{ m/s} \approx 6 \text{ mph}$$

You *can* walk this fast, though it becomes energetically unfavorable to do so at speeds above 4 mph. Most people make a transition to a running gait at about this speed. Children, with their shorter legs, must make a transition to a running gait at a much lower speed.

STOP TO THINK 6.3 A block on a string spins in a horizontal circle on a frictionless table. Rank in order, from largest to smallest, the tensions T_A to T_E acting on the blocks A to E.

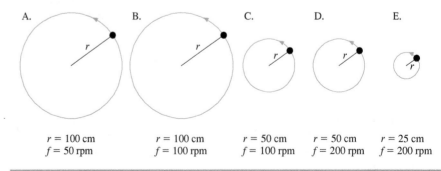

A.	B.	C.	D.	E.
$r = 100$ cm	$r = 100$ cm	$r = 50$ cm	$r = 50$ cm	$r = 25$ cm
$f = 50$ rpm	$f = 100$ rpm	$f = 100$ rpm	$f = 200$ rpm	$f = 200$ rpm

6.4 Apparent Forces in Circular Motion

FIGURE 6.19 shows a carnival ride that spins the riders around inside a large cylinder. The people are "stuck" to the inside wall of the cylinder! As you probably know from experience, the riders *feel* that they are being pushed outward, into the wall. But our analysis has found that an object in circular motion must have an *inward* force to create the centripetal acceleration. How can we explain this apparent difference?

FIGURE 6.19 Inside the Gravitron, a rotating circular room.

Centrifugal Force?

If you are a passenger in a car that turns a corner quickly, you may feel "thrown" by some mysterious force against the door. But is there really such a force? FIGURE 6.20 shows a bird's-eye view of you riding in a car as it makes a left turn. You try to continue moving in a straight line, obeying Newton's first law, when—without having been provoked—the door starts to turn in toward you and so runs into you! You do then feel the force of the door because it is now the force of the door, pushing *inward* toward the center of the curve, that is causing you to turn the corner. But you were not "thrown" into the door; the door ran into you.

A "force" that *seems* to push an object to the outside of a circle is called a *centrifugal force*. Despite having a name, there really is no such force. What you feel is your body trying to move ahead in a straight line (which would take you away from the center of the circle) as outside forces act to turn you in a circle. The only real forces, those that appear on free-body diagrams, are the ones pushing inward toward the center. **A centrifugal force will never appear on a free-body diagram and never be included in Newton's laws.**

With this in mind, let's revisit the rotating carnival ride. A person watching from above would see the riders in the cylinder moving in a circle with the walls providing the inward force that causes their centripetal acceleration. The riders *feel* as if they're being pushed outward because their natural tendency to move in a straight line is being resisted by the wall of the cylinder, which keeps getting in the way. But feelings aren't forces. The only actual force is the contact force of the cylinder wall pushing *inward*.

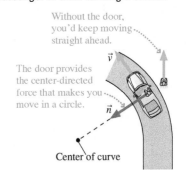

FIGURE 6.20 Bird's-eye view of a passenger in a car turning a corner.

Apparent Weight in Circular Motion

Imagine swinging a bucket of water over your head. If you swing the bucket quickly, the water stays in. But you'll get a shower if you swing too slowly. Why does the water stay in the bucket? Or think about a roller coaster that does a loop-the-loop. How does the car stay on the track when it's upside down? You might have said that there was a centrifugal force holding the water in the bucket and the car on the track, but we have seen that there really isn't a centrifugal force. Analyzing these questions will tell us a lot about forces in general and circular motion in particular.

FIGURE 6.21a shows a roller coaster car going around a vertical loop-the-loop of radius r. If you've ever ridden a roller coaster, you know that your sensation of weight changes as you go over the crests and through the dips. To understand why, let's look at the forces on passengers going through the loop. To simplify our analysis, we will assume that the speed of the car stays constant as it moves through the loop.

FIGURE 6.21b shows a passenger's free-body diagram at the top and the bottom of the loop. Let's start by examining the forces on the passenger at the bottom of the loop. The only forces acting on her are her weight $\vec{w}$ and the normal force $\vec{n}$ of the seat pushing up on her. Recall from Chapter 5 that a person's apparent weight is the magnitude of the force that supports her. Here the seat is supporting the passenger with the normal force $\vec{n}$, so her apparent weight is $w_{app} = n$. Based on our understanding of circular motion, we can say:

- She's moving in a circle, so there must be a net force directed toward the center of the circle—currently directly above her head—to provide the centripetal acceleration.

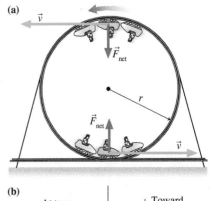

FIGURE 6.21 A roller coaster car going around a loop-the-loop.

(a)

(b)

When "down" is up BIO You can tell, even with your eyes closed, what direction is down. This sense is due to small crystals of calcium carbonate, called *otoliths,* in your inner ears. Gravity pulls the otoliths down, so a normal force from a sensitive supporting membrane must push them up. Your brain interprets "down" as the opposite of this normal force. Normally, what your ears tell you is "down" is really down. But at the top of a loop in a roller coaster, the normal force is directed down, so your inner ear tells you that "down" is up! If your ears tell you one thing and your eyes another, it can be disorienting.

- The net force points *upward,* so it must be the case that $n > w$.
- Her apparent weight is $w_{app} = n$, so her apparent weight is greater than her true weight ($w_{app} > w$). Thus she "feels heavy" at the bottom of the circle.

This situation is the same as for the car driving through a valley in Conceptual Example 6.8. To analyze the situation quantitatively, we'll apply the steps of Problem-Solving Strategy 6.1. As always, we choose the x-axis to point toward the center of the circle or, in this case, vertically upward. Then Newton's second law is

$$\sum F_x = n_x + w_x = n - w = \frac{mv^2}{r}$$

From this equation, her apparent weight is

$$w_{app} = n = w + \frac{mv^2}{r} \tag{6.11}$$

The passenger's apparent weight at the bottom is *greater* than her true weight w, which agrees with your experience when you go through a dip or a valley.

Now let's look at the roller coaster car as it crosses the top of the loop. Things are a little trickier here. As Figure 6.21b shows, whereas the normal force of the seat pushes up when the passenger is at the bottom of the circle, it pushes *down* when she is at the top and the seat is above her. It's worth thinking carefully about this diagram to make sure you understand what it is showing.

The passenger is still moving in a circle, so there must be a net force *downward,* toward the center of the circle, to provide her centripetal acceleration. As always, we define the x-axis to be toward the center of the circle, so here the x-axis points vertically downward. Newton's second law gives

$$\sum F_x = n_x + w_x = n + w = \frac{mv^2}{r}$$

Note that w_x is now *positive* because the x-axis is directed downward. We can solve for her apparent weight:

$$w_{app} = n = \frac{mv^2}{r} - w \tag{6.12}$$

If v is sufficiently large, her apparent weight can exceed the true weight, just as it did at the bottom of the track.

But let's look at what happens if the car goes slower. Notice from Equation 6.12 that, as v decreases, there comes a point when $mv^2/r = w$ and n becomes zero. At that point, the seat is *not* pushing against the passenger at all! Instead, she is able to complete the circle because her weight force alone provides sufficient centripetal acceleration.

The speed for which $n = 0$ is called the *critical speed* v_c. Because for n to be zero we must have $mv_c^2/r = w$, the critical speed is

$$v_c = \sqrt{\frac{rw}{m}} = \sqrt{\frac{rmg}{m}} = \sqrt{gr} \tag{6.13}$$

What happens if the speed is slower than the critical speed? In this case, Equation 6.12 gives a *negative* value for n if $v < v_c$. But that is physically impossible. The seat can push against the passenger ($n > 0$), but it can't *pull* on her, so the slowest possible speed is the speed for which $n = 0$ at the top. Thus, **the critical speed is the slowest speed at which the car can complete the circle.** If $v < v_c$, the passenger cannot turn the full loop but, instead, will fall from the car as a projectile! (This is why you're always strapped into a roller coaster.)

Water stays in a bucket swung over your head for the same reason. The bottom of the bucket pushes against the water to provide the inward force that causes circular motion. If you swing the bucket too slowly, the force of the bucket on the water drops to zero. At that point, the water leaves the bucket and becomes a projectile following a parabolic trajectory onto your head!

A fast-spinning world Saturn, a gas giant planet composed largely of fluid matter, is quite a bit larger than the earth. It also rotates much more quickly, completing one rotation in just under 11 hours. The rapid rotation decreases the apparent weight at the equator enough to distort the fluid surface; the planet is noticeably out of round, as the red circle shows. The diameter at the equator is 11% greater than the diameter at the poles.

EXAMPLE 6.12 How slow can you go?

A motorcyclist in the Globe of Death, pictured at the start of the chapter, rides in a 2.2-m-radius vertical loop. To keep control of the bike, the rider wants the normal force on his tires at the top of the loop to equal or exceed his and the bike's combined weight. What is the minimum speed at which the rider can take the loop?

PREPARE The visual overview for this problem is shown in FIGURE 6.22. At the top of the loop, the normal force of the cage on the tires is a *downward* force. In accordance with Problem-

FIGURE 6.22 Riding in a vertical loop around the Globe of Death.

Solving Strategy 6.1, we've chosen the x-axis to point toward the center of the circle.

SOLVE We will consider the forces at the top point of the loop. Because the x-axis points downward, Newton's second law is

$$\sum F_x = w + n = \frac{mv^2}{r}$$

The minimum acceptable speed occurs when $n = w$; thus

$$2w = 2mg = \frac{mv_{min}^2}{r}$$

Solving for the speed, we find

$$v_{min} = \sqrt{2gr} = \sqrt{2(9.8 \text{ m/s}^2)(2.2 \text{ m})} = 6.6 \text{ m/s}$$

ASSESS The minimum speed is ≈15 mph, which isn't all that fast; the bikes can easily reach this speed. But normally several bikes are in the globe at one time. The big challenge is to keep all of the riders in the cage moving at this speed in synchrony. The period for the circular motion at this speed is $T = 2\pi r/v \approx 2$ s, leaving little room for error!

Centrifuges

The *centrifuge*, an important biological application of circular motion, is used to separate the components of a liquid with different densities. Typically these are different types of cells, or the components of cells, suspended in water. You probably know that small particles suspended in water will eventually settle to the bottom. However, the downward motion due to gravity for extremely small objects such as cells is so slow that it could take days or even months for the cells to settle out. It's not practical to wait for biological samples to separate due to gravity alone.

The separation would go faster if the force of gravity could be increased. Although we can't change gravity, we can increase the apparent weight of objects in the sample by spinning them very fast, and that is what the centrifuge in FIGURE 6.23 does. By using very high angular velocities, the centrifuge produces centripetal accelerations that are thousands of times greater than free-fall acceleration. As the centrifuge effectively increases gravity to thousands of times its normal value, the cells or cell components settle out and separate by density in a matter of minutes or hours.

A centrifuge.

EXAMPLE 6.13 Analyzing the ultracentrifuge

An 18-cm-diameter ultracentrifuge produces an extraordinarily large centripetal acceleration of 250,000g, where g is the free-fall acceleration due to gravity. What is its frequency in rpm? What is the apparent weight of a sample with a mass of 0.0030 kg?

PREPARE The acceleration in SI units is

$$a = 250,000(9.80 \text{ m/s}^2) = 2.45 \times 10^6 \text{ m/s}^2$$

The radius is half the diameter, or $r = 9.0$ cm $= 0.090$ m.

SOLVE The centripetal acceleration is related to the angular speed by $a = \omega^2 r$. Thus

$$\omega = \sqrt{\frac{a}{r}} = \sqrt{\frac{2.45 \times 10^6 \text{ m/s}^2}{0.090 \text{ m}}} = 5.22 \times 10^3 \text{ rad/s}$$

FIGURE 6.23 The operation of a centrifuge.

The high angular velocity requires a large normal force, which leads to a large apparent weight.

Continued

Human centrifuge BIO If you spin your arm rapidly in a vertical circle, the motion will produce an effect like that in a centrifuge. The motion will assist outbound blood flow in your arteries and retard inbound blood flow in your veins. There will be a buildup of fluid in your hand that you will be able to see (and feel!) quite easily.

By Equation 6.6, this corresponds to a frequency

$$f = \frac{\omega}{2\pi} = \frac{5.22 \times 10^3 \text{ rad/s}}{2\pi} = 830 \text{ rev/s}$$

Converting to rpm, we find

$$830 \frac{\text{rev}}{\text{s}} \times \frac{60 \text{ s}}{1 \text{ min}} = 50,000 \text{ rpm}$$

At this rotation rate, the 0.0030 kg mass has an apparent weight

$$w_{\text{app}} = ma = (3.0 \times 10^{-3} \text{ kg})(2.45 \times 10^6 \text{ m/s}^2) = 7.4 \times 10^3 \text{ N}$$

The three gram sample has an effective weight of about 1700 pounds!

ASSESS Because the acceleration is 250,000g, the apparent weight is 250,000 times the actual weight. The forces in the ultracentrifuge are very large and can destroy the machine if it is not carefully balanced.

STOP TO THINK 6.4 A car is rolling over the top of a hill at constant speed v. At this instant,

A. $n > w$.
B. $n < w$.
C. $n = w$.
D. We can't tell about n without knowing v.

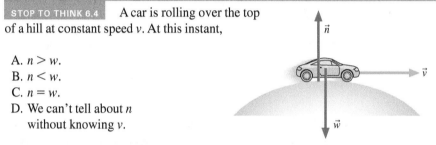

6.5 Circular Orbits and Weightlessness

The Space Shuttle orbits the earth in a circular path at a speed of over 15,000 miles per hour. What forces act on it? Why does it move in a circle? Before we start considering the physics of orbital motion, let's return, for a moment, to projectile motion. Projectile motion occurs when the only force on an object is gravity. Our analysis of projectiles made an implicit assumption that the earth is flat and that the free-fall acceleration, due to gravity, is everywhere straight down. This is an acceptable approximation for projectiles of limited range, such as baseballs or cannon balls, but there comes a point where we can no longer ignore the curvature of the earth.

Orbital Motion

FIGURE 6.24 Projectiles being launched at increasing speeds from height h on a smooth, airless planet.

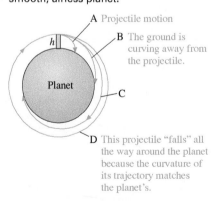

A Projectile motion
B The ground is curving away from the projectile.
C
D This projectile "falls" all the way around the planet because the curvature of its trajectory matches the planet's.

FIGURE 6.24 shows a perfectly smooth, spherical, airless planet with a vertical tower of height h. A projectile is launched from this tower with initial speed v_i parallel to the ground. If v_i is very small, as in trajectory A, the "flat-earth approximation" is valid and the problem is identical to Example 3.11 in which a car drove off a cliff. The projectile simply falls to the ground along a parabolic trajectory.

As the initial speed v_i is increased, it seems to the projectile that the ground is curving out from beneath it. It is still falling the entire time, always getting closer to the ground, but the distance that the projectile travels before finally reaching the ground—that is, its range—increases because the projectile must "catch up" with the ground that is curving away from it. Trajectories B and C are like this.

If the launch speed v_i is sufficiently large, there comes a point at which the curve of the trajectory and the curve of the earth are parallel. In this case, the projectile "falls" but it never gets any closer to the ground! This is the situation for trajectory D. The projectile returns to the point from which it was launched, at the same speed at which it was launched, making a closed trajectory. Such a closed trajectory around a planet or star is called an **orbit.**

The most important point of this qualitative analysis is that, in the absence of air resistance, **an orbiting projectile is in free fall.** This is, admittedly, a strange idea, but one worth careful thought. An orbiting projectile is really no different from a thrown baseball or a car driving off a cliff. The only force acting on it is gravity, but its tangential velocity is so great that the curvature of its trajectory matches the curvature of the earth. When this happens, the projectile "falls" under the influence of gravity but never gets any closer to the surface, which curves away beneath it.

When we first studied free fall in Chapter 2, we said that free-fall acceleration is always directed vertically downward. As we see in FIGURE 6.25, "downward" really means "toward the center of the earth." For a projectile in orbit, the direction of the force of gravity changes, always pointing toward the center of the earth.

FIGURE 6.25 The force of gravity is really directed toward the center of the earth.

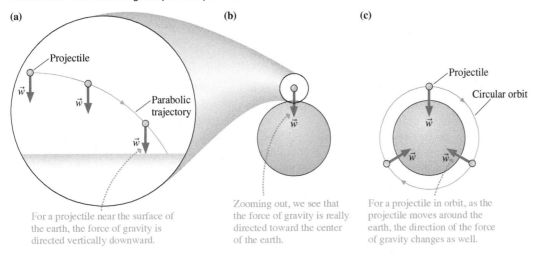

(a) For a projectile near the surface of the earth, the force of gravity is directed vertically downward.

(b) Zooming out, we see that the force of gravity is really directed toward the center of the earth.

(c) For a projectile in orbit, as the projectile moves around the earth, the direction of the force of gravity changes as well.

As you have learned, a force of constant magnitude that always points toward the center of a circle causes the centripetal acceleration of uniform circular motion. Because the only force acting on the orbiting projectile in Figure 6.25 is gravity, and we're assuming the projectile is very near the surface of the earth, we can write

$$a = \frac{F_{net}}{m} = \frac{w}{m} = \frac{mg}{m} = g \qquad (6.14)$$

An object moving in a circle of radius r at speed v_{orbit} will have this centripetal acceleration if

$$a = \frac{(v_{orbit})^2}{r} = g \qquad (6.15)$$

That is, if an object moves parallel to the surface with the speed

$$v_{orbit} = \sqrt{gr} \qquad (6.16)$$

then the free-fall acceleration provides exactly the centripetal acceleration needed for a circular orbit of radius r. An object with any other speed will not follow a circular orbit.

The earth's radius is $r = R_e = 6.37 \times 10^6$ m. The orbital speed of a projectile just skimming the surface of a smooth, airless earth is

$$v_{orbit} = \sqrt{gR_e} = \sqrt{(9.80 \text{ m/s}^2)(6.37 \times 10^6 \text{ m})} = 7900 \text{ m/s} \approx 18,000 \text{ mph}$$

We can use v_{orbit} to calculate the period of the satellite's orbit:

$$T = \frac{2\pi r}{v_{orbit}} = 2\pi\sqrt{\frac{r}{g}} \qquad (6.17)$$

For this earth-skimming orbit, $T = 5065$ s $= 84.4$ min.

Of course, this orbit is unrealistic; even if there were no trees and mountains, a real projectile moving at this speed would burn up from the friction of air resistance. Suppose, however, that we launched the projectile from a tower of height $h = 200$ mi $\approx 3.2 \times 10^5$ m, above most of the earth's atmosphere. This is approximately the height of low-earth-orbit satellites, such as the Space Shuttle. Note that $h \ll R_e$, so the radius of the orbit $r = R_e + h = 6.69 \times 10^6$ m is only 5% larger than the earth's radius. Many people have a mental image that satellites orbit far above the earth, but in fact most satellites come pretty close to skimming the surface.

At this slightly larger value of r, Equation 6.17 gives $T = 87$ min. The actual period of the Space Shuttle at an altitude of 200 mi is about 91 minutes, so our calculation is very good—but not perfect. As we'll see in the next section, a correct calculation must take into account the fact that the force of gravity gradually gets weaker at higher elevations above the earth's surface.

Weightlessness in Orbit

When we discussed *weightlessness* in Chapter 5, we saw that it occurs during free fall. We asked the question, at the end of Section 5.4, whether astronauts and their spacecraft are in free fall. We can now give an affirmative answer: They are, indeed, in free fall. They are falling continuously around the earth, under the influence of only the gravitational force, but never getting any closer to the ground because the earth's surface curves beneath them. Weightlessness in space is no different from the weightlessness in a free-falling elevator. **Weightlessness does *not* occur from an absence of weight or an absence of gravity.** Instead, the astronaut, the spacecraft, and everything in it are "weightless" (i.e., their *apparent* weight is zero) because they are all falling together.

Zero apparent weight in the Space Shuttle.

The Orbit of the Moon

If a satellite is simply "falling" around the earth, with the gravitational force causing a centripetal acceleration, then what about the moon? Is it obeying the same laws of physics? Or do celestial objects obey laws that we cannot discover by experiments here on earth?

The radius of the moon's orbit around the earth is 3.84×10^8 m. If we use Equation 6.17 to calculate the period of the moon's orbit, the time the moon takes to circle the earth once, we get

$$T = 2\pi\sqrt{\frac{r}{g}} = 2\pi\sqrt{\frac{3.84 \times 10^8 \text{ m}}{9.80 \text{ m/s}^2}} = 655 \text{ min} \approx 11 \text{ h} \qquad (6.18)$$

This is clearly wrong; the period of the moon's orbit is approximately one month.

Newton believed that the laws of motion he had discovered were *universal* and so should apply to the motion of the moon as well as to the motion of objects in the laboratory. But why should we assume that the free-fall acceleration g is the same at the distance of the moon as it is on or near the earth's surface? If gravity is the force of the earth pulling on an object, it seems plausible that the size of that force, and thus the size of g, should diminish with increasing distance from the earth.

Newton proposed the idea that the earth's force of gravity decreases with the square of the distance from the earth. This is the basis of *Newton's law of gravity,* a

Rotating space stations **BIO** The weightlessness astronauts experience in orbit has serious physiological consequences. Astronauts who spend time in weightless environments lose bone and muscle mass and suffer other adverse effects. One solution is to introduce "artificial gravity." On a space station, the easiest way to do this would be to make the station rotate, producing an apparent weight. The designers of this space station model for the movie *2001: A Space Odyssey* made it rotate for just that reason.

topic we will study in the next section. The force of gravity is less at the distance of the moon—exactly the strength needed to make the moon orbit at the observed rate. The moon, just like the Space Shuttle, is simply "falling" around the earth!

6.6 Newton's Law of Gravity

A popular image has Newton thinking of the idea of gravity after an apple fell on his head. This amusing story is at least close to the truth. Newton himself said that the "notion of gravitation" came to him as he "sat in a contemplative mood" and "was occasioned by the fall of an apple." It occurred to him that, perhaps, the apple was attracted to the center of the earth but was prevented from getting there by the earth's surface. And if the apple was so attracted, why not the moon? Newton's genius was his sudden realization that **the force that attracts the moon to the earth (and the planets to the sun) was identical to the force that attracts an apple to the earth.** In other words, gravitation is a *universal* force between all objects in the universe! This is not shocking today, but no one before Newton had ever thought that the mundane motion of objects on earth had any connection at all with the stately motion of the planets around the sun.

Isaac Newton was born to a poor farming family in 1642, the year of Galileo's death. He entered Trinity College at Cambridge University at age 19 as a "subsizar," a poor student who had to work his way through school. Newton graduated in 1665, at age 23, just as an outbreak of the plague in England forced the universities to close for two years. He returned to his family farm for that period, during which he made important experimental discoveries in optics, laid the foundations for his theories of mechanics and gravitation, and made major progress toward his invention of calculus as a whole new branch of mathematics.

Gravity Obeys an Inverse-Square Law

Newton also recognized that the strength of gravity must decrease with distance. These two notions about gravity—that it is universal and that it decreases with distance—form the basis for Newton's law of gravity.

Newton proposed that *every* object in the universe attracts *every other* object with a force that has the following properties:

1. The force is inversely proportional to the square of the distance between the objects.
2. The force is directly proportional to the product of the masses of the two objects.

FIGURE 6.26 shows two spherical objects with masses m_1 and m_2 separated by distance r. Each object exerts an attractive force on the other, a force that we call the **gravitational force.** These two forces form an action/reaction pair, so $\vec{F}_{1\,\text{on}\,2}$ is equal in magnitude and opposite in direction to $\vec{F}_{2\,\text{on}\,1}$. The magnitude of the forces is given by Newton's law of gravity.

MP **PhET: Gravity Force Lab**

FIGURE 6.26 The gravitational forces on masses m_1 and m_2.

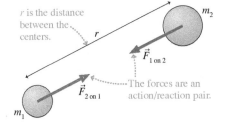

r is the distance between the centers.

The forces are an action/reaction pair.

Newton's law of gravity If two objects with masses m_1 and m_2 are a distance r apart, the objects exert attractive forces on each other of magnitude

$$F_{1\,\text{on}\,2} = F_{2\,\text{on}\,1} = \frac{Gm_1m_2}{r^2} \qquad (6.19)$$

The forces are directed along the line joining the two objects.

The constant G is called the **gravitational constant.** In the SI system of units,

$$G = 6.67 \times 10^{-11} \text{ N} \cdot \text{m}^2/\text{kg}^2$$

NOTE ▶ Strictly speaking, Newton's law of gravity applies to *particles* with masses m_1 and m_2. However, it can be shown that the law also applies to the force between two spherical objects if r is the distance between their centers. ◀

As the distance r between two objects increases, the gravitational force between them decreases. Because the distance appears squared in the denominator, Newton's law of gravity is what we call an **inverse-square** law. Doubling the distance between two masses causes the force between them to decrease by a factor of 4. This mathematical form is one we will see again, so it is worth our time to explore it in more detail.

Inverse-square relationships

Two quantities have an **inverse-square relationship** if y is inversely proportional to the *square* of x. We write the mathematical relationship as

$$y = \frac{A}{x^2}$$

y is inversely proportional to x^2

Here, A is a constant. This relationship is sometimes written as $y \propto 1/x^2$.

SCALING As the graph shows, inverse-square scaling means, for example:

- If you double x, you decrease y by a factor of 4.
- If you halve x, you increase y by a factor of 4.
- If you increase x by a factor of 3, you decrease y by a factor of 9.
- If you decrease x by a factor of 3, you increase y by a factor of 9.

Generally, **if x increases by a factor of C, y decreases by a factor of C^2. If x decreases by a factor of C, y increases by a factor of C^2.**

RATIOS For any two values of x—say, x_1 and x_2—we have

$$y_1 = \frac{A}{x_1^2} \quad \text{and} \quad y_2 = \frac{A}{x_2^2}$$

Dividing the y_1-equation by the y_2-equation, we find

$$\frac{y_1}{y_2} = \frac{A/x_1^2}{A/x_2^2} = \frac{A}{x_1^2}\frac{x_2^2}{A} = \frac{x_2^2}{x_1^2}$$

That is, the ratio of y-values is the inverse of the ratio of the squares of the corresponding values of x.

LIMITS As x becomes large, y becomes very small; as x becomes small, y becomes very large.

Exercises 23, 24

CONCEPTUAL EXAMPLE 6.14   **Varying gravitational force**

The gravitational force between two giant lead spheres is 0.010 N when the centers of the spheres are 20 m apart. What is the distance between their centers when the gravitational force between them is 0.160 N?

REASON We can solve this problem without knowing the masses of the two spheres. The key is to consider the ratios of forces and distances. Gravity is an inverse-square relationship; the force is related to the inverse square of the distance. The force *increases* by a factor of (0.160 N)/(0.010 N) = 16, so the distance must *decrease* by a factor of $\sqrt{16} = 4$. The distance is thus (20 m)/4 = 5.0 m.

ASSESS This type of ratio reasoning is a very good way to get a quick handle on the solution to a problem.

EXAMPLE 6.15 Gravitational force between two people

You are seated in your physics class next to another student 0.60 m away. Estimate the magnitude of the gravitational force between you. Assume that you each have a mass of 65 kg.

PREPARE We will model each of you as a sphere; this is not a particularly good model, but it will do for making an estimate. We will take the 0.60 m as the distance between your centers.

SOLVE The gravitational force is given by Equation 6.19:

$$F_{(\text{you})\text{on}(\text{other student})} = \frac{Gm_{\text{you}}m_{\text{other student}}}{r^2}$$

$$= \frac{(6.67 \times 10^{-11} \text{ N} \cdot \text{m}^2/\text{kg}^2)(65 \text{ kg})(65 \text{ kg})}{(0.60 \text{ m})^2}$$

$$= 7.8 \times 10^{-7} \text{ N}$$

ASSESS The force is quite small, roughly the weight of one hair on your head.

There is a gravitational force between all objects in the universe, but the gravitational force between two ordinary-sized objects is extremely small. Only when one (or both) of the masses is exceptionally large does the force of gravity become important. The downward force of the earth on you—your weight—is large because the earth has an enormous mass. And the attraction is mutual; by Newton's third law, you exert an upward force on the earth that is equal to your weight. However, the large mass of the earth makes the effect of this force on the earth negligible.

EXAMPLE 6.16 Gravitational force of the earth on a person

What is the magnitude of the gravitational force of the earth on a 60 kg person? The earth has mass 5.98×10^{24} kg and radius 6.37×10^6 m.

PREPARE We'll again model the person as a sphere. The distance r in Newton's law of gravity is the distance between the *centers* of the two spheres. The size of the person is negligible compared to the size of the earth, so we can use the earth's radius as r.

SOLVE The force of gravity on the person due to the earth can be computed using Equation 6.19:

$$F_{\text{earth on person}} = \frac{GM_e m}{R_e^2} = \frac{(6.67 \times 10^{-11} \text{ N} \cdot \text{m}^2/\text{kg}^2)(5.98 \times 10^{24} \text{ kg})(60 \text{ kg})}{(6.37 \times 10^6 \text{ m})^2}$$

$$= 590 \text{ N}$$

ASSESS This force is exactly the same as we would calculate using the formula for the weight force, $w = mg$. This isn't surprising, though. Chapter 5 introduced the weight of an object as simply the "force of gravity" acting on it. Newton's law of gravity is a more fundamental law for calculating the force of gravity, but it's still the same force that we earlier called "weight."

NOTE ▶ We will use uppercase R and M to represent the large mass and radius of a star or planet, as we did in Example 6.16. ◀

The force of gravitational attraction between the earth and you is responsible for your weight. If you were to venture to another planet, your *mass* would be the same but your *weight* would vary, as we discussed in Chapter 5. We will now explore this concept in more detail.

Gravity on Other Worlds

When astronauts ventured to the moon, television images showed them walking—and even jumping and skipping—with some ease, even though they were wearing life support systems with a mass of over 80 kg. This was a visible reminder that the weight of objects is less on the moon. Let's consider why this is so.

FIGURE 6.27 on the next page shows an astronaut on the moon weighing a rock of mass m. When we compute the weight of an object on the surface of the earth, we

Variable gravity When we calculated the force of the earth's gravity, we assumed that the earth's shape and composition are uniform. Neither is quite true, so there is a very small variation in gravity at the surface of the earth, as shown in this image. Red means slightly stronger surface gravity; blue, slightly weaker. These variations are caused by differing distances from the earth's center and by unevenness in the density of the earth's crust. Though these variations are important for scientists studying the earth, they are small enough that we can ignore them for the computations we'll do in this textbook.

FIGURE 6.27 An astronaut weighing a mass on the moon.

"Little g" perspective:
$F = mg_{moon}$

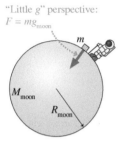

"Big G" perspective:
$F = \dfrac{GM_{moon}\,m}{R_{moon}^2}$

use the formula $w = mg$. We can do the same calculation for a mass on the moon, as long as we use the value of g on the moon:

$$w = mg_{moon} \tag{6.20}$$

This is the "little g" perspective. Falling-body experiments on the moon would give the value of g_{moon} as 1.62 m/s^2.

But we can also take a "big G" perspective. The weight of the rock comes from the gravitational attraction of the moon, and we can compute this weight using Equation 6.19. The distance r is the radius of the moon, which we'll call R_{moon}. Thus

$$F_{moon\,on\,m} = \frac{GM_{moon}\,m}{R_{moon}^2} \tag{6.21}$$

Because Equations 6.20 and 6.21 are two names and two expressions for the same force, we can equate the right-hand sides to find that

$$g_{moon} = \frac{GM_{moon}}{R_{moon}^2}$$

We have done this calculation for an object on the moon, but the result is completely general. At the surface of a planet (or a star), the free-fall acceleration g, a consequence of gravity, can be computed as

$$g_{planet} = \frac{GM_{planet}}{R_{planet}^2} \tag{6.22}$$

Free-fall acceleration on the surface of a planet

If we use values for the mass and the radius of the moon from the table inside the cover of the book, we can compute $g_{moon} = 1.62 \text{ m/s}^2$. This means that an object would weigh less on the moon than it would on the earth, where g is 9.80 m/s^2. A 70 kg astronaut wearing an 80 kg spacesuit would weigh over 330 lb on the earth but only 54 lb on the moon.

The low lunar gravity makes walking very easy, but a walking pace on the moon would be very slow. Earlier in the chapter we found that the maximum walking speed is $v_{max} = \sqrt{gr}$, where r is the length of the leg. For a typical leg length of 0.7 m and the gravity of the moon, the *maximum* walking speed would be about 1 m/s, just over 2 mph—a very gentle stroll!

Equation 6.22 gives g at the surface of a planet. More generally, imagine an object at distance $r > R$ from the center of a planet. Its free-fall acceleration at this distance is

$$g = \frac{GM}{r^2} \tag{6.23}$$

This more general result agrees with Equation 6.22 if $r = R$, but it allows us to determine the "local" free-fall acceleration at distances $r > R$. Equation 6.23 expresses Newton's idea that the size of g should decrease as you get farther from the earth.

As you're flying in a jet airplane at a height of about 10 km, the free-fall acceleration is about 0.3% less than on the ground. At the height of the Space Shuttle, about 300 km, Equation 6.23 gives $g = 8.9 \text{ m/s}^2$, about 10% less than the free-fall acceleration on the earth's surface. If you use this slightly smaller value of g in Equation 6.17 for the period of a satellite's orbit, you'll get the correct period of about 90 minutes. This value of g, only slightly less than the ground-level value, emphasizes the

◀ **Walking on the moon** BIO The low lunar gravity made walking at a reasonable pace difficult for the Apollo astronauts, but the reduced weight made jumping quite easy. Videos from the surface of the moon often show the astronauts getting from place to place by hopping or skipping—not for fun, but for speed and efficiency.

point that an object in orbit is not "weightless" due to the absence of gravity, but rather because it is in free fall.

EXAMPLE 6.17   **Gravity on Saturn**

Saturn, at 5.68×10^{26} kg, has nearly 100 times the mass of the earth. It is also much larger, with a radius of 5.85×10^7 m. What is the value of g on the surface of Saturn?

SOLVE We can use Equation 6.22 to compute the value of g_{Saturn}:

$$g_{\text{Saturn}} = \frac{GM_{\text{Saturn}}}{R_{\text{Saturn}}^2} = \frac{(6.67 \times 10^{-11} \text{ N} \cdot \text{m}^2/\text{kg}^2)(5.68 \times 10^{26} \text{ kg})}{(5.85 \times 10^7 \text{ m})^2} = 11.1 \text{ m/s}^2$$

ASSESS Even though Saturn is much more massive than the earth, its larger radius gives it a surface gravity that is not markedly different from that of the earth. If Saturn had a solid surface, you could walk and move around quite normally.

EXAMPLE 6.18   **Finding the speed to orbit Deimos**

Mars has two moons, each much smaller than the earth's moon. The smaller of these two bodies, Deimos, has an average radius of only 6.3 km and a mass of 1.8×10^{15} kg. At what speed would a projectile move in a very low orbit around Deimos?

SOLVE The free-fall acceleration at the surface of Deimos is quite small:

$$g_{\text{Deimos}} = \frac{GM_{\text{Deimos}}}{R_{\text{Deimos}}^2} = \frac{(6.67 \times 10^{-11} \text{ N} \cdot \text{m}^2/\text{kg}^2)(1.8 \times 10^{15} \text{ kg})}{(6.3 \times 10^3 \text{ m})^2}$$

$$= 0.0030 \text{ m/s}^2$$

Given this, we can use Equation 6.16 to calculate the orbital speed:

$$v_{\text{orbit}} = \sqrt{gr} = \sqrt{(0.0030 \text{ m/s}^2)(6.3 \times 10^3 \text{ m})} = 4.3 \text{ m/s} \approx 10 \text{ mph}$$

ASSESS This is quite slow. With a good jump, you could easily launch yourself into an orbit around Deimos!

STOP TO THINK 6.5   Rank in order, from largest to smallest, the free-fall accelerations on the surfaces of the following planets.

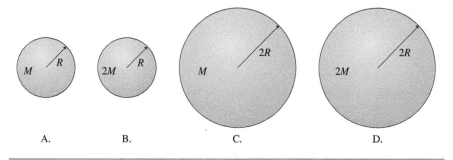

A.   B.   C.   D.

6.7 Gravity and Orbits

The planets of the solar system orbit the sun because the sun's gravitational pull, a force that points toward the center, causes the centripetal acceleration of circular motion. Mercury, the closest planet, experiences the largest acceleration, while Pluto, the most distant, has the smallest.

FIGURE 6.28 on the following page shows a large body of mass M, such as the earth or the sun, with a much smaller body of mass m orbiting it. The smaller body is called a **satellite,** even though it may be a planet orbiting the sun. Newton's second law tells us that $F_{M\text{on}m} = ma$, where $F_{M\text{on}m}$ is the gravitational force of the large body

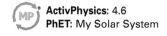

ActivPhysics: 4.6
PhET: My Solar System

FIGURE 6.28 The orbital motion of a satellite is due to the force of gravity.

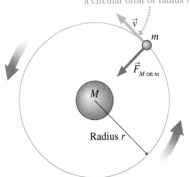

The satellite must have speed $\sqrt{GM/r}$ to maintain a circular orbit of radius r.

on the satellite and a is the satellite's acceleration. $F_{M\,\text{on}\,m}$ is given by Equation 6.19, and, because it's moving in a circular orbit, the satellite's acceleration is its centripetal acceleration, mv^2/r. Thus Newton's second law gives

$$F_{M\,\text{on}\,m} = \frac{GMm}{r^2} = ma = \frac{mv^2}{r} \tag{6.24}$$

Solving for v, we find that the speed of a satellite in a circular orbit is

$$v = \sqrt{\frac{GM}{r}} \tag{6.25}$$

Speed of a satellite in a circular orbit of radius r
about a star or planet of mass M

A satellite must have this specific speed in order to maintain a circular orbit of radius r about the larger mass M. If the velocity differs from this value, the orbit will become elliptical rather than circular. Notice that the orbital speed does not depend on the satellite's mass m. This is consistent with our previous discoveries that free-fall motion and projectile motion due to gravity are independent of the mass.

For a planet orbiting the sun, the period T is the time to complete one full orbit. The relationship among speed, radius, and period is the same as for any circular motion, $v = 2\pi r/T$. Combining this with the value of v for a circular orbit from Equation 6.25 gives

$$\sqrt{\frac{GM}{r}} = \frac{2\pi r}{T}$$

If we square both sides and rearrange, we find the period of a satellite:

$$T^2 = \left(\frac{4\pi^2}{GM}\right)r^3 \tag{6.26}$$

Relationship between the orbital period T and radius r for a
satellite in a circular orbit around an object of mass M

In other words, **the square of the period of the orbit is proportional to the cube of the radius of the orbit.**

NOTE ▶ The mass M in Equation 6.26 is the mass of the object at the center of the orbit. ◀

This relationship between radius and period had been deduced from naked-eye observations of planetary motions by the 17th-century astronomer Johannes Kepler. One of Newton's major scientific accomplishments was to use his law of gravity and his laws of motion to prove what Kepler had deduced from observations. Even today, Newton's law of gravity and equations such as Equation 6.26 are essential tools for the NASA engineers who launch probes to other planets in the solar system.

The table inside the back cover of this book contains astronomical information about the sun and the planets that will be useful for many of the end-of-chapter problems. Note that planets farther from the sun have longer periods, in agreement with Equation 6.26.

EXAMPLE 6.19 Locating a geostationary satellite

Communication satellites appear to "hover" over one point on the earth's equator. A satellite that appears to remain stationary as the earth rotates is said to be in a *geostationary orbit*. What is the radius of the orbit of such a satellite?

PREPARE For the satellite to remain stationary with respect to the earth, the satellite's orbital period must be 24 hours; in seconds this is $T = 8.64 \times 10^4$ s.

SOLVE We solve for the radius of the orbit by rearranging Equation 6.26. The mass at the center of the orbit is the earth:

$$r = \left(\frac{GM_eT^2}{4\pi^2}\right)^{\frac{1}{3}} = \left(\frac{(6.67 \times 10^{-11}\ \text{N} \cdot \text{m}^2/\text{kg}^2)(5.98 \times 10^{24}\ \text{kg})(8.64 \times 10^4\ \text{s})^2}{4\pi^2}\right)^{\frac{1}{3}}$$

$$= 4.22 \times 10^7\ \text{m}$$

ASSESS This is a high orbit; the radius is about 7 times the radius of the earth. Recall that the radius of the Space Shuttle's orbit is only about 5% larger than that of the earth.

Gravity on a Grand Scale

Although relatively weak, gravity is a long-range force. No matter how far apart two objects may be, there is a gravitational attraction between them. Consequently, gravity is the most ubiquitous force in the universe. It not only keeps your feet on the ground, but also is at work on a much larger scale. The Milky Way galaxy, the collection of stars of which our sun is a part, is held together by gravity. But why doesn't the attractive force of gravity simply pull all of the stars together?

The reason is that all of the stars in the galaxy are in orbit around the center of the galaxy. The gravitational attraction keeps the stars moving in orbits around the center of the galaxy rather than falling inward, much as the planets orbit the sun rather than falling into the sun. In the nearly 5 billion years that our solar system has existed, it has orbited the center of the galaxy approximately 20 times.

The galaxy as a whole doesn't rotate at a fixed angular speed, though. All of the stars in the galaxy are different distances from the galaxy's center, and so orbit with different periods. Stars closer to the center complete their orbits in less time, as we would expect from Equation 6.26. As the stars orbit, their relative positions shift. Stars that are relatively near neighbors now could be on opposite sides of the galaxy at some later time.

The rotation of a *rigid body* like a wheel is much simpler. As a wheel rotates, all of the points keep the same relationship to each other; every point on the wheel moves with the same angular velocity. The rotational dynamics of such rigid bodies is a topic we will take up in the next chapter.

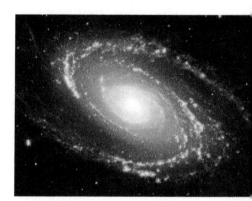

A spiral galaxy, similar to our Milky Way galaxy.

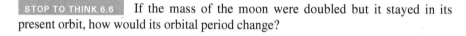

STOP TO THINK 6.6   If the mass of the moon were doubled but it stayed in its present orbit, how would its orbital period change?

A. The period would increase.
B. The period would decrease.
C. The period would stay the same.

INTEGRATED EXAMPLE 6.20   **A hunter and his sling**

A Stone Age hunter stands on a cliff overlooking a flat plain. He places a 1.0 kg rock in a sling, ties the sling to a 1.0-m-long vine, then swings the rock in a horizontal circle around his head. The plane of the motion is 25 m above the plain below. The tension in the vine increases as the rock goes faster and faster. Suddenly, just as the tension reaches 200 N, the vine snaps. If the rock is moving toward the cliff at this instant, how far out on the plain (from the base of the cliff) will it land?

PREPARE We model the rock as a particle in uniform circular motion. We can use Problem-Solving Strategy 6.1 to analyze this part of the motion. Once the vine breaks, the rock undergoes projectile motion with an initial velocity that is horizontal.

The force identification diagram of FIGURE 6.29a on the next page shows that the only contact force acting on the rock is the tension in the vine. Because the rock moves in a horizontal circle, you may be tempted to draw a free-body diagram like FIGURE 6.29b, on the next page where $\vec{T}$ is directed along the x-axis. You will quickly run into trouble, however, because in this diagram the net force has a downward y-component that would cause the rock to rapidly accelerate downward. But we know that it moves in a horizontal circle and that the net force must point toward the center of the circle. In this free-body diagram, the weight force $\vec{w}$ points straight down and is certainly correct, so the difficulty must be with $\vec{T}$.

Continued

FIGURE 6.29 Visual overview of a hunter swinging a rock.

(a)

(b)

(c)

(d)

As an experiment, tie a small weight to a string, swing it over your head, and check the angle of the string. You will discover that the string is not horizontal but, instead, is angled downward. The sketch of FIGURE 6.29c labels this angle θ. Notice that the rock moves in a *horizontal* circle, so the center of the circle is not at his hand. The x-axis points horizontally, to the center of the circle, but the tension force is directed along the vine. Thus the correct free-body diagram is the one in FIGURE 6.29d.

Once the vine breaks, the visual overview of the situation is shown in FIGURE 6.30. The important thing to note here is that the initial x-component of velocity is the speed the rock had an instant before the vine broke.

SOLVE From the free-body diagram of Figure 6.29d, Newton's second law for circular motion is

$$\sum F_x = T \cos \theta = \frac{mv^2}{r}$$
$$\sum F_y = T \sin \theta - mg = 0$$

where θ is the angle of the vine below the horizontal. We can use the y-equation to find the angle of the vine:

$$\sin \theta = \frac{mg}{T}$$
$$\theta = \sin^{-1}\left(\frac{mg}{T}\right) = \sin^{-1}\left(\frac{(1.0 \text{ kg})(9.8 \text{ m/s}^2)}{200 \text{ N}}\right) = 2.81°$$

where we've evaluated the angle at the maximum tension of 200 N. The vine's angle of inclination is small but not zero.

Turning now to the x-equation, we find the rock's speed around the circle is

$$v = \sqrt{\frac{rT \cos \theta}{m}}$$

Be careful! The radius r of the circle is not the length L of the vine. You can see in Figure 6.29c that $r = L \cos \theta$. Thus

$$v = \sqrt{\frac{LT \cos^2 \theta}{m}} = \sqrt{\frac{(1.0 \text{ m})(200 \text{ N})(\cos 2.81°)^2}{1.0 \text{ kg}}} = 14 \text{ m/s}$$

Because this is the horizontal speed of the rock just when the vine breaks, the initial velocity $(v_x)_i$ in the visual overview of the projectile motion, Figure 6.30, must be $(v_x)_i = 14 \text{ m/s}$. Recall that a projectile has no horizontal acceleration, so the rock's final position is

$$x_f = x_i + (v_x)_i \Delta t = 0 \text{ m} + (14 \text{ m/s})\Delta t$$

where Δt is the time the projectile is in the air. We're not given Δt, but we can find it from the vertical motion. For a projectile, the vertical motion is just free-fall motion, so we have

$$y_f = y_i + (v_y)_i \Delta t - \frac{1}{2}g(\Delta t)^2$$

The initial height is $y_i = 25 \text{ m}$, the final height is $y_f = 0 \text{ m}$, and the initial vertical velocity is $(v_y)_i = 0 \text{ m/s}$. With these values, we have

$$0 \text{ m} = 25 \text{ m} + (0 \text{ m/s})\Delta t - \frac{1}{2}(9.8 \text{ m/s}^2)(\Delta t)^2$$

Solving this for Δt gives

$$\Delta t = \sqrt{\frac{2(25 \text{ m})}{9.8 \text{ m/s}^2}} = 2.3 \text{ s}$$

Now we can use this time to find

$$x_f = 0 \text{ m} + (14 \text{ m/s})(2.3 \text{ s}) = 32 \text{ m}$$

The rock lands 32 m from the base of the cliff.

ASSESS The circumference of the rock's circle is $2\pi r$, or about 6 m. At a speed of 14 m/s, the rock takes roughly half a second to go around once. This seems reasonable. The 32 m distance is about 100 ft, which seems easily attainable from a cliff over 75 feet high.

FIGURE 6.30 Visual overview of the rock in projectile motion.

Known

$y_i = 25m, \ y_f = 0m$

$(v_y)_i = 0 \text{ m/s}$

$t_i = 0 s$

$x_i = 0 m$

$(v_x)_i = $ speed of circular motion when vine breaks

Find

x_f

SUMMARY

The goal of Chapter 6 has been to learn about motion in a circle, including orbital motion under the influence of a gravitational force.

GENERAL PRINCIPLES

Uniform Circular Motion

An object moving in a circular path is in uniform circular motion if v is constant.

- The speed is constant, but the direction of motion is constantly changing.

- The **centripetal acceleration** is directed toward the center of the circle and has magnitude

$$a = \frac{v^2}{r}$$

- This acceleration requires a net force directed toward the center of the circle. Newton's second law for circular motion is

$$\vec{F}_{net} = m\vec{a} = \left(\frac{mv^2}{r}, \text{ toward center of circle}\right)$$

Universal Gravitation

Two objects with masses m_1 and m_2 that are distance r apart exert attractive gravitational forces on each other of magnitude

$$F_{1\,on\,2} = F_{2\,on\,1} = \frac{Gm_1m_2}{r^2}$$

where the gravitational constant is

$$G = 6.67 \times 10^{-11} \text{ N} \cdot \text{m}^2/\text{kg}^2$$

This is **Newton's law of gravity.** Gravity is an inverse-square law.

IMPORTANT CONCEPTS

Describing circular motion

We define new variables for circular motion. By convention, counterclockwise is positive.

Angular position: θ

Angular displacement: $\Delta\theta = \theta_f - \theta_i$

Angular velocity: $\omega = \dfrac{\Delta\theta}{\Delta t}$

Angles are measured in radians, where $1 \text{ rev} = 360° = 2\pi \text{ rad}$. The SI units of angular velocity are rad/s.

Period: $T = $ time for one complete circle.

Frequency: $f = \dfrac{1}{T}$

Uniform circular motion kinematics

For uniform circular motion:

$$\omega = 2\pi f \qquad \theta_f - \theta_i = \Delta\theta = \omega\,\Delta t$$

The velocity, acceleration, and circular motion variables are related as follows:

$$v = \frac{2\pi r}{T}$$
$$v = \omega r$$
$$a = \frac{v^2}{r} = \omega^2 r$$

APPLICATIONS

Apparent weight and weightlessness

Circular motion requires a net force pointing to the center. The apparent weight $w_{app} = n$ is usually not the same as the true weight w. n must be > 0 for the object to be in contact with a surface.

In orbital motion, the net force is provided by gravity. An astronaut and his spacecraft are both in free fall, so he feels weightless.

Planetary gravity and orbital motion

For a planet of mass M and radius R, the free-fall acceleration on the surface is

$$g = \frac{GM}{R^2}$$

The speed of a satellite in a low orbit is

$$v = \sqrt{gr}$$

A **satellite** in a circular orbit of radius r around an object of mass M moves at a speed v given by

$$v = \sqrt{\frac{GM}{r}}$$

The period and radius are related as follows:

$$T^2 = \left(\frac{4\pi^2}{GM}\right)r^3$$

Problem difficulty is labeled as | (straightforward) to |||| (challenging). Problems labeled 🖉 can be done on a Workbook Dynamics Worksheet; INT integrate significant material from earlier chapters; BIO are of biological or medical interest.

For homework assigned on MasteringPhysics, go to www.masteringphysics.com

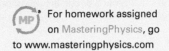
Scan this QR code to launch a Video Tutor Solution that will help you solve problems for this chapter.

QUESTIONS

Conceptual Questions

1. The batter in a baseball game hits a home run. As he circles the bases, is his angular velocity positive or negative?

2. Viewed from somewhere in space above the north pole, would a point on the earth's equator have a positive or negative angular velocity due to the earth's rotation?

3. A cyclist goes around a level, circular track at constant speed. Do you agree or disagree with the following statement? "Since the cyclist's speed is constant, her acceleration is zero." Explain.

4. In uniform circular motion, which of the following quantities are constant: speed, instantaneous velocity, angular velocity, centripetal acceleration, the magnitude of the net force?

5. A particle moving along a straight line can have nonzero acceleration even when its speed is zero (for instance, a ball in free fall at the top of its path). Can a particle moving in a circle have nonzero *centripetal* acceleration when its speed is zero? If so, give an example. If not, why not?

6. Would having four-wheel drive on a car make it possible to drive faster around corners on an icy road, without slipping, than the same car with two-wheel drive? Explain.

7. BIO Large birds like pheasants often walk short distances. Small birds like chickadees never walk. They either hop or fly. Why might this be?

8. When you drive fast on the highway with muddy tires, you can hear the mud flying off the tires into your wheel wells. Why does the mud fly off?

9. A ball on a string moves in a vertical circle as in Figure Q6.9. When the ball is at its lowest point, is the tension in the string greater than, less than, or equal to the ball's weight? Explain. (You may want to include a free-body diagram as part of your explanation.)

FIGURE Q6.9

10. Give an everyday example of circular motion for which the centripetal acceleration is mostly or completely due to a force of the type specified: (a) Static friction. (b) Tension.

11. Give an everyday example of circular motion for which the centripetal acceleration is mostly or completely due to a force of the type specified: (a) Gravity. (b) Normal force.

12. It's been proposed that future space stations create "artificial gravity" by rotating around an axis. (The space station would have to be much larger than the present space station for this to be feasible.)
    a. How would this work? Explain.
    b. Would the artificial gravity be equally effective throughout the space station? If not, where in the space station would the residents want to live and work?

13. A car coasts at a constant speed over a circular hill. Which of the free-body diagrams in Figure Q6.13 is correct? Explain.

FIGURE Q6.13   A.   B.   C.

14. Riding in the back of a pickup truck can be very dangerous. If the truck turns suddenly, the riders can be thrown from the truck bed. Why are the riders ejected from the bed?

15. Variation in your apparent weight is desirable when you ride a roller coaster; it makes the ride fun. However, too much variation over a short period of time can be painful. For this reason, the loops of real roller coasters are not simply circles like Figure 6.21a. A typical loop is shown in Figure Q6.15. The radius of the circle that matches the track at the top of the loop is much smaller than that of a matching circle at other places on the track. Explain why this shape gives a more comfortable ride than a circular loop.

FIGURE Q6.15

16. A small projectile is launched parallel to the ground at height $h = 1$ m with sufficient speed to orbit a completely smooth, airless planet. A bug rides in a small hole inside the projectile. Is the bug weightless? Explain.

17. Why is it impossible for an astronaut inside an orbiting space shuttle to go from one end to the other by walking normally?

18. If every object in the universe feels an attractive gravitational force due to every other object, why don't you feel a pull from someone seated next to you?

19. A mountain climber's weight is less on the top of a tall mountain than at the base, though his mass is the same. Why?

20. Is the earth's gravitational force on the sun larger, smaller, or equal to the sun's gravitational force on the earth? Explain.

Multiple-Choice Questions

21. | A ball on a string moves around a complete circle, once a second, on a frictionless, horizontal table. The tension in the string is measured to be 6.0 N. What would the tension be if the ball went around in only half a second?
    A. 1.5 N B. 3.0 N C. 12 N D. 24 N

22. | As seen from above, a car rounds the curved path shown in Figure Q6.22 at a constant speed. Which vector best represents the net force acting on the car?

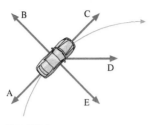

FIGURE Q6.22

23. | Suppose you and a friend, each of mass 60 kg, go to the park and get on a 4.0-m-diameter merry-go-round. You stand on the outside edge of the merry-go-round, while your friend pushes so that it rotates once every 6.0 s. What is the magnitude of the (apparent) outward force that you feel?
    A. 7 N B. 63 N C. 130 N D. 260 N

24. | The cylindrical space station in Figure Q6.24, 200 m in diameter, rotates in order to provide artificial gravity of g for the occupants. How much time does the station take to complete one rotation?
    A. 3 s B. 20 s C. 28 s D. 32 s

200 m

FIGURE Q6.24

25. || Two cylindrical space stations, the second four times the diameter of the first, rotate so as to provide the same amount of artificial gravity. If the first station makes one rotation in the time T, then the second station makes one rotation in time
    A. $T/4$ B. $2T$ C. $4T$ D. $16T$

26. | A newly discovered planet has twice the mass and three times the radius of the earth. What is the free-fall acceleration at its surface, in terms of the free-fall acceleration g at the surface of the earth?
    A. $\frac{2}{9}g$ B. $\frac{2}{3}g$ C. $\frac{3}{4}g$ D. $\frac{4}{3}g$

27. || Suppose one night the radius of the earth doubled but its mass stayed the same. What would be an approximate new value for the free-fall acceleration at the surface of the earth?
    A. 2.5 m/s² B. 5.0 m/s² C. 10 m/s² D. 20 m/s²

28. | Currently, the moon goes around the earth once every 27.3 days. If the moon could be brought into a new circular orbit with a smaller radius, its orbital period would be
    A. More than 27.3 days.
    B. 27.3 days.
    C. Less than 27.3 days.

29. || Two planets orbit a star. Planet 1 has orbital radius r_1 and planet 2 has $r_2 = 4r_1$. Planet 1 orbits with period T_1. Planet 2 orbits with period
    A. $T_2 = \frac{1}{2}T_1$ B. $T_2 = 2T_1$ C. $T_2 = 4T_1$ D. $T_2 = 8T_1$

30. | A particle undergoing circular motion in the xy-plane stops on the positive y-axis. Which of the following does *not* describe its angular position?
    A. $\pi/2$ rad B. π rad C. $5\pi/2$ rad D. $-3\pi/2$ rad

Questions 31 through 33 concern a classic figure-skating jump called the axel. A skater starts the jump moving forward as shown in Figure Q6.31, leaps into the air, and turns one-and-a-half revolutions before landing. The typical skater is in the air for about 0.5 s, and the skater's hands are located about 0.8 m from the rotation axis.

FIGURE Q6.31

31. || What is the approximate angular speed of the skater during the leap?
    A. 2 rad/s B. 6 rad/s C. 9 rad/s D. 20 rad/s

32. | The skater's arms are fully extended during the jump. What is the approximate centripetal acceleration of the skater's hand?
    A. 10 m/s² B. 30 m/s² C. 300 m/s² D. 450 m/s²

33. | What is the approximate speed of the skater's hand?
    A. 1 m/s B. 3 m/s C. 9 m/s D. 15 m/s

PROBLEMS

Section 6.1 Uniform Circular Motion

1. || What is the angular position in radians of the minute hand of a clock at (a) 5:00, (b) 7:15, and (c) 3:35?

2. | A child on a merry-go-round takes 3.0 s to go around once. What is his angular displacement during a 1.0 s time interval?

3. ||| What is the angular speed of the tip of the minute hand on a clock, in rad/s?

4. || An old-fashioned vinyl record rotates on a turntable at 45 rpm. What are (a) the angular speed in rad/s and (b) the period of the motion?

5. ||| The earth's radius is about 4000 miles. Kampala, the capital of Uganda, and Singapore are both nearly on the equator. The distance between them is 5000 miles.
    a. Through what angle do you turn, relative to the earth, if you fly from Kampala to Singapore? Give your answer in both radians and degrees.
    b. The flight from Kampala to Singapore takes 9 hours. What is the plane's angular speed relative to the earth?

6. ▐ A Ferris wheel rotates at an angular velocity of 0.036 rad/s. At $t = 0$ min, your friend Seth is at the very top of the ride. What is Seth's angular position at $t = 3.0$ min, measured counterclockwise from the top? Give your answer as an angle in degrees between 0° and 360°.

7. ▐▐ A turntable rotates counterclockwise at 78 rpm. A speck of dust on the turntable is at $\theta = 0.45$ rad at $t = 0$ s. What is the angle of the speck at $t = 8.0$ s? Your answer should be between 0 and 2π rad.

8. ▐ A fast-moving superhero in a comic book runs around a circular, 70-m-diameter track five and a half times (ending up directly opposite her starting point) in 3.0 s. What is her angular speed, in rad/s?

9. ▐ Figure P6.9 shows the angular position of a potter's wheel.
   a. What is the angular displacement of the wheel between $t = 5$ s and $t = 15$ s?
   b. What is the angular velocity of the wheel at $t = 15$ s?

FIGURE P6.9

10. ▐ The angular velocity (in rpm) of the blade of a blender is given in Figure P6.10.
    a. If $\theta = 0$ rad at $t = 0$ s, what is the blade's angular position at $t = 20$ s?
    b. At what time has the blade completed 10 full revolutions?

FIGURE P6.10

Section 6.2 Speed, Velocity, and Acceleration in Uniform Circular Motion

11. ▐ A 5.0-m-diameter merry-go-round is turning with a 4.0 s period. What is the speed of a child on the rim?

12. ▏ The blade on a table saw spins at 3450 rpm. Its diameter is 25.0 cm. What is the speed of a tooth on the edge of the blade, in both m/s and mph?

13. ▐ The horse on a carousel is 4.0 m from the central axis.
    a. If the carousel rotates at 0.10 rev/s, how long does it take the horse to go around twice?
    b. How fast is a child on the horse going (in m/s)?

14. ▐▐ The radius of the earth's very nearly circular orbit around the sun is 1.50×10^{11} m. Find the magnitude of the earth's (a) velocity, (b) angular velocity, and (c) centripetal acceleration as it travels around the sun. Assume a year of 365 days.

15. ▐ Your roommate is working on his bicycle and has the bike upside down. He spins the 60-cm-diameter wheel, and you notice that a pebble stuck in the tread goes by three times every second. What are the pebble's speed and acceleration?

16. ▐ To withstand "g-forces" of up to 10g, caused by suddenly pulling out of a steep dive, fighter jet pilots train on a "human centrifuge." 10g is an acceleration of 98 m/s². If the length of the centrifuge arm is 12 m, at what speed is the rider moving when she experiences 10g?

Section 6.3 Dynamics of Uniform Circular Motion

17. ▐▐▐ Figure P6.17 is a bird's-eye view of particles on a string moving in horizontal circles on a tabletop. All are moving at the same speed. Rank in order, from largest to smallest, the tensions T_1 to T_4.

FIGURE P6.17

18. ▐ A 200 g block on a 50-cm-long string swings in a circle on a horizontal, frictionless table at 75 rpm.
    a. What is the speed of the block?
    b. What is the tension in the string?

19. ▐ A 1500 kg car drives around a flat 200-m-diameter circular track at 25 m/s. What are the magnitude and direction of the net force on the car? What causes this force?

20. ▐ A fast pitch softball player does a "windmill" pitch, illustrated in Figure P6.20, moving her hand through a circular arc to pitch a ball at 70 mph. The 0.19 kg ball is 50 cm from the pivot point at her shoulder. At the lowest point of the circle, the ball has reached its maximum speed.
    a. At the bottom of the circle, just before the ball leaves her hand, what is its centripetal acceleration?
    b. What are the magnitude and direction of the force her hand exerts on the ball at this point?

FIGURE P6.20

21. ▐ A baseball pitching machine works by rotating a light and stiff rigid rod about a horizontal axis until the ball is moving toward the target. Suppose a 144 g baseball is held 85 cm from the axis of rotation and released at the major league pitching speed of 85 mph.
    a. What is the ball's centripetal acceleration just before it is released?
    b. What is the magnitude of the net force that is acting on the ball just before it is released?

22. ▐ You're driving your pickup truck around a curve with a radius of 20 m. A box in the back of the truck is pressed up against the wall of the truck. How fast must you drive so that the force of the wall on the box equals the weight of the box?

Section 6.4 Apparent Forces in Circular Motion

23. ⫼ The passengers in a roller coaster car feel 50% heavier than their true weight as the car goes through a dip with a 30 m radius of curvature. What is the car's speed at the bottom of the dip?

24. ⫶ You hold a bucket in one hand. In the bucket is a 500 g rock. You swing the bucket so the rock moves in a vertical circle 2.2 m in diameter. What is the minimum speed the rock must have at the top of the circle if it is to always stay in contact with the bottom of the bucket?

25. ⫼ As a roller coaster car crosses the top of a 40-m-diameter loop-the-loop, its apparent weight is the same as its true weight. What is the car's speed at the top?

26. ⫼ A typical laboratory centrifuge rotates at 4000 rpm. Test tubes have to be placed into a centrifuge very carefully because of the very large accelerations.
    BIO
    INT a. What is the acceleration at the end of a test tube that is 10 cm from the axis of rotation?
    b. For comparison, what is the magnitude of the acceleration a test tube would experience if stopped in a 1.0-ms-long encounter with a hard floor after falling from a height of 1.0 m?

Section 6.5 Circular Orbits and Weightlessness

27. ⫼ A satellite orbiting the moon very near the surface has a period of 110 min. Use this information, together with the radius of the moon from the table on the inside of the back cover, to calculate the free-fall acceleration on the moon's surface.

Section 6.6 Newton's Law of Gravity

28. ⫼⫼ The centers of a 10 kg lead ball and a 100 g lead ball are separated by 10 cm.
    a. What gravitational force does each exert on the other?
    b. What is the ratio of this gravitational force to the weight of the 100 g ball?

29. ⫶ The gravitational force of a star on an orbiting planet 1 is F_1. Planet 2, which is twice as massive as planet 1 and orbits at twice the distance from the star, experiences gravitational force F_2. What is the ratio F_2/F_1?

30. ⫶ The free-fall acceleration at the surface of planet 1 is 20 m/s². The radius and the mass of planet 2 are twice those of planet 1. What is the free-fall acceleration on planet 2?

31. ⫼⫼ What is the ratio of the sun's gravitational force on you to the earth's gravitational force on you?

32. ⫼ Suppose the free-fall acceleration at some location on earth was exactly 9.8000 m/s². What would it be at the top of a 1000-m-tall tower at this location? (Give your answer to five significant figures.)

33. ⫶ a. What is the gravitational force of the sun on the earth?
    b. What is the gravitational force of the moon on the earth?
    c. The moon's force is what percent of the sun's force?

34. ⫶ What is the free-fall acceleration at the surface of (a) Mars and (b) Jupiter?

Section 6.7 Gravity and Orbits

35. ⫼⫼ Planet X orbits the star Omega with a "year" that is 200 earth days long. Planet Y circles Omega at four times the distance of Planet X. How long is a year on Planet Y?

36. ⫼⫼ Satellite A orbits a planet with a speed of 10,000 m/s. Satellite B is twice as massive as satellite A and orbits at twice the distance from the center of the planet. What is the speed of satellite B?

37. ⫼⫼ The Space Shuttle is in a 250-mile-high orbit. What are the shuttle's orbital period, in minutes, and its speed?

38. ⫶ The *asteroid belt* circles the sun between the orbits of Mars and Jupiter. One asteroid has a period of 5.0 earth years. What are the asteroid's orbital radius and speed?

39. ⫼⫼ An earth satellite moves in a circular orbit at a speed of 5500 m/s. What is its orbital period?

General Problems

40. ⫶ How fast must a plane fly along the earth's equator so that the sun stands still relative to the passengers? In which direction must the plane fly, east to west or west to east? Give your answer in both km/h and mph. The radius of the earth is 6400 km.

41. ⫼⫼ The car in Figure P6.41 travels at a constant speed along the road shown. Draw vectors showing its acceleration at the three points A, B, and C, or write $\vec{a} = \vec{0}$. The lengths of your vectors should correspond to the magnitudes of the accelerations.

FIGURE P6.41

42. ⫼⫼ In the Bohr model of the hydrogen atom, an electron (mass $m = 9.1 \times 10^{-31}$ kg) orbits a proton at a distance of 5.3×10^{-11} m. The proton pulls on the electron with an electric force of 8.2×10^{-8} N. How many revolutions per second does the electron make?

43. ⫶ A 75 kg man weighs himself at the north pole and at the equator. Which scale reading is higher? By how much? Assume the earth is a perfect sphere. Explain why the readings differ.

44. ⫶ A 1500 kg car takes a 50-m-radius unbanked curve at 15 m/s. What is the size of the friction force on the car?

45. ⫼⫼ A 500 g ball swings in a vertical circle at the end of a 1.5-m-long string. When the ball is at the bottom of the circle, the tension in the string is 15 N. What is the speed of the ball at that point?

46. ⫼⫼ Suppose the moon were held in its orbit not by gravity but by a massless cable attached to the center of the earth. What would be the tension in the cable? See the inside of the back cover for astronomical data.

47. ⫼⫼ A 30 g ball rolls around a 40-cm-diameter L-shaped track, shown in Figure P6.47, at 60 rpm. Rolling friction can be neglected.

FIGURE P6.47

    a. How many different contact forces does the track exert on the ball? Name them.
    b. What is the magnitude of the net force on the ball?

48. ⫶ A 5.0 g coin is placed 15 cm from the center of a turntable. The coin has static and kinetic coefficients of friction with the turntable surface of $\mu_s = 0.80$ and $\mu_k = 0.50$. The turntable very slowly speeds up to 60 rpm. Does the coin slide off?
    INT

49. ⫼ A *conical pendulum* is formed by attaching a 500 g ball to a 1.0-m-long string, then allowing the mass to move in a horizontal circle of radius 20 cm. Figure P6.49 shows that the string traces out the surface of a cone, hence the name.
    a. What is the tension in the string?
    b. What is the ball's angular velocity, in rpm?
    Hint: Determine the horizontal and vertical components of the forces acting on the ball, and use the fact that the vertical component of acceleration is zero since there is no vertical motion.

FIGURE P6.49

50. ⫼ In an old-fashioned amusement park ride, passengers stand inside a 3.0-m-tall, 5.0-m-diameter hollow steel cylinder with their backs against the wall. The cylinder begins to rotate about a vertical axis. Then the floor on which the passengers are standing suddenly drops away! If all goes well, the passengers will "stick" to the wall and not slide. Clothing has a static coefficient of friction against steel in the range 0.60 to 1.0 and a kinetic coefficient in the range 0.40 to 0.70. What is the minimum rotational frequency, in rpm, for which the ride is safe?

51. ⫼ The 0.20 kg puck on the frictionless, horizontal table in Figure P6.51 is connected by a string through a hole in the table to a hanging 1.20 kg block. With what speed must the puck rotate in a circle of radius 0.50 m if the block is to remain hanging at rest?

FIGURE P6.51

52. ⫼ While at the county fair, you decide to ride the Ferris wheel. Having eaten too many candy apples and elephant ears, you find the motion somewhat unpleasant. To take your mind off your stomach, you wonder about the motion of the ride. You estimate the radius of the big wheel to be 15 m, and you use your watch to find that each loop around takes 25 s.
    a. What are your speed and magnitude of your acceleration?
    b. What is the ratio of your apparent weight to your true weight at the top of the ride?
    c. What is the ratio of your apparent weight to your true weight at the bottom?

53. ⫼ A car drives over the top of a hill that has a radius of 50 m. What maximum speed can the car have without flying off the road at the top of the hill?

54. ⫼ A 100 g ball on a 60-cm-long string is swung in a vertical circle whose center is 200 cm above the floor. The string suddenly breaks when it is parallel to the ground and the ball is moving upward. The ball reaches a height 600 cm above the floor. What was the tension in the string an instant before it broke?

55. ⫼ While a person is walking, his arms (each with typical length 70 cm measured from the shoulder joint) swing through approximately a 45° angle in 0.50 s. As a reasonable approximation, we can assume that the arm moves with constant speed during each swing.
    a. What is the acceleration of a 1.0 g drop of blood in the fingertips at the bottom of the swing?
    b. Draw a free-body diagram for the drop of blood in part a.
    c. Find the magnitude and direction of the force that the blood vessel must exert on the drop of blood.
    d. What force would the blood vessel exert if the arm were not swinging?

56. ⫼ The two identical pucks in Figure P6.56 rotate together on a frictionless, horizontal table. They are tied together by strings 1 and 2, each of length *l*. If their common angular speed is ω, what are the tensions in the two strings?

FIGURE P6.56

57. ⫼ The ultracentrifuge is an important tool for separating and analyzing proteins in biological research. Because of the enormous centripetal accelerations that can be achieved, the apparatus (see Figure 6.23) must be carefully balanced so that each sample is matched by another on the opposite side of the rotor shaft. Failure to do so is a costly mistake, as seen in Figure P6.57. Any difference in mass of the opposing samples will cause a net force in the horizontal plane on the shaft of the rotor. Suppose that a scientist makes a slight error in sample preparation, and one sample has a mass 10 mg greater than the opposing sample. If the samples are 10 cm from the axis of the rotor and the ultracentrifuge spins at 70,000 rpm, what is the magnitude of the net force on the rotor due to the unbalanced samples?

FIGURE P6.57

58. ⫼ The Space Shuttle orbits 300 km above the surface of the earth.
    a. What is the force of gravity on a 1.0 kg sphere inside the Space Shuttle?
    b. The sphere floats around inside the Space Shuttle, apparently "weightless." How is this possible?

59. ⫼ A sensitive gravimeter at a mountain observatory finds that the free-fall acceleration is 0.0075 m/s² less than that at sea level. What is the observatory's altitude?

60. ⫼ Suppose we could shrink the earth without changing its mass. At what fraction of its current radius would the free-fall acceleration at the surface be three times its present value?

61. ⫼ Planet Z is 10,000 km in diameter. The free-fall acceleration on Planet Z is 8.0 m/s².
    a. What is the mass of Planet Z?
    b. What is the free-fall acceleration 10,000 km above Planet Z's north pole?

62. ⫼ What are the speed and altitude of a geostationary satellite (see Example 6.19) orbiting Mars? Mars rotates on its axis once every 24.8 hours.

63. ⫼ a. What is the free-fall acceleration on Mars?
    b. Estimate the maximum speed at which an astronaut can walk on the surface of Mars.

64. ⫼ How long will it take a rock dropped from 2.0 m above the surface of Mars to reach the ground?

65. ⫾ A 20 kg sphere is at the origin and a 10 kg sphere is at
INT $(x, y) = (20 \text{ cm}, 0 \text{ cm})$. At what point or points could you place
a small mass such that the net gravitational force on it due to the
spheres is zero?

66. ⫾ a. At what height above the earth is the free-fall acceleration
10% of its value at the surface?
    b. What is the speed of a satellite orbiting at that height?

67. ⫾ Mars has a small moon, Phobos, that orbits with a period of 7 h
39 min. The radius of Phobos' orbit is 9.4×10^6 m. Use only this
information (and the value of G) to calculate the mass of Mars.

68. ⫾ You are the science officer on a visit to a distant solar system.
Prior to landing on a planet you measure its diameter to be
1.80×10^7 m and its rotation period to be 22.3 h. You have previously determined that the planet orbits 2.20×10^{11} m from its
star with a period of 402 earth days. Once on the surface you
find that the free-fall acceleration is 12.2 m/s². What are the
masses of (a) the planet and (b) the star?

69. ⫾ Europa, a satellite of Jupiter,
BIO is believed to have a liquid
ocean of water (with a possibility of life) beneath its icy surface. In planning a future mission
to Europa, what is the fastest
that an astronaut with legs of
length 0.70 m could walk on the
surface of Europa? Europa is
3100 km in diameter and has a
mass of 4.8×10^{22} kg.

In Problems 70 through 73 you are given the equation (or equations)
used to solve a problem. For each of these, you are to

a. Write a realistic problem for which this is the correct equation.
The last two questions should involve real planets. Be sure that
the answer your problem requests is consistent with the equation
given.

b. Finish the solution of the problem.

70. ⫾ $60 \text{ N} = (0.30 \text{ kg})\omega^2(0.50 \text{ m})$

71. ⫾ $(1500 \text{ kg})(9.80 \text{ m/s}^2) - 11{,}760 \text{ N} = (1500 \text{ kg})v^2/(200 \text{ m})$

72. ⫾ $$\frac{(6.67 \times 10^{-11} \text{ N} \cdot \text{m}^2/\text{kg}^2)(1.90 \times 10^{27} \text{ kg})}{r^2}$$
$$= \frac{(6.67 \times 10^{-11} \text{ N} \cdot \text{m}^2/\text{kg}^2)(5.98 \times 10^{24} \text{ kg})}{(6.37 \times 10^6 \text{ m})^2}$$

73. ⫾ $$\frac{(6.67 \times 10^{-11} \text{ N} \cdot \text{m}^2/\text{kg}^2)(5.98 \times 10^{24} \text{ kg})(1000 \text{ kg})}{r^2}$$
$$= \frac{(1000 \text{ kg})(1997 \text{ m/s})^2}{r}$$

Passage Problems

Orbiting the Moon

Suppose a spacecraft orbits the moon in a very low, circular orbit,
just a few hundred meters above the lunar surface. The moon has a
diameter of 3500 km, and the free-fall acceleration at the surface is
1.6 m/s².

74. ⫾ The direction of the net force on the craft is
    A. Away from the surface of the moon.
    B. In the direction of motion.
    C. Toward the center of the moon.
    D. Nonexistent, because the net force is zero.

75. ⫾ How fast is this spacecraft moving?
    A. 53 m/s   B. 75 m/s   C. 1700 m/s   D. 2400 m/s

76. ⫾ How much time does it take for the spacecraft to complete
one orbit?
    A. 38 min   B. 76 min   C. 110 min   D. 220 min

77. ⫾ The material that comprises the side of the moon facing the
earth is actually slightly more dense than the material on the far
side. When the spacecraft is above a more dense area of the surface, the moon's gravitational force on the craft is a bit stronger. In
order to stay in a circular orbit of constant height and speed, the
spacecraft could fire its rockets while passing over the denser
area. The rockets should be fired so as to generate a force on the
craft
    A. Away from the surface of the moon.
    B. In the direction of motion.
    C. Toward the center of the moon.
    D. Opposite the direction of motion.

STOP TO THINK ANSWERS

Stop to Think 6.1: A. Because $5\pi/2 \text{ rad} = 2\pi \text{ rad} + \pi/2 \text{ rad}$, the
particle's position is one complete revolution (2π rad) plus an extra
$\pi/2$ rad. This extra $\pi/2$ rad puts the particle at position A.

Stop to Think 6.2: D > B > C > A. The centripetal acceleration
is $\omega^2 r$. Changing r by a factor of 2 changes the centripetal acceleration by a factor of 2, but changing ω by a factor of 2 changes the centripetal acceleration by a factor of 4.

Stop to Think 6.3: $T_D > T_B = T_E > T_C > T_A$. The center-
directed force is $m\omega^2 r$. Changing r by a factor of 2 changes the tension by a factor of 2, but changing f (and thus ω) by a factor of 2
changes the tension by a factor of 4.

Stop to Think 6.4: B. The car is moving in a circle, so there must
be a net force toward the center of the circle. The center of the circle
is below the car, so the net force must point downward. This can be
true only if $w > n$.

Stop to Think 6.5: B > A > D > C. The free-fall acceleration is
proportional to the mass, but inversely proportional to the square of
the radius.

Stop to Think 6.6: C. The period of the orbit does not depend on the
mass of the orbiting object.

7 Rotational Motion

To get the roulette wheel spinning, the croupier must give the wheel a push in the direction of its motion. Does it matter if she pushes closer to the rim or nearer the center?

LOOKING AHEAD ▶▶

The goal of Chapter 7 is to understand the physics of rotating objects.

The Rotation of a Rigid Body

A **rigid body** is an extended object whose size and shape do not change as it moves.

A rigid body whose angular velocity is changing has an **angular acceleration.**

The angular velocity is increasing.

Boomerangs and bicycle wheels are examples of rigid bodies.

Looking Back ◀◀
6.1–6.2 Uniform circular motion

Newton's Second Law for Rotational Motion

You've learned Newton's second law of motion for *translational* motion: **A net force causes an object to accelerate.** In this chapter, we'll study Newton's second law for *rotational* motion: **A net torque causes an object to have an *angular* acceleration.**

To make the merry-go-round speed up, the girl has to apply a torque to it by pushing at its edge.

Looking Back ◀◀
4.6 Newton's second law

Torque

Torque is the rotational equivalent of force. To get an object rotating, you need to apply a torque to it. The farther from the axis of rotation a force is applied, the greater the torque.

Gravitational Torque

For the purpose of calculating torque, the entire weight of an object can be considered as acting at a single point, the **center of gravity.**

By applying forces at the edge of the large wheel, the sailor can exert a large torque upon it.

The weight of this tree, acting at its center of gravity, tries to rotate the tree about its base.

Moment of Inertia

We have learned that *mass* is the property of an object that resists acceleration. The property of an object that resists angular acceleration is its *moment of inertia*. The moment of inertia of an object depends not only on its mass but also on how that mass is distributed.

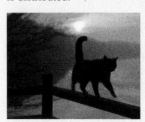

By extending its tail, this cat increases its moment of inertia. This increases its resistance to angular acceleration, making it harder for it to fall.

7.1 The Rotation of a Rigid Body

So far, our study of physics has focused almost exclusively on the *particle model* in which an entire object is represented as a single point in space. The particle model is entirely adequate for understanding motion in a wide variety of situations, but there are also cases for which we need to consider the motion of an *extended object*—a system of particles for which the size and shape *do* make a difference and cannot be neglected.

A **rigid body** is an extended object whose size and shape do not change as it moves. For example, a bicycle wheel can be thought of as a rigid body. FIGURE 7.1 shows a rigid body as a collection of atoms held together by the rigid "massless rods" of molecular bonds.

Real molecular bonds are, of course, not perfectly rigid. That's why an object seemingly as rigid as a bicycle wheel can flex and bend. Thus Figure 7.1 is really a simplified *model* of an extended object, the **rigid-body model.** The rigid-body model is a very good approximation for many real objects of practical interest, such as wheels and axles. Even nonrigid objects can often be modeled as rigid bodies during segments of their motion. For example, a diver is well described as a rotating rigid body while she's in the tuck position.

FIGURE 7.2 illustrates the three basic types of motion of a rigid body: **translational motion, rotational motion,** and **combination motion.** We've already studied translational motion of a rigid body using the particle model. If a rigid body doesn't rotate, this model is often adequate for describing its motion. The rotational motion of a rigid body will be the main focus of this chapter. We'll also discuss an important case of combination motion—that of a *rolling* object—later in this chapter.

ActivPhysics: 7.7

FIGURE 7.1 The rigid-body model of an extended object.

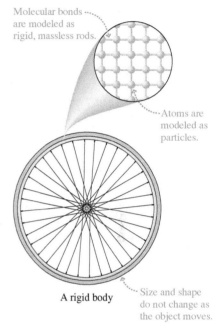

Molecular bonds are modeled as rigid, massless rods.

Atoms are modeled as particles.

A rigid body

Size and shape do not change as the object moves.

FIGURE 7.2 Three basic types of motion of a rigid body.

Trajectory

Translational motion:
The object as a whole moves along a trajectory but does not rotate.

Rotational motion:
The object rotates about a fixed point. Every point on the object moves in a circle.

Combination motion:
An object rotates as it moves along a trajectory.

Rotational Motion of a Rigid Body

FIGURE 7.3 shows a wheel rotating on an axle. Notice that as the wheel rotates for a time interval Δt, two points 1 and 2 on the wheel, marked with dots, turn through the *same angle,* even through their distances r from the axis of rotation may be different; that is, $\Delta\theta_1 = \Delta\theta_2$ during the time interval Δt. As a consequence, the two points have equal angular velocities: $\omega_1 = \omega_2$. In general, **every point on a rotating rigid body has the same angular velocity.** Because of this, we can refer to the angular velocity ω *of the wheel.*

Recall from Chapter 6 that the speed of a particle moving in a circle is $v = \omega r$, so two points of a rotating object will have different *speeds* if they have different distances from the axis of rotation, but *all* points have the *same* angular velocity ω. Thus angular velocity is one of the most important parameters of a rotating object.

Because every point on a rotating object moves in a circle, we can carry forward all the results for circular motion from Chapter 6. Thus the angular displacement of any point on the wheel shown in Figure 7.3 is found from Equation 6.4 as $\Delta\theta = \omega \Delta t$; the speed of any particle in the wheel is $v = \omega r$, where r is the particle's distance from the axis; and the particle's centripetal acceleration is $a = \omega^2 r$.

FIGURE 7.3 All points on a wheel rotate with the same angular velocity.

Every point on the wheel undergoes circular motion with the same angular velocity ω.

ω

$\Delta\theta_1$

$\Delta\theta_2$

Same angles

Axle

FIGURE 7.4 A rotating wheel with a changing angular velocity.

The angular velocity is *changing*, so the wheel has an angular acceleration.

FIGURE 7.5 Determining the sign of the angular acceleration.

α is *positive* when the rigid body is . . .

. . . rotating counter–clockwise and speeding up.

. . . rotating clockwise and slowing down.

α is *negative* when the rigid body is . . .

. . . rotating counter–clockwise and slowing down.

. . . rotating clockwise and speeding up.

Angular Acceleration

If you push on the edge of a bicycle wheel, it begins to rotate. If you continue to push, it rotates ever faster. Its angular velocity is *changing*. To understand the dynamics of rotating objects, we'll need to be able to describe this case of changing angular velocity—that is, the case of *nonuniform* circular motion.

FIGURE 7.4 shows a bicycle wheel whose angular velocity is changing. The dot represents a particular point on the wheel at successive times. At time t_i the angular velocity is ω_i; at a later time $t_f = t_i + \Delta t$ the angular velocity has changed to ω_f. The change in angular velocity during this time interval is

$$\Delta\omega = \omega_f - \omega_i$$

Recall that in Chapter 2 we defined the *linear* acceleration as

$$a_x = \frac{\Delta v_x}{\Delta t} = \frac{(v_x)_f - (v_x)_i}{\Delta t}$$

By analogy, we now define the **angular acceleration** as

$$\alpha = \frac{\text{change in angular velocity}}{\text{time interval}} = \frac{\Delta\omega}{\Delta t} \qquad (7.1)$$

Angular acceleration for a particle in nonuniform circular motion

We use the symbol α (Greek alpha) for angular acceleration. Because the units of ω are rad/s, the units of angular acceleration are (rad/s)/s, or rad/s^2. From Equation 7.1, the sign of α is the same as the sign of $\Delta\omega$. FIGURE 7.5 shows how to determine the sign of α. Be careful with the sign of α; just as with linear acceleration, positive and negative values of α can't be interpreted as simply "speeding up" and "slowing down." Like ω, the angular acceleration α is the same for every point on a rotating rigid body.

In Chapter 6 we found analogies between linear and angular positions and velocities. Here we've extended those analogies to include linear and angular accelerations. Table 7.1 summarizes all of these analogies between linear and circular motion.

NOTE ▶ Don't confuse the angular acceleration with the centripetal acceleration introduced in Chapter 6. The angular acceleration indicates how rapidly the *angular* velocity is changing. The centripetal acceleration is a vector quantity that points toward the center of a particle's circular path; it is nonzero even if the angular velocity is constant. ◀

In addition, the various equations of one-dimensional kinematics have analogs for rotational or circular motion. Table 7.2 lists the equations for one-dimensional motion and the analogous equations for the kinematics of circular motion.

TABLE 7.1 Linear and circular motion variables

Linear motion	Circular motion
Position x	Angular position θ
Velocity $v_x = \Delta x/\Delta t$	Angular velocity $\omega = \Delta\theta/\Delta t$
Acceleration $a_x = \Delta v_x/\Delta t$	Angular acceleration $\alpha = \Delta\omega/\Delta t$

TABLE 7.2 Linear and circular motion equations

Linear motion	Circular motion
Displacement at constant speed: $\Delta x = v\,\Delta t$	Angular displacement at constant angular speed: $\Delta\theta = \omega\,\Delta t$
Change in velocity at constant acceleration: $\Delta v = a\,\Delta t$	Change in angular velocity at constant angular acceleration: $\Delta\omega = \alpha\,\Delta t$
Displacement at constant acceleration: $\Delta x = v_i\,\Delta t + \frac{1}{2}a\,\Delta t^2$	Angular displacement at constant angular acceleration: $\Delta\theta = \omega_i\,\Delta t + \frac{1}{2}\alpha\,\Delta t^2$

EXAMPLE 7.1 Spinning up a computer disk

The disk in a computer disk drive spins up to 5400 rpm in 2.00 s. What is the angular acceleration of the disk? At the end of 2.00 s, how many revolutions has the disk made?

PREPARE The initial angular velocity is $\omega_i = 0$ rad/s. The final angular velocity is $\omega_f = 5400$ rpm. However, this value is not in the correct SI units of rad/s. The conversion is

$$\omega_f = \frac{5400 \text{ rev}}{\text{min}} \times \frac{1 \text{ min}}{60 \text{ s}} \times \frac{2\pi \text{ rad}}{1 \text{ rev}} = 565 \text{ rad/s}$$

SOLVE From the definition of angular acceleration, we have

$$\alpha = \frac{\Delta\omega}{\Delta t} = \frac{565 \text{ rad/s} - 0 \text{ rad/s}}{2.00 \text{ s}} = 283 \text{ rad/s}^2$$

We can compute the angular displacement during this acceleration by using the angular displacement equation from Table 7.2:

$$\Delta\theta = \omega_i \Delta t + \tfrac{1}{2}\alpha \, \Delta t^2$$
$$= (0 \text{ rad/s})(2.00 \text{ s}) + \tfrac{1}{2}(283 \text{ rad/s}^2)(2.00 \text{ s})^2$$
$$= 566 \text{ rad}$$

Each revolution corresponds to an angular displacement of 2π, so we have

$$\text{number of revolutions} = \frac{566 \text{ rad}}{2\pi \text{ rad/revolution}}$$
$$= 90 \text{ revolutions}$$

The disk completes 90 revolutions during the first 2 seconds.

ASSESS It seems reasonable that a fast-spinning disk would turn 90 times in a few seconds.

Graphs for Rotational Motion with Constant Angular Acceleration

In Chapter 2 we studied position, velocity, and acceleration graphs for motion with constant acceleration. A review of Section 2.5 is highly recommended. Because of the analogies between linear and angular quantities in Table 7.1, the rules for graphing angular variables are identical with those for linear variables. In particular, **the angular velocity is the slope of the angular position-versus-time graph** (as we discussed in Chapter 6), and **the angular acceleration is the slope of the angular velocity-versus-time graph.** When the angular acceleration is constant, the equations for circular motion in Table 7.2 show that the angular velocity graph is linear while the angular position graph is parabolic.

 PhET: Ladybug Revolution

EXAMPLE 7.2 Graphing angular quantities

FIGURE 7.6 shows the angular velocity-versus-time graph for the propeller of a ship.

a. Describe the motion of the propeller.
b. Draw the angular acceleration graph for the propeller.

FIGURE 7.6 The propeller's angular velocity.

PREPARE The angular acceleration graph is the slope of the angular velocity graph.

SOLVE

a. Initially the propeller has a negative angular velocity, so it is turning clockwise. It slows down until, at $t = 4$ s, it is instantaneously stopped. It then speeds up in the opposite direction until it is turning counterclockwise at a constant angular velocity.

b. The angular acceleration graph is the slope of the angular velocity graph. From $t = 0$ s, to $t = 8$ s, the slope is

$$\frac{\Delta\omega}{\Delta t} = \frac{\omega_f - \omega_i}{\Delta t} = \frac{(8.0 \text{ rad/s}) - (-8.0 \text{ rad/s})}{8.0 \text{ s}} = 2.0 \text{ rad/s}^2$$

After $t = 8$ s, the slope is zero, so the angular acceleration is zero. This graph is plotted in FIGURE 7.7.

FIGURE 7.7 Angular acceleration graph for a propeller.

ASSESS A comparison of these graphs with their linear analogs in Figure 2.24 suggests that we're on the right track.

FIGURE 7.8 Uniform and nonuniform circular motion.

(a) Uniform circular motion

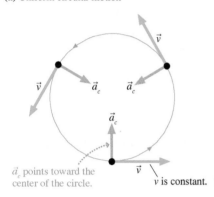

$\vec{a}_c$ points toward the center of the circle.

v is constant.

(b) Nonuniform circular motion

The tangential acceleration $\vec{a}_t$ causes the particle's *speed* to change. There's a tangential acceleration *only* when the particle is speeding up or slowing down.

v is increasing.

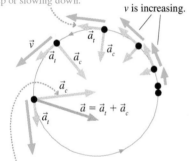

$\vec{a} = \vec{a}_t + \vec{a}_c$

The centripetal acceleration $\vec{a}_c$ causes the particle's *direction* to change. As the particle speeds up, a_c gets larger. Circular motion *always* has a centripetal acceleration.

Tangential Acceleration

As you learned in Chapter 6, and as **FIGURE 7.8a** reminds you, a particle undergoing uniform circular motion has an acceleration directed inward toward the center of the circle. This centripetal acceleration $\vec{a}_c$ is due to the change in the *direction* of the particle's velocity. Recall that the magnitude of the centripetal acceleration is $a_c = v^2/r = \omega^2 r$.

> **NOTE** ▶ Centripetal acceleration will now be denoted a_c to distinguish it from tangential acceleration a_t, discussed below. ◀

If the particle's circular motion is *nonuniform,* so that the particle's speed is changing, then the particle will have another component to its acceleration. **FIGURE 7.8b** shows a particle whose speed is increasing as it moves around its circular path. Because the *magnitude* of the velocity is increasing, this second component of the acceleration is directed *tangentially* to the circle, in the same direction as the velocity. This component of acceleration is called the **tangential acceleration.** As shown in Figure 7.8b, **the full acceleration $\vec{a}$ is then the vector sum of these two components:** the centripetal acceleration $\vec{a}_c$ and the tangential acceleration $\vec{a}_t$.

The tangential acceleration measures the rate at which the particle's speed around the circle increases. Thus its magnitude is

$$a_t = \frac{\Delta v}{\Delta t}$$

We can relate the tangential acceleration to the *angular* acceleration by using the relation $v = \omega r$ between the speed of a particle moving in a circle of radius r and its angular velocity ω. We have

$$a_t = \frac{\Delta v}{\Delta t} = \frac{\Delta(\omega r)}{\Delta t} = \frac{\Delta \omega}{\Delta t} r$$

or, because $\alpha = \Delta \omega / \Delta t$ from Equation 7.1,

$$a_t = \alpha r \tag{7.2}$$

Relationship between tangential and angular acceleration

We've seen that all points on a rotating rigid body have the same angular acceleration. From Equation 7.2, however, the centripetal and tangential accelerations of a point on a rotating object depends on the point's distance r from the axis, so that these accelerations are *not* the same for all points.

> **STOP TO THINK 7.1** A ball on the end of a string swings in a horizontal circle once every second. State whether the magnitude of each of the following quantities is zero, constant (but not zero), or changing.
>
> a. Velocity   d. Angular acceleration
> b. Angular velocity   e. Tangential acceleration
> c. Centripetal acceleration

7.2 Torque

Class Video

Newton's genius, summarized in his second law of motion, was to recognize force as the cause of acceleration. But what about *angular* acceleration? What do Newton's laws tell us about rotational motion? To begin our study of rotational motion, we'll need to find a rotational equivalent of force.

Consider the common experience of pushing open a heavy door. FIGURE 7.9 is a top view of a door that is hinged on the left. Four forces are shown, all of equal strength. Which of these will be most effective at opening the door?

Force $\vec{F}_1$ will open the door, but force $\vec{F}_2$, which pushes straight at the hinge, will not. Force $\vec{F}_3$ will open the door, but not as easily as $\vec{F}_1$. What about $\vec{F}_4$? It is perpendicular to the door and it has the same magnitude as $\vec{F}_1$, but you know from experience that pushing close to the hinge is not as effective as pushing at the outer edge of the door.

The ability of a force to cause a rotation thus depends on three factors:

1. The magnitude F of the force
2. The distance r from the pivot—the axis about which the object can rotate—to the point at which the force is applied
3. The angle at which the force is applied

We can incorporate these three observations into a single quantity called the **torque** τ (Greek tau). Loosely speaking, τ measures the "effectiveness" of a force at causing an object to rotate about a pivot. **Torque is the rotational equivalent of force.** In Figure 7.9, for instance, the torque τ_1 due to $\vec{F}_1$ is greater than τ_4 due to $\vec{F}_4$.

To make these ideas specific, FIGURE 7.10 shows a force $\vec{F}$ applied at one point of a wrench that's loosening a nut. Figure 7.10 defines the distance r from the pivot to the point at which the force is applied; the **radial line**, the line starting at the pivot and extending through this point; and the angle ϕ (Greek phi) measured from the radial line to the direction of the force.

We saw in Figure 7.9 that force $\vec{F}_1$, which was directed perpendicular to the door, was effective in opening it, but force $\vec{F}_2$, directed toward the hinges, had no effect on its rotation. As shown in FIGURE 7.11, this suggests breaking the force $\vec{F}$ applied to the wrench into two component vectors: $\vec{F}_\perp$ directed perpendicular to the radial line, and $\vec{F}_\parallel$ directed parallel to it. Because $\vec{F}_\parallel$ points either directly toward or away from the pivot, it has no effect on the wrench's rotation, and thus contributes nothing to the torque. Only $\vec{F}_\perp$ tends to cause rotation of the wrench, so it is this component of the force that determines the torque.

NOTE ▶ The perpendicular component $\vec{F}_\perp$ is pronounced "F perpendicular" and the parallel component $\vec{F}_\parallel$ is "F parallel." ◀

We've seen that a force applied at a greater distance r from the pivot has a greater effect on rotation, so we expect a larger value of r to give a greater torque. We also saw that only $\vec{F}_\perp$ contributes to the torque. Both these observations are contained in our first expression for torque:

$$\tau = rF_\perp \qquad (7.3)$$

Torque due to a force with perpendicular component $F_\perp$
acting at a distance r from the pivot

From this equation, we see that the SI units of torque are newton-meters, abbreviated N·m.

FIGURE 7.9 The four forces are the same strength, but they have different effects on the swinging door.

FIGURE 7.10 Force $\vec{F}$ exerts a torque about the pivot point.

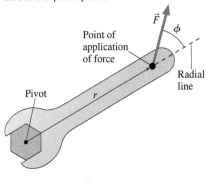

FIGURE 7.11 Torque is due to the component of the force perpendicular to the radial line.

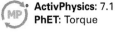
ActivPhysics: 7.1
PhET: Torque

EXAMPLE 7.3 **Torque in opening a door**

In trying to open a stuck door, Ryan pushes it at a point 0.75 m from the hinges with a 240 N force directed 20° away from being perpendicular to the door. What torque does Ryan exert on the door?

PREPARE In FIGURE 7.12 on the next page the radial line is shown drawn from the pivot—the hinge—through the point at

which the force $\vec{F}$ is applied. We see that the component of $\vec{F}$ that is perpendicular to the radial line is $F_\perp = F \cos 20° = 226$ N. The distance from the hinge to the point at which the force is applied is $r = 0.75$ m.

Continued

FIGURE 7.12 Ryan's force exerts a torque on the door.

Top view of door

$\vec{F}$
240 N
$\vec{F}_\perp$
20°

$r = 0.75$ m

Hinge

Radial line

SOLVE We can find the torque on the door from Equation 7.3:

$$\tau = rF_\perp = (0.75 \text{ m})(226 \text{ N}) = 170 \text{ N} \cdot \text{m}$$

ASSESS Ryan could slightly increase the torque he exerts by pushing with the same force but exactly perpendicular to the door.

FIGURE 7.13 You can also calculate torque in terms of the moment arm between the pivot and the line of action.

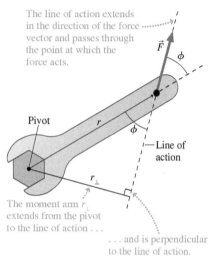

The line of action extends in the direction of the force vector and passes through the point at which the force acts.

$\vec{F}$
ϕ

Pivot
r
ϕ
—Line of action

$r_\perp$

The moment arm $r_\perp$ extends from the pivot to the line of action . . .

. . . and is perpendicular to the line of action.

FIGURE 7.13 shows an alternative way to calculate torque. The line that is in the direction of the force, and passes through the point at which the force acts, is called the *line of action*. The perpendicular distance from this line to the pivot is called the **moment arm** (or *lever arm*) $r_\perp$. You can see from the figure that $r_\perp = r\sin\phi$. Further, Figure 7.11 showed that $F_\perp = F\sin\phi$. We can then write Equation 7.3 as $\tau = rF\sin\phi = F(r\sin\phi) = Fr_\perp$. Thus an equivalent expression for the torque is

$$\tau = r_\perp F \tag{7.4}$$

Torque due to a force F with moment arm $r_\perp$

CONCEPTUAL EXAMPLE 7.4 | **Starting a bike**

It is hard to get going if you try to start your bike with the pedal at the highest point. Why is this?

REASON Aided by the weight of the body, the greatest force can be applied to the pedal straight down. But with the pedal at the top, this force is exerted almost directly toward the pivot, causing only a small torque. We could say either that the perpendicular component of the force is small or that the moment arm is small.

ASSESS If you've ever climbed a steep hill while standing on the pedals, you know that you get the greatest forward motion when one pedal is completely forward with the crank parallel to the ground. This gives the maximum possible torque because the force you apply is entirely perpendicular to the radial line, and the moment arm is as long as it can be.

We've seen that Equation 7.3 can be written as $\tau = rF_\perp = r(F\sin\phi)$, and Equation 7.4 as $\tau = r_\perp F = (r\sin\phi)F$. This shows that both methods of calculating torque lead to the same expression for torque—namely:

$$\tau = rF\sin\phi \tag{7.5}$$

Torque due to a force F applied at a distance r from the pivot, at an angle ϕ to the radial line

---

◀ Torque versus speed To start and stop quickly, the basketball player needs to apply a large torque to her wheel. To make the torque as large as possible, the handrim—the outside wheel that she actually grabs—is almost as big as the wheel itself. The racer needs to move continuously at high speed, so his wheel spins much faster. To allow his hands to keep up, his handrim is much smaller than his chair's wheel, making its linear velocity correspondingly lower. The smaller radius means, however, that the torque he can apply is lower as well.

NOTE ▶ Torque differs from force in a very important way. Torque is calculated or measured *about a particular point.* To say that a torque is 20 N · m is meaningless without specifying the point about which the torque is calculated. Torque can be calculated about any point, but its value depends on the point chosen because this choice determines r and ϕ. In practice, we usually calculate torques about a hinge, pivot, or axle. ◀

Equations 7.3–7.5 are three different ways of thinking about—and calculating— the torque due to a force. Depending on the problem at hand, one might be easier to use than the others. But they all calculate the *same* torque, and all will give the same value for the torque.

These equations give only the magnitude of the torque. But torque, like a force component, has a sign. **A torque that tends to rotate the object in a counterclockwise direction is positive, while a torque that tends to rotate the object in a clockwise direction is negative.** FIGURE 7.14 summarizes the signs. Notice that a force pushing straight toward the pivot or pulling straight out from the pivot exerts *no* torque.

NOTE ▶ When calculating a torque, you must supply the appropriate sign by observing the direction in which the torque acts. ◀

FIGURE 7.14 Signs and strengths of the torque.

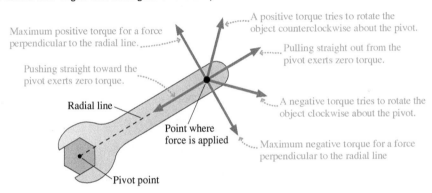

EXAMPLE 7.5 **Calculating the torque on a nut**

Luis uses a 20-cm-long wrench to turn a nut. The wrench handle is tilted 30° above the horizontal, and Luis pulls straight down on the end with a force of 100 N. How much torque does Luis exert on the nut?

PREPARE FIGURE 7.15 shows the situation. The two illustrations correspond to two methods of calculating torque, corresponding to Equations 7.3 and 7.4.

FIGURE 7.15 A wrench being used to turn a nut.

SOLVE According to Equation 7.3 and 7.5, the torque can be calculated as $\tau = rF_\perp = rF\sin\phi$. From Figure 7.15a we see that

the angle between the force and the radial line is $\phi = 30° + 90° = 120°$. The torque is then

$$\tau = -rF\sin\phi = -(0.20\text{ m})(100\text{ N})(\sin 120°) = -17\text{ N} \cdot \text{m}$$

We put in the minus sign because the torque is negative—it tries to rotate the nut in a *clockwise* direction.

Alternatively, we can use Equation 7.4 to find the torque. Figure 7.15b shows the moment arm $r_\perp$, the perpendicular distance from the pivot to the line of action. From the figure we see that

$$r_\perp = r\cos 30° = (0.20\text{ m})(\cos 30°) = 0.17\text{ m}$$

Then the torque is

$$\tau = -r_\perp F = -(0.17\text{ m})(100\text{ N}) = -17\text{ N} \cdot \text{m}$$

Again, we insert the minus sign because the torque acts to give a clockwise rotation.

ASSESS Both methods give the same answer for the torque, as expected. In general, however, you need use only one of Equations 7.3–7.5 to find the torque in any given situation. In using any of these methods to find the torque, remember to include the minus sign if the torque acts to rotate the object in a clockwise direction.

Rank in order, from largest to smallest, the five torques τ_A to τ_E. The rods all have the same length and are pivoted at the dot.

A.   B.   C.   D.   E.

FIGURE 7.16 The forces exert a net torque about the pivot point.

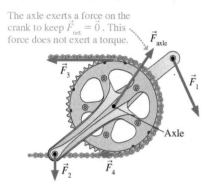

The axle exerts a force on the crank to keep $\vec{F}_{net} = \vec{0}$. This force does not exert a torque.

Net Torque

FIGURE 7.16 shows the forces acting on the crankset of a bicycle. Forces $\vec{F}_1$ and $\vec{F}_2$ are due to the rider pushing on the pedals, and $\vec{F}_3$ and $\vec{F}_4$ are tension forces from the chain. The crankset is free to rotate about a fixed axle, but the axle prevents it from having any translational motion with respect to the bike frame. It does so by exerting force $\vec{F}_{axle}$ on the object to balance the other forces and keep $\vec{F}_{net} = \vec{0}$.

Forces $\vec{F}_1$, $\vec{F}_2$, $\vec{F}_3$, and $\vec{F}_4$ exert torques τ_1, τ_2, τ_3, and τ_4 on the crank (measured about the axle), but $\vec{F}_{axle}$ does *not* exert a torque because it is applied at the pivot point—the axle—and so has zero moment arm. Thus the *net* torque about the axle is the sum of the torques due to the *applied* forces:

$$\tau_{net} = \tau_1 + \tau_2 + \tau_3 + \tau_4 + \cdots = \sum \tau \tag{7.6}$$

EXAMPLE 7.6   Force in turning a capstan

A capstan is a device used on old sailing ships to raise the anchor. A sailor pushes the long lever, turning the capstan and winding up the anchor rope. If the capstan turns at a constant speed, the net torque on it, as we'll learn later in the chapter, is zero.

Suppose the rope tension due to the weight of the anchor is 1500 N. If the distance from the axis to the point on the lever where the sailor pushes is exactly seven times the radius of the capstan around which the rope is wound, with what force must the sailor push if the net torque on the capstan is to be zero?

PREPARE Shown in FIGURE 7.17 is a view looking down from above the capstan. The rope pulls with a tension force $\vec{T}$ at distance R from the axis of rotation. The sailor pushes with a force $\vec{F}$ at distance $7R$ from the axis. Both forces are perpendicular to their radial lines, so ϕ in Equation 7.5 is 90°.

FIGURE 7.17 Top view of a sailor turning a capstan.

The sailor pushes the capstan in a clockwise direction . . .

. . . while the tension force tries to turn it counterclockwise.

$7R$

R

SOLVE The torque due to the tension in the rope is

$$\tau_T = RT \sin 90° = RT$$

We don't know the capstan radius, so we'll just leave it as R for now. This torque is positive because it tries to turn the capstan counterclockwise. The torque due to the sailor is

$$\tau_S = -(7R)F \sin 90° = -7RF$$

We put the minus sign in because this torque acts in the clockwise (negative) direction. The net torque is zero, so we have $\tau_T + \tau_S = 0$, or

$$RT - 7RF = 0$$

Note that the radius R cancels, leaving

$$F = \frac{T}{7} = \frac{1500 \text{ N}}{7} = 210 \text{ N}$$

ASSESS 210 N is about 50 lb, a reasonable number. The force the sailor must exert is one-seventh the force the rope exerts: The long lever helps him lift the heavy anchor. In the HMS *Warrior*, built in 1860, it took 200 men turning the capstan to lift the huge anchor that weighed close to 55,000 N!

Note that forces $\vec{F}$ and $\vec{T}$ point in different directions. Their torques depend only on their directions with respect to their own radial lines, not on the directions of the forces with respect to each other. The force the sailor needs to apply remains unchanged as he circles the capstan.

STOP TO THINK 7.3 Two forces act on the wheel shown. What third force, acting at point P, will make the net torque on the wheel zero?

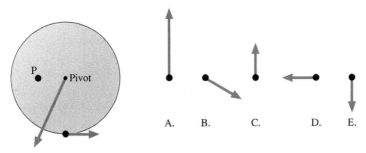

A.   B.   C.   D.   E.

7.3 Gravitational Torque and the Center of Gravity

As the gymnast in FIGURE 7.18 pivots around the bar, a torque due to the force of gravity causes her to rotate toward a vertical position. A falling tree and a car hood slamming shut are other examples where gravity exerts a torque on an object. Stationary objects can also experience a torque due to gravity. A diving board experiences a gravitational torque about its fixed end. It doesn't rotate because of a counteracting torque provided by forces from the base at its fixed end.

We've learned how to calculate the torque due to a single force acting on an object. But gravity doesn't act at a single point on an object. It pulls downward on *every particle* that makes up the object, as shown for the gymnast in Figure 7.18a, and so each particle experiences a small torque due to the force of gravity that acts upon it. The gravitational torque on the object as a whole is then the *net* torque exerted on all the particles. We won't prove it, but the gravitational torque can be calculated by assuming that the net force of gravity—that is, the object's weight $\vec{w}$—acts at a single special point on the object called its **center of gravity** (symbol ☉). Then we can calculate the torque due to gravity by the methods learned earlier for a single force ($\vec{w}$) acting at a single point (the center of gravity). Figure 7.18b shows how we can consider the gymnast's weight as acting at her center of gravity.

FIGURE 7.18 The center of gravity is the point where the weight appears to act.

(a) Gravity exerts a force and a torque on each particle that makes up the gymnast.····   Rotation axis

(b)   The weight force provides a torque about the rotation axis.····

Center of gravity

$\vec{w}$

The gymnast responds *as if* her entire weight acts at her center of gravity.

EXAMPLE 7.7 The torque on a flagpole

A 3.2 kg flagpole extends from a wall at an angle of 25° from the horizontal. Its center of gravity is 1.6 m from the point where the pole is attached to the wall. What is the gravitational torque on the flagpole about the point of attachment?

PREPARE FIGURE 7.19 shows the situation. For the purpose of calculating torque, we can consider the entire weight of the pole as acting at the center of gravity. We can use any of the three

FIGURE 7.19 Visual overview of the flagpole.

Known
$m = 3.2$ kg
$r = 1.6$ m
$\theta = 25°$

Find
Torque τ

methods discussed in Section 7.2 to calculate the torque. Because the moment arm $r_\perp$ is simple to visualize here, we'll use Equation 7.4 for the torque.

SOLVE From Figure 7.19, we see that the moment arm is $r_\perp = (1.6 \text{ m}) \cos 25° = 1.5 \text{ m}$. Thus the gravitational torque on the flagpole, about the point where it attaches to the wall, is

$$\tau = -r_\perp w = -r_\perp mg = -(1.5 \text{ m})(3.2 \text{ kg})(9.8 \text{ m/s}^2) = -47 \text{ N} \cdot \text{m}$$

We inserted the minus sign because the torque tries to rotate the pole in a clockwise direction.

ASSESS If the pole were attached to the wall by a hinge, the gravitational torque would cause the pole to fall. However, the actual rigid connection provides a counteracting (positive) torque to the pole that prevents this.

FIGURE 7.20 Method for finding the center of gravity of an object.

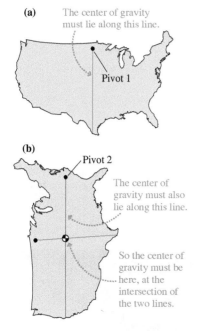

(a) The center of gravity must lie along this line.

Pivot 1

(b) Pivot 2

The center of gravity must also lie along this line.

So the center of gravity must be here, at the intersection of the two lines.

Video Tutor Demonstration

Finding the Center of Gravity

To calculate the gravitational torque, we need to locate the object's center of gravity. There is a simple experimental method for finding the center of gravity of any object, based on the observation that **any object free to rotate about a pivot will come to rest with its center of gravity directly below the pivot.** To see this, consider the cutout map of the continental United States in FIGURE 7.20a. If the center of gravity is to the right or left of the blue line, a gravitational torque will cause the map to swing. If the center of gravity lies directly *below* the pivot, however, the weight force lies along the line of action and the torque is zero. The map can then remain at rest with no tendency to swing.

We know that the center of gravity lies somewhere along the blue line, but we don't yet know where. To find out, we need to suspend the map from a second pivot, as shown in FIGURE 7.20b. Then the center of gravity will fall somewhere along the red line shown. Because the center of gravity must lie on both the blue and red lines, it must be at their *intersection*. Interestingly, the geographical center of the continental United States is defined in just this way, as the center of gravity of a map of the contiguous United States. This point is one mile northwest of Lebanon, Kansas.

For a simple symmetrical object, such as a rod, sphere, or cube made of a uniform material, FIGURE 7.21 shows that **the center of gravity of a symmetrical object lies at its geometrical center.** A particularly simple case of this is a point particle, whose center of gravity lies at the position of the particle.

FIGURE 7.21 The center of gravity of a symmetrical object lies at its center.

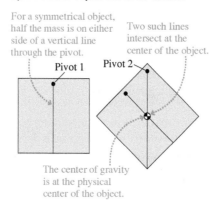

For a symmetrical object, half the mass is on either side of a vertical line through the pivot.

Two such lines intersect at the center of the object.

Pivot 1   Pivot 2

The center of gravity is at the physical center of the object.

FIGURE 7.22 Balancing a ruler.

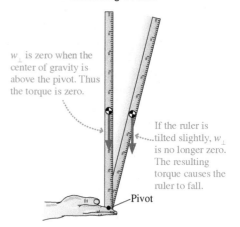

$w_\perp$ is zero when the center of gravity is above the pivot. Thus the torque is zero.

If the ruler is tilted slightly, $w_\perp$ is no longer zero. The resulting torque causes the ruler to fall.

Pivot

As we've seen, an object free to pivot will rotate until its center of gravity is directly below the pivot. If the center of gravity lies directly *above* the pivot, as in FIGURE 7.22, there is no torque due to the object's weight and it can remain balanced. However, if the object is even slightly displaced to either side, the gravitational torque will no longer be zero and the object will begin to rotate. This question of *balance*—the behavior of an object whose center of gravity lies above the pivot— will be explored in depth in Chapter 8.

Calculating the Position of the Center of Gravity

It is nice to know you can locate an object's center of gravity by suspending it from a pivot, but it is rarely a practical technique. More often, we would like to calculate the center of gravity of an object made up of a combination of particles and objects whose center-of-gravity positions are known.

Because there's no gravitational torque when the center of gravity lies either directly above or directly below the pivot, it must be the case that **the torque due to gravity when the pivot is *at* the center of gravity is zero.** We can use this fact to find a general expression for the position of the center of gravity.

Consider the dumbbell shown in FIGURE 7.23. If we slide the triangular pivot back and forth until the dumbbell balances, the pivot must then be at the center of gravity (at position x_{cg}), and the torque due to gravity must therefore be zero. But we can calculate the gravitational torque directly by calculating and summing the torques about this point due to the two individual weights. Gravity acts on weight 1 with moment arm r_1, so the torque about the pivot at position x_{cg} is

$$\tau_1 = r_1 w_1 = (x_{cg} - x_1)m_1 g$$

Similarly, the torque due to weight 2 is

$$\tau_2 = -r_2 w_2 = -(x_2 - x_{cg})m_2 g$$

This torque is negative because it tends to rotate the dumbbell in a clockwise direction. We've just argued that the net torque must be zero because the pivot is directly under the center of gravity, so

$$\tau_{net} = 0 = \tau_1 + \tau_2 = (x_{cg} - x_1)m_1 g - (x_2 - x_{cg})m_2 g$$

We can solve this equation for the position of the center of gravity x_{cg}:

$$x_{cg} = \frac{x_1 m_1 + x_2 m_2}{m_1 + m_2} \tag{7.7}$$

The following Tactics Box shows how Equation 7.7 can be generalized to find the center of gravity of *any* number of particles. If the particles don't all lie along the x-axis, then we'll also need to find the y-coordinate of the center of gravity.

FIGURE 7.23 Finding the center of gravity of a dumbbell.

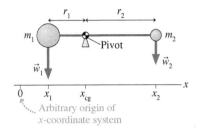

TACTICS BOX 7.1 Finding the center of gravity

❶ Choose an origin for your coordinate system. You can choose any convenient point as the origin.
❷ Determine the coordinates (x_1, y_1), (x_2, y_2), (x_3, y_3), ... for the particles of masses $m_1, m_2, m_3, \ldots$, respectively.
❸ The x-coordinate of the center of gravity is

$$x_{cg} = \frac{x_1 m_1 + x_2 m_2 + x_3 m_3 + \cdots}{m_1 + m_2 + m_3 + \cdots} \tag{7.8}$$

❹ Similarly, the y-coordinate of the center of gravity is

$$y_{cg} = \frac{y_1 m_1 + y_2 m_2 + y_3 m_3 + \cdots}{m_1 + m_2 + m_3 + \cdots} \tag{7.9}$$

Exercises 12–15

Holding steady Many movie-making scenes require handheld shots for which the cameraman must walk along, following the action. The stabilizer shown reduces unwanted camera motion as the cameraman walks. The center of gravity of the camera and its hanging weight arm is located exactly at a pivot that can swing freely in any direction. The frictionless pivot exerts no torque on the camera and arm. Neither does the weight, because it acts at the pivot. With no torque acting on it, the camera has no tendency to rotate. The long arm also increases the system's *moment of inertia*, further decreasing unwanted rotations. More about this later!

Because the center of gravity depends on products such as $x_1 m_1$, objects with large masses count more heavily than objects with small masses. Consequently, **the center of gravity tends to lie closer to the heavier objects or particles** that make up the entire object.

EXAMPLE 7.8 Where should the dumbbell be lifted?

A 1.0-m-long dumbbell has a 10 kg mass on the left and a 5.0 kg mass on the right. Find the position of the center of gravity, the point where the dumbbell should be lifted in order to remain balanced.

PREPARE We'll treat the two masses as point particles separated by a massless rod. Then we can use the steps from Tactics

Box 7.1 to find the center of gravity. Let's choose the origin to be at the position of the 10 kg mass on the left, making $x_1 = 0$ m and $x_2 = 1.0$ m. Because the dumbbell masses lie on the x-axis, the y-coordinate of the center of gravity must also lie on the x-axis. Thus we only need to solve for the x-coordinate of the center of gravity.

Continued

SOLVE The *x*-coordinate of the center of gravity is found from Equation 7.8:

$$x_{cg} = \frac{x_1 m_1 + x_2 m_2}{m_1 + m_2} = \frac{(0 \text{ m})(10 \text{ kg}) + (1.0 \text{ m})(5.0 \text{ kg})}{(10 \text{ kg}) + (5.0 \text{ kg})}$$

$$= 0.33 \text{ m}$$

The center of gravity is 0.33 m from the 10 kg mass or, equivalently, 0.17 m left of the center of the bar.

ASSESS The position of the center of gravity is closer to the larger mass. This agrees with our general statement that the center of gravity tends to lie closer to the heavier particles.

FIGURE 7.24 Body segment masses and centers of gravity.

2.2 kg
1.3 kg
0.5 kg
47 kg
8.0 kg
3.4 kg
1.1 kg

The center of gravity of an extended object can often be found by considering the object as made up of pieces, each with mass and center of gravity that are known or can be found. Then the coordinates of the entire object's center of gravity are given by Equations 7.8 and 7.9, with (x_1, y_1), (x_2, y_2), (x_3, y_3), ... the coordinates of the center of gravity of each piece and $m_1, m_2, m_3,$ ... their masses.

This method is widely used in biomechanics and kinesiology to calculate the center of gravity of the human body. **FIGURE 7.24** shows how the body can be considered to be made of segments, each of whose mass and center of gravity have been measured. The numbers shown are appropriate for a man with a total mass of 80 kg. For a given posture the positions of the segments and their centers of gravity can be found, and thus the whole-body center of gravity from Equations 7.8 and 7.9 (and a third equation for the *z*-coordinate). Example 7.9 explores a simplified version of this method.

EXAMPLE 7.9 **Finding the center of gravity of a gymnast**

A gymnast performing on the rings holds himself in the pike position. **FIGURE 7.25** shows how we can consider his body to be made up of two segments whose masses and center-of-gravity positions are shown. The upper segment includes his head, trunk, and arms, while the lower segment consists of his legs. Locate the overall center of gravity of the gymnast.

FIGURE 7.25 Centers of gravity of two segments of a gymnast.

y (cm)

80
60
40
20
0

Center of gravity of head, trunk, and arms

Center of gravity of entire body (to be calculated)

Center of gravity of legs

45 kg

30 kg

20   40   60   80   100   *x* (cm)

PREPARE From Figure 7.25 we can find the *x*- and *y*-coordinates of the segment centers of gravity:

$$x_{\text{trunk}} = 15 \text{ cm} \qquad y_{\text{trunk}} = 50 \text{ cm}$$
$$x_{\text{legs}} = 30 \text{ cm} \qquad y_{\text{legs}} = 20 \text{ cm}$$

SOLVE The *x*- and *y*-coordinates of the center of gravity are given by Equations 7.8 and 7.9:

$$x_{cg} = \frac{x_{\text{trunk}} m_{\text{trunk}} + x_{\text{legs}} m_{\text{legs}}}{m_{\text{trunk}} + m_{\text{legs}}}$$

$$= \frac{(15 \text{ cm})(45 \text{ kg}) + (30 \text{ cm})(30 \text{ kg})}{45 \text{ kg} + 30 \text{ kg}} = 21 \text{ cm}$$

and

$$y_{cg} = \frac{y_{\text{trunk}} m_{\text{trunk}} + y_{\text{legs}} m_{\text{legs}}}{m_{\text{trunk}} + m_{\text{legs}}}$$

$$= \frac{(50 \text{ cm})(45 \text{ kg}) + (20 \text{ cm})(30 \text{ kg})}{45 \text{ kg} + 30 \text{ kg}} = 38 \text{ cm}$$

ASSESS The center-of-gravity position of the entire body, shown in Figure 7.25, is closer to that of the heavier trunk segment than to that of the lighter legs. It also lies along a line connecting the two segment centers of gravity, just as it would for the center of gravity of two point particles. Note also that the gymnast's hands—the pivot point—must lie directly below his center of gravity. Otherwise he would rotate forward or backward.

STOP TO THINK 7.4   The balls are connected by very lightweight rods pivoted at the point indicated by a dot. The rod lengths are all equal except for A, which is twice as long. Rank in order, from least to greatest, the magnitudes of the gravitational torques about the pivots for arrangements A to E.

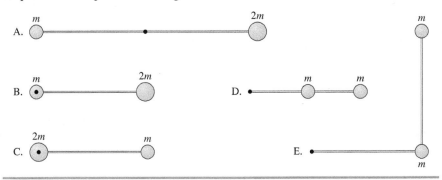

7.4 Rotational Dynamics and Moment of Inertia

In Section 7.2 we asked: What do Newton's laws tell us about rotational motion? We can now answer that question: **A torque causes an angular acceleration.** This is the rotational equivalent of our earlier discovery, for motion along a line, that a force causes an acceleration.

To see where this connection between torque and angular acceleration comes from, let's start by examining a *single particle* subject to a torque. **FIGURE 7.26** shows a particle of mass m attached to a lightweight, rigid rod of length r that constrains the particle to move in a circle. The particle is subject to two forces. Because it's moving in a circle, there must be a force—here, the tension $\vec{T}$ from the rod—directed toward the center of the circle. As we learned in Chapter 6, this is the force responsible for changing the *direction* of the particle's velocity. The acceleration associated with this change in the particle's velocity is the centripetal acceleration $\vec{a}_c$.

But the particle in Figure 7.26 is also subject to the force $\vec{F}$ that changes the *speed* of the particle. This force causes a tangential acceleration $\vec{a}_t$. Applying Newton's second law in the direction tangent to the circle gives

$$a_t = \frac{F}{m} \tag{7.10}$$

Now the tangential and angular accelerations are related by $a_t = \alpha r$, so we can rewrite Equation 7.10 as $\alpha r = F/m$, or

$$\alpha = \frac{F}{mr} \tag{7.11}$$

We can now connect this angular acceleration to the torque because force $\vec{F}$, which is perpendicular to the radial line, exerts torque

$$\tau = rF$$

With this relation between F and τ, we can write Equation 7.11 as

$$\alpha = \frac{\tau}{mr^2} \tag{7.12}$$

Equation 7.12 gives a relationship between the torque on a single particle and its angular acceleration. Now all that remains is to expand this idea from a single particle to an extended object.

FIGURE 7.26 A tangential force $\vec{F}$ exerts a torque on the particle and causes an angular acceleration.

This large granite ball, with a mass of 26,400 kg, floats with nearly zero friction on a thin layer of pressurized water. Even though the girl exerts a large torque on the ball, its angular acceleration is small because of its large moment of inertia.

Newton's Second Law for Rotational Motion

FIGURE 7.27 The forces on a rigid body exert a torque about the rotation axis.

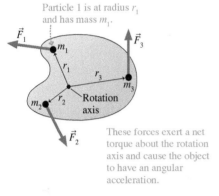

Particle 1 is at radius r_1 and has mass m_1.

Rotation axis

These forces exert a net torque about the rotation axis and cause the object to have an angular acceleration.

ActivPhysics: 7.6

FIGURE 7.27 shows a rigid body that undergoes rotation about a fixed and unmoving axis. According to the rigid-body model, we can think of the object as consisting of particles with masses $m_1, m_2, m_3, \ldots$ at fixed distances $r_1, r_2, r_3, \ldots$ from the axis. Suppose forces $\vec{F}_1, \vec{F}_2, \vec{F}_3, \ldots$ act on these particles. These forces exert torques around the rotation axis, so the object will undergo an angular acceleration α. Because all the particles that make up the object rotate together, each particle has this *same* angular acceleration α. Rearranging Equation 7.12 slightly, we can write the torques on the particles as

$$\tau_1 = m_1 r_1^2 \alpha \qquad \tau_2 = m_2 r_2^2 \alpha \qquad \tau_3 = m_3 r_3^2 \alpha$$

and so on for every particle in the object. If we add up all these torques, the *net* torque on the object is

$$\tau_{net} = \tau_1 + \tau_2 + \tau_3 + \cdots = m_1 r_1^2 \alpha + m_2 r_2^2 \alpha + m_3 r_3^2 \alpha + \cdots$$
$$= \alpha(m_1 r_1^2 + m_2 r_2^2 + m_3 r_3^2 + \cdots) = \alpha \sum m_i r_i^2 \qquad (7.13)$$

By factoring α out of the sum, we're making explicit use of the fact that every particle in a rotating rigid body has the *same* angular acceleration α.

The quantity $\sum m r^2$ in Equation 7.13, which is the proportionality constant between angular acceleration and net torque, is called the object's **moment of inertia** I:

$$I = m_1 r_1^2 + m_2 r_2^2 + m_3 r_3^2 + \cdots = \sum m_i r_i^2 \qquad (7.14)$$

Moment of inertia of a collection of particles

The units of moment of inertia are mass times distance squared, or $kg \cdot m^2$. An object's moment of inertia, like torque, *depends on the axis of rotation*. Once the axis is specified, allowing the values of $r_1, r_2, r_3, \ldots$ to be determined, the moment of inertia *about that axis* can be calculated from Equation 7.14.

NOTE ▶ The word "moment" in "moment of inertia" and "moment arm" has nothing to do with time. It stems from the Latin *momentum,* meaning "motion." ◀

Substituting the moment of inertia into Equation 7.13 puts the final piece of the puzzle into place, giving us the fundamental equation for rigid-body dynamics:

Newton's second law for rotation An object that experiences a net torque τ_{net} about the axis of rotation undergoes an angular acceleration

$$\alpha = \frac{\tau_{net}}{I} \qquad (7.15)$$

where I is the moment of inertia of the object *about the rotation axis.*

In practice we often write $\tau_{net} = I\alpha$, but Equation 7.15 better conveys the idea that **a net torque is the cause of angular acceleration.** In the absence of a net torque ($\tau_{net} = 0$), the object has zero angular acceleration α, so it either does not rotate ($\omega = 0$) or rotates with *constant* angular velocity ($\omega = $ constant).

Interpreting the Moment of Inertia

Before rushing to calculate moments of inertia, let's get a better understanding of its meaning. First, notice that **moment of inertia is the rotational equivalent of mass.** It plays the same role in Equation 7.15 as does mass m in the now-familiar $\vec{a} = \vec{F}_{net}/m$. Recall that objects with larger mass have a larger *inertia,* meaning that they're harder to accelerate. Similarly, an object with a larger moment of inertia is

TRY IT YOURSELF

Hammering home inertia Most of the mass of a hammer is in its head, so the hammer's moment of inertia is large when calculated about an axis passing through the end of the handle (far from the head), but small when calculated about an axis passing through the head itself. You can *feel* this difference by attempting to wave a hammer back and forth about the handle end and the head end. It's much harder to do about the handle end because the large moment of inertia keeps the angular acceleration small.

harder to get rotating: It takes a larger torque to spin up an object with a larger moment of inertia than an object with a smaller moment of inertia. The fact that "moment of inertia" retains the word "inertia" reminds us of this.

But why does the moment of inertia depend on the distances r from the rotation axis? Think about trying to start a merry-go-round from rest, as shown in FIGURE 7.28. By pushing on the rim of the merry-go-round, you exert a torque on it, and its angular velocity begins to increase. If your friends sit at the rim of the merry-go-round, as in Figure 7.28a, their distances r from the axle are large. The moment of inertia is large, according to Equation 7.14, and it will be difficult to get the merry-go-round rotating. If, however, your friends sit near the axle, as in Figure 7.28b, then r and the moment of inertia are small. You'll find it's much easier to get the merry-go-round going.

Thus an object's moment of inertia depends not only on the object's mass but also on *how the mass is distributed* around the rotation axis. This is well known to bicycle racers. Every time a cyclist accelerates, she has to "spin up" the wheels and tires. The larger the moment of inertia, the more effort it takes and the slower her acceleration. For this reason, racers use the lightest possible tires, and they put those tires on wheels that have been designed to keep the mass as close as possible to the center without sacrificing the necessary strength and rigidity.

Table 7.3 summarizes the analogies between linear and rotational dynamics.

FIGURE 7.28 Moment of inertia depends on both the mass and how the mass is distributed.

(a) Mass concentrated around the rim

(b) Mass concentrated at the center

Larger moment of inertia, harder to get rotating

Smaller moment of inertia, easier to get rotating

TABLE 7.3 Rotational and linear dynamics

Rotational dynamics		Linear dynamics	
Torque	τ_{net}	Force	$\vec{F}_{net}$
Moment of inertia	I	Mass	m
Angular acceleration	α	Acceleration	$\vec{a}$
Second law	$\alpha = \tau_{net}/I$	Second law	$\vec{a} = \vec{F}_{net}/m$

EXAMPLE 7.10 **Calculating the moment of inertia**

Your friend is creating an abstract sculpture that consists of three small, heavy spheres attached by very lightweight 10-cm-long rods as shown in FIGURE 7.29. The spheres have masses $m_1 = 1.0$ kg, $m_2 = 1.5$ kg, and $m_3 = 1.0$ kg. What is the object's moment of inertia if it is rotated about axis a? About axis b?

FIGURE 7.29 Three point particles separated by lightweight rods.

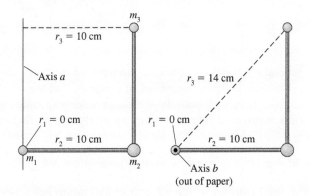

PREPARE We'll use Equation 7.14 for the moment of inertia:

$$I = m_1 r_1^2 + m_2 r_2^2 + m_3 r_3^2$$

In this expression, r_1, r_2, and r_3 are the distances of each particle from the axis of rotation, so they depend on the axis chosen. Particle 1 lies on both axes, so $r_1 = 0$ cm in both cases. Particle 2 lies

10 cm (0.10 m) from both axes. Particle 3 is 10 cm from axis a, but farther from axis b. We can find r_3 for axis b by using the Pythagorean theorem, which gives $r_3 = 14$ cm. These distances are indicated in the figure.

SOLVE For each axis, we can prepare a table of the values of r, m, and mr^2 for each particle, then add the values of mr^2. For axis a we have

Particle	r	m	mr^2
1	0 m	1.0 kg	0 kg·m²
2	0.10 m	1.5 kg	0.015 kg·m²
3	0.10 m	1.0 kg	0.010 kg·m²
			$I_a = 0.025$ kg·m²

For axis b we have

Particle	r	m	mr^2
1	0 m	1.0 kg	0 kg·m²
2	0.10 m	1.5 kg	0.015 kg·m²
3	0.14 m	1.0 kg	0.020 kg·m²
			$I_b = 0.035$ kg·m²

ASSESS We've already noted that the moment of inertia of an object is higher when its mass is distributed farther from the axis of rotation. Here, m_3 is farther from axis b than from axis a, leading to a higher moment of inertia about that axis.

The Moments of Inertia of Common Shapes

Newton's second law for rotational motion is easy to write, but we can't make use of it without knowing an object's moment of inertia. Unlike mass, we can't measure moment of inertia by putting an object on a scale. And although we can guess that the center of gravity of a symmetrical object is at the physical center of the object, we can *not* guess the moment of inertia of even a simple object.

For an object consisting of only a few point particles connected by massless rods, we can use Equation 7.14 to directly calculate I. But such an object is pretty unrealistic. All real objects are made up of solid material that is itself composed of countless atoms. To calculate the moment of inertia of even a simple object requires integral calculus and is beyond the scope of this text. A short list of common moments of inertia is given in Table 7.4. We use a capital M for the total mass of an extended object.

TABLE 7.4 Moments of inertia of objects with uniform density and total mass M

Object and axis	Picture	I	Object and axis	Picture	I
Thin rod (of any cross section), about center		$\frac{1}{12}ML^2$	Cylinder or disk, about center		$\frac{1}{2}MR^2$
Thin rod (of any cross section), about end		$\frac{1}{3}ML^2$	Cylindrical hoop, about center		MR^2
Plane or slab, about center		$\frac{1}{12}Ma^2$	Solid sphere, about diameter		$\frac{2}{5}MR^2$
Plane or slab, about edge		$\frac{1}{3}Ma^2$	Spherical shell, about diameter		$\frac{2}{3}MR^2$

We can make some general observations about the moments of inertia in Table 7.4. For instance, the cylindrical hoop is composed of particles that are all the same distance R from the axis. Thus each particle of mass m makes the *same* contribution mR^2 to the hoop's moment of inertia. Adding up all these contributions gives

$$I = m_1R^2 + m_2R^2 + m_3R^2 + \cdots = (m_1 + m_2 + m_3 + \cdots)R^2 = MR^2$$

as given in the table. The solid cylinder of the same mass and radius has a *lower* moment of inertia than the hoop because much of the cylinder's mass is nearer its center. In the same way we can see why a slab rotated about its center has a lower moment of inertia than the same slab rotated about its edge: In the latter case, some of the mass is twice as far from the axis as the farthest mass in the former case. Those particles contribute *four times* as much to the moment of inertia, leading to an overall larger moment of inertia for the slab rotated about its edge.

► **Novel golf clubs** The latest craze in golf putters is heads with high moments of inertia. When the putter hits the ball, the ball—by Newton's third law—exerts a force on the putter and thus exerts a torque that causes the head of the putter to rotate around the shaft. Any rotation while the putter is still in contact with the ball will affect the ball's direction. If the putter's mass is largely placed rather far from the shaft (the rotation axis), the moment of inertia about the shaft can be greatly increased. The large moment of inertia of the head will keep its angular acceleration small—reducing unwanted rotation and allowing a truer putt.

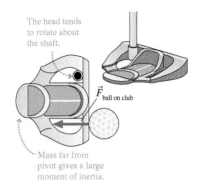

The head tends to rotate about the shaft.

$\vec{F}_{\text{ball on club}}$

Mass far from pivot gives a large moment of inertia.

STOP TO THINK 7.5 Four very lightweight disks of equal radii each have three identical heavy marbles glued to them as shown. Rank in order, from largest to smallest, the moments of inertia of the disks about the indicated axis.

Axis

A.   B.   C.   D.

7.5 Using Newton's Second Law for Rotation

In this section we'll look at several examples of rotational dynamics for rigid bodies that rotate about a *fixed axis*. The restriction to a fixed axis avoids complications that arise for an object undergoing a combination of rotational and translational motion. The problem-solving strategy for rotational dynamics is very similar to that for linear dynamics in Chapter 5.

MP **ActivPhysics:** 7.8, 7.9, 7.10

PROBLEM-SOLVING
STRATEGY 7.1   Rotational dynamics problems   **MP**

PREPARE Model the object as a simple shape. Draw a pictorial representation to clarify the situation, define coordinates and symbols, and list known information.

■ Identify the axis about which the object rotates.
■ Identify the forces and determine their distance from the axis.
■ Calculate the torques caused by the forces, and find the signs of the torques.

SOLVE The mathematical representation is based on Newton's second law for rotational motion:

$$\tau_{\text{net}} = I\alpha \qquad \text{or} \qquad \alpha = \frac{\tau_{\text{net}}}{I}$$

■ Find the moment of inertia either by direct calculation using Equation 7.14 or from Table 7.4 for common shapes of objects.
■ Use rotational kinematics to find angular positions and velocities.

ASSESS Check that your result has the correct units, is reasonable, and answers the question.

Exercise 25

EXAMPLE 7.11 **Starting an airplane engine**

The engine in a small airplane is specified to have a torque of 500 N · m. This engine drives a 2.0-m-long, 40 kg single-blade propeller. On start-up, how long does it take the propeller to reach 2000 rpm?

PREPARE The propeller can be modeled as a rod that rotates about its center. The engine exerts a torque on the propeller. FIGURE 7.30 shows the propeller and the rotation axis.

FIGURE 7.30 A rotating airplane propeller.

The torque from the engine rotates the propeller.

$M = 40$ kg

$L = 2.0$ m

Axis

SOLVE The moment of inertia of a rod rotating about its center is found from Table 7.4:

$$I = \tfrac{1}{12}ML^2 = \tfrac{1}{12}(40 \text{ kg})(2.0 \text{ m})^2 = 13.3 \text{ kg} \cdot \text{m}^2$$

The 500 N · m torque of the engine causes an angular acceleration of

$$\alpha = \frac{\tau}{I} = \frac{500 \text{ N} \cdot \text{m}}{13.3 \text{ kg} \cdot \text{m}^2} = 37.5 \text{ rad/s}^2$$

The time needed to reach $\omega_f = 2000$ rpm $= 33.3$ rev/s $= 209$ rad/s is

$$\Delta t = \frac{\Delta \omega}{\alpha} = \frac{\omega_f - \omega_i}{\alpha} = \frac{209 \text{ rad/s} - 0 \text{ rad/s}}{37.5 \text{ rad/s}^2} = 5.6 \text{ s}$$

ASSESS We've assumed a constant angular acceleration, which is reasonable for the first few seconds while the propeller is still turning slowly. Eventually, air resistance and friction will cause opposing torques and the angular acceleration will decrease. At full speed, the negative torque due to air resistance and friction cancels the torque of the engine. Then $\tau_{net} = 0$ and the propeller turns at *constant* angular velocity with no angular acceleration.

EXAMPLE 7.12 **Angular acceleration of a falling pole**

A 7.0-m-tall telephone pole with a mass of 260 kg has just been placed in the ground. Before the wires can be connected, the pole is hit by lightning, nearly severing the pole at its base. The pole begins to fall, rotating about the part still connected to the base. Estimate the pole's angular acceleration when it has fallen by 25° from the vertical.

PREPARE The situation is shown in FIGURE 7.31, where we define our symbols and list the known information. Two forces are acting on the pole: the pole's weight $\vec{w}$, which acts at the center of gravity, and the force of the base on the pole (not shown).

FIGURE 7.31 A falling telephone pole undergoes an angular acceleration due to a gravitational torque.

Known
$L = 7.0$ m
$m = 260$ kg
$\theta = 25°$

Find: α

$w_\perp = w\sin\theta$

The torque on the pole is due only to its weight.

θ

$L/2$

$\vec{w}$

No torque due to the force that acts at axis

Rotation axis

This second force exerts no torque because it acts at the axis of rotation. The torque on the pole is thus due only to gravity. From the figure we see that this torque tends to rotate the pole in a counterclockwise direction, so the torque is positive.

SOLVE We'll model the pole as a uniform thin rod rotating about one end. Its center of gravity is at its center, a distance $L/2$ from the axis. You can see from the figure that the perpendicular component of $\vec{w}$ is $w_\perp = w\sin\theta$. Thus the torque due to gravity is

$$\tau_{net} = \left(\frac{L}{2}\right)w_\perp = \left(\frac{L}{2}\right)w\sin\theta = \frac{mgL}{2}\sin\theta$$

From Table 7.4, the moment of inertia of a thin rod rotated about its end is $I = \tfrac{1}{3}mL^2$. Thus, from Newton's second law for rotational motion, the angular acceleration is

$$\alpha = \frac{\tau_{net}}{I} = \frac{\tfrac{1}{2}mgL\sin\theta}{\tfrac{1}{3}mL^2} = \frac{3g\sin\theta}{2L}$$

$$= \frac{3(9.8 \text{ m/s}^2)\sin 25°}{2(7.0 \text{ m})} = 0.9 \text{ rad/s}^2$$

ASSESS The answer is given to only one significant figure because the problem asked for an *estimate* of the angular acceleration. This is usually a hint that you should make some simplifying assumptions, as we did here in modeling the pole as a thin rod.

Balancing a meter stick

You've probably tried balancing a rod-shaped object vertically on your fingertip. If the object is very long, like a meter stick or a baseball bat, it's not too hard. But if it's short, like a pencil, it's almost impossible. Why is this?

REASON Suppose you've managed to balance a vertical stick on your fingertip, but then it starts to fall. You'll need to quickly adjust your finger to bring the stick back into balance. As Example 7.12 showed, the angular acceleration α of a thin rod is *inversely proportional* to L. Thus a long object like a meter stick

topples much more slowly than a short one like a pencil. Your reaction time is fast enough to correct for a slowly falling meter stick but not for a rapidly falling pencil.

ASSESS If we double the length of a rod, its mass doubles and its center of gravity is twice as high, so the gravitational torque τ on it is four times as much. But because a rod's moment of inertia is $I = \frac{1}{3}ML^2$, the longer rod's moment of inertia will be *eight* times greater, so the angular acceleration will be only half as large.

Constraints Due to Ropes and Pulleys

Many important applications of rotational dynamics involve objects that are attached to ropes that pass over pulleys. FIGURE 7.32 shows a rope passing over a pulley and connected to an object in linear motion. If the pulley turns *without the rope slipping on it*, then the rope's speed v_{rope} must exactly match the speed of the rim of the pulley, which is $v_{\text{rim}} = \omega R$. If the pulley has an angular acceleration, the rope's acceleration a_{rope} must match the *tangential* acceleration of the rim of the pulley, $a_t = \alpha R$.

The object attached to the other end of the rope has the same speed and acceleration as the rope. Consequently, the object must obey the constraints

$$v_{\text{obj}} = \omega R$$
$$a_{\text{obj}} = \alpha R \qquad (7.16)$$

Motion constraints for an object connected to a pulley of radius R by a nonslipping rope

FIGURE 7.32 The rope's motion must match the motion of the rim of the pulley.

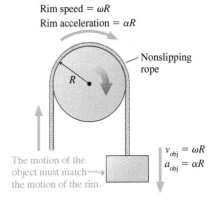

Rim speed $= \omega R$
Rim acceleration $= \alpha R$

Nonslipping rope

The motion of the object must match····▶ the motion of the rim.

$v_{\text{obj}} = \omega R$
$a_{\text{obj}} = \alpha R$

These constraints are similar to the acceleration constraints introduced in Chapter 5 for two objects connected by a string or rope.

NOTE ▶ The constraints are given as magnitudes. Specific problems will require you to specify signs that depend on the direction of motion and on the choice of coordinate system. ◀

EXAMPLE 7.14   **Time for a bucket to fall**

Josh has just raised a 2.5 kg bucket of water using a well's winch when he accidentally lets go of the handle. The winch consists of a rope wrapped around a 3.0 kg, 4.0-cm-diameter cylinder, which rotates on an axle through the center. The bucket is released from rest 4.0 m above the water level of the well. How long does it take to reach the water?

PREPARE Assume the rope is massless and does not slip. FIGURE 7.33a gives a visual overview of the falling bucket. FIGURE 7.33b shows the free-body diagrams for the cylinder and the bucket. The rope tension exerts an upward force on the bucket and a downward force on the outer edge of the cylinder. The rope is massless, so these two tension forces have equal magnitudes, which we'll call T.

FIGURE 7.33 Visual overview of a falling bucket.

(a)

$R = 2.0$ cm
$M = 3.0$ kg

Axle

$y_i = 4.0$ m
$v_i = 0$ m/s
$m = 2.5$ kg

$y_f = 0$ m

(b)

$\vec{n}$

Cylinder

$\vec{w}_c$
$\vec{T}_c$

$\vec{T}_b$

Bucket

$\vec{w}_b$

Continued

SOLVE Newton's second law applied to the linear motion of the bucket is

$$ma_y = T - mg$$

where, as usual, the y-axis points upward. What about the cylinder? There is a normal force $\vec{n}$ on the cylinder due to the axle and the weight of the cylinder $\vec{w}_c$. However, neither of these forces exerts a torque because each passes through the rotation axis. The only torque comes from the rope tension. The moment arm for the tension is $r_\perp = R$, and the torque is positive because the rope turns the cylinder counterclockwise. Thus $\tau_{\text{rope}} = TR$, and Newton's second law for the rotational motion is

$$\alpha = \frac{\tau_{\text{net}}}{I} = \frac{TR}{\frac{1}{2}MR^2} = \frac{2T}{MR}$$

The moment of inertia of a cylinder rotating about a center axis was taken from Table 7.4.

The last piece of information we need is the constraint due to the fact that the rope doesn't slip. Equation 7.16 relates only the magnitudes of the linear and angular accelerations, but in this problem α is positive (counterclockwise acceleration), while a_y is negative (downward acceleration). Hence

$$a_y = -\alpha R$$

Using α from the cylinder's equation in the constraint, we find

$$a_y = -\alpha R = -\frac{2T}{MR}R = -\frac{2T}{M}$$

Thus the tension is $T = -\frac{1}{2}Ma_y$. If we use this value of the tension in the bucket's equation, we can solve for the acceleration:

$$ma_y = -\tfrac{1}{2}Ma_y - mg$$

$$a_y = -\frac{g}{(1 + M/2m)} = -6.1 \text{ m/s}^2$$

The time to fall through $\Delta y = y_f - y_i = -4.0$ m is found from kinematics:

$$\Delta y = \tfrac{1}{2}a_y(\Delta t)^2$$

$$\Delta t = \sqrt{\frac{2\Delta y}{a_y}} = \sqrt{\frac{2(-4.0 \text{ m})}{-6.1 \text{ m/s}^2}} = 1.1 \text{ s}$$

ASSESS The expression for the acceleration gives $a_y = -g$ if $M = 0$. This makes sense because the bucket would be in free fall if there were no cylinder. When the cylinder has mass, the downward force of gravity on the bucket has to accelerate the bucket *and* spin the cylinder. Consequently, the acceleration is reduced and the bucket takes longer to fall.

7.6 Rolling Motion

FIGURE 7.34 The trajectories of the center of a wheel and of a point on the rim are seen in a time-exposure photograph.

Rolling is a *combination motion* in which an object rotates about an axis that is moving along a straight-line trajectory. For example, FIGURE 7.34 is a time-exposure photo of a rolling wheel with one lightbulb on the axis and a second lightbulb at the edge. The axis light moves straight ahead, but the edge light follows a curve called a *cycloid*. Let's see if we can understand this interesting motion. We'll consider only objects that roll without slipping.

To understand rolling motion, consider FIGURE 7.35, which shows a round object—a wheel or a sphere—that rolls forward, *without slipping*, exactly one revolution. The point initially at the bottom follows the blue curve to the top and then back to the bottom. The overall position of the object is measured by the position x of the object's center. Because the object doesn't slip, in one revolution the center moves forward exactly one circumference, so that $\Delta x = 2\pi R$. The time for the

FIGURE 7.35 An object rolling through one revolution.

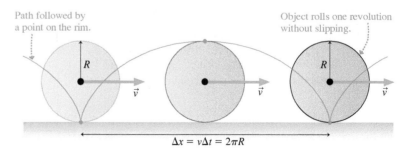

object to turn one revolution is its period T, so we can compute the speed of the object's center as

$$v = \frac{\Delta x}{T} = \frac{2\pi R}{T} \qquad (7.17)$$

But $2\pi/T$ is the angular velocity ω, as you learned in Chapter 6, which leads to

$$v = \omega R \qquad (7.18)$$

Equation 7.18 is the **rolling constraint,** the basic link between translation and rotation for objects that roll without slipping.

We can find the velocity for any point on a rolling object by adding the velocity of that point when the object is in pure translation, without rolling, to the velocity of the point when the object is in pure rotation, without translating. FIGURE 7.36 shows how the velocity vectors at the top, center, and bottom of a rotating wheel are found in this way.

Ancient movers The great stone *moai* of Easter Island were moved as far as 16 km from a quarry to their final positions. Archeologists believe that one possible method of moving these 14 ton statues was to place them on rollers. One disadvantage of this method is that the statues, placed on top of the rollers, move twice as fast as the rollers themselves. Thus rollers are continuously left behind and have to be carried back to the front and reinserted. Sadly, the indiscriminate cutting of trees for moving *moai* may have hastened the demise of this island civilization.

FIGURE 7.36 Rolling is a combination of translation and rotation.

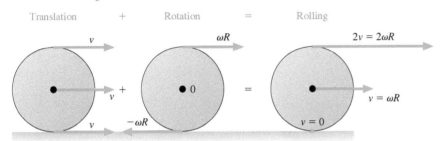

Thus the point at the top of the wheel has a forward speed of v due to its translational motion plus a forward speed of $\omega R = v$ due to its rotational motion. The speed of a point at the top of a wheel is then $2v = 2\omega R$, or *twice* the speed of its center of mass. On the other hand, the point at the bottom of the wheel, where it touches the ground, still has a forward speed of v due to its translational motion. But its velocity due to rotation points *backward* with a magnitude of $\omega R = v$. Adding these, we find that the velocity of this lowest point is *zero*. In other words, **the point on the bottom of a rolling object is instantaneously at rest.**

Although this seems surprising, it is really what we mean by "rolling without slipping." If the bottom point had a velocity, it would be moving horizontally relative to the surface. In other words, it would be slipping or sliding across the surface. To roll without slipping, the bottom point, the point touching the surface, must be at rest.

EXAMPLE 7.15 **Rotating your tires**

The diameter of your tires is 0.60 m. You take a 60 mile trip at a speed of 45 mph.

a. During this trip, what was your tires' angular speed?
b. How many times did they revolve?

PREPARE The angular speed is related to the speed of a wheel's center by Equation 7.18: $v = \omega R$. Because the center of the wheel turns on an axle fixed to the car, the speed v of the wheel's center is the same as that of the car. We prepare by converting the car's speed to SI units:

$$v = (45 \text{ mph}) \times \left(0.447 \, \frac{\text{m/s}}{\text{mph}} \right) = 20 \text{ m/s}$$

Once we know the angular speed, we can find the number of times the tires turned from the rotational-kinematic equation $\Delta\theta = \omega \, \Delta t$. We'll need to find the time traveled Δt from $v = \Delta x/\Delta t$.

SOLVE a. From Equation 7.18 we have

$$\omega = \frac{v}{R} = \frac{20 \text{ m/s}}{0.30 \text{ m}} = 67 \text{ rad/s}$$

b. The time of the trip is

$$\Delta t = \frac{\Delta x}{v} = \frac{60 \text{ mi}}{45 \text{ mi/h}} = 1.33 \text{ h} \times \frac{3600 \text{ s}}{1 \text{ h}} = 4800 \text{ s}$$

Continued

Thus the total angle through which the tires turn is

$$\Delta\theta = \omega\,\Delta t = (67\text{ rad/s})(4800\text{ s}) = 3.2 \times 10^5\text{ rad}$$

Because each turn of the wheel is 2π rad, the number of turns is

$$\frac{3.2 \times 10^5\text{ rad}}{2\pi\text{ rad}} = 51{,}000\text{ turns}$$

ASSESS You probably know from seeing tires on passing cars that a tire rotates several times a second at 45 mph. Because there are 3600 s in an hour, and your 60 mile trip at 45 mph is going to take over an hour—say, $\approx$5000 s—you would expect the tire to make many thousands of revolutions. So 51,000 turns seems to be a reasonable answer. You can see that your tires rotate roughly a thousand times per mile. During the lifetime of a tire, about 50,000 miles, it will rotate about 50 million times!

STOP TO THINK 7.6 A wheel rolls without slipping. Which is the correct velocity vector for point P on the wheel?

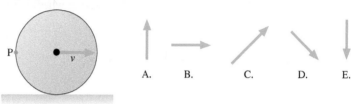

A.   B.   C.   D.   E.

INTEGRATED EXAMPLE 7.16   Spinning a gyroscope

A gyroscope is a top-like toy consisting of a heavy ring attached by light spokes to a central axle. The axle and ring are free to turn on bearings. To get the gyroscope spinning, a 30-cm-long string is wrapped around the 2.0-mm-diameter axle, then pulled with a constant force of 5.0 N. If the ring's diameter is 5.0 cm and its mass is 30 g, at what rate is it spinning, in rpm, once the string is completely unwound?

PREPARE Because the ring is heavy compared to the spokes and the axle, we'll model it as a cylindrical hoop, taking its moment of inertia from Table 7.4 to be $I = MR^2$. FIGURE 7.37 shows a visual overview of the problem. Two points are worth noting. First, rule 2 of Tactics Box 5.2 tells us that the tension in the string has the same magnitude as the force that pulls on the string, so the tension is $T = 5.0$ N. Second, it is a good idea to convert all the known quantities in the problem statement to SI units, and to collect them all in one place as we have done in the visual overview of Figure 7.37. Here, radius R is half the 5.0 cm ring diameter, and radius r is half the 2.0 mm axle diameter.

We are asked at what rate the ring is spinning when the string is unwound. This is a question about the ring's final *angular velocity*, which we've labeled ω_f. We've assumed that the initial angular velocity is $\omega_i = 0$ rad/s. Because the angular velocity is changing, the ring must have an angular acceleration that, as we know, is caused by a torque. So a good strategy will be to find the torque on the ring, from which we can find its angular acceleration and, using kinematics, the final angular velocity.

FIGURE 7.37 Visual overview of a gyroscope being spun.

String completely wound   String completely unwound

Known
$T = 5.0$ N
$L = 0.30$ m
$r = 0.0010$ m
$R = 0.025$ m
$M = 0.030$ kg
$\omega_i = 0$ rad/s

Find
ω_f

SOLVE The torque on the ring is due to the tension in the string. Because the string—and the line of action of the tension—is tangent to the axle, the moment arm of the tension force is the radius r of the axle. Thus $\tau = r_\perp T = rT$. Now we can apply Newton's second law for rotational motion, Equation 7.15, to find the angular acceleration:

$$\alpha = \frac{\tau_{net}}{I} = \frac{rT}{MR^2} = \frac{(0.0010 \text{ m})(5.0 \text{ N})}{(0.030 \text{ kg})(0.025 \text{ m})^2} = 267 \text{ rad/s}^2$$

We next use constant-angular-acceleration kinematics to find the final angular velocity. For the equation $\Delta\theta = \omega_i \Delta t + \frac{1}{2}\alpha \Delta t^2$ of Table 7.2, we know α and ω_i, and we should be able to find $\Delta\theta$ from the length of string unwound, but we don't know Δt. For the equation $\Delta\omega = \omega_f - \omega_i = \alpha \Delta t$, we know α and ω_i, and ω_f is what we want to find, but again we don't know Δt. To find an equation that doesn't contain Δt, we first write

$$\Delta t = \frac{\omega_f - \omega_i}{\alpha}$$

from the second kinematic equation. Inserting this value for Δt into the first equation gives

$$\Delta\theta = \omega_i \frac{\omega_f - \omega_i}{\alpha} + \frac{1}{2}\alpha\left(\frac{\omega_f - \omega_i}{\alpha}\right)^2$$

which can be simplified to

$$\omega_f^2 = \omega_i^2 + 2\alpha \Delta\theta$$

This equation, which is the rotational analog of the linear motion Equation 2.13, will allow us to find ω_f once $\Delta\theta$ is known.

FIGURE 7.38 shows how to find $\Delta\theta$. As a segment of string of length s unwinds, the axle turns through an angle (based on the

FIGURE 7.38 Relating the angle turned to the length of string unwound.

definition of radian measure) $\theta = s/r$. Thus as the whole string, of length L, unwinds, the axle (and the ring) turns through an angular displacement

$$\Delta\theta = \frac{L}{r} = \frac{0.30 \text{ m}}{0.0010 \text{ m}} = 300 \text{ rad}$$

Now we can use our kinematic equation to find that

$$\omega_f^2 = \omega_i^2 + 2\alpha\Delta\theta = (0 \text{ rad/s})^2 + 2(267 \text{ rad/s}^2)(300 \text{ rad})$$

$$= 160{,}000 \text{ (rad/s)}^2$$

from which we find that $\omega_f = 400 \text{ rad/s}$. Converting rad/s to rpm, we find that the gyroscope ring is spinning at

$$400 \text{ rad/s} = \left(\frac{400 \text{ rad}}{\text{s}}\right)\left(\frac{60 \text{ s}}{1 \text{ min}}\right)\left(\frac{1 \text{ rev}}{2\pi \text{ rad}}\right) = 3800 \text{ rpm}$$

ASSESS This is fast, about the speed of your car engine when its on the highway, but if you've ever played with a gyroscope or a string-wound top, you know you can really get it spinning fast.

SUMMARY

The goal of Chapter 7 has been to understand the physics of rotating objects.

GENERAL PRINCIPLES

Newton's Second Law for Rotational Motion

If a net torque τ_{net} acts on an object, the object will experience an angular acceleration given by $\alpha = \tau_{net}/I$, where I is the object's moment of inertia about the rotation axis.

This law is analogous to Newton's second law for linear motion, $\vec{a} = \vec{F}_{net}/m$.

IMPORTANT CONCEPTS

Torque is the rotational analog of force. Just as a force causes an object to undergo a linear acceleration, a torque causes an object to undergo an angular acceleration.

There are two interpretations of torque:

Interpretation 1: $\tau = rF_\perp$ Interpretation 2: $\tau = r_\perp F$

The component of $\vec{F}$ that is *perpendicular* to the radial line causes a torque.

$F_\perp = F \sin\phi$

The moment arm $r_\perp$ extends from the pivot to the line of action.

$r_\perp = r \sin\phi$

Pivot

Both interpretations give the same expression for the magnitude of the torque: $\tau = rF\sin\phi$.

A torque is positive if it tends to rotate the object counterclockwise; negative if it tends to rotate the object clockwise.

The moment of inertia is the rotational equivalent of mass. The larger an object's moment of inertia, the more difficult it is to get the object rotating. For an object made up of particles of masses $m_1, m_2, \ldots$ at distances $r_1, r_2, \ldots$ from the axis, the moment of inertia is

$$I = m_1 r_1^2 + m_2 r_2^2 + m_3 r_3^2 + \cdots = \sum mr^2$$

Angular and tangential acceleration

A particle moving in a circle has

- A velocity tangent to the circle.
- A centripetal acceleration $\vec{a}_c$ directed toward the center of the circle.

Centripetal acceleration   Angular velocity

$\vec{a}_t$ $\vec{a}_c$

Tangential acceleration

Velocity

If the particle's speed is increasing, it will also have

- A tangential acceleration $\vec{a}_t$ directed tangent to the circle.
- An angular acceleration α.

The angular and tangential accelerations are related by $a_t = \alpha r$.

For a **rigid body,** the angular velocity and angular acceleration are the same for every point on the object.

Center of gravity

The **center of gravity** of an object is the point at which gravity can be considered as acting.

Gravity acts on each particle that makes up the object.

The object responds *as if* its entire weight acts at the center of gravity.

$\vec{w}$

The **position of the center of gravity** depends on the distance $x_1, x_2, \ldots$ of each particle of mass $m_1, m_2, \ldots$ from the origin:

$$x_{cg} = \frac{x_1 m_1 + x_2 m_2 + x_3 m_3 + \cdots}{m_1 + m_2 + m_3 + \cdots}$$

APPLICATIONS

Moments of inertia of common shapes

MR^2

$\frac{1}{2}MR^2$

$\frac{2}{5}MR^2$

$\frac{1}{3}ML^2$

$\frac{2}{3}MR^2$

$\frac{1}{12}ML^2$

Rotation about a fixed axis

When a net torque is applied to an object that rotates about a fixed axis, the object will undergo an **angular acceleration** given by

$$\alpha = \frac{\tau_{net}}{I}$$

If a rope unwinds from a pulley of radius R, the linear motion of an object tied to the rope is related to the angular motion of the pulley by

$$a_{obj} = \alpha R \qquad v_{obj} = \omega R$$

Rolling motion

For an object that rolls without slipping,

$$v = \omega R$$

The velocity of a point at the top of the object is twice that of the center.

$2\vec{v}$

$\vec{v}$

Problem difficulty is labeled as | (straightforward) to |||| (challenging). Problems labeled INT integrate significant material from earlier chapters; BIO are of biological or medical interest.

 For homework assigned on MasteringPhysics, go to www.masteringphysics.com

 Scan this QR code to launch a **Video Tutor Solution** that will help you solve problems for this chapter.

QUESTIONS

Conceptual Questions

1. Figure Q7.1 shows four pulleys, each with a heavy and a light block strung over them. The blocks' velocities are shown. What are the signs (+ or −) of the angular velocity and angular acceleration of the pulley in each case?

(a)   (b)   (c)   (d)

FIGURE Q7.1

2. If you are using a wrench to loosen a very stubborn nut, you can make the job easier by using a "cheater pipe." This is a piece of pipe that slides over the handle of the wrench, as shown in Figure Q7.2, making it effectively much longer. Explain why this would help you loosen the nut.

FIGURE Q7.2

3. Five forces are applied to a door, as seen from above in Figure Q7.3. For each force, is the torque about the hinge positive, negative, or zero?

FIGURE Q7.3

4. A screwdriver with a very thick handle requires less force to operate than one with a very skinny handle. Explain why this is so.

5. If you have ever driven a truck, you likely found that it had a steering wheel with a larger diameter than that of a passenger car. Why is this?

6. A common type of door stop is a wedge made of rubber. Is such a stop more effective when jammed under the door near or far from the hinges? Why?

7. Suppose you are hanging from a tree branch. If you move out along the branch, farther away from the trunk, the branch will be more likely to break. Explain why this is so.

8. A student gives a quick push to a ball at the end of a massless, rigid rod, causing the ball to rotate clockwise in a *horizontal* circle as shown in Figure Q7.8. The rod's pivot is frictionless.

   a. As the student is pushing, is the torque about the pivot positive, negative, or zero?
   b. After the push has ended, what does the ball's angular velocity do? Steadily increase? Increase for a while, then hold steady? Hold steady? Decrease for a while, then hold steady? Steadily decrease? Explain.

FIGURE Q7.8

   c. Right after the push has ended, is the torque positive, negative, or zero?

9. The two ends of the dumbbell shown in Figure Q7.9 are made of the same material. Is the dumbbell's center of gravity at point 1, 2, or 3? Explain.

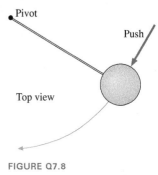

FIGURE Q7.9

10. When you rise from a chair, you have to lean quite far forward (try it!). Why is this?

11. Suppose you have two identical-looking metal spheres of the same size and the same mass. One of them is solid, the other is hollow. How can you tell which is which?

12. The moment of inertia of a uniform rod about an axis through its center is $ML^2/12$. The moment of inertia about an axis at one end is $ML^2/3$. Explain *why* the moment of inertia is larger about the end than about the center.

13. A heavy steel rod, 1.0 m long, and a light pencil, 0.15 m long, are held 15° from the vertical with one end on a table, then released simultaneously. Which will hit the table first? Or will it be a tie? Explain.

14. The wheel in Figure Q7.14 is rolling to the right without slipping. Rank in order, from fastest to slowest, the *speeds* of the points labeled 1 through 5. Explain your reasoning.

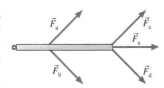

FIGURE Q7.14

15. A car traveling at 60 mph has a pebble stuck in one of its tires. Eventually the pebble works loose, and at the instant of release it is at the top of the tire. Explain why the pebble then slams *hard* into the *front* of the wheel well.

Multiple-Choice Questions

16. | A nut needs to be tightened with a wrench. Which force shown in Figure Q7.16 will apply the greatest torque to the nut?

FIGURE Q7.16

17. | Suppose a bolt on your car engine needs to be tightened to a torque of 20 N · m. You are using a 15-cm-long wrench, and you apply a force at the very end in the direction that produces maximum torque. What force should you apply?
A. 1300 N   B. 260 N   C. 130 N   D. 26 N

18. | A machine part is made up of two pieces, with centers of gravity shown in Figure Q7.18. Which point could be the center of gravity of the entire part?

19. ||| A typical compact disk has a mass of 15 g and a diameter of 120 mm. What is

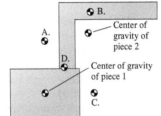

FIGURE Q7.18

its moment of inertia about an axis through its center, perpendicular to the disk?
A. 2.7×10^{-5} kg · m^2 B. 5.4×10^{-5} kg · m^2
C. 1.1×10^{-4} kg · m^2 D. 2.2×10^{-4} kg · m^2

20. ||| Suppose you make a new kind of compact disk that is the same thickness as a current disk but twice the diameter. By what factor will the moment of inertia increase?
A. 2   B. 4   C. 8   D. 16

21. | Doors 1 and 2 have the same mass, height, and thickness. Door 2 is twice as wide as door 1. Bob pushes straight against the outer edge of door 2 with force F, and Barb pushes straight against the outer edge of door 1 with force $2F$. How do the angular accelerations α_1 and α_2 of the two doors compare?
A. $\alpha_1 > \alpha_2$ B. $\alpha_1 = \alpha_2$ C. $\alpha_1 < \alpha_2$

22. | A baseball bat has a heavy barrel and a thin handle. If you want to hold a baseball bat on your palm so that it balances vertically, you should
A. Put the end of the handle in your palm, with the barrel up.
B. Put the end of the barrel in your palm, with the handle up.
C. The bat will be equally easy to balance in either configuration.

23. | A car traveling at a steady 30 m/s has 74-cm-diameter tires. What is the approximate acceleration of a piece of the tread on any of the tires?
A. 24 m/s^2 B. 48 m/s^2 C. 2400 m/s^2 D. 4800 m/s^2

PROBLEMS

Section 7.1 The Rotation of a Rigid Body

1. ||| To throw a discus, the thrower holds it with a fully outstretched arm. Starting from rest, he begins to turn with a constant angular acceleration, releasing the discus after making one complete revolution. The diameter of the circle in which the discus moves is about 1.8 m. If the thrower takes 1.0 s to complete one revolution, starting from rest, what will be the speed of the discus at release?

2. ||| A computer hard disk starts from rest, then speeds up with an angular acceleration of 190 rad/s^2 until it reaches its final angular speed of 7200 rpm. How many revolutions has the disk made 10.0 s after it starts up?

3. ||| The crankshaft in a race car goes from rest to 3000 rpm in 2.0 s.
   a. What is the crankshaft's angular acceleration?
   b. How many revolutions does it make while reaching 3000 rpm?

Section 7.2 Torque

4. | Reconsider the situation in Example 7.5. If Luis pulls straight down on the end of a wrench that is in the same orientation but is 35 cm long, rather than 20 cm, what force must he apply to exert the same torque?

5. ||| Balls are attached to light rods and can move in horizontal circles as shown in Figure P7.5. Rank in order, from smallest to

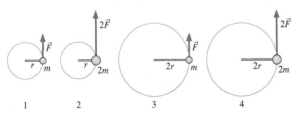

FIGURE P7.5

largest, the torques τ_1 to τ_4 about the centers of the circles. Explain.

6. ||| Six forces, each of magnitude either F or $2F$, are applied to a door as seen from above in Figure P7.6. Rank in order, from smallest to largest, the six torques τ_1 to τ_6 about the hinge.

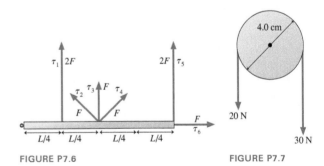

FIGURE P7.6   FIGURE P7.7

7. | What is the net torque about the axle on the pulley in Figure P7.7?

8. ||| The tune-up specifications of a car call for the spark plugs to be tightened to a torque of 38 N · m. You plan to tighten the plugs by pulling on the end of a 25-cm-long wrench. Because of the cramped space under the hood, you'll need to pull at an angle of 120° with respect to the wrench shaft. With what force must you pull?

9. ||| A professor's office door is 0.91 m wide, 2.0 m high, and 4.0 cm thick; has a mass of 25 kg; and pivots on frictionless hinges. A "door closer" is attached to the door and the top of the door frame. When the door is open and at rest, the door closer exerts a torque of 5.2 N · m. What is the least force that you need to apply to the door to hold it open?

10. || In Figure P7.10, force $\vec{F}_2$ acts half as far from the pivot as $\vec{F}_1$. What magnitude of $\vec{F}_2$ causes the net torque on the rod to be zero?

FIGURE P7.10

11. ||| Tom and Jerry both push on the 3.00-m-diameter merry-go-round shown in Figure P7.11.
   a. If Tom pushes with a force of 40.0 N and Jerry pushes with a force of 35.2 N, what is the net torque on the merry-go-round?
   b. What is the net torque if Jerry reverses the direction he pushes by 180° without changing the magnitude of his force?

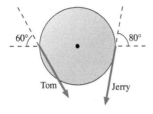

FIGURE P7.11

12. || What is the net torque of the bar shown in Figure P7.12, about the axis indicated by the dot?

FIGURE P7.12   FIGURE P7.13

13. || What is the net torque of the bar shown in Figure P7.13, about the axis indicated by the dot?

14. || What is the net torque of the bar shown in Figure P7.14, about the axis indicated by the dot?

FIGURE P7.14

15. || A 1.7-m-long barbell has a 20 kg weight on its left end and a 35 kg weight on its right end.
   a. If you ignore the weight of the bar itself, how far from the left end of the barbell is the center of gravity?
   b. Where is the center of gravity if the 8.0 kg mass of the barbell itself is taken into account?

Section 7.3 Gravitational Torque and the Center of Gravity

16. || Three identical coins lie on three corners of a square 10.0 cm on a side, as shown in Figure P7.16. Determine the x and y coordinates of the center of gravity of the three coins.

17. | Hold your arm outstretched so that it is horizontal. Estimate the mass of your arm and the position of its center of gravity. What is the gravitational torque on your arm in this position, computed around the shoulder joint?

BIO

FIGURE P7.16

18. ||| A solid cylinder sits on top of a solid cube as shown in Figure P7.18. How far above the table's surface is the center of gravity of the combined object?

FIGURE P7.18   FIGURE P7.19

19. || The 2.0 kg, uniform, horizontal rod in Figure P7.19 is seen from the side. What is the gravitational torque about the point shown?

20. ||| A 4.00-m-long, 500 kg steel beam extends horizontally from the point where it has been bolted to the framework of a new building under construction. A 70.0 kg construction worker stands at the far end of the beam. What is the magnitude of the torque about the point where the beam is bolted into place?

21. ||| An athlete at the gym holds a 3.0 kg steel ball in his hand. His arm is 70 cm long and has a mass of 4.0 kg. What is the magnitude of the torque about his shoulder if he holds his arm
BIO
   a. Straight out to his side, parallel to the floor?
   b. Straight, but 45° below horizontal?

22. ||| The 2.0-m-long, 15 kg beam in Figure P7.22 is hinged at its left end. It is "falling" (rotating clockwise, under the influence of gravity), and the figure shows its position at three different times. What is the gravitational torque on the beam about an axis through the hinged end when the beam is at the
   a. Upper position?
   b. Middle position?
   c. Lower position?

FIGURE P7.22

23. ||| Two thin beams are joined end-to-end as shown in Figure P7.23 to make a single object. The left beam is 10.0 kg and 1.00 m long and the right one is 40.0 kg and 2.00 m long.
   a. How far from the left end of the left beam is the center of gravity of the object?
   b. What is the gravitational torque on the object about an axis through its left end? The object is seen from the side.

FIGURE P7.23

24. ||| Figure P7.24 shows two thin beams joined at right angles. The vertical beam is 15.0 kg and 1.00 m long and the horizontal beam is 25.0 kg and 2.00 m long.
   a. Find the center of gravity of the two joined beams. Express your answer in the form (x, y), taking the origin at the corner where the beams join.
   b. Calculate the gravitational torque on the joined beams about an axis through the corner. The beams are seen from the side.

FIGURE P7.24

Section 7.4 Rotational Dynamics and Moment of Inertia

25. ‖ A regulation table tennis ball has a mass of 2.7 g and is 40 mm in diameter. What is its moment of inertia about an axis that passes through its center?

26. ‖ Three pairs of balls are connected by very light rods as shown in Figure P7.26. Rank in order, from smallest to largest, the moments of inertia I_1, I_2, and I_3 about axes through the centers of the rods.

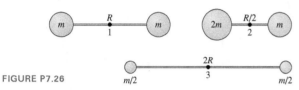

FIGURE P7.26

27. ‖ A playground toy has four seats, each 5.0 kg, attached to very light, 1.5-m-long rods, as seen from above in Figure P7.27. If two children, with masses of 15 kg and 20 kg, sit in seats opposite one another, what is the moment of inertia about the rotation axis?

FIGURE P7.27

28. ‖‖ A solid cylinder with a radius of 4.0 cm has the same mass as a solid sphere of radius R. If the cylinder and sphere have the same moment of inertia about their centers, what is the sphere's radius?

29. ‖ A bicycle rim has a diameter of 0.65 m and a moment of inertia, measured about its center, of 0.19 kg·m². What is the mass of the rim?

Section 7.5 Using Newton's Second Law for Rotation

30. ‖ The left part of Figure P7.30 shows a bird's-eye view of two identical balls connected by a light rod that rotates about a vertical axis through its center. The right part shows a ball of twice the mass connected to a light rod of half the length, that rotates about its left end. If equal forces are applied as shown in the figure, which of the two rods will have the greater angular acceleration?

FIGURE P7.30

31. ‖‖ a. What is the moment of inertia of the door in Problem 9?
    b. If you let go of the open door, what is its angular acceleration immediately afterward?

32. ‖ A small grinding wheel has a moment of inertia of 4.0×10^{-5} kg·m². What net torque must be applied to the wheel for its angular acceleration to be 150 rad/s²?

33. ‖ While sitting in a swivel chair, you push against the floor with your heel to make the chair spin. The 7.0 N frictional force is applied at a point 40 cm from the chair's rotation axis, in the direction that causes the greatest angular acceleration. If that angular acceleration is 1.8 rad/s², what is the total moment of inertia about the axis of you and the chair?

34. ‖ An object's moment of inertia is 2.0 kg·m². Its angular velocity is increasing at the rate of 4.0 rad/s per second. What is the net torque on the object?

35. ‖‖ A 200 g, 20-cm-diameter plastic disk is spun on an axle through its center by an electric motor. What torque must the motor supply to take the disk from 0 to 1800 rpm in 4.0 s?

36. ‖‖ The 2.5 kg object shown in Figure P7.36 has a moment of inertia about the rotation axis of 0.085 kg·m². The rotation axis is horizontal. When released, what will be the object's initial angular acceleration?

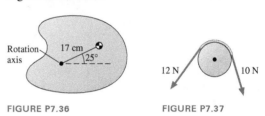

FIGURE P7.36   FIGURE P7.37

37. ‖‖ A frictionless pulley, which can be modeled as a 0.80 kg solid cylinder with a 0.30 m radius, has a rope going over it, as shown in Figure P7.37. The tension in the rope is 10 N on one side and 12 N on the other. What is the angular acceleration of the pulley?

38. ‖‖ If you lift the front wheel of a poorly maintained bicycle off the ground and then start it spinning at 0.72 rev/s, friction in the bearings causes the wheel to stop in just 12 s. If the moment of inertia of the wheel about its axle is 0.30 kg·m², what is the magnitude of the frictional torque?

39. ‖‖ A toy top with a spool of diameter 5.0 cm has a moment of inertia of 3.0×10^{-5} kg·m² about its rotation axis. To get the top spinning, its string is pulled with a tension of 0.30 N. How long does it take for the top to complete the first five revolutions? The string is long enough that it is wrapped around the top more than five turns.

40. ‖‖ A 34-cm-diameter potter's wheel with a mass of 20 kg is spinning at 180 rpm. Using her hands, a potter forms a pot, centered on the wheel, with a 14 cm diameter. Her hands apply a net friction force of 1.3 N to the edge of the pot. If the power goes out, so that the wheel's motor no longer provides any torque, how long will it take for the wheel to come to a stop in her hands?

41. ‖‖ A 1.5 kg block and a 2.5 kg block are attached to opposite ends of a light rope. The rope hangs over a solid, frictionless pulley that is 30 cm in diameter and has a mass of 0.75 kg. When the blocks are released, what is the acceleration of the lighter block?

Section 7.6 Rolling Motion

42. ‖‖ A bicycle with 0.80-m-diameter tires is coasting on a level road at 5.6 m/s. A small blue dot has been painted on the tread of the rear tire.
    a. What is the angular speed of the tires?
    b. What is the speed of the blue dot when it is 0.80 m above the road?
    c. What is the speed of the blue dot when it is 0.40 m above the road?

43. ‖‖ A 1.2 g pebble is stuck in a tread of a 0.76-m-diameter automobile tire, held in place by static friction that can be at most 3.6 N. The car starts from rest and gradually accelerates on a straight road. How fast is the car moving when the pebble flies out of the tire tread?

General Problems

44. | Figure P7.44 shows the angular position-versus-time graph
INT for a particle moving in a circle.
a. Write a description of the particle's motion.
b. Draw the angular velocity-versus-time graph.

FIGURE P7.44   FIGURE P7.45

45. | The graph in Figure P7.45 shows the angular velocity of the
INT crankshaft in a car. Draw a graph of the angular acceleration
versus time. Include appropriate numerical scales on both axes.

46. ⅲ A computer disk is 8.0 cm in diameter. A reference dot on the
edge of the disk is initially located at $\theta = 45°$. The disk accelerates steadily for 0.50 s, reaching 2000 rpm, then coasts at steady
angular velocity for another 0.50 s.
a. What is the tangential acceleration of the reference dot at
$t = 0.25$ s?
b. What is the centripetal acceleration of the reference dot at
$t = 0.25$ s?
c. What is the angular position of the reference dot at $t = 1.0$ s?
d. What is the speed of the reference dot at $t = 1.0$ s?

47. ⅱ A car with 58-cm-diameter tires accelerates uniformly from
INT rest to 20 m/s in 10 s. How many times does each tire rotate?

48. ⅱ The cable lifting an elevator is wrapped around a 1.0-m-
diameter cylinder that is turned by the elevator's motor. The
elevator is moving upward at a speed of 1.6 m/s. It then slows to
a stop, while the cylinder turns one complete revolution. How
long does it take for the elevator to stop?

49. ⅲ The 20-cm-diameter disk
in Figure P7.49 can rotate on
an axle through its center.
What is the net torque about
the axle?

50. ⅲ A combination lock has a
INT 1.0-cm-diameter knob that is
part of the dial you turn to
unlock the lock. To turn that
knob, you grip it between
your thumb and forefinger
with a force of 0.60 N as you
twist your wrist. Suppose the
coefficient of static friction between the knob and your fingers
is only 0.12 because some oil accidentally got onto the knob.
What is the most torque you can exert on the knob without having it slip between your fingers?

51. ⅲⅲ A 70 kg man's arm, including the hand, can be modeled as a
BIO 75-cm-long uniform cylinder with a mass of 3.5 kg. In raising
both his arms, from hanging down to straight up, by how much
does he raise his center of gravity?

52. ⅲ A penny has a mass of 2.5 g and is 1.5 mm thick; a nickel has a
mass of 5.7 g and is 1.9 mm thick. If you make a stack of coins on
a table, starting with five nickels and finishing with four pennies,
how far above the tabletop is the center of gravity of the stack?

FIGURE P7.49

53. ⅲⅲ The machinist's
square shown in
Figure P7.53 consists
of a thin, rectangular
blade connected to a
rectangular handle.
a. Determine the x
and y coordinates
of the center of
gravity. Let the lower left corner be $x = 0, y = 0$.
b. Sketch how the tool would hang if it were allowed to freely
pivot about the point $x = 0, y = 0$.
c. When hanging from that point, what angle would the long
side of the blade make with the vertical?

FIGURE P7.53

54. ⅲⅲ The four masses shown in
Figure P7.54 are connected by
massless, rigid rods.
a. Find the coordinates of the
center of gravity.
b. Find the moment of inertia
about an axis that passes
through mass A and is perpendicular to the page.
c. Find the moment of inertia
about a diagonal axis that
passes through masses B
and D.

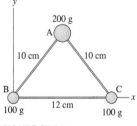

FIGURE P7.54

55. ⅲⅲ Three 0.10 kg balls are connected by light rods to form an
equilateral triangle with a side length of 0.30 m. What is the
moment of inertia of this triangle about an axis perpendicular to
its plane and passing through one of the balls?

56. ⅲⅲ The three masses shown in
Figure P7.56 are connected by
massless, rigid rods.
a. Find the coordinates of the
center of gravity.
b. Find the moment of inertia
about an axis that passes
through mass A and is perpendicular to the page.
c. Find the moment of inertia
about an axis that passes
through masses B and C.

FIGURE P7.56

57. ⅱ A reasonable estimate of the moment of inertia of an ice
BIO skater spinning with her arms at her sides can be made by modeling most of her body as a uniform cylinder. Suppose the
skater has a mass of 64 kg. One-eighth of that mass is in her
arms, which are 60 cm long and 20 cm from the vertical axis
about which she rotates. The rest of her mass is approximately
in the form of a 20-cm-radius cylinder.
a. Estimate the skater's moment of inertia to two significant
figures.
b. If she were to hold her arms outward, rather than at her
sides, would her moment of inertia increase, decrease, or
remain unchanged? Explain.

58. ⅱ Starting from rest, a 12-cm-diameter compact disk takes 3.0 s
to reach its operating angular velocity of 2000 rpm. Assume
that the angular acceleration is constant. The disk's moment of
inertia is 2.5×10^{-5} kg·m².
a. How much torque is applied to the disk?
b. How many revolutions does it make before reaching full speed?

59. ⫼ The ropes in Figure P7.59 are each wrapped around a cylinder, and the two cylinders are fastened together. The smaller cylinder has a diameter of 10 cm and a mass of 5.0 kg; the larger cylinder has a diameter of 20 cm and a mass of 20 kg. What is the angular acceleration of the cylinders? Assume that the cylinders turn on a frictionless axle.

FIGURE P7.59

60. ⫼ Flywheels are large, massive wheels used to store energy. They can be spun up slowly, then the wheel's energy can be released quickly to accomplish a task that demands high power. An industrial flywheel has a 1.5 m diameter and a mass of 250 kg. A motor spins up the flywheel with a constant torque of 50 N · m. How long does it take the flywheel to reach top angular speed of 1200 rpm?

61. ⫼ A 1.0 kg ball and a 2.0 kg ball are connected by a 1.0-m-long rigid, massless rod. The rod and balls are rotating clockwise about their center of gravity at 20 rpm. What torque will bring the balls to a halt in 5.0 s?

62. ⫼ A 1.5 kg block is connected by a rope across a 50-cm-diameter, 2.0 kg, frictionless pulley, as shown in Figure P7.62. A constant 10 N tension is applied to the other end of the rope. Starting from rest, how long does it take the block to move 30 cm?

10 N

1.5 kg

FIGURE P7.62

63. ⫼ The two blocks in Figure P7.63 are connected by a massless rope that passes over a pulley. The pulley is 12 cm in diameter and has a mass of 2.0 kg. As the pulley turns, friction at the axle exerts a torque of magnitude 0.50 N · m. If the blocks are released from rest, how long does it take the 4.0 kg block to reach the floor?

FIGURE P7.63   FIGURE P7.64

64. ⫼ The 2.0 kg, 30-cm-diameter disk in Figure P7.64 is spinning at 300 rpm. How much friction force must the brake apply to the rim to bring the disk to a halt in 3.0 s?

65. ⫼ A tradesman sharpens a knife by pushing it against the rim of a grindstone. The 30-cm-diameter stone is spinning at 200 rpm and has a mass of 28 kg. The coefficient of kinetic friction between the knife and the stone is 0.20. If the stone loses 10% of its speed in 10 s of grinding, what is the force with which the man presses the knife against the stone?

66. ⫼ The bunchberry flower has the fastest-moving parts ever BIO seen in a plant. Initially, the stamens are held by the petals in a bent position, storing elastic energy like a coiled spring. As the petals release, the tips of the stamens act like medieval catapults, flipping through a 60° angle in just 0.30 ms to launch pollen from the anther sacs at their ends. The human eye just sees a burst of pollen; careful photography (see Figure P7.66a) reveals the details. As shown in Figure P7.66b, we can model a stamen tip as a 1.0-mm-long, 10 μg rigid rod with a 10 μg anther sac at one end and a pivot point at the opposite end. Although oversimplifying, we will assume that the angular acceleration is constant throughout the motion.

FIGURE P7.66

a. What is the tangential acceleration of the anther sac during the motion?
b. What is the speed of the anther sac as it releases its pollen?
c. How large is the "straightening torque"? Neglect gravitational forces in your calculation.
d. Compute the gravitational torque on the stamen tip (including the anther sac) in its initial orientation. Was it reasonable to neglect the gravitational torque in part c?

Passage Problems

The Illusion of Flight

The grand jeté is a classic ballet maneuver in which a dancer executes a horizontal leap while moving her arms and legs up and then down. At the center of the leap, the arms and legs are gracefully extended, as we see in Figure P7.67a. The goal of the leap is to create the illusion of flight. As discussed in Section 7.3, the center of mass—and hence the center of gravity—of an extended object follows a parabolic trajectory when undergoing projectile motion. But when you watch a dancer leap through the air, you don't watch her center of gravity, you watch her head. If the translational motion of her head is horizontal—not parabolic—this creates the illusion that she is flying through the air, held up by unseen forces.

FIGURE P7.67

Figure P7.67b illustrates how the dancer creates this illusion. While in the air, she changes the position of her center of gravity relative to her body by moving her arms and legs up, then down. Her center of gravity moves in a parabolic path, but her head moves in a straight line. It's not flight, but it will appear that way, at least for a moment.

67. | To perform this maneuver, the dancer relies on the fact that the position of her center of gravity
    A. Is near the center of the torso.
    B. Is determined by the positions of her arms and legs.
    C. Moves in a horizontal path.
    D. Is outside of her body.

68. | Suppose you wish to make a vertical leap with the goal of getting your head as high as possible above the ground. At the top of your leap, your arms should be
    A. Held at your sides.
    B. Raised above your head.
    C. Outstretched, away from your body.

69. | When the dancer is in the air, is there a gravitational torque on her? Take the dancer's rotation axis to be through her center of gravity.
    A. Yes, there is a gravitational torque.
    B. No, there is not a gravitational torque.
    C. It depends on the positions of her arms and legs.

70. | In addition to changing her center of gravity, a dancer may change her moment of inertia. Consider her moment of inertia about a vertical axis through the center of her body. When she raises her arms and legs, this
    A. Increases her moment of inertia.
    B. Decreases her moment of inertia.
    C. Does not change her moment of inertia.

STOP TO THINK ANSWERS

Stop to Think 7.1: a. constant (but not zero), b. constant (but not zero), c. constant (but not zero), d. zero, e. zero. The angular velocity ω is constant. Thus the magnitude of the velocity $v = \omega r$ and the centripetal acceleration $a_c = \omega^2 r$ are constant. This also means that the ball's angular acceleration α and tangential acceleration $a_t = \alpha r$ are both zero.

Stop to Think 7.2: $\tau_E > \tau_A = \tau_D > \tau_B > \tau_C$. The perpendicular component in E is larger than 2 N.

Stop to Think 7.3: A. The force acting at the axis exerts no torque. Thus the third force needs to exert an equal but opposite torque to that exerted by the force acting at the rim. Force A, which

has twice the magnitude but acts at half the distance from the axis, does so.

Stop to Think 7.4: $\tau_E = \tau_B > \tau_D > \tau_A = \tau_C$. The torques are $\tau_B = \tau_E = 2mgL$, $\tau_D = \frac{3}{2}mgL$, and $\tau_A = \tau_C = mgL$, where L is the length of the rod in B.

Stop to Think 7.5: $I_D > I_A > I_C > I_B$. The moments of inertia are $I_B \approx 0$, $I_C = 2mr^2$, $I_A = 3mr^2$, and $I_D = mr^2 + m(2r)^2 = 5mr^2$.

Stop to Think 7.6: C. The velocity of P is the vector sum of $\vec{v}$ directed to the right and an upward velocity of the same magnitude due to the rotation of the wheel.

8 Equilibrium and Elasticity

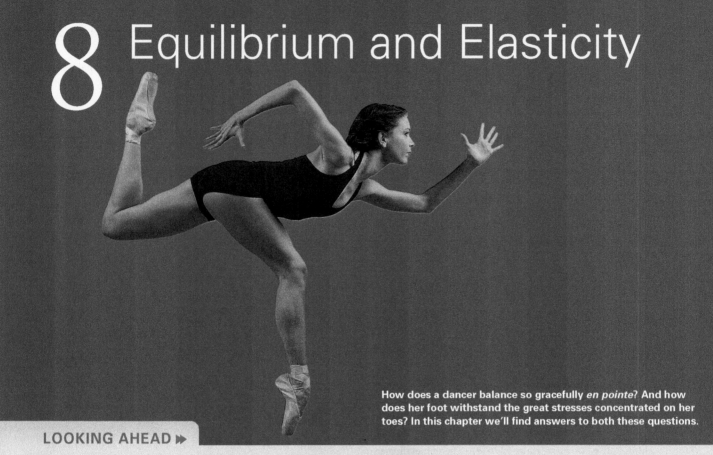

How does a dancer balance so gracefully *en pointe*? And how does her foot withstand the great stresses concentrated on her toes? In this chapter we'll find answers to both these questions.

LOOKING AHEAD ▶

The goals of Chapter 8 are to learn about the static equilibrium of extended objects and to understand the basic properties of springs and elastic materials.

Torque and Static Equilibrium

In Chapter 5 we found that a particle can be in static equilibrium only if the net force acting on it is zero. For an extended object such as the dancer shown above, we'll learn that the net torque on the object must also be zero for it to be in equilibrium.

For this cyclist and his bike to stand motionless, the net force *and* net torque on them must be zero.

Looking Back ◀◀
5.1 Equilibrium

Springs

We'll study springs and similar elastic objects, and we'll find the important result that the spring force is proportional to the distance the spring is stretched or compressed from its natural length.

You can get a better workout by stretching the band farther, because the farther it stretches, the harder it is to pull.

Looking Back ◀◀
4.3 Spring forces

Stability and Balance

Why are some objects more *stable* than others; that is, why are some easy to tip over while others are more solidly planted? We'll learn that an object is more stable when its center of gravity is low and its contact points with the ground are widely separated.

For maximal stability, this football player keeps his center of gravity low and his stance wide.

The girls on this tree trunk have a hard time balancing because of their tall stance and narrow footprint.

Looking Back ◀◀
7.2–7.3 Torque, center of gravity, gravitational torque

Elastic Materials

All materials, even seemingly rigid ones like glass or steel, stretch slightly when you pull on them—they act like very stiff springs. We'll learn how to calculate the amount a solid object stretches or compresses as forces are applied to it.

Each of the steel cables suspending this bridge is 24" in diameter, yet the designers must carefully compensate for the slight stretch in each cable due to the enormous load of the bridge.

Biological Materials

The elastic properties of biological materials such as bone, tendon, and even spider silk play an important role in the world of living things. Bone, of course, is quite rigid, but did you know that spider silk is as strong as steel?

8.1 Torque and Static Equilibrium

We have now spent several chapters studying motion and its causes. In many disciplines, it is just as important to understand the conditions under which objects do *not* move. In structural engineering, buildings and dams must be designed such that they remain motionless, even when huge forces act on them. In sports science, a correct stationary position is often the starting point for a successful athletic event. And joints in the body must sustain large forces when the body is supporting heavy loads, as in holding or carrying heavy objects.

Recall from Section 5.1 that an object at rest is in *static equilibrium*. As long as an object can be modeled as a *particle,* the condition necessary for static equilibrium is that the net force $\vec{F}_{net}$ on the particle is zero. Such a situation is shown in FIGURE 8.1a, where the two forces applied to the particle balance and the particle can remain at rest.

But in Chapter 7 we moved beyond the particle model to study extended objects that can rotate. Consider, for example, the block in FIGURE 8.1b. In this case the two forces act along the same line, the net force is zero, and the block is in equilibrium. But what about the block in FIGURE 8.1c? The net force is still zero, but this time the block begins to rotate because the two forces exert a net *torque*. For an extended object, $\vec{F}_{net} = \vec{0}$ is not by itself enough to ensure static equilibrium. There is a second condition for static equilibrium of an extended object: The net torque τ_{net} on the object must also be zero.

If we write the net force in component form, the conditions for static equilibrium of an extended object are

$$\left.\begin{array}{l} \sum F_x = 0 \\ \sum F_y = 0 \end{array}\right\} \ \text{No net force}$$

$$\sum \tau = 0 \ \} \ \text{No net torque} \qquad (8.1)$$

Conditions for static equilibrium of an extended object

If motion is possible in the z-direction, we'd also require that $\sum F_z = 0$. In this chapter, however, we'll consider only motion restricted to the xy-plane.

FIGURE 8.1 A block with no net force acting on it may still be out of equilibrium.

(a) When the net force on a particle is zero, the particle is in static equilibrium.

(b) Both the net force and the net torque are zero, so the block is in static equilibrium.

(c) The net force is still zero, but the net torque is *not* zero. The block is not in equilibrium.

EXAMPLE 8.1   Finding the force from the biceps tendon

Weightlifting can exert extremely large forces on the body's joints and tendons. In the *strict curl* event, a standing athlete lifts a barbell by moving only his forearms, which pivot at the elbow. The record weight lifted in the strict curl is over 200 pounds (about 900 N). FIGURE 8.2 shows the arm bones and the main lifting muscle when the forearm is horizontal. The distance from the tendon to the elbow joint is 4.0 cm, and from the barbell to the elbow 35 cm.

a. What is the tension in the tendon connecting the biceps muscle to the bone while a 900 N barbell is held stationary in this position?

b. What is the force exerted by the elbow on the forearm bones?

PREPARE FIGURE 8.3 shows a simplified model of the arm and the forces acting on the forearm. $\vec{F}_t$ is the tension force due to the muscle, $\vec{F}_b$ is the downward force of the barbell, and $\vec{F}_e$ is the force of the elbow joint on the forearm. As a simplification, we've neglected the weight of the arm itself because it is so much less than the weight of the barbell. Because $\vec{F}_t$ and $\vec{F}_b$ have no x-component, neither can $\vec{F}_e$. If it did, the net force in the x-direction would not be zero, and the forearm could not be in equilibrium. Because each arm supports half the weight of the barbell, the magnitude of the barbell force is $F_b = 450$ N.

FIGURE 8.2 An arm holding a barbell.

Lifting muscle (*biceps*)

Tendon

Elbow joint

4.0 cm

35 cm

Continued

FIGURE 8.3 Visual overview of holding a barbell.

FIGURE 8.3 Visual overview of holding a barbell.

due to each of the three forces in terms of their magnitudes F and moment arms $r_\perp$ as $\tau = r_\perp F$. The moment arm is the perpendicular distance between the pivot and the "line of action" along which the force is applied. Figure 8.3 shows that the moment arms for $\vec{F}_t$ and $\vec{F}_b$ are the distances d_t and d_b, respectively, measured along the beam representing the forearm. The moment arm for $\vec{F}_e$ is zero, because this force acts directly at the pivot. Thus we have

$$\tau_{net} = F_e \times 0 + F_t d_t - F_b d_b = 0$$

The tension in the tendon tries to rotate the arm counterclockwise, so it produces a positive torque; the torque due to the barbell, which tries to rotate the arm in a clockwise direction, is negative. We can solve the torque equation for F_t:

$$F_t = F_b \frac{d_b}{d_t} = (450 \text{ N}) \frac{35 \text{ cm}}{4.0 \text{ cm}} = 3900 \text{ N}$$

b. We now need to make use of the force equation:

$$F_e = F_t - F_b = 3900 \text{ N} - 450 \text{ N} = 3450 \text{ N}$$

ASSESS This large value for F_t makes sense: The short distance d_t from the tendon to the elbow joint means that the force supplied by the biceps has to be very large to counter the torque generated by a force applied at the opposite end of the forearm.

SOLVE a. For the forearm to be in static equilibrium, the net force and net torque on it must both be zero. Setting the net force to zero gives

$$\sum F_y = F_t - F_e - F_b = 0$$

We don't know either of the forces F_t and F_e, nor does the force equation give us enough information to find them. But the fact that in static equilibrium the torque also must be zero gives us the extra information that we need.

Recall that the torque must be calculated about a particular point. Here, a natural choice is the elbow joint, about which the forearm can pivot. Given this pivot, we can calculate the torque

---

STOP TO THINK 8.1 Which of these objects is in static equilibrium?

A.   B.   C.   D.

Choosing the Pivot Point

In Example 8.1, we calculated the net torque using the elbow joint as the axis of rotation or pivot point. But we learned in Chapter 7 that the torque depends on which point is chosen as the pivot point. Was there something special about our choice of the elbow joint?

Consider the hammer shown in FIGURE 8.4, supported on a pegboard by two pegs A and B. Because the hammer is in static equilibrium, the net torque around the pivot at peg A must be zero: The clockwise torque due to the weight $\vec{w}$ is exactly balanced by the counterclockwise torque due to the force $\vec{n}_B$ of peg B. (Recall that the torque due to $\vec{n}_A$ is zero, because here $\vec{n}_A$ acts at the pivot A.) But if instead we take B as the pivot, the net torque is still zero. The counterclockwise torque due to $\vec{w}$ (with a large force but small moment arm) balances the clockwise torque due to $\vec{n}_A$ (with a small force but large moment arm). Indeed, **for an object in static equilibrium, the net torque about *every* point must be zero.** This means you can pick *any* point you wish as a pivot point for calculating the torque.

Although any choice of a pivot point will work, some choices are better because they simplify the calculations. Often, there is a "natural" axis of rotation in the problem, an axis about which rotation *would* occur if the object were not in static equilibrium. Example 8.1 is of this type, with the elbow joint as a natural axis of rotation.

FIGURE 8.4 A hammer resting on two pegs.

The net torque on an object in static equilibrium is zero when calculated about *any* pivot point.

If no point naturally suggests itself as an axis, look for a point on the object at which several forces act, or at which a force acts whose magnitude you don't know. Such a point is a good choice because any force acting at that point does not contribute to the torque. For instance, the woman in FIGURE 8.5 is in equilibrium as she rests on the rock wall. A good choice of pivot point would be where her foot contacts the wall because this choice eliminates the torque due to the force $\vec{F}$ of the wall on her foot. But don't agonize over the choice of a pivot point! You can still solve the problem no matter which point you choose.

FIGURE 8.5 Choosing the pivot for a woman rappelling down a rock wall.

The torque due to $\vec{F}$ about this point is zero. This makes this point a good choice as the pivot.

PROBLEM-SOLVING
STRATEGY 8.1   **Static equilibrium problems**

PREPARE Model the object as a simple shape. Draw a visual overview that shows all forces and distances. List known information.

■ Pick an axis or pivot about which the torques will be calculated.
■ Determine the torque about this pivot point due to each force acting on the object. The torques due to any forces acting *at* the pivot are zero.
■ Determine the sign of each torque about this pivot point.

SOLVE The mathematical steps are based on the fact that an object in static equilibrium has no net force and no net torque:

$$\vec{F}_{net} = \vec{0} \quad \text{and} \quad \tau_{net} = 0$$

■ Write equations for $\sum F_x = 0$, $\sum F_y = 0$, and $\sum \tau = 0$.
■ Solve the resulting equations.

ASSESS Check that your result is reasonable and answers the question.

ActivPhysics: 7.2, 7.3, 7.4, 7.5
PhET: Molecular Motors

EXAMPLE 8.2   **Forces on a board on sawhorses**

A board weighing 100 N sits across two sawhorses, as shown in FIGURE 8.6. What are the magnitudes of the normal forces of the sawhorses acting on the board?

FIGURE 8.6 A board sitting on two sawhorses.

PREPARE The board and the forces acting on it are shown in FIGURE 8.7. $\vec{n}_1$ and $\vec{n}_2$ are the normal forces on the board due to the sawhorses, and $\vec{w}$ is the weight of the board acting at the center of gravity. The distance d_1 to the center of the board is half the board's length, or 1.5 m. Then d_2 is $d_1 - 1.0$ m, or 0.5 m.

As discussed above, a good choice for the pivot is a point at which an unknown force acts, because that force contributes nothing to the torque. Either the point where $\vec{n}_1$ acts or the point where $\vec{n}_2$ acts will work; let's choose the left end of the board, where $\vec{n}_1$ acts, for this example. With this choice of pivot point, the moment arm for $\vec{w}$ is $d_1 = 1.5$ m. Because $\vec{w}$ tends to rotate

the board clockwise, its torque is negative. The moment arm for $\vec{n}_2$ is the distance $d_1 + d_2 = 2.0$ m, and its torque is positive.

FIGURE 8.7 Visual overview of a board on two sawhorses.

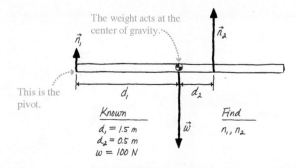

SOLVE The board is in static equilibrium, so the net force $\vec{F}_{net}$ and the net torque τ_{net} must both be zero. The forces have only y-components, so the force equation is

$$\sum F_y = n_1 - w + n_2 = 0$$

The torque equation, computed around the left end of the board, is

$$\tau_{net} = -d_1 w + (d_1 + d_2)n_2 = 0$$

Continued

We now have two simultaneous equations with the two unknowns n_1 and n_2. To solve these, let's solve for n_2 in the torque equation and then substitute that result into the force equation. From the torque equation,

$$n_2 = \frac{d_1 w}{d_1 + d_2} = \frac{(1.5 \text{ m})(100 \text{ N})}{2.0 \text{ m}} = 75 \text{ N}$$

The force equation is then $n_1 - 100 \text{ N} + 75 \text{ N} = 0$, which we can solve for n_1:

$$n_1 = w - n_2 = 100 \text{ N} - 75 \text{ N} = 25 \text{ N}$$

ASSESS It seems reasonable that $n_2 > n_1$ because more of the board sits over the right sawhorse.

STOP TO THINK 8.2 A beam with a pivot on its left end is suspended from a rope. In which direction is the force of the pivot on the beam?

An interesting application of static equilibrium is to find the center of gravity of the human body. Because the human body is highly flexible, the position of the center of gravity is quite variable and depends on just how the body is posed. The horizontal position of the body's center of gravity can be located accurately from simple measurements with a *reaction board* and a scale. The following example shows how this is done.

EXAMPLE 8.3 Finding the center of gravity of the human body

A woman weighing 600 N lies on a 2.5-m-long, 60 N reaction board with her feet over the pivot. The scale on the right reads 250 N. What is the distance d from the woman's feet to her center of gravity?

PREPARE The forces and distances in the problem are shown in FIGURE 8.8. We'll consider the board and woman as a single object. We've assumed that the board is uniform, so its center of gravity is at its midpoint. To eliminate the unknown magnitude of

FIGURE 8.8 Visual overview of the reaction board and woman.

The subject's weight acts at her center of gravity.

Scale

Pivot

The board's weight acts at its center of gravity.

Known
$w = 600$ N
$w_b = 60$ N
$L = 2.5$ m
$F = 250$ N

Find
d

$\vec{n}$ from the torque equation, we'll choose the pivot to be the left end of the board. The torque due to $\vec{F}$ is positive, and those due to $\vec{w}$ and $\vec{w}_b$ are negative.

SOLVE Because the board and woman are in static equilibrium, the net force and net torque on them must be zero. The force equation reads

$$\sum F_y = n - w_b - w + F = 0$$

and the torque equation gives

$$\sum \tau = -\frac{L}{2} w_b - dw + LF = 0$$

In this case, the force equation isn't needed because we can solve the torque equation for d:

$$d = \frac{LF - \frac{1}{2}Lw_b}{w} = \frac{(2.5 \text{ m})(250 \text{ N}) - \frac{1}{2}(2.5 \text{ m})(60 \text{ N})}{600 \text{ N}}$$
$$= 0.92 \text{ m}$$

ASSESS If the woman is 5′ 6″ (1.68 m) tall, her center of gravity is $(0.92 \text{ m})/(1.68 \text{ m}) = 55\%$ of her height, or a little more than halfway up her body. This seems reasonable.

EXAMPLE 8.4 Will the ladder slip?

A 3.0-m-long ladder leans against a frictionless wall at an angle of 60° with respect to the floor. What is the minimum value of μ_s, the coefficient of static friction with the ground, that will prevent the ladder from slipping?

PREPARE The ladder is a rigid rod of length L. To not slip, both the net force and net torque on the ladder must be zero. FIGURE 8.9 shows the ladder and the forces acting on it. The bottom corner of the ladder is a good choice of a pivot point because two of the

FIGURE 8.9 Visual overview of a ladder in static equilibrium.

Known
$L = 3.0$ m

Find
μ_s

Center of gravity

$\vec{n}_2$

$\vec{n}_1$

$\vec{w}$

$\vec{f}_s$ 60°

d_2

d_1

$\tau_{net} = 0$ about this point.

Weight acts at the center of gravity.

Static friction prevents slipping.

forces pass through this point and thus produce no torque about it. With this choice, the weight of the ladder, acting at the center of gravity, exerts torque $d_1 w$ and the force of the wall exerts torque $-d_2 n_2$. The signs are based on the observation that $\vec{w}$ would cause the ladder to rotate counterclockwise, while $\vec{n}_2$ would cause it to rotate clockwise.

SOLVE The x- and y-components of $\vec{F}_{net} = \vec{0}$ are

$$\sum F_x = n_2 - f_s = 0$$
$$\sum F_y = n_1 - w = n_1 - Mg = 0$$

The torque about the bottom corner is

$$\tau_{net} = d_1 w - d_2 n_2 = \frac{1}{2}(L\cos 60°)Mg - (L\sin 60°)n_2 = 0$$

Altogether, we have three equations with the three unknowns n_1, n_2, and f_s. If we solve the third equation for n_2,

$$n_2 = \frac{\frac{1}{2}(L\cos 60°)Mg}{L\sin 60°} = \frac{Mg}{2\tan 60°}$$

we can then substitute this into the first equation to find

$$f_s = \frac{Mg}{2\tan 60°}$$

Our model of static friction is $f_s \leq f_{s\,max} = \mu_s n_1$. We can find n_1 from the second equation: $n_1 = Mg$. From this, the model of friction tells us that

$$f_s \leq \mu_s Mg$$

Comparing these two expressions for f_s, we see that μ_s must obey

$$\mu_s \geq \frac{1}{2\tan 60°} = 0.29$$

Thus the minimum value of the coefficient of static friction is 0.29.

ASSESS You know from experience that you can lean a ladder or other object against a wall if the ground is "rough," but it slips if the surface is too smooth. 0.29 is a "medium" value for the coefficient of static friction, which is reasonable.

8.2 Stability and Balance

If you tilt a box up on one edge by a small amount and let go, it falls back down. If you tilt it too much, it falls over. And if you tilt it "just right," you can get the box to balance on its edge. What determines these three possible outcomes?

FIGURE 8.10 illustrates the idea with a car, but the results are general and apply in many situations. An extended object, whether it's a car, a box, or a person, has a *base of support* on which it rests when in static equilibrium. If you tilt the object, one edge of the base of support becomes a pivot point. As long as the object's center of gravity remains over the base of support, torque due to gravity will rotate the object back toward its stable equilibrium position; we say that the object is **stable.** This is the

Class Video

FIGURE 8.10 A car—or any object—will fall over when tilted too far.

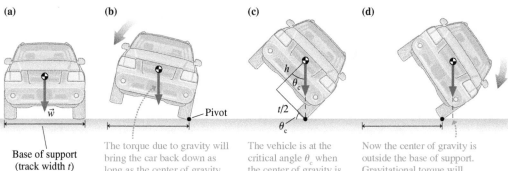

(a)

$\vec{w}$

Base of support (track width t)

(b)

Pivot

The torque due to gravity will bring the car back down as long as the center of gravity is over the base of support.

(c)

h

θ_c

$t/2$

θ_c

The vehicle is at the critical angle θ_c when the center of gravity is directly over the pivot.

(d)

Now the center of gravity is outside the base of support. Gravitational torque will cause it to roll over.

FIGURE 8.11 Compared to a passenger car, an SUV has a high center of gravity relative to its width.

For the car the center-of-gravity height h is 33% of t.

For the SUV, the center-of-gravity height h is 47% of t.

situation in Figure 8.10b. But if the center of gravity gets outside the base of support, as in Figure 8.10d, the gravitational torque causes a rotation in the opposite direction. Now the car rolls over; it is **unstable.**

A *critical angle* θ_c is reached when the center of gravity is directly over the pivot point. This is the point of balance, with no net torque. For vehicles, the distance between the tires—the base of support—is called the *track width* t. If the height of the center of gravity is h, you can see from Figure 8.10c that the critical angle is

$$\theta_c = \tan^{-1}\left(\frac{t/2}{h}\right) = \tan^{-1}\left(\frac{t}{2h}\right) \qquad (8.2)$$

If an accident (or taking a corner too fast) causes a vehicle to pivot up onto two wheels, it will roll back to an upright position as long as $\theta < \theta_c$ but it will roll over if $\theta > \theta_c$. Notice that it's the height-to-width ratio that's important, not the absolute height of the center of gravity.

FIGURE 8.11 compares a passenger car and a sport utility vehicle (SUV). For the passenger car, with $h \approx 0.33t$, the critical angle is $\theta_c \approx 57°$. But for the SUV, with its higher center of gravity ($h \approx 0.47t$), the critical angle is only $\theta_c \approx 47°$. Loading an SUV with cargo further raises the center of gravity, especially if the roof rack is used, thus reducing θ_c even more. Various automobile safety groups have determined that a vehicle with $\theta_c > 50°$ is unlikely to roll over in an accident. A rollover becomes increasingly likely when θ_c is less than 50°. The same argument that leads to Equation 8.2 for tilted vehicles can be made for any object, leading to the general rule that **a wider base of support and/or a lower center of gravity improve stability.**

CONCEPTUAL EXAMPLE 8.5 **How far to walk the plank?**

A cat walks along a plank that extends out from a table. If the cat walks too far out on the plank, the plank will begin to tilt. What determines when this happens?

REASON An object is stable if its center of gravity lies over its base of support, and unstable otherwise. Let's take the cat and the plank to be one combined object whose center of gravity lies along a line between the cat's center of gravity and that of the plank.

In FIGURE 8.12a, when the cat is near the left end of the plank, the combined center of gravity is over the base of support and the plank is stable. As the cat moves to the right, he reaches a point where the combined center of gravity is directly over the edge of the table, as shown in FIGURE 8.12b. If the cat takes one more step, the cat and plank will become unstable and the plank will begin to tilt.

FIGURE 8.12 Changing stability as a cat walks on a plank.

ASSESS Because the plank's center of gravity must be to the left of the edge for it to be stable by itself, the cat can actually walk a short distance out onto the unsupported part of the plank before it starts to tilt. The heavier the plank is, the farther the cat can walk.

TRY IT YOURSELF

Balancing a soda can Try to balance a soda can—full or empty—on the narrow bevel at the bottom. It can't be done because, either full or empty, the center of gravity is near the center of the can. If the can is tilted enough to sit on the bevel, the center of gravity lies far outside this small base of support. But if you put about 2 ounces (60 ml) of water in an empty can, the center of gravity will be right over the bevel and the can will balance.

Stability and Balance of the Human Body

The human body is remarkable for its ability to constantly adjust its stance to remain stable on just two points of support. In walking, running, or even in the simple act of rising from a chair, the position of the body's center of gravity is constantly changing. To maintain stability, we unconsciously adjust the positions of our arms and legs to keep our center of gravity over our base of support.

A simple example of how the body naturally realigns its center of gravity is found in the act of standing up on tiptoes. FIGURE 8.13a shows the body in its normal standing position. Notice that the center of gravity is well centered over the base of support (the feet), ensuring stability. If the subject were now to stand on tiptoes *without* otherwise adjusting the body position, her center of gravity would fall behind the base of support, which is now the balls of the feet, and she would fall backward. To prevent this, as shown in FIGURE 8.13b, the body naturally leans forward, regaining stability by moving the center of gravity over the balls of the feet.

FIGURE 8.13 Standing on tiptoes.

STOP TO THINK 8.3 Rank in order, from least stable to most stable, the three objects shown in the figure. The positions of their centers of gravity are marked. (For the centers of gravity to be positioned like this, the objects must have a nonuniform composition.)

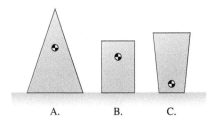

A.   B.   C.

TRY IT YOURSELF

Impossible balance Stand facing a wall with your toes touching the base of the wall. Now rise onto your tiptoes. You will not be able to do so without falling backward. As we see from Figure 8.13b, your body has to lean forward to stand on tiptoes. With the wall in your way, you cannot lean enough to maintain your balance, and you will begin to topple backward.

8.3 Springs and Hooke's Law

We have assumed that objects in equilibrium maintain their shape as forces and torques are applied to them. In reality this is an oversimplification. Every solid object stretches, compresses, or deforms when a force acts upon it. This change is easy to see when you press on a green twig on a tree, but even the largest branch on the tree will bend slightly under your weight.

If you stretch a rubber band, there is a force that tries to pull the rubber band back to its equilibrium, or unstretched, length. A force that restores a system to an equilibrium position is called a **restoring force**. Systems that exhibit such restoring forces are called **elastic**. The most basic examples of **elasticity** are things like springs and rubber bands. If you stretch a spring, a tension-like force pulls back. Similarly, a compressed spring tries to re-expand to its equilibrium length. Elasticity and restoring forces are properties of much stiffer systems as well. The steel beams of a bridge bend slightly as you drive your car over it, but they are restored to equilibrium after your car passes by. Your leg bones flex a bit during each step you take. Nearly everything that stretches, compresses, bends, or twists exhibits a restoring force and can be called elastic.

The behavior of a simple spring illustrates the basic ideas of elasticity. When no forces act on a spring to compress or extend it, it will relax to its **equilibrium length.** If we now stretch the spring by a displacement Δx, how hard does it pull back? FIGURE 8.14 shows what happens: The farther we stretch the spring, the harder the restoring force of the spring pulls back.

 PhET: Masses and Springs

FIGURE 8.14 The spring force depends on how far the spring is stretched.

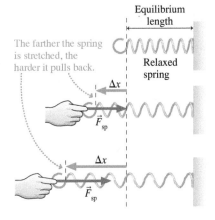

FIGURE 8.15 Measured data for the restoring force of a real spring.

FIGURE 8.16 The spring force is always directed opposite the displacement.

Elasticity in action A golf ball compresses quite a bit when struck. The restoring force that pushes the ball back into its original shape helps launch the ball off the face of the club, making for a longer drive.

In FIGURE 8.15, data for the magnitude of the restoring force of a real spring show that **the force of the spring is *proportional* to the displacement of the end of the spring.** That is, compressing or stretching the spring twice as far results in a restoring force that is twice as large. This is a *linear relationship,* and the slope k of the line is the proportionality constant:

$$F_{sp} = k\,\Delta x \qquad (8.3)$$

A second important fact about spring forces is illustrated in FIGURE 8.16. If the spring is compressed, as in Figure 8.16a, Δx is positive and, because $\vec{F}_{sp}$ points to the left, its component $(F_{sp})_x$ is negative. If, however, the spring is stretched, as in Figure 8.16b, Δx is negative and, because $\vec{F}_{sp}$ points to the right, its component $(F_{sp})_x$ is positive. In general, **the spring force always points in the opposite direction to the displacement from equilibrium.** We can express this fact, along with what we've learned about the magnitude of the spring force, by rewriting Equation 8.3 in terms of the *component* of the spring force:

$$(F_{sp})_x = -k\,\Delta x \qquad (8.4)$$

Hooke's law for the force due to a spring

PROPORTIONAL

The minus sign in Equation 8.4 reflects the fact that $(F_{sp})_x$ and Δx are always of opposite sign. (For motion in the vertical (y) direction, Hooke's law is $(F_{sp})_y = -k\,\Delta y$.)

The proportionality constant k is called the **spring constant.** The units of the spring constant are N/m. The spring constant k is a property that characterizes a spring, just as mass m characterizes a particle. If k is large, it takes a large pull to cause a significant stretch, and we call the spring a "stiff" spring. If k is small, we can stretch the spring with very little force, and we call it a "soft" spring. Every spring has its own, unique value of k. The spring constant for the spring in Figure 8.15 can be determined from the slope of the straight line to be $k = 3.5$ N/m.

Equation 8.4 for the restoring force of a spring was first suggested by Robert Hooke, a contemporary (and sometimes bitter rival) of Newton. Hooke's law is not a true "law of nature," in the sense that Newton's laws are, but is actually just a *model* of a restoring force. It works extremely well for some springs, as in Figure 8.15, but less well for others. Hooke's law will fail for any spring if it is compressed or stretched too far.

NOTE ▶ Just as we used massless strings, we will adopt the idealization of a *massless spring.* Though not a perfect description, it is a good approximation if the mass attached to a spring is much greater than the mass of the spring itself. ◀

EXAMPLE 8.6   **Weighing a fish**

A scale used to weigh fish consists of a spring connected to the ceiling. The spring's equilibrium length is 30 cm. When a 4.0 kg fish is suspended from the end of the spring, it stretches to a length of 42 cm.

a. What is the spring constant k for this spring?
b. If an 8.0 kg fish is suspended from the spring, what will be the length of the spring?

PREPARE The visual overview in FIGURE 8.17 shows the details for the first part of the problem. The fish hangs in static equilibrium, so the net force in the y-direction and the net torque must be zero.

FIGURE 8.17 Visual overview of a mass suspended from a spring.

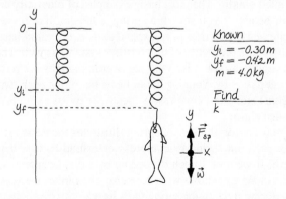

Known
$y_i = -0.30\,m$
$y_f = -0.42\,m$
$m = 4.0\,kg$

Find
k

SOLVE a. Because the fish is in static equilibrium, we have

$$\sum F_y = (F_{sp})_y + w_y = -k\,\Delta y - mg = 0$$

so that $k = -mg/\Delta y$. (The net torque is zero because the fish's center of gravity comes to rest directly under the pivot point of the hook.) From Figure 8.17, the displacement of the spring from equilibrium is $\Delta y = y_f - y_i = (-0.42\text{ m}) - (-0.30\text{ m}) = -0.12\text{ m}$. This displacement is *negative* because the fish moves in the $-y$-direction. We can now solve for the spring constant:

$$k = -\frac{mg}{\Delta y} = -\frac{(4.0\text{ kg})(9.8\text{ m/s}^2)}{-0.12\text{ m}} = 330\text{ N/m}$$

b. The restoring force is proportional to the displacement of the spring from its equilibrium length. If we double the mass (and thus the weight) of the fish, the displacement of the end of the spring will double as well, to $\Delta y = -0.24\text{ m}$. Thus the spring will be 0.24 m longer, so its new length is $0.30\text{ m} + 0.24\text{ m} = 0.54\text{ m}$.

ASSESS A spring constant of 330 N/m means that when the spring is stretched by 1.0 m it will exert a force of 330 N (about 75 lb). This seems reasonable for a spring used to weigh objects of 10 or 20 lb.

EXAMPLE 8.7   **When does the block slip?**

FIGURE 8.18 shows a spring attached to a 2.0 kg block. The other end of the spring is pulled by a motorized toy train that moves forward at 5.0 cm/s. The spring constant is 50 N/m, and the coefficient of static friction between the block and the surface is 0.60. The spring is at its equilibrium length at $t = 0$ s when the train starts to move. When does the block slip?

FIGURE 8.18 A toy train stretches the spring until the block slips.

5.0 cm/s

2.0 kg

PREPARE We model the block as a particle and the spring as a massless spring. **FIGURE 8.19** is a free-body diagram for the block. We convert the speed of the train into m/s: $v = 0.050\text{ m/s}$.

FIGURE 8.19 Free-body diagram for the block.

When the spring force exceeds the maximum force of static friction, the block will slip.

$\vec{f}_s$ $\vec{n}$ y x $\vec{w}$ $\vec{F}_{sp}$

SOLVE Recall that the tension in a massless string pulls equally at *both* ends of the string. The same is true for the spring force: It pulls (or pushes) equally at *both* ends. Imagine holding a rubber band with your left hand and stretching it with your right hand. Your left hand feels the pulling force, even though it was the right end of the rubber band that moved.

This is the key to solving the problem. As the right end of the spring moves, stretching the spring, the spring pulls backward on the train *and* forward on the block with equal strength. The train is moving to the right, and so the spring force pulls to the left on the train—as we would expect. But the block is at the other end of the spring; the spring force pulls to the right on the block, as shown in Figure 8.19. As the spring stretches, the static friction force on the block increases in magnitude to keep the block at rest. The block is in static equilibrium, so

$$\sum F_x = (F_{sp})_x + (f_s)_x = F_{sp} - f_s = 0$$

where F_{sp} is the magnitude of the spring force. This magnitude is $F_{sp} = k\,\Delta x$, where $\Delta x = vt$ is the distance the train has moved. Thus

$$f_s = F_{sp} = k\,\Delta x$$

The block slips when the static friction force reaches its maximum value $f_{s\,max} = \mu_s n = \mu_s mg$. This occurs when the train has moved a distance

$$\Delta x = \frac{f_{s\,max}}{k} = \frac{\mu_s mg}{k} = \frac{(0.60)(2.0\text{ kg})(9.8\text{ m/s}^2)}{50\text{ N/m}} = 0.235\text{ m}$$

The time at which the block slips is

$$t = \frac{\Delta x}{v} = \frac{0.235\text{ m}}{0.050\text{ m/s}} = 4.7\text{ s}$$

ASSESS The result of about 5 s seems reasonable for a slowly moving toy train to stretch the spring enough for the block to slip.

STOP TO THINK 8.4   A 1.0 kg weight is suspended from a spring, stretching it by 5.0 cm. How much does the spring stretch if the 1.0 kg weight is replaced by a 3.0 kg weight?

A. 5.0 cm   B. 10.0 cm   C. 15.0 cm   D. 20.0 cm

FIGURE 8.20 Stretching a steel rod.

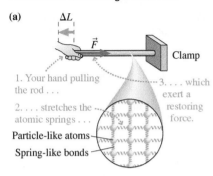

(a)

1. Your hand pulling the rod . . .

2. . . . stretches the atomic springs . . .

3. . . . which exert a restoring force.

Particle-like atoms

Spring-like bonds

(b) Data for a 1.0-m-long, 1.0-cm-diameter steel rod

F (kN) ········ 1 kN = 1000 N

Slope = k = 1.6 × 10⁷ N/m

Change in the rod's length

ΔL (mm)

FIGURE 8.21 A rod stretched by length ΔL.

ΔL Restoring force

Area A

$\vec{F}$

L

TABLE 8.1 Young's modulus for rigid materials

Material	Young's modulus (10^{10} N/m^2)
Cast iron	20
Steel	20
Silicon	13
Copper	11
Aluminum	7
Glass	7
Concrete	3
Wood (Douglas Fir)	1

8.4 Stretching and Compressing Materials

In Chapter 4 we noted that we could model most solid materials as being made of particle-like atoms connected by spring-like bonds. We can model a steel rod this way, as illustrated in FIGURE 8.20a. The spring-like bonds between the atoms in steel are quite stiff, but they can be stretched or compressed, meaning that even a steel rod is elastic. If you pull on the end of a steel rod, as in Figure 8.20a, you will slightly stretch the bonds between the particles that make it up, and the rod itself will stretch. The stretched bonds pull back on your hand with a restoring force that causes the rod to return to its original length when released. In this sense, the entire rod acts like a very stiff spring. As is the case for a spring, a restoring force is also produced by compressing the rod.

In FIGURE 8.20b, real data for a 1.0-m-long, 1.0-cm-diameter steel rod show that, just as for a spring, the restoring force is proportional to the change in length. However, the *scale* of the stretch of the rod and the restoring force is much different from that for a spring. It would take a force of 16,000 N to stretch the rod by only 1 mm, corresponding to a spring constant of 1.6 × 10⁷ N/m! Steel is elastic, but under normal forces, it experiences only very small changes in dimension. Materials of this sort are called **rigid.**

The behavior of other materials, such as the rubber in a rubber band, can be quite different. A rubber band can be stretched quite far—several times its equilibrium length—with a very small force, and then snaps back to its original shape when released. Materials that show large deformations with small forces are called **pliant.**

A rod's spring constant depends on several factors, as shown in FIGURE 8.21. First, we expect that a thick rod, with a large cross-section area A, will be more difficult to stretch than a thinner rod. Second, a rod with a long length L will be easier to stretch by a given amount than a short rod (think of trying to stretch a rope by 1 cm—this would be easy to do for a 10-m-long rope, but it would be pretty hard for a piece of rope only 10 cm long). Finally, the stiffness of the rod will depend on the material that it's made of. Experiments bear out these observations, and it is found that the spring constant of the rod can be written as

$$k = \frac{YA}{L} \qquad (8.5)$$

where the constant Y is called **Young's modulus.** Young's modulus is a property of the *material* from which the rod is made—it does not depend on the object's shape or size. All rods made from steel have the same Young's modulus, regardless of their length or area, while aluminum rods have a different Young's modulus.

From Equation 8.3, the magnitude of the restoring force for a spring is related to the change in its length as $F_{sp} = k \, \Delta x$. Writing the change in the length of a rod as ΔL, as shown in Figure 8.21, we can use Equation 8.5 to write the restoring force F of a rod as

$$F = \frac{YA}{L} \, \Delta L \qquad (8.6)$$

Equation 8.6 applies both to elongation (stretching) and to compression.

It's useful to rearrange Equation 8.6 in terms of two new ratios, the *stress* and the *strain*:

The ratio of force to cross-section area is called **stress.**

$$\frac{F}{A} = Y\left(\frac{\Delta L}{L}\right) \qquad (8.7)$$

The ratio of the change in length to the original length is called **strain.**

The unit of stress is N/m². If the stress is due to stretching, we call it a **tensile stress.** The strain is the fractional change in the rod's length. If the rod's length changes by 1%, the strain is 0.01. Because strain is dimensionless, Young's modulus Y has the same units as stress. Table 8.1 gives values of Young's modulus for several

PhET: Stretching DNA

rigid materials. Large values of Y characterize materials that are stiff. "Softer" materials have smaller values of Y. Because the values of Young's modulus for materials such as steel or aluminum are very large, it takes a significant stress to produce even a small strain.

EXAMPLE 8.8 Finding the stretch of a wire

A *Foucault pendulum* in a physics department (used to prove that the earth rotates) consists of a 120 kg steel ball that swings at the end of a 6.0-m-long steel cable. The cable has a diameter of 2.5 mm. When the ball was first hung from the cable, by how much did the cable stretch?

PREPARE The amount by which the cable stretches depends on the elasticity of the steel cable. Young's modulus for steel is given in Table 8.1 as $Y = 20 \times 10^{10} \text{ N/m}^2$.

SOLVE Equation 8.7 relates the stretch of the cable ΔL to the restoring force F and to the properties of the cable. Rearranging terms, we find that the cable stretches by

$$\Delta L = \frac{LF}{AY}$$

The cross-section area of the cable is

$$A = \pi r^2 = \pi(0.00125 \text{ m})^2 = 4.91 \times 10^{-6} \text{ m}^2$$

The restoring force of the cable is equal to the ball's weight:

$$F = w = mg = (120 \text{ kg})(9.8 \text{ m/s}^2) = 1180 \text{ N}$$

The change in length is thus

$$\Delta L = \frac{(6.0 \text{ m})(1180 \text{ N})}{(4.91 \times 10^{-6} \text{ m}^2)(20 \times 10^{10} \text{ N/m}^2)}$$
$$= 0.0072 \text{ m} = 7.2 \text{ mm}$$

ASSESS If you've ever strung a guitar with steel strings, you know that the strings stretch several millimeters with the force you can apply by turning the tuning pegs. So a stretch of 7 mm under a 120 kg load seems reasonable.

Beyond the Elastic Limit

In the previous section, we found that if we stretch a rod by a small amount ΔL, it will pull back with a restoring force F, according to Equation 8.6. But if we continue to stretch the rod, this simple linear relationship between ΔL and F will eventually break down. FIGURE 8.22 is a graph of the rod's restoring force from the start of the stretch until the rod finally breaks.

As you can see, the graph has a *linear region,* the region where F and ΔL are proportional to each other, obeying Hooke's law: $F = k \Delta L$. **As long as the stretch stays within the linear region, a solid rod acts like a spring and obeys Hooke's law.**

How far can you stretch the rod before damaging it? As long as the stretch is less than the **elastic limit,** the rod will return to its initial length L when the force is removed. The elastic limit is the end of the **elastic region.** Stretching the rod beyond the elastic limit will permanently deform it, and the rod won't return to its original length. Finally, at a certain point the rod will reach a breaking point, where it will snap in two. The maximum stress that a material can be subjected to before failing is called the **tensile strength.** Table 8.2 lists values of tensile strength for rigid materials. When we speak of the *strength* of a material, we are referring to its tensile strength.

FIGURE 8.22 Stretch data for a steel rod.

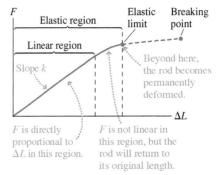

EXAMPLE 8.9 Breaking a pendulum cable

After a late night of studying physics, several 80 kg students decide it would be fun to swing on the Foucault pendulum of Example 8.8. What's the maximum number of students that the pendulum cable could support?

PREPARE The tensile strength, given for steel in Table 8.2 as $1000 \times 10^6 \text{ N/m}^2$, or $1.0 \times 10^9 \text{ N/m}^2$, is the largest stress the cable can sustain. Because the stress in the cable is F/A, we can find the maximum force F_{max} that can be applied to the cable before it fails.

Continued

TABLE 8.2 Tensile strengths of rigid materials

Material	Tensile strength (N/m^2)
Polypropylene	20×10^6
Glass	60×10^6
Cast iron	150×10^6
Aluminum	400×10^6
Steel	1000×10^6

Spider silk BIO The glands on the abdomen of a spider produce different kinds of silk. The silk that is used in webs can be quite stretchy; that used to subdue prey is generally not. An individual strand of silk may be a mix of fibers of different types, allowing spiders great flexibility in their material.

FIGURE 8.23 **Stress-versus-strain graphs for steel and spider silk.**

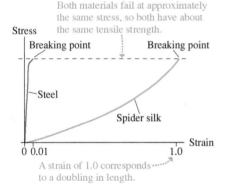

Both materials fail at approximately the same stress, so both have about the same tensile strength.

Stress

Breaking point   Breaking point

Steel

Spider silk

0 0.01   1.0   Strain

A strain of 1.0 corresponds to a doubling in length.

FIGURE 8.24 **Cross section of a long bone.**

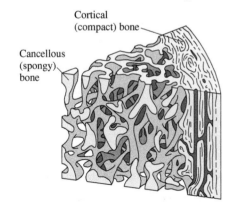

Cortical (compact) bone

Cancellous (spongy) bone

SOLVE We have

$$F_{max} = A(1.0 \times 10^9 \text{ N/m}^2)$$

From Example 8.8, the diameter of the cable is 2.5 mm, so its radius is 0.00125 m. Thus

$$F_{max} = \left(\pi(0.00125 \text{ m})^2\right)(1.0 \times 10^9 \text{ N/m}^2) = 4.9 \times 10^3 \text{ N}$$

This force is the weight of the heaviest mass the cable can support: $w = m_{max}g$. The maximum mass that can be supported is

$$m_{max} = \frac{F_{max}}{g} = 500 \text{ kg}$$

The ball has a mass of 120 kg, leaving 380 kg for the students. Four students have a mass of 320 kg, which is less than this value. But five students, totaling 400 kg, would cause the cable to break.

ASSESS Steel has a very large tensile strength. This very narrow wire can still support 4900 N $\approx$ 1100 lb.

Biological Materials

Suppose we take equal lengths of spider silk and steel wire, stretch each, and measure the restoring force of each until it breaks. The graph of stress versus strain might appear as in FIGURE 8.23.

The spider silk is certainly less stiff: For a given stress, the silk will stretch about 100 times farther than steel. Interestingly, though, spider silk and steel eventually fail at approximately the same stress. In this sense, spider silk is "as strong as steel." Many pliant biological materials share this combination of low stiffness and large tensile strength. These materials can undergo significant deformations without failing. Tendons, the walls of arteries, and the web of a spider are all quite strong but nonetheless capable of significant stretch.

Bone is an interesting example of a rigid biological material. Most bones in your body are made of two different kinds of bony material: dense and rigid cortical (or compact) bone on the outside, and porous, flexible cancellous (or spongy) bone on the inside. FIGURE 8.24 shows a cross section of a typical bone. Cortical and cancellous bones have very different values of Young's modulus. Young's modulus for cortical bone approaches that of concrete, so it is very rigid with little ability to stretch or compress. In contrast, cancellous bone has a much lower Young's modulus. Consequently, the elastic properties of bones can be well modeled as those of a hollow cylinder.

The structure of bones in birds actually approximates a hollow cylinder quite well. FIGURE 8.25 shows that a typical bone is a thin-walled tube of cortical bone with a tenuous structure of cancellous bone inside. Most of a cylinder's rigidity comes from the material near its surface. A hollow cylinder retains most of the rigidity of a solid one, but it is much lighter. Bird bones carry this idea to its extreme.

FIGURE 8.25 **Section of a bone from a bird.**

Table 8.3 gives values of Young's modulus for biological materials. Note the large difference between pliant and rigid materials. Table 8.4 shows the tensile strengths for biological materials. Interestingly, spider silk, a pliant material, has a greater tensile strength than bone!

The values in Table 8.4 are for static forces—forces applied for a long time in a testing machine. Bone can withstand significantly greater stresses if the forces are applied for only a very short period of time.

| EXAMPLE 8.10 | Finding the compression of a bone |

The femur, the long bone in the thigh, can be modeled as a tube of cortical bone for most of its length. A 70 kg person has a femur with a cross-section area (of the cortical bone) of 4.8×10^{-4} m^2, a typical value.

a. If this person supports his entire weight on one leg, what fraction of the tensile strength of the bone does this stress represent?
b. By what fraction of its length does the femur shorten?

PREPARE The stress on the femur is F/A. Here F, the force compressing the femur, is the person's weight, so $F = mg$. The fractional change $\Delta L/L$ in the femur is the strain, which we can find using Equation 8.7, taking the value of Young's modulus for cortical bone from Table 8.3.

SOLVE

a. The person's weight is $mg = (70 \text{ kg})(9.8 \text{ m/s}^2) = 690$ N. The resulting stress on the femur is

$$\frac{F}{A} = \frac{690 \text{ N}}{4.8 \times 10^{-4} \text{ m}^2} = 1.4 \times 10^6 \text{ N/m}^2$$

A stress of 1.4×10^6 N/m^2 is 1.4% of the tensile strength of cortical bone given in Table 8.4.

b. We can compute the strain as

$$\frac{\Delta L}{L} = \left(\frac{1}{Y}\right)\frac{F}{A} = \left(\frac{1}{1.6 \times 10^{10} \text{ N/m}^2}\right)(1.4 \times 10^6 \text{ N/m}^2) = 8.8 \times 10^{-5} \approx 0.0001$$

The femur compression is $\Delta L \approx 0.0001L$, or $\approx 0.01\%$ of its length.

ASSESS It makes sense that, under ordinary standing conditions, the stress on the femur is only a percent or so of the maximum value it can sustain.

TABLE 8.3 Young's modulus for biological materials

Material	Young's modulus (10^{10} N/m^2)
Tooth enamel	6
Cortical bone	1.6
Cancellous bone	0.02–0.3
Spider silk	0.2
Tendon	0.15
Cartilage	0.0001
Blood vessel (aorta)	0.00005

TABLE 8.4 Tensile strength of biological materials

Material	Tensile strength (N/m^2)
Cancellous bone	5×10^6
Cortical bone	100×10^6
Tendon	100×10^6
Spider silk	1000×10^6

The dancer in the chapter-opening photo stands *en pointe*, balanced delicately on the tip of her shoe with her entire weight supported on a very small area. The stress on the bones in her toes is very large, but it is still much less than the tensile strength of bone.

| STOP TO THINK 8.5 | A 10 kg mass is hung from a 1-m-long cable, causing the cable to stretch by 2 mm. Suppose a 10 kg mass is hung from a 2 m length of the same cable. By how much does the cable stretch?

A. 0.5 mm   B. 1 mm   C. 2 mm   D. 3 mm   E. 4 mm

| INTEGRATED EXAMPLE 8.11 | Holding a barrel on a hill |

FIGURE 8.26 shows a 60-cm-diameter barrel of sand, with a mass of 600 kg, being held in place on a hill by a polypropylene rope wrapped around the barrel. The coefficient of static friction between the barrel and the hill is 0.25.

a. What is the tension in the rope?
b. What is the steepest hill that the barrel could rest on without slipping?

FIGURE 8.26 A barrel being held by a rope.

c. What is the smallest-diameter rope that can be used without the rope breaking?

PREPARE We'll follow Problem-Solving Strategy 8.1: For an object in static equilibrium, the net torque is zero, $\Sigma\tau = 0$, and the net force is zero, $\Sigma F_x = 0$ and $\Sigma F_y = 0$. To find the net torque on the barrel, we'll redraw it in **FIGURE 8.27** on the next page with all the forces shown at the points at which they act. To find the components of the net force, we'll draw the free-body diagram of Figure 8.27. As usual, we tilt our x-axis so that it's parallel to the surface of the hill. Recall from Figure 5.14 that the angle between the weight vector and the $-y$-axis is the same as the angle of the slope.

The direction of the static friction force is chosen to keep the bottom of the barrel from slipping down the hill. Imagine what

Continued

FIGURE 8.27 Visual overview of the barrel.

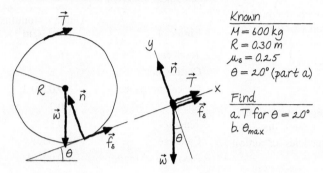

Known
$$M = 600\,kg$$
$$R = 0.30\,m$$
$$\mu_s = 0.25$$
$$\theta = 20° \ (part\ a)$$

Find
a. T for $\theta = 20°$
b. θ_{max}

would happen if friction suddenly vanished while the rope was holding the top of the barrel in place.

We need to pick a pivot about which the torque will be calculated. If we choose the point of contact of the barrel with the hill as our pivot, then the unknown forces $\vec{n}$ and $\vec{f}_s$, which act at that point, make no contribution to the torque. Only the weight, whose magnitude we know, and the tension, which is what we want to find, contribute to the torque.

For part c, the rope will fail if the stress exceeds the tensile strength of polypropylene, given in Table 8.2 as $2.0 \times 10^7\ \text{N/m}^2$.

SOLVE

a. **FIGURE 8.28** shows how to calculate the torque. Forces $\vec{n}$ and $\vec{f}_s$ are not shown because, as just discussed, they act at the pivot and do not contribute to the torque. In Figure 8.28a, the tension $\vec{T}$ acts perpendicular to the radial line, at a distance $2R$ from the pivot, so the torque due to the tension is $\tau_T = -2RT$. It's negative because the tension tries to rotate the barrel clockwise.

FIGURE 8.28 Calculating the torque.

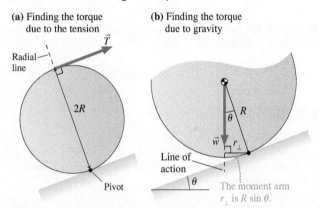

(a) Finding the torque due to the tension

(b) Finding the torque due to gravity

Radial line

$2R$

$\vec{T}$

Pivot

Line of action

$\vec{w}$ $r_\perp$

R

θ

θ

The moment arm $r_\perp$ is $R \sin \theta$.

We'll use Equation 7.4, $\tau = r_\perp F$, to find the torque due to the weight, which acts at the center of gravity. From Figure 8.28b we see that the moment arm $r_\perp$, the perpendicular distance from the line of action to the pivot, is $r_\perp = R \sin \theta$. The magnitude of the weight force is Mg, so the torque due to the weight is $\tau_w = MgR \sin \theta$.

We can now write the condition that the net torque is zero as

$$\tau_{net} = \tau_w + \tau_T = MgR \sin \theta - 2RT = 0$$

Solving this equation for the tension gives

$$T = \tfrac{1}{2} Mg \sin \theta = \frac{(600\ \text{kg})(9.8\ \text{m/s}^2)}{2} \sin 20° = 1000\ \text{N}$$

Note that R cancels, so the tension does not depend on the radius of the barrel.

b. Part a was solved using only the net torque equation. For this part, we'll need the two force equations as well. From the free-body diagram of Figure 8.27, we can write

$$\sum F_x = T + f_s - Mg \sin \theta = 0$$

$$\sum F_y = n - Mg\cos\theta = 0$$

We can solve the first of these equations for the friction force:

$$f_s = Mg \sin \theta - T = Mg \sin \theta - \tfrac{1}{2}Mg \sin \theta = \tfrac{1}{2}Mg \sin \theta$$

Here we used the result for the tension T found in part a.

The static friction must have this value to keep the barrel from slipping. But static friction can't exceed the maximum possible value, $f_{s\,max} = \mu_s n$. From the y force equation, the normal force is $n = Mg \cos \theta$, so $f_{s\,max} = \mu_s Mg \cos \theta$. The barrel will slip when the friction force equals its maximum possible value, or when

$$f_s = \tfrac{1}{2} Mg \sin \theta = f_{s\,max} = \mu_s Mg \cos \theta$$

The factor Mg cancels from both sides of this equation, giving $\tfrac{1}{2} \sin \theta = \mu_s \cos \theta$, which, after dividing both sides by $\cos \theta$, can be written as $\tfrac{1}{2} \tan \theta = \mu_s$. Thus the angle at which the barrel will slip is given by $\tan \theta = 2\mu_s$, or

$$\theta = \tan^{-1}(2\mu_s) = \tan^{-1}(2 \cdot 0.25) = 27°$$

c. The maximum possible stress in the rope, when it is at its breaking point, is

$$\frac{F}{A} = \frac{T}{\pi r^2} = \frac{1000\ \text{N}}{\pi r^2} = 2.0 \times 10^7\ \text{N/m}^2$$

The radius of the rope at this level of stress is

$$r = \sqrt{\frac{1000\ \text{N}}{\pi(2.0 \times 10^7\ \text{N/m}^2)}} = 4.0 \times 10^{-3}\ \text{m}$$

The minimum rope diameter is twice this radius, or 8.0 mm. If the rope were any smaller, the stress would exceed the tensile strength of polypropylene and the rope would break.

ASSESS Back in Example 5.14, we found that an object will *slide* (without rolling) down a slope when the angle exceeds $\tan^{-1}\mu_s$, a *smaller* angle than for our rolling object. This makes sense because for the barrel there is an extra uphill force—the tension—that is absent for a sliding object. This uphill force allows the slope to be steeper before a round object begins to slip.

SUMMARY

The goals of Chapter 8 have been to learn about the static equilibrium of extended objects and to understand the basic properties of springs and elastic materials.

GENERAL PRINCIPLES

Static Equilibrium

An object in **static equilibrium** must have no net force on it and no net torque. Mathematically, we express this as

$$\sum F_x = 0$$
$$\sum F_y = 0$$
$$\sum \tau = 0$$

Since the net torque is zero about *any* point, the pivot point for calculating the torque can be chosen at any convenient location.

Springs and Hooke's Law

When a spring is stretched or compressed, it exerts a force proportional to the change Δx in its length but in the opposite direction. This is known as **Hooke's law:**

$$(F_{sp})_x = -k\,\Delta x$$

The constant of proportionality k is called the **spring constant.** It is larger for a "stiff" spring.

IMPORTANT CONCEPTS

Stability

An object is **stable** if its center of gravity is over its base of support; otherwise, it is **unstable.**

Stable   Unstable

Base of support

If an object is tipped, it will reach the limit of its stability when its center of gravity is over the edge of the base. This defines the **critical angle** θ_c.

This object is at its critical angle.

This object has a wider base of support and hence a larger critical angle.

This object has a lower center of gravity, so its critical angle is larger too.

Greater stability is possible with a lower center of gravity or a broader base of support.

Elastic materials and Young's modulus

ΔL Restoring force

Area A $\vec{F}$

L

A solid rod illustrates how materials respond when stretched or compressed.

Stress is the restoring force of the rod divided by its cross-section area.

$$\left(\frac{F}{A}\right) = Y\left(\frac{\Delta L}{L}\right)$$

Strain is the fractional change in the rod's length.

Young's modulus

This equation can also be written as

This is the "spring constant" k for the rod.

$$F = \left(\frac{YA}{L}\right)\Delta L$$

showing that a rod obeys Hooke's law and acts like a very stiff spring.

APPLICATIONS

Forces in the body

Muscles and tendons apply the forces and torques needed to maintain static equilibrium. These forces may be quite large.

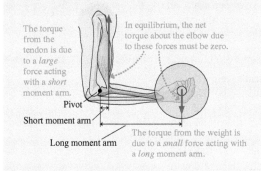

The torque from the tendon is due to a *large* force acting with a *short* moment arm.

In equilibrium, the net torque about the elbow due to these forces must be zero.

Pivot

Short moment arm

Long moment arm

The torque from the weight is due to a *small* force acting with a *long* moment arm.

The elastic limit and beyond

If a rod or other object is not stretched too far, when released it will return to its original shape.

If stretched too far, an object will permanently deform, and finally break. The stress at which an object breaks is its **tensile stress.**

If not stretched beyond here, the object will return to its original length.

F

Hooke's law applies

Breaking point

If stretched to this region, the object will be permanently deformed.

ΔL

QUESTIONS

Conceptual Questions

1. An object is acted upon by two (and only two) forces that are of equal magnitude and oppositely directed. Is the object necessarily in static equilibrium?
2. Sketch a force acting at point P in Figure Q8.2 that would make the rod be in static equilibrium. Is there only one such force?
3. Could a ladder on a level floor lean against a wall in static equilibrium if there were no friction forces? Explain.
4. Suppose you are hanging from a tree branch. If you move out the branch, farther away from the trunk, the branch will be more likely to break. Explain why this is so.
5. As divers stand on tiptoes on the edge of a diving platform, in preparation for a high dive, as shown in Figure Q8.5, they usually extend their arms in front of them. Why do they do this?
6. Where are the centers of gravity of the two people doing the classic yoga poses shown in Figure Q8.6?

FIGURE Q8.2

FIGURE Q8.5

FIGURE Q8.6

7. You must lean quite far forward as you rise from a chair (try it!). Explain why.
8. A spring exerts a 10 N force after being stretched by 1 cm from its equilibrium length. By how much will the spring force *increase* if the spring is stretched from 4 cm away from equilibrium to 5 cm from equilibrium?
9. The left end of a spring is attached to a wall. When Bob pulls on the right end with a 200 N force, he stretches the spring by 20 cm. The same spring is then used for a tug-of-war between Bob and Carlos. Each pulls on his end of the spring with a 200 N force.
   a. How far does Bob's end of the spring move? Explain.
   b. How far does Carlos's end of the spring move? Explain.

10. A spring is attached to the floor and pulled straight up by a string. The string's tension is measured. The graph in Figure Q8.10 shows the tension in the spring as a function of the spring's length *L*.
    a. Does this spring obey Hooke's law? Explain.
    b. If it does, what is the spring constant?

FIGURE Q8.10

11. Take a spring and cut it in half to make two springs. Is the spring constant of these smaller springs larger, smaller, or the same as the spring constant of the original spring? Explain.
12. A wire is stretched right to its breaking point by a 5000 N force. A longer wire made of the same material has the same diameter. Is the force that will stretch it right to its breaking point larger than, smaller than, or equal to 5000 N? Explain.
13. Steel nails are rigid and unbending. Steel wool is soft and squishy. How would you account for this difference?

Multiple-Choice Questions

14. II Two children carry a lightweight 1.8-m-long horizontal pole with a water bucket hanging from it. The older child supports twice as much weight as the younger child. How far is the bucket from the older child?
    A. 0.3 m   B. 0.6 m
    C. 0.9 m   D. 1.2 m
15. II The uniform rod in Figure Q8.15 has a weight of 14.0 N. What is the magnitude of the normal force exerted on the rod by the surface?
    A. 7 N   B. 14 N
    C. 20 N   D. 28 N

Frictionless surface

FIGURE Q8.15

16. I A student lies on a very light, rigid board with a scale under each end. Her feet are directly over one scale, and her body is positioned as shown in Figure Q8.16. The two scales read the values shown in the figure. What is the student's weight?
    A. 65 lb   B. 75 lb
    C. 100 lb   D. 165 lb

FIGURE Q8.16

17. I For the student in Figure Q8.16, approximately how far from her feet is her center of gravity?
    A. 0.6 m   B. 0.8 m
    C. 1.0 m   D. 1.2 m

Questions 18 through 20 use the information in the following paragraph and figure.

Suppose you stand on one foot while holding your other leg up behind you. Your muscles will have to apply a force to hold your leg in this raised position. We can model this situation as in Figure Q8.18. The leg pivots at the knee joint, and the force to hold the leg up is provided by a tendon attached to the lower leg as shown. Assume that the lower leg and the foot together have a combined mass of 4.0 kg, and that their combined center of gravity is at the center of the lower leg.

The tendon provides the torque to raise the lower leg.

5.0 cm

50 cm

FIGURE Q8.18

18. | How much force must the tendon exert to keep the leg in this
BIO position?
A. 40 N   B. 200 N   C. 400 N   D. 1000 N
19. | As you hold your leg in this position, the upper leg exerts a
BIO force on the lower leg at the knee joint. What is the direction of this force?
A. Up   B. Down   C. Right   D. Left
20. | What is the magnitude of the force of the upper leg on the
BIO lower leg at the knee joint?
A. 40 N   B. 160 N   C. 200 N   D. 240 N

21. ‖ You have a heavy piece of equipment hanging from a 1.0-mm-diameter wire. Your supervisor asks that the length of the wire be doubled without changing how far the wire stretches. What diameter must the new wire have?
A. 1.0 mm   B. 1.4 mm   C. 2.0 mm   D. 4.0 mm
22. ‖ A 30.0-cm-long board is placed on a table such that its right end hangs over the edge by 8.0 cm. A second identical board is stacked on top of the first, as shown in Figure Q8.22. What is the largest that the distance x can be before both boards topple over?
A. 4.0 cm   B. 8.0 cm
C. 14 cm   D. 15 cm

30.0 cm

x

8.0 cm

FIGURE Q8.22

23. ‖ Two 20 kg blocks are connected by a 2.0-m-long, 5.0-mm-diameter rope. Young's modulus for this rope is 1.5×10^9 N/m². The rope is then hung over a pulley, so that the blocks, hanging from each side of the pulley, are in static equilibrium. By how much does the rope stretch?
A. 3.0 mm   B. 6.3 mm
C. 9.3 mm   D. 13 mm

PROBLEMS

Section 8.1 Torque and Static Equilibrium

1. ‖ A 64 kg woman stands on a very light, rigid board that rests on a bathroom scale at each end, as shown in Figure P8.1. What is the reading on each of the scales?

1.5 m

2.0 m

FIGURE P8.1

2. ‖ Suppose the woman in Figure P8.1 is 54 kg, and the board she is standing on has a 10 kg mass. What is the reading on each of the scales?
3. ‖ How close to the right edge of the 56 kg picnic table shown in Figure P8.3 can a 70 kg man stand without the table tipping over?

2.10 m

0.74 m   0.55 m

FIGURE P8.3

4. ‖ In Figure P8.4, a 70 kg man walks out on a 10 kg beam that rests on, but is not attached to, two supports. When the beam just starts to tip, what is the force exerted on the beam by the right support?

FIGURE P8.4

5. ‖ You're carrying a 3.6-m-long, 25 kg pole to a construction site when you decide to stop for a rest. You place one end of the pole on a fence post and hold the other end of the pole 35 cm from its tip. How much force must you exert to keep the pole motionless in a horizontal position?

6. ‖ How much torque must the pin exert to keep the rod in Figure P8.6 from rotating? Calculate this torque about an axis that passes through the point where the pin enters the rod and is perpendicular to the plane of the figure.

80 cm

2.0 kg

Pin

500 g

FIGURE P8.6

7. ‖ Is the object in Figure P8.7 in equilibrium? Explain.

100 N

2.0 m

1.0 m

2.0 m   1.0 m

4.0 kg

40 N   Massless   60 N d 1.0 kg

FIGURE P8.7   FIGURE P8.8

8. ‖ The two objects in Figure P8.8 are balanced on the pivot. What is distance d?

9. ⫽ A 60 kg diver stands at the end of a 30 kg springboard, as shown in Figure P8.9. The board is attached to a hinge at the left end but simply rests on the right support. What is the magnitude of the vertical force exerted by the hinge on the board?

FIGURE P8.9

10. ⫽ A uniform beam of length 1.0 m and mass 10 kg is attached to a wall by a cable, as shown in Figure P8.10. The beam is free to pivot at the point where it attaches to the wall. What is the tension in the cable?

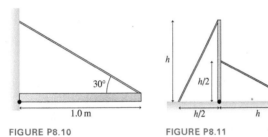

FIGURE P8.10   FIGURE P8.11

11. ⫽ Figure P8.11 shows a vertical pole of height h that can rotate about a hinge at the bottom. The pole is held in position by two wires under tension. What is the ratio of the tension in the left wire to the tension in the right wire?

Section 8.2 Stability and Balance

12. ⫽ You want to slowly push a stiff board across a 20 cm gap between two tabletops that are at the same height. If you apply only a horizontal force, how long must the board be so that it doesn't tilt down into the gap before reaching the other side?

13. ⎮ A magazine rack has a center of gravity 16 cm above the floor, as shown in Figure P8.13. Through what maximum angle, in degrees, can the rack be tilted without falling over?

14. ⫽ A car manufacturer claims that you can drive its new vehicle across a hill with a 47° slope before the vehicle starts to tip. If the vehicle is 2.0 m wide, how high is its center of gravity?

FIGURE P8.13

15. ⫽ A thin 2.00 kg box rests on a 6.00 kg board that hangs over the end of a table, as shown in Figure P8.15. How far can the center of the box be from the end of the table before the board begins to tilt?

FIGURE P8.15   FIGURE P8.16

16. ⫽ The object shown in Figure P8.16 is made of a uniform material. What is the greatest that x can be without the object tipping over?

Section 8.3 Springs and Hooke's Law

17. ⎮ One end of a spring is attached to a wall. A 25 N pull on the other end causes the spring to stretch by 3.0 cm. What is the spring constant?

18. ⎮ Experiments using "optical tweezers" measure the elasticity
BIO of individual DNA molecules. For small enough changes in length, the elasticity has the same form as that of a spring. A DNA molecule is anchored at one end, then a force of 1.5 nN $(1.5 \times 10^{-9}$ N) pulls on the other end, causing the molecule to stretch by 5.0 nm $(5.0 \times 10^{-9}$ m). What is the spring constant of that DNA molecule?

19. ⫽ A spring has an unstretched length of 10 cm. It exerts a restoring force F when stretched to a length of 11 cm.
   a. For what total stretched length of the spring is its restoring force $3F$?
   b. At what compressed length is the restoring force $2F$?

20. ⫽ A 10-cm-long spring is attached to the ceiling. When a 2.0 kg mass is hung from it, the spring stretches to a length of 15 cm.
   a. What is the spring constant?
   b. How long is the spring when a 3.0 kg mass is suspended from it?

21. ⫽ A spring stretches 5.0 cm when a 0.20 kg block is hung from it. If a 0.70 kg block replaces the 0.20 kg block, how far does the spring stretch?

22. ⫽ A 1.2 kg block is hung from a vertical spring, causing the spring to stretch by 2.4 cm. How much farther will the spring stretch if a 0.60 kg block is added to the 1.2 kg block?

23. ⫽ A runner wearing spiked shoes pulls a 20 kg sled across frictionless ice using a horizontal spring with spring constant 1.5×10^2 N/m. The spring is stretched 20 cm from its equilibrium length. What is the acceleration of the sled?

24. ⎮ You need to make a spring scale to measure the mass of objects hung from it. You want each 1.0 cm length along the scale to correspond to a mass difference of 0.10 kg. What should be the value of the spring constant?

Section 8.4 Stretching and Compressing Materials

25. ⫽ A force stretches a wire by 1.0 mm.
   a. A second wire of the same material has the same cross section and twice the length. How far will it be stretched by the same force?
   b. A third wire of the same material has the same length and twice the diameter as the first. How far will it be stretched by the same force?

26. ⫽⫽ What hanging mass will stretch a 2.0-m-long, 0.50-mm-diameter steel wire by 1.0 mm?

27. ⫽⫽ How much force does it take to stretch a 10-m-long, 1.0-cm-diameter steel cable by 5.0 mm?

28. ⫽⫽ An 80-cm-long, 1.0-mm-diameter steel guitar string must be tightened to a tension of 2.0 kN by turning the tuning screws. By how much is the string stretched?

29. ⫽⫽ A 2000 N force stretches a wire by 1.0 mm.
   a. A second wire of the same material is twice as long and has twice the diameter. How much force is needed to stretch it by 1.0 mm? Explain.
   b. A third wire of the same material is twice as long as the first and has the same diameter. How far is it stretched by a 4000 N force?

30. ⫽⫽ A 1.2-m-long steel rod with a diameter of 0.50 cm hangs vertically from the ceiling. An auto engine weighing 4.7 kN is hung from the rod. By how much does the rod stretch?

31. ▌▌▌ A mine shaft has an elevator hung from a single steel-wire cable of diameter 2.5 cm. When the cable is fully extended, the end of the cable is 500 m below the support. How much does the fully extended cable stretch when 3000 kg of ore is loaded into the elevator?

32. ▌▌ The normal force of the ground on the foot can reach three
BIO times a runner's body weight when the foot strikes the pavement. By what amount does the 52-cm-long femur of an 80 kg runner compress at this moment? The cross-section area of the bone of the femur can be taken as 5.2×10^{-4} m².

33. ▌▌▌ A three-legged wooden bar stool made out of solid Douglas fir has legs that are 2.0 cm in diameter. When a 75 kg man sits on the stool, by what percent does the length of the legs decrease? Assume, for simplicity, that the stool's legs are vertical and that each bears the same load.

34. ▌▌ A 3.0-m-tall, 50-cm-diameter concrete column supports a 200,000 kg load. By how much is the column compressed?

General Problems

35. ▌▌▌▌ A 3.0-m-long rigid beam with a mass of 100 kg is supported at each end, as shown in Figure P8.35. An 80 kg student stands 2.0 m from support 1. How much upward force does each support exert on the beam?

FIGURE P8.35

36. ▌▌ An 80 kg construction worker sits down 2.0 m from the end of a 1450 kg steel beam to eat his lunch, as shown in Figure P8.36. The cable supporting the beam is rated at 15,000 N. Should the worker be worried?

FIGURE P8.36

37. ▌▌▌▌ Using the information in Figure 8.2, calculate the tension in
BIO the biceps tendon if the hand is holding a 10 kg ball while the forearm is held 45° below horizontal.

38. ▌▌▌ A woman weighing 580 N does a
BIO pushup from her knees, as shown in Figure P8.38. What are the normal forces of the floor on (a) each of her hands and (b) each of her knees?

FIGURE P8.38

39. ▌▌▌▌ When you bend over, a series of large
BIO muscles, the erector spinae, pull on your spine to hold you up. Figure P8.39 shows a simplified model of the spine as a rod of length L that pivots at its lower end. In this model, the center of gravity of the 320 N weight of the upper torso is at the center of the spine. The 160 N weight of the head and arms acts at the top of the spine. The erector spinae muscles are modeled as a single muscle that acts at an 12° angle to the spine. Suppose the

person in Figure P8.39 bends over to an angle of 30° from the horizontal.

a. What is the tension in the erector muscle?
Hint: Align your x-axis with the axis of the spine.

b. A force from the pelvic girdle acts on the base of the spine. What is the component of this force in the direction of the spine? (This large force is the cause of many back injuries).

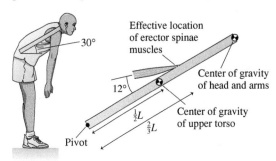

FIGURE P8.39

40. ▌ The woman lying on the reaction board in Example 8.3 spreads her arms out in the plane of the board. The reading of the scale is observed to increase by 10 N. By how much does the distance from her feet to her center of gravity change?

41. ▌▌▌ A man is attempting to raise a 7.5-m-long, 28 kg flagpole that has a hinge at the base by pulling on a rope attached to the top of the pole, as shown in Figure P8.41. With what force does the man have to pull on the rope to hold the pole motionless in this position?

FIGURE P8.41

42. ▌▌▌▌ A library ladder of length L rolls on wheels as shown in Figure P8.42. The two legs of the ladder freely pivot at the hinge at the top. The legs are kept from splaying apart by a lightweight chain that is attached halfway up the ladder. If the ladder weighs 200 N, and the angle between each leg and the vertical is 25°, what is the tension in the chain?

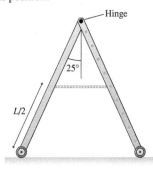

FIGURE P8.42

43. ▌▌▌▌ A 40 kg, 5.0-m-long beam is supported by, but not attached to, the two posts in Figure P8.43. A 20 kg boy starts walking along the beam. How close can he get to the right end of the beam without it tipping?

FIGURE P8.43   FIGURE P8.44

44. ▌▌▌ The wheel of mass m in Figure P8.44 is pulled on by a horizontal force applied at its center. The wheel is touching a curb whose height is half the wheel's radius. What is the minimum force required to just raise the wheel off the ground?

45. ‖ A 5.0 kg mass hanging from a spring scale is slowly lowered onto a vertical spring, as shown in Figure P8.45. The scale reads in newtons.

FIGURE P8.45

   a. What does the spring scale read just before the mass touches the lower spring?
   b. The scale reads 20 N when the lower spring has been compressed by 2.0 cm. What is the value of the spring constant for the lower spring?
   c. At what compression distance will the scale read zero?

46. ‖‖ Two identical, side-by-side springs with spring constant 240 N/m support a 2.00 kg hanging box. By how much is each spring stretched?

47. ‖ Two springs have the same equilibrium length but different spring constants. They are arranged as shown in Figure P8.47, then a block is pushed against them, compressing both by 1.00 cm. With what net force do they push back on the block?

FIGURE P8.47   FIGURE P8.48

48. ‖ Two springs have the same spring constant $k = 130$ N/m but different equilibrium lengths, 3.0 cm and 5.0 cm. They are arranged as shown in Figure P8.48, then a block is pushed against them, compressing both to a length of 2.5 cm. With what net force do they push back on the block?

49. ‖ Figure P8.49 shows two springs attached to a block that can slide on a frictionless surface. In the block's equilibrium position, the left spring is compressed by 2.0 cm.

FIGURE P8.49

   a. By how much is the right spring compressed?
   b. What is the net force on the block if it is moved 15 cm to the right of its equilibrium position?

50. ‖‖ Figure P8.50 shows two springs attached to each other, and also attached to a box that can slide on a frictionless surface. In the block's equilibrium position, neither spring is stretched. What is the net force on the block if it is moved 15 cm to the right of its equilibrium position?
   Hint: There is zero net force on the point where the two springs meet. This implies a relationship between the amounts the two springs stretch.

51. ‖ A 60 kg student is standing atop a spring in an elevator that is accelerating upward at 3.0 m/s². The spring constant is 2.5×10^3 N/m. By how much is the spring compressed?

52. ‖‖ A 25 kg child bounces on a pogo stick. The pogo stick has a spring with spring constant 2.0×10^4 N/m. When the child makes a nice big bounce, she finds that at the bottom of the bounce she is accelerating *upward* at 9.8 m/s². How much is the spring compressed?

53. ‖‖‖ Two 3.0 kg blocks on a level, frictionless surface are connected by a spring with spring constant 1000 N/m, as shown in Figure P8.53.

FIGURE P8.53

   The left block is pushed by a horizontal force $\vec{F}$. At $t = 0$ s, both blocks have velocity 3.2 m/s to the right. For the next second, the spring's compression is a constant 1.5 cm.
   a. What is the velocity of the right block at $t = 1.0$ s?
   b. What is the magnitude of $\vec{F}$ during that 1.0 s interval?

54. ‖ What is the effective spring constant (that is, the ratio of force to change in length) of a copper cable that is 5.0 mm in diameter and 5.0 m long?

55. ‖‖ Figure P8.55 shows a 100 kg plank supported at its right end by a 7.0-mm-diameter rope with a tensile strength of 6.0×10^7 N/m². How far along the plank, measured from the pivot, can the center of gravity of an 800 kg piece of heavy machinery be placed before the rope snaps?

FIGURE P8.55

56. ‖‖‖ When you walk, your Achilles tendon, which connects your heel to your calf muscles, repeatedly stretches and contracts, much like a spring. This helps make walking more efficient. Suppose your Achilles tendon is 15 cm long and has a cross-section area of 110 mm², typical values. If you model the Achilles tendon as a spring, what is its spring constant?

57. ‖‖‖ There is a disk of cartilage between each pair of vertebrae in your spine. Suppose a disk is 0.50 cm thick and 4.0 cm in diameter. If this disk supports half the weight of a 65 kg person, by what fraction of its thickness does the disk compress?

58. ‖‖ In Example 8.1, the tension in the biceps tendon for a person doing a strict curl of a 900 N barbell was found to be 3900 N. What fraction does this represent of the maximum possible tension the biceps tendon can support? You can assume a typical cross-section area of 130 mm².

59. ‖‖‖ Larger animals have sturdier bones than smaller animals. A mouse's skeleton is only a few percent of its body weight, compared to 16% for an elephant. To see why this must be so, recall, from Example 8.10, that the stress on the femur for a man standing on one leg is 1.4% of the bone's tensile strength. Suppose we scale this man up by a factor of 10 in all dimensions, keeping the same body proportions. Use the data for Example 8.10 to compute the following.
   a. Both the inside and outside diameter of the femur, the region of cortical bone, will increase by a factor of 10. What will be the new cross-section area?
   b. The man's body will increase by a factor of 10 in each dimension. What will be his new mass?
   c. If the scaled-up man now stands on one leg, what fraction of the tensile strength is the stress on the femur?

60. ‖ Orb spiders make silk with a typical diameter of 0.15 mm.
   a. A typical large orb spider has a mass of 0.50 g. If this spider suspends itself from a single 12-cm-long strand of silk, by how much will the silk stretch?
   b. What is the maximum weight that a single thread of this silk could support?

Passage Problems

Standing on Tiptoes BIO

When you stand on your tiptoes, your feet pivot about your ankle. As shown in Figure P8.61, the forces on your foot are an upward force on your toes from the floor, a downward force on your ankle from the lower leg bone, and an upward force on the heel of your foot from your Achilles tendon. Suppose a 60 kg woman stands on tiptoes with the sole of her foot making a 25° angle with the floor. Assume that each foot supports half her weight.

Achilles tendon

Ankle pivot

15 cm

20 cm

FIGURE P8.61

61. ‖‖ What is the upward force of the floor on the toes of one foot?
    A. 140 N   B. 290 N
    C. 420 N   D. 590 N

62. ‖ What upward force does the Achilles tendon exert on the heel of her foot?
    A. 290 N   B. 420 N
    C. 590 N   D. 880 N

63. ‖‖ The tension in the Achilles tendon will cause it to stretch. If the Achilles tendon is 15 cm long and has a cross-section area of 110 mm², by how much will it stretch under this force?
    A. 0.2 mm   B. 0.8 mm
    C. 2.3 mm   D. 5.2 mm

STOP TO THINK ANSWERS

Stop to Think 8.1: D. Only object D has both zero net force and zero net torque.

Stop to Think 8.2: B. The tension in the rope and the weight have no horizontal component. To make the net force zero, the force due to the pivot must also have no horizontal component, so we know it points either up or down. Now consider the torque about the point where the rope is attached. The tension provides no torque. The weight exerts a counterclockwise torque. To make the net torque zero, the pivot force must exert a *clockwise* torque, which it can do only if it points *up*.

Stop to Think 8.3: B, A, C. The critical angle θ_c, shown in the figure, measures how far the object can be tipped before falling. B has the smallest critical angle, followed by A, then C.

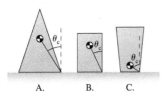

A.   B.   C.

Stop to Think 8.4: C. The restoring force of the spring is proportional to the stretch. Increasing the restoring force by a factor of 3 requires increasing the stretch by a factor of 3.

Stop to Think 8.5: E. The cables have the same diameter, and the force is the same, so the stress is the same in both cases. This means that the strain, $\Delta L/L$, is the same. The 2 m cable will experience twice the change in length of the 1 m cable.

Force and Motion

The goal of Part I has been to discover the connection between force and motion. We started with kinematics, the mathematical description of motion; then we proceeded to dynamics, the explanation of motion in terms of forces. We then used these descriptions to analyze and explain motions ranging from the motion of the moon about the earth to the forces in your elbow when you lift a weight. Newton's three laws of motion formed the basis of all of our explanations.

The table below is a *knowledge structure* for force and motion. The knowledge structure does not represent everything you have learned over the past eight chapters. It's a summary of the "big picture," outlining the basic goals, the general principles, and the primary applications of the part of the book we have just finished. When you are immersed in a chapter, it may be hard to see the connections among all

of the different topics. Before we move on to new topics, we will finish each part of the book with a knowledge structure to make these connections clear.

Work through the knowledge structure from top to bottom. First are the goals and general principles. There aren't that many general principles, but we can use them along with the general problem-solving strategy to solve a wide range of problems. Once you recognize a problem as a dynamics problem, you immediately know to start with Newton's laws. You can then determine the category of motion and apply Newton's second law in the appropriate form. The kinematic equations for that category of motion then allow you to reach the solution you seek. These equations and other detailed information from the chapters are summarized in the bottom section.

KNOWLEDGE STRUCTURE I Force and Motion

BASIC GOALS

How can we describe motion? How does an object respond to a force?
How do systems interact? What is the nature of the force of gravity?
How can we analyze the motion and deformation of extended objects?

GENERAL PRINCIPLES

Newton's first law   An object with no forces acting on it will remain at rest or move in a straight line at a constant speed.

Newton's second law $\vec{F}_{net} = m\vec{a}$

Newton's third law $\vec{F}_{A\,on\,B} = -\vec{F}_{B\,on\,A}$

Newton's law of gravity $F_{1\,on\,2} = F_{2\,on\,1} = \dfrac{Gm_1 m_2}{r^2}$

BASIC PROBLEM-SOLVING STRATEGY

Use Newton's second law for each particle or system. Use Newton's third law to equate the magnitudes of the two members of an action/reaction pair.

Types of forces:
$$\vec{w} = (mg,\ \text{downward})$$
$$\vec{f}_k = (\mu_k n,\ \text{opposite motion})$$
$$(F_{sp})_x = -k\,\Delta x$$

Linear and projectile motion:
$$\left.\begin{array}{l}\sum F_x = ma_x \\ \sum F_y = 0\end{array}\right\} \text{ or } \left\{\begin{array}{l}\sum F_x = 0 \\ \sum F_y = ma_y\end{array}\right.$$

Circular motion:

The force is directed to the center:
$$\vec{F}_{net} = \left(\dfrac{mv^2}{r},\ \text{toward center of circle}\right)$$

Rigid-body motion:
When a torque is exerted on an object with moment of inertia I,
$$\tau_{net} = I\alpha$$

Equilibrium:
For an object at rest,
$$\sum F_x = 0 \quad \sum \tau = 0$$
$$\sum F_y = 0$$

Linear and projectile kinematics

Uniform motion: $x_f = x_i + v_x\,\Delta t$
$(a_x = 0,\ v_x = \text{constant})$

Constant acceleration: $(v_x)_f = (v_x)_i + a_x\,\Delta t$
$(a_x = \text{constant})$
$$x_f = x_i + (v_x)_i\,\Delta t + \tfrac{1}{2}a_x(\Delta t)^2$$
$$(v_x)_f^2 = (v_x)_i^2 + 2a_x\,\Delta x$$

Projectile motion:
Projectile motion is uniform horizontal motion and constant-acceleration vertical motion with $a_y = -g$.

Velocity is the slope of the position-versus-time graph.
Acceleration is the slope of the velocity-versus-time graph.

Circular kinematics

Uniform circular motion:
$$f = \dfrac{1}{T} \qquad \omega = 2\pi f$$
$$v = \dfrac{2\pi r}{T} = \omega r \qquad a = \dfrac{v^2}{r} = \omega^2 r$$

Rigid bodies

Torque $\tau = rF_\perp = r_\perp F$

Center of gravity $x_{cg} = \dfrac{x_1 m_1 + x_2 m_2 + \cdots}{m_1 + m_2 + \cdots}$

Moment of inertia $I = \sum mr^2$

Dark Matter and the Structure of the Universe

The idea that the earth exerts a gravitational force on us is something we now accept without questioning. But when Isaac Newton developed this idea to show that the gravitational force also holds the moon in its orbit, it was a remarkable, ground-breaking insight. It changed the way that we look at the universe we live in.

Newton's laws of motion and gravity are tools that allow us to continue Newton's quest to better understand our place in the cosmos. But it sometimes seems that the more we learn, the more we realize how little we actually know and understand.

Here's an example. Advances in astronomy over the past 100 years have given us great insight into the structure of the universe. But everything our telescopes can see appears to be only a small fraction of what is out there. As much as 90% of the mass in the universe is *dark matter*—matter that gives off no light or other radiation that we can detect. Everything that we have ever seen through a telescope is merely the tip of the cosmic iceberg.

What is this dark matter? Black holes? Neutrinos? Some form of exotic particle? No one knows. It could be any of these, or all of them—or something entirely different that no one has yet dreamed of. You might wonder how we know that such matter exists if no one has seen it. Even though we can't directly observe dark matter, we see its effects. And you now know enough physics to understand why.

Whatever dark matter is, it has mass, and so it has gravity. This picture of the Andromeda galaxy shows a typical spiral galaxy structure: a dense collection of stars in the center surrounded by a disk of stars and other matter. This is the shape of our own Milky Way galaxy.

The spiral Andromeda galaxy.

This structure is reminiscent of the structure of the solar system: a dense mass (the sun) in the center surrounded by a disk of other matter (the planets, asteroids, and comets). The sun's gravity keeps the planets in their orbits, but the planets would fall into the sun unless they were in constant motion around it. The same is true of a spiral galaxy; everything in the galaxy orbits its center. Our solar system orbits the center of our galaxy with a period of about 200 million years.

The orbital speed of an object depends on the mass that pulls on it. If you analyze our sun's motion about the center of the Milky Way, or the motion of stars in the Andromeda galaxy about its center, you find that the orbits are much faster than they should be, based on how many stars we see. There must be some other mass present.

There's another problem with the orbital motion of stars around the center of their galaxies. We know that the orbital speeds of planets decrease with distance from the sun; Neptune orbits at a much slower speed than the earth. We might expect something similar for galaxies: Stars farther from the center should orbit at reduced speeds. But they don't. As we measure outward from the center of the galaxy, the orbital speed stays about the same—even as we get to the edge of the visible disk. There must be some other mass—the invisible dark matter—exerting a gravitational force on the stars. This dark matter, which far outweighs the matter we can see, seems to form a halo around the centers of galaxies, providing the gravitational force necessary to produce the observed rotation. Other observations of the motions of galaxies with respect to each other verify this basic idea.

On a cosmic scale, the picture is even stranger. The universe is currently expanding. The mutual gravitational attraction of all matter—regular and dark—in the universe should slow this expansion. But recent observations of the speeds of distant galaxies imply that the expansion of the universe is accelerating, so there must be yet another component to the universe, something that "pushes out". The best explanation at present is that the acceleration is caused by *dark energy*. The nature of dark matter isn't known, but the nature of dark energy is even more mysterious. If current theories hold, it's the most abundant stuff in the universe. And we don't know what it is.

This sort of mystery is what drives scientific investigation. It's what drove Newton to wonder about the connection between the fall of an apple and the motion of the moon, and what drove investigators to develop all of the techniques and theories you will learn about in the coming chapters.

The following questions are related to the passage "Dark Matter and the Structure of the Universe" on the previous page.

1. As noted in the passage, our solar system orbits the center of the Milky Way galaxy in about 200 million years. If there were no dark matter in our galaxy, this period would be
   A. Longer.
   B. The same.
   C. Shorter.
2. Saturn is approximately 10 times as far away from the sun as the earth. This means that its orbital acceleration is _____ that of the earth.
   A. 1/10
   B. 1/100
   C. 1/1000
   D. 1/10,000

3. Saturn is approximately 10 times as far away from the sun as the earth. If dark matter changed the orbital properties of the planets so that Saturn had the same orbital speed as the earth, Saturn's orbital acceleration would be _____ that of the earth.
   A. 1/10
   B. 1/100
   C. 1/1000
   D. 1/10,000
4. Which of the following might you expect to be an additional consequence of the fact that galaxies contain more mass than expected?
   A. The gravitational force between galaxies is greater than expected.
   B. Galaxies appear less bright than expected.
   C. Galaxies are farther away than expected.
   D. There are more galaxies than expected.

The following passages and associated questions are based on the material of Part I.

Animal Athletes BIO

Different animals have very different capacities for running. A horse can maintain a top speed of 20 m/s for a long distance but has a maximum acceleration of only 6.0 m/s², half what a good human sprinter can achieve with a block to push against. Greyhounds, dogs especially bred for feats of running, have a top speed of 17 m/s, but their acceleration is much greater than that of the horse. Greyhounds are particularly adept at turning corners at a run.

FIGURE I.1

5. If a horse starts from rest and accelerates at the maximum value until reaching its top speed, how much time elapses, to the nearest second?
   A. 1 s   B. 2 s
   C. 3 s   D. 4 s
6. If a horse starts from rest and accelerates at the maximum value until reaching its top speed, how far does it run, to the nearest 10 m?
   A. 40 m   B. 30 m
   C. 20 m   D. 10 m
7. A greyhound on a racetrack turns a corner at a constant speed of 15 m/s with an acceleration of 7.1 m/s². What is the radius of the turn?
   A. 40 m   B. 30 m
   C. 20 m   D. 10 m
8. A human sprinter of mass 70 kg starts a run at the maximum possible acceleration, pushing backward against a block set in the track. What is the force of his foot on the block?
   A. 1500 N   B. 840 N
   C. 690 N   D. 420 N
9. In the photograph of the greyhounds in Figure I.1, what is the direction of the net force on each dog?
   A. Up
   B. Down
   C. Left, toward the outside of the turn
   D. Right, toward the inside of the turn

Sticky Liquids BIO

The drag force on an object moving in a liquid is quite different from that in air. Drag forces in air are largely the result of the object having to push the air out of its way as it moves. For an object moving slowly through a liquid, however, the drag force is mostly due to the *viscosity* of the liquid, a measure of how much resistance to flow the fluid has. Honey, which drizzles slowly out of its container, has a much higher viscosity than water, which flows fairly freely.

The *viscous drag* force in a liquid depends on the shape of the object, but there is a simple result called *Stokes's law* for the drag on a sphere. The drag force on a sphere of radius r moving at speed v through a fluid with viscosity η is

$$\vec{D} = (6\pi\eta rv, \text{ direction opposite motion})$$

At small scales, viscous drag becomes very important. To a paramecium (Figure I.2), a single-celled animal that can propel itself through water with fine hairs on its body, swimming through water feels like swimming through honey would to you. We can model a paramecium as a sphere of diameter 50 μm, with a mass of 6.5×10^{-11} kg. Water has a viscosity of 0.0010 N · s/m².

FIGURE I.2

10. A paramecium swimming at a constant speed of 0.25 mm/s ceases propelling itself and slows to a stop. At the instant it stops swimming, what is the magnitude of its acceleration?
    A. 0.2g   B. 0.5g
    C. 2g   D. 5g
11. If the acceleration of the paramecium in Problem 10 were to stay constant as it comes to rest, approximately how far would it travel before stopping?
    A. 0.02 μm   B. 0.2 μm
    C. 2 μm   D. 20 μm
12. If the paramecium doubles its swimming speed, how does this change the drag force?
    A. The drag force decreases by a factor of 2.
    B. The drag force is unaffected.
    C. The drag force increases by a factor of 2.
    D. The drag force increases by a factor of 4.

13. You can test the viscosity of a liquid by dropping a steel sphere into it and measuring the speed at which it sinks. For viscous fluids, the sphere will rapidly reach a terminal speed. At this terminal speed, the net force on the sphere is
   A. Directed downward.
   B. Zero.
   C. Directed upward.

Pulling Out of a Dive BIO

Falcons are excellent fliers that can reach very high speeds by diving nearly straight down. To pull out of such a dive, a falcon extends its wings and flies through a circular arc that redirects its motion. The forces on the falcon that control its motion are its weight and an upward lift force—like an airplane—due to the air flowing over its wings. At the bottom of the arc, as in Figure I.3, a falcon can easily achieve an acceleration of 15 m/s².

FIGURE I.3

14. At the bottom of the arc, as in Figure I.3, what is the direction of the net force on the falcon?
   A. To the left, opposite the motion
   B. To the right, in the direction of the motion
   C. Up
   D. Down
   E. The net force is zero.
15. Suppose the falcon weighs 8.0 N and is turning with an acceleration of 15 m/s² at the lowest point of the arc. What is the magnitude of the upward lift force at this instant?
   A. 8.0 N   B. 12 N
   C. 16 N   D. 20 N
16. A falcon starts from rest, does a free-fall dive from a height of 30 m, and then pulls out by flying in a circular arc of radius 50 m. Which segment of the motion has a higher acceleration?
   A. The free-fall dive
   B. The circular arc
   C. The two accelerations are equal.

Bending Beams

If you bend a rod down, it compresses the lower side of the rod and stretches the top, resulting in a restoring force. Figure I.4 shows a

If the beam is pushed down, there is an upward restoring force.

FIGURE I.4

beam of length L, width w, and thickness t fixed at one end and free to move at the other. Deflecting the end of the beam causes a restoring force F at the end of the beam. The magnitude of the restoring force F depends on the dimensions of the beam, the Young's modulus Y for the material, and the deflection d. For small values of the deflection, the restoring force is

$$F = \left[\frac{Ywt^3}{4L^3}\right]d$$

This is similar to the formula for the restoring force of a spring, with the quantity in brackets playing the role of the spring constant k.
   When a 70 kg man stands on the end of a springboard (a type of diving board), the board deflects by 4.0 cm.
17. If a 35 kg child stands at the end of the board, the deflection is
   A. 1.0 cm.   B. 2.0 cm.
   C. 3.0 cm.   D. 4.0 cm.
18. A 70 kg man jumps up and lands on the end of the board, deflecting it by 12 cm. At this instant, what is the approximate magnitude of the upward force the board exerts on his feet?
   A. 700 N   B. 1400 N
   C. 2100 N   D. 2800 N
19. If the board is replaced by one that is half the length but otherwise identical, how much will it deflect when a 70 kg man stands on the end?
   A. 0.50 cm   B. 1.0 cm
   C. 2.0 cm   D. 4.0 cm

Additional Integrated Problems

20. You go to the playground and slide down the slide, a 3.0-m-long ramp at an angle of 40° with respect to horizontal. The pants that you've worn aren't very slippery; the coefficient of kinetic friction between your pants and the slide is $\mu_k = 0.45$. A friend gives you a very slight push to get you started. How long does it take you to reach the bottom of the slide?
21. If you stand on a scale at the equator, the scale will read slightly less than your true weight due to your circular motion with the rotation of the earth.
   a. Draw a free-body diagram to show why this is so.
   b. By how much is the scale reading reduced for a person with a true weight of 800 N?
22. Dolphins and other sea creatures can leap to great heights by swimming straight up and exiting the water at a high speed. A 210 kg dolphin leaps straight up to a height of 7.0 m. When the dolphin reenters the water, drag from the water brings it to a stop in 1.5 m. Assuming that the force of the water on the dolphin stays constant as it slows down,
   a. How much time does it take for the dolphin to come to rest?
   b. What is the force of the water on the dolphin as it is coming to rest?

PART

II

Conservation Laws

The kestrel is pulling in its wings to begin a steep dive, in which it can achieve a speed of 60 mph. How does the bird achieve such a speed, and why does this speed help the kestrel catch its prey? Such questions are best answered by considering the conservation of energy and momentum.

Why Some Things Stay the Same

Part I of this textbook was about *change*. Simple observations show us that most things in the world around us are changing. Even so, there are some things that *don't* change even as everything else is changing around them. Our emphasis in Part II will be on things that stay the same.

Consider, for example, a strong, sealed box in which you have replaced all the air with a mixture of hydrogen and oxygen. The mass of the box plus the gases inside is 600.0 g. Now, suppose you use a spark to ignite the hydrogen and oxygen. As you know, this is an explosive reaction, with the hydrogen and oxygen combining to create water—and quite a bang. But the strong box contains the explosion and all of its products.

What is the mass of the box after the reaction? The gas inside the box is different now, but a careful measurement would reveal that the mass hasn't changed—it's still 600.0 g! We say that the mass is *conserved*. Of course, this is true only if the box has stayed sealed. For conservation of mass to apply, the system must be *closed*.

Conservation Laws

A closed system of interacting particles has another remarkable property. Each system is characterized by a certain number, and no matter how complex the interactions, the value of this number never changes. This number is called the *energy* of the system, and the fact that it never changes is called the *law of conservation of energy*. It is, perhaps, the single most important physical law ever discovered.

The law of conservation of energy is much more general than Newton's laws. Energy can be converted to many different forms, and, in all cases, the total energy stays the same:

- Gasoline, diesel, and jet engines convert the energy of a fuel into the mechanical energy of moving pistons, wheels, and gears.
- A solar cell converts the electromagnetic energy of light into electrical energy.
- An organism converts the chemical energy of food into a variety of other forms of energy, including kinetic energy, sound energy, and thermal energy.

Energy will be *the* most important concept throughout the remainder of this textbook, and much of Part II will focus on understanding what energy is and how it is used.

But energy is not the only conserved quantity. We will begin Part II with the study of two other quantities that are conserved in a closed system: *momentum* and *angular momentum*. Their conservation will help us understand a wide range of physical processes, from the forces when two rams butt heads to the graceful spins of ice skaters.

Conservation laws will give us a new and different *perspective* on motion. Some situations are most easily analyzed from the perspective of Newton's laws, but others make much more sense when analyzed from a conservation-law perspective. An important goal of Part II is to learn which perspective is best for a given problem.

9 Momentum

Male rams butt heads at high speeds in a ritual to assert their dominance. How can the force of this collision be minimized so as to avoid damage to their brains?

LOOKING AHEAD ▸

The goals of Chapter 9 are to introduce the ideas of impulse, momentum, and angular momentum and to learn a new problem-solving strategy based on conservation laws.

Impulse

We'll begin by studying what happens to an object subject to a strong but short-duration **impulsive force.**

We say that the club has delivered an **impulse** to the ball.

Looking Back ◂◂
5.2 Newton's second law

A golf ball being struck by a club is subject to a brief but very large force.

Momentum

The **momentum** of an object is the product of its mass and its velocity. A heavy, fast-moving object such as a car has much greater momentum than a light, slow-moving one such as a falling raindrop.

The momentum of a moving car is a billion times greater than that of a falling raindrop.

Momentum and Impulse

We'll discover how an impulse delivered to an object *changes* the object's momentum.

The player's head delivers an impulse to the ball, changing its momentum and thus its direction.

Conservation of Momentum

When two or more objects interact only with each other, the total momentum of these objects is conserved—it is the same after the interaction as it was before. This **law of conservation of momentum** will lead us to a powerful new *before-and-after* problem-solving strategy.

Before:

After:

Conservation of momentum is an important tool for analyzing *explosions*, like the ball shot from this toy gun, or *collisions*, like two pool balls hitting and flying apart.

Looking Back ◂◂
4.8 Newton's third law
5.7 Interacting objects

Angular Momentum

Rotating objects have *angular* momentum. Angular momentum is changed by an applied torque. When no torques act on a rotating object, its angular momentum is conserved.

Conservation of angular momentum causes this skater's spin to increase as she pulls her arms in toward her body.

Looking Back ◂◂
7.2, 7.4 Torque and moment of inertia

9.1 Impulse

Suppose that two or more objects have an intense and perhaps complex interaction, such as a collision or an explosion. Our goal is to find a relationship between the velocities of the objects before the interaction and their velocities after the interaction. We'll start by looking at collisions.

A **collision** is a short-duration interaction between two objects. The collision between a tennis ball and a racket, or a baseball and a bat, may seem instantaneous to your eye, but that is a limitation of your perception. A careful look at the tennis ball/racket collision in FIGURE 9.1 reveals that the right side of the ball is flattened and pressed up against the strings of the racket. It takes time to compress the ball, and more time for the ball to re-expand as it leaves the racket.

The duration of a collision depends on the materials from which the objects are made, but 1 to 10 ms (0.001 to 0.010 s) is typical. This is the time during which the two objects are in contact with each other. The harder the objects, the shorter the contact time. A collision between two steel balls lasts less than 1 ms, while that between a tennis ball and racket might last 10 ms.

FIGURE 9.2 A sequence of high-speed photos of a soccer ball being kicked.

Let's begin our discussion by considering a collision that most of us have experienced: kicking a soccer ball. A sequence of high-speed photos of a soccer kick is shown in FIGURE 9.2. As the foot and the ball just come into contact, as shown in the left frame, the ball is just beginning to compress. By the middle frame of Figure 9.2, the ball has sped up and become greatly compressed. Finally, as shown in the right frame, the ball, now moving very fast, is again only slightly compressed.

The amount by which the ball is compressed is a measure of the magnitude of the force the foot exerts on the ball; more compression indicates a greater force. If we were to graph this force versus time, it would look something like FIGURE 9.3. The force is zero until the foot first contacts the ball, rises quickly to a maximum value, and then falls back to zero as the ball leaves the foot. Thus there is a well-defined duration Δt of the force. A large force like this exerted during a short interval of time is called an **impulsive force**. The forces of a hammer on a nail and of a bat on a baseball are other examples of impulsive forces.

A harder kick (i.e., a taller force curve) or a kick of longer duration (a wider force curve) causes the ball to leave the kicker's foot with a higher speed; that is, the *effect* of the kick is larger. Now a taller or wider force-versus-time curve has a larger *area* between the curve and the axis (i.e., the area "under" the force curve is larger), so we can say that **the effect of an impulsive force is proportional to the area under the force-versus-time curve.** This area, shown in FIGURE 9.4a, is called the **impulse** J of the force.

Impulsive forces can be complex, and the shape of the force-versus-time graph often changes in a complicated way. Consequently, it is often useful to think of the collision in terms of an *average* force F_{avg}. As FIGURE 9.4b shows, F_{avg} is defined to be the constant force that has the same duration Δt and the same area under the force curve as the real force. You can see from the figure that the area under the force curve can be written simply as $F_{avg} \Delta t$. Thus

$$\text{impulse } J = \text{area under the force curve} = F_{avg} \, \Delta t \qquad (9.1)$$

Impulse due to a force acting for a duration Δt

FIGURE 9.1 A tennis ball collides with a racket. Notice that the right side of the ball is flattened.

FIGURE 9.3 The force on a soccer ball changes rapidly.

FIGURE 9.4 Looking at the impulse graphically.

(a)

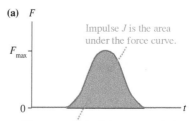

The area under both force curves is the same; thus, both forces deliver the same impulse. This means that they have the same effect on the object.

(b)

From Equation 9.1 we see that impulse has units of N · s, but you should be able to show that N · s are equivalent to kg · m/s. We'll see shortly why the latter are the preferred units for impulse.

So far, we've been assuming the force is directed along a coordinate axis, such as the x-axis. In this case impulse is a *signed* quantity—it can be positive or negative. A positive impulse results from an average force directed in the positive x-direction (that is, F_{avg} is positive), while a negative impulse is due to a force directed in the negative x-direction (F_{avg} is negative). More generally, the impulse is a *vector* quantity pointing in the direction of the average force vector:

$$\vec{J} = \vec{F}_{avg}\,\Delta t \tag{9.2}$$

EXAMPLE 9.1 **Finding the impulse on a bouncing ball**

A rubber ball experiences the force shown in FIGURE 9.5 as it bounces off the floor.

a. What is the impulse on the ball?
b. What is the average force on the ball?

PREPARE The impulse is the area under the force curve. Here the shape of the graph is triangular, so we'll need to use the fact that the area of a triangle is $\frac{1}{2}$ × height × base.

FIGURE 9.5 The force of the floor on a bouncing ball.

SOLVE a. The impulse is

$$J = \tfrac{1}{2}(300\ \text{N})(0.0080\ \text{s}) = 1.2\ \text{N·s} = 1.2\ \text{kg·m/s}$$

b. From Equation 9.1, $J = F_{avg}\,\Delta t$, we can find the average force that would give this same impulse:

$$F_{avg} = \frac{J}{\Delta t} = \frac{1.2\ \text{N·s}}{0.0080\ \text{s}} = 150\ \text{N}$$

ASSESS In this particular example, the average value of the force is half the maximum value. This is not surprising for a triangular force because the area of a triangle is *half* the base times the height.

Class Video

9.2 Momentum and the Impulse-Momentum Theorem

We've noted that the effect of an impulsive force depends on the impulse delivered to the object. The effect also depends on the object's mass. Our experience tells us that giving a kick to a heavy object will change its velocity much less than giving the same kick to a light object. We want now to find a quantitative relationship for impulse, mass, and velocity change.

Consider the puck of mass m in FIGURE 9.6, sliding with an initial velocity $\vec{v}_i$. It is struck by a hockey stick that delivers an impulse $\vec{J} = \vec{F}_{avg}\,\Delta t$ to the puck. After the impulse, the puck leaves the stick with a final velocity $\vec{v}_f$. How is this final velocity related to the initial velocity?

From Newton's second law, the average acceleration of the puck during the time the stick is in contact with it is

$$\vec{a}_{avg} = \frac{\vec{F}_{avg}}{m} \tag{9.3}$$

The average acceleration is related to the change in the velocity by

$$\vec{a}_{avg} = \frac{\Delta\vec{v}}{\Delta t} = \frac{\vec{v}_f - \vec{v}_i}{\Delta t} \tag{9.4}$$

Combining Equations 9.3 and 9.4, we have

$$\frac{\vec{F}_{avg}}{m} = \vec{a}_{avg} = \frac{\vec{v}_f - \vec{v}_i}{\Delta t}$$

or, rearranging,

$$\vec{F}_{avg}\,\Delta t = m\vec{v}_f - m\vec{v}_i \tag{9.5}$$

FIGURE 9.6 The stick exerts an impulse on the puck, changing its speed.

$\vec{v}_i$

While the stick is in contact with the puck, it exerts a force $\vec{F}_{avg}$ on the puck, causing it to accelerate.

$\vec{F}_{avg}$

$\vec{v}_f$

We recognize the left side of this equation as the impulse $\vec{J}$. The right side is the *change* in the quantity $m\vec{v}$. This quantity, the product of the object's mass and velocity, is called the **momentum** of the object. The symbol for momentum is $\vec{p}$:

$$\vec{p} = m\vec{v} \qquad (9.6)$$

Momentum of an object of mass m and velocity $\vec{v}$

From Equation 9.6, the units of momentum are those of mass times velocity, or kg · m/s. We noted above that kg · m/s are the preferred units of impulse. Now we see that the reason for that preference is to match the units of momentum.

FIGURE 9.7 shows that the momentum $\vec{p}$ is a *vector* quantity that points in the same direction as the velocity vector $\vec{v}$. Like any vector, $\vec{p}$ can be decomposed into x- and y-components. Equation 9.6, which is a vector equation, is a shorthand way to write the two equations

$$p_x = mv_x$$
$$p_y = mv_y \qquad (9.7)$$

NOTE ▶ One of the most common errors in momentum problems is failure to use the correct signs. The momentum component p_x has the same sign as v_x. Just like velocity, momentum is positive for a particle moving to the right (on the x-axis) or up (on the y-axis), but *negative* for a particle moving to the left or down. ◀

The *magnitude* of an object's momentum is simply the product of the object's mass and speed, or $p = mv$. A heavy, fast-moving object will have a great deal of momentum, while a light, slow-moving object will have very little. Two objects with very different masses can have similar momenta if their speeds are very different as well. Table 9.1 gives some typical values of the momenta (the plural of *momentum*) of various moving objects. You can see that the momenta of a bullet and a fastball are similar. The momentum of a moving car is almost a billion times greater than that of a falling raindrop.

FIGURE 9.7 A particle's momentum vector $\vec{p}$ can be decomposed into x- and y-components.

Momentum is a vector that points in the same direction as the object's velocity.

TABLE 9.1 Some typical momenta (approximate)

Object	Mass (kg)	Speed (m/s)	Momentum (kg · m/s)
Falling raindrop	2×10^{-5}	5	10^{-4}
Bullet	0.004	500	2
Pitched baseball	0.15	40	6
Running person	70	3	200
Car on highway	1000	30	3×10^4

The Impulse-Momentum Theorem

We can now write Equation 9.5 in terms of impulse and momentum:

$$\vec{J} = \vec{p}_f - \vec{p}_i = \Delta\vec{p} \qquad (9.8)$$

Impulse-momentum theorem

where $\vec{p}_i = m\vec{v}_i$ is the object's initial momentum, $\vec{p}_f = m\vec{v}_f$ is its final momentum after the impulse, and $\Delta\vec{p} = \vec{p}_f - \vec{p}_i$ is the *change* in its momentum. This expression is known as the **impulse-momentum theorem**. It states that **an impulse delivered to an object causes the object's momentum to change.** That is, the *effect* of an impulsive force is to change the object's momentum from $\vec{p}_i$ to

$$\vec{p}_f = \vec{p}_i + \vec{J} \qquad (9.9)$$

Equation 9.8 can also be written in terms of its x- and y-components as

$$J_x = \Delta p_x = (p_x)_f - (p_x)_i = m(v_x)_f - m(v_x)_i$$
$$J_y = \Delta p_y = (p_y)_f - (p_y)_i = m(v_y)_f - m(v_y)_i \qquad (9.10)$$

The impulse-momentum theorem is illustrated by two examples in FIGURE 9.8 on the next page. In the first, the putter strikes the ball, exerting a force on it and delivering an impulse $\vec{J} = \vec{F}_{avg} \Delta t$. Notice that the direction of the impulse is the same as

Legging it BIO A frog making a jump wants to gain as much momentum as possible before leaving the ground. This means that he wants the greatest impulse $J = F_{avg} \Delta t$ delivered to him by the ground. There is a maximum force that muscles can exert, limiting F_{avg}. But the time interval Δt over which the force is exerted can be greatly increased by having long legs. Many animals that are good jumpers have particularly long legs.

FIGURE 9.8 Impulse causes a *change* in momentum.

(a)

$\vec{p}_i = \vec{0}$ $\vec{J}$ $\vec{p}_f$

(b)

$\vec{p}_i$ $\vec{J}$ $\vec{p}_f$ $\vec{p}_i$ $\vec{p}_f$ $\vec{J}$

Vector addition shows that $\vec{p}_f = \vec{p}_i + \vec{J}$.

that of the force. Because $\vec{p}_i = \vec{0}$ in this situation, we can use the impulse-momentum theorem to find that the ball leaves the putter with momentum $\vec{p}_f = \vec{p}_i + \vec{J} = \vec{J}$.

> **NOTE** ► You can think of the putter as changing the ball's momentum by transferring momentum to it as an impulse. Thus we say the putter *delivers* an impulse to the ball, and the ball *receives* an impulse from the putter. ◄

The soccer player in Figure 9.8b presents a more complicated case. Here, the initial momentum of the ball is directed downward to the left. The impulse delivered to it by the player's head, upward to the right, is strong enough to reverse the ball's motion and send it off in a new direction. The graphical addition of vectors in Figure 9.8b again shows that $\vec{p}_f = \vec{p}_i + \vec{J}$.

EXAMPLE 9.2   **Calculating the change in momentum**

A ball of mass $m = 0.25$ kg rolling to the right at 1.3 m/s strikes a wall and rebounds to the left at 1.1 m/s. What is the change in the ball's momentum? What is the impulse delivered to it by the wall?

PREPARE A visual overview of the ball bouncing is shown in FIGURE 9.9. This is a new kind of visual overview, one in which we show the situation "before" and "after" the interaction. We'll have more to say about before-and-after pictures in the next section. The ball is moving along the x-axis, so we'll write the momentum in component form, as in Equation 9.7. The change in

FIGURE 9.9 Visual overview for a ball bouncing off a wall.

Before:

$m = 0.25$ kg

$(v_x)_i = 1.3$ m/s

$\vec{F}$

Find: $\Delta p_x, J_x$

x

After:

$(v_x)_f = -1.1$ m/s

momentum is then the difference between the final and initial values of the momentum. By the impulse-momentum theorem, the impulse is equal to this change in momentum.

SOLVE The x-component of the initial momentum is

$$(p_x)_i = m(v_x)_i = (0.25 \text{ kg})(1.3 \text{ m/s}) = 0.33 \text{ kg} \cdot \text{m/s}$$

The y-component of the momentum is zero both before and after the bounce. After the ball rebounds, the x-component of its momentum is

$$(p_x)_f = m(v_x)_f = (0.25 \text{ kg})(-1.1 \text{ m/s}) = -0.28 \text{ kg} \cdot \text{m/s}$$

It is particularly important to notice that the x-component of the momentum, like that of the velocity, is negative. This indicates that the ball is moving to the *left*. The change in momentum is

$$\Delta p_x = (p_x)_f - (p_x)_i = (-0.28 \text{ kg} \cdot \text{m/s}) - (0.33 \text{ kg} \cdot \text{m/s})$$

$$= -0.61 \text{ kg} \cdot \text{m/s}$$

The change in the momentum is negative. By the impulse-momentum theorem, the impulse delivered to the ball by the wall is equal to this change, so

$$J_x = \Delta p_x = -0.61 \text{ kg} \cdot \text{m/s}$$

ASSESS The impulse is negative, indicating that the force causing the impulse is pointing to the left, which makes sense.

▶ **Water balloon catch** If you've ever tried to catch a water balloon, you may have learned the hard way not to catch it with your arms rigidly extended. The brief collision time implies a large, balloon-bursting force. A better way to catch a water balloon is to pull your arms in toward your body as you catch it, lengthening the collision time and hence reducing the force on the balloon.

TRY IT YOURSELF

An interesting application of the impulse-momentum theorem is to the question of how to slow down a fast-moving object in the gentlest possible way. For instance, a car is headed for a collision with a bridge abutment. How can this crash be made survivable? How do the rams in the chapter-opening photo avoid injury when they collide?

In these examples, the object has momentum $\vec{p}_i$ just before impact and zero momentum after (i.e., $\vec{p}_f = \vec{0}$). The impulse-momentum theorem tells us that

$$\vec{J} = \vec{F}_{avg}\,\Delta t = \Delta\vec{p} = \vec{p}_f - \vec{p}_i = -\vec{p}_i$$

or

$$\vec{F}_{avg} = -\frac{\vec{p}_i}{\Delta t} \qquad (9.11)$$

That is, the average force needed to stop an object is *inversely proportional* to the duration Δt of the collision. **If the duration of the collision can be increased, the force of the impact will be decreased.** This is the principle used in most impact-lessening techniques.

For example, obstacles such as bridge abutments are made safer by placing a line of water-filled barrels in front of them. Water is heavy but deformable. In case of a collision, the time it takes for the car to plow through these barrels is much longer than the time it would take it to stop if it hit the abutment head-on. The force on the car (and on the driver from his or her seat belt) is greatly reduced by the longer-duration collision with the barrels.

The spines of a hedgehog obviously help protect it from predators. But they serve another function as well. If a hedgehog falls from a tree—a not uncommon occurrence—it simply rolls itself into a ball before it lands. Indeed, hedgehogs have been observed to purposely descend to the ground by simply dropping from the tree. Its thick spines then cushion the blow by increasing the time it takes for the animal to come to rest. Along with its small size, this adaptation allows the hedgehog to easily survive long falls unhurt.

The butting rams shown in the photo at the beginning of this chapter also have adaptations that allow them to collide at high speeds without injury to their brains. The cranium has a double wall to prevent skull injuries, and there is a thick spongy mass that increases the time it takes for the brain to come to rest upon impact, again reducing the magnitude of the force on the brain.

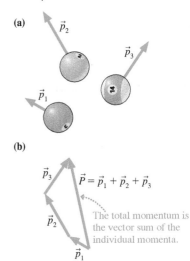

A hedgehog is its own crash cushion!

FIGURE 9.10 The total momentum of three pool balls.

Total Momentum

If we have more than one object moving—a *system* of particles—then the system as a whole has an overall momentum. The **total momentum** $\vec{P}$ (note the capital P) of a system of particles is the vector sum of the momenta of the individual particles:

$$\vec{P} = \vec{p}_1 + \vec{p}_2 + \vec{p}_3 + \cdots$$

FIGURE 9.10 shows how the momentum vectors of three moving pool balls are graphically added to find the total momentum. The concept of total momentum will be of key importance when we discuss the conservation law for momentum in Section 9.4.

STOP TO THINK 9.1   The cart's change of momentum is

A. -30 kg · m/s.
B. -20 kg · m/s.
C. -10 kg · m/s.
D. 10 kg · m/s.
E. 20 kg · m/s.
F. 30 kg · m/s.

Before:

2 m/s   10 kg

x

After:

1 m/s

9.3 Solving Impulse and Momentum Problems

Visual overviews have become an important problem-solving tool. The visual overviews and free-body diagrams that you learned to draw in Chapters 1–8 were oriented toward the use of Newton's laws and a subsequent kinematical analysis. Now we are interested in making a connection between "before" and "after."

TACTICS
BOX 9.1   **Drawing a before-and-after visual overview**

❶ **Sketch the situation.** Use two drawings, labeled "Before" and "After," to show the objects *immediately before* they interact and again *immediately after* they interact.
❷ **Establish a coordinate system.** Select your axes to match the motion.
❸ **Define symbols.** Define symbols for the masses and for the velocities before and after the interaction. Position and time are not needed.
❹ **List known information.** List the values of quantities known from the problem statement or that can be found quickly with simple geometry or unit conversions. Before-and-after pictures are usually simpler than the pictures you used for dynamics problems, so listing known information on the sketch is often adequate.
❺ **Identify the desired unknowns.** What quantity or quantities will allow you to answer the question? These should have been defined as symbols in step 3.

Exercises 9–11

EXAMPLE 9.3   **Force in hitting a baseball**

A 150 g baseball is thrown with a speed of 20 m/s. It is hit straight back toward the pitcher at a speed of 40 m/s. The impulsive force of the bat on the ball has the shape shown in FIGURE 9.11. What is the *maximum* force F_{max} that the bat exerts on the ball? What is the *average* force that the bat exerts on the ball?

FIGURE 9.11 The interaction force between the baseball and the bat.

PREPARE We can model the interaction as a collision. FIGURE 9.12 is a before-and-after visual overview in which the steps from Tactics Box 9.1 are explicitly noted. Because F_x is positive (a force to the right), we know the ball was initially moving toward the left and is hit back toward the right. Thus we converted the statements about *speeds* into information about *velocities*, with $(v_x)_i$ negative.

SOLVE In the last several chapters we've started the mathematical solution with Newton's second law. Now we want to use the impulse-momentum theorem:

$$\Delta p_x = J_x = \text{area under the force curve}$$

FIGURE 9.12 A before-and-after visual overview.

❶ Draw the before-and-after pictures.

Before:

$(v_x)_i = -20$ m/s

❷ Establish a coordinate system.

$m = 0.15$ kg

0 x

After:

❸ Define symbols.

❹ List known information.

$(v_x)_f = 40$ m/s.

Find: F_{max} and F_{avg}

❺ Identify desired unknowns.

We know the velocities before and after the collision, so we can find the change in the ball's momentum:

$$\Delta p_x = m(v_x)_f - m(v_x)_i = (0.15 \text{ kg})(40 \text{ m/s} - (-20 \text{ m/s}))$$

$$= 9.0 \text{ kg} \cdot \text{m/s}$$

The force curve is a triangle with height F_{max} and width 0.60 ms. As in Example 9.1, the area under the curve is

$$J_x = \text{area} = \tfrac{1}{2} \times F_{max} \times (6.0 \times 10^{-4} \text{ s})$$

$$= (F_{max})(3.0 \times 10^{-4})$$

According to the impulse-momentum theorem, $\Delta p_x = J_x$, so we have

$$9.0 \text{ kg} \cdot \text{m/s} = (F_{max})(3.0 \times 10^{-4} \text{ s})$$

Thus the *maximum* force is

$$F_{max} = \frac{9.0 \text{ kg} \cdot \text{m/s}}{3.0 \times 10^{-4} \text{ s}} = 30{,}000 \text{ N}$$

Using Equation 9.1, we find that the *average* force, which depends on the collision duration $\Delta t = 6.0 \times 10^{-4}$ s, has the smaller value:

$$F_{avg} = \frac{J_x}{\Delta t} = \frac{\Delta p_x}{\Delta t} = \frac{9.0 \text{ kg} \cdot \text{m/s}}{6.0 \times 10^{-4} \text{ s}} = 15{,}000 \text{ N}$$

ASSESS F_{max} is a large force, but quite typical of the impulsive forces during collisions.

The Impulse Approximation

When two objects interact during a collision or other brief interaction, such as that between the bat and ball of Example 9.3, the forces *between* them are generally quite large. Other forces may also act on the interacting objects, but usually these forces are *much* smaller than the interaction forces. In Example 9.3, for example, the 1.5 N weight of the ball is vastly less than the 30,000 N force of the bat on the ball. We can reasonably neglect these small forces *during* the brief time of the impulsive force. Doing so is called the **impulse approximation**.

When we use the impulse approximation, $(p_x)_i$ and $(p_x)_f$—and $(v_x)_i$ and $(v_x)_f$—are then the momenta (and velocities) *immediately* before and *immediately* after the collision. For example, the velocities in Example 9.3 are those of the ball just before and after it collides with the bat. We could then do a follow-up problem, including weight and drag, to find the ball's speed a second later as the second baseman catches it.

EXAMPLE 9.4   **Height of a bouncing ball**

A 100 g rubber ball is thrown straight down onto a hard floor so that it strikes the floor with a speed of 11 m/s. FIGURE 9.13 shows the force that the floor exerts on the ball. Estimate the height of the ball's bounce.

PREPARE The ball experiences an impulsive force while in contact with the

FIGURE 9.13 The force of the floor on a bouncing rubber ball.

F_y

800 N

0

5.0 ms

floor. Using the impulse approximation, we'll neglect the ball's weight during these 5.0 ms. The ball's rise after the bounce is free-fall motion—that is, motion subject only to the force of gravity. We'll use free-fall kinematics to describe the motion after the bounce.

FIGURE 9.14 on the next page is a visual overview. Here we have a two-part problem, an impulsive collision followed by upward free fall. The overview thus shows the ball just before the collision, where we label its velocity as v_{1y}; just after the collision, where its velocity is v_{2y}; and at the highest point of its rising free fall, where its velocity is $v_{3y} = 0$.

Continued

FIGURE 9.14 Before-and-after visual overview for a bouncing ball.

SOLVE The impulse-momentum theorem tells us that $J_y = \Delta p_y = p_{2y} - p_{1y}$, so that $p_{2y} = p_{1y} + J_y$. The initial momentum, just before the collision, is $p_{1y} = mv_{1y} = (0.10 \text{ kg})(-11 \text{ m/s}) = -1.1 \text{ kg} \cdot \text{m/s}$.

Next, we need to find the impulse J_y, which is the area under the curve in Figure 9.13. Because the force is given as a smooth curve, we'll have to *estimate* this area. Recall that the area can be written as $F_{avg} \Delta t$. From the curve, we might estimate F_{avg} to be about 400 N, or half the maximum value of the force. With this estimate we have

J_y = area under the force curve $\approx (400 \text{ N}) \times (0.0050 \text{ s})$

$$= 2.0 \text{ N} \cdot \text{s} = 2.0 \text{ kg} \cdot \text{m/s}$$

Thus

$$p_{2y} = p_{1y} + J_y = (-1.1 \text{ kg} \cdot \text{m/s}) + 2.0 \text{ kg} \cdot \text{m/s}$$

$$= 0.9 \text{ kg} \cdot \text{m/s}$$

and the post-collision velocity is

$$v_{2y} = \frac{p_{2y}}{m} = \frac{0.9 \text{ kg} \cdot \text{m/s}}{0.10 \text{ kg}} = 9 \text{ m/s}$$

The rebound speed is less than the impact speed, as expected. Finally, we can use free-fall kinematics to find

$$v_{3y}^2 = 0 = v_{2y}^2 - 2g \Delta y = v_{2y}^2 - 2gy_3$$

$$y_3 = \frac{v_{2y}^2}{2g} = \frac{(9 \text{ m/s})^2}{2(9.8 \text{ m/s}^2)} = 4 \text{ m}$$

We estimate that the ball bounces to a height of 4 m.

ASSESS This is a reasonable height for a rubber ball thrown down quite hard.

STOP TO THINK 9.2 A 10 g rubber ball and a 10 g clay ball are each thrown at a wall with equal speeds. The rubber ball bounces; the clay ball sticks. Which ball receives the greater impulse from the wall?

A. The clay ball receives a greater impulse because it sticks.
B. The rubber ball receives a greater impulse because it bounces.
C. They receive equal impulses because they have equal momenta.
D. Neither receives an impulse because the wall doesn't move.

FIGURE 9.15 A collision between two balls.

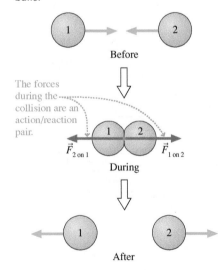

9.4 Conservation of Momentum

The impulse-momentum theorem was derived from Newton's second law and is really just an alternative way of looking at that law. It is used in the context of single-particle dynamics, much as we used Newton's law in Chapters 4–7.

However, consider two objects, such as the rams shown in the opening photo of this chapter, that interact during the brief moment of a collision. During a collision, two objects exert forces on each other that vary in a complex way. We usually don't even know the magnitudes of these forces. Using Newton's second law alone to predict the outcome of such a collision would thus be a daunting challenge. However, by using Newton's *third* law in the language of impulse and momentum, we'll find that it's possible to describe the *outcome* of a collision—the final speeds and directions of the colliding objects—in a simple way. Newton's third law will lead us to one of the most important conservation laws in physics.

FIGURE 9.15 shows two balls initially headed toward each other. The balls collide, then bounce apart. The forces during the collision, when the balls are interacting, are the action/reaction pair $\vec{F}_{1 \text{ on } 2}$ and $\vec{F}_{2 \text{ on } 1}$. For now, we'll continue to assume that the motion is one dimensional along the x-axis.

During the collision, the impulse J_{2x} delivered to ball 2 by ball 1 is the average value of $\vec{F}_{1\,on\,2}$ multiplied by the collision time Δt. Likewise, the impulse J_{1x} delivered to ball 1 by ball 2 is the average value of $\vec{F}_{2\,on\,1}$ multiplied by Δt. Because $\vec{F}_{1\,on\,2}$ and $\vec{F}_{2\,on\,1}$ form an action/reaction pair, they have equal magnitudes but opposite directions. As a result, the two impulses J_{1x} and J_{2x} are also equal in magnitude but opposite in sign, so that $J_{1x} = -J_{2x}$.

According to the impulse-momentum theorem, the change in the momentum of ball 1 is $\Delta p_{1x} = J_{1x}$ and the change in the momentum of ball 2 is $\Delta p_{2x} = J_{2x}$. Because $J_{1x} = -J_{2x}$, the change in the momentum of ball 1 is equal in magnitude but opposite in sign to the change in momentum of ball 2. If ball 1's momentum increases by a certain amount during the collision, ball 2's momentum will *decrease* by exactly the same amount. This implies that **the total momentum $P_x = p_{1x} + p_{2x}$ of the two balls is *unchanged* by the collision;** that is,

$$(P_x)_f = (P_x)_i \tag{9.12}$$

Because it doesn't change during the collision, we say that the x-component of total momentum is *conserved*. Equation 9.12 is our first example of a *conservation law*.

Law of Conservation of Momentum

The same arguments just presented for the two colliding balls can be extended to systems containing any number of objects. FIGURE 9.16 shows the idea. Each pair of particles in the system (the boundary of which is denoted by the red line) interacts via forces that are an action/reaction pair. Exactly as for the two-particle collision, the change in momentum of particle 2 due to the force from particle 3 is equal in magnitude, but opposite in direction, to the change in particle 3's momentum due to particle 2. The *net* change in the momentum of these two particles due to their inter-action forces is thus zero. The same argument holds for every pair, with the result that, no matter how complicated the forces between the particles, **there is no change in the *total* momentum $\vec{P}$ of the system.** The total momentum of the system remains constant: It is *conserved*.

Figure 9.16 showed particles interacting only with other particles inside the system. Forces that act only between particles within the system are called **internal forces.** As we've just seen, **the total momentum of a system subject only to inter-nal forces is conserved.**

Most systems are also subject to forces from agents outside the system. These forces are called **external forces.** For example, the system consisting of a student on a skateboard is subject to three external forces—the normal force of the ground on the skateboard, the force of gravity on the student, and the force of gravity on the board. How do external forces affect the momentum of a system of particles?

In FIGURE 9.17 we show the same three-particle system of Figure 9.16, but now with *external* forces acting on the three particles. These external forces *can* change the momentum of the system. During a time interval Δt, for instance, the external force $\vec{F}_{ext\,on\,1}$ acting on particle 1 changes its momentum, according to the impulse-momentum theorem, by $\Delta \vec{p}_1 = (\vec{F}_{ext\,on\,1})\Delta t$. The momenta of the other two particles change similarly. Thus the change in the total momentum is

$$\begin{aligned}
\Delta \vec{P} &= \Delta \vec{p}_1 + \Delta \vec{p}_2 + \Delta \vec{p}_3 \\
&= (\vec{F}_{ext\,on\,1}\Delta t) + (\vec{F}_{ext\,on\,2}\Delta t) + (\vec{F}_{ext\,on\,3}\Delta t) \\
&= (\vec{F}_{ext\,on\,1} + \vec{F}_{ext\,on\,2} + \vec{F}_{ext\,on\,3})\Delta t \\
&= \vec{F}_{net}\Delta t
\end{aligned} \tag{9.13}$$

where $\vec{F}_{net}$ is the net force due to *external forces*.

Equation 9.13 has a very important implication in the case where the net force on a system is zero: If $\vec{F}_{net} = \vec{0}$ the *total* momentum $\vec{P}$ of the system does not change. The total momentum remains constant, *regardless* of whatever interactions are going on *inside* the system.

FIGURE 9.16 A system of three particles.

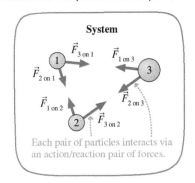

Each pair of particles interacts via an action/reaction pair of forces.

FIGURE 9.17 A system of particles subject to external forces.

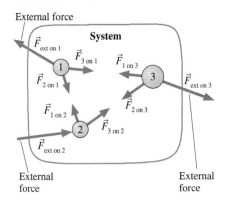

Earlier, we found that a system's total momentum is conserved when the system has no external forces acting on it. Now we've found that the system's total momentum is also conserved when the net external force acting on it is zero. With no external forces acting that can change its momentum, we call a system with $\vec{F}_{net} = \vec{0}$ an **isolated system.**

The importance of these results is sufficient to elevate them to a law of nature, alongside Newton's laws.

> **Law of conservation of momentum** The total momentum $\vec{P}$ of an isolated system is a constant. Interactions within the system do not change the system's total momentum.

NOTE ▶ It is worth emphasizing the critical role of Newton's third law in the derivation of Equation 9.13. The law of conservation of momentum is a direct consequence of the fact that interactions within an isolated system are action/reaction pairs. ◀

Mathematically, the law of conservation of momentum for an isolated system is

$$\vec{P}_f = \vec{P}_i \tag{9.14}$$

Law of conservation of momentum for an isolated system

The total momentum after an interaction is equal to the total momentum before the interaction. Because Equation 9.14 is a vector equation, the equality is true for each of the components of the momentum vector; that is,

$$
\begin{array}{l}
x\text{-component} \longrightarrow (p_{1x})_f + (p_{2x})_f + (p_{3x})_f + \cdots = (p_{1x})_i + (p_{2x})_i + (p_{3x})_i + \cdots \\
\qquad\qquad\qquad \text{Particle 1 Particle 2 Particle 3} \\
y\text{-component} \longrightarrow (p_{1y})_f + (p_{2y})_f + (p_{3y})_f + \cdots = (p_{1y})_i + (p_{2y})_i + (p_{3y})_i + \cdots
\end{array}
\tag{9.15}
$$

Final momentum   Initial momentum

EXAMPLE 9.5   **Speed of ice skaters pushing off**

Two ice skaters, Sandra and David, stand facing each other on frictionless ice. Sandra has a mass of 45 kg, David a mass of 80 kg. They then push off from each other. After the push, Sandra moves off at a speed of 2.2 m/s. What is David's speed?

PREPARE The two skaters interact with each other, but they form an isolated system because, for each skater, the upward normal force of the ice balances their downward weight force to make $\vec{F}_{net} = \vec{0}$. Thus the total momentum of the system of the two skaters is conserved.

FIGURE 9.18 shows a before-and-after visual overview for the two skaters. The total momentum before they push off is $\vec{P}_i = \vec{0}$ because both skaters are at rest. Consequently, the total momentum will still be $\vec{0}$ *after* they push off.

SOLVE Since the motion is only in the x-direction, we'll only need to consider x-components of momentum. We write Sandra's initial momentum as $(p_{Sx})_i = m_S(v_{Sx})_i$, where m_S is her mass and

FIGURE 9.18 Before-and-after visual overview for two skaters pushing off from each other.

Before:

$(v_{Dx})_i = 0$ m/s
$m_D = 80$ kg

$(v_{Sx})_i = 0$ m/s
$m_S = 45$ kg

After:

$(v_{Dx})_f$

$(v_{Sx})_f = 2.2$ m/s

Find: $(v_{Dx})_f$

$(v_{Sx})_i$ her initial velocity. Similarly, we write David's initial momentum as $(p_{Dx})_i = m_D(v_{Dx})_i$. Both these momenta are zero because both skaters are initially at rest.

We can now apply the mathematical statement of momentum conservation, Equation 9.15. Writing the final momentum of Sandra as $m_S(v_{Sx})_f$ and that of David as $m_D(v_{Dx})_f$, we have

$$\underbrace{m_S(v_{Sx})_f + m_D(v_{Dx})_f}_{\text{The skaters' final momentum ...}} = \underbrace{m_S(v_{Sx})_i + m_D(v_{Dx})_i}_{\text{... equals their initial momentum ...}} = \underbrace{0}_{\text{... which was zero.}}$$

Solving for $(v_{Dx})_f$, we find

$$(v_{Dx})_f = -\frac{m_S}{m_D}(v_{Sx})_f = -\frac{45\ \text{kg}}{80\ \text{kg}} \times 2.2\ \text{m/s} = -1.2\ \text{m/s}$$

David moves backward with a *speed* of 1.2 m/s.

Notice that we didn't need to know any details about the force between David and Sandra in order to find David's final speed. Conservation of momentum *mandates* this result.

ASSESS The *total* momentum of the system is zero both before and after they push off, but the individual momenta are not zero. Because $(p_{Sx})_f$ is positive (Sandra moves to the right), $(p_{Dx})_f$ must have the same magnitude but the opposite sign (David moves to the left).

A Strategy for Conservation of Momentum Problems

Our derivation of the law of conservation of momentum, and the conditions under which it holds, suggests a problem-solving strategy.

 ActivPhysics: 6.3, 6.4, 6.6, 6.7, 6.10

PROBLEM-SOLVING STRATEGY 9.1 Conservation of momentum problems

PREPARE Clearly define *the system*.

- If possible, choose a system that is isolated ($\vec{F}_{net} = \vec{0}$) or within which the interactions are sufficiently short and intense that you can ignore external forces for the duration of the interaction (the impulse approximation). Momentum is then conserved.
- If it's not possible to choose an isolated system, try to divide the problem into parts such that momentum is conserved during one segment of the motion. Other segments of the motion can be analyzed using Newton's laws or, as you'll learn in Chapter 10, conservation of energy.

Following Tactics Box 9.1, draw a before-and-after visual overview. Define symbols that will be used in the problem, list known values, and identify what you're trying to find.

SOLVE The mathematical representation is based on the law of conservation of momentum: $\vec{P}_f = \vec{P}_i$. In component form, this is

$$(p_{1x})_f + (p_{2x})_f + (p_{3x})_f + \cdots = (p_{1x})_i + (p_{2x})_i + (p_{3x})_i + \cdots$$

$$(p_{1y})_f + (p_{2y})_f + (p_{3y})_f + \cdots = (p_{1y})_i + (p_{2y})_i + (p_{3y})_i + \cdots$$

ASSESS Check that your result has the correct units, is reasonable, and answers the question.

Exercise 17

EXAMPLE 9.6 Getaway speed of a cart

Bob is running from the police and thinks he can make a faster getaway by jumping on a stationary cart in front of him. He runs toward the cart, jumps on, and rolls along the horizontal street. Bob has a mass of 75 kg and the cart's mass is 25 kg. If Bob's speed is 4.0 m/s when he jumps onto the cart, what is the cart's speed after Bob jumps on?

PREPARE When Bob lands on and sticks to the cart, a "collision" occurs between Bob and the cart. If we take Bob and the cart together to be the system, the forces involved in this collision—friction forces between Bob's feet and the cart—are internal forces. Because the normal force balances the weight of both Bob and the cart, the net external force on the system is zero, so the

Continued

total momentum of Bob + cart is conserved: It is the same before and after the collision.

The visual overview in FIGURE 9.19 shows the important point that Bob and the cart move together after he lands on the cart, so $(v_x)_f$ is their common final velocity.

FIGURE 9.19 Before-and-after visual overview of Bob and the cart.

Before:
$m_B = 75$ kg
$(v_{Bx})_i = 4.0$ m/s
$(v_{Cx})_i = 0$ m/s
$m_C = 25$ kg

After:
Find: $(v_x)_f$
$(v_{Bx})_f = (v_{Cx})_f = (v_x)_f$

System

SOLVE To solve for the final velocity of Bob and the cart, we'll use conservation of momentum: $(P_x)_f = (P_x)_i$. Written in terms of the individual momenta, we have

$$(P_x)_i = m_B(v_{Bx})_i + m_C \underbrace{(v_{Cx})_i}_{0 \text{ m/s}} = m_B(v_{Bx})_i$$

$$(P_x)_f = m_B(v_x)_f + m_C(v_x)_f = (m_B + m_C)(v_x)_f$$

In the second equation, we've used the fact that both Bob and the cart travel at the common velocity of $(v_x)_f$. Equating the final and initial total momenta gives

$$(m_B + m_C)(v_x)_f = m_B(v_{Bx})_i$$

Solving this for $(v_x)_f$, we find

$$(v_x)_f = \frac{m_B}{m_B + m_C}(v_{Bx})_i = \frac{75 \text{ kg}}{100 \text{ kg}} \times 4.0 \text{ m/s} = 3.0 \text{ m/s}$$

The cart's speed is 3.0 m/s immediately after Bob jumps on.

ASSESS It makes sense that Bob has *lost* speed because he had to share his initial momentum with the cart. Not a good way to make a getaway!

Notice how easy this was! No forces, no kinematic equations, no simultaneous equations. Why didn't we think of this before? Although conservation laws are indeed powerful, they can answer only certain questions. Had we wanted to know how far Bob slid across the cart before sticking to it, how long the slide took, or what the cart's acceleration was during the collision, we would not have been able to answer such questions on the basis of the conservation law. There is a price to pay for finding a simple connection between before and after, and that price is the loss of information about the details of the interaction. If we are satisfied with knowing only about before and after, then conservation laws are a simple and straightforward way to proceed. But many problems *do* require us to understand the interaction, and for these there is no avoiding Newton's laws and all they entail.

It Depends on the System

The first step in the problem-solving strategy asks you to clearly define *the system*. This is worth emphasizing, because many problem-solving errors arise from trying to apply momentum conservation to an inappropriate system. **The goal is to choose a system whose momentum will be conserved.** Even then, it is the *total* momentum of the system that is conserved, not the momenta of the individual particles within the system.

In Example 9.6, we chose the system to be Bob and the cart. Why this choice? Let's see what would happen if we had chosen the system to be Bob alone, as shown in FIGURE 9.20. As the free-body diagram shows, as Bob lands on the cart, there are three forces acting on him: the normal force $\vec{n}$ of the cart on Bob, his weight $\vec{w}$, and a friction force $\vec{f}_{C \text{ on B}}$ of the cart on Bob. This last force is subtle. We know that Bob's feet must exert a rightward-directed friction force $\vec{f}_{B \text{ on C}}$ *on the cart* as he lands; it is this friction force that causes the cart to speed up. By Newton's third law, then, the cart exerts a leftward directed force $\vec{f}_{C \text{ on B}}$ on Bob.

The free-body diagram of Figure 9.20 then shows that there is a net force on Bob directed to the left. Thus the system consisting of Bob alone is *not* isolated, and Bob's momentum will not be conserved. Indeed, we know that Bob slows down after landing on the cart, so that his momentum clearly *decreases*.

If we had chosen the cart to be the system, the unbalanced rightward force $\vec{f}_{B \text{ on C}}$ of Bob on the cart would also lead to a nonzero net force. Thus the cart's momentum would not be conserved; in fact, we know it *increases* because the cart speeds up.

Only by choosing the system to be Bob and the cart *together* is the net force on the system zero and the total momentum conserved. The momentum lost by Bob is gained by the cart, so the total momentum of the two is unchanged.

FIGURE 9.20 An analysis of the system consisting of Bob alone.

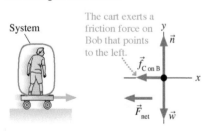

System

The cart exerts a friction force on Bob that points to the left.

$\vec{f}_{C \text{ on B}}$

$\vec{n}$

y

x

$\vec{F}_{\text{net}}$

$\vec{w}$

Explosions

An **explosion,** where the particles of the system move apart after a brief, intense interaction, is the opposite of a collision. The explosive forces, which could be from an expanding spring or from expanding hot gases, are *internal* forces. If the system is isolated, its total momentum during the explosion will be conserved.

Video Tutor Demonstration

EXAMPLE 9.7 **Recoil speed of a rifle**

A 30 g ball is fired from a 1.2 kg spring-loaded toy rifle with a speed of 15 m/s. What is the recoil speed of the rifle?

PREPARE As the ball moves down the barrel, there are complicated forces exerted on the ball and on the rifle. However, if we take the system to be the ball + rifle, these are *internal* forces that do not change the total momentum.

The *external* forces of the rifle's and ball's weights are balanced by the external force exerted by the person holding the

FIGURE 9.21 Before-and-after visual overview for a toy rifle.

Before:

$m_B = 0.030$ kg
$(v_{Bx})_i = 0$ m/s

System

$m_R = 1.2$ kg
$(v_{Rx})_i = 0$ m/s

After:

$(v_{Rx})_f$ Find: $(v_{Rx})_f$ $(v_{Bx})_f = 15$ m/s

rifle, so $\vec{F}_{net} = \vec{0}$. This is an isolated system and the law of conservation of momentum applies.

FIGURE 9.21 shows a visual overview before and after the ball is fired. We'll assume the ball is fired in the $+x$-direction.

SOLVE The x-component of the total momentum is $P_x = p_{Bx} + p_{Rx}$. Everything is at rest before the trigger is pulled, so the initial momentum is zero. After the trigger is pulled, the internal force of the spring pushes the ball down the barrel *and* pushes the rifle backward. Conservation of momentum gives

$$(P_x)_f = m_B(v_{Bx})_f + m_R(v_{Rx})_f = (P_x)_i = 0$$

Solving for the rifle's velocity, we find

$$(v_{Rx})_f = -\frac{m_B}{m_R}(v_{Bx})_f = -\frac{0.030 \text{ kg}}{1.2 \text{ kg}} \times 15 \text{ m/s} = -0.38 \text{ m/s}$$

The minus sign indicates that the rifle's recoil is to the left. The recoil *speed* is 0.38 m/s.

ASSESS Real rifles fire their bullets at much higher velocities, and their recoil is correspondingly higher. Shooters need to brace themselves against the "kick" of the rifle back against their shoulder.

We would not know where to begin to solve a problem such as this using Newton's laws. But Example 9.7 is a simple problem when approached from the before-and-after perspective of a conservation law. The selection of ball + rifle as "the system" was the critical step. For momentum conservation to be a useful principle, we had to select a system in which the complicated forces due to the spring and to friction were all internal forces. The rifle by itself is *not* an isolated system, so its momentum is *not* conserved.

Much the same reasoning explains how a rocket or jet aircraft accelerates. FIGURE 9.22 shows a rocket with a parcel of fuel on board. Burning converts the fuel to hot gases that are expelled from the rocket motor. If we choose rocket + gases to be the system, then the burning and expulsion are internal forces. In deep space there are no other forces, so the total momentum of the rocket + gases system must be conserved. The rocket gains forward velocity and momentum as the exhaust gases are shot out the back, but the *total* momentum of the system remains zero.

Many people find it hard to understand how a rocket can accelerate in the vacuum of space because there is nothing to "push against." Thinking in terms of momentum, you can see that the rocket does not push against anything *external,* but only against the gases that it pushes out the back. In return, in accordance with Newton's third law, the gases push forward on the rocket.

FIGURE 9.22 Rocket propulsion is an example of conservation of momentum.

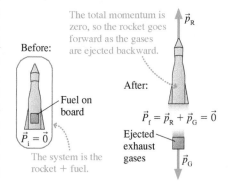

The total momentum is zero, so the rocket goes forward as the gases are ejected backward.

$\vec{p}_R$

Before:

Fuel on board

$\vec{P}_i = \vec{0}$

The system is the rocket + fuel.

After:

$\vec{P}_f = \vec{p}_R + \vec{p}_G = \vec{0}$

Ejected exhaust gases

$\vec{p}_G$

 PhET: Lunar Lander

▶ **Squid propulsion** BIO Squids use a form of "rocket propulsion" to make quick movements to escape enemies or catch prey. The squid draws in water through a pair of valves in its outer sheath, or mantle, and then quickly expels the water through a funnel, propelling the squid backward. The funnel's direction is adjustable, allowing the squid to move in any backward direction.

STOP TO THINK 9.3 An explosion in a rigid pipe shoots three balls out of its ends. A 6 g ball comes out the right end. A 4 g ball comes out the left end with twice the speed of the 6 g ball. From which end, left or right, does the third ball emerge?

9.5 Inelastic Collisions

Collisions can have different possible outcomes. A rubber ball dropped on the floor bounces—it's *elastic*—but a ball of clay sticks to the floor without bouncing; we call such a collision *inelastic*. A golf club hitting a golf ball causes the ball to rebound away from the club (elastic), but a bullet striking a block of wood becomes embedded in the block (inelastic).

A collision in which the two objects stick together and move with a common final velocity is called a **perfectly inelastic collision**. The clay hitting the floor and the bullet embedding itself in the wood are examples of perfectly inelastic collisions. Other examples include railroad cars coupling together upon impact and darts hitting a dart board. FIGURE 9.23 emphasizes the fact that the two objects have a common final velocity after they collide. (We have drawn the combined object moving to the right, but it could have ended up moving to the left, depending on the objects' masses and initial velocities.)

In an *elastic collision*, by contrast, the two objects bounce apart. We've looked at some examples of elastic collisions, but a full analysis requires some ideas about energy. We will return to elastic collisions in Chapter 10.

FIGURE 9.23 A perfectly inelastic collision.

Two objects approach and collide.

Before: $(v_{1x})_i$ $(v_{2x})_i$ m_1 m_2

They stick and move together.

After: $(v_x)_f$

Combined mass $m_1 + m_2$ Common final velocity

EXAMPLE 9.8 **Speeds in a perfectly inelastic glider collision**

In a laboratory experiment, a 200 g air-track glider and a 400 g air-track glider are pushed toward each other from opposite ends of the track. The gliders have Velcro tabs on their fronts so that they will stick together when they collide. The 200 g glider is pushed with an initial speed of 3.0 m/s. The collision causes it to reverse direction at 0.50 m/s. What was the initial speed of the 400 g glider?

PREPARE We model the gliders as particles and define the two gliders as the system. This is an isolated system, so its total momentum is conserved in the collision. The gliders stick together, so this is a perfectly inelastic collision.

FIGURE 9.24 Before-and-after visual overview for two gliders colliding on an air track.

Before:

$m_1 = 200$ g $(v_{1x})_i = 3.0$ m/s $(v_{2x})_i$ $m_2 = 400$ g

x

After:
$(v_x)_f = -0.50$ m/s $m_1 + m_2$

Find: $(v_{2x})_i$

FIGURE 9.24 shows a visual overview. We've chosen to let the 200 g glider (glider 1) start out moving to the right, so $(v_{1x})_i$ is a positive 3.0 m/s. The gliders move to the left after the collision, so their common final velocity is $(v_x)_f = -0.50$ m/s. You can see that velocity $(v_{2x})_i$ must be negative in order to "turn around" both gliders.

SOLVE The law of conservation of momentum, $(P_x)_f = (P_x)_i$, is

$$(m_1 + m_2)(v_x)_f = m_1(v_{1x})_i + m_2(v_{2x})_i$$

where we made use of the fact that the combined mass $m_1 + m_2$ moves together after the collision. We can easily solve for the initial velocity of the 400 g glider:

$$(v_{2x})_i = \frac{(m_1 + m_2)(v_x)_f - m_1(v_{1x})_i}{m_2}$$

$$= \frac{(0.60 \text{ kg})(-0.50 \text{ m/s}) - (0.20 \text{ kg})(3.0 \text{ m/s})}{0.40 \text{ kg}}$$

$$= -2.3 \text{ m/s}$$

The negative sign, which we anticipated, indicates that the 400 g glider started out moving to the left. The initial *speed* of the glider, which we were asked to find, is 2.3 m/s.

ASSESS The key step in solving inelastic collision problems is that both objects move after the collision with the same velocity. You should thus choose a single symbol (here, $(v_x)_f$) for this common velocity.

STOP TO THINK 9.4 The two particles shown collide and stick together. After the collision, the combined particles

A. Move to the right as shown.
B. Move to the left.
C. Are at rest.

2.5 m/s   1.5 m/s
①→   ←②   ①② ???→
0.40 kg Before 0.80 kg   After

9.6 Momentum and Collisions in Two Dimensions

Our examples thus far have been confined to motion along a one-dimensional axis. Many practical examples of momentum conservation involve motion in a plane. The total momentum $\vec{P}$ is the *vector* sum of the momenta $\vec{p} = m\vec{v}$ of the individual particles. Consequently, as Equation 9.15 showed, momentum is conserved only if each component of $\vec{P}$ is conserved:

$$(p_{1x})_f + (p_{2x})_f + (p_{3x})_f + \cdots = (p_{1x})_i + (p_{2x})_i + (p_{3x})_i + \cdots$$
$$(p_{1y})_f + (p_{2y})_f + (p_{3y})_f + \cdots = (p_{1y})_i + (p_{2y})_i + (p_{3y})_i + \cdots \qquad (9.16)$$

In this section we'll apply momentum conservation to motion in two dimensions.

Collisions and explosions often involve motion in two dimensions.

EXAMPLE 9.9 Analyzing a peregrine falcon strike

Peregrine falcons often grab their prey from above while both falcon and prey are in flight. A falcon, flying at 18 m/s, swoops down at a 45° angle from behind a pigeon flying horizontally at 9.0 m/s. The falcon has a mass of 0.80 kg and the pigeon a mass of 0.36 kg. What are the speed and direction of the falcon (now holding the pigeon) immediately after impact?

PREPARE This is a perfectly inelastic collision because after the collision the falcon and pigeon move at a common velocity. The total momentum of the falcon + pigeon system is conserved. For a two-dimensional collision, this means that the x-component of the total momentum before the collision must equal the x-component

FIGURE 9.25 Before-and-after visual overview for a falcon catching a pigeon.

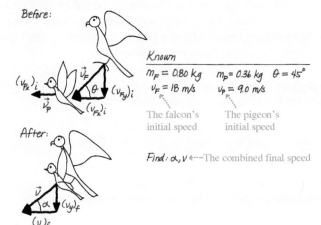

Before:

Known
$m_F = 0.80$ kg $m_P = 0.36$ kg $\theta = 45°$
$v_F = 18$ m/s $v_P = 9.0$ m/s

The falcon's initial speed   The pigeon's initial speed

After:

Find: α, v ←····The combined final speed

of the total momentum after the collision, and similarly for the y-components. **FIGURE 9.25** is a before-and-after visual overview.

SOLVE We'll start by finding the x- and y-components of the momentum before the collision. For the x-component we have

The x-component of the initial momentum . . .   (Both velocity components are negative, since they point to the left.)

$$(P_x)_i = m_F(v_{Fx})_i + m_P(v_{Px})_i = m_F(-v_F \cos\theta) + m_P(-v_P)$$

. . . equals the x-component of the initial momentum of the falcon . . .   . . . plus the x-component of the initial momentum of the pigeon.

$$= (0.80 \text{ kg})(-18 \text{ m/s})(\cos 45°) + (0.36 \text{ kg})(-9.0 \text{ m/s})$$

$$= -13.4 \text{ kg} \cdot \text{m/s}$$

Similarly, for the y-component of the initial momentum we have

$$(P_y)_i = m_F(v_{Fy})_i + m_P(v_{Py})_i = m_F(-v_F \sin\theta) + 0$$

$$= (0.80 \text{ kg})(-18.0 \text{ m/s})(\sin 45°) = -10.2 \text{ kg} \cdot \text{m/s}$$

After the collision, the two birds move with a common velocity $\vec{v}$ that is directed at an angle α from the horizontal. The x-component of the final momentum is then

$$(P_x)_f = (m_F + m_P)(v_x)_f$$

Continued

Momentum conservation requires $(P_x)_f = (P_x)_i$, so

$$(v_x)_f = \frac{(P_x)_i}{m_F + m_P} = \frac{-13.4 \text{ kg} \cdot \text{m/s}}{(0.80 \text{ kg}) + (0.36 \text{ kg})} = -11.6 \text{ m/s}$$

Similarly, $(P_y)_f = (P_y)_i$ gives

$$(v_y)_f = \frac{(P_y)_i}{m_F + m_P} = \frac{-10.2 \text{ kg} \cdot \text{m/s}}{(0.80 \text{ kg}) + (0.36 \text{ kg})} = -8.79 \text{ m/s}$$

From the figure we see that $\tan\alpha = (v_y)_f / (v_x)_f$, so that

$$\alpha = \tan^{-1}\left(\frac{(v_y)_f}{(v_x)_f}\right) = \tan^{-1}\left(\frac{-8.79 \text{ m/s}}{-11.6 \text{ m/s}}\right) = 37°$$

The magnitude of the final velocity (i.e., the speed) can be found from the Pythagorean theorem as

$$v = \sqrt{(v_x)_f^2 + (v_y)_f^2}$$
$$= \sqrt{(-11.6 \text{ m/s})^2 + (-8.79 \text{ m/s})^2} = 15 \text{ m/s}$$

Thus immediately after impact the falcon, with its meal, is moving 37° below horizontal at a speed of 15 m/s.

ASSESS It makes sense that the falcon slows down after catching the slower-moving pigeon. Also, the final angle is closer to the horizontal than the falcon's initial angle. This seems reasonable because the pigeon was initially flying horizontally, making the total momentum vector more horizontal than the direction of the falcon's initial momentum.

FIGURE 9.26 The momentum vectors of the falcon strike.

The total momentum is the same before and after the collision.

$\vec{P} = \vec{p}_F + \vec{p}_P$

It's instructive to examine this collision with a picture of the momentum vectors. The vectors $\vec{p}_F$ and $\vec{p}_P$ before the collision, and their sum $\vec{P} = \vec{p}_F + \vec{p}_P$, are shown in FIGURE 9.26. You can see that the total momentum vector makes a 53° angle with the negative y-axis. The individual momenta change in the collision, *but the total momentum does not.*

PhET: Torque

Class Video

FIGURE 9.27 By applying a torque to the merry-go-round, the girl is increasing its angular momentum.

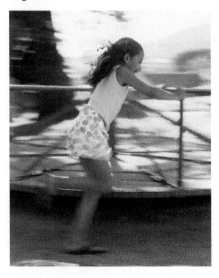

9.7 Angular Momentum

For a single particle, we can think of the law of conservation of momentum as an alternative way of stating Newton's first law. Rather than saying that a particle will continue to move in a straight line at constant velocity unless acted on by a net force, we can say that the momentum of an isolated particle is conserved. Both express the idea that a particle moving in a straight line tends to "keep going" unless something acts on it to change its motion.

Another important motion you've studied is motion in a circle. The momentum $\vec{p}$ is *not* conserved for a particle undergoing circular motion. Momentum is a vector, and the momentum of a particle in circular motion changes as the direction of motion changes.

Nonetheless, a spinning bicycle wheel would keep turning if it were not for friction, and a ball moving in a circle at the end of a string tends to "keep going" in a circular path. The quantity that expresses this idea for circular motion is called *angular momentum.*

Let's start by looking at an example from everyday life: pushing a merry-go-round, as in FIGURE 9.27. If you push tangentially to the rim, you are applying a *torque* to the merry-go-round. As we learned in Chapter 7, the merry-go-round's angular speed will continue to increase for as long as you apply this torque. If you push *harder* (greater torque) or for a *longer time,* the greater the increase in its angular velocity will be. How can we quantify these observations?

Let's apply a constant torque τ_{net} to the merry-go-round for a time Δt. By how much will the merry-go-round's angular speed increase? In Section 7.4 we found that the angular acceleration α is given by the rotational equivalent of Newton's second law, or

$$\alpha = \frac{\tau_{\text{net}}}{I} \tag{9.17}$$

where I is the merry-go-round's moment of inertia.

Now the angular acceleration is the rate of change of the angular velocity, so

$$\alpha = \frac{\Delta\omega}{\Delta t} \tag{9.18}$$

Setting Equations 9.17 and 9.18 equal to each other gives

$$\frac{\Delta\omega}{\Delta t} = \frac{\tau_{net}}{I}$$

or, rearranging,

$$\tau_{net}\,\Delta t = I\,\Delta\omega \qquad (9.19)$$

If you recall the impulse-momentum theorem for *linear* motion, which is

$$\vec{F}_{net}\,\Delta t = m\,\Delta\vec{v} = \Delta\vec{p} \qquad (9.20)$$

you can see that Equation 9.19 is an analogous statement about rotational motion. Because the quantity $I\omega$ is evidently the rotational equivalent of $m\vec{v}$, the linear momentum $\vec{p}$, it seems reasonable to define the **angular momentum** L to be

$$L = I\omega \qquad (9.21)$$

Angular momentum of an object with moment
of inertia I rotating at angular velocity ω

The SI units of angular momentum are those of moment of inertia times angular velocity, or $kg \cdot m^2/s$.

Just as an object in linear motion can have a large momentum by having either a large mass or a high speed, a rotating object can have a large angular momentum by having a large moment of inertia or a large angular velocity. The merry-go-round in Figure 9.27 has a larger angular momentum if it's spinning fast than if it's spinning slowly. Also, the merry-go-round (large I) has a much larger angular momentum than a toy top (small I) spinning with the same angular velocity.

Table 9.2 summarizes the analogies between linear and rotational quantities that you learned in Chapter 7 and adds the analogy between linear momentum and angular momentum.

TABLE 9.2 Rotational and linear dynamics

Rotational dynamics	Linear dynamics
Torque τ_{net}	Force $\vec{F}_{net}$
Moment of inertia I	Mass m
Angular velocity ω	Velocity $\vec{v}$
Angular momentum $L = I\omega$	Linear momentum $\vec{p} = m\vec{v}$

Conservation of Angular Momentum

Having now defined angular momentum, we can write Equation 9.19 as

$$\tau_{net}\,\Delta t = \Delta L \qquad (9.22)$$

in exact analogy with its linear dynamics equivalent, Equation 9.20. This equation states that the change in the angular momentum of an object is proportional to the net torque applied to the object. If the net external torque on an object is *zero,* the rotational analog of an isolated system, then the change in the angular momentum is zero as well. That is, a rotating object will continue to rotate with *constant* angular velocity—to "keep going"—unless acted upon by an external torque. We can state this conclusion as the *law of conservation of angular momentum*:

 ActivPhysics: 7.14

Video Tutor Demonstration   Video Tutor Demonstration

Law of conservation of angular momentum The angular momentum of a rotating object subject to no net external torque ($\tau_{net} = 0$) is a constant. The final angular momentum L_f is equal to the initial angular momentum L_i.

This law is analogous to that for the conservation of linear momentum; there, linear momentum is conserved if the net *force* is zero. Because the angular momentum is $L = I\omega$, the mathematical statement of the law of conservation of angular momentum is

$$I_f\omega_f = I_i\,\omega_i \qquad (9.23)$$

EXAMPLE 9.10 Period of a merry-go-round

Joey, whose mass is 36 kg, stands at the center of a 200 kg merry-go-round that is rotating once every 2.5 s. While it is rotating, Joey walks out to the edge of the merry-go-round, 2.0 m from its center. What is the rotational period of the merry-go-round when Joey gets to the edge?

PREPARE Take the system to be Joey + merry-go-round and assume frictionless bearings. There is no external torque on this system, so the angular momentum of the system will be conserved. As shown in the visual overview of FIGURE 9.28, we model the merry-go-round as a uniform disk of radius $R = 2.0$ m. From Table 7.2, the moment of inertia of a disk is $I_{disk} = \frac{1}{2}MR^2$. If we model Joey as a particle of mass m, his moment of inertia is zero when he is at the center, but it increases to mR^2 when he reaches the edge.

FIGURE 9.28 Visual overview of the merry-go-round.

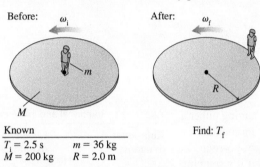

Before: ω_i After: ω_f

m

M

R

Known		Find: T_f
$T_i = 2.5$ s	$m = 36$ kg	
$M = 200$ kg	$R = 2.0$ m	

SOLVE The mathematical statement of the law of conservation of momentum is $L_i = L_f$ or, from Equation 9.23, $I_f \omega_f = I_i \omega_i$, which we can rewrite as

$$\omega_f = \frac{I_i}{I_f} \omega_i$$

As Joey moves out to the edge, the moment of inertia of the system increases and, as a result, the angular velocity decreases. Initially, the moment of inertia of the system is just that of the merry-go-round because Joey's contribution is zero. Thus

$$I_i = I_{disk} = \tfrac{1}{2}MR^2 = \tfrac{1}{2}(200 \text{ kg})(2.0 \text{ m})^2 = 400 \text{ kg} \cdot \text{m}^2$$

When Joey reaches the edge, the total moment of inertia becomes

$$I_f = I_{disk} + mR^2 = 400 \text{ kg} \cdot \text{m}^2 + (36 \text{ kg})(2.0 \text{ m})^2$$
$$= 540 \text{ kg} \cdot \text{m}^2$$

The initial angular velocity is related to the initial period of rotation T_i by

$$\omega_i = \frac{2\pi}{T_i} = \frac{2\pi}{2.5 \text{ s}} = 2.5 \text{ rad/s}$$

Thus the final angular velocity is

$$\omega_f = \frac{I_i}{I_f}\omega_i = \frac{400 \text{ kg} \cdot \text{m}^2}{540 \text{ kg} \cdot \text{m}^2}(2.5 \text{ rad/s}) = 1.9 \text{ rad/s}$$

When Joey reaches the edge, the period of the merry-go-round has increased to

$$T_f = \frac{2\pi}{\omega_f} = \frac{2\pi}{1.9 \text{ rad/s}} = 3.3 \text{ s}$$

ASSESS The merry-go-round rotates *more slowly* after Joey moves out to the edge. This makes sense because if the system's moment of inertia increases, as it does when Joey moves out, the angular velocity must decrease to keep the angular momentum constant.

FIGURE 9.29 A spinning figure skater.

Large moment of inertia; slow spin

Small moment of inertia; fast spin

Conservation of momentum enters into many aspects of sports. Because no external torques act, the angular momentum of a platform diver is conserved while she's in the air. Just as for Joey and the merry-go-round of Example 9.10, she spins slowly when her moment of inertia is large; by decreasing her moment of inertia, she increases her rate of spin. Divers can thus markedly increase their spin rate by changing their body from an extended posture to a tuck position. Figure skaters also increase their spin rate by decreasing their moment of inertia, as shown in FIGURE 9.29. The following example gives a simplified treatment of this process.

EXAMPLE 9.11 Analyzing a spinning ice skater

An ice skater spins around on the tips of his blades while holding a 5.0 kg weight in each hand. He begins with his arms straight out from his body and his hands 140 cm apart. While spinning at 2.0 rev/s, he pulls the weights in and holds them 50 cm apart against his shoulders. If we neglect the mass of the skater, how fast is he spinning after pulling the weights in?

PREPARE Although the mass of the skater is larger than the mass of the weights, neglecting the skater's mass is not a bad approximation. Moment of inertia depends on the *square* of the distance of the mass from the axis of rotation. The skater's mass is concentrated in his torso, which has an effective radius (i.e., where most of the mass is concentrated) of only 9 or 10 cm. The weights move in much larger circles and have a disproportionate influence on his motion. The skater's arms exert radial forces on the weights just to keep them moving in circles, and even larger radial forces as he pulls them in. But there is no external torque on the weights, so their total angular momentum is conserved. FIGURE 9.30 shows a before-and-after visual overview, as seen from above.

FIGURE 9.30 Top view visual overview of the spinning ice skater.

SOLVE The two weights have the same mass, move in circles with the same radius, and have the same angular velocity. Thus the total angular momentum is twice that of one weight. The mathematical statement of angular momentum conservation, $I_f\omega_f = I_i\omega_i$, is

There are two weights.

$$(2\,mr_f^2)\omega_f = (2\,mr_i^2)\omega_i$$
$$\underbrace{\qquad}_{I_f} \qquad \underbrace{\qquad}_{I_i}$$

Because the angular velocity is related to the rotation frequency f by $\omega = 2\pi f$, this equation simplifies to

$$f_f = \left(\frac{r_i}{r_f}\right)^2 f_i$$

When he pulls the weights in, his rotation frequency increases to

$$f_f = \left(\frac{0.70\text{ m}}{0.25\text{ m}}\right)^2 \times 2.0\text{ rev/s} = 16\text{ rev/s}$$

ASSESS Pulling in the weights increases the skater's spin from 2 rev/s to 16 rev/s. This is somewhat high, because we neglected the mass of the skater, but it illustrates how skaters do "spin up" by pulling their mass in toward the rotation axis.

Solving either of these two examples using Newton's laws would be quite difficult. We would have to deal with internal forces, such as Joey's feet against the merry-go-round, and other complications. For problems like these, where we're interested only in the before-and-after aspects of the motion, using a conservation law makes the solution much simpler.

▶ The eye of a hurricane As air masses from the slowing rotating outer zones are drawn toward the low-pressure center, their moment of inertia decreases. Because the angular momentum of these air masses is conserved, their speed must *increase* as they approach the center, leading to the high wind speeds near the center of the storm.

STOP TO THINK 9.5 The left figure shows two boys of equal mass standing halfway to the edge on a turntable that is freely rotating at angular speed ω_i. They then walk to the positions shown in the right figure. The final angular speed ω_f is

A. Greater than ω_i. B. Less than ω_i. C. Equal to ω_i.

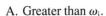

INTEGRATED EXAMPLE 9.12   **Aerial firefighting**

A forest fire is easiest to attack when it's just getting started. In remote locations, this often means using airplanes to rapidly deliver large quantities of water and fire suppressant to the blaze.

The "Superscooper" is an amphibious aircraft that can pick up a 6000 kg load of water by skimming over the surface of a river or lake and scooping water directly into its storage tanks. As it approaches the water's surface at a speed of 35 m/s, an empty Superscooper has a mass of 13,000 kg.

a. It takes the plane 12 s to pick up a full load of water. If we ignore the force on the plane due to the thrust of its propellers, what is its speed immediately after picking up the water?
b. What is the impulse delivered to the plane by the water?
c. What is the average force of the water on the plane?
d. The plane then flies over the fire zone at 40 m/s. It releases water by opening doors in the belly of the plane, allowing the water to fall straight down with respect to the plane. What is the plane's speed after dropping the water if it takes 5.0 s to do so?

PREPARE We can solve part a, and later part d, using conservation of momentum, following Problem-Solving Strategy 9.1. We'll need to choose the system with care, so that $\vec{F}_{net} = \vec{0}$. The plane alone is not an appropriate system for using conservation of momentum: As the plane scoops up the water, the water exerts a large external drag force on the plane, so $\vec{F}_{net}$ is definitely not zero. Instead, we should choose the plane *and* the water it is going to scoop up as the system. Then there are no external forces in the *x*-direction, and the net force in the *y*-direction is zero, since neither plane nor water accelerates appreciably in this direction during the scooping process. The complicated forces between plane and water are now *internal* forces that do not change the total momentum of the plane + water system.

With the system chosen, we follow the steps of Tactics Box 9.1 to prepare the before-and-after visual overview shown in FIGURE 9.31.

Parts b and c are impulse-and-momentum problems, so to solve them we'll use the impulse-momentum theorem, Equation 9.8. The impulse-momentum theorem considers the dynamics of a *single* object—here, the plane—subject to external forces—in this case, from the water.

FIGURE 9.31 Visual overview of the plane and water.

SOLVE a. Conservation of momentum in the *x*-direction is

$$(P_x)_f = (P_x)_i$$

or

$$(m_P + m_W)(v_x)_f = m_P(v_{Px})_i + m_W(v_{Wx})_i = m_P(v_{Px})_i + 0$$

Here we've used the facts that the initial velocity of the water is zero and that the final situation, as in an inelastic collision, has the combined mass of the plane and water moving with the same velocity $(v_x)_f$. Solving for $(v_x)_f$, we find

$$(v_x)_f = \frac{m_P(v_{Px})_i}{m_P + m_W} = \frac{(13,000 \text{ kg})(35 \text{ m/s})}{(13,000 \text{ kg}) + (6000 \text{ kg})} = 24 \text{ m/s}$$

b. The impulse-momentum theorem is $J_x = \Delta p_x$, where $\Delta p_x = m_P \Delta v_x$ is the change in the plane's momentum. Thus

$$J_x = m_P \Delta v_x = m_P[(v_x)_f - (v_{Px})_i]$$
$$= (13,000 \text{ kg})(24 \text{ m/s} - 35 \text{ m/s}) = -1.4 \times 10^5 \text{ kg} \cdot \text{m/s}$$

c. From Equation 9.1, the definition of impulse, we have

$$(F_{avg})_x = \frac{J_x}{\Delta t} = \frac{-1.4 \times 10^5 \text{ kg} \cdot \text{m/s}}{12 \text{ s}} = -12,000 \text{ N}$$

d. Because the water drops straight down *relative to the plane*, it has the same *x*-component of velocity immediately after being dropped as before being dropped. That is, simply opening the doors doesn't cause the water to speed up or slow down horizontally, so the water's horizontal momentum doesn't change upon being dropped. Because the total momentum of the plane + water system is conserved, the momentum of the plane doesn't change either. The plane's speed after the drop is still 40 m/s.

ASSESS The mass of the water is nearly half that of the plane, so the significant decrease in the plane's velocity as it scoops up the water is reasonable. The force of the water on the plane is large, but is still only about 10% of the plane's weight, $mg = 130,000$ N, so the answer seems to be reasonable.

SUMMARY

The goals of Chapter 9 have been to introduce the ideas of impulse, momentum, and angular momentum and to learn a new problem-solving strategy based on conservation laws.

GENERAL PRINCIPLES

Law of Conservation of Momentum

The total momentum $\vec{P} = \vec{p}_1 + \vec{p}_2 + \cdots$ of an isolated system is a constant. Thus

$$\vec{P}_f = \vec{P}_i$$

Conservation of Angular Momentum

The angular momentum L of a rotating object subject to zero external torque does not change. Thus

$$L_f = L_i$$

This can be written in terms of the moment of inertia and angular velocity as

$$I_f\omega_f = I_i\omega_i$$

Solving Momentum Conservation Problems

PREPARE Choose an isolated system or a system that is isolated during at least part of the problem. Draw a visual overview of the system before and after the interaction.

SOLVE Write the law of conservation of momentum in terms of vector components:

$$(p_{1x})_f + (p_{2x})_f + \cdots = (p_{1x})_i + (p_{2x})_i + \cdots$$

$$(p_{1y})_f + (p_{2y})_f + \cdots = (p_{1y})_i + (p_{2y})_i + \cdots$$

In terms of masses and velocities, this is

$$m_1(v_{1x})_f + m_2(v_{2x})_f + \cdots = m_1(v_{1x})_i + m_2(v_{2x})_i + \cdots$$

$$m_1(v_{1y})_f + m_2(v_{2y})_f + \cdots = m_1(v_{1y})_i + m_2(v_{2y})_i + \cdots$$

ASSESS Is the result reasonable?

IMPORTANT CONCEPTS

Momentum $\vec{p} = m\vec{v}$

Impulse J_x = area under force curve

Impulse and momentum are related by the impulse-momentum theorem

$$\Delta p_x = J_x$$

This is an alternative statement of Newton's second law.

Angular momentum $L = I\omega$ is the rotational analog of linear momentum $\vec{p} = m\vec{v}$.

System A group of interacting particles.

Isolated system A system on which the net external force is zero.

Internal forces

Before-and-after visual overview

- Define the system.

- Use two drawings to show the system *before* and *after* the interaction.

- List known information and identify what you are trying to find.

Before: m_1 ① $(v_{1x})_i$ → ← $(v_{2x})_i$ ② m_2
After: ← ① ② → $(v_{1x})_f$ $(v_{2x})_f$

APPLICATIONS

Collisions Two or more particles come together. In a perfectly inelastic collision, they stick together and move with a common final velocity.

① → ← ②
$(v_{1x})_i$ $(v_{2x})_i$

Explosions Two or more particles move away from each other.

← ① ② →
$(v_{1x})_f$ $(v_{2x})_f$

Two dimensions Both the x- and y-components of the total momentum P must be conserved, giving two simultaneous equations.

① $\vec{v}_{1f}$
① $\vec{v}_{1i}$ →
$\vec{v}_{2i}$ ② ② $\vec{v}_{2f}$

Problem difficulty is labeled as I (straightforward) to IIIII (challenging). Problems labeled 🖉 can be done on a Workbook Momentum Worksheet; INT integrate significant material from earlier chapters; BIO are of biological or medical interest.

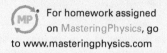

For homework assigned on MasteringPhysics, go to www.masteringphysics.com

Scan this QR code to launch a Video Tutor Solution that will help you solve problems for this chapter.

QUESTIONS

Conceptual Questions

1. Rank in order, from largest to smallest, the momenta p_{1x} through p_{5x} of the objects presented in Figure Q9.1. Explain.

FIGURE Q9.1

2. Starting from rest, object 1 is subject to a 12 N force for 2.0 s. Object 2, with twice the mass, is subject to a 15 N force for 3.0 s. Which object has the greater final speed? Explain.

3. A 0.2 kg plastic cart and a 20 kg lead cart can roll without friction on a horizontal surface. Equal forces are used to push both carts forward for a time of 1 s, starting from rest. After the force is removed at $t = 1$ s, is the momentum of the plastic cart greater than, less than, or equal to the momentum of the lead cart? Explain.

4. Two pucks, of mass m and $4m$, lie on a frictionless table. Equal forces are used to push both pucks forward a distance of 1 m.
   a. Which puck takes longer to travel the distance? Explain.
   b. Which puck has the greater momentum upon completing the distance? Explain.

5. A stationary firecracker explodes into three pieces. One piece travels off to the east; a second travels to the north. Which of the vectors of Figure Q9.5 could be the velocity of the third piece? Explain.

6. Two students stand at rest, facing each other on frictionless skates. They then start tossing a heavy ball back and forth between them. Describe their subsequent motion.

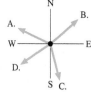

FIGURE Q9.5

7. Two particles collide, one of which was initially moving and the other initially at rest.
   a. Is it possible for *both* particles to be at rest after the collision? Give an example in which this happens, or explain why it can't happen.
   b. Is it possible for *one* particle to be at rest after the collision? Give an example in which this happens, or explain why it can't happen.

8. Automobiles are designed with "crumple zones" intended to collapse in a collision. Why would a manufacturer design part of a car so that it collapses in a collision?

9. You probably know that it feels better to catch a baseball if you are wearing a padded glove. Explain why this is so, using the ideas of momentum and impulse.

10. In the early days of rocketry, some people claimed that rockets couldn't fly in outer space as there was no air for the rockets to push against. Suppose you were an early investigator in the field of rocketry and met someone who made this argument. How would you convince the person that rockets could travel in space?

11. Two ice skaters, Megan and Jason, push off from each other on frictionless ice. Jason's mass is twice that of Megan.
    a. Which skater, if either, experiences the greater impulse during the push? Explain.
    b. Which skater, if either, has the greater speed after the push-off? Explain.

12. Suppose a rubber ball and a steel ball collide. Which, if either, receives the larger impulse? Explain.

13. While standing still on a basketball court, you throw the ball to a teammate. Why do you not move backward as a result? Is the law of conservation of momentum violated?

14. To win a prize at the county fair, you're trying to knock down a heavy bowling pin by hitting it with a thrown object. Should you choose to throw a rubber ball or a beanbag of equal size and weight? Explain.

15. Rank in order, from largest to smallest, the angular momenta L_1 through L_5 of the balls shown in Figure Q9.15. Explain.

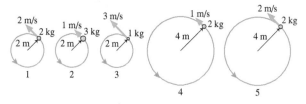

FIGURE Q9.15

16. Figure Q9.16 shows two masses held together by a thread on a rod that is rotating about its center with angular velocity ω. If the thread breaks, the masses will slide out to the ends of the rod. If that happens, will the rod's angular velocity increase, decrease, or remain unchanged? Explain.

FIGURE Q9.16

17. If the earth warms significantly, the polar ice caps will melt. Water will move from the poles, near the earth's rotation axis, and will spread out around the globe. In principle, this will change the length of the day. Why? Will the length of the day increase or decrease?

18. The disks shown in Figure Q9.18 have equal mass. Is the angular momentum of disk 2, on the right, larger than, smaller than, or equal to the angular momentum of disk 1? Explain.

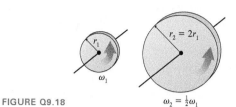

FIGURE Q9.18

Multiple-Choice Questions

19. | Curling is a sport played with 20 kg stones that slide across an ice surface. Suppose a curling stone sliding at 1 m/s strikes another stone and comes to rest in 2 ms. Approximately how much force is there on the stone during the impact?
    A. 200 N   B. 1000 N   C. 2000 N   D. 10,000 N

20. | Two balls are hung from cords. The first ball, of mass 1.0 kg, is pulled to the side and released, reaching a speed of 2.0 m/s at the bottom of its arc. Then, as shown in Figure Q9.20, it hits and sticks to another ball. The speed of the pair just after the collision is 1.2 m/s. What is the mass of the second ball?
    A. 0.67 kg
    B. 2.0 kg
    C. 1.7 kg
    D. 1.0 kg

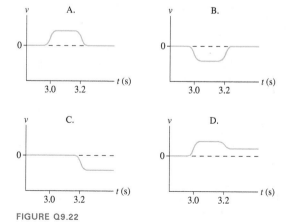

FIGURE Q9.20

21. | Figure Q9.21 shows two blocks sliding on a frictionless surface. Eventually the smaller block overtakes the larger one, collides with it, and sticks. What is the speed of the two blocks after the collision?
    A. $v_i/2$ B. $4v_i/5$ C. v_i D. $5v_i/4$ E. $2v_i$

FIGURE Q9.21

22. | Two friends are sitting in a stationary canoe. At $t = 3.0$ s the person at the front tosses a sack to the person in the rear, who catches the sack 0.2 s later. Which plot in Figure Q9.22 shows

FIGURE Q9.22

the velocity of the boat as a function of time? Positive velocity is forward, negative velocity is backward. Neglect any drag force on the canoe from the water.

23. ‖ Two blocks, with masses $m_1 = 2.5$ kg and $m_2 = 14$ kg, approach each other along a horizontal, frictionless track. The initial velocities of the blocks are $v_1 = 12.0$ m/s to the right and $v_2 = 3.4$ m/s to the left. The two blocks then collide and stick together. Which of the graphs could represent the force of block 1 on block 2 during the collision?

FIGURE Q9.23

24. | A small puck is sliding to the right with momentum $\vec{p}_i$ on a horizontal, frictionless surface, as shown in Figure Q9.24. A force is applied to the puck for a short time and its momentum afterward is $\vec{p}_f$. Which lettered arrow shows the direction of the impulse that was delivered to the puck?

FIGURE Q9.24

25. | A red ball, initially at rest, is simultaneously hit by a blue ball traveling from west to east at 3 m/s and a green ball traveling east to west at 3 m/s. All three balls have equal mass. Afterward, the red ball is traveling south and the green ball is moving to the east. In which direction is the blue ball traveling?
    A. West
    B. North
    C. Between north and west
    D. Between north and east
    E. Between south and west

26. | A 24 g, 3-cm-diameter thin, hollow sphere rotates at 30 rpm about a vertical, frictionless axis through its center. A 4 g bug stands at the top of the sphere. He then walks along the surface of the sphere until he reaches its "equator." When he reaches the equator, the sphere is rotating at
    A. 15 rpm
    B. 24 rpm
    C. 30 rpm
    D. 37 rpm
    E. 45 rpm

27. | A 5.0 kg solid cylinder of radius 12 cm rotates with $\omega_i = 3.7$ rad/s about an axis through its center. A torque of 0.040 N·m is applied to the cylinder for 5.0 s. By how much does the cylinder's angular momentum change?
    A. 0.12 kg·m²/s
    B. 0.20 kg·m²/s
    C. 0.38 kg·m²/s
    D. 0.52 kg·m²/s
    E. 0.88 kg·m²/s

PROBLEMS

Section 9.1 Impulse

Section 9.2 Momentum and the Impulse-Momentum Theorem

1. | At what speed do a bicycle and its rider, with a combined mass of 100 kg, have the same momentum as a 1500 kg car traveling at 5.0 m/s?

2. | A 57 g tennis ball is served at 45 m/s. If the ball started from rest, what impulse was applied to the ball by the racket?

3. || A student throws a 120 g snowball at 7.5 m/s at the side of the schoolhouse, where it hits and sticks. What is the magnitude of the average force on the wall if the duration of the collision is 0.15 s?

4. |||| In Figure P9.4, what value of F_{max} gives an impulse of 6.0 N · s?

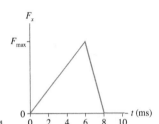

FIGURE P9.4

5. | A sled and rider, gliding over horizontal, frictionless ice at 4.0 m/s, have a combined mass of 80 kg. The sled then slides over a rough spot in the ice, slowing down to 3.0 m/s. What impulse was delivered to the sled by the friction force from the rough spot?

Section 9.3 Solving Impulse and Momentum Problems

6. || Use the impulse-momentum theorem to find how long a stone falling straight down takes to increase its speed from 5.5 m/s to 10.4 m/s.

7. || a. A 2.0 kg object is moving to the right with a speed of 1.0 m/s when it experiences the force shown in Figure P9.7a. What are the object's speed and direction after the force ends?
   b. Answer this question for the force shown in Figure P9.7b.

FIGURE P9.7

8. |||| A 60 g tennis ball with an initial speed of 32 m/s hits a wall and rebounds with the same speed. Figure P9.8 shows the force of the wall on the ball during the collision. What is the value of F_{max}, the maximum value of the contact force during the collision?

FIGURE P9.8

9. || A child is sliding on a sled at 1.5 m/s to the right. You stop the sled by pushing on it for 0.50 s in a direction opposite to its motion. If the mass of the child and sled is 35 kg, what average force do you need to apply to stop the sled? Use the concepts of impulse and momentum.

10. ||| An ice hockey puck slides along the ice at 12 m/s. A hockey stick delivers an impulse of 4.0 kg · m/s, causing the puck to move off in the opposite direction with the same speed. What is the mass of the puck?

11. | As part of a safety investigation, two 1400 kg cars traveling at 20 m/s are crashed into different barriers. Find the average forces exerted on (a) the car that hits a line of water barrels and takes 1.5 s to stop, and (b) the car that hits a concrete barrier and takes 0.1 s to stop.

12. || In a Little League baseball game, the 145 g ball enters the strike zone with a speed of 15.0 m/s. The batter hits the ball, and it leaves his bat with a speed of 20.0 m/s in exactly the opposite direction.
    a. What is the magnitude of the impulse delivered by the bat to the ball?
    b. If the bat is in contact with the ball for 1.5 ms, what is the magnitude of the average force exerted by the bat on the ball?

Section 9.4 Conservation of Momentum

13. |||| A small, 100 g cart is moving at 1.20 m/s on an air track when it collides with a larger, 1.00 kg cart at rest. After the collision, the small cart recoils at 0.850 m/s. What is the speed of the large cart after the collision?

14. || A man standing on very slick ice fires a rifle horizontally. The mass of the man together with the rifle is 70 kg, and the mass of the bullet is 10 g. If the bullet leaves the muzzle at a speed of 500 m/s, what is the final speed of the man?

15. ||| A 2.7 kg block of wood sits on a table. A 3.0 g bullet, fired horizontally at a speed of 500 m/s, goes completely through the block, emerging at a speed of 220 m/s. What is the speed of the block immediately after the bullet exits?

16. | A strong man is compressing a lightweight spring between two weights. One weight has a mass of 2.3 kg, the other a mass of 5.3 kg. He is holding the weights stationary, but then he loses his grip and the weights fly off in opposite directions. The lighter of the two is shot out at a speed of 6.0 m/s. What is the speed of the heavier weight?

17. || A 10,000 kg railroad car is rolling at 2.00 m/s when a 4000 kg load of gravel is suddenly dropped in. What is the car's speed just after the gravel is loaded?

18. | A 5000 kg open train car is rolling on frictionless rails at 22.0 m/s when it starts pouring rain. A few minutes later, the car's speed is 20.0 m/s. What mass of water has collected in the car?

19. || A 50.0 kg archer, standing on frictionless ice, shoots a 40 g arrow at a speed of 60 m/s. What is the recoil speed of the archer?

20. || A 9.5 kg dog takes a nap in a canoe and wakes up to find the canoe has drifted out onto the lake but now is stationary. He walks along the length of the canoe at 0.50 m/s, relative to the water, and the canoe simultaneously moves in the opposite direction at 0.15 m/s. What is the mass of the canoe?

Section 9.5 Inelastic Collisions

21. ‖ A 300 g bird flying along at 6.0 m/s sees a 10 g insect heading straight toward it with a speed of 30 m/s. The bird opens its mouth wide and enjoys a nice lunch. What is the bird's speed immediately after swallowing?

22. ‖ A 71 kg baseball player jumps straight up to catch a line drive. If the 140 g ball is moving horizontally at 28 m/s, and the catch is made when the ballplayer is at the highest point of his leap, what is his speed immediately after stopping the ball?

23. ‖‖ A kid at the junior high cafeteria wants to propel an empty milk carton along a lunch table by hitting it with a 3.0 g spit ball. If he wants the speed of the 20 g carton just after the spit ball hits it to be 0.30 m/s, at what speed should his spit ball hit the carton?

24. ‖ The parking brake on a 2000 kg Cadillac has failed, and it is rolling slowly, at 1 mph, toward a group of small children. Seeing the situation, you realize you have just enough time to drive your 1000 kg Volkswagen head-on into the Cadillac and save the children. With what speed should you impact the Cadillac to bring it to a halt?

25. ‖ A 2.0 kg block slides along a frictionless surface at 1.0 m/s. A second block, sliding at a faster 4.0 m/s, collides with the first from behind and sticks to it. The final velocity of the combined blocks is 2.0 m/s. What was the mass of the second block?

Section 9.6 Momentum and Collisions in Two Dimensions

26. ‖‖‖ A 20 g ball of clay traveling east at 3.0 m/s collides with a 30 g ball of clay traveling north at 2.0 m/s. What are the speed and the direction of the resulting 50 g ball of clay?

27. ‖ Two particles collide and bounce apart. Figure P9.27 shows the initial momenta of both and the final momentum of particle 2. What is the final momentum of particle 1? Show your answer by copying the figure and drawing the final momentum vector on the figure.

FIGURE P9.27

28. ‖ A 20 g ball of clay traveling east at 2.0 m/s collides with a 30 g ball of clay traveling 30° south of west at 1.0 m/s. What are the speed and direction of the resulting 50 g blob of clay?

29. ‖ A firecracker in a coconut blows the coconut into three pieces. Two pieces of equal mass fly off south and west, perpendicular to each other, at 20 m/s. The third piece has twice the mass as the other two. What are the speed and direction of the third piece?

Section 9.7 Angular Momentum

30. ‖‖‖ What is the angular momentum of the moon around the earth? The moon's mass is 7.4×10^{22} kg and it orbits 3.8×10^8 m from the earth.

31. ‖‖‖ A little girl is going on the merry-go-round for the first time, and wants her 47 kg mother to stand next to her on the ride, 2.6 m from the merry-go-round's center. If her mother's speed is 4.2 m/s when the ride is in motion, what is her angular momentum around the center of the merry-go-round?

32. ‖ What is the angular momentum about the axle of the 500 g rotating bar in Figure P9.32?

FIGURE P9.32   FIGURE P9.33

33. ‖‖‖ What is the angular momentum about the axle of the 2.0 kg, 4.0-cm-diameter rotating disk in Figure P9.33?

34. ‖ Divers change their body position in midair while rotating about their center of mass. In one dive, the diver leaves the board with her body nearly straight, then tucks into a somersault position. If the moment of inertia of the diver in a straight position is 14 kg · m² and in a tucked position is 4.0 kg · m², by what factor is her angular velocity when tucked greater than when straight?

35. ‖ Ice skaters often end their performances with spin turns, where they spin very fast about their center of mass with their arms folded in and legs together. Upon ending, their arms extend outward, proclaiming their finish. Not quite as noticeably, one leg goes out as well. Suppose that the moment of inertia of a skater with arms out and one leg extended is 3.2 kg · m² and for arms and legs in is 0.80 kg · m². If she starts out spinning at 5.0 rev/s, what is her angular speed (in rev/s) when her arms and one leg open outward?

General Problems

36. ‖‖‖ What is the impulse on a 3.0 kg particle that experiences the force described by the graph in Figure P9.36?

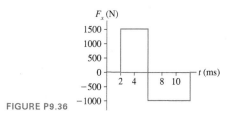

FIGURE P9.36

37. ‖‖‖ A 600 g air-track glider collides with a spring at one end of the track. Figure P9.37 shows the glider's velocity and the force exerted on the glider by the spring. How long is the glider in contact with the spring?

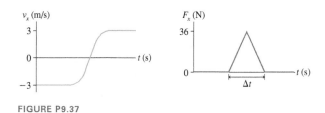

FIGURE P9.37

38. ‖ Far in space, where gravity is negligible, a 425 kg rocket traveling at 75.0 m/s in the positive *x*-direction fires its engines. Figure P9.38 shows the thrust force as a function of time. The mass lost by the rocket during these 30.0 s is negligible.
    a. What impulse does the engine impart to the rocket?
    b. At what time does the rocket reach its maximum speed? What is the maximum speed?

FIGURE P9.38

FIGURE P9.39

39. ‖‖‖ A 200 g ball is dropped from a height of 2.0 m, bounces on a hard floor, and rebounds to a height of 1.5 m. Figure P9.39 shows the impulse received from the floor. What maximum force does the floor exert on the ball?

40. ‖‖‖ A 200 g ball is dropped from a height of 2.0 m and bounces on a hard floor. The force on the ball from the floor is shown in Figure P9.40. How high does the ball rebound?

FIGURE P9.40

FIGURE P9.41

41. ‖‖ Figure P9.41 is a graph of the force exerted by the floor on a woman making a vertical jump. At what speed does she leave the ground?
    Hint: The force of the floor is not the only force acting on the woman.

42. ‖ A sled slides along a horizontal surface for which the coefficient of kinetic friction is 0.25. Its velocity at point A is 8.0 m/s and at point B is 5.0 m/s. Use the impulse-momentum theorem to find how long the sled takes to travel from A to B.

43. ‖‖‖ A 140 g baseball is moving horizontally to the right at 35 m/s when it is hit by the bat. The ball flies off to the left at 55 m/s, at an angle of 25° above the horizontal. What are the magnitude and direction of the impulse that the bat delivers to the ball?

44. ‖ Squids rely on jet propulsion, a versatile technique to move around in water. A 1.5 kg squid at rest suddenly expels 0.10 kg of water backward to quickly get itself moving forward at 3.0 m/s. If other forces (such as the drag force on the squid) are ignored, what is the speed with which the squid expels the water?

45. ‖‖‖ The flowers of the bunchberry plant open with astonishing force and speed, causing the pollen grains to be ejected out of the flower in a mere 0.30 ms at an acceleration of 2.5×10^4 m/s². If the acceleration is constant, what impulse is delivered to a pollen grain with a mass of 1.0×10^{-7} g?

46. ‖‖ a. With what speed are pollen grains ejected from a bunchberry flower? See Problem 45 for information.
    b. Suppose that 1000 ejected pollen grains slam into the abdomen of a 5.0 g bee that is hovering just above the flower. If the collision is perfectly inelastic, what is the bee's speed immediately afterward? Is the bee likely to notice?

47. ‖‖‖ A tennis player swings her 1000 g racket with a speed of 10 m/s. She hits a 60 g tennis ball that was approaching her at a speed of 20 m/s. The ball rebounds at 40 m/s.
    a. How fast is her racket moving immediately after the impact? You can ignore the interaction of the racket with her hand for the brief duration of the collision.
    b. If the tennis ball and racket are in contact for 10 ms, what is the average force that the racket exerts on the ball?

48. ‖ A 20 g ball of clay is thrown horizontally at 30 m/s toward a 1.0 kg block sitting at rest on a frictionless surface. The clay hits and sticks to the block.
    a. What is the speed of the block and clay right after the collision?
    b. Use the block's initial and final speeds to calculate the impulse the clay exerts on the block.
    c. Use the clay's initial and final speeds to calculate the impulse the block exerts on the clay.
    d. Does $\vec{J}_{\text{block on clay}} = -\vec{J}_{\text{clay on block}}$?

49. ‖ Dan is gliding on his skateboard at 4.0 m/s. He suddenly jumps backward off the skateboard, kicking the skateboard forward at 8.0 m/s. How fast is Dan going as his feet hit the ground? Dan's mass is 50 kg and the skateboard's mass is 5.0 kg.

50. ‖ James and Sarah stand on a stationary cart with frictionless wheels. The total mass of the cart and riders is 130 kg. At the same instant, James throws a 1.0 kg ball to Sarah at 4.5 m/s, while Sarah throws a 0.50 kg ball to James at 1.0 m/s. James's throw is to the right and Sarah's is to the left.
    a. While the two balls are in the air, what are the speed and direction of the cart and its riders?
    b. After the balls are caught, what are the speed and direction of the cart and riders?

51. ‖‖‖ Ethan, whose mass is 80 kg, stands at one end of a very long, stationary wheeled cart that has a mass of 500 kg. He then starts sprinting toward the other end of the cart. He soon reaches his top speed of 8.0 m/s, measured relative to the cart. What is the speed of the cart when Ethan has reached his top speed?

52. ‖ The cars of a long coal train are filled by pulling them under a hopper, from which coal falls into the cars at a rate of 10,000 kg/s. Ignoring friction due to the rails, what is the average force that the engine must exert on the coal train to keep it moving under the hopper at a speed of 0.50 m/s?

53. ‖ Three identical train cars, coupled together, are rolling east at 2.0 m/s. A fourth car traveling east at 4.0 m/s catches up with the three and couples to make a four-car train. A moment later, the train cars hit a fifth car that was at rest on the tracks, and it couples to make a five-car train. What is the speed of the five-car train?

54. ‖ A 110 kg linebacker running at 2.0 m/s and an 82 kg quarterback running at 3.0 m/s have a head-on collision in midair. The linebacker grabs and holds onto the quarterback. Who ends up moving forward after they hit?

55. ‖ Most geologists believe that the dinosaurs became extinct 65 million years ago when a large comet or asteroid struck the earth, throwing up so much dust that the sun was blocked out for a period of many months. Suppose an asteroid with a diameter of 2.0 km and a mass of 1.0×10^{13} kg hits the earth with an impact speed of 4.0×10^4 m/s.
    a. What is the earth's recoil speed after such a collision? (Use a reference frame in which the earth was initially at rest.)
    b. What percentage is this of the earth's speed around the sun? (Use the astronomical data inside the back cover.)

56. ‖ At the center of a 50-m-diameter circular ice rink, a 75 kg skater traveling north at 2.5 m/s collides with and holds onto a 60 kg skater who had been heading west at 3.5 m/s.
    a. How long will it take them to glide to the edge of the rink?
    b. Where will they reach it? Give your answer as an angle north of west.

57. ‖ Two ice skaters, with masses of 50 kg and 75 kg, are at the center of a 60-m-diameter circular rink. The skaters push off against each other and glide to opposite edges of the rink. If the heavier skater reaches the edge in 20 s, how long does the lighter skater take to reach the edge?

58. ‖ One billiard ball is shot east at 2.00 m/s. A second, identical billiard ball is shot west at 1.00 m/s. The balls have a glancing collision, not a head-on collision, deflecting the second ball by 90° and sending it north at 1.41 m/s. What are the speed and direction of the first ball after the collision?

59. ‖ A 10 g bullet is fired into a 10 kg wood block that is at rest on a wood table. The block, with the bullet embedded, slides 5.0 cm across the table. What was the speed of the bullet?

60. ‖ You are part of a search-and-rescue mission that has been called out to look for a lost explorer. You've found the missing explorer, but you're separated from him by a 200-m-high cliff and a 30-m-wide raging river, as shown in Figure P9.60. To save his life, you need to get a 5.0 kg package of emergency supplies across the river. Unfortunately, you can't throw the package hard enough to make

FIGURE P9.60

it across. Fortunately, you happen to have a 1.0 kg rocket intended for launching flares. Improvising quickly, you attach a sharpened stick to the front of the rocket, so that it will impale itself into the package of supplies, then fire the rocket at ground level toward the supplies. What minimum speed must the rocket have just before impact in order to save the explorer's life?

61. ‖‖ A 1500 kg weather rocket accelerates upward at 10.0 m/s². It explodes 2.00 s after liftoff and breaks into two fragments, one twice as massive as the other. Photos reveal that the lighter fragment traveled straight up and reached a maximum height of 530 m. What were the speed and direction of the heavier fragment just after the explosion?

62. ‖ Two 500 g blocks of wood are 2.0 m apart on a frictionless table. A 10 g bullet is fired at 400 m/s toward the blocks. It passes all the way through the first block, then embeds itself in the second block. The speed of the first block immediately afterward is 6.0 m/s. What is the speed of the second block after the bullet stops?

63. ‖ A 500 kg cannon fires a 10 kg cannonball with a speed of 200 m/s relative to the muzzle. The cannon is on wheels that roll without friction. When the cannon fires, what is the speed of the cannonball relative to the earth?

64. ‖‖ Laura, whose mass is 35 kg, jumps horizontally off a 55 kg canoe at 1.5 m/s relative to the canoe. What is the canoe's speed just after she jumps?

65. ‖ A spaceship of mass 2.0×10^6 kg is cruising at a speed of 5.0×10^6 m/s when the antimatter reactor fails, blowing the ship into three pieces. One section, having a mass of 5.0×10^5 kg, is blown straight backward with a speed of 2.0×10^6 m/s. A second piece, with mass 8.0×10^5 kg, continues forward at 1.0×10^6 m/s. What are the direction and speed of the third piece?

66. ‖ A proton is shot at 5.0×10^7 m/s toward a gold target. The nucleus of a gold atom, with a mass 197 times that of the proton, repels the proton and deflects it straight back with 90% of its initial speed. What is the recoil speed of the gold nucleus?

67. ‖ Figure P9.67 shows a collision between three balls of clay. The three hit simultaneously and stick together. What are the speed and direction of the resulting blob of clay?

FIGURE P9.67

68. ‖ The carbon isotope ^{14}C is used for carbon dating of archeological artifacts. ^{14}C (mass 2.34×10^{-26} kg) decays by the process known as *beta decay* in which the nucleus emits an electron (the beta particle) and a subatomic particle called a neutrino. In one such decay, the electron and the neutrino are emitted at right angles to each other. The electron (mass 9.11×10^{-31} kg) has a speed of 5.00×10^7 m/s and the neutrino has a momentum of 8.00×10^{-24} kg · m/s. What is the recoil speed of the nucleus?

69. ‖ A 1.0-m-long massless rod is pivoted at one end and swings around in a circle on a frictionless table. A block with a hole through the center can slide in and out along the rod. Initially, a small piece of wax holds the block 30 cm from the pivot. The block is spun at 50 rpm, then the temperature of the rod is slowly increased. When the wax melts, the block slides out to the end of the rod. What is the final angular speed? Give your answer in rpm.

70. ‖ A 200 g puck revolves in a circle on a frictionless table at the end of a 50.0-cm-long string. The puck's angular momentum about the center of the circle is 3.00 kg · m²/s. What is the tension in the string?

71. ‖ Figure P9.71 shows a 100 g puck revolving in a 20-cm-radius circle on a frictionless table. The string passes through a hole in the center of the table and is tied to two 200 g weights.
    a. What speed does the puck need to support the two weights?

FIGURE P9.71

    b. The lower weight is a light bag filled with sand. Suppose a pin pokes a hole in the bag and the sand slowly leaks out while the puck is revolving. What will be the puck's speed and the radius of its trajectory after all of the sand is gone?

72. ‖ A 2.0 kg, 20-cm-diameter turntable rotates at 100 rpm on frictionless bearings. Two 500 g blocks fall from above, hit the turntable simultaneously at opposite ends of a diagonal, and stick. What is the turntable's angular speed, in rpm, just after this event?

73. ‖ Joey, from Example 9.10, stands at rest at the outer edge of the frictionless merry-go-round of Figure 9.28. The merry-go-round is also at rest. Joey then begins to run around the perimeter of the merry-go-round, finally reaching a constant speed, measured relative to the ground, of 5.0 m/s. What is the final angular speed of the merry-go-round?

74. ▥ A 3.0-m-diameter merry-go-round with a mass of 250 kg is spinning at 20 rpm. John runs around the merry-go-round at 5.0 m/s, in the same direction that it is turning, and jumps onto the outer edge. John's mass is 30 kg. What is the merry-go-round's angular speed, in rpm, after John jumps on?

75. ▥ Disk A, with a mass of 2.0 kg and a radius of 40 cm, rotates clockwise about a frictionless vertical axle at 30 rev/s. Disk B, also 2.0 kg but with a radius of 20 cm, rotates counterclockwise about that same axle, but at a greater height than disk A, at 30 rev/s. Disk B slides down the axle until it lands on top of disk A, after which they rotate together. After the collision, what is their common angular speed (in rev/s) and in which direction do they rotate?

Passage Problems

Hitting a Golf Ball

Consider a golf club hitting a golf ball. To a good approximation, we can model this as a collision between the rapidly moving head of the golf club and the stationary golf ball, ignoring the shaft of the club and the golfer.

A golf ball has a mass of 46 g. Suppose a 200 g club head is moving at a speed of 40 m/s just before striking the golf ball. After the collision, the golf ball's speed is 60 m/s.

76. ▯ What is the momentum of the club + ball system right before the collision?
    A. 1.8 kg · m/s   B. 8.0 kg · m/s
    C. 3220 kg · m/s   D. 8000 kg · m/s

77. ▯ Immediately after the collision, the momentum of the club + ball system will be
    A. Less than before the collision.
    B. The same as before the collision.
    C. More than before the collision.

78. ▯ A manufacturer makes a golf ball that compresses more than a traditional golf ball when struck by a club. How will this affect the average force during the collision?
    A. The force will decrease.
    B. The force will not be affected.
    C. The force will increase.

79. ▯ By approximately how much does the club head slow down as a result of hitting the ball?
    A. 4 m/s   B. 6 m/s   C. 14 m/s   D. 26 m/s

STOP TO THINK ANSWERS

Stop to Think 9.1: F. The cart is initially moving in the negative x-direction, so $(p_x)_i = -20 \text{ kg} \cdot \text{m/s}$. After it bounces, $(p_x)_f = 10 \text{ kg} \cdot \text{m/s}$. Thus $\Delta p = (10 \text{ kg} \cdot \text{m/s}) - (-20 \text{ kg} \cdot \text{m/s}) = 30 \text{ kg} \cdot \text{m/s}$.

Stop to Think 9.2: B. The clay ball goes from $(v_x)_i = v$ to $(v_x)_f = 0$, so $J_{clay} = \Delta p_x = -mv$. The rubber ball rebounds, going from $(v_x)_i = v$ to $(v_x)_f = -v$ (same speed, opposite direction). Thus $J_{rubber} = \Delta p_x = -2mv$. The rubber ball has a greater momentum change, and this requires a greater impulse.

Stop to Think 9.3: Right end. The balls started at rest, so the total momentum of the system is zero. It's an isolated system, so the total momentum after the explosion is still zero. The 6 g ball has momentum $6v$. The 4 g ball, with velocity $-2v$, has momentum $-8v$. The combined momentum of these two balls is $-2v$. In order for P to be zero, the third ball must have a *positive* momentum ($+2v$) and thus a positive velocity.

Stop to Think 9.4: B. The momentum of particle 1 is $(0.40 \text{ kg})(2.5 \text{ m/s}) = 1.0 \text{ kg} \cdot \text{m/s}$, while that of particle 2 is $(0.80 \text{ kg})(-1.5 \text{ m/s}) = -1.2 \text{ kg} \cdot \text{m/s}$. The total momentum is then $1.0 \text{ kg} \cdot \text{m/s} - 1.2 \text{ kg} \cdot \text{m/s} = -0.2 \text{ kg} \cdot \text{m/s}$. Because it's negative, the total momentum, and hence the final velocity of the particles, is directed to the left.

Stop to Think 9.5: B. Angular momentum $L = I\omega$ is conserved. Both boys have mass m and initially stand distance $R/2$ from the axis. Thus the initial moment of inertia is $I_i = I_{disk} + 2 \times m(R/2)^2 = I_{disk} + \frac{1}{2}mR^2$. The final moment of inertia is $I_f = I_{disk} + 0 + mR^2$, because the boy standing at the axis contributes nothing to the moment of inertia. Because $I_f > I_i$ we must have $\omega_f < \omega_i$.

10 Energy and Work

As this bungee jumper falls, he gains kinetic energy, the energy of motion. Where does this energy come from? And where does it go as he slows at the bottom of his fall?

LOOKING AHEAD ▶

The goals of Chapter 10 are to introduce the concept of energy and to learn a new problem-solving strategy based on conservation of energy.

Forms of Energy

A principal goal of this chapter is to learn about several important forms of energy.

Kinetic energy is the energy of motion. This heavy, fast-moving rhinoceros has lots of kinetic energy.

These passengers gain **potential energy,** the energy of position, as they ride up the escalator.

The **thermal energy** of this red-hot horseshoe is associated with the microscopic motion of its molecules.

Looking Back ◀
2.5 Motion with constant acceleration
7.1, 7.4 Rotation and moment of inertia
8.3 Hooke's law

The Law of Conservation of Energy

One of the most fundamental laws of physics, the **law of conservation of energy** states that the total energy of an
isolated system is a constant.

How fast are these water sliders moving at the bottom? How fast does the rock fly out of the slingshot? We'll use conservation of energy and the before-and-after analysis introduced in Chapter 9 to solve these kinds of problems.

Looking Back ◀
9.2–9.3 Before-and after visual overviews

Transferring Energy

Energy can be *transferred* into a system by pushing on it, a process called **work.**

The bobsledders do work on the sled, *transferring* energy to it and causing it to speed up.

Transforming Energy

Energy of one kind can change into energy of a different kind. These **energy transformations** are what make the world an interesting place.

As this race car skids to a stop, its kinetic energy is being *transformed* into thermal energy, making the tires hot enough to smoke.

Power

We're very often interested in **power,** the *rate* at which energy is transformed from one kind into another.

As they climb, this truck and these jets both transform the chemical energy of their fuel into potential energy. But the jet engines transform energy at a rate 70 times that of the truck's engine—their *power* is much greater.

10.1 The Basic Energy Model

Energy. It's a word you hear all the time. We use chemical energy to heat our homes and bodies, electric energy to run our lights and computers, and solar energy to grow our crops and forests. We're told to use energy wisely and not to waste it. Athletes and weary students consume "energy bars" and "energy drinks."

But just what is energy? The concept of energy has grown and changed over time, and it is not easy to define in a general way just what energy is. Rather than starting with a formal definition, we'll let the concept of energy expand slowly over the course of several chapters. In this chapter we introduce several fundamental forms of energy, including kinetic energy, potential energy, and thermal energy. Our goal is to understand the characteristics of energy, how energy is used, and, especially important, how energy is transformed from one form into another. Much of modern technology is concerned with transforming energy, such as changing the chemical energy of oil molecules into electric energy or into the kinetic energy of your car.

We'll also learn how energy can be transferred to or from a system by the application of mechanical forces. By pushing on a sled, you increase its speed, and hence its energy of motion. By lifting a heavy object, you increase its gravitational potential energy.

These observations will lead us to discover a very powerful conservation law for energy. Energy is neither created nor destroyed: If one form of energy in a system decreases, it must appear in an equal amount in another form. Many scientists consider the law of conservation of energy to be the most important of all the laws of nature. This law will have implications throughout the rest of this book.

Systems and Energy

In Chapter 9 we introduced the idea of a *system* of interacting objects. A system can be as simple as a falling acorn or as complex as a city. But whether simple or complex, every system in nature has associated with it a quantity we call its **total energy** E. The total energy is the sum of the different kinds of energies present in the system. In the table below, we give a brief overview of some of the more important forms of energy; in the rest of the chapter, we'll look at several of these forms of energy in much greater detail.

A system may have many of these kinds of energy at one time. For instance, a moving car has kinetic energy of motion, chemical energy stored in its gasoline, thermal energy in its hot engine, and many other forms of energy. The total energy of the system, E, is the *sum* of all the different energies present in the system:

$$E = K + U_g + U_s + E_{th} + E_{chem} + \cdots \tag{10.1}$$

The energies shown in this sum are the forms of energy in which we'll be most interested in this and the next chapter. The ellipses ($\cdots$) stand for other forms of energy, such as nuclear or electric, that also might be present. We'll treat these and others in later chapters.

Some important forms of energy

Kinetic energy K	Gravitational potential energy U_g	Elastic or spring potential energy U_s
Kinetic energy is the energy of *motion*. All moving objects have kinetic energy. The heavier an object and the faster it moves, the more kinetic energy it has. The wrecking ball in this picture is effective in part because of its large kinetic energy.	Gravitational potential energy is *stored* energy associated with an object's *height above the ground*. As this coaster ascends, energy is stored as gravitational potential energy. As it descends, this stored energy is converted into kinetic energy.	Elastic potential energy is energy stored when a spring or other elastic object, such as this archer's bow, is *stretched*. This energy can later be transformed into the kinetic energy of the arrow.

Continued

Thermal energy E_{th}

Hot objects have more *thermal energy* than cold ones because the molecules in a hot object jiggle around more than those in a cold object. Thermal energy is the sum of the microscopic kinetic and potential energies of all the molecules in an object. In boiling water, some molecules have enough energy to escape the water as steam.

Chemical energy E_{chem}

Electric forces cause atoms to bind together to make molecules. Energy can be stored in these bonds, energy that can later be released as the bonds are rearranged during chemical reactions. When we burn fuel to run our car or eat food to power our bodies, we are using *chemical energy.*

Nuclear energy $E_{nuclear}$

An enormous amount of energy is stored in the *nucleus,* the tiny core of an atom. Certain nuclei can be made to break apart, releasing some of this *nuclear energy,* which is transformed into the kinetic energy of the fragments and then into thermal energy. The ghostly blue glow of a nuclear reactor results from high-energy fragments as they travel through water.

Energy Transformations

We've seen that all systems contain energy in many different forms. But if the amounts of each form of energy never changed, the world would be a very dull place. What makes the world interesting is that **energy of one kind can be *transformed* into energy of another kind.** The gravitational potential energy of the roller coaster at the top of the track is rapidly transformed into kinetic energy as the coaster descends; the chemical energy of gasoline is transformed into the kinetic energy of your moving car. The following table illustrates a few common energy transformations. In this table, we use an arrow $\rightarrow$ as a shorthand way of representing an energy transformation.

Some energy transformations

A weightlifter lifts a barbell over her head
The barbell has much more gravitational potential energy when high above her head than when on the floor. To lift the barbell, she is transforming chemical energy in her body into gravitational potential energy of the barbell.

$$E_{chem} \rightarrow U_g$$

A base runner slides into the base
When running, he has lots of kinetic energy. After sliding, he has none. His kinetic energy is transformed mainly into thermal energy: The ground and his legs are slightly warmer.

$$K \rightarrow E_{th}$$

A burning campfire
The wood contains considerable chemical energy. When the carbon in the wood combines chemically with oxygen in the air, this chemical energy is transformed largely into thermal energy of the hot gases and embers.

$$E_{chem} \rightarrow E_{th}$$

A springboard diver
Here's a two-step energy transformation. At the instant shown, the board is flexed to its maximum extent, so that elastic potential energy stored in the board. Soon this energy will begin to be transformed into kinetic energy; as the diver rises into the air and slows, this kinetic energy will be transformed into gravitational potential energy.

$$U_s \rightarrow K \rightarrow U_g$$

FIGURE 10.1 Energy transformations occur within the system.

The *environment* is everything that is *not* part of the system.

Environment

System

$E = K + U + E_{\text{th}} + E_{\text{chem}} + \cdots$

Class Video

FIGURE 10.2 The basic energy model shows that work and heat are energy transfers into and out of the system, while energy transformations occur within the system.

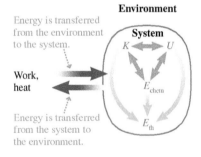

Environment

System

Energy is transferred from the environment to the system.

Work, heat

Energy is transferred from the system to the environment.

FIGURE 10.1 reinforces the idea that **energy transformations are changes of energy *within* the system from one form to another.** (The U in this figure is a generic potential energy; it could be gravitational potential energy U_g, spring potential energy U_s, or some other form of potential energy.) Note that it is easy to convert kinetic, potential, and chemical energies into thermal energy, but converting thermal energy back into these other forms is not so easy. How it can be done, and what possible limitations there might be in doing so, will form a large part of the next chapter.

Energy Transfers and Work

We've just seen that energy *transformations* occur between forms of energy *within* a system. But every physical system also interacts with the world around it—that is, with its *environment.* In the course of these interactions, the system can exchange energy with the environment. **An exchange of energy between system and environment is called an energy *transfer.*** There are two primary energy-transfer processes: **work,** the *mechanical* transfer of energy to or from a system by pushing or pulling on it, and **heat,** the *nonmechanical* transfer of energy from the environment to the system (or vice versa) because of a temperature difference between the two.

FIGURE 10.2, which we call the **basic energy model,** shows how our energy model is modified to include energy transfers into and out of the system as well as energy transformations within the system. In this chapter we'll consider only energy transfers by means of work; the concept of heat will be developed much further in Chapters 11 and 12.

"Work" is a common word in the English language, with many meanings. When you first think of work, you probably think of physical effort or the job you do to make a living. After all, we talk about "working out," or we say, "I just got home from work." But that is not what work means in physics.

In physics, "work" is the process of *transferring* energy from the environment to a system, or from a system to the environment, by the application of mechanical forces—pushes and pulls—to the system. Once the energy has been transferred to the system, it can appear in many forms. Exactly what form it takes depends on the details of the system and how the forces are applied. The table below gives three examples of energy transfers due to work. We use W as the symbol for work.

Energy transfers: work

Putting a shot

The system: The shot

The environment: The athlete

As the athlete pushes on the shot to get it moving, he is doing work on the system; that is, he is transferring energy from himself to the ball. The energy transferred to the system appears as kinetic energy.

The transfer: $W \to K$

Striking a match

The system: The match and matchbox

The environment: The hand

As the hand quickly pulls the match across the box, the hand does work on the system, increasing its thermal energy. The match head becomes hot enough to ignite.

The transfer: $W \to E_{\text{th}}$

Firing a slingshot

The system: The slingshot

The environment: The boy

As the boy pulls back on the elastic bands, he does work on the system, increasing its elastic potential energy.

The transfer: $W \to U_s$

Notice that in each example on the previous page, the environment applies a force while the system undergoes a *displacement*. Energy is transferred as work only when the system *moves* while the force acts. A force applied to a stationary object, such as when you push against a wall, transfers no energy to the object and thus does no work.

NOTE ▶ In the table on the previous page, energy is being transferred *from* the athlete *to* the shot by the force of his hand. We say he "does work" on the shot, or "work is done" by the force of his hand. ◀

The Law of Conservation of Energy

Work done on a system represents energy that is transferred into or out of the system. This transferred energy *changes* the system's energy by exactly the amount of work W that was done. Writing the change in the system's energy as ΔE, we can represent this idea mathematically as

$$\Delta E = W \qquad (10.2)$$

Now the total energy E of a system is, according to Equation 10.1, the sum of the different energies present in the system. Thus the change in E is the sum of the *changes* of the different energies present. Then Equation 10.2 gives what is called the *work-energy equation*:

The work-energy equation The total energy of a system changes by the amount of work done on it:

$$\Delta E = \Delta K + \Delta U_g + \Delta U_s + \Delta E_{th} + \Delta E_{chem} + \cdots = W \qquad (10.3)$$

NOTE ▶ Equation 10.3, the work-energy equation, is the mathematical representation of the basic energy model of Figure 10.2. Together, they are the heart of what the subject of energy is all about. ◀

Suppose now we have an **isolated system,** one that is separated from its surrounding environment in such a way that no energy is transferred into or out of the system. This means that *no work is done on the system*. The energy within the system may be transformed from one form into another, but it is a deep and remarkable fact of nature that, during these transformations, the total energy of an isolated system—the *sum* of all the individual kinds of energy—remains *constant,* as shown in FIGURE 10.3. We say that **the total energy of an isolated system is *conserved*.**

For an isolated system, we must set $W = 0$ in Equation 10.3, leading to the following *law of conservation of energy:*

Law of conservation of energy The total energy of an isolated system remains constant:

$$\Delta E = \Delta K + \Delta U_g + \Delta U_s + \Delta E_{th} + \Delta E_{chem} + \cdots = 0 \qquad (10.4)$$

The law of conservation of energy is similar to the law of conservation of momentum. Momentum changes when an impulse acts on a system; the total momentum of an isolated system doesn't change. Similarly, energy changes when external forces do work on a system; the total energy of an isolated system doesn't change.

In solving momentum problems, we adopted a new before-and-after perspective: The momentum *after* an interaction was the same as the momentum *before* the interaction. We will introduce a similar before-and-after perspective for energy that will lead to an extremely powerful problem-solving strategy.

FIGURE 10.3 An isolated system.

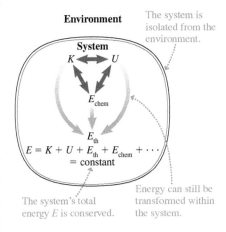

Environment

The system is isolated from the environment.

System

$K \longleftrightarrow U$

E_{chem}

E_{th}

$E = K + U + E_{th} + E_{chem} + \cdots$
$= \text{constant}$

The system's total energy E is conserved.

Energy can still be transformed within the system.

Before using energy ideas to solve problems, however, we first need to develop quantitative expressions for work, kinetic energy, potential energy, and thermal energy. This will be our task in the next several sections.

STOP TO THINK 10.1   A child slides down a playground slide at constant speed. The energy transformation is

A. $U_g \rightarrow K$ B. $K \rightarrow U_g$ C. $W \rightarrow K$ D. $U_g \rightarrow E_{th}$ E. $K \rightarrow E_{th}$

10.2 Work

Our first task is to learn how work is calculated. We've just seen that work is the transfer of energy to or from a system by the application of forces exerted on the system by the environment. Thus work is done on a system by forces from *outside* the system; we call such forces *external forces*. Only external forces can change the energy of a system. *Internal forces*—forces between objects *within* the system—cause energy transformations within the system but don't change the system's total energy.

We also learned that in order for energy to be transferred as work, the system must undergo a displacement—it must *move*—during the time that the force is applied. Let's further investigate the relationship among work, force, and displacement.

Consider a system consisting of a windsurfer at rest, as shown on the left in FIGURE 10.4. Let's assume that there is no friction between his board and the water. Initially the system has no kinetic energy. But if a force from outside the system, such as the force due to the wind, begins to act on the system, the surfer will begin to speed up, and his kinetic energy will increase. In terms of energy transfers, we would say that the energy of the system has increased because of the work done on the system by the force of the wind.

What determines how much work is done by the force of the wind? First, we note that the greater the distance over which the wind pushes the surfer, the faster the surfer goes, and the more his kinetic energy increases. This implies a greater transfer of energy. So, **the larger the displacement, the greater the work done.** Second, if the wind pushes with a stronger force, the surfer speeds up more rapidly, and the change in his kinetic energy is greater than with a weaker force. **The stronger the force, the greater the work done.**

This experiment suggests that the amount of energy transferred to a system by a force $\vec{F}$—that is, the amount of work done by $\vec{F}$—depends on both the magnitude F of the force *and* the displacement d of the system. Many experiments of this kind have established that the amount of work done by $\vec{F}$ is *proportional* to both F and d. For the simplest case described above, where the force $\vec{F}$ is constant and points in the direction of the object's displacement, the expression for the work done is found to be

$$W = Fd \tag{10.5}$$

Work done by a constant force $\vec{F}$ in the direction of a displacement $\vec{d}$

The unit of work, that of force multiplied by distance, is N·m. This unit is so important that it has been given its own name, the **joule** (rhymes with *tool*). We define:

$$1 \text{ joule} = 1 \text{ J} = 1 \text{ N·m}$$

Because work is simply energy being transferred, **the joule is the unit of *all* forms of energy.** Note that work is a *scalar* quantity.

FIGURE 10.4 The force of the wind does work on the system, increasing its kinetic energy K.

The system's kinetic energy increases and the boarder speeds up.

The force of the wind $\vec{F}$ does work on the system.

EXAMPLE 10.1 **Work done in pushing a crate**

Sarah pushes a heavy crate 3.0 m along the floor at a constant speed. She pushes with a constant horizontal force of magnitude 70 N. How much work does Sarah do on the crate?

PREPARE We begin with the visual overview in FIGURE 10.5. Sarah pushes with a constant force in the direction of the crate's motion, so we can use Equation 10.5 to find the work done.

FIGURE 10.5 Sarah pushing a crate.

Known
$F = 70$ N
$d = 3.0$ m
$v =$ constant

Find
W

SOLVE The work done by Sarah is

$$W = Fd = (70 \text{ N})(3.0 \text{ m}) = 210 \text{ J}$$

ASSESS Work represents a transfer of energy into a system, so here the energy of the system—the box and the floor—increases. Unlike the windsurfer, the box doesn't speed up, so its kinetic energy doesn't increase. Instead, the work increases the thermal energy in the crate and the part of the floor along which it slides, increasing the temperature of both. Using the notation of Equation 10.3, we can write this energy transfer as $\Delta E_{th} = W$.

Force at an Angle to the Displacement

A force does the greatest possible amount of work on an object when the force points in the same direction as the object's displacement. Less work is done when the force acts at an angle to the displacement. To see this, consider the kite buggy of FIGURE 10.6a, pulled along a horizontal path by the angled force of the kite string $\vec{F}$. As shown in FIGURE 10.6b, we can divide $\vec{F}$ into a component $F_\perp$ perpendicular to the motion, and a component $F_\parallel$ parallel to the motion. Only the parallel component acts to accelerate the rider and increase his kinetic energy, so only the parallel component does work on the rider. From Figure 10.6b, we see that if the angle between $\vec{F}$ and the displacement is θ, then the parallel component is $F_\parallel = F \cos \theta$. So, when the force acts at an angle θ to the direction of the displacement, we have

$$W = F_\parallel d = Fd \cos \theta \tag{10.6}$$

Work done by a constant force $\vec{F}$ at an angle θ to the displacement $\vec{d}$

Notice that this more general definition of work agrees with Equation 10.5 if $\theta = 0°$.

Tactics Box 10.1 shows how to calculate the work done by a force at any angle to the direction of motion. The system illustrated is a block sliding on a frictionless, horizontal surface, so that only the kinetic energy is changing. However, the same relationships hold for any object undergoing a displacement.

The quantities F and d are always positive, so **the sign of W is determined entirely by the angle θ between the force and the displacement.** Note that Equation 10.6, $W = Fd \cos \theta$, is valid for any angle θ. In three special cases, $\theta = 0°$, $\theta = 90°$, and $\theta = 180°$, however, there are simple versions of Equation 10.6 that you can use. These are noted in Tactics Box 10.1.

FIGURE 10.6 Finding the work done when the force is at an angle to the displacement.

(a)

(b) The rider undergoes a displacement $\vec{d}$.

$F_\parallel = F \cos \theta$

The component of $\vec{F}$ parallel to the displacement accelerates the rider.

The component of $\vec{F}$ perpendicular to the displacement only pulls up on the rider. It doesn't accelerate him.

MP **ActivPhysics:** 5.1

TACTICS
BOX 10.1   Calculating the work done by a constant force

Direction of force relative to displacement	Angles and work done	Sign of W	Energy transfer
Before: $\vec{v}_i$ After: $\vec{v}_f$ $\vec{d}$ $\theta = 0°$ $\vec{F}$	$\theta = 0°$ $\cos\theta = 1$ $W = Fd$	+	The force is in the direction of motion. The block has its greatest positive acceleration. K increases the most: **Maximum energy transfer to system.**
$\theta < 90°$ $\vec{F}$ $\vec{d}$	$\theta < 90°$ $W = Fd\cos\theta$	+	The component of force parallel to the displacement is less than F. The block has a smaller positive acceleration. K increases less: **Decreased energy transfer to system.**
$\theta = 90°$ $\vec{F}$ $\vec{d}$	$\theta = 90°$ $\cos\theta = 0$ $W = 0$	0	There is no component of force in the direction of motion. The block moves at constant speed. No change in K: **No energy transferred.**
$\theta > 90°$ $\vec{F}$ $\vec{d}$	$\theta > 90°$ $W = Fd\cos\theta$	−	The component of force parallel to the displacement is opposite the motion. The block slows down, and K decreases: **Decreased energy transfer *out* of system.**
$\theta = 180°$ $\vec{F}$ $\vec{d}$	$\theta = 180°$ $\cos\theta = -1$ $W = -Fd$	−	The force is directly opposite the motion. The block has its greatest deceleration. K decreases the most: **Maximum energy transfer *out* of system.**

Exercises 5–6

EXAMPLE 10.2   **Work done in pulling a suitcase**

A strap inclined upward at a 45° angle pulls a suitcase through the airport. The tension in the strap is 20 N. How much work does the tension do if the suitcase is pulled 100 m at a constant speed?

PREPARE FIGURE 10.7 shows a visual overview. Since the suitcase moves at a constant speed, there must be a rolling friction force acting to the left.

SOLVE We can use Equation 10.6, with force $F = T$, to find that the tension does work:

$$W = Td\cos\theta = (20 \text{ N})(100 \text{ m})\cos 45° = 1400 \text{ J}$$

ASSESS Because a person is pulling on the other end of the strap, causing the tension, we would say informally that the person does 1400 J of work on the suitcase. This work represents

FIGURE 10.7 A suitcase pulled by a strap.

energy transferred into the suitcase + floor system. Since the suitcase moves at a constant speed, the system's kinetic energy doesn't change. Thus, just as for Sarah pushing the crate in Example 10.1, the work done goes entirely into increasing the thermal energy E_{th} of the suitcase and the floor.

Work done by a parachute

A drag racer is slowed by a parachute. What is the sign of the work done?

REASON The drag force on the drag racer is shown in FIGURE 10.8, along with the dragster's displacement as it slows. The force points in the direction opposite the displacement, so that the angle θ in

FIGURE 10.8 The force acting on a drag racer.

Equation 10.6 is 180°. Then $\cos\theta = \cos(180°) = -1$. Because F and d in Equation 10.6 are magnitudes, and hence positive, the work $W = Fd\cos\theta = -Fd$ done by the drag force is *negative*.

ASSESS Applying Equation 10.3 to this situation, we have

$$\Delta K = W$$

because the only system energy that changes is the racer's kinetic energy K. Because the kinetic energy is decreasing, its change ΔK is negative. This agrees with the sign of W. This example illustrates the general principle that **negative work represents a transfer of energy out of the system.**

If several forces act on an object that undergoes a displacement, each does work on the object. The **total** (or **net**) **work** W_{total} is the sum of the work done by each force. The total work represents the total energy transfer *to* the system from the environment (if $W_{total} > 0$) or *from* the system to the environment (if $W_{total} < 0$).

Forces That Do No Work

The fact that a force acts on an object doesn't mean that the force will do work on the object. The table below shows three common cases where a force does no work.

Forces that do no work

If the object undergoes no displacement while the force acts, no work is done.	**A force perpendicular to the displacement does no work.**	**If the part of the object on which the force acts undergoes no displacement, no work is done.**
This can sometimes seem counterintuitive. The weightlifter struggles mightily to hold the barbell over his head. But during the time the barbell remains stationary, he does no work on it because its displacement is zero. Why then is it so hard for him to hold it there? We'll see in Chapter 11 that it takes a rapid conversion of his internal chemical energy to keep his arms extended under this great load.	The woman exerts only a vertical force on the briefcase she's carrying. This force has no component in the direction of the displacement, so the briefcase moves at a constant velocity and its kinetic energy remains constant. Since the energy of the briefcase doesn't change, it must be that no energy is being transferred to it as work. (This is the case where $\theta = 90°$ in Tactics Box 10.1.)	Even though the wall pushes on the skater with a normal force $\vec{n}$ and she undergoes a displacement $\vec{d}$, the wall does no work on her, because the point of her body on which $\vec{n}$ acts—her hands—undergoes no displacement. This makes sense: How could energy be transferred as work from an inert, stationary object? So where does her kinetic energy come from? This will be the subject of much of Chapter 11. Can you guess?

Which force does the most work?

A. The 10 N force.
B. The 8 N force.
C. The 6 N force.
D. They all do the same
   amount of work.

10.3 Kinetic Energy

FIGURE 10.9 The work done by the tow rope increases the car's kinetic energy.

Before: After:

ActivPhysics: 6.1
PhET: The Ramp

We've already qualitatively discussed kinetic energy, an object's energy of motion. Let's now use what we've learned about work, and some simple kinematics, to find a quantitative expression for kinetic energy. Consider a car being pulled by a tow rope, as in FIGURE 10.9. The rope pulls with a constant force $\vec{F}$ while the car undergoes a displacement $\vec{d}$, so the force does work $W = Fd$ on the car. If we ignore friction and drag, the work done by $\vec{F}$ is transferred entirely into the car's energy of motion—its kinetic energy. In this case, the change in the car's kinetic energy is given by the work-energy equation, Equation 10.3, as

$$W = \Delta K = K_f - K_i \tag{10.7}$$

Using kinematics, we can find another expression for the work done, in terms of the car's initial and final speeds. Recall from Chapter 2 the kinematic equation

$$v_f^2 = v_i^2 + 2a\Delta x$$

Applied to the motion of our car, $\Delta x = d$ is the car's displacement and, from Newton's second law, the acceleration is $a = F/m$. Thus we can write

$$v_f^2 = v_i^2 + \frac{2Fd}{m} = v_i^2 + \frac{2W}{m}$$

where we have replaced Fd with the work W. If we now solve for the work, we find

$$W = \frac{1}{2}m\left(v_f^2 - v_i^2\right) = \frac{1}{2}mv_f^2 - \frac{1}{2}mv_i^2$$

If we compare this result with Equation 10.7, we see that

$$K_f = \frac{1}{2}mv_f^2 \quad \text{and} \quad K_i = \frac{1}{2}mv_i^2$$

In general, then, an object of mass m moving with speed v has kinetic energy

$$K = \frac{1}{2}mv^2 \tag{10.8}$$

Kinetic energy of an object of mass m moving with speed v

QUADRATIC

TABLE 10.1 Some approximate kinetic energies

Object	Kinetic energy
Ant walking	1×10^{-8} J
Penny dropped 1 m	2.5×10^{-3} J
Person walking	70 J
Fastball, 100 mph	150 J
Bullet	5000 J
Car, 60 mph	5×10^5 J
Supertanker, 20 mph	2×10^{10} J

From Equation 10.8, the units of kinetic energy are those of mass times speed squared, or $kg \cdot (m/s)^2$. But

$$1 \ kg \cdot (m/s)^2 = 1 \ kg \cdot (m/s^2) \cdot m = 1 \ N \cdot m = 1 \ J$$

We see that the units of kinetic energy are the same as those of work, as they must be. Table 10.1 gives some approximate kinetic energies. Everyday kinetic energies range from a tiny fraction of a fraction of a joule to nearly a million joules for a speeding car.

CONCEPTUAL EXAMPLE 10.4 Kinetic energy changes for a car

Compare the increase in a 1000 kg car's kinetic energy as it speeds up by 5.0 m/s, starting from 5.0 m/s, to its increase in kinetic energy as it speeds up by 5.0 m/s, starting from 10 m/s.

REASON The change in the car's kinetic energy in going from 5.0 m/s to 10 m/s is

$$\Delta K_{5 \to 10} = \frac{1}{2}mv_{\rm f}^2 - \frac{1}{2}mv_{\rm i}^2$$

This gives

$$\Delta K_{5 \to 10} = \frac{1}{2}(1000 \text{ kg})(10 \text{ m/s})^2 - \frac{1}{2}(1000 \text{ kg})(5.0 \text{ m/s})^2$$

$$= 3.8 \times 10^4 \text{ J}$$

Similarly, increasing from 10 m/s to 15 m/s requires

$$\Delta K_{10 \to 15} = \frac{1}{2}(1000 \text{ kg})(15 \text{ m/s})^2 - \frac{1}{2}(1000 \text{ kg})(10 \text{ m/s})^2$$

$$= 6.3 \times 10^4 \text{ J}$$

Even though the increase in the car's *speed* is the same in both cases, the increase in kinetic energy is substantially greater in the second case.

ASSESS Kinetic energy depends on the *square* of the speed v. In FIGURE 10.10, which plots kinetic energy versus speed, we see that the energy of the car increases rapidly with speed. We can also see graphically why the change in K for a 5 m/s change in v is greater at high speeds than at low speeds. In part this is why it's harder to accelerate your car at high speeds than at low speeds.

FIGURE 10.10 The kinetic energy increases as the *square* of the speed.

EXAMPLE 10.5 Speed of a bobsled after pushing

A two-man bobsled has a mass of 390 kg. Starting from rest, the two racers push the sled for the first 50 m with a net force of 270 N. Neglecting friction, what is the sled's speed at the end of the 50 m?

PREPARE We can find the sled's final speed if we can find its final kinetic energy. We can do so by equating the work done by the racers as they push on the sled to the change in its kinetic energy. FIGURE 10.11 lists the known quantities and the quantity ($v_{\rm f}$) that we want to find.

FIGURE 10.11 The work done by the pushers increases the sled's kinetic energy.

Known	Find: $v_{\rm f}$
$m = 390 \text{ kg} \quad F = 270 \text{ N}$	
$d = 50 \text{ m} \quad v_{\rm i} = 0 \text{ m/s}$	

SOLVE From Equation 10.3, the work-energy equation, the change in the sled's kinetic energy is $\Delta K = K_{\rm f} - K_{\rm i} = W$. The sled's final kinetic energy is thus

$$K_{\rm f} = K_{\rm i} + W$$

Using our expressions for kinetic energy and work, we get

$$\frac{1}{2}mv_{\rm f}^2 = \frac{1}{2}mv_{\rm i}^2 + Fd$$

Because $v_{\rm i} = 0$, the work-energy equation reduces to

$$\frac{1}{2}mv_{\rm f}^2 = Fd$$

We can solve for the final speed to get

$$v_{\rm f} = \sqrt{\frac{2Fd}{m}} = \sqrt{\frac{2(270 \text{ N})(50 \text{ m})}{390 \text{ kg}}} = 8.3 \text{ m/s}$$

ASSESS 8.3 m/s, about 18 mph, seems a reasonable speed for two fast pushers to attain.

STOP TO THINK 10.3 Rank in order, from greatest to least, the kinetic energies of the sliding pucks.

1 kg 2 m/s   1 kg 3 m/s   –2 m/s 1 kg   2 kg 2 m/s

A.   B.   C.   D.

FIGURE 10.12 The large rotating blades of a windmill have a great deal of kinetic energy.

FIGURE 10.13 Rotational kinetic energy is due to the circular motion of the particles.

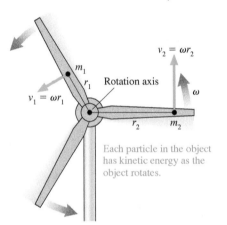

Each particle in the object has kinetic energy as the object rotates.

Video Tutor Demonstration

Rotational Kinetic Energy

We've just found an expression for the kinetic energy of an object moving along a line or some other path. This energy is called **translational kinetic energy**. Consider now an object rotating about a fixed axis, such as the windmill blades in FIGURE 10.12. Although the blades have no overall translational motion, each particle in the blade is moving and hence has kinetic energy. Adding up the kinetic energy for each particle that makes up the blades, we find that the blades have **rotational kinetic energy,** the kinetic energy due to rotation.

FIGURE 10.13 shows two of the particles making up a windmill blade that rotates with angular velocity ω. Recall from Section 6.2 that a particle moving with angular velocity ω in a circle of radius r has a speed $v = \omega r$. Thus particle 1, which rotates in a circle of radius r_1, moves with speed $v_1 = r_1\omega$ and so has kinetic energy $\frac{1}{2}m_1v_1^2 = \frac{1}{2}m_1r_1^2\omega^2$. Similarly, particle 2, which rotates in a circle with a larger radius r_2, has kinetic energy $\frac{1}{2}m_2r_2^2\omega^2$. The object's rotational kinetic energy is the sum of the kinetic energies of *all* the particles:

$$K_{\text{rot}} = \frac{1}{2}m_1r_1^2\omega^2 + \frac{1}{2}m_2r_2^2\omega^2 + \cdots = \frac{1}{2}\left(\sum mr^2\right)\omega^2$$

You will recognize the term in parentheses as our old friend, the moment of inertia I. Thus the rotational kinetic energy is

$$K_{\text{rot}} = \frac{1}{2}I\omega^2 \qquad (10.9)$$

Rotational kinetic energy of an object with moment of inertia I and angular velocity ω

QUADRATIC

NOTE ▶ Rotational kinetic energy is *not* a new form of energy. It is the ordinary kinetic energy of motion, only now expressed in a form that is especially convenient for rotational motion. Comparison with the familiar $\frac{1}{2}mv^2$ shows again that the moment of inertia I is the rotational equivalent of mass. ◀

A rolling object, such as a wheel, is undergoing both rotational *and* translational motions. Consequently, its total kinetic energy is the sum of its rotational and translational kinetic energies:

$$K = K_{\text{trans}} + K_{\text{rot}} = \frac{1}{2}mv^2 + \frac{1}{2}I\omega^2 \qquad (10.10)$$

This illustrates an important fact: **The kinetic energy of a rolling object is always greater than that of a nonrotating object moving at the same speed.**

◀ **Rotational recharge** The International Space Station (ISS) gets its electric power from solar panels. But during each 92-minute orbit, the ISS is in the earth's shadow for 30 minutes. The batteries that currently provide power during these blackouts need periodic replacement, which is very expensive in space. A promising new technology would replace the batteries with a *flywheel*—a cylinder rotating at a very high angular speed. Energy from the solar panels is used to speed up the flywheel, storing energy as rotational kinetic energy, which can then be converted back into electric energy when the ISS is in shadow.

EXAMPLE 10.6 | Kinetic energy of a bicycle

Bike 1 has a 10.0 kg frame and 1.00 kg wheels; bike 2 has a 9.00 kg frame and 1.50 kg wheels. Both bikes thus have the same 12.0 kg total mass. What is the kinetic energy of each bike when they are ridden at 12.0 m/s? Model each wheel as a hoop of radius 35.0 cm.

PREPARE Each bike's frame has only translational kinetic energy $K_{\text{frame}} = \frac{1}{2}mv^2$, where m is the mass of the frame. The kinetic energy of each rolling wheel is given by Equation 10.10. From Table 7.4, we find that I for a hoop is MR^2, where M is the mass of one wheel.

SOLVE From Equation 10.10 the kinetic energy of each rolling wheel is

$$K_{\text{wheel}} = \frac{1}{2}Mv^2 + \frac{1}{2}I\omega^2 = \frac{1}{2}Mv^2 + \frac{1}{2}\underbrace{(MR^2)}_{I}\underbrace{\left(\frac{v}{R}\right)^2}_{\omega^2} = Mv^2$$

Then the total kinetic energy of a bike is

$$K = K_{\text{frame}} + 2K_{\text{wheel}} = \frac{1}{2}mv^2 + 2Mv^2$$

The factor of 2 in the second term occurs because each bike has two wheels. Thus the kinetic energies of the two bikes are

$$K_1 = \frac{1}{2}(10.0 \text{ kg})(12.0 \text{ m/s})^2 + 2(1.00 \text{ kg})(12.0 \text{ m/s})^2$$
$$= 1010 \text{ J}$$

$$K_2 = \frac{1}{2}(9.00 \text{ kg})(12.0 \text{ m/s})^2 + 2(1.50 \text{ kg})(12.0 \text{ m/s})^2$$
$$= 1080 \text{ J}$$

The kinetic energy of bike 2 is about 7% higher than that of bike 1. Note that the radius of the wheels was not needed in this calculation.

ASSESS As the cyclists on these bikes accelerate from rest to 12 m/s, they must convert some of their internal chemical energy into the kinetic energy of the bikes. Racing cyclists want to use as little of their own energy as possible. Although both bikes have the same total mass, the one with the lighter wheels will take less energy to get it moving. Shaving a little extra weight off your wheels is more useful than taking that same weight off your frame.

It's important that racing bike wheels are as light as possible.

10.4 Potential Energy

When two or more objects in a system interact, it is sometimes possible to *store* energy in the system in a way that the energy can be easily recovered. For instance, the earth and a ball interact by the gravitational force between them. If the ball is lifted up into the air, energy is stored in the ball + earth system, energy that can later be recovered as kinetic energy when the ball is released and falls. Similarly, a spring is a system made up of countless atoms that interact via their atomic "springs." If we push a box against a spring, energy is stored that can be recovered when the spring later pushes the box across the table. This sort of stored energy is called **potential energy,** since it has the *potential* to be converted into other forms of energy, such as kinetic or thermal energy.

The forces due to gravity and springs are special in that they allow for the storage of energy. Other interaction forces do not. When a crate is pushed across the floor, the crate and the floor interact via the force of friction, and the work done on the system is converted into thermal energy. But this energy is *not* stored up for later recovery—it slowly diffuses into the environment and cannot be recovered.

Interaction forces that can store useful energy are called **conservative forces.** The name comes from the important fact that, as we'll see, the mechanical energy of a system is *conserved* when only conservative forces act. Gravity and elastic forces are conservative forces, and later we'll find that the electric force is a conservative force as well. Friction, on the other hand, is a **nonconservative force.** When two objects interact via a friction force, energy is not stored. It is usually transformed into thermal energy.

Let's look more closely at the potential energies associated with the two conservative forces—gravity and springs—that we'll study in this chapter.

Gravitational Potential Energy

To find an expression for gravitational potential energy, let's consider the system of the book and the earth shown in FIGURE 10.14a on the next page. The book is lifted at a constant speed from its initial position at y_i to a final height y_f. The lifting force of the hand is external to the system and so does work W on the system, increasing its energy. The book is lifted at a constant speed, so its kinetic energy doesn't change. Because there's no friction, the book's thermal energy doesn't change either. Thus

FIGURE 10.14 Lifting a book increases the system's gravitational potential energy.

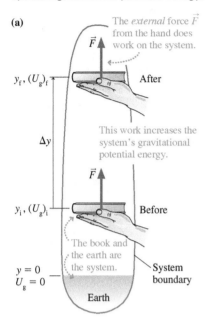

(a)

The *external* force $\vec{F}$ from the hand does work on the system.

$\vec{F}$

After

$y_f, (U_g)_f$

Δy

This work increases the system's gravitational potential energy.

$\vec{F}$

$y_i, (U_g)_i$

Before

The book and the earth are the system.

$y = 0$
$U_g = 0$

System boundary

Earth

(b)

Because the book is being lifted at a constant speed, it is in dynamic equilibrium with $\vec{F}_{net} = 0$. Thus $F = w = mg$.

$\vec{F}$

$\vec{w}$

the work done goes entirely into increasing the gravitational potential energy of the system. According to Equation 10.3, the work-energy equation, $\Delta U_g = W$. Because $\Delta U_g = (U_g)_f - (U_g)_i$, Equation 10.3 can be written

$$(U_g)_f = (U_g)_i + W \qquad (10.11)$$

The work done is $W = Fd$, where $d = \Delta y = y_f - y_i$ is the vertical distance that the book is lifted. From the free-body diagram of FIGURE 10.14b, we see that $F = mg$. Thus $W = mg\,\Delta y$, and so

$$(U_g)_f = (U_g)_i + mg\,\Delta y \qquad (10.12)$$

Because our final height was greater than our initial height, Δy is positive and $(U_g)_f > (U_g)_i$. **The higher the object is lifted, the greater the gravitational potential energy in the object + earth system.**

Equation 10.12 gives the final gravitational potential energy $(U_g)_f$ in terms of its initial value $(U_g)_i$. But what is the value of $(U_g)_i$? We can gain some insight by writing Equation 10.12 in terms of energy *changes*:

$$(U_g)_f - (U_g)_i = \Delta U_g = mg\,\Delta y$$

For example, if we lift a 1.5 kg book up by $\Delta y = 2.0$ m, we increase the system's gravitational potential energy by $\Delta U_g = (1.5 \text{ kg})(9.8 \text{ m/s}^2)(2.0 \text{ m}) = 29.4$ J. This increase is *independent* of the book's starting height: The gravitational potential energy increases by 29.4 J whether we lift the book 2.0 m starting at sea level or starting at the top of the Washington Monument. This illustrates an important general fact about *every* form of potential energy: **Only *changes* in potential energy are significant.**

Because of this fact, we are free to choose a *reference level* where we define U_g to be zero. Our expression for U_g is particularly simple if we choose this reference level to be at $y = 0$. We then have

$$U_g = mgy \qquad (10.13)$$

Gravitational potential energy of an object of mass m at height y
(assuming $U_g = 0$ when the object is at $y = 0$)

NOTE ▶ We've emphasized that gravitational potential energy is an energy of the earth + object *system*. In solving problems using the law of conservation of energy, you'll need to include the earth as part of your system. For simplicity, we'll usually speak of "the gravitational potential energy of the ball," but what we really mean is the potential energy of the earth + ball system. ◀

EXAMPLE 10.7 **Racing up a skyscraper**

In the Empire State Building Run-Up, competitors race up the 1576 steps of the Empire State Building, climbing a total vertical distance of 320 m. How much gravitational potential energy does a 70 kg racer gain during this race?

Racers head up the staircase in the Empire State Building Run-Up.

PREPARE We choose $y = 0$ m and $U_g = 0$ J at the ground floor of the building.

SOLVE At the top, the racer's gravitational potential energy is

$$U_g = mgy = (70 \text{ kg})(9.8 \text{ m/s}^2)(320 \text{ m}) = 2.2 \times 10^5 \text{ J}$$

Because the racer's gravitational potential energy was 0 J at the ground floor, the change in his potential energy is 2.2×10^5 J.

ASSESS This is a large amount of energy. According to Table 10.1, it's comparable to the energy of a speeding car. But if you think how hard it would be to climb the Empire State Building, it seems like a plausible result.

An important conclusion from Equation 10.13 is that gravitational potential energy depends only on the height of the object above the reference level $y = 0$, not on the object's horizontal position. To understand why, consider carrying a briefcase while walking on level ground at a constant speed. As shown in the table on page 297, the vertical force of your hand on the briefcase is *perpendicular* to the displacement. *No work* is done on the briefcase, so its gravitational potential energy remains constant as long as its height above the ground doesn't change.

This idea can be applied to more complicated cases, such as the 82 kg hiker in FIGURE 10.15. His gravitational potential energy depends *only* on his height y above the reference level. Along path A, it's the same value $U_g = mgy = 80$ kJ at any point where he is at height $y = 100$ m above the reference level. If he had instead taken path B, his gravitational potential energy at $y = 100$ m would be the same 80 kJ. It doesn't matter *how* he gets to the 100 m elevation; his potential energy at that height is always the same. **Gravitational potential energy depends only on the *height* of an object and not on the path the object took to get to that position.** This fact will allow us to use the law of conservation of energy to easily solve a variety of problems that would be very difficult to solve using Newton's laws alone.

FIGURE 10.15 The hiker's gravitational potential energy depends only on his height above the $y = 0$ m reference level.

The hiker's potential energy at the top is 160 kJ regardless of whether he took path A or path B.

$U_g = 160$ kJ

His potential energy is the same at any point where his elevation is 100 m.

200 m

100 m

$U_g = 80$ kJ

Path A

Path B

0 m

The reference level $y = 0$ m is where $U_g = 0$ J.

STOP TO THINK 10.4 Rank in order, from largest to smallest, the gravitational potential energies of identical balls 1 through 4.

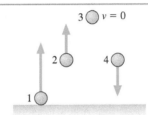

Elastic Potential Energy

Energy can also be stored in a compressed or extended spring as **elastic (or spring) potential energy** U_s. We can find out how much energy is stored in a spring by using an external force to slowly compress the spring. This external force does work on the spring, transferring energy to the spring. Since only the elastic potential energy of the spring is changing, Equation 10.3 reads

$$\Delta U_s = W \tag{10.14}$$

That is, we can find out how much elastic potential energy is stored in the spring by calculating the amount of work needed to compress the spring.

FIGURE 10.16 shows a spring being compressed by a hand. In Section 8.3 we found that the force the spring exerts on the hand is $F_s = -k\Delta x$ (Hooke's law), where Δx is the displacement of the end of the spring from its equilibrium position and k is the spring constant. In Figure 10.16 we have set the origin of our coordinate system at the equilibrium position. The displacement from equilibrium Δx is therefore equal to x, and the spring force is then $-kx$. By Newton's third law, the force that the hand exerts on the spring is thus $F = +kx$.

As the hand pushes the end of the spring from its equilibrium position to a final position x, the applied force increases from 0 to kx. This is not a constant force, so we can't use Equation 10.5, $W = Fd$, to find the work done. However, it seems reasonable to calculate the work by using the *average* force in Equation 10.5. Because the force varies from $F_i = 0$ to $F_f = kx$, the average force used to compress the spring is $F_{avg} = \frac{1}{2}kx$. Thus the work done by the hand is

$$W = F_{avg}d = F_{avg}x = \left(\frac{1}{2}kx\right)x = \frac{1}{2}kx^2$$

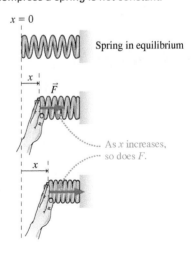

FIGURE 10.16 The force required to compress a spring is not constant.

$x = 0$

Spring in equilibrium

x

$\vec{F}$

As x increases, so does F.

x

Calf muscle

Achilles tendon

On each stride, the tendon stretches, storing about 35 J of energy.

Spring in your step BIO As you run, you lose some of your mechanical energy each time your foot strikes the ground; this energy is transformed into unrecoverable thermal energy. Luckily, about 35% of the decrease of your mechanical energy when your foot lands is stored as elastic potential energy in the stretchable Achilles tendon of the lower leg. On each plant of the foot, the tendon is stretched, storing some energy. The tendon springs back as you push off the ground again, helping to propel you forward. This recovered energy reduces the amount of internal chemical energy you use, increasing your efficiency.

This work is stored as potential energy in the spring, so we can use Equation 10.14 to find that as the spring is compressed, the elastic potential energy increases by

$$\Delta U_s = \frac{1}{2}kx^2$$

Just as in the case of gravitational potential energy, we have found an expression for the *change* in U_s, not U_s itself. Again, we are free to set $U_s = 0$ at any convenient spring extension. An obvious choice is to set $U_s = 0$ at the point where the spring is in equilibrium, neither compressed nor stretched—that is, at $x = 0$. With this choice we have

$$U_s = \frac{1}{2}kx^2 \qquad (10.15)$$

Elastic potential energy of a spring displaced a distance x from equilibrium (assuming $U_s = 0$ when the end of the spring is at $x = 0$)

NOTE ▶ Because U_s depends on the *square* of the displacement x, U_s is the same whether x is positive (the spring is compressed as in Figure 10.16) or negative (the spring is stretched). ◀

EXAMPLE 10.8 **Pulling back on a bow**

An archer pulls back the string on her bow to a distance of 70 cm from its equilibrium position. To hold the string at this position takes a force of 140 N. How much elastic potential energy is stored in the bow?

PREPARE A bow is an elastic material, so we will model it as obeying Hooke's law, $F_s = -kx$, where x is the distance the string is pulled back. We can use the force required to hold the string, and the distance it is pulled back, to find the bow's spring constant k. Then we can use Equation 10.15 to find the elastic potential energy.

SOLVE From Hooke's law, the spring constant is

$$k = \frac{F}{x} = \frac{140\ \text{N}}{0.70\ \text{m}} = 200\ \text{N/m}$$

Then the elastic potential energy of the flexed bow is

$$U_s = \frac{1}{2}kx^2 = \frac{1}{2}(200\ \text{N/m})(0.70\ \text{m})^2 = 49\ \text{J}$$

ASSESS When the arrow is released, this elastic potential energy will be transformed into the kinetic energy of the arrow. Because arrows are quite light, 49 J of kinetic energy will correspond to a very high speed.

FIGURE 10.17 A molecular view of thermal energy.

Hot object: Fast-moving molecules have lots of kinetic and elastic potential energy.

Cold object: Slow-moving molecules have little kinetic and elastic potential energy.

STOP TO THINK 10.5 When a spring is stretched by 5 cm, its elastic potential energy is 1 J. What will its elastic potential energy be if it is *compressed* by 10 cm?

A. −4 J   B. −2 J   C. 2 J   D. 4 J

10.5 Thermal Energy

We noted earlier that thermal energy is related to the microscopic motion of the molecules of an object. As FIGURE 10.17 shows, the molecules in a hot object jiggle around their average positions more than the molecules in a cold object. This has two consequences. First, each atom is on average moving faster in the hot object. This means that each atom has a higher *kinetic energy*. Second, each atom in the hot object tends to stray farther from its equilibrium position, leading to a greater stretching or compressing of the spring-like molecular bonds. This means that each atom has on average a higher *potential energy*. The potential energy stored in any one bond and the kinetic energy of any one atom are both exceedingly small, but there are incredibly many bonds and atoms. The sum of all these microscopic potential and kinetic energies is what we call **thermal energy**. Increasing an object's thermal energy corresponds to increasing its temperature.

Creating Thermal Energy

FIGURE 10.18 shows a thermogram of a heavy box and the floor across which it has just been dragged. In this image, warmer areas appear light blue or green. You can see that the bottom of the box and the region of the floor that the box moved over are noticeably warmer than their surroundings. In the process of dragging the box, thermal energy has appeared in the box and the floor.

We can find a quantitative expression for the change in thermal energy by considering such a box pulled by a rope at a constant speed. As the box is pulled across the floor, the rope exerts a constant forward force $\vec{F}$ on the box, while the friction force $\vec{f}_k$ exerts a constant force on the box that is directed backward. Because the box moves at a constant speed, the magnitudes of these two forces are equal: $F = f_k$.

As the box moves through a displacement $d = \Delta x$, the rope does work $W = F\Delta x$ on the box. This work represents energy transferred into the system, so the system's energy must *increase*. In what form is this increased energy? The box's speed remains constant, so there is no change in its kinetic energy ($\Delta K = 0$). And its height doesn't change, so its gravitational potential energy is unchanged as well ($\Delta U_g = 0$). Instead, the increased energy must be in the form of *thermal* energy E_{th}. As Figure 10.18 shows, this energy appears as an increased temperature of both the box *and* the floor across which it was dragged.

We can write the work-energy equation, Equation 10.3, for the case where only thermal energy changes:

$$\Delta E_{th} = W$$

or, because the work is $W = F\Delta x = f_k\Delta x$,

$$\Delta E_{th} = f_k\Delta x \qquad (10.16)$$

This increase in thermal energy is a general feature of any system where friction between sliding objects is present. An atomic-level explanation is shown in FIGURE 10.19. Although we arrived at Equation 10.16 by considering energy transferred into the system via work done by an external force, the equation is equally valid for the transformation of mechanical energy into thermal energy when, for instance, an object slides to a halt on a rough surface. Equation 10.16 also applies to rolling friction; we need only replace f_k by f_r.

FIGURE 10.18 A thermograph of a box that's been dragged across the floor.

FIGURE 10.19 How friction causes an increase in thermal energy.

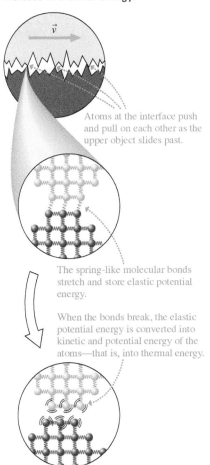

Atoms at the interface push and pull on each other as the upper object slides past.

The spring-like molecular bonds stretch and store elastic potential energy.

When the bonds break, the elastic potential energy is converted into kinetic and potential energy of the atoms—that is, into thermal energy.

TRY IT YOURSELF

◀**Agitating atoms** Vigorously rub a somewhat soft object such as a blackboard eraser on your desktop for about 10 seconds. If you then pass your fingers over the spot where you rubbed, you'll feel a distinct warm area. Congratulations: You've just set some 100,000,000,000,000,000,000,000 atoms into motion!

EXAMPLE 10.9   Creating thermal energy by rubbing

A 0.30 kg block of wood is rubbed back and forth against a wood table 30 times in each direction. The block is moved 8.0 cm during each stroke and pressed against the table with a force of 22 N. How much thermal energy is created in this process?

PREPARE The hand holding the block does work to push the block back and forth. Work transfers energy into the block + table system, where it appears as thermal energy according to Equation 10.16. The force of friction can be found from the model of kinetic friction introduced in Chapter 5, $f_k = \mu_k n$; from Table 5.1 the coefficient of kinetic friction for wood sliding on wood is $\mu_k = 0.20$. To find the normal force n acting on the block, we draw the free-body diagram of FIGURE 10.20, which shows only the *vertical* forces acting on the block.

FIGURE 10.20 Free-body diagram (vertical forces only) for a block being rubbed against a table.

SOLVE From Equation 10.16 we have $\Delta E_{th} = f_k \Delta x$, where $f_k = \mu_k n$. The block is not accelerating in the y-direction, so from the free-body diagram Newton's second law gives

$$\sum F_y = n - w - F = ma_y = 0$$

or

$$n = w + F = mg + F = (0.30 \text{ kg})(9.8 \text{ m/s}^2) + 22 \text{ N} = 25 \text{ N}$$

The friction force is then $f_k = \mu_k n = (0.20)(25 \text{ N}) = 5.0 \text{ N}$. The total displacement of the block is $2 \times 30 \times 8.0$ cm = 4.8 m. Thus the thermal energy created is

$$\Delta E_{th} = f_k \Delta x = (5.0 \text{ N})(4.8 \text{ m}) = 24 \text{ J}$$

ASSESS This modest amount of thermal energy seems reasonable for a person to create by rubbing.

PhET: Energy Skate Park (MP)

Class Video

10.6 Using the Law of Conservation of Energy

The law of conservation of energy, Equation 10.4, states that **the total energy of an isolated system is conserved** so that its change is zero:

$$\Delta E = \Delta K + \Delta U_g + \Delta U_s + \Delta E_{th} + \Delta E_{chem} + \cdots = 0 \qquad (10.17)$$

This law applies to every form of energy, from kinetic to chemical to nuclear. For the rest of this chapter, however, we'll narrow our focus and concern ourselves with only the forms of energy typically transformed during the motion of ordinary objects. These forms are kinetic energy K, gravitational and elastic potential energies U_g and U_s, and thermal energy E_{th}.

We defined an isolated system as one on which external forces do no work, so that no energy is transferred into or out of the system. The following table shows how to choose an isolated system for four common situations.

TABLE 10.2   Choosing an isolated system

An object in free fall	An object sliding down a frictionless ramp	An object compressing a spring	An object sliding along a surface with friction
We choose the ball *and* the earth as the system, so that the forces between them are *internal* forces. There are no external forces to do work, so the system is isolated.	The external force the ramp exerts on the object is perpendicular to the motion, and so does no work. The object and the earth together form an isolated system.	We choose the object and the spring to be the system. The forces between them are internal forces, so no work is done.	The block and the surface interact via kinetic friction forces, but these forces are internal to the system. There are no external forces to do work, so the system is isolated.

Just as for momentum conservation, we wish to develop a before-and-after perspective for energy conservation. We can do so by noting that $\Delta K = K_f - K_i$, $\Delta U_g = (U_g)_f - (U_g)_i$, and so on. Then Equation 10.17 can be written as

$$K_f + (U_g)_f + (U_s)_f + \Delta E_{th} = K_i + (U_g)_i + (U_s)_i \qquad (10.18)$$

Equation 10.18 is the before-and-after version of the law of conservation of energy: It equates the final value of an isolated system's energy to its initial energy. This equation will be the basis for a powerful problem-solving strategy.

NOTE ▶ We don't write ΔE_{th} as $(E_{th})_f - (E_{th})_i$ because the initial and final values of the thermal energy are typically unknown; only their *difference* ΔE_{th} can be measured. ◀

Conservation of Mechanical Energy

If we further restrict ourselves to cases where friction can be neglected, so that $\Delta E_{th} = 0$, the law of conservation of energy, Equation 10.18, becomes

$$K_f + (U_g)_f + (U_s)_f = K_i + (U_g)_i + (U_s)_i \qquad (10.19)$$

 ActivPhysics: 5.2, 5.3, 5.4, 5.5, 5.6, 5.7, 7.11, 7.12, 7.13

The sum of the kinetic and potential energies, $K + U_g + U_s$, is called the **mechanical energy** of the system, so Equation 10.19 says that **the mechanical energy is conserved for an isolated system without friction.**

These observations about the conservation of energy suggest the following problem-solving strategy.

PROBLEM-SOLVING STRATEGY 10.1   Conservation of energy problems

PREPARE Referring to Table 10.2, choose your system so that it is isolated. Draw a before-and-after visual overview, as was outlined in Tactics Box 9.1. Note the known quantities, and identify what you're trying to find.

SOLVE There are two important situations:

- If the system is isolated *and* there's no friction, the mechanical energy is conserved:

$$K_f + (U_g)_f + (U_s)_f = K_i + (U_g)_i + (U_s)_i$$

- If the system is isolated but there is friction within the system, the total energy is conserved:

$$K_f + (U_g)_f + (U_s)_f + \Delta E_{th} = K_i + (U_g)_i + (U_s)_i$$

Depending on the problem, you'll need to calculate the initial and/or final values of these energies; you can then solve for the unknown energies, and from these any unknown speeds (from K), heights (from U_g and U_s), or displacements or friction forces (from $\Delta E_{th} = f_k \Delta x$).

ASSESS Check the signs of your energies. Kinetic energy is always positive, as is the change in thermal energy. Check that your result has the correct units, is reasonable, and answers the question.

Exercise 23 🖉

Spring into action **BIO** A locust can jump as far as 1 meter, an impressive distance for such a small animal. To make such a jump, its legs must extend much more rapidly than muscles can ordinarily contract. Thus, instead of using its muscles to make the jump directly, the locust uses them to more slowly stretch an internal "spring" near its knee joint. This stores elastic potential energy in the spring. When the muscles relax, the spring is suddenly released, and its energy is rapidly converted into kinetic energy of the insect.

EXAMPLE 10.10   Hitting the bell

At the county fair, Katie tries her hand at the ring-the-bell attraction, as shown in FIGURE 10.21 on the next page. She swings the mallet hard enough to give the ball an initial upward speed of 8.0 m/s. Will the ball ring the bell, 3.0 m from the bottom?

PREPARE We'll follow the steps of Problem-Solving Strategy 10.1. From Table 10.2, we see that once the ball is in the air, the system consisting of the ball and the earth is isolated. If we assume that the track along which the ball moves is frictionless, then the

Continued

system's mechanical energy is conserved. Figure 10.21 shows a before-and-after visual overview in which we've chosen $y = 0$ m to be at the ball's starting point. We can then use conservation of mechanical energy, Equation 10.19.

FIGURE 10.21 Before-and-after visual overview of the ring-the-bell attraction.

We'll calculate how high the ball would go if the bell weren't there. Then we'll see if that height is enough to have reached the bell.

After:
y_f
$v_f = 0$ m/s

Find: y_f

3.0 m

Before:
$v_i = 8.0$ m/s
$y_i = 0$ m

SOLVE Equation 10.19 tells us that $K_f + (U_g)_f = K_i + (U_g)_i$. We can use our expressions for kinetic and potential energy to write this as

$$\frac{1}{2}mv_f^2 + mgy_f = \frac{1}{2}mv_i^2 + mgy_i$$

Let's ignore the bell for the moment and figure out how far the ball would rise if there were nothing in its way. We know that the ball starts at $y_i = 0$ m and that its speed v_f at the highest point is 0 m/s. Thus the energy equation simplifies to

$$mgy_f = \frac{1}{2}mv_i^2$$

This is easily solved for the height y_f:

$$y_f = \frac{v_i^2}{2g} = \frac{(8.0 \text{ m/s})^2}{2(9.8 \text{ m/s}^2)} = 3.3 \text{ m}$$

This is higher than the point where the bell sits, so the ball would actually hit it on the way up.

ASSESS It seems reasonable that Katie could swing the mallet hard enough to make the ball rise by about 3 m.

EXAMPLE 10.11 **Speed at the bottom of a water slide**

Still at the county fair, Katie tries the water slide, whose shape is shown in FIGURE 10.22. The starting point is 9.0 m above the ground. She pushes off with an initial speed of 2.0 m/s. If the slide is frictionless, how fast will Katie be traveling at the bottom?

PREPARE Table 10.2 showed that the system consisting of Katie and the earth is isolated because the normal force of the slide is perpendicular to Katie's motion and does no work. If we assume the slide is frictionless, we can use the conservation of mechanical energy equation. Figure 10.22 is a visual overview of the problem.

FIGURE 10.22 Before-and-after visual overview of Katie on the water slide.

y

Before:
$y_i = 9.0$ m
$v_i = 2.0$ m/s

Find: v_f

After:
$y_f = 0$ m
v_f

0

SOLVE Conservation of mechanical energy gives

$$K_f + (U_g)_f = K_i + (U_g)_i$$

or

$$\frac{1}{2}mv_f^2 + mgy_f = \frac{1}{2}mv_i^2 + mgy_i$$

Taking $y_f = 0$ m, we have

$$\frac{1}{2}mv_f^2 = \frac{1}{2}mv_i^2 + mgy_i$$

which we can solve to get

$$v_f = \sqrt{v_i^2 + 2gy_i}$$
$$= \sqrt{(2.0 \text{ m/s})^2 + 2(9.8 \text{ m/s}^2)(9.0 \text{ m})} = 13 \text{ m/s}$$

ASSESS This speed is about 30 mph. This is probably faster than you really would go on a water slide but, because we have ignored friction, our answer is reasonable. It is important to realize that the *shape* of the slide does not matter because gravitational potential energy depends only on the *height* above a reference level. **If you slide down any (frictionless) slide of the same height, your speed at the bottom is the same.**

EXAMPLE 10.12 **Speed of a spring-launched ball**

A spring-loaded toy gun is used to launch a 10 g plastic ball. The spring, which has a spring constant of 10 N/m, is compressed by 10 cm as the ball is pushed into the barrel. When the trigger is pulled, the spring is released and shoots the ball back out. What is the ball's speed as it leaves the barrel? Assume that friction is negligible.

PREPARE Assume the spring obeys Hooke's law, $F_s = -kx$, and is massless so that it has no kinetic energy of its own. Using Table 10.2, we choose the isolated system to be the spring and the ball. There's no friction; hence the system's mechanical energy $K + U_s$ is conserved.

FIGURE 10.23 Before-and-after visual overview of a ball being shot out of a spring-loaded toy gun.

Before: $v_i = 0$ m/s

$x_i = -10$ cm $x = 0$

After: v_f

$x_f = 0$ cm

Find: v_f

FIGURE 10.23 shows a before-and-after visual overview. The compressed spring will push on the ball until the spring has returned to its equilibrium length. We have chosen the origin of the coordinate system at the equilibrium position of the free end of the spring, making $x_i = -10$ cm and $x_f = 0$ cm.

SOLVE The energy conservation equation is $K_f + (U_s)_f = K_i + (U_s)_i$. We can use the elastic potential energy of the spring, Equation 10.15, to write this as

$$\tfrac{1}{2}mv_f^2 + \tfrac{1}{2}kx_f^2 = \tfrac{1}{2}mv_i^2 + \tfrac{1}{2}kx_i^2$$

We know that $x_f = 0$ m and $v_i = 0$ m/s, so this simplifies to

$$\tfrac{1}{2}mv_f^2 = \tfrac{1}{2}kx_i^2$$

It is now straightforward to solve for the ball's speed:

$$v_f = \sqrt{\frac{kx_i^2}{m}} = \sqrt{\frac{(10\text{ N/m})(-0.10\text{ m})^2}{0.010\text{ kg}}} = 3.2\text{ m/s}$$

ASSESS This is *not* a problem that we could have easily solved with Newton's laws. The acceleration is not constant, and we have not learned how to handle the kinematics of nonconstant acceleration. But with conservation of energy—it's easy!

Friction and Thermal Energy

Thermal energy is always created when kinetic friction is present, so we must use the more general conservation of energy equation, Equation 10.18, which includes thermal-energy changes ΔE_{th}. Furthermore, we know from Section 10.5 that the change in the thermal energy when an object slides a distance Δx while subject to a friction force f_k is $\Delta E_{th} = f_k\Delta x$.

EXAMPLE 10.13 | **Where will the sled stop?**

A sledder, starting from rest, slides down a 10-m-high hill. At the bottom of the hill is a long horizontal patch of rough snow. The hill is nearly frictionless, but the coefficient of friction between the sled and the rough snow at the bottom is $\mu_k = 0.30$. How far will the sled slide along the rough patch?

PREPARE In order to be isolated, the system must include the sled, the earth, *and* the rough snow. As Table 10.2 shows, this makes the friction force an internal force so that no work is done on the system. We can use conservation of energy, but we will need to include thermal energy. A visual overview of the problem is shown in FIGURE 10.24.

FIGURE 10.24 Visual overview of a sledder sliding downhill.

SOLVE At the top of the hill the sled has only gravitational potential energy $(U_g)_i = mgy_i$. It has no kinetic or potential energy after stopping at the bottom of the hill, so $K_f = (U_g)_f = 0$. However, friction in the rough patch causes an increase in thermal energy. Thus our conservation of energy equation $K_f + (U_g)_f + \Delta E_{th} = K_i + (U_g)_i$ is

$$\Delta E_{th} = (U_g)_i = mgy_i$$

The change in thermal energy is $\Delta E_{th} = f_k\Delta x = \mu_k n\Delta x$. The normal force $\vec{n}$ balances the sled's weight $\vec{w}$ as it crosses the rough patch, so $n = w = mg$. Thus

$$\Delta E_{th} = \mu_k n\Delta x = \mu_k(mg)\Delta x = mgy_i$$

from which we find

$$\Delta x = \frac{y_i}{\mu_k} = \frac{10\text{ m}}{0.30} = 33\text{ m}$$

ASSESS It seems reasonable that the sledder would slide a distance that is greater than the height of the hill he started down.

10.7 Energy in Collisions

In Chapter 9 we studied collisions between two objects. We found that if no external forces are acting on the objects, the total *momentum* of the objects will be conserved. Now we wish to study what happens to *energy* in collisions. The energetics of

 ActivPhysics: 6.2, 6.5, 6.8, 6.9

collisions are important in many applications in biokinetics, such as designing safer automobiles and bicycle helmets.

Let's first re-examine a perfectly inelastic collision. We studied just such a collision in Example 9.8. Recall that in such a collision the two objects stick together and then move with a common final velocity. What happens to the energy?

EXAMPLE 10.14 **Energy transformations in a perfectly inelastic collision**

FIGURE 10.25 shows two air-track gliders that are pushed toward each other, collide, and stick together. In Example 9.8, we used conservation of momentum to find the final velocity shown in Figure 10.25 from the given initial velocities. How much thermal energy is created in this collision?

FIGURE 10.25 Before-and-after visual overview of a completely inelastic collision.

PREPARE We'll choose our system to be the two gliders. Because the track is horizontal, there is no change in potential energy. Thus the law of conservation of energy, Equation 10.18, is $K_f + \Delta E_{th} = K_i$. The total energy before the collision must equal the total energy afterward, but the *mechanical* energies need not be equal.

SOLVE The initial kinetic energy is

$$K_i = \frac{1}{2}m_1(v_{1x})_i^2 + \frac{1}{2}m_2(v_{2x})_i^2$$

$$= \frac{1}{2}(0.200 \text{ kg})(3.00 \text{ m/s})^2 + \frac{1}{2}(0.400 \text{ kg})(-2.25 \text{ m/s})^2$$

$$= 1.91 \text{ J}$$

Because the gliders stick together and move as a single object with mass $m_1 + m_2$, the final kinetic energy is

$$K_f = \frac{1}{2}(m_1 + m_2)(v_x)_f^2$$

$$= \frac{1}{2}(0.600 \text{ kg})(-0.500 \text{ m/s})^2 = 0.0750 \text{ J}$$

From the conservation of energy equation above, we find that the thermal energy increases by

$$\Delta E_{th} = K_i - K_f = 1.91 \text{ J} - 0.075 \text{ J} = 1.84 \text{ J}$$

This amount of the initial kinetic energy is transformed into thermal energy during the impact of the collision.

ASSESS About 96% of the initial kinetic energy is transformed into thermal energy. This is typical of many real-world collisions.

Elastic Collisions

Figure 9.1 showed a collision of a tennis ball with a racket. The ball is compressed and the racket strings stretch as the two collide, then the ball expands and the strings relax as the two are pushed apart. In the language of energy, the kinetic energy of the objects is transformed into the elastic potential energy of the ball and strings, then back into kinetic energy as the two objects spring apart. If *all* of the kinetic energy is stored as elastic potential energy, and *all* of the elastic potential energy is transformed back into the post-collision kinetic energy of the objects, then mechanical energy is conserved. A collision for which mechanical energy is conserved is called a **perfectly elastic collision.**

Needless to say, most real collisions fall somewhere between perfectly elastic and perfectly inelastic. A rubber ball bouncing on the floor might "lose" 20% of its kinetic energy on each bounce and return to only 80% of the height of the preceding bounce. But collisions between two very hard objects, such as two pool balls or two steel balls, come close to being perfectly elastic. And collisions between microscopic particles, such as atoms or electrons, can be perfectly elastic.

FIGURE 10.26 on the next page shows a head-on, perfectly elastic collision of a ball of mass m_1, having initial velocity $(v_{1x})_i$, with a ball of mass m_2 that is initially at rest. The balls' velocities after the collision are $(v_{1x})_f$ and $(v_{2x})_f$. These are velocities, not speeds, and have signs. Ball 1, in particular, might bounce backward and have a negative value for $(v_{1x})_f$.

In a collision between a cue ball and a stationary ball, the mechanical energy of the balls is almost perfectly conserved.

The collision must obey two conservation laws: conservation of momentum (obeyed in any collision) and conservation of mechanical energy (because the collision is perfectly elastic). Although the energy is transformed into potential energy during the collision, the mechanical energy before and after the collision is purely kinetic energy. Thus,

momentum conservation: $\quad m_1(v_{1x})_i = m_1(v_{1x})_f + m_2(v_{2x})_f$

energy conservation: $\quad \dfrac{1}{2}m_1(v_{1x})_i^2 = \dfrac{1}{2}m_1(v_{1x})_f^2 + \dfrac{1}{2}m_2(v_{2x})_f^2$

Momentum conservation alone is not sufficient to analyze the collision because there are two unknowns: the two final velocities. That is why we did not consider perfectly elastic collisions in Chapter 9. Energy conservation gives us another condition. The complete solution of these two equations involves straightforward but rather lengthy algebra. We'll just give the solution here:

$$(v_{1x})_f = \frac{m_1 - m_2}{m_1 + m_2}(v_{1x})_i \qquad (v_{2x})_f = \frac{2m_1}{m_1 + m_2}(v_{1x})_i \qquad (10.20)$$

Perfectly elastic collision with object 2 initially at rest

Equations 10.20 allow us to compute the final velocity of each object. Let's look at a common and important example: a perfectly elastic collision between two objects of equal mass.

FIGURE 10.26 A perfectly elastic collision.

Video Tutor Demonstration

EXAMPLE 10.15   **Velocities in an air hockey collision**

On an air hockey table, a moving puck, traveling to the right at 2.3 m/s, makes a head-on collision with an identical puck at rest. What is the final velocity of each puck?

PREPARE The before-and-after visual overview is shown in FIGURE 10.27. We've shown the final velocities in the picture, but we don't really know yet which way the pucks will move. Because one puck was initially at rest, we can use Equation 10.20

FIGURE 10.27 A moving puck collides with a stationary puck.

Before: $(v_{1x})_i = 2.3$ m/s $(v_{2x})_i = 0$ m/s

$\vec{v}_{1i}$ $\vec{v}_{2i} = \vec{0}$

After: Find: $(v_{1x})_f$ and $(v_{2x})_f$

$\vec{v}_{1f}$ $\vec{v}_{2f}$

to find the final velocities of the pucks. The pucks are identical, so we have $m_1 = m_2 = m$.

SOLVE We use Equation 10.20 with $m_1 = m_2 = m$ to get

$$(v_{1x})_f = \frac{m - m}{m + m}(v_{1x})_i = 0 \text{ m/s}$$

$$(v_{2x})_f = \frac{2m}{m + m}(v_{1x})_i = (v_{1x})_i = 2.3 \text{ m/s}$$

The incoming puck stops dead, and the initially stationary puck goes off with the same velocity that the incoming one had.

ASSESS You can see that momentum and energy are conserved: The incoming puck's momentum and energy are completely transferred to the outgoing puck. If you've ever played pool, you've probably seen this sort of collision when you hit a ball head-on with the cue ball. The cue ball stops and the other ball picks up the cue ball's velocity.

Other cases where the colliding objects have unequal masses will be treated in the end-of-chapter problems.

Forces in Collisions

The collision between two pool balls occurs very quickly, and the forces are typically very large and difficult to calculate. Fortunately, by using the concepts of momentum and energy conservation, we can often calculate the final velocities of the balls without having to know the forces between them. There are collisions, however, where knowing the forces involved is of critical importance. The following example shows how a helmet helps protect the head from the large forces involved in a bicycle accident.

EXAMPLE 10.16   **Protecting your head**

A bike helmet—basically a shell of hard, crushable foam—is tested by being strapped onto a 5.0 kg head-form and dropped from a height of 2.0 m onto a hard anvil. What force is encountered by the headform if the impact crushes the foam by 3.0 cm?

The foam inside a bike helmet is designed to crush upon impact.

PREPARE A before-and-after visual overview of the test is shown in FIGURE 10.28. We've chosen the endpoint of the problem to be when the headform comes to rest with the foam crushed. We can use the work-energy equation, Equation 10.3, to calculate the force on the headform. We'll choose the head-form and the earth to be the system; the foam in the helmet is part of the environment. We make this choice so that the force on the headform due to the foam is an *external* force that does work W on the headform.

SOLVE The work-energy equation $\Delta K + \Delta U_g + \Delta E_{th} = W$ tells us that the work done by external forces—in this case, the force of the foam on the headform—changes the energy of the system. The headform starts at rest, speeds up as it falls, then returns to rest during the impact. Overall, then, $\Delta K = 0$. Furthermore, $\Delta E_{th} = 0$ because there's no friction to increase the thermal energy. Only the gravitational potential energy changes, giving

$$\Delta U_g = (U_g)_f - (U_g)_i = W$$

The upward force of the foam on the headform is opposite the downward displacement of the headform. Referring to Tactics Box 10.1, we see that the work done is negative: $W = -Fd$, where we've assumed that the force is relatively constant. Using this result in the work-energy equation and solving for F, we find

$$F = -\frac{(U_g)_f - (U_g)_i}{d} = \frac{(U_g)_i - (U_g)_f}{d}$$

Taking our reference height to be $y = 0$ m at the anvil, we have $(U_g)_f = 0$. We're left with $(U_g)_i = mgy_i$, so

$$F = \frac{mgy_i}{d} = \frac{(5.0 \text{ kg})(9.8 \text{ m/s})(2.0 \text{ m})}{0.030 \text{ m}} = 3300 \text{ N}$$

This is the force that acts on the head to bring it to a halt in 3.0 cm. More important from the perspective of possible brain injury is the head's *acceleration:*

$$a = \frac{F}{m} = \frac{3300 \text{ N}}{5.0 \text{ kg}} = 660 \text{ m/s}^2 = 67g$$

ASSESS The accepted threshold for serious brain injury is around $300g$, so this helmet would protect the rider in all but the most serious accidents. Without the helmet, the rider's head would come to a stop in a much shorter distance and thus be subjected to a much larger acceleration.

FIGURE 10.28 Before-and-after visual overview of the bike helmet test.

The headform is dropped from a height of 2.0 m.

The helmet has just touched the anvil. The foam is now pushing up on the headform.

$-y_i, v_i$

$y = 0$

The headform is subject to a large force from the foam. This force does negative work on the headform, slowing it down.

$\vec{F}$

$\vec{F}$

d

y_f, v_f

$d = 0.030$ m

Before:
$y_i = 2.0$ m, $v_i = 0$ m/s

After:
$y_f = 0$ m, $v_f = 0$ m/s

Find: F

10.8 Power

We've now studied how energy can be transformed from one kind into another and how it can be transferred between the environment and the system as work. In many situations we would like to know *how quickly* the energy is transformed or transferred. Is a transfer of energy very rapid, or does it take place over a long time? In passing a truck, your car needs to transform a certain amount of the chemical energy in its fuel into kinetic energy. It makes a *big* difference whether your engine can do this in 20 s or 60 s!

The question How quickly? implies that we are talking about a *rate*. For example, the velocity of an object—how fast it is going—is the *rate of change* of position. So, when we raise the issue of how fast the energy is transformed, we are talking about the *rate of transformation* of energy. Suppose in a time interval Δt an amount of energy ΔE is transformed from one form to another. The rate at which this energy is transformed is called the **power** P and is defined as

$$P = \frac{\Delta E}{\Delta t} \qquad (10.21)$$

Power when an amount of energy ΔE is transformed in a time interval Δt

The unit of power is the **watt,** which is defined as 1 watt = 1 W = 1 J/s.

Power also measures the rate at which energy is transferred into or out of a system as work W. If work W is done in time interval Δt, the rate of energy *transfer* is

$$P = \frac{W}{\Delta t} \qquad (10.22)$$

Power when an amount of work W is done in a time interval Δt

A force that is doing work (i.e., transferring energy) at a rate of 3 J/s has an "output power" of 3 W. A system that is gaining energy at the rate of 3 J/s is said to "consume" 3 W of power. Common prefixes used for power are mW (milliwatts), kW (kilowatts), and MW (megawatts).

We can express Equation 10.22 in a different form. If in the time interval Δt an object undergoes a displacement Δx, the work done by a force acting on the object is $W = F\Delta x$. Then Equation 10.22 can be written as

$$P = \frac{W}{\Delta t} = \frac{F\Delta x}{\Delta t} = F\frac{\Delta x}{\Delta t} = Fv$$

The rate at which energy is transferred to an object as work—the power—is the product of the force that does the work and the velocity of the object:

$$P = Fv \qquad (10.23)$$

Rate of energy transfer due to a force F acting on an object moving at velocity v

Both these cars take about the same energy to reach 60 mph, but the race car gets there in a much shorter time, so its *power* is much greater.

The English unit of power is the *horsepower.* The conversion factor to watts is

1 horsepower = 1 hp = 746 W

Many common appliances, such as motors, are rated in hp.

EXAMPLE 10.17 **Power to pass a truck**

Your 1500 kg car is behind a truck traveling at 60 mph (27 m/s). To pass it, you speed up to 75 mph (34 m/s) in 6.0 s. What engine power is required to do this?

PREPARE Your engine is transforming the chemical energy of its fuel into the kinetic energy of the car. We can calculate the rate of transformation by finding the change ΔK in the kinetic energy and using the known time interval.

SOLVE We have

$$K_i = \frac{1}{2}mv_i^2 = \frac{1}{2}(1500 \text{ kg})(27 \text{ m/s})^2 = 5.47 \times 10^5 \text{ J}$$
$$K_f = \frac{1}{2}mv_f^2 = \frac{1}{2}(1500 \text{ kg})(34 \text{ m/s})^2 = 8.67 \times 10^5 \text{ J}$$

so that

$$\Delta K = K_f - K_i$$
$$= (8.67 \times 10^5 \text{ J}) - (5.47 \times 10^5 \text{ J}) = 3.20 \times 10^5 \text{ J}$$

To transform this amount of energy in 6 s, the power required is

$$P = \frac{\Delta K}{\Delta t} = \frac{3.20 \times 10^5 \text{ J}}{6.0 \text{ s}} = 53,000 \text{ W} = 53 \text{ kW}$$

This is about 71 hp. This power is in addition to the power needed to overcome drag and friction and cruise at 60 mph, so the total power required from the engine will be even greater than this.

ASSESS You use a large amount of energy to perform a simple driving maneuver such as this. 3.20×10^5 J is enough energy to lift an 80 kg person 410 m in the air—the height of a tall skyscraper. And 53 kW would lift him there in only 6 s!

STOP TO THINK 10.6 Four students run up the stairs in the times shown. Rank in order, from largest to smallest, their power outputs P_A through P_D.

INTEGRATED EXAMPLE 10.18   **Stopping a runaway truck**

A truck's brakes can overheat and fail while descending mountain highways, leading to an extremely dangerous runaway truck. Some highways have *runaway-truck ramps* to safely bring out-of-control trucks to a stop. These uphill ramps are covered with a deep bed of gravel. The uphill slope and the large coefficient of rolling friction as the tires sink into the gravel bring the truck to a safe halt.

A runaway-truck ramp along Interstate 70 in Colorado.

A 22,000 kg truck heading down a 3.5° slope at 20 m/s ($\approx$45 mph) suddenly has its brakes fail. Fortunately, there's a runaway-truck ramp 600 m ahead. The ramp slopes upward at an angle of 10°, and the coefficient of rolling friction between the truck's tires and the loose gravel is $\mu_r = 0.40$. Ignore air resistance and rolling friction as the truck rolls down the highway.

a. Use conservation of energy to find how far along the ramp the truck travels before stopping.
b. By how much does the thermal energy of the truck and ramp increase as the truck stops?

PREPARE Parts a and b can be solved using energy conservation by following Problem-Solving Strategy 10.1. FIGURE 10.29 shows a before-and-after visual overview. Because we're going to need to determine friction forces to calculate the increase in thermal energy, we've also drawn a free-body diagram for the truck as it moves up the ramp. One slight complication is that the y-axis of free-body diagrams is drawn perpendicular to the slope, whereas the calculation of gravitational potential energy needs a vertical y-axis to measure height. We've dealt with this by labeling the free-body diagram axis the y'-axis.

FIGURE 10.29 Visual overview of the runaway truck.

SOLVE a. The law of conservation of energy for the motion of the truck, from the moment its brakes fail to when it finally stops, is

$$K_f + (U_g)_f + \Delta E_{th} = K_i + (U_g)_i$$

Because friction is present only along the ramp, thermal energy will be created only as the truck moves up the ramp. This thermal energy is then given by $\Delta E_{th} = f_r \Delta x_2$, because Δx_2 is the length of the ramp. The conservation of energy equation then is

$$\frac{1}{2}mv_f^2 + mgy_f + f_r\Delta x_2 = \frac{1}{2}mv_i^2 + mgy_i$$

From Figure 10.29 we have $y_i = \Delta x_1 \sin\theta_1$, $y_f = \Delta x_2 \sin\theta_2$, and $v_f = 0$, so the equation becomes

$$mg\Delta x_2 \sin\theta_2 + f_r\Delta x_2 = \frac{1}{2}mv_i^2 + mg\Delta x_1 \sin\theta_1$$

To find $f_r = \mu_r n$ we need to find the normal force n. The free-body diagram shows that

$$\sum F_{y'} = n - mg\cos\theta_2 = a_{y'} = 0$$

from which $f_r = \mu_r n = \mu_r mg \cos\theta_2$. With this result for f_r, our conservation of energy equation is

$$mg\Delta x_2 \sin\theta_2 + \mu_r mg\cos\theta_2 \Delta x_2 = \frac{1}{2}mv_i^2 + mg\Delta x_1 \sin\theta_1$$

which, after we divide both sides by mg, simplifies to

$$\Delta x_2 \sin\theta_2 + \mu_r \cos\theta_2 \Delta x_2 = \frac{v_i^2}{2g} + \Delta x_1 \sin\theta_1$$

Solving this for Δx_2 gives

$$\Delta x_2 = \frac{\dfrac{v_i^2}{2g} + \Delta x_1 \sin\theta_1}{\sin\theta_2 + \mu_r\cos\theta_2}$$

$$= \frac{\dfrac{(20\text{ m/s})^2}{2(9.8\text{ m/s}^2)} + (600\text{ m})(\sin 3.5°)}{\sin 10° + 0.40(\cos 10°)} = 100\text{ m}$$

b. We know that $\Delta E_{th} = f_r\Delta x_2 = (\mu_r mg\cos\theta_2)\Delta x_2$, so that

$$\Delta E_{th} = (0.40)(22{,}000\text{ kg})(9.8\text{ m/s}^2)(\cos 10°)(100\text{ m})$$

$$= 8.5 \times 10^6\text{ J}$$

ASSESS It seems reasonable that a truck that speeds up as it rolls 600 m downhill takes only 100 m to stop on a steeper, high-friction ramp. We also expect the thermal energy to be roughly comparable to the kinetic energy of the truck, since it's largely the kinetic energy that is transformed into thermal energy. At the top of the hill the truck's kinetic energy is $K_i = \frac{1}{2}mv_i^2 = \frac{1}{2}(22{,}000\text{ kg})(20\text{ m/s})^2 = 4.4 \times 10^6\text{ J}$, which is of the same order of magnitude as ΔE_{th}. Our answer is reasonable.

SUMMARY

The goals of Chapter 10 are to introduce the concept of energy and to learn a new problem-solving strategy based on conservation of energy.

GENERAL PRINCIPLES

Basic Energy Model

Within a system, energy can be **transformed** between various forms.

Energy can be **transferred** into or out of a system in two basic ways:

- **Work:** The transfer of energy by mechanical forces.

- **Heat:** The nonmechanical transfer of energy from a hotter to a colder object.

Energy is *transformed* within the system.

Environment

System

$K \longleftrightarrow U$

E_{chem}

E_{th}

Work, heat

Energy is *transferred* to or from the system from or to the environment.

Conservation of Energy

When work W is done on a system, the system's total energy changes by the amount of work done. In mathematical form, this is the **work-energy equation:**

$$\Delta E = \Delta K + \Delta U_g + \Delta U_s + \Delta E_{th} + \Delta E_{chem} + \cdots = W$$

A system is **isolated** when no energy is transferred into or out of the system. This means the work is zero, giving the **law of conservation of energy:**

$$\Delta K + \Delta U_g + \Delta U_s + \Delta E_{th} + \Delta E_{chem} + \cdots = 0$$

Solving Energy Conservation Problems

PREPARE Choose your system so that it's isolated. Draw a before-and-after visual overview.

SOLVE

- If the system is isolated and there's no friction, then mechanical energy is conserved:

$$K_f + (U_g)_f + (U_s)_f = K_i + (U_g)_i + (U_s)_i$$

- If the system is isolated but there's friction present, then the total energy is conserved:

$$K_f + (U_g)_f + (U_s)_f + \Delta E_{th} = K_i + (U_g)_i + (U_s)_i$$

ASSESS Kinetic energy is always positive, as is the change in thermal energy.

IMPORTANT CONCEPTS

Kinetic energy is an energy of motion:

$$K = \tfrac{1}{2}mv^2 + \tfrac{1}{2}I\omega^2$$

Translational · · · · ·↗   ↖· · · · · Rotational

Potential energy is energy stored in a system of interacting objects.

- **Gravitational potential energy:** $U_g = mgy$

- **Elastic potential energy:** $U_s = \dfrac{1}{2}kx^2$

Mechanical energy is the sum of a system's kinetic and potential energies:

$$\text{Mechanical energy} = K + U = K + U_g + U_s$$

Thermal energy is the sum of the microscopic kinetic and potential energies of all the molecules in an object. The hotter an object, the more thermal energy it has. When kinetic (sliding) friction is present, the increase in the thermal energy is $\Delta E_{th} = f_k \Delta x$.

Work is the process by which energy is transferred to or from a system by the application of mechanical forces.

If a particle moves through a displacement $\vec{d}$ while acted upon by a constant force $\vec{F}$, the force does work

$$W = F_\parallel d = Fd\cos\theta$$

Only the component of the force parallel to the displacement does work.

APPLICATIONS

Perfectly elastic collisions
Both mechanical energy and momentum are conserved.

$$(v_{1x})_f = \frac{m_1 - m_2}{m_1 + m_2}(v_{1x})_i$$

$$(v_{2x})_f = \frac{2m_1}{m_1 + m_2}(v_{1x})_i$$

Object 2 initially at rest

Before: ① $(v_{1x})_i$ → ② K_i

After: $K_f = K_i$ ① → ② →
$(v_{1x})_f$ $(v_{2x})_f$

Power is the rate at which energy is transformed . . .

$$P = \frac{\Delta E}{\Delta t}$$
· · · · · Amount of energy transformed
· · · · · Time required to transform it

. . . or at which work is done.

$$P = \frac{W}{\Delta t}$$
· · · · · Amount of work done
· · · · · Time required to do work

Problem difficulty is labeled as I (straightforward) to IIIII (challenging). Problems labeled ✎ can be done on a Workbook Energy Worksheet; INT integrate significant material from earlier chapters; BIO are of biological or medical interest.

For homework assigned on MasteringPhysics, go to www.masteringphysics.com

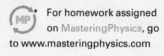

Scan this QR code to launch a Video Tutor Solution that will help you solve problems for this chapter.

QUESTIONS

Conceptual Questions

1. The brake shoes of your car are made of a material that can tolerate very high temperatures without being damaged. Why is this so?
2. When you pound a nail with a hammer, the nail gets quite warm. Describe the energy transformations that lead to the addition of thermal energy in the nail.

For Questions 3 through 10, give a specific example of a system with the energy transformation shown. In these questions, W is the work done on the system, and K, U, and E_{th} are the kinetic, potential, and thermal energies of the system, respectively. Any energy not mentioned in the transformation is assumed to remain constant; if work is not mentioned, it is assumed to be zero.

3. $W \rightarrow K$
4. $W \rightarrow U$
5. $K \rightarrow U$
6. $K \rightarrow W$
7. $U \rightarrow K$
8. $W \rightarrow \Delta E_{th}$
9. $U \rightarrow \Delta E_{th}$
10. $K \rightarrow \Delta E_{th}$

11. A ball of putty is dropped from a height of 2 m onto a hard floor, where it sticks. What object or objects need to be included within the system if the system is to be isolated during this process?
12. A 0.5 kg mass on a 1-m-long string swings in a circle on a horizontal, frictionless table at a steady speed of 2 m/s. How much work does the tension in the string do on the mass during one revolution? Explain.
13. Particle A has less mass than particle B. Both are pushed forward across a frictionless surface by equal forces for 1 s. Both start from rest.
    a. Compare the amount of work done on each particle. That is, is the work done on A greater than, less than, or equal to the work done on B? Explain.
    b. Compare the impulses delivered to particles A and B. Explain.
    c. Compare the final speeds of particles A and B. Explain.
14. The meaning of the word "work" is quite different in physics from its everyday usage. Give an example of an action a person could do that "feels like work" but that does not involve any work as we've defined it in this chapter.
15. To change a tire, you need to use a jack to raise one corner of your car. While doing so, you happen to notice that pushing the jack handle down 20 cm raises the car only 0.2 cm. Use energy concepts to explain why the handle must be moved so far to raise the car by such a small amount.
16. You drop two balls from a tower, one of mass m and the other of mass $2m$. Just before they hit the ground, which ball, if either, has the larger kinetic energy? Explain.

17. A roller coaster car rolls down a frictionless track, reaching speed v at the bottom.
    a. If you want the car to go twice as fast at the bottom, by what factor must you increase the height of the track?
    b. Does your answer to part a depend on whether the track is straight or not? Explain.
18. A spring gun shoots out a plastic ball at speed v. The spring is then compressed twice the distance it was on the first shot.
    a. By what factor is the spring's potential energy increased?
    b. By what factor is the ball's speed increased? Explain.
19. Sandy and Chris stand on the edge of a cliff and throw identical mass rocks at the same speed. Sandy throws her rock horizontally while Chris throws his upward at an angle of 45° to the horizontal. Are the rocks moving at the same speed when they hit the ground, or is one moving faster than the other? If one is moving faster, which one? Explain.
20. A solid cylinder and a cylindrical shell have the same mass, same radius, and turn on frictionless, horizontal axles. (The cylindrical shell has lightweight spokes connecting the shell to the axle.) A rope is wrapped around each cylinder and tied to a block. The blocks have the same mass and are held the same height above the ground as shown in Figure Q10.20. Both blocks are released simultaneously. The ropes do not slip. Which block hits the ground first? Or is it a tie? Explain.

FIGURE Q10.20

21. You are much more likely to be injured if you fall and your head
BIO strikes the ground than if your head strikes a gymnastics pad. Use energy and work concepts to explain why this is so.

Multiple-Choice Questions

22. II If you walk up a flight of stairs at constant speed, gaining vertical height h, the work done on you (the system, of mass m) is
    A. $+mgh$, by the normal force of the stairs.
    B. $-mgh$, by the normal force of the stairs.
    C. $+mgh$, by the gravitational force of the earth.
    D. $-mgh$, by the gravitational force of the earth.
23. I You and a friend each carry a 15 kg suitcase up two flights of stairs, walking at a constant speed. Take each suitcase to be the system. Suppose you carry your suitcase up the stairs in 30 s while your friend takes 60 s. Which of the following is true?
    A. You did more work, but both of you expended the same power.
    B. You did more work and expended more power.
    C. Both of you did equal work, but you expended more power.
    D. Both of you did equal work, but you expended less power.

24. | A woman uses a pulley and a rope to raise a 20 kg weight to a height of 2 m. If it takes 4 s to do this, about how much power is she supplying?
    A. 100 W   B. 200 W   C. 300 W   D. 400 W

25. | A hockey puck sliding along frictionless ice with speed v to the right collides with a horizontal spring and compresses it by 2.0 cm before coming to a momentary stop. What will be the spring's maximum compression if the same puck hits it at a speed of $2v$?
    A. 2.0 cm   B. 2.8 cm   C. 4.0 cm
    D. 5.6 cm   E. 8.0 cm

26. ‖ A block slides down a smooth ramp, starting from rest at a height h. When it reaches the bottom it's moving at speed v. It then continues to slide up a second smooth ramp. At what height is its speed equal to $v/2$?
    A. $h/4$ B. $h/2$ C. $3h/4$ D. $2h$

27. | A wrecking ball is suspended from a 5.0-m-long cable that makes a 30° angle with the vertical. The ball is released and swings down. What is the ball's speed at the lowest point?
    A. 7.7 m/s   B. 4.4 m/s   C. 3.6 m/s   D. 3.1 m/s

PROBLEMS

Section 10.2 Work

1. ‖ During an etiquette class, you walk slowly and steadily at 0.20 m/s for 2.5 m with a 0.75 kg book balanced on top of your head. How much work does your head do on the book?

2. ‖ A 2.0 kg book is lying on a 0.75-m-high table. You pick it up and place it on a bookshelf 2.3 m above the floor.
   a. How much work does gravity do on the book?
   b. How much work does your hand do on the book?

3. ‖ The two ropes seen in Figure P10.3 are used to lower a 255 kg piano exactly 5 m from a second-story window to the ground. How much work is done by each of the three forces?

FIGURE P10.3   FIGURE P10.4

4. | The two ropes shown in the bird's-eye view of Figure P10.4 are used to drag a crate exactly 3 m across the floor. How much work is done by each of the ropes on the crate?

5. ‖ a. At the airport, you ride a "moving sidewalk" that carries you horizontally for 25 m at 0.70 m/s. Assuming that you were moving at 0.70 m/s before stepping onto the moving sidewalk and continue at 0.70 m/s afterward, how much work does the moving sidewalk do on you? Your mass is 60 kg.
   b. An escalator carries you from one level to the next in the airport terminal. The upper level is 4.5 m above the lower level, and the length of the escalator is 7.0 m. How much work does the up escalator do on you when you ride it from the lower level to the upper level?
   c. How much work does the down escalator do on you when you ride it from the upper level to the lower level?

6. | A boy flies a kite with the string at a 30° angle to the horizontal. The tension in the string is 4.5 N. How much work does the string do on the boy if the boy
   a. Stands still?
   b. Walks a horizontal distance of 11 m away from the kite?
   c. Walks a horizontal distance of 11 m toward the kite?

Section 10.3 Kinetic Energy

7. | Which has the larger kinetic energy, a 10 g bullet fired at 500 m/s or a 10 kg bowling ball sliding at 10 m/s?

8. ‖ At what speed does a 1000 kg compact car have the same kinetic energy as a 20,000 kg truck going 25 km/hr?

9. | A car is traveling at 10 m/s.
   a. How fast would the car need to go to double its kinetic energy?
   b. By what factor does the car's kinetic energy increase if its speed is doubled to 20 m/s?

10. ‖ Sam's job at the amusement park is to slow down and bring to a stop the boats in the log ride. If a boat and its riders have a mass of 1200 kg and the boat drifts in at 1.2 m/s, how much work does Sam do to stop it?

11. ‖ A 20 g plastic ball is moving to the left at 30 m/s. How much work must be done on the ball to cause it to move to the right at 30 m/s?

12. ‖ The turntable in a microwave oven has a moment of inertia of $0.040 \text{ kg} \cdot \text{m}^2$ and is rotating once every 4.0 s. What is its kinetic energy?

13. ‖‖ An energy storage system based on a flywheel (a rotating disk) can store a maximum of 4.0 MJ when the flywheel is rotating at 20,000 revolutions per minute. What is the moment of inertia of the flywheel?

Section 10.4 Potential Energy

14. ‖ The lowest point in Death Valley is 85.0 m below sea level. The summit of nearby Mt. Whitney has an elevation of 4420 m. What is the change in gravitational potential energy of an energetic 65.0 kg hiker who makes it from the floor of Death Valley to the top of Mt. Whitney?

15. | a. What is the kinetic energy of a 1500 kg car traveling at a speed of 30 m/s ($\approx$65 mph)?
    b. From what height should the car be dropped to have this same amount of kinetic energy just before impact?
    c. Does your answer to part b depend on the car's mass?

16. | The world's fastest humans can reach speeds of about 11 m/s. In order to increase his gravitational potential energy by an amount equal to his kinetic energy at full speed, how high would such a sprinter need to climb?

17. | A 72 kg bike racer climbs a 1200-m-long section of road that has a slope of 4.3°. By how much does his gravitational potential energy change during this climb?

18. ‖ A 1000 kg wrecking ball hangs from a 15-m-long cable. The ball is pulled back until the cable makes an angle of 25° with the vertical. By how much has the gravitational potential energy of the ball changed?

19. ‖ How far must you stretch a spring with $k = 1000$ N/m to store 200 J of energy?

20. ‖ How much energy can be stored in a spring with a spring constant of 500 N/m if its maximum possible stretch is 20 cm?

21. ‖‖‖ The elastic energy stored in your tendons can contribute up to BIO 35% of your energy needs when running. Sports scientists have studied the change in length of the knee extensor tendon in sprinters and nonathletes. They find (on average) that the sprinters' tendons stretch 41 mm, while nonathletes' stretch only 33 mm. The spring constant for the tendon is the same for both groups, 33 N/mm. What is the difference in maximum stored energy between the sprinters and the nonathletes?

Section 10.5 Thermal Energy

22. ‖ Marissa drags a 23 kg duffel bag 14 m across the gym floor. If the coefficient of kinetic friction between the floor and bag is 0.15, how much thermal energy does Marissa create?

23. ‖ Mark pushes his broken car 150 m down the block to his friend's house. He has to exert a 110 N horizontal force to push the car at a constant speed. How much thermal energy is created in the tires and road during this short trip?

24. ‖‖‖ A 900 N crate slides 12 m down a ramp that makes an angle of 35° with the horizontal. If the crate slides at a constant speed, how much thermal energy is created?

25. ‖‖‖ A 25 kg child slides down a playground slide at a *constant speed*. The slide has a height of 3.0 m and is 7.0 m long. Using energy considerations, find the magnitude of the kinetic friction force acting on the child.

Section 10.6 Using the Law of Conservation of Energy

26. ‖ A boy reaches out of a window and tosses a ball straight up with a speed of 10 m/s. The ball is 20 m above the ground as he releases it. Use conservation of energy to find
   a. The ball's maximum height above the ground.
   b. The ball's speed as it passes the window on its way down.
   c. The speed of impact on the ground.

27. ‖ a. With what minimum speed must you toss a 100 g ball straight up to just barely hit the 10-m-high ceiling of the gymnasium if you release the ball 1.5 m above the floor? Solve this problem using energy.
   b. With what speed does the ball hit the floor?

28. ‖‖‖ What minimum speed does a 100 g puck need to make it to the top of a frictionless ramp that is 3.0 m long and inclined at 20°?

29. ‖ A car is parked at the top of a 50-m-high hill. It slips out of gear and rolls down the hill. How fast will it be going at the bottom? (Ignore friction.)

30. ‖‖‖ A 1500 kg car is approaching the hill shown in Figure P10.30 at 10 m/s when it suddenly runs out of gas.
   a. Can the car make it to the top of the hill by coasting?
   b. If your answer to part a is yes, what is the car's speed after coasting down the other side?

FIGURE P10.30

31. ‖ A 10 kg runaway grocery cart runs into a spring with spring constant 250 N/m and compresses it by 60 cm. What was the speed of the cart just before it hit the spring?

32. ‖ As a 15,000 kg jet lands on an aircraft carrier, its tail hook snags a cable to slow it down. The cable is attached to a spring with spring constant 60,000 N/m. If the spring stretches 30 m to stop the plane, what was the plane's landing speed?

33. ‖ Your friend's Frisbee has become stuck 16 m above the ground in a tree. You want to dislodge the Frisbee by throwing a rock at it. The Frisbee is stuck pretty tight, so you figure the rock needs to be traveling at least 5.0 m/s when it hits the Frisbee. If you release the rock 2.0 m above the ground, with what minimum speed must you throw it?

34. ‖ A fireman of mass 80 kg slides down a pole. When he reaches the bottom, 4.2 m below his starting point, his speed is 2.2 m/s. By how much has thermal energy increased during his slide?

35. ‖ A 20 kg child slides down a 3.0-m-high playground slide. She starts from rest, and her speed at the bottom is 2.0 m/s.
   a. What energy transfers and transformations occur during the slide?
   b. What is the total change in the thermal energy of the slide and the seat of her pants?

36. ‖ A hockey puck is given an initial speed of 5.0 m/s. If the coefficient of kinetic friction between the puck and the ice is 0.05, how far does the puck slide before coming to rest? Solve this problem using conservation of energy.

Section 10.7 Energy in Collisions

37. ‖ A 50 g marble moving at 2.0 m/s strikes a 20 g marble at rest. What is the speed of each marble immediately after the collision? Assume the collision is perfectly elastic and the marbles collide head-on.

38. ‖ Ball 1, with a mass of 100 g and traveling at 10 m/s, collides head-on with ball 2, which has a mass of 300 g and is initially at rest. What are the final velocities of each ball if the collision is (a) perfectly elastic? (b) perfectly inelastic?

39. ‖ An air-track glider undergoes a perfectly inelastic collision with an identical glider that is initially at rest. What fraction of the first glider's initial kinetic energy is transformed into thermal energy in this collision?

40. ‖ Two balls undergo a perfectly elastic head-on collision, with one ball initially at rest. If the incoming ball has a speed of 200 m/s, what are the final speed and direction of each ball if
   a. The incoming ball is *much* more massive than the stationary ball?
   b. The stationary ball is *much* more massive than the incoming ball?

Section 10.8 Power

41. ‖ a. How much work must you do to push a 10 kg block of steel across a steel table at a steady speed of 1.0 m/s for 3.0 s? The coefficient of kinetic friction for steel on steel is 0.60.
   b. What is your power output while doing so?

42. ‖ a. How much work does an elevator motor do to lift a 1000 kg elevator a height of 100 m?
   b. How much power must the motor supply to do this in 50 s at constant speed?

43. ‖‖‖ A 1000 kg sports car accelerates from 0 to 30 m/s in 10 s. What is the average power of the engine?

44. ‖‖‖ In just 0.30 s, you compress a spring (spring constant 5000 N/m), which is initially at its equilibrium length, by 4.0 cm. What is your average power output?

45. ‖‖‖ In the winter sport of curling, players give a 20 kg stone a push across a sheet of ice. A curler accelerates a stone to a speed of 3.0 m/s over a time of 2.0 s.
   a. How much force does the curler exert on the stone?
   b. What average power does the curler use to bring the stone up to speed?

46. ‖ A 710 kg car drives at a constant speed of 23 m/s. It is subject to a drag force of 500 N. What power is required from the car's engine to drive the car
    a. On level ground?
    b. Up a hill with a slope of 2.0°?
47. ‖‖ An elevator weighing 2500 N ascends at a constant speed of 8.0 m/s. How much power must the motor supply to do this?

General Problems

48. ‖ A 2.3 kg box, starting from rest, is pushed up a ramp by a 10 N force parallel to the ramp. The ramp is 2.0 m long and tilted at 17°. The speed of the box at the top of the ramp is 0.80 m/s. Consider the system to be the box + ramp + earth.
    a. How much work W does the force do on the system?
    b. What is the change ΔK in the kinetic energy of the system?
    c. What is the change ΔU_g in the gravitational potential energy of the system?
    d. What is the change ΔE_{th} in the thermal energy of the system?

49. ‖ A 55 kg skateboarder wants to just make it to the upper edge of a "half-pipe" with a radius of 3.0 m, as shown in Figure P10.49. What speed v_i does he need at the bottom if he is to coast all the way up?

FIGURE P10.49

3.0 m

   a. First do the calculation treating the skateboarder and board as a point particle, with the entire mass nearly in contact with the half-pipe.
   b. More realistically, the mass of the skateboarder in a deep crouch might be thought of as concentrated 0.75 m from the half-pipe. Assuming he remains in that position all the way up, what v_i is needed to reach the upper edge?

50. ‖‖ Fleas have remarkable jumping ability. A 0.50 mg flea, jumping straight up, would reach a height of 40 cm if there were no air resistance. In reality, air resistance limits the height to 20 cm.
    a. What is the flea's kinetic energy as it leaves the ground?
    b. At its highest point, what fraction of the initial kinetic energy has been converted to potential energy?

51. ‖‖ A marble slides without friction in a *vertical* plane around the inside of a smooth, 20-cm-diameter horizontal pipe. The marble's speed at the bottom is 3.0 m/s; this is fast enough so that the marble makes a complete loop, never losing contact with the pipe. What is its speed at the top?

52. ‖ A 20 kg child is on a swing that hangs from 3.0-m-long chains, as shown in Figure P10.52. What is her speed v_i at the bottom of the arc if she swings out to a 45° angle before reversing direction?

FIGURE P10.52

FIGURE P10.53

53. ‖ Suppose you lift a 20 kg box by a height of 1.0 m.
    a. How much work do you do in lifting the box?
       Instead of lifting the box straight up, suppose you push it up a 1.0-m-high ramp that makes a 30° degree angle with the horizontal, as shown in Figure P10.53. Being clever, you choose a ramp with no friction.

    b. How much force F is required to push the box straight up the slope at a constant speed?
    c. How long is the ramp?
    d. Use your force and distance results to calculate the work you do in pushing the box up the ramp. How does this compare to your answer to part a?

54. ‖ A cannon tilted up at a 30° angle fires a cannon ball at 80 m/s from atop a 10-m-high fortress wall. What is the ball's impact speed on the ground below? Ignore air resistance.

55. ‖ The sledder shown in Figure P10.55 starts from the top of a frictionless hill and slides down into the valley. What initial speed v_i does the sledder need to just make it over the next hill?

FIGURE P10.55

56. ‖‖‖‖ In a physics lab experiment, a spring clamped to the table shoots a 20 g ball horizontally. When the spring is compressed 20 cm, the ball travels horizontally 5.0 m and lands on the floor 1.5 m below the point at which it left the spring. What is the spring constant?

57. ‖‖‖ A 50 g ice cube can slide without friction up and down a 30° slope. The ice cube is pressed against a spring at the bottom of the slope, compressing the spring 10 cm. The spring constant is 25 N/m. When the ice cube is released, what distance will it travel up the slope before reversing direction?

58. ‖‖‖‖ The maximum energy a bone can absorb without breaking is surprisingly small. For a healthy human of mass 60 kg, experimental data show that the leg bones can absorb about 200 J.
    a. From what maximum height could a person jump and land rigidly upright on both feet without breaking his legs? Assume that all the energy is absorbed in the leg bones in a rigid landing.
    b. People jump from much greater heights than this; explain how this is possible.

    Hint: Think about how people land when they jump from greater heights.

59. ‖ In an amusement park water slide, people slide down an essentially frictionless tube. They drop 3.0 m and exit the slide, moving horizontally, 1.2 m above a swimming pool. What horizontal distance do they travel from the exit point before hitting the water? Does the mass of the person make any difference?

60. ‖ The 5.0-m-long rope in Figure P10.60 hangs vertically from a tree right at the edge of a ravine. A woman wants to use the rope to swing to the other side of the ravine. She runs as fast as she can, grabs the rope, and swings out over the ravine.

FIGURE P10.60

    a. As she swings, what energy conversion is taking place?
    b. When she's directly over the far edge of the ravine, how much higher is she than when she started?
    c. Given your answers to parts a and b, how fast must she be running when she grabs the rope in order to swing all the way across the ravine?

61. ▌▌▌ You have been asked to design a "ballistic spring system" to measure the speed of bullets. A bullet of mass m is fired into a block of mass M. The block, with the embedded bullet, then slides across a frictionless table and collides with a horizontal spring whose spring constant is k. The opposite end of the spring is anchored to a wall. The spring's maximum compression d is measured.

 a. Find an expression for the bullet's initial speed v_B in terms of m, M, k, and d.

 Hint: This is a two-part problem. The bullet's collision with the block is an inelastic collision. What quantity is conserved in an inelastic collision? Subsequently the block hits a spring on a frictionless surface. What quantity is conserved in this collision?

 b. What was the speed of a 5.0 g bullet if the block's mass is 2.0 kg and if the spring, with $k = 50$ N/m, was compressed by 10 cm?

 c. What fraction of the bullet's initial kinetic energy is "lost"? Where did it go?

62. ▌▌▌ A new event, shown in Figure P10.62, has been proposed for the Winter Olympics. An athlete will sprint 100 m, starting from rest, then leap onto a 20 kg bobsled. The person and bobsled will then slide down a 50-m-long ice-covered ramp, sloped at 20°, and into a spring with a carefully calibrated spring constant of 2000 N/m. The athlete who compresses the spring the farthest wins the gold medal. Lisa, whose mass is 40 kg, has been training for this event. She can reach a maximum speed of 12 m/s in the 100 m dash.

FIGURE P10.62

 a. How far will Lisa compress the spring?

 b. The Olympic committee has very exact specifications about the shape and angle of the ramp. Is this necessary? If the committee asks your opinion, what factors about the ramp will you tell them are important?

63. ▌▌ Boxes A and B in Figure P10.63 have masses of 12.0 kg and 4.0 kg, respectively. The two boxes are released from rest. Use conservation of energy to find the boxes' speed when box B has fallen a distance of 0.50 m. Assume a frictionless upper surface.

FIGURE P10.63

64. ▌▌▌ What would be the speed of the boxes in Problem 63 if the coefficient of kinetic friction between box A and the surface it slides on were 0.20? Use conservation of energy.

65. ▌▌▌ A 20 g ball is fired horizontally with initial speed v_i toward a 100 g ball that is hanging motionless from a 1.0-m-long string. The balls undergo a head-on, perfectly elastic collision, after which the 100 g ball swings out to a maximum angle $\theta_{max} = 50°$. What was v_i?

66. ▌▌ Two coupled boxcars are rolling along at 2.5 m/s when they collide with and couple to a third, stationary boxcar.

 a. What is the final speed of the three coupled boxcars?

 b. What fraction of the cars' initial kinetic energy is transformed into thermal energy?

67. ▌▌ A fish scale, consisting of a spring with spring constant $k = 200$ N/m, is hung vertically from the ceiling. A 5.0 kg fish is attached to the end of the unstretched spring and then released. The fish moves downward until the spring is fully stretched, then starts to move back up as the spring begins to contract. What is the maximum distance through which the fish falls?

68. ▌ A 70 kg human sprinter can accelerate from rest to 10 m/s in 3.0 s. During the same interval, a 30 kg greyhound can accelerate from rest to 20 m/s. Compute (a) the change in kinetic energy and (b) the average power output for each.

69. ▌▌▌ A 50 g ball of clay traveling at speed v_i hits and sticks to a 1.0 kg block sitting at rest on a frictionless surface.

 a. What is the speed of the block after the collision?

 b. Show that the mechanical energy is *not* conserved in this collision. What percentage of the ball's initial kinetic energy is "lost"? Where did this kinetic energy go?

70. ▌▌ A package of mass m is released from rest at a warehouse loading dock and slides down a 3.0-m-high frictionless chute to a waiting truck. Unfortunately, the truck driver went on a break without having removed the previous package, of mass $2m$, from the bottom of the chute as shown in Figure P10.70.

 a. Suppose the packages stick together. What is their common speed after the collision?

 b. Suppose the collision between the packages is perfectly elastic. To what height does the package of mass m rebound?

FIGURE P10.70

71. ▌▌▌▌ A 50 kg sprinter, starting from rest, runs 50 m in 7.0 s at constant acceleration.

 a. What is the magnitude of the horizontal force acting on the sprinter?

 b. What is the sprinter's average power output during the first 2.0 s of his run?

 c. What is the sprinter's average power output during the final 2.0 s?

72. ▌▌ Bob can throw a 500 g rock with a speed of 30 m/s. He moves his hand forward 1.0 m while doing so.

 a. How much force, assumed to be constant, does Bob apply to the rock?

 b. How much work does Bob do on the rock?

73. ▌▌▌ A 2.0 hp electric motor on a water well pumps water from 10 m below the surface. The density of water is 1.0 kg per L. How many liters of water can the motor pump in 1 h?

74. ▌▌ The human heart has to pump the average adult's 6.0 L of blood through the body every minute. The heart must do work to overcome frictional forces that resist the blood flow. The average blood pressure is 1.3×10^4 N/m^2.

 a. Compute the work done moving the 6.0 L of blood completely through the body, assuming the blood pressure always takes its average value.

 b. What power output must the heart have to do this task once a minute?

 Hint: When the heart contracts, it applies force to the blood. Pressure is just force/area, so we can write work = (pressure)(area)(distance). But (area)(distance) is just the blood volume passing through the heart.

Passage Problems

Tennis Ball Testing

A tennis ball bouncing on a hard surface compresses and then rebounds. The details of the rebound are specified in tennis regulations. Tennis balls, to be acceptable for tournament play, must have a mass of 57.5 g. When dropped from a height of 2.5 m onto a concrete surface, a ball must rebound to a height of 1.4 m. During impact, the ball compresses by approximately 6 mm.

75. | How fast is the ball moving when it hits the concrete surface? (Ignore air resistance.)
   A. 5 m/s B. 7 m/s C. 25 m/s D. 50 m/s
76. | If the ball accelerates uniformly when it hits the floor, what is its approximate acceleration as it comes to rest before rebounding?
   A. 1000 m/s^2 B. 2000 m/s^2 C. 3000 m/s^2 D. 4000 m/s^2
77. | The ball's kinetic energy just after the bounce is less than just before the bounce. In what form does this lost energy end up?
   A. Elastic potential energy
   B. Gravitational potential energy
   C. Thermal energy
   D. Rotational kinetic energy
78. | By approximately what percent does the kinetic energy decrease?
   A. 35% B. 45% C. 55% D. 65%
79. | When a tennis ball bounces from a racket, the ball loses approximately 30% of its kinetic energy to thermal energy. A ball that hits a racket at a speed of 10 m/s will rebound with approximately what speed?
   A. 8.5 m/s B. 7.0 m/s C. 4.5 m/s D. 3.0 m/s

Work and Power in Cycling

When you ride a bicycle at constant speed, almost all of the energy you expend goes into the work you do against the drag force of the air. In this problem, assume that *all* of the energy expended goes into working against drag. As we saw in Section 5.6, the drag force on an object is approximately proportional to the square of its speed with respect to the air. For this problem, assume that $F \propto v^2$ exactly and that the air is motionless with respect to the ground unless noted otherwise. Suppose a cyclist and her bicycle have a combined mass of 60 kg and she is cycling along at a speed of 5 m/s.

80. | If the drag force on the cyclist is 10 N, how much energy does she use in cycling 1 km?
   A. 6 kJ B. 10 kJ C. 50 kJ D. 100 kJ
81. | Under these conditions, how much power does she expend as she cycles?
   A. 10 W B. 50 W C. 100 W D. 200 W
82. | If she doubles her speed to 10 m/s, how much energy does she use in cycling 1 km?
   A. 20 kJ B. 40 kJ C. 200 kJ D. 400 kJ
83. | How much power does she expend when cycling at that speed?
   A. 100 W B. 200 W C. 400 W D. 1000 W
84. | Upon reducing her speed back down to 5 m/s, she hits a headwind of 5 m/s. How much power is she expending now?
   A. 100 W B. 200 W C. 500 W D. 1000 W

STOP TO THINK ANSWERS

Stop to Think 10.1: D. Since the child slides at a constant speed, his kinetic energy doesn't change. But his gravitational potential energy decreases as he descends. It is transformed into thermal energy in the slide and his bottom.

Stop to Think 10.2: C. $W = Fd\cos\theta$. The 10 N force at 90° does no work at all. $\cos 60° = \frac{1}{2}$, so the 8 N force does less work than the 6 N force.

Stop to Think 10.3: B > D > A = C. $K = (1/2)mv^2$. Using the given masses and velocities, we find $K_A = 2.0$ J, $K_B = 4.5$ J, $K_C = 2.0$ J, $K_D = 4.0$ J.

Stop to Think 10.4: $(U_g)_3 > (U_g)_2 = (U_g)_4 > (U_g)_1$. Gravitational potential energy depends only on height, not speed.

Stop to Think 10.5: D. The potential energy of a spring depends on the *square* of the displacement x, so the energy is positive whether the spring is compressed or extended. Furthermore, if the spring is compressed by twice the amount it had been stretched, the energy will increase by a factor of $2^2 = 4$. So the energy will be 4×1 J $= 4$ J.

Stop to Think 10.6: $P_B > P_A = P_C > P_D$. The power here is the rate at which each runner's internal chemical energy is converted into gravitational potential energy. The change in gravitational potential energy is $mg\Delta y$, so the power is $mg\Delta y/\Delta t$. For runner A, the ratio $m\Delta y/\Delta t$ equals (80 kg)(10 m)/(10 s) = 80 kg·m/s. For C, it's the same. For B, it's 100 kg·m/s, while for D the ratio is 64 kg·m/s.

11 Using Energy

The odd hopping gait of a kangaroo has a very practical purpose: It lets the kangaroo cover great distances with minimal energy input. How is this efficiency possible?

LOOKING AHEAD ▶

The goals of Chapter 11 are to learn more about energy transformations and transfers, the laws of thermodynamics, and theoretical and practical limitations on energy use.

Efficiency

In this chapter, we'll look at practical limits on energy transfers and transformations.

> **Looking Back ◀◀**
> 10.1 Basic energy concepts; forms of energy
> 10.6 The law of conservation of energy

Both bulbs put out the same amount of light, but the one on the right uses 1/4 the electric power. Both bulbs perform the same transformation, but one is much more efficient.

Energy in the Body

All the energy that your body uses for all of the tasks you complete during the day comes from food. How efficient is your body at converting this energy? How much energy does your body actually use to run, climb, and move?

Climbing stairs requires a change in potential energy. How much energy does your body use to make this climb?

These fighters wear masks that allow a direct measurement of the energy used by their bodies as they exercise.

Thermal Energy and Temperature

An object's temperature is related to its thermal energy, the energy of motion on an atomic scale.

We'll use the ideal gas model to help us understand the nature of thermal energy and temperature.

> **Looking Back ◀◀**
> 10.7 Thermal energy

Heat and Thermodynamics

Processes in which only thermal energy changes are the domain of **thermodynamics.**

The thermal energy of the kettle is increased by the heat from the burner, which is at a higher temperature.

Heat Engines and Heat Pumps

A **heat engine** can convert thermal energy into other forms of energy. A **heat pump** moves thermal energy from one place to another.

This geothermal plant uses volcanic thermal energy to generate electricity. "Waste" heat warms the lagoon. Why must any energy be "wasted"?

The inside of a refrigerator is cold because heat has been "pumped" out. What's the energy cost to move this heat?

Entropy

Entropy is a measure of disorder at an atomic level that helps us explain some basic observations about the world.

When you stir a cup of coffee, the cream mixes in. This is irreversible; stirring backward won't cause it to unmix. The concept of entropy explains why the future is different from the past and why there are theoretical limits on energy use.

11.1 Transforming Energy

As we saw in Chapter 10, energy can't be created or destroyed; it can only be converted from one form to another. When we say we are *using energy,* we mean that we are transforming it, such as transforming the chemical energy of food into the kinetic energy of your body. Let's revisit the idea of energy transformations, considering some realistic situations that have interesting theoretical and practical limitations.

Energy transformations

 Light energy hitting a solar cell on top of these walkway lights is converted to electric energy and then stored as chemical energy in a battery.

 Light energy is absorbed by photosynthetic pigments in soybean plants, which use this energy to create concentrated chemical energy.

 A wind turbine converts the translational kinetic energy of moving air into electric energy.

 At night, the battery's chemical energy is converted to electric energy that is then converted to light energy in a light-emitting diode.

 The soybeans are harvested and their oil is used to make candles. When the candle burns, the stored chemical energy is transformed into light energy and thermal energy.

 Miles away, this energy can be used by a fan, which transforms the electric energy back into the kinetic energy of moving air.

In each of the processes in the table, energy is transformed from one form into another, ending up in the same form as it began. But some energy appears to have been "lost" along the way. The garden lights certainly shine with a glow that is much less bright than the sun that shined on them. No energy is really lost because energy is conserved; it is merely converted to other forms that are less useful to us.

The table also illustrates another key point: We are broadening our scope to include forms of energy beyond those we considered in Chapter 10, including radiant energy (the light that hits the solar cells and the plants) and electric energy (energy that is transferred from the windmill to the fan).

Recall the work-energy equation from Chapter 10:

$$\Delta E = \Delta K + \Delta U + \Delta E_{th} + \Delta E_{chem} + \cdots = W \qquad (11.1)$$

This equation includes work, an energy transfer. Work can be positive or negative; it's positive when energy is transferred into a system, negative when energy is transferred out of a system. In Chapter 10 we defined work as a mechanical transfer of energy; in this chapter we'll broaden our definition of work to include electric energy into and out of motors and generators.

Electric power companies sometimes use excess electric energy to pump water uphill to a reservoir. They reclaim some of this energy when demand increases by letting the water generate electricity as it flows back down. FIGURE 11.1 shows the energy transformations in this process, assuming 100 J of electric energy at the start. We define the system as the water and the network of pipes, pumps, and generators that makes up the plant. The electric energy to run the pump is a work input, and so it is positive; the electric energy that is extracted at the end is a work output, and so is negative. Pumping the water uphill requires 100 J of work; this increases the potential energy of the water by only 75 J. The "lost" energy is simply the energy transformed to thermal energy due to friction in the pump and other causes, as we can see by applying Equation 11.1 to this situation:

$$\Delta E_{th} = W - \Delta U = 100 \text{ J} - 75 \text{ J} = 25 \text{ J}$$

FIGURE 11.1 Energy transformations for a pumped storage system.

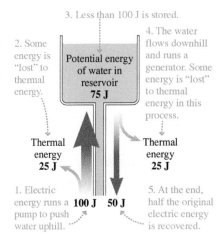

3. Less than 100 J is stored.

2. Some energy is "lost" to thermal energy.

Potential energy of water in reservoir 75 J

4. The water flows downhill and runs a generator. Some energy is "lost" to thermal energy in this process.

Thermal energy 25 J

Thermal energy 25 J

1. Electric energy runs a **100 J** pump to push water uphill.

50 J

5. At the end, half the original electric energy is recovered.

When the water flows back downhill, the potential energy decreases, meaning a negative value of ΔU. Energy is transferred out of the system as work, meaning a negative value for W in the conservation of energy equation as well. The change in thermal energy in this case is

$$E_{th} = W - \Delta U = (-50 \text{ J}) - (-75 \text{ J}) = 25 \text{ J}$$

For the pumped storage scheme of Figure 11.1, as for the cases in the table on the previous page, the energy output is in the same form as the energy input, but some energy appears to have been "lost" as the transfers and transformations took place. The power company put in 100 J of electric energy at the start, but only 50 J of electric energy was recovered at the end. No energy was actually lost, of course, but, as we'll see, when other forms of energy are transformed into thermal energy, this change is *irreversible*: We cannot easily recover this thermal energy and convert it back to electric energy. In other words, **the energy isn't lost, but it is lost to our use.** In order to look at losses in energy transformations in more detail, we will define the notion of efficiency.

Efficiency

To get 50 J of energy out of your pumped storage plant, you would actually need to *pay* to put in 100 J of energy, as we saw in Figure 11.1. Because only 50% of the energy is returned as useful energy, we can say that this plant has an efficiency of 50%. Generally, we can define efficiency as

$$e = \frac{\text{what you get}}{\text{what you had to pay}} \tag{11.2}$$

General definition of efficiency

The larger the energy losses in a system, the lower its efficiency.
Reductions in efficiency can arise from two different sources:

- **Process limitations.** In some cases, energy losses may be due to practical details of an energy transformation process. You could, in principle, design a process that entailed smaller losses.
- **Fundamental limitations.** In other cases, energy losses are due to physical laws that cannot be circumvented. The best process that could theoretically be designed will have less than 100% efficiency. As we will see, these limitations result from the difficulty of transforming thermal energy into other forms of energy.

If you are of average weight, walking up a typical flight of stairs increases your body's potential energy by about 1800 J. But a measurement of the energy used by your body to climb the stairs would show that your body uses about 7200 J to complete this task. The 1800 J increase in potential energy is "what you get"; the 7200 J your body uses is "what you had to pay." We can use Equation 11.2 to compute the efficiency for this action:

$$e = \frac{1800 \text{ J}}{7200 \text{ J}} = 0.25 = 25\%$$

This relatively low efficiency is due to *process limitations*. The efficiency is less than 100% because of the biochemistry of how your food is digested and the biomechanics of how you move. The process could be made more efficient by, for example, changing the angle of the stairs.

The electric energy you use daily must be generated from other sources—in most cases the chemical energy in coal or other fossil fuels. In a coal-fired power plant, the

These cooling towers release thermal energy from a coal-fired power plant.

chemical energy is converted to thermal energy by burning, and the resulting thermal energy is converted to electric energy. A typical power-plant cycle is shown in FIGURE 11.2. "What you get" is the energy output, the 35 J of electric energy. "What you had to pay" is the energy input, the 100 J of chemical energy, giving an efficiency of

$$e = \frac{35\ J}{100\ J} = 0.35 = 35\%$$

Unlike your stair-climbing efficiency, the rather modest power-plant efficiency turns out to be largely due to a *fundamental limitation:* Thermal energy cannot be transformed into other forms of energy with 100% efficiency. A 35% efficiency is close to the theoretical maximum, and no power plant could be designed that would do better than this maximum. In later sections, we will explore the fundamental properties of thermal energy that make this so.

FIGURE 11.2 Energy transformations in a coal-fired power plant.

2. Steam with 100 J of thermal energy enters the turbine.

3. The turbine turns a generator, producing 35 J of electric energy.

1. Burning coal produces 100 J of thermal energy.

4. 65 J of thermal energy is exhausted into the environment.

PROBLEM-SOLVING STRATEGY 11.1 Energy efficiency problems

PREPARE There are two key components to define before we compute efficiency:

1. Choose what energy to count as "what you get." This could be the useful energy output of an engine or process or the work that is done in completing a process. For example, when you climb a flight of stairs, "what you get" is your change in potential energy.
2. "What you had to pay" will generally be the total energy input needed for an engine, task, or process. For example, when you run your air conditioner, "what you had to pay" is the electric energy input.

SOLVE You may need to do additional calculations:

- Compute values for "what you get" and "what you had to pay."
- Be certain that all energy values are in the same units.

After this, compute the efficiency using $e = \frac{\text{what you get}}{\text{what you had to pay}}$.

ASSESS Check your answer to see if it is reasonable, given what you know about typical efficiencies for the process under consideration.

EXAMPLE 11.1 Lightbulb efficiency

A 15 W compact fluorescent bulb and a 75 W incandescent bulb each produce 3.0 W of visible-light energy. What are the efficiencies of these two types of bulbs for converting electric energy into light?

PREPARE The problem statement doesn't give us values for energy; we are given values for power. But 15 W is 15 J/s, so we will consider the value for the power to be the energy in 1 second.

FIGURE 11.3 Incandescent and compact fluorescent bulbs.

For each of the bulbs, "what you get" is the visible-light output—3.0 J of light every second for each bulb. "What you had to pay" is the electric energy to run the bulb. This is how the bulbs are rated. A bulb labeled "15 W" uses 15 J of electric energy each second. A 75 W bulb uses 75 J each second.

SOLVE The efficiencies of the two bulbs are computed using the energy in 1 second:

$$e(\text{compact fluorescent bulb}) = \frac{3.0\ J}{15\ J} = 0.20 = 20\%$$

$$e(\text{incandescent bulb}) = \frac{3.0\ J}{75\ J} = 0.040 = 4\%$$

ASSESS Both bulbs produce the same visible-light output, but the compact fluorescent bulb does so with a significantly lower energy input, so it is more efficient. Compact fluorescent bulbs are more efficient than incandescent bulbs, but their efficiency is still relatively low—only 20%.

STOP TO THINK 11.1   Crane 1 uses 10 kJ of energy to lift a 50 kg box to the roof of a building. Crane 2 uses 20 kJ to lift a 100 kg box the same distance. Which crane is more efficient?

A. Crane 1.
B. Crane 2.
C. Both cranes have the same efficiency.

11.2 Energy in the Body: Energy Inputs

In this section, we will look at energy in the body, which will give us the opportunity to explore a number of different energy transformations and transfers in a practical context. FIGURE 11.4 shows the body considered as the system for energy analysis. The chemical energy in food provides the necessary energy input for your body to function. It is this energy that is used for energy transfers with the environment.

FIGURE 11.4 Energy of the body, considered as the system.

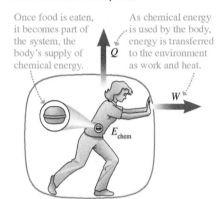

Once food is eaten, it becomes part of the system, the body's supply of chemical energy.

As chemical energy is used by the body, energy is transferred to the environment as work and heat.

Getting Energy from Food

When you walk up a flight of stairs, where does the energy come from to increase your body's potential energy? At some point, the energy came from the food you ate, but what were the intermediate steps? The chemical energy in food is made available to the cells in the body by a two-step process. First, the digestive system breaks down food into simpler molecules such as glucose, a simple sugar, or long chains of glucose molecules called glycogen. These molecules are delivered via the bloodstream to cells in the body, where they are metabolized by combining with oxygen, as in Equation 11.3:

Glucose from the digestion of food combines with oxygen that is breathed in to produce ...   ... carbon dioxide, which is exhaled; water, which can be used by the body; and energy.

$$C_6H_{12}O_6 + 6O_2 \longrightarrow 6CO_2 + 6H_2O + \text{energy} \qquad (11.3)$$

Glucose   Oxygen   Carbon dioxide   Water

This metabolism releases energy, much of which is stored in a molecule called ATP, or adenosine triphosphate. Cells in the body use this ATP to do all the work of life: Muscle cells use it to contract, nerve cells use it to produce electrical signals, and so on.

Oxidation reactions like those in Equation 11.3 "burn" the fuel that you obtain by eating. The oxidation of 1 g of glucose (or any other carbohydrate) will release approximately 17 kJ of energy. Table 11.1 compares the energy content of carbohydrates and other foods to other familiar sources of chemical energy.

It is possible to measure the chemical energy content of food by burning it. Burning food may seem quite different from metabolizing it, but if glucose is burned, the chemical formula for the reaction is Equation 11.3; the two reactions are the same. Burning food transforms all of its chemical energy into thermal energy, which can be easily measured. Thermal energy is often measured in units of **calories (cal)** rather than in joules; 1.00 calorie is equivalent to 4.19 joules.

TABLE 11.1 Energy in fuels

Fuel	Energy in 1 g of fuel (in kJ)
Hydrogen	121
Gasoline	44
Fat (in food)	38
Coal	27
Carbohydrates (in food)	17
Wood chips	15

NOTE ▶ The energy content of food is usually given in Calories (Cal) (with a capital "C"); one Calorie (also called a "food calorie") is equal to 1000 calories or 1 kcal. If a candy bar contains 230 Cal, this means that, if burned, it would produce 230,000 cal (or 964 kJ) of thermal energy. ◀

EXAMPLE 11.2 **Energy in food**

A 12 oz can of soda contains approximately 40 g (or a bit less than 1/4 cup) of sugar, a simple carbohydrate. What is the chemical energy in joules? How many Calories is this?

SOLVE 1 g of sugar contains 17 kJ of energy; 40 g contains

$$40 \text{ g} \times \frac{17 \times 10^3 \text{ J}}{1 \text{ g}} = 68 \times 10^4 \text{ J} = 680 \text{ kJ}$$

Converting to Calories, we get

$$680 \text{ kJ} = 6.8 \times 10^5 \text{ J} = (6.8 \times 10^5 \text{ J})\frac{1.00 \text{ cal}}{4.19 \text{ J}}$$

$$= 1.6 \times 10^5 \text{ cal} = 160 \text{ Cal}$$

ASSESS 160 Calories is a typical value for the energy content of a 12 oz can of soda (check the nutrition label on one to see), so this result seems reasonable.

The first item on the nutrition label on packaged foods is Calories—a measure of the chemical energy in the food. (In Europe, where SI units are standard, you will find the energy content listed in kJ.) The energy content of some common foods is given in Table 11.2.

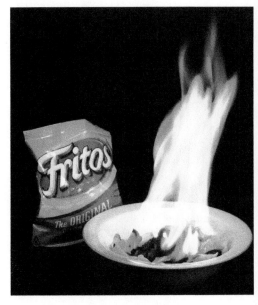

Counting calories BIO Most foods burn quite well, as this photo of corn chips illustrates. You could set food on fire to measure its energy content, but this isn't really necessary. The chemical energies of the basic components of food (carbohydrates, proteins, fats) have been carefully measured—by burning—in a device called a *calorimeter*. Foods are analyzed to determine their composition, and their chemical energy can then be calculated.

TABLE 11.2 Energy content of foods

Food	Energy content in Cal	Energy content in kJ	Food	Energy content in Cal	Energy content in kJ
Carrot (large)	30	125	Slice of pizza	300	1260
Fried egg	100	420	Frozen burrito	350	1470
Apple (large)	125	525	Apple pie slice	400	1680
Beer (can)	150	630	Fast-food meal:		
BBQ chicken wing	180	750	burger, fries,		
Latte (whole milk)	260	1090	drink (large)	1350	5660

11.3 Energy in the Body: Energy Outputs

Your body uses energy in many ways. Even at rest, your body uses energy for tasks such as building and repairing tissue, digesting food, and keeping warm. The numbers of joules used per second (that is, the power in watts) by different tissues in the resting body are listed in Table 11.3.

Your body uses energy at the rate of approximately 100 W when at rest. This energy, from chemical energy in your body's stores, is ultimately converted entirely to thermal energy, which is then transferred as heat to the environment. A hundred people in a lecture hall add thermal energy to the room at a rate of 10,000 W, and the air conditioning must be designed to take account of this.

TABLE 11.3 Energy use at rest

Organ	Resting power (W) of 68 kg individual
Liver	26
Brain	19
Heart	7
Kidneys	11
Skeletal muscle	18
Remainder of body	19
Total	**100**

Energy Use in Activities

Your body stores very little energy as ATP. As your body uses energy, your cells must continuously metabolize carbohydrates, which requires oxygen, as we saw in Equation 11.3. Physiologists can precisely measure the body's energy use by measuring how much oxygen the body is taking up with a respiratory apparatus, as

FIGURE 11.5 The odd masks worn by the fighters measure respiration—the oxygen used by their bodies.

FIGURE 11.5 The odd masks worn by the fighters measure respiration—the oxygen used by their bodies.

TABLE 11.4 Metabolic power use during activities

Activity	Metabolic power (W) of 68 kg individual
Typing	125
Ballroom dancing	250
Walking at 5 km/h	380
Cycling at 15 km/h	480
Swimming at a fast crawl	800
Running at 15 km/h	1150

FIGURE 11.6 Climbing a set of stairs.

seen in FIGURE 11.5. The device determines the body's *total metabolic energy use*—all of the energy used by the body while performing an activity. This total will include all of the body's basic processes such as breathing plus whatever additional energy is needed to perform the activity. This corresponds to measuring "what you had to pay."

The metabolic energy used in an activity depends on an individual's size, level of fitness, and other variables. But we can make reasonable estimates for the power used in various activities for a typical individual. Some values are given in Table 11.4.

Efficiency of the Human Body

Suppose you climb a set of stairs at a constant speed, as in FIGURE 11.6. What is your body's efficiency for this process? In this case, we can do a conservation of energy calculation similar to those in Chapter 10; when you climb stairs, "what you get" is a change in potential energy.

For such problems, we can adapt the work-energy equation to include only those energy changes that we need to consider. If you climb at a constant speed, there's no change in kinetic energy. And given how we define the system, there is no work—there is no external input of energy, as there would be if you took the elevator. As you climb the stairs, your body uses chemical energy to run your muscles for the climb; chemical energy decreases and potential energy increases. As with other cases we've seen, thermal energy increases as well. This is something you know well: If you climb several sets of stairs, you certainly warm up in the process!

For this case of climbing stairs, the work-energy equation reduces to

$$\Delta E_{chem} + \Delta U_g + \Delta E_{th} = 0 \qquad (11.4)$$

Thermal energy and gravitational potential energy are increasing, so ΔE_{th} and ΔU_g are positive; chemical energy is being used, so ΔE_{chem} is a negative number. We can get a better feeling about what is happening by rewriting Equation 11.4 as

$$|\Delta E_{chem}| = \Delta U_g + \Delta E_{th}$$

The *magnitude* of the change in the chemical energy is equal to the sum of the changes in the gravitational potential and thermal energies. Chemical energy from your body is converted into potential energy and thermal energy; in the final position, you are at a greater height and your body is slightly warmer.

Earlier in the chapter, we noted that the efficiency for stair climbing is about 25%. Let's see where that number comes from.

1. *What you get.* What you get is the change in potential energy: You have raised your body to the top of the stairs. If you climb a flight of stairs of vertical height Δy, we can easily compute the increase in potential energy $\Delta U_g = mg\Delta y$. Assuming a mass of 68 kg and a change in height of 2.7 m (about 9 ft, a reasonable value for a flight of stairs), we compute (to two significant figures)

$$\Delta U_g = (68 \text{ kg})(9.8 \text{ m/s}^2)(2.7 \text{ m}) = 1800 \text{ J}$$

2. *What you had to pay.* The cost is the metabolic energy your body used in completing the task. As we've seen, physiologists can measure directly how much energy $|\Delta E_{chem}|$ your body uses to perform a task. A typical value for climbing a flight of stairs is

$$|E_{chem}| = 7200 \text{ J}$$

Given the definition of efficiency in Equation 11.2, we can compute an efficiency for climbing the stairs:

$$e = \frac{\Delta U_g}{|\Delta E_{chem}|} = \frac{1800 \text{ J}}{7200 \text{ J}} = 0.25 = 25\%$$

▶ **High heating costs?** BIO The daily energy use of mammals is much higher than that of reptiles, largely because mammals use energy to maintain a constant body temperature. A 40 kg timber wolf uses approximately 19,000 kJ during the course of a day. A Komodo dragon, a reptilian predator of the same size, uses only 2100 kJ.

For the types of activities we will consider in this chapter, such as running, walking, and cycling, the body's efficiency is typically in the range of 20–30%. **We will generally use a value of 25% for the body's efficiency for our calculations.** Efficiency varies from individual to individual and from activity to activity, but this rough approximation will be sufficient for our purposes in this chapter.

The metabolic power values given in Table 11.4 represent the energy *used by the body* while these activities are being performed. Given that we assume an efficiency of 25%, the body's actual *useful power output* is quite a bit less than this. The table's value for cycling at 15 km/h (a bit less than 10 mph) is 480 W. If we assume that the efficiency for cycling is 25%, the actual power going to forward propulsion will only be 120 W. An elite racing cyclist whizzing along at 35 km/h is using about 300 W for forward propulsion. This is a surprisingly low figure, as noted in FIGURE 11.7.

The energy you use per second while running is proportional to your speed; running twice as fast takes approximately twice as much power. But running twice as fast takes you twice as far in the same time, so the energy you use to run a certain distance doesn't depend on how fast you run! Running a marathon takes approximately the same amount of energy whether you complete it in 2 hours, 3 hours, or 4 hours; it is only the power that varies.

FIGURE 11.7 Amazingly, a racing cyclist moving at 35 km/h uses about the same power as an electric scooter moving at 5 km/h.

NOTE ▶ It is important to remember the distinction between the metabolic energy used to perform a task and the work done in a physics sense; these values can be quite different. Your muscles use power when applying a force, even when there is no motion. Holding a weight above your head involves no external work, but it clearly takes metabolic power to keep the weight in place! ◀

This distinction—between the work done (what you get) and the energy used by the body (what you had to pay)—is important to keep in mind when you do calculations on energy used by the body. We'll consider two different cases:

■ For some tasks, such as climbing stairs, we compute the energy change that is the outcome of the task; that is, we compute what you get. If we assume an efficiency of 25%, the energy used by the body (what you had to pay) is 4 times this amount.

■ For other tasks, such as cycling, we use data from metabolic studies (such as data in Table 11.4). This is the actual power used by the body to complete a task—in other words, what you had to pay. If we assume an efficiency of 25%, the useful power output (what you get) is 1/4 of this value.

CONCEPTUAL EXAMPLE 11.3 **Energy in weightlifting**

A weightlifter lifts a 50 kg bar from the floor to a position over his head and back to the floor again 10 times in succession. At the end of this exercise, what energy transformations have taken place?

REASON We will take the system to be the weightlifter plus the bar. The environment does no work on the system, and we will assume that the time is short enough that no heat is transferred from the system to the environment. The bar has returned to its starting position and is not moving, so there has been no change in potential or kinetic energy. The equation for energy conservation is thus

$$\Delta E_{\text{chem}} + \Delta E_{\text{th}} = 0$$

This equation tells us that ΔE_{chem} must be negative. This makes sense because the muscles *use* chemical energy—depleting the body's store—each time the bar is raised or lowered. Ultimately, all of this energy is transformed into thermal energy.

ASSESS Most exercises in the gym—lifting weights, running on a treadmill—involve only the transformation of chemical energy into thermal energy.

EXAMPLE 11.4 **Energy usage for a cyclist**

A cyclist pedals for 20 min at a speed of 15 km/h. How much metabolic energy is required? How much energy is used for forward propulsion?

PREPARE Table 11.4 gives a value of 480 W for the power used in cycling at a speed of 15 km/h. 480 W is the power used by the body; the power going into forward propulsion is much less than this. The cyclist uses energy at this rate for 20 min, or 1200 s.

SOLVE We know the power and the time, so we can compute the energy needed by the body as follows:

$$\Delta E = P\Delta t = (480 \text{ J/s})(1200 \text{ s}) = 580 \text{ kJ}$$

If we assume an efficiency of 25%, only 25%, or 140 kJ, of this energy is used for forward propulsion. The remainder goes into thermal energy.

ASSESS How much energy is 580 kJ? A look at Table 11.2 shows that this is slightly more than the amount of energy available in a large apple, and only 10% of the energy available in a large fast-food meal. If you eat such a meal and plan to "work it off" by cycling, you should plan on cycling at a pretty good clip for a bit over 3 h.

EXAMPLE 11.5 **How many flights?**

How many flights of stairs could you climb on the energy contained in a 12 oz can of soda? Assume that your mass is 68 kg and that a flight of stairs has a vertical height of 2.7 m (9 ft).

PREPARE In Example 11.2 we found that the soda contains 680 kJ of chemical energy. We'll assume that all of this added energy is available to be transformed into the mechanical energy of climbing stairs, at the typical 25% efficiency. We'll also assume you ascend the stairs at constant speed, so your kinetic energy doesn't change. What you get in this case is increased gravitational potential energy, and what you had to pay is the 680 kJ obtained by "burning" the chemical energy of the soda.

SOLVE At 25% efficiency, the amount of chemical energy transformed into increased potential energy is

$$\Delta U_g = (0.25)(680 \times 10^3 \text{ J}) = 1.7 \times 10^5 \text{ J}$$

Because $\Delta U_g = mg\Delta y$, the height gained is

$$\Delta y = \frac{\Delta U_g}{mg} = \frac{1.7 \times 10^5 \text{ J}}{(68 \text{kg})(9.8 \text{ m/s}^2)} = 255 \text{ m}$$

With each flight of stairs having a height of 2.7 m, the number of flights climbed is

$$\frac{255 \text{ m}}{2.7 \text{ m}} \cong 94 \text{ flights}$$

ASSESS This is almost enough to get to the top of the Empire State Building—all fueled by one can of soda! This is a remarkable result.

Energy Storage

The body gets energy from food; if this energy is not used, it will be stored. A small amount of energy needed for immediate use is stored as ATP. A larger amount of energy is stored as chemical energy of glycogen and glucose in muscle tissue and the liver. A healthy adult might store 400 g of these carbohydrates, which is a little more carbohydrate than is typically consumed in one day.

If the energy input from food continuously exceeds the energy outputs of the body, this energy will be stored in the form of fat under the skin and around the organs. From an energy point of view, gaining weight is simply explained!

EXAMPLE 11.6 **Running out of fuel**

The body stores about 400 g of carbohydrates. Approximately how far could a 68 kg runner travel on this stored energy?

PREPARE Table 11.1 gives a value of 17 kJ per g of carbohydrate. The 400 g of carbohydrates in the body contain an energy of

$$E_{chem} = (400 \text{ g})(17 \times 10^3 \text{ J/g}) = 6.8 \times 10^6 \text{ J}$$

SOLVE Table 11.4 gives the power used in running at 15 km/hr as 1150 W. The time that the stored chemical energy will last at this rate is

$$\Delta t = \frac{\Delta E_{chem}}{P} = \frac{6.8 \times 10^6 \text{ J}}{1150 \text{ W}} = 5.91 \times 10^3 \text{ s} = 1.64 \text{ h}$$

And the distance that can be covered during this time at 15 km/h is

$$\Delta x = v\Delta t = (15 \text{ km/h})(1.64 \text{ h}) = 25 \text{ km}$$

to two significant figures.

ASSESS A marathon is longer than this—just over 42 km. Even with "carbo loading" before the event (eating high-carbohydrate meals), many marathon runners "hit the wall" before the end of the race as they reach the point where they have exhausted their store of carbohydrates. The body has other energy stores (in fats, for instance), but the rate that they can be drawn on is much lower.

Energy and Locomotion

When you walk at a constant speed on level ground, your kinetic energy is constant. Your potential energy is also constant. So why does your body need energy to walk? Where does this energy go?

We use energy to walk because of mechanical inefficiencies in our gait. FIGURE 11.8 shows how the speed of your foot typically changes during each stride. The kinetic energy of your leg and foot increases, only to go to zero at the end of the stride. The kinetic energy is mostly transformed into thermal energy in your muscles and in your shoe. This thermal energy is lost; it can't be used for making more strides.

Footwear can be designed to minimize the loss of kinetic energy to thermal energy. A spring in the sole of the shoe can store potential energy, which can be returned to kinetic energy during the next stride. Such a spring will make the collision with the ground more elastic. We saw in Chapter 10 that the tendons in the ankle do store a certain amount of energy during a stride; very stout tendons in the legs of kangaroos store energy even more efficiently. Their peculiar hopping gait is efficient at high speeds.

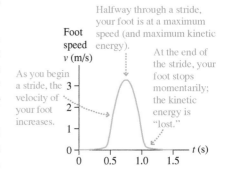

FIGURE 11.8 Human locomotion analysis.

Halfway through a stride, your foot is at a maximum speed (and maximum kinetic energy).

As you begin a stride, the velocity of your foot increases.

At the end of the stride, your foot stops momentarily; the kinetic energy is "lost."

Foot speed v (m/s)

> **STOP TO THINK 11.2** A runner is moving at a constant speed on level ground. Chemical energy in the runner's body is being transformed into other forms of energy; most of the chemical energy is transformed into
>
> A. Kinetic energy.   B. Potential energy.   C. Thermal energy.

11.4 Thermal Energy and Temperature

We have frequently spoken of the energy that is transformed into thermal energy as being "lost." Regardless of whether "the system" is a car, a power plant, or your body, this thermal energy is simply exhausted into the environment. But why isn't thermal energy in your body and other systems converted to other forms of energy and used for practical purposes? To continue our study of how energy is used, we need to understand a bit more about one particular kind of energy—thermal energy.

What do you mean when you say something is "hot"? Do you mean that it has a high temperature? Or do you mean that it has a lot of thermal energy? Are both of these definitions the same? Let's give some thought to the definitions of temperature and thermal energy, and the relationship between them.

Where do you wear the weights? BIO If you wear a backpack with a mass equal to 1% of your body mass, your energy expenditure for walking will increase by 1%. But if you wear ankle weights with a combined mass of 1% of your body mass, the increase in energy expenditure is 6%, because you must repeatedly accelerate this extra mass. If you want to "burn more fat," wear the weights on your ankles, not on your back! If you are a runner who wants to shave seconds off your time in the mile, you might try lighter shoes.

An Atomic View of Thermal Energy and Temperature

Consider the simplest possible atomic system, the **ideal gas** of atoms seen in FIGURE 11.9. In Chapter 10, we defined thermal energy to be the energy associated with the motion of the atoms and molecules that make up an object. Because there are no molecular bonds, the atoms in an ideal gas have only the kinetic energy of their motion. Thus, **the thermal energy of an ideal gas is equal to the total kinetic energy of the moving atoms in the gas.**

If you take a container of an ideal gas and place it over a flame, as in FIGURE 11.10 on the next page, energy will be transferred from the hot flame to the cooler gas. This is a new type of energy transfer, one we'll call **heat**. We will define the nature of heat later in the chapter; for now, we'll focus on the changes in the gas when it is heated.

FIGURE 11.9 Motion of atoms in an ideal gas.

The gas is made up of a large number N of atoms, each moving randomly.

The only interactions among the atoms are elastic collisions.

FIGURE 11.10 Heating an ideal gas.

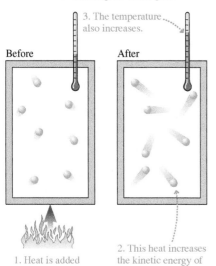

3. The temperature also increases.

Before   After

1. Heat is added to an ideal gas.

2. This heat increases the kinetic energy of the gas atoms.

Thermal expansion of the liquid in the thermometer pushes it higher when immersed in hot water than in ice water.

As Figure 11.10 shows, heating the gas causes the atoms to move faster and thus increases the thermal energy of the gas. Heating the gas also increases its temperature. The observation that both increase suggests that temperature must be related to the kinetic energy of the gas atoms, but how? We can get an important hint from the following fact: The temperature of a system does not depend on the size of the system. If you mix together two glasses of water, each at a temperature of 20°C, you will have a larger volume of water at the same temperature of 20°C. The combined volume has more atoms, and therefore more *total* thermal energy, but each atom is moving about just as it was before, and so the *average* kinetic energy per atom is unchanged. It is this average kinetic energy of the atoms that is related to the temperature. **The temperature of an ideal gas is a measure of the *average* kinetic energy of the atoms that make up the gas.**

We'll formalize and extend these ideas in Chapter 12, but, for now, we'll be able to say quite a bit about temperature and thermal energy by referring to the properties of this simple model.

Temperature Scales

Temperature, in an ideal gas, is related to the average kinetic energy of atoms. We can make a similar statement about other materials, be they solid, liquid, or gas: The higher the temperature, the faster the atoms move. But how do you measure temperature? The common glass-tube thermometer works by allowing a small volume of mercury or alcohol to expand or contract when placed in contact with a "hot" or "cold" object. Other thermometers work in different ways, but all—at a microscopic level—depend on the speed of the object's atoms as they collide with the atoms in the thermometer. That is, all thermometers are sampling the average kinetic energy of the atoms in the object.

A thermometer needs a temperature scale to be a useful measuring device. The scale used in scientific work (and in almost every country in the world) is the *Celsius scale*. As you likely know, the Celsius scale is defined so that the freezing point of water is 0°C and the boiling point is 100°C. The units of the Celsius temperature scale are "degrees Celsius," which we abbreviate as °C. The Fahrenheit scale, still widely used in the United States, is related to the Celsius scale by

$$T(°C) = \frac{5}{9}\left(T(°F) - 32°\right) \qquad T(°F) = \frac{9}{5}T(°C) + 32° \qquad (11.5)$$

Both the Celsius and the Fahrenheit scales have a zero point that is arbitrary—simply an agreed-upon convention—and both allow negative temperatures. If, instead, we use the average kinetic energy of ideal-gas atoms as our basis for the definition of temperature, our temperature scale will have a natural zero—the point at which kinetic energy is zero. Kinetic energy is always positive, so the zero on our temperature scale will be an **absolute zero;** no temperature below this is possible.

This is how zero is defined on the temperature scale called the *Kelvin scale:* **Zero degrees is the point at which the kinetic energy of atoms is zero.** All temperatures on the Kelvin scale are positive, so it is often called an *absolute temperature scale.* The units of the Kelvin temperature scale are "kelvin" (not degrees kelvin!), abbreviated K.

The spacing between divisions on the Kelvin scale is the same as that of the Celsius scale; the only difference is the position of the zero point. Absolute zero—the temperature at which atoms would cease moving—is −273°C. The conversion between Celsius and Kelvin temperatures is therefore quite straightforward:

$$T(K) = T(°C) + 273 \qquad T(°C) = T(K) - 273 \qquad (11.6)$$

The size of a degree on the Kelvin and Celsius scales is the same. This means that a temperature *difference* is the same on both scales:

$$\Delta T(K) = \Delta T(°C)$$

On the Kelvin scale, the freezing point of water at $0°C$ is $T = 0 + 273 = 273$ K. A $30°C$ warm summer day is $T = 303$ K on the Kelvin scale. FIGURE 11.11 gives a side-by-side comparison of these scales.

NOTE ▶ From now on, we will use the symbol T for temperature in kelvin. We will denote other scales by showing the units in parentheses. In the equations in this chapter and the rest of the text, **T must be interpreted as a temperature in kelvin.** ◀

FIGURE 11.11 Celsius and Kelvin temperature scales.

Temperature *differences* are the same on the Celsius and Kelvin scales. The temperature difference between the freezing point and boiling point of water is $100°C$ or 100 K.

EXAMPLE 11.7 Temperature scales

The coldest temperature ever measured on earth was $-129°F$, in Antarctica. What is this in $°C$ and K?

SOLVE We use Equation 11.5 to convert the temperature to the Celsius scale:

$$T(°C) = \frac{5}{9}(-129° - 32°) = -89°C$$

We can then use Equation 11.6 to convert this to kelvin:

$$T = -89 + 273 = 184 \text{ K}$$

ASSESS This is cold, but quite a bit warmer than the coldest temperatures achieved in the laboratory.

Relating Temperature and Thermal Energy

We noted above that the temperature of an ideal gas is a measure of the average kinetic energy of the atoms. It can be shown that temperature on the Kelvin scale is related to the average kinetic energy per atom by

$$T = \frac{2}{3}\frac{K_{avg}}{k_B} \tag{11.7}$$

where k_B is a constant known as **Boltzmann's constant**. Its value is

$$k_B = 1.38 \times 10^{-23} \text{ J/K}$$

We can rearrange Equation 11.7 to give the average kinetic energy in terms of the temperature:

$$K_{avg} = \frac{3}{2}k_B T \tag{11.8}$$

The thermal energy of an ideal gas consisting of N atoms is the sum of the kinetic energies of the individual atoms:

$$E_{th} = NK_{avg} = \frac{3}{2}Nk_B T \tag{11.9}$$

Thermal energy of an ideal gas of N atoms

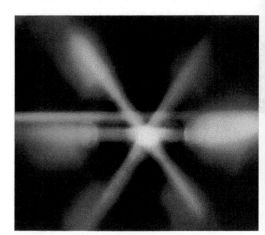

Optical molasses It isn't possible to reach absolute zero, where the atoms would be still, but it is possible to get quite close by slowing the atoms down directly. These crossed laser beams produce what is known as "optical molasses." As we will see in Chapter 28, light is made of photons, which carry energy and momentum. Interactions of the atoms of a diffuse gas with the photons cause the atoms to slow down. In this manner atoms can be slowed to speeds that correspond to a temperature as cold as 5×10^{-10} K!

For an ideal gas, **thermal energy is directly proportional to temperature.** Consequently, a change in the thermal energy of an ideal gas is proportional to a change in temperature:

$$\Delta E_{th} = \frac{3}{2}Nk_B \Delta T \tag{11.10}$$

ActivPhysics: 8.1, 8.2, 8.3

Is it cold in space? The Space Shuttle orbits in the upper thermosphere, about 300 km above the surface of the earth. There is still a trace of atmosphere left at this altitude, and it has quite a high temperature—over 1000°C. Although the average speed of the air molecules here is high, there are so few air molecules present that the thermal energy is extremely low.

This relationship between a change in temperature and a change in thermal energy is for an ideal gas, but solids, liquids, and other gases all follow similar rules, as we will see in the next chapter. For now, we will simply note two important conclusions that apply to any substance:

1. The thermal energy of a substance is proportional to the number of atoms. A gas with more atoms has more thermal energy than a gas at the same temperature with fewer atoms.
2. A change in temperature causes a proportional change in the substance's thermal energy. A larger temperature change causes a larger change in thermal energy.

EXAMPLE 11.8 **Energy needed to warm up a room**

A large bedroom contains about 1×10^{27} molecules of air. (In the next chapter, we'll see how to calculate this.) Estimate the energy required to raise the temperature of the air in the room by 5°C.

PREPARE We'll model the air as an ideal gas. Equation 11.10 relates the change in thermal energy of an ideal gas to a change in temperature. The actual temperature of the gas doesn't matter—only the change. The temperature increase is given as 5°C, implying a change in the absolute temperature by the same amount: $\Delta T = 5$ K.

SOLVE We can use Equation 11.10 to calculate the amount by which the room's thermal energy must be increased:

$$\Delta E_{th} = \frac{3}{2}Nk_B\Delta T = \frac{3}{2}(1 \times 10^{27})(1.38 \times 10^{-23}\ \text{J/K})(5\ \text{K}) = 1 \times 10^5\ \text{J} = 100\ \text{kJ}$$

This is the energy we would have to supply—probably in the form of heat from a furnace—to raise the temperature.

ASSESS 100 kJ isn't that much energy. Table 11.2 shows it to be less than the food energy in a carrot! This seems reasonable because you know that your furnace can quickly warm up the air in a room. Heating up the walls and furnishings is another story.

STOP TO THINK 11.3 Two samples of ideal gas, sample 1 and sample 2, have the same thermal energy. Sample 1 has twice as many atoms as sample 2. What can we say about the temperatures of the two samples?

A. $T_1 > T_2$ B. $T_1 = T_2$ C. $T_1 < T_2$

11.5 Heat and the First Law of Thermodynamics

In Chapter 10, we saw that a system could exchange energy with the environment through two different means: work and heat. Work was treated in some detail in Chapter 10; now it is time to look at the transfer of energy by heat. This will begin our study of a topic called *thermodynamics,* the study of thermal energy and heat and their relationships to other forms of energy and energy transfer.

What Is Heat?

Heat is a more elusive concept than work. We use the word "heat" very loosely in the English language, often as synonymous with "hot." We might say, on a very hot day, "This heat is oppressive." If your apartment is cold, you may say, "Turn up the heat." It's time to develop more precise language to discuss these concepts.

Suppose you put a pan of cold water on the stove. If you light the burner so that there is a hot flame under the pan, as in FIGURE 11.12a, the temperature of the water increases. We've added energy to the system—the pan of water—as heat. You know, from everyday experience, that heat always flows "downhill" in the sense that energy is transferred from a hotter object to a colder object. If there is no temperature difference, no energy is transferred. We'll explore this idea further, but, for now, we can use this familiar observation as a definition of heat: **Heat is energy transferred between two objects at different temperatures.**

FIGURE 11.12 Two different means of raising the temperature of a pan of water.

(a) Energy is transferred from the flame to the water as heat.

Q

The thermal energy and the temperature of the water increase.

(b) The spinning paddle does work on the water.

W

The thermal energy and the temperature of the water increase.

Energetic cooking You can do a modern version of Joule's experiment in the kitchen. Next time you mix food in a blender, notice that it actually warms the food. As the blades rotate, friction increases the thermal energy of the food in the blender. A blender uses about as much power as a microwave, and most of this energy ends up as thermal energy in the food, so the temperature rises as the food is chopped and blended.

FIGURE 11.12b shows the same system, but this time work is being done on the system by means of a rapidly spinning paddle. Careful experiments by the British physicist James Joule in the 1840s found that doing work on the system also increases the temperature. In fact, the temperature increase and the final state of the system are exactly the same regardless of whether energy is added as heat or an equal amount of energy is added by doing work. This implies that heat and work are in some sense equivalent: **Heat and work are simply two different ways of transferring energy to or from a system.**

An Atomic Model of Heat

Let's consider an atomic model to explain why thermal energy is transferred from higher temperatures to lower. FIGURE 11.13 shows a rigid, insulated container that is divided into two sections by a very thin membrane. Each side is filled with a gas of the same kind of atoms. The left side, which we'll call system 1, is at an initial temperature T_{1i}. System 2 on the right is at an initial temperature T_{2i}. We imagine the membrane to be so thin that atoms can collide at the boundary as if the membrane were not there, yet it is a barrier that prevents atoms from moving from one side to the other.

Suppose that system 1 is initially at a higher temperature: $T_{1i} > T_{2i}$. This means that the atoms in system 1 have a higher average kinetic energy. Figure 11.13 shows a fast atom and a slow atom approaching the barrier from opposite sides. They undergo a perfectly elastic collision at the barrier. Although no net energy is lost in a perfectly elastic collision, the faster atom loses energy while the slower one gains energy. In other words, there is an energy *transfer* from the faster atom's side to the slower atom's side.

Because the atoms in system 1 are, on average, more energetic than the atoms in system 2, *on average* the collisions transfer energy from system 1 to system 2. This is not true for every collision. Sometimes a fast atom in system 2 collides with a slow atom in system 1, transferring energy from 2 to 1. But the net energy transfer, from all collisions, is from the warmer system 1 to the cooler system 2. This transfer of energy is heat; **thermal energy is transferred from the faster moving atoms on the warmer side to the slower moving atoms on the cooler side.**

FIGURE 11.13 Collisions at a barrier transfer energy from faster molecules to slower molecules.

Insulation prevents heat from entering or leaving the container.

A thin barrier prevents atoms from moving from system 1 to 2 but still allows them to collide.

System 1
T_{1i}
Fast

System 2
T_{2i}
Slow

Elastic collision

Loses energy | Gains energy

System 1 is initially at a higher temperature, and so has atoms with a higher average speed.

Collisions transfer energy to the atoms in system 2.

FIGURE 11.14 Two systems in thermal contact exchange thermal energy.

Collisions transfer energy from the warmer system to the cooler system. This energy transfer is heat.

Thermal equilibrium occurs when the systems have the same average kinetic energy and thus the same temperature.

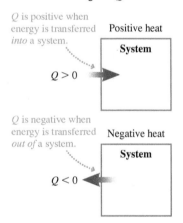

FIGURE 11.15 The sign of Q.

Q is positive when energy is transferred *into* a system.

Positive heat

System

$Q > 0$

Q is negative when energy is transferred *out of* a system.

Negative heat

System

$Q < 0$

Class Video

This transfer will continue until a stable situation is reached. This is a situation we call **thermal equilibrium.** How do the systems "know" when they've reached thermal equilibrium? Energy transfer continues until the atoms on both sides of the barrier have the *same average kinetic energy.* Once the average kinetic energies are the same, individual collisions will still transfer energy from one side to the other. But since both sides have atoms with the same average kinetic energies, the amount of energy transferred from 1 to 2 will equal that transferred from 2 to 1. Once the average kinetic energies are the same, there will be no more net energy transfer.

As we've seen, the average kinetic energy of the atoms in a system is directly proportional to the system's temperature. If two systems exchange energy until their atoms have the same average kinetic energy, we can say that

$$T_{1f} = T_{2f} = T_f$$

That is, heat is transferred until the two systems reach a common final temperature; we call this final state **thermal equilibrium.** We considered a rather artificial system in this case, but the result is quite general: **Two systems placed in thermal contact will transfer thermal energy from hot to cold until their final temperatures are the same.** This process is illustrated in FIGURE 11.14.

Heat is a transfer of energy. The sign that we use for transfers is defined in FIGURE 11.15. In the process of Figure 11.14, Q_1 is negative because system 1 loses energy; Q_2 is positive because system 2 gains energy. No energy escapes from the container, so all of the energy that was lost by system 1 was gained by system 2. We can write that as:

$$Q_2 = -Q_1$$

The heat energy lost by one system is gained by the other.

The First Law of Thermodynamics

We need to broaden our work-energy equation, Equation 11.1, to include energy transfers in the form of heat. The sign conventions for heat, as shown in Figure 11.15, have the same form as those for work—a positive value means a transfer into the system, a negative value means a transfer out of the system. Thus, when we include heat Q in the work-energy equation, it appears on the right side of the equation along with work W:

$$\Delta K + \Delta U + \Delta E_{th} + \Delta E_{chem} + \cdots = W + Q \tag{11.11}$$

This equation is our most general statement to date about energy and the conservation of energy; it includes all of the energy transfers and transformations we have discussed.

In Chapter 10, we focused on systems where the potential and kinetic energies could change, such as a sled moving down a hill. Earlier in this chapter, we looked at the body, where the chemical energy changes. Now let's consider systems in which only the thermal energy changes. That is, we will consider systems that aren't moving, that aren't changing chemically, but whose temperatures can change. Such systems are the province of what is called **thermodynamics.** The question of how to keep your house cool in the summer is a question of thermodynamics. If energy is transferred into your house, the thermal energy increases and the temperature rises. To reduce the temperature, you must transfer energy out of the house. This is the purpose of an air conditioner, as we'll see in a later section.

If we consider cases in which only thermal energy changes, Equation 11.11 can be simplified. This simpler version is a statement of conservation of energy for systems in which only the thermal energy changes; we call it the **first law of thermodynamics:**

First law of thermodynamics For systems in which only the thermal energy changes, the change in thermal energy is equal to the energy transferred into or out of the system as work W, heat Q, or both:

$$\Delta E_{th} = W + Q \qquad (11.12)$$

FIGURE 11.16 Energy transfers in a thermodynamic system.

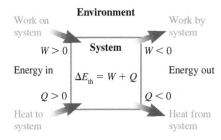

Only work and heat, two ways of transferring energy between a system and the environment, cause the system's energy to change. In thermodynamic systems, the only energy change will be a change in thermal energy. Whether this energy increases or decreases depends on the signs of W and Q, as we've seen. The possible energy transfers between a system and the environment are illustrated in FIGURE 11.16.

CONCEPTUAL EXAMPLE 11.9 **Compressing a gas**

Suppose a gas is in an insulated container, so that no heat energy can escape. If a piston is used to compress the gas, what happens to the temperature of the gas?

REASON The piston applies a force to the gas, and there is a displacement. This means that work is done on the gas by the piston ($W > 0$). No thermal energy can be exchanged with the environment, meaning $Q = 0$. Since energy is transferred into the system,

the thermal energy of the gas must increase. This means that the temperature must increase as well.

ASSESS This result makes sense in terms of everyday observations you may have made. When you use a bike pump to inflate a tire, the pump and the tire get warm. This temperature increase is largely due to the warming of the air by the compression.

EXAMPLE 11.10 **Work and heat in an ideal gas**

Suppose an uninsulated container holds 5.0×10^{22} molecules of an ideal gas. 50 J of work are done on the gas by a piston that compresses it. The temperature of the gas increases by 30°C during this process. How much heat is transferred to or from the environment?

PREPARE This is an energy conservation problem. We can first use the temperature increase to determine the change in thermal energy of the gas; then use this to determine how much heat energy goes in or out.

SOLVE For an ideal gas, the change in thermal energy is given by Equation 11.10:

$$\Delta E_{th} = \frac{3}{2} N k_B \Delta T$$
$$= \left(\frac{3}{2}\right)(5.0 \times 10^{22})(1.38 \times 10^{-23} \text{ J/K})(30 \text{ K}) = 31 \text{ J}$$

The first law of thermodynamics, Equation 11.12, tells us that the change in thermal energy ΔE_{th} of the gas is the sum of W and Q, the total energy added to the system. W is known, and we have just calculated ΔE_{th}. Combining, we get

$$Q = \Delta E_{th} - W = 31 \text{ J} - 50 \text{ J} = -19 \text{ J}$$

ASSESS Q is negative, meaning that energy is transferred outward from the hot gas to the cooler environment in this process.

Energy-Transfer Diagrams

Suppose you drop a hot rock into the ocean. Heat is transferred from the rock to the ocean until the rock and ocean are the same temperature. Although the ocean warms up ever so slightly, ΔT_{ocean} is so small as to be completely insignificant.

An **energy reservoir** is an object or a part of the environment so large that, like the ocean, its temperature does not noticeably change when heat is transferred between the system and the reservoir. A reservoir at a higher temperature than the system is called a *hot reservoir*. A vigorously burning flame is a hot reservoir for small objects placed in the flame. A reservoir at a lower temperature than the system is called a *cold reservoir*. The ocean is a cold reservoir for the hot rock. We will use T_H and T_C to designate the temperatures of the hot and cold reservoirs.

Heat energy is transferred between a system and a reservoir if they have different temperatures. We will define

    Q_H = amount of heat transferred to or from a hot reservoir

    Q_C = amount of heat transferred to or from a cold reservoir

By definition, Q_H and Q_C are *positive* quantities.

FIGURE 11.17a shows a heavy copper bar placed between a hot reservoir (at temperature T_H) and a cold reservoir (at temperature T_C). Heat Q_H is transferred from the hot

FIGURE 11.17 Energy-transfer diagrams.

(a)

(b)

FIGURE 11.18 An impossible energy transfer.

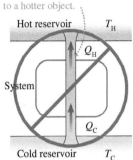

Heat is never spontaneously transferred from a colder object to a hotter object.

reservoir into the copper, and heat Q_C is transferred from the copper to the cold reservoir. FIGURE 11.17b is an **energy-transfer diagram** for this process. The hot reservoir is generally drawn at the top, the cold reservoir at the bottom, and the system—the copper bar in this case—between them. The reservoirs and the system are connected by "pipes" that show the energy transfers. Figure 11.17b shows heat Q_H being transferred into the system and Q_C being transferred out.

FIGURE 11.18 illustrates an important fact about heat transfers that we have discussed: Spontaneous transfers go in one direction only, from hot to cold. This is an important result that has significant practical implications.

CONCEPTUAL EXAMPLE 11.11 **Energy transfers and the body**

Why—in physics terms—is it more taxing on the body to exercise in very hot weather?

REASON Your body continuously converts chemical energy to thermal energy, as we have seen. In order to maintain a constant body temperature, your body must continuously transfer heat to the environment. This is a simple matter in cool weather when heat is spontaneously transferred to the environment, but when the air temperature is higher than your body temperature, your body cannot cool itself this way and must use other mechanisms to transfer this energy, such as perspiring. These mechanisms require additional energy expenditure.

ASSESS Strenuous exercise in hot weather can easily lead to a rise in body temperature if the body cannot exhaust heat quickly enough.

Falling water turns a waterwheel.

STOP TO THINK 11.4 You have driven your car for a while and now turn off the engine. Your car's radiator is at a higher temperature than the air around it. Considering the radiator as the system, we can say that

A. $Q > 0$ B. $Q = 0$ C. $Q < 0$

11.6 Heat Engines

In the early stages of the industrial revolution, most of the energy needed to run mills and factories came from water power. Water in a high reservoir will naturally flow downhill. A waterwheel can be used to harness this natural flow of water to produce some useful energy because some of the potential energy lost by the water as it flows downhill can be converted into other forms.

It is possible to do something similar with heat. Thermal energy is naturally transferred from a hot reservoir to a cold reservoir; it is possible to take some of this energy as it is transferred and convert it to other forms. This is the job of a device known as a **heat engine.**

A simple example of a heat engine is shown in FIGURE 11.19a. Here a *Peltier device*—a device that produces a voltage if there is a temperature difference between its two sides—is sandwiched between two aluminum vanes that sit in cups of water. The cup of water on the left is hot; the cup on the right is cold. The temperature difference produces a voltage that drives the fan.

FIGURE 11.19 A simple heat engine.

(a)

Peltier device

Hot water   Cold water

(b)

W_{out} Energy is extracted to run the fan.

System

Q_H Q_C

Heat energy is transferred from the hot water.

Excess heat energy is transferred into the cold water.

FIGURE 11.19b is a diagram that illustrates the operation of this device in thermodynamic terms. The Peltier device is the system. Heat energy is transferred through the device from the hot water to the cold water. As the transfer occurs, some of this energy is transformed into electric energy to run the fan.

The energy-transfer diagram of FIGURE 11.20 on the next page illustrates the basic physics of a heat engine. It takes in energy as heat from the hot reservoir, turns some of it into useful work, and exhausts the balance as waste heat in the cold reservoir. Any heat engine has exactly the same schematic.

Efficiency of a Heat Engine

We assume, for a heat engine, that the engine's thermal energy doesn't change. This means that there is no net energy transfer into or out of the heat engine. Because energy is conserved, we can say that the useful work extracted is equal to the difference between the heat energy transferred from the hot reservoir and the heat exhausted into the cold reservoir:

$$W_{out} = Q_H - Q_C$$

The energy input to the engine is Q_H and the energy output is W_{out}.

NOTE ▶ We earlier defined Q_H and Q_C to be positive quantities. We also define the energy output of a heat engine W_{out} to be a positive quantity. For heat engines, the directions of the transfers will always be clear, and we will take all of these basic quantities to be positive. ◀

We can use the definition of efficiency, from earlier in the chapter, to compute the heat engine's efficiency:

$$e = \frac{\text{what you get}}{\text{what you had to pay}} = \frac{W_{out}}{Q_H} = \frac{Q_H - Q_C}{Q_H} \qquad (11.13)$$

Q_H is what you had to pay because this is the energy of the fuel burned—and, quite literally, paid for—to provide the high temperature of the hot reservoir. The heat energy that is not converted to work ends up in the cold reservoir as waste heat.

Why should we waste energy this way? Why don't we make a heat engine like the one shown in FIGURE 11.21 that converts 100% of the heat into useful work? The surprising answer is that we can't. **No heat engine can operate without exhausting some fraction of the heat into a cold reservoir**. This isn't a limitation on our engineering abilities. As we'll see, it's a fundamental law of nature.

The maximum possible efficiency of a heat engine is fixed by the *second law of thermodynamics*, which we will explore in detail in Section 11.8. We will not do a detailed derivation, but simply note that the second law gives the maximum efficiency of a heat engine as

$$e_{max} = 1 - \frac{T_C}{T_H} \qquad (11.14)$$

Theoretical maximum efficiency of a heat engine

The maximum efficiency of any heat engine is therefore fixed by the ratio of the temperatures of the hot and cold reservoirs. It is possible to increase the efficiency of a heat engine by increasing the temperature of the hot reservoir or decreasing the temperature of the cold reservoir. The efficiency of Equation 11.14 is also called the *Carnot efficiency*, after a particular heat engine that achieves this maximum possible efficiency. The actual efficiency of real heat engines is usually much less than the theoretical maximum.

NOTE ▶ The temperatures in Equation 11.14 *must* be in K, not °C. ◀

Because $e_{max} < 1$, the work done is always less than the heat input ($W_{out} < Q_H$). Consequently, there *must* be heat Q_C exhausted to the cold reservoir. That is why the heat engine of Figure 11.21 is impossible. Think of a heat engine as analogous to a water wheel: The engine "siphons off" some of the energy that is spontaneously flowing from hot to cold, but it can't completely shut off the flow.

The fact that heat engine efficiency is limited—and that heat must be exhausted into a cold reservoir—is of tremendous practical importance. Most of the energy that you use daily comes from the conversion of chemical energy into thermal energy and the subsequent conversion of that energy into other forms. Let's look at some common examples of heat engines.

FIGURE 11.20 The operation of a heat engine.

1. Heat energy Q_H is transferred from the hot reservoir to the system.

2. Part of the energy is used to do useful work W_{out}.

3. The remaining energy $Q_C = Q_H - W_{out}$ is exhausted to the cold reservoir as waste heat.

FIGURE 11.21 A perfect (and impossible!) heat engine.

This is impossible! No heat engine can convert 100% of heat into useful work.

Heat engines

Most of the electricity that you use was generated by heat engines. Coal or other fossil fuels are burned to produce high-temperature, high-pressure steam. The steam does work by spinning a turbine attached to a generator, which produces electricity. Some of the energy of the steam is extracted in this way, but more than half simply flows "downhill" and is deposited in a cold reservoir, often a lake or a river.

Your car gets the energy it needs to run from the chemical energy in gasoline. The gasoline is burned; the resulting hot gases are the hot reservoir. Some of the thermal energy is converted into the kinetic energy of the moving vehicle, but more than 90% is lost as heat to the surrounding air via the radiator and the exhaust, as shown in this thermogram.

There are many small, simple heat engines that are part of things you use daily. This fan, which can be put on top of a wood stove, uses the thermal energy of the stove to provide power to drive air around the room. Where are the hot and cold reservoirs in this device?

EXAMPLE 11.12 **The efficiency of a nuclear power plant**

Energy from nuclear reactions in the core of a nuclear reactor produces high-pressure steam at a temperature of 290°C. After the steam is used to spin a turbine, it is condensed (by using cooling water from a nearby river) back to water at 20°C. The excess heat is deposited in the river. The water is then reheated, and the cycle beings again. What is the maximum possible efficiency that this plant could achieve?

PREPARE A nuclear power plant is a heat engine, with energy transfers as illustrated in Figure 11.20. Q_H is the heat energy transferred to the steam in the reactor core. T_H is the temperature of the steam, 290°C. The steam is cooled and condensed, and the heat Q_C is exhausted to the river. The river is the cold reservoir, so T_C is 20°C.

In kelvin, these temperatures are

$$T_H = 290°C = 563 \text{ K} \qquad T_C = 20°C = 293 \text{ K}$$

SOLVE We use Equation 11.14 to compute the maximum possible efficiency:

$$e_{max} = 1 - \frac{T_C}{T_H} = 1 - \frac{293 \text{ K}}{563 \text{ K}} = 0.479 \approx 48\%$$

ASSESS This is the maximum possible efficiency. There are practical limitations as well that limit real power plants, whether nuclear or coal- or gas-fired, to an efficiency $e \approx 0.35$. This means that 65% of the energy from the fuel is exhausted as waste heat into a river or lake, where it may cause problematic warming in the local environment.

Heat engines take energy from a hot reservoir, transform some into useful forms of energy, such as mechanical or electric energy, and deposit the rest as thermal energy in a cold reservoir. The laws of physics say that some energy must be deposited in the cold reservoir, but this energy need not be "wasted." Those of you who live in cold climates use the heat energy from your car's engine to warm the car's interior—heat that would otherwise simply be deposited in the environment. There is no cost to warm your car's interior on a chilly day; you are simply putting this "waste" heat to good use. Many college campuses have combined heat and power systems in which the exhausted heat from an electric power plant is used to warm campus buildings. This scheme is quite common in cities in Europe and, increasingly, the United States.

STOP TO THINK 11.5 Which of the following changes (there may be more than one) would increase the maximum theoretical efficiency of a heat engine?

A. Increase T_H B. Increase T_C C. Decrease T_H D. Decrease T_C

11.7 Heat Pumps

The inside of your refrigerator is colder than the air in your kitchen, so heat energy will be transferred from the room to the inside of the refrigerator, warming it. This happens every time you open the door and as heat "leaks" through the walls. But you want the inside of the refrigerator to stay cool. To keep it cool, you need some way to move this heat back out to the warmer room. Transferring heat energy from a cold reservoir to a hot reservoir—the opposite of the natural direction—is the job of a **heat pump.**

The Peltier device that we saw in the last section can also be used as a heat pump. If an electric current is put through the device, a temperature difference develops between the two sides. As time goes by, the cold side gets colder and the hot side gets hotter. A practical application of such a heat pump is the water cooler/heater shown in FIGURE 11.22. The energy that is removed from the cold water ends up as increased thermal energy in the hot water. A single process cools the cold water and heats the hot water.

The heat pump in a refrigerator transfers heat from the cold air *inside* the refrigerator to the warmer air in the room. Coils inside the refrigerator that are colder than the inside air take in thermal energy. This energy is transferred to warm coils *outside* the refrigerator that transfer heat to the room. In the antique refrigerator shown on the next page, the cold coils are in the metal bracket at the top of the cabinet, the warm coils are outside the cabinet in the cylindrical unit on top. When the refrigerator is running, these top coils are quite warm. If you look closely at your refrigerator, you will find warm coils or a warm air exhaust that transfers heat to the room, heat that was removed from the inside.

An air conditioner works similarly, transferring heat from the cool air of a house (or a car) to the warmer air outside. You have probably seen room air conditioners that are single units meant to fit in a window. The side of the air conditioner that faces the room is the cool side; the other side of the air conditioner is warm. Heat is pumped from the cool side to the warm side, cooling the room.

You can also use a heat pump to *warm* your house in the winter by moving thermal energy from outside your house to inside. A unit outside the house takes in heat energy that is pumped to a unit inside the house, warming the inside air.

In all of these cases, we are moving energy against the natural direction it would flow. This requires an energy input—work must be done—as shown in the energy–transfer diagram of a heat pump in FIGURE 11.23. Energy must be conserved, so the heat deposited in the hot side must equal the sum of the heat removed from the cold side and the work input:

$$Q_H = Q_C + W_{in}$$

For heat pumps, rather than compute efficiency, we compute an analogous quantity called the **coefficient of performance (COP).** There are two different ways that one can use a heat pump, as noted above. A refrigerator uses a heat pump for cooling, removing heat from a cold reservoir to keep it cold. As Figure 11.23 shows, we must do work to make this happen.

If we use a heat pump for cooling, we define the coefficient of performance as

$$COP = \frac{\text{what you get}}{\text{what you had to pay}} = \frac{\text{energy removed from the cold reservoir}}{\text{work required to perform the transfer}} = \frac{Q_C}{W_{in}}$$

The second law of thermodynamics limits the efficiency of a heat pump just as it limits the efficiency of a heat engine. The maximum possible coefficient of performance is related to the temperatures of the hot and cold reservoirs:

$$COP_{max} = \frac{T_C}{T_H - T_C} \qquad (11.15)$$

Theoretical maximum coefficient of performance
of a heat pump used for cooling

FIGURE 11.22 A heat pump provides hot and cold water.

Electric energy does work on the Peltier unit . . .

W_{in}

Q_H Q_C

Hot water   Cold water

. . . causing heat to be transferred from the cold water to the hot water.

FIGURE 11.23 The operation of a heat pump.

The amount of heat exhausted to the hot reservoir is larger than the amount of heat extracted from the cold reservoir.

Hot reservoir T_H

Q_H

W_{in} Heat pump

Q_C

Cold reservoir T_C

External work is used to remove heat from a cold reservoir and exhaust heat to a hot reservoir.

Hot or cold lunch? Small coolers like this use Peltier devices that run off the 12 V electrical system of your car. They can transfer heat from the interior of the cooler to the outside, keeping food or drinks cool. But Peltier devices, like some other heat pumps, are reversible; switching the direction of current reverses the direction of heat transfer. A flick of a switch will cause heat to be transferred into the interior, keeping your lunch warm!

A refrigerator from 1934.

We can also use a heat pump for heating, moving heat from a cold reservoir to a hot reservoir to keep it warm. In that case, we define the coefficient of performance as

$$COP = \frac{\text{what you get}}{\text{what you had to pay}} = \frac{\text{energy added to the hot reservoir}}{\text{work required to perform the transfer}} = \frac{Q_H}{W_{in}}$$

In this case, the maximum possible coefficient of performance is

$$COP_{max} = \frac{T_H}{T_H - T_C} \tag{11.16}$$

Theoretical maximum coefficient of performance
of a heat pump used for heating

In both cases, **a larger coefficient of performance means a more efficient heat pump.** Unlike the efficiency of a heat engine, which must be less than 1, the COP of a heat pump can be—and usually is—greater than 1. The following example shows that the COP can be quite high for typical temperatures.

EXAMPLE 11.13 **Coefficient of performance of a refrigerator**

The inside of your refrigerator is approximately 0°C. Heat from the inside of your refrigerator is deposited into the air in your kitchen, which has a temperature of approximately 20°C. At these operating temperatures, what is the maximum possible coefficient of performance of your refrigerator?

PREPARE The temperatures of the hot side and the cold side must be expressed in kelvin:

$$T_H = 20°C = 293 \text{ K} \qquad T_C = 0°C = 273 \text{ K}$$

SOLVE We use Equation 11.15 to compute the maximum coefficient of performance:

$$COP_{max} = \frac{T_C}{T_H - T_C} = \frac{273 \text{ K}}{293 \text{ K} - 273 \text{ K}} = 13.6$$

ASSESS A coefficient of performance of 13.6 means that we pump 13.6 J of heat for an energy cost of 1 J. Due to practical limitations, the coefficient of performance of an actual refrigerator is typically ≈5. Other factors affect the overall efficiency of the appliance, including how well insulated it is.

CONCEPTUAL EXAMPLE 11.14 **Keeping your cool?**

It's a hot day, and your apartment is rather warm. Your roommate suggests cooling off the apartment by keeping the door of the refrigerator open. Will this help the situation?

REASON It's time for a physics lesson for your roommate! What you want to do is remove heat from the room. Your refrigerator, a heat pump, is designed to transfer heat from its inside to the outside. If you leave the door open, all parts of the refrigerator are exposed to the room air. It simply transfers heat from one part of the room to another—it won't make the room cooler.

ASSESS An air conditioner is a heat pump too. It must have a hot side that is outside the house, so that there is a net transfer of heat from inside to outside.

STOP TO THINK 11.6 Which of the following changes would allow your refrigerator to use less energy to run? (There may be more than one correct answer.)

A. Increasing the temperature inside the refrigerator
B. Increasing the temperature of the kitchen
C. Decreasing the temperature inside the refrigerator
D. Decreasing the temperature of the kitchen

11.8 Entropy and the Second Law of Thermodynamics

Throughout the chapter, we have noticed certain trends and certain limitations in energy transformations and transfers. Heat is transferred spontaneously from hot to cold, not from cold to hot. Once energy is transformed to thermal energy, it is (in some sense) "lost." The spontaneous transfer of heat from hot to cold is an example of an **irreversible** process, a process that can happen in only one direction. Why are some processes irreversible? The spontaneous transfer of heat from cold to hot would not violate any law of physics that we have seen to this point, but it is never observed. There must be another law of physics that prevents it. In this section we will explore the basis for this law, which we will call the **second law of thermodynamics.**

FIGURE 11.24 Molecular collisions are reversible.

(a) Forward movie

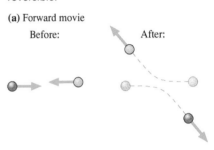

(b) The backward movie is equally plausible.

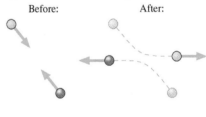

Reversible and Irreversible Processes

Stirring the cream in your coffee mixes the cream and coffee together. No amount of stirring ever unmixes them. If you watched a movie of someone stirring a cup of coffee and unmixing the cream, you'd be quite certain that the movie was running backward. In fact, a reasonable definition of an irreversible process is one for which a backward-running movie shows a physically impossible process.

At a microscopic level, collisions between molecules are completely reversible. In FIGURE 11.24 we see two possible movies of a collision between two gas molecules, one forward and the other backward. You can't tell by looking which is really going forward and which is being played backward. Nothing in either collision looks wrong, and no measurements you might make on either would reveal any violations of Newton's laws. Interactions at the molecular level are reversible processes.

At a macroscopic level, it's a different story. FIGURE 11.25 shows two possible movies of the collision of a car with a barrier. One movie is being run forward, the other backward. The backward movie of Figure 11.25b is obviously wrong. But what has been violated in the backward movie? To have the car return to its original shape and spring away from the wall would not violate any laws of physics we have so far discussed.

If microscopic motions are all reversible, how can macroscopic phenomena such as the car crash end up being irreversible? If reversible collisions can cause heat to be transferred from hot to cold, why do they never cause heat to be transferred from cold to hot? There must be something at work that can distinguish the past from the future.

FIGURE 11.25 Macroscopic collisions are not reversible.

(a) Forward movie

Before: After:

(b) The backward movie is physically impossible.

Before: After:

Which Way to Equilibrium?

How do two systems initially at different temperatures "know" which way to go to reach equilibrium? Perhaps an analogy will help.

FIGURE 11.26 on the next page shows two boxes, numbered 1 and 2, containing identical balls. Box 1 starts with more balls than box 2, so $N_{1i} > N_{2i}$. Once every second, a ball in one of the two boxes is chosen at random and moved to the other box. This is a reversible process because a ball can move from box 2 to box 1 just as easily as from box 1 to box 2. What do you expect to see if you return several hours later?

(MP) **PhET: Reversible Reactions**

FIGURE 11.26 Moving balls between boxes.

Balls are chosen at random
and moved from one box
to the other.

Box 1
N_1 balls

Box 2
N_2 balls

Because balls are chosen at random, and because $N_{1i} > N_{2i}$, it's initially more likely that a ball will move from box 1 to box 2 than from box 2 to box 1. Sometimes a ball will move "backward" from box 2 to box 1, but overall there's a net movement of balls from box 1 to box 2. The system will evolve until $N_1 \approx N_2$. We have reached a stable situation—equilibrium!—with an equal number of balls moving in both directions.

But couldn't it go the other way, with N_1 getting even larger while N_2 decreases? In principle, any arrangement of the balls is possible. But certain arrangements are more likely. Each ball is equally likely to be in either box. With four balls, the odds are 1 in 2^4, or 1 in 16, that, at a randomly chosen instant of time, you would find all the balls in box 1. Were you to do so, you wouldn't find that to be terribly surprising. But with 100 balls, the probability has dropped to about 1 in 1,000,000,000,000,000,000,000,000,000,000, or 1 in 10^{30}, that all of the balls will be in box 1.

Although each transfer is reversible, **the statistics of large numbers make it overwhelmingly likely that the system will evolve toward a state in which $N_1 \approx N_2$.** For the 10^{23} or so particles in a realistic system of atoms or molecules, we will never see a state that deviates appreciably from the equilibrium case.

So imagine: Is it possible that all of the air molecules in the room in which you are sitting could, in the next second, end up moving to one side of the room, leaving the other side empty? In principle it's possible, but this situation is so extraordinarily unlikely that we can, in good conscience, call it impossible.

A system reaches thermal equilibrium not by any plan or by outside intervention, but simply because **equilibrium is the most probable state in which to be.** The consequence of having a vast number of random events is that the system evolves in one direction, toward equilibrium, and not the other. Reversible microscopic events lead to irreversible macroscopic behavior because some macroscopic states are vastly more probable than others.

Order, Disorder, and Entropy

FIGURE 11.27 Ordered and disordered arrangements of atoms in a gas.

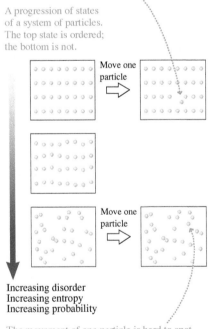

The arrangement is unlikely; all of the particles must be precisely arranged. The movement of one particle is easy to notice.

A progression of states of a system of particles. The top state is ordered; the bottom is not.

Move one particle

Move one particle

Increasing disorder
Increasing entropy
Increasing probability

The movement of one particle is hard to spot. Many arrangements have a similar appearance, so an arrangement like this is quite likely.

FIGURE 11.27 shows microscopic views of three containers of gas. The top diagram shows a group of atoms arranged in a regular pattern. This is a highly ordered and nonrandom system, with each atom's position precisely specified. Contrast this with the system on the bottom, in which there is no order at all. It is extremely improbable that the atoms in a container would *spontaneously* arrange themselves into the ordered pattern of the top picture; even a small change in the pattern is quite noticeable. By contrast, there are a vast number of arrangements like the one on the bottom that randomly fill the container. A small change in the pattern is hard to detect.

Scientists and engineers use the term **entropy** to quantify the probability that a certain state of a system will occur. The ordered arrangement of the top system, which has a very small probability of spontaneous occurrence, has a very low entropy. The entropy of the randomly filled container is high; it has a large probability of occurrence. The entropy in Figure 11.27 increases as you move from the ordered system on the top to the disordered system on the bottom.

Suppose you ordered the atoms in Figure 11.27 as they are in the top diagram, and then you let them go. After some time, you would expect their arrangement to appear as in the bottom diagram. In fact, the series of diagrams from top to bottom may be thought of as a series of movie frames showing the evolution of the positions of the atoms after they are released, moving toward a state of higher entropy. You would correctly expect this process to be irreversible—the particles will never spontaneously recreate their initial ordered state.

Two thermally interacting systems with different temperatures have a low entropy. These systems are ordered: The faster atoms are on one side of the barrier, the slower atoms on the other. The most random possible distribution of energy, and hence the least ordered system, corresponds to the situation where the two systems are in thermal equilibrium with equal temperatures. **Entropy increases as two systems with initially different temperatures move toward thermal equilibrium.**

▶ **Typing Shakespeare** Make a new document in your word processor. Close your eyes and type randomly for a while. Now open your eyes. Did you type any recognizable words? There is a chance that you did, but you probably didn't. One thousand chimps in a room, typing away randomly, *could* type the works of Shakespeare. Molecular collisions *could* transfer energy from a cold object to a hot object. But, the probability is so tiny that the outcome is never seen in the real world.

TRY IT YOURSELF

The fact that macroscopic systems evolve irreversibly toward equilibrium is a new law of physics, **the second law of thermodynamics:**

Second law of thermodynamics The entropy of an isolated system never decreases. The entropy either increases, until the system reaches equilibrium, or, if the system began in equilibrium, stays the same.

NOTE ▶ The qualifier "isolated" is crucial. We can order the system by reaching in from the outside, perhaps using little tweezers to place atoms in a lattice. Similarly, we can transfer heat from cold to hot by using a refrigerator. The second law is about what a system can or cannot do *spontaneously,* on its own, without outside intervention. ◀

The second law of thermodynamics tells us that an isolated system evolves such that:

- Order turns into disorder and randomness.
- Information is lost rather than gained.
- The system "runs down" as other forms of energy are transformed into thermal energy.

An isolated system never spontaneously generates order out of randomness. It is not that the system "knows" about order or randomness, but rather that there are vastly more states corresponding to randomness than there are corresponding to order. As collisions occur at the microscopic level, the laws of probability dictate that the system will, on average, move inexorably toward the most probable and thus most random macroscopic state.

Entropy and Thermal Energy

Suppose we have a very cold, moving baseball, with essentially no thermal energy, and a stationary helium balloon at room temperature, as shown in FIGURE 11.28. The atoms in the baseball and the atoms in the balloon are all moving, but there is a big difference in their motions. The atoms in the baseball are all moving in the same direction at the same speed, but the atoms in the balloon are moving in random directions. The ordered, organized motion of the baseball has low entropy, while the disorganized, random motion of the gas atoms—what we have called thermal energy—has high entropy. You can see that a conversion of macroscopic kinetic energy into thermal energy means an increase in entropy. We saw, in Section 11.5, that the conversion of other forms of energy into thermal energy was irreversible. Now, we can explain why: **When another form of energy is converted into thermal energy, there is an increase in entropy.**

This is why converting thermal energy into other forms of energy can't be done with 100% efficiency. We have redrawn our schematic diagram of a heat engine in FIGURE 11.29 on the next page, adding arrows representing entropy. Now we can see why heat must be exhausted into the cold reservoir: We need to get rid of entropy! Efficiencies or coefficients of performance higher than those in Equations 11.14, 11.15, and 11.16 would reduce entropy and thus violate the second law of thermodynamics.

FIGURE 11.28 Kinetic energy and thermal energy compared.

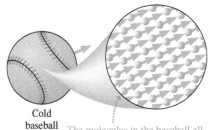

Cold baseball   The molecules in the baseball all move in the same direction at the same speed. This ordered motion is the ball's kinetic energy.

Helium balloon   The molecules in the gas move in different directions at different speeds. This random motion is the thermal energy of the gas.

FIGURE 11.29 A diagram of a heat engine, with entropy changes noted.

1. Heat energy Q_H comes into the system from the hot reservoir. Entropy is added to the heat engine.

2. The work out contains no entropy. The only way that entropy can leave is via heat flow to the cold reservoir.

3. Heat energy Q_C goes out of the heat engine into the cold reservoir. Entropy is removed from the heat engine.

Of all of the forms of energy we've seen, only thermal energy has entropy; the others are all ordered. As long as thermal energy isn't involved, you can freely and reversibly convert between different forms of energy, as we've seen. When you toss a ball into the air, the kinetic energy is converted to potential energy as the ball rises, then back to kinetic energy as the ball falls. But when some form of energy is transformed into thermal energy, entropy has increased, and the second law of thermodynamics tells us that this change is irreversible. When you drop a ball on the floor, it bounces several times and then stops moving. The kinetic energy of the ball in motion has become thermal energy of the slightly warmer ball at rest. This process won't reverse—the ball won't suddenly cool and jump into the air! This process would conserve energy, but it would reduce entropy, and so would violate this new law of physics.

This property of thermal energy has consequences for the efficiencies of heat engines, as we've seen, but it has consequences for the efficiencies of other devices as well.

CONCEPTUAL EXAMPLE 11.15 **Efficiency of hybrid vehicles**

Hybrid vehicles are powered by a gasoline engine paired with an electric motor and batteries. They get much better mileage in the stop and go of city driving than conventional vehicles do. When you brake to a stop in a conventional car, friction converts the kinetic energy of the car's motion into thermal energy in the brakes. In a typical hybrid car, some of this energy is converted into chemical energy in a battery. Explain how this makes a hybrid vehicle more efficient.

REASON When energy is transformed into thermal energy, the increase in entropy makes this change irreversible. When you brake a conventional car, the kinetic energy is transformed into the thermal energy of hot brakes and is lost to your use. In a hybrid vehicle, the kinetic energy is converted into chemical energy in a battery. This change is reversible; when the car starts again, the energy can be transformed back into kinetic energy.

ASSESS Whenever energy is converted to thermal energy, it is in some sense "lost," which reduces efficiency. The hybrid vehicle avoids this transformation, and so is more efficient.

STOP TO THINK 11.7 Which of the following processes does not involve a change in entropy?

A. An electric heater raises the temperature of a cup of water by 20°C.
B. A ball rolls up a ramp, decreasing in speed as it rolls higher.
C. A basketball is dropped from 2 m and bounces until it comes to rest.
D. The sun shines on a black surface and warms it.

11.9 Systems, Energy, and Entropy

Over the past two chapters, we have learned a good deal about energy and how it is used. By introducing the concept of entropy, we were able to see how limits on our ability to use energy come about. We will close this chapter, and this part of the book, by considering a few final questions that bring these different pieces together.

The Conservation of Energy and Energy Conservation

We have all heard for many years that it is important to "conserve energy." We are asked to turn off lights when we leave rooms, to drive our cars less, to turn down our thermostats. But this brings up an interesting question: If we have a law of conservation of energy, which states that energy can't be created or destroyed, what do we really mean by "conserving energy"? If energy can't be created or destroyed, how can there be an "energy crisis"?

We started this chapter looking at energy transformations. We saw that whenever energy is transformed, some of it is "lost." And now we know what this means: The energy isn't really lost, but it is converted into thermal energy. This change is irreversible; thermal energy can't be efficiently converted back into other forms of energy.

And that's the problem. We aren't, as a society or as a planet, running out of energy. We can't! What we can run out of is high-quality sources of energy. Oil is a good example. A gallon of gasoline contains a great deal of chemical energy. It is a liquid, so is easily transported, and it is easily burned in a host of devices to generate heat, electricity, or motion. When you burn gasoline in your car, you don't use up its energy—you simply convert its chemical energy into thermal energy. As you do this, you decrease the amount of high-quality chemical energy in the world and increase the supply of thermal energy. The amount of energy in the world is still the same; it's just in a less useful form.

Perhaps the best way to "conserve energy" is to concentrate on efficiency, to reduce "what you had to pay." More efficient lightbulbs, more efficient cars—all of these use less energy to produce the same final result.

Entropy and Life

The second law of thermodynamics predicts that systems will "run down," that ordered states will evolve toward disorder and randomness. But living organisms seem to violate this rule:

- Plants grow from simple seeds to complex entities.
- Single-celled fertilized eggs grow into complex adult organisms.
- Over the last billion years or so, life has evolved from simple unicellular organisms to very complex forms.

How can this be?

There is an important qualification in the second law of thermodynamics: It applies only to isolated systems, systems that do not exchange energy with their environment. The situation is entirely different if energy is transferred into or out of the system.

Your body is not an isolated system. Every day, you take in chemical energy in the food you eat. As you use this energy, most of it ends up as thermal energy that you exhaust as heat into the environment, taking away the entropy created by natural processes in your body. An energy and entropy diagram of this situation is given in FIGURE 11.30. Each second, as you sit quietly and read this book, your body is using 100 J of chemical energy and exhausting 100 J of thermal energy to the environment. The entropy of your body is staying approximately constant, but the entropy of the environment is increasing due to the thermal energy from your body. To grow and develop, organisms must take in high-quality forms of energy and exhaust thermal energy. This continuous exchange of energy (and entropy) with the environment makes your life—and all life—possible without violating any laws of physics.

Sealed, but not isolated BIO This glass container is a completely sealed system containing living organisms, shrimp and algae. But the organisms will live and grow for many years. The reason this is possible is that the glass sphere, though sealed, is not an *isolated* system. Energy can be transferred in and out as light and heat. If the container were placed in a darkened room, the organisms would quickly perish.

FIGURE 11.30 Thermodynamic view of the body.

Chemical energy comes into your body in the food you eat.

Energy leaves your body mostly as heat, meaning entropy is transferred as well.

E_{in} Q_{out}

Entropy out

INTEGRATED EXAMPLE 11.16 Efficiency of an automobile

In the absence of external forces, Newton's first law tells us that a car would continue at a constant speed once it was moving. So why can't you get your car up to speed and then take your foot off the gas? Because there *are* external forces. At highway speeds, nearly all of the force opposing your car's motion is the drag force of the air. (Rolling friction is much smaller than drag at highway speeds, so we'll ignore it.) FIGURE 11.31 shows that as your car moves through the air it pushes the air aside. Doing so takes energy, and your car's engine must keep running to replace this lost energy.

FIGURE 11.31 A wind-tunnel test shows airflow around a car.

Sports cars, with their aerodynamic shape, are often those that lose the least energy to drag. A typical sports car has a 350 hp engine, a drag coefficient of 0.30, and a low profile with the area of the front of the car being a modest 1.8 m^2. Such a car gets about 25 miles per gallon of gasoline at a highway speed of 30 m/s (just over 65 mph).

Suppose this car is driven 25 miles at 30 m/s. It will consume 1 gallon of gasoline, containing 1.4×10^8 J of chemical energy. What is the car's efficiency for this trip?

PREPARE We can use what we learned about the drag force in Chapter 5 to compute the amount of energy needed to move the car forward through the air. We can use this value in Equation 11.2 as what you get; it is the minimum amount of energy that *could* be used to move the car forward at this speed. We can then use the mileage data to calculate what you had to pay; this is the energy actually used by the car's engine. Once we have these two pieces of information, we can calculate efficiency.

SOLVE Heat and work both play a role in this process, so we need to use our most general equation about energy and energy conservation, Equation 11.11:

$$\Delta K + \Delta U + \Delta E_{th} + \Delta E_{chem} + \cdots = W + Q$$

The car is moving at a constant speed, so its kinetic energy is not changing. The road is assumed to be level, so there is no change in potential energy. Once the car is warmed up, its temperature will be constant, so its thermal energy isn't changing. Equation 11.11 reduces to

$$\Delta E_{chem} = W + Q$$

The car's engine is using chemical energy as it burns fuel. The engine transforms some of this energy to work—the propulsion force pushing the car forward against the opposing force of air drag. But the engine also transforms much of the chemical energy

to "waste heat" that is transferred to the environment through the radiator and the exhaust. ΔE_{chem} is negative because the amount of energy stored in the gas tank is decreasing as gasoline is burned. W and Q are also negative, according to the sign convention of Figure 11.16, because these energies are being transferred *out* of the system to the environment.

In Chapter 5 we saw that the drag force on an object moving at a speed v is given by

$$\vec{D} = \left(\tfrac{1}{2} C_D \rho A v^2, \text{ direction opposite the motion} \right)$$

where C_D is the drag coefficient, ρ is the density of air (approximately 1.2 kg/m^3), and A is the area of the front of the car. The drag force on the car moving at 30 m/s is

$$D = \tfrac{1}{2}(0.30)(1.2 \text{ kg/m}^3)(1.8 \text{ m}^2)(30 \text{ m/s})^2 = 290 \text{ N}$$

The drag force opposes the motion. To move the car forward at constant speed, and thus with no *net* force, requires a propulsion force $F = 290$ N in the forward direction. In Chapter 10 we found that the power—the rate of energy expenditure—to move an object at speed v with force F is $P = Fv$. Thus the power the car must supply—at the wheels—to keep the car moving down the highway is

$$P = Fv = (290 \text{ N})(30 \text{ m/s}) = 8700 \text{ W}$$

It's interesting to compare this to the engine power by converting to horsepower:

$$P = 8700 \text{ W} \left(\frac{1 \text{ hp}}{746 \text{ W}} \right) = 12 \text{ hp}$$

Only a small fraction of the engine's 350 horsepower is needed to keep the car moving at highway speeds.

The distance traveled is

$$\Delta x = 25 \text{ mi} \times \frac{1.6 \text{ km}}{1 \text{ mi}} \times \frac{1000 \text{ m}}{1 \text{ km}} = 40,000 \text{ m}$$

and the time required to travel it is $\Delta t = (40,000 \text{ m})/(30 \text{ m/s}) = 1333$ s. Thus the minimum energy needed to travel 40 km—the energy needed simply to push the air aside—is

$$E_{min} = P\Delta t = (8700 \text{ W})(1333 \text{ s}) = 1.2 \times 10^7 \text{ J}$$

In traveling this distance, the car uses 1 gallon of gas, with 1.4×10^8 J of chemical energy. This is, quite literally, what you had to pay to drive this distance. Thus the car's efficiency is

$$e = \frac{\text{what you get}}{\text{what you had to pay}} = \frac{1.2 \times 10^7 \text{ J}}{1.4 \times 10^8 \text{ J}} = 0.086 = 8.6\%$$

ASSESS The efficiency of the car is quite low, even compared to other engines that we've seen. Nonetheless, our calculation agrees reasonably well with actual measurements. Gasoline-powered vehicles simply are inefficient, which is one factor favoring more efficient alternative vehicles. Smaller mass and better aerodynamic design would improve the efficiency of vehicles, but a large part of the inefficiency of a gasoline-powered vehicle is inherent in the thermodynamics of the engine itself and in the complex drive train needed to transfer the engine's power to the wheels.

SUMMARY

The goals of Chapter 11 have been to learn more about energy transformations and transfers, the
laws of thermodynamics, and theoretical and practical limitations on energy use.

GENERAL PRINCIPLES

Energy and Efficiency

When energy is transformed from one form into another, some
may be "lost," usually to thermal energy, due to practical or
theoretical constraints. This limits the efficiency of processes. We
define **efficiency** as

$$e = \frac{\text{what you get}}{\text{what you had to pay}}$$

Entropy and Irreversibility

Systems move toward more
probable states. These
states have higher
entropy—more disorder.
This change is irreversible.
Changing other forms of
energy to thermal energy is
irreversible.

Increasing probability
Increasing entropy

The Laws of Thermodynamics

The **first law of thermodynamics** is a statement of conservation
of energy for systems in which only thermal energy changes:

$$\Delta E_{th} = W + Q$$

The **second law of thermodynamics** specifies the way that isolated systems can evolve:

The entropy of an isolated system always increases.

This law has practical consequences:

- Heat energy spontaneously flows only from hot to cold.
- A transformation of energy into thermal energy is irreversible.
- No heat engine can be 100% efficient.

Heat is energy transferred between
two objects at different temperatures.
Energy will be transferred until
thermal equilibrium is reached.

IMPORTANT CONCEPTS

Thermal energy

- For a gas, the thermal energy
  is the **total kinetic energy** of
  motion of the atoms.
- Thermal energy is random kinetic
  energy and so has entropy.

$$E_{th} = NK_{avg} = \frac{3}{2}Nk_BT$$

Temperature

- For a gas, temperature is
  proportional to the **average kinetic
  energy** of the motion of the atoms.

$$T = \frac{2}{3}\frac{K_{avg}}{k_B}$$

- Two systems are in **thermal
  equilibrium** if they are at the
  same temperature. No heat
  energy is transferred at thermal
  equilibrium.

A **heat engine** converts thermal
energy from a hot reservoir into
useful work. Some heat is
exhausted into a cold reservoir,
limiting efficiency.

$$e_{max} = 1 - \frac{T_C}{T_H}$$

A **heat pump** uses an energy
input to transfer heat from a cold
side to a hot side. The **coefficient
of performance** is analogous to
efficiency. For cooling, it is:

$$COP_{max} = \frac{T_C}{T_H - T_C}$$

APPLICATIONS

Efficiencies

Energy in the body
Cells in the body metabolize chemical energy
in food. Efficiency for most actions is about 25%.

Energy used by body
at rate of 480 W

Energy for forward
propulsion at rate of
120 W

Power plants
A typical power plant converts about
1/3 of the energy input into useful work.
The rest is exhausted as waste heat.

Chemical energy in

Waste
heat

Useful
work
out

Temperature scales

Zero on the **Kelvin temperature scale**
is the temperature at which the kinetic
energy of atoms is zero. This is
absolute zero. The conversion from
°C to K is

$$T(K) = T(°C) + 273$$

▶ All temperatures in equations must
be in kelvin. ◀

Problem difficulty is labeled as | (straightforward) to ||||| (challenging). Problems labeled INT integrate significant material from earlier chapters; BIO are of biological or medical interest.

For homework assigned on MasteringPhysics, go to www.masteringphysics.com

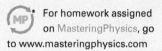

Scan this QR code to launch a **Video Tutor Solution** that will help you solve problems for this chapter.

QUESTIONS

Conceptual Questions

1. Rub your hands together vigorously. What happens? Discuss the energy transfers and transformations that take place.

2. Write a few sentences describing the energy transformations that occur from the time moving water enters a hydroelectric plant until you see some water being pumped out of a nozzle in a public fountain. Use the "Energy transformations" table on page 324 as an example.

3. BIO Describe the energy transfers and transformations that occur from the time you sit down to breakfast until you've completed a fast bicycle ride.

4. BIO According to Table 11.4, cycling at 15 km/h requires less metabolic energy than running at 15 km/h. Suggest reasons why this is the case.

5. You're stranded on a remote desert island with only a chicken, a bag of corn, and a shade tree. To survive as long as possible in hopes of being rescued, should you eat the chicken at once and then the corn? Or eat the corn, feeding enough to the chicken to keep it alive, and then eat the chicken when the corn is gone? Or are your survival chances the same either way? Explain.

6. For most automobiles, the number of miles per gallon decreases as highway speed increases. Fuel economy drops as speeds increase from 55 to 65 mph, then decreases further as speeds increase to 75 mph. Explain why this is the case.

7. When the space shuttle returns to earth, its surfaces get very hot as it passes through the atmosphere at high speed.
   a. Has the space shuttle been heated? If so, what was the source of the heat? If not, why is it hot?
   b. Energy must be conserved. What happens to the space shuttle's initial kinetic energy?

8. One end of a short aluminum rod is in a campfire and the other end is in a block of ice, as shown in Figure Q11.8. If 100 J of energy are transferred from the fire to the rod, and if the temperature at every point in the rod has reached a steady value, how much energy goes from the rod into the ice?

FIGURE Q11.8

9. Two blocks of copper, one of mass 1 kg and the second of mass 3 kg, are at the same temperature. Which block has more thermal energy? If the blocks are placed in thermal contact, will the thermal energy of the blocks change? If so, how?

10. If the temperature T of an ideal gas doubles, by what factor does the average kinetic energy of the atoms change?

11. A bottle of helium gas and a bottle of argon gas contain equal numbers of atoms at the same temperature. Which bottle, if either, has the greater total thermal energy?

For Questions 12 through 17, give a specific example of a process that has the energy changes and transfers described. (For example, if the question states "$\Delta E_{th} > 0$, $W = 0$," you are to describe a process

that has an increase in thermal energy and no transfer of energy by work. You could write "Heating a pan of water on the stove.")

12. $\Delta E_{th} < 0$, $W = 0$

13. $\Delta E_{th} > 0$, $Q = 0$

14. $\Delta E_{th} < 0$, $Q = 0$

15. $\Delta E_{th} > 0$, $W \neq 0$, $Q \neq 0$

16. $\Delta E_{th} < 0$, $W \neq 0$, $Q \neq 0$

17. $\Delta E_{th} = 0$, $W \neq 0$, $Q \neq 0$

18. A fire piston—an impressive physics demonstration—ignites a fire without matches. The operation is shown in Figure Q11.18. A wad of cotton is placed at the bottom of a sealed syringe with a tight-fitting plunger. When the plunger is rapidly depressed, the air temperature in the syringe rises enough to ignite the cotton. Explain why the air temperature rises, and why the plunger must be pushed in very quickly.

FIGURE Q11.18

19. In a gasoline engine, fuel vapors are ignited by a spark. In a diesel engine, a fuel–air mixture is drawn in, then rapidly compressed to as little as 1/20 the original volume, in the process increasing the temperature enough to ignite the fuel–air mixture. Explain why the temperature rises during the compression.

20. A drop of green ink falls into a beaker of clear water. First *describe* what happens. Then *explain* the outcome in terms of entropy.

21. If you hold a rubber band loosely between two fingers and then stretch it, you can tell by touching it to the sensitive skin of your forehead that stretching the rubber band has increased its temperature. If you then let the rubber band rest against your forehead, it soon returns to its original temperature. What are the signs of W and Q for the entire process?

22. In areas in which the air temperature drops very low in the winter, the exterior unit of a heat pump designed for heating is sometimes buried underground in order to use the earth as a thermal reservoir. Why is it worthwhile to bury the heat exchanger, even if the underground unit costs more to purchase and install than one above ground?

23. Assuming improved materials and better processes, can engineers ever design a heat engine that exceeds the maximum efficiency indicated by Equation 11.14? If not, why not?

24. Electric vehicles increase speed by using an electric motor that draws energy from a battery. When the vehicle slows, the motor runs as a generator, recharging the battery. Explain why this means that an electric vehicle can be more efficient than a gasoline-fueled vehicle.

25. When the sun's light hits the earth, the temperature rises. Is there an entropy change to accompany this transformation? Explain.

26. When you put an ice cube tray filled with liquid water in your freezer, the water eventually becomes solid ice. The solid is more ordered than the liquid—it has less entropy. Explain how this transformation is possible without violating the second law of thermodynamics.

27. A company markets an electric heater that is described as 100% efficient at converting electric energy to thermal energy. Does this violate the second law of thermodynamics?

Multiple-Choice Questions

28. ‖ A person is walking on level ground at constant speed. What energy transformation is taking place?
    A. Chemical energy is being transformed to thermal energy.
    B. Chemical energy is being transformed to kinetic energy.
    C. Chemical energy is being transformed to kinetic energy and thermal energy.
    D. Chemical energy and thermal energy are being transformed to kinetic energy.

29. | A person walks 1 km, turns around, and runs back to where he started. Compare the energy used and the power during the two segments.
    A. The energy used and the power are the same for both.
    B. The energy used while walking is greater, the power while running is greater.
    C. The energy used while running is greater, the power while running is greater.
    D. The energy used is the same for both segments, the power while running is greater.

30. | The temperature of the air in a basketball increases as it is pumped up. This means that
    A. The total kinetic energy of the air is increasing and the average kinetic energy of the molecules is decreasing.
    B. The total kinetic energy of the air is increasing and the average kinetic energy of the molecules is increasing.
    C. The total kinetic energy of the air is decreasing and the average kinetic energy of the molecules is decreasing.
    D. The total kinetic energy of the air is decreasing and the average kinetic energy of the molecules is increasing.

31. | The thermal energy of a container of helium gas is halved. What happens to the temperature, in kelvin?
    A. It decreases to one-fourth its initial value.
    B. It decreases to one-half its initial value.
    C. It stays the same.
    D. It increases to twice its initial value.

32. | An inventor approaches you with a device that he claims will take 100 J of thermal energy input and produce 200 J of electricity. You decide not to invest your money because this device would violate
    A. The first law of thermodynamics.
    B. The second law of thermodynamics.
    C. Both the first and second laws of thermodynamics.

33. | While keeping your food cold, your refrigerator transfers energy from the inside to the surroundings. Thus thermal energy goes from a colder object to a warmer one. What can you say about this?
    A. It is a violation of the second law of thermodynamics.
    B. It is not a violation of the second law of thermodynamics because refrigerators can have efficiency of 100%.
    C. It is not a violation of the second law of thermodynamics because the second law doesn't apply to refrigerators.
    D. The second law of thermodynamics applies in this situation, but it is not violated because the energy did not spontaneously go from cold to hot.

34. ‖ An electric power plant uses energy from burning coal to generate steam at 450°C. The plant is cooled by 20°C water from a nearby river. If burning coal provides 100 MJ of heat, what is the theoretical minimum amount of heat that must be transferred to the river during the conversion of heat to electric energy?
    A. 100 MJ   B. 90 MJ
    C. 60 MJ   D. 40 MJ

35. ‖ A refrigerator's freezer compartment is set at −10°C; the kitchen is 24°C. What is the theoretical minimum amount of electric energy necessary to pump 1.0 J of energy out of the freezer compartment?
    A. 0.89 J   B. 0.87 J
    C. 0.13 J   D. 0.11 J

PROBLEMS

Section 11.1 Transforming Energy

1. ‖ A 10% efficient engine accelerates a 1500 kg car from rest to 15 m/s. How much energy is transferred to the engine by burning gasoline?

2. ‖ A 60% efficient device uses chemical energy to generate 600 J of electric energy.
   a. How much chemical energy is used?
   b. A second device uses twice as much chemical energy to generate half as much electric energy. What is its efficiency?

3. | A typical photovoltaic cell delivers 4.0×10^{-3} W of electric energy when illuminated with 1.2×10^{-1} W of light energy. What is the efficiency of the cell?

4. ‖ An individual white LED (light-emitting diode) has an efficiency of 20% and uses 1.0 W of electric power. How many LEDs must be combined into one light source to give a total of 1.6 W of visible-light output (comparable to the light output of a 40 W incandescent bulb)? What total power is necessary to run this LED light source?

Section 11.2 Energy in the Body: Energy Inputs

5. ‖ BIO A fast-food hamburger (with cheese and bacon) contains 1000 Calories. What is the burger's energy in joules?

6. ‖ BIO In an average human, basic life processes require energy to be supplied at a steady rate of 100 W. What daily energy intake, in Calories, is required to maintain these basic processes?

7. | BIO An "energy bar" contains 6.0 g of fat. How much energy is this in joules? In calories? In Calories?

8. | BIO An "energy bar" contains 22 g of carbohydrates. How much energy is this in joules? In calories? In Calories?

Section 11.3 Energy in the Body: Energy Outputs

9. ‖ BIO An "energy bar" contains 22 g of carbohydrates. If the energy bar was his only fuel, how far could a 68 kg person walk at 5.0 km/h?

10. ‖ BIO Suppose your body was able to use the chemical energy in gasoline. How far could you pedal a bicycle at 15 km/h on the energy in 1 gal of gas? (1 gal of gas has a mass of 3.2 kg.)

11. ‖‖‖ The label on a candy bar says 400 Calories. Assuming a
BIO typical efficiency for energy use by the body, if a 60 kg person
were to use the energy in this candy bar to climb stairs, how
high could she go?

12. ‖ A weightlifter curls a 30 kg bar, raising it each time a
BIO distance of 0.60 m. How many times must he repeat this exercise to burn off the energy in one slice of pizza?

13. ‖ A weightlifter works out at the gym each day. Part of her rou-
BIO tine is to lie on her back and lift a 40 kg barbell straight up from
chest height to full arm extension, a distance of 0.50 m.
   a. How much work does the weightlifter do to lift the barbell
      one time?
   b. If the weightlifter does 20 repetitions a day, what total
      energy does she expend on lifting, assuming a typical effi-
      ciency for energy use by the body.
   c. How many 400 Calorie donuts can she eat a day to supply
      that energy?

Section 11.4 Thermal Energy and Temperature

14. ‖ The planet Mercury's surface temperature varies from 700 K
during the day to 90 K at night. What are these values in °C
and °F?

15. ‖ An ideal gas is at 20°C. If we double the average kinetic
energy of the gas atoms, what is the new temperature in °C?

16. ‖ An ideal gas is at 20°C. The gas is cooled, reducing the thermal energy by 10%. What is the new temperature in °C?

17. ‖ An ideal gas at 0°C consists of 1.0×10^{23} atoms. 10 J of
thermal energy are added to the gas. What is the new temperature in °C?

18. ‖ An ideal gas at 20°C consists of 2.2×10^{22} atoms. 4.3 J of
thermal energy are removed from the gas. What is the new temperature in °C?

Section 11.5 Heat and the First Law of Thermodynamics

19. ‖ 500 J of work are done on a system in a process that
decreases the system's thermal energy by 200 J. How much
energy is transferred to or from the system as heat?

20. ‖ 600 J of heat energy are transferred to a system that does 400 J
of work. By how much does the system's thermal energy change?

21. ‖ 300 J of energy are transferred to a system in the form of heat
while the thermal energy increases by 150 J. How much work is
done on or by the system?

22. ‖ 10 J of heat are removed from a gas sample while it is being
compressed by a piston that does 20 J of work. What is the
change in the thermal energy of the gas? Does the temperature
of the gas increase or decrease?

Section 11.6 Heat Engines

23. ‖ A heat engine extracts 55 kJ from the hot reservoir and
exhausts 40 kJ into the cold reservoir. What are (a) the work
done and (b) the efficiency?

24. ‖ A heat engine does 20 J of work while exhausting 30 J of
waste heat. What is the engine's efficiency?

25. ‖ A heat engine does 200 J of work while exhausting 600 J of
heat to the cold reservoir. What is the engine's efficiency?

26. ‖ A heat engine with an efficiency of 40% does 100 J of work.
How much heat is (a) extracted from the hot reservoir and
(b) exhausted into the cold reservoir?

27. ‖ a. At what cold-reservoir temperature (in °C) would an engine
operating at maximum theoretical efficiency with a hot-
reservoir temperature of 427°C have an efficiency of 60%?

   b. If another engine, operating at maximum theoretical effi-
      ciency with a hot-reservoir temperature of 400°C, has the
      same efficiency, what is its cold-reservoir temperature?

28. ‖ A heat engine operating between energy reservoirs at 20°C
and 600°C has 30% of the maximum possible efficiency. How
much energy does this engine extract from the hot reservoir to
do 1000 J of work?

29. ‖ A newly proposed device for generating electricity from the
sun is a heat engine in which the hot reservoir is created by
focusing sunlight on a small spot on one side of the engine. The
cold reservoir is ambient air at 20°C. The designer claims that
the efficiency will be 60%. What minimum hot-reservoir temperature, in °C, would be required to produce this efficiency?

30. ‖ Converting sunlight to electricity with solar cells has an
efficiency of $\approx 15\%$. It's possible
to achieve a higher efficiency
(though currently at higher cost)
by using concentrated sunlight as
the hot reservoir of a heat engine.
Each dish in Figure P11.30 con-
centrates sunlight on one side of

FIGURE P11.30

a heat engine, producing a hot-reservoir temperature of 650°C.
The cold reservoir, ambient air, is approximately 30°C. The
actual working efficiency of this device is $\approx 30\%$. What is the
theoretical maximum efficiency?

Section 11.7 Heat Pumps

31. ‖ A refrigerator takes in 20 J of work and exhausts 50 J of heat.
What is the refrigerator's coefficient of performance?

32. ‖ Air conditioners are rated by their coefficient of performance at
80°F inside temperature and 95°F outside temperature. An efficient but realistic air conditioner has a coefficient of performance
of 3.2. What is the maximum possible coefficient of performance?

33. ‖ 50 J of work are done on a refrigerator with a coefficient of
performance of 4.0. How much heat is (a) extracted from the
cold reservoir and (b) exhausted to the hot reservoir?

34. ‖ Find the maximum possible coefficient of performance for a
heat pump used to heat a house in a northerly climate in winter.
The inside is kept at 20°C while the outside is −20°C.

Section 11.8 Entropy and the Second Law of Thermodynamics

35. ‖ Which, if any, of the heat engines in Figure P11.35 below
violate (a) the first law of thermodynamics or (b) the second
law of thermodynamics? Explain.

FIGURE P11.35

36. | Which, if any, of the refrigerators in Figure P11.36 below violate (a) the first law of thermodynamics or (b) the second law of thermodynamics? Explain.

FIGURE P11.36

37. ‖ Draw all possible distinct arrangements in which three balls (labeled A, B, C) are placed into two different boxes (1 and 2), as in Figure 11.26. If all arrangements are equally likely, what is the probability that all three will be in box 1?

General Problems

38. ‖‖‖ How many slices of pizza must you eat to walk for 1.0 h at a
BIO speed of 5.0 km/h? (Assume your mass is 68 kg.)

39. ‖ A 60 kg hiker climbs to the top of a 500-m-high hill. Ignoring the energy needed for horizontal motion and assuming a typical efficiency for energy use by the body, how many frozen burritos would be needed to fuel this climb?

40. ‖‖‖ For how long would a 68 kg athlete have to swim at a fast
BIO crawl to use all the energy available in a typical fast-food meal of burger, fries, and a drink?

41. ‖ a. How much metabolic energy is required for a 68 kg
BIO runner to run at a speed of 15 km/h for 20 min?
    b. How much metabolic energy is required for this runner to walk at a speed of 5.0 km/h for 60 min? Compare your result to your answer to part a.
    c. Compare your results of parts a and b to the result of Example 11.4. Of these three modes of human motion, which is the most efficient?

42. | To a good approximation, the only external force that does
BIO work on a cyclist moving on level ground is the force of air resistance. Suppose a cyclist is traveling at 15 km/h on level ground. Assume he is using 480 W of metabolic power.
    a. Estimate the amount of power he uses for forward motion.
    b. How much force must he exert to overcome the force of air resistance?

43. | The winning time for the 2005 annual race up 86 floors of the
BIO Empire State Building was 10 min and 49 s. The winner's mass was 60 kg.
    a. If each floor was 3.7 m high, what was the winner's change in gravitational potential energy?

b. If the efficiency in climbing stairs is 25%, what total energy did the winner expend during the race?
    c. How many food Calories did the winner "burn" in the race?
    d. Of those Calories, how many were converted to thermal energy?
    e. What was the winner's metabolic power in watts during the race up the stairs?

44. ‖‖ Championship swimmers take about 22 s and about 30 arm
BIO strokes to move through the water in a 50 m freestyle race.
INT a. From Table 11.4, a swimmer's metabolic power is 800 W. If the efficiency for swimming is 25%, how much energy is expended moving through the water in a 50 m race?
    b. If half the energy is used in arm motion and half in leg motion, what is the energy expenditure per arm stroke?
    c. Model the swimmer's hand as a paddle. During one arm stroke, the paddle moves halfway around a 90-cm-radius circle. If all the swimmer's forward propulsion during an arm stroke comes from the hand pushing on the water and none from the arm (somewhat of an oversimplification), what is the average force of the hand on the water?

45. ‖‖‖ A 68 kg hiker walks at 5.0 km/h up a 7% slope. What is the
BIO necessary metabolic power? **Hint:** You can model her power needs as the sum of the power to walk on level ground plus the power needed to raise her body by the appropriate amount.

46. ‖‖‖ A 70 kg student consumes 2500 Cal each day and stays the
BIO same weight. One day, he eats 3500 Cal and, wanting to keep
INT from gaining weight, decides to "work off" the excess by jumping up and down. With each jump, he accelerates to a speed of 3.3 m/s before leaving the ground. How many jumps must he make? Assume that the efficiency of the body in using energy is 25%

47. ‖ To make your workouts more productive, you can get a gen-
BIO erator that you drive with the rear wheel of your bicycle when it is mounted in a stand.
    a. Your laptop charger uses 75 W. What is your body's metabolic power use while running the generator to power your laptop charger, given the typical efficiency for such tasks? Assume 100% efficiency for the generator.
    b. Your laptop takes 1 hour to recharge. If you run the generator for 1 hour, how much energy does your body use? Express your result in joules and in Calories.

48. ‖ The resistance of an exercise bike is often provided by a gen-
BIO erator; that is, the energy that you expend is used to generate electric energy, which is then dissipated. Rather than dissipate the energy, it could be used for practical purposes.
    a. A typical person can maintain a steady energy expenditure of 400 W on a bicycle. Assuming a typical efficiency for the body and a generator that is 80% efficient, what useful electric power could you produce with a bicycle-powered generator?
    b. How many people would need to ride bicycle generators simultaneously to power a 400 W TV in the gym?

49. ‖ Smaller mammals use proportionately more energy than
BIO larger mammals; that is, it takes more energy per gram to power a mouse than a human. A typical mouse has a mass of 20 g and, at rest, needs to consume 3.0 Cal each day for basic body processes.
    a. If a 68 kg human used the same energy per kg of body mass as a mouse, how much energy would be needed each day?
    b. What resting power does this correspond to? How much greater is this than the resting power noted in the chapter?

50. ‖ Larger animals use propor-
BIO tionately less energy than smaller
animals; that is, it takes less
energy per kg to power an elephant than to power a human. A
5000 kg African elephant requires
about 70,000 Cal for basic needs
for one day.

   a. If a 68 kg human required
   the same energy per kg of
   body mass as an elephant,
   how much energy would be
   required each day?
   b. What resting power does this correspond to? How much
   less is this than the resting power noted in the chapter?

51. ‖ A large horse can perform work at a steady rate of about
BIO 1 horsepower, as you might expect.
   a. Assuming a 25% efficiency, how many Calories would a
   horse need to consume to work at 1.0 hp for 1.0 h?
   b. Dry hay contains about 10 MJ per kg. How many kilograms
   of hay would the horse need to eat to perform this work?

52. ‖ A college student is working on her physics homework in
her dorm room. Her room contains a total of 6.0×10^{26} gas
molecules. As she works, her body is converting chemical
energy into thermal energy at a rate of 125 W. If her dorm room
were an isolated system (dorm rooms can certainly feel like
that) and if all of this thermal energy were transferred to the air
in the room, by how much would the temperature increase in
10 min?

53. ‖ A container holding argon atoms changes temperature by
20°C when 30 J of heat are removed. How many atoms are in
the container?

54. ‖ A heat engine with a high-temperature reservoir at 400 K has
an efficiency of 0.20. What is the maximum possible temperature of the cold reservoir?

55. ‖ An engine does 10 J of work and exhausts 15 J of waste heat.
   a. What is the engine's efficiency?
   b. If the cold-reservoir temperature is 20°C, what is the minimum possible temperature in °C of the hot reservoir?

56. ‖ The heat exhausted to the cold reservoir of an engine operating at maximum theoretical efficiency is two-thirds the heat
extracted from the hot reservoir. What is the temperature ratio
T_C/T_H?

57. ‖ An engine operating at maximum theoretical efficiency
whose cold-reservoir temperature is 7°C is 40% efficient. By
how much should the temperature of the hot reservoir be
increased to raise the efficiency to 60%?

58. ‖ Some heat engines can run on very small temperature differences. One manufacturer claims to have a very small heat
engine that can run on the temperature difference between your
hand and the air in the room. Estimate the theoretical maximum
efficiency of this heat engine.

59. ‖ The coefficient of performance of a refrigerator is 5.0.
   a. If the compressor uses 10 J of energy, how much heat is
   exhausted to the hot reservoir?
   b. If the hot-reservoir temperature is 27°C, what is the lowest
   possible temperature in °C of the cold reservoir?

60. ‖ An engineer claims to have measured the characteristics of a
heat engine that takes in 100 J of thermal energy and produces
50 J of useful work. Is this engine possible? If so, what is the
smallest possible ratio of the temperatures (in kelvin) of the hot
and cold reservoirs?

61. ‖ A 32% efficient electric power plant produces 900 MJ of
electric energy per second and discharges waste heat into 20°C
ocean water. Suppose the waste heat could be used to heat
homes during the winter instead of being discharged into the
ocean. A typical American house requires an average 20 kW for
heating. How many homes could be heated with the waste heat
of this one power plant?

62. ‖ A typical coal-fired power plant burns 300 metric tons of
coal *every hour* to generate 2.7×10^6 MJ of electric energy.
1 metric ton = 1000 kg; 1 metric ton of coal has a volume of
1.5 m³. The heat of combustion of coal is 28 MJ/kg. Assume
that *all* heat is transferred from the fuel to the boiler and that
all the work done in spinning the turbine is transformed into
electric energy.
   a. Suppose the coal is piled up in a 10 m × 10 m room. How
   tall must the pile be to operate the plant for one day?
   b. What is the power plant's efficiency?

63. ‖ Each second, a nuclear power plant generates 2000 MJ of
thermal energy from nuclear reactions in the reactor's core.
This energy is used to boil water and produce high-pressure
steam at 300°C. The steam spins a turbine, which produces
700 MJ of electric power, then the steam is condensed and the
water is cooled to 30°C before starting the cycle again.
   a. What is the maximum possible efficiency of the plant?
   b. What is the plant's actual efficiency?

64. ‖ 250 students sit in an auditorium listening to a physics lecture. Because they are thinking hard, each is using 125 W of
metabolic power, slightly more than they would use at rest. An
air conditioner with a COP of 5.0 is being used to keep the room
at a constant temperature. What minimum electric power must
be used to operate the air conditioner?

65. ‖ Driving on asphalt roads entails very little rolling resistance,
INT so most of the energy of the engine goes to overcoming air
resistance. But driving slowly in dry sand is another story. If a
1500 kg car is driven in sand at 5.0 m/s, the coefficient of
rolling friction is 0.06. In this case, nearly all of the energy that
the car uses to move goes to overcoming rolling friction, so you
can ignore air drag in this problem.
   a. What propulsion force is needed to keep the car moving forward at a constant speed?
   b. What power is required for propulsion at 5.0 m/s?
   c. If the car gets 15 mpg when driving on sand, what is the
   car's efficiency?

66. ‖ Air conditioners sold in the United States are given a seasonal energy-efficiency ratio (SEER) rating that consumers can
use to compare different models. A SEER rating is the ratio of
heat pumped to energy input, similar to a COP but using English units, so a higher SEER rating means a more efficient model.
You can determine the COP of an air conditioner by dividing
the SEER rating by 3.4. For typical inside and outside temperatures when you'd be using air conditioning, estimate the theoretical maximum SEER rating of an air conditioner. (New air
conditioners must have a SEER rating that exceeds 13, quite a
bit less than the theoretical maximum, but there are practical
issues that reduce efficiency.)

67. ‖ The surface waters of tropical oceans are at a temperature
of 27°C while water at a depth of 1200 m is at 3°C. It has
been suggested these warm and cold waters could be the
energy reservoirs for a heat engine, allowing us to do work or
generate electricity from the thermal energy of the ocean.
What is the maximum efficiency possible of such a heat
engine?

68. ‖ The light energy that falls on a square meter of ground over the course of a typical sunny day is about 20 MJ. The average rate of electric energy consumption in one house is 1.0 kW.
    a. On average, how much energy does one house use during each 24 h day?
    b. If light energy to electric energy conversion using solar cells is 15% efficient, how many square miles of land must be covered with solar cells to supply the electrical energy for 250,000 houses? Assume there is no cloud cover.

Passage Problems

Kangaroo Locomotion BIO

Kangaroos have very stout tendons in their legs that can be used to store energy. When a kangaroo lands on its feet, the tendons stretch, transforming kinetic energy of motion to elastic potential energy. Much of this energy can be transformed back into kinetic energy as the kangaroo takes another hop. The kangaroo's peculiar hopping gait is not very efficient at low speeds but is quite efficient at high speeds.

Figure P11.69 shows the energy cost of human and kangaroo locomotion. The graph shows oxygen uptake (in mL/s) per kg of body mass, allowing a direct comparison between the two species.

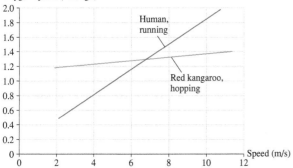

FIGURE P11.69 Oxygen uptake (a measure of energy use per second) for a running human and a hopping kangaroo.

For humans, the energy used per second (i.e., power) is proportional to the speed. That is, the human curve nearly passes through the origin, so running twice as fast takes approximately twice as much power. For a hopping kangaroo, the graph of energy use has only a very small slope. In other words, the energy used per second changes very little with speed. Going faster requires very little additional power. Treadmill tests on kangaroos and observations in the wild have shown that they do not become winded at any speed at which they are able to hop. No matter how fast they hop, the necessary power is approximately the same.

69. ∣ A person runs 1 km. How does his speed affect the total energy needed to cover this distance?
    A. A faster speed requires less total energy.
    B. A faster speed requires more total energy.
    C. The total energy is about the same for a fast speed and a slow speed.
70. ∣ A kangaroo hops 1 km. How does its speed affect the total energy needed to cover this distance?
    A. A faster speed requires less total energy.
    B. A faster speed requires more total energy.
    C. The total energy is about the same for a fast speed and a slow speed.
71. ∣ At a speed of 4 m/s,
    A. A running human is more efficient than an equal-mass hopping kangaroo.
    B. A running human is less efficient than an equal-mass hopping kangaroo.
    C. A running human and an equal-mass hopping kangaroo have about the same efficiency.
72. ∣ At approximately what speed would a human use half the power of an equal-mass kangaroo moving at the same speed?
    A. 3 m/s   B. 4 m/s   C. 5 m/s   D. 6 m/s
73. ∣ At what speed does the hopping motion of the kangaroo become more efficient than the running gait of a human?
    A. 3 m/s   B. 5 m/s   C. 7 m/s   D. 9 m/s

STOP TO THINK ANSWERS

Stop to Think 11.1: C. In each case, what you get is the potential-energy change of the box. Crane 2 lifts a box with twice the mass the same distance as crane 1, so you get twice as much energy with crane 2. How about what you have to pay? Crane 2 uses 20 kJ, crane 1 only 10 kJ. Comparing crane 1 and crane 2, we find crane 2 has twice the energy out for twice the energy in, so the efficiencies are the same.

Stop to Think 11.2: C. As the body uses chemical energy from food, approximately 75% is transformed into thermal energy. Also, kinetic energy of motion of the legs and feet is transformed into thermal energy with each stride. Most of the chemical energy is transformed into thermal energy.

Stop to Think 11.3: C. Samples 1 and 2 have the same thermal energy, which is the total kinetic energy of all the atoms. Sample 1 has twice as many atoms, so the average energy per atom, and thus the temperature, must be less.

Stop to Think 11.4: C. The radiator is at a higher temperature than the surrounding air. Thermal energy is transferred out of the system to the environment, so $Q < 0$.

Stop to Think 11.5: A, D. The efficiency is fixed by the ratio of T_C to T_H. Decreasing this ratio increases efficiency; the heat engine will be more efficient with a hotter hot reservoir or a colder cold reservoir.

Stop to Think 11.6: A, D. The closer the temperatures of the hot and cold reservoirs, the more efficient the heat pump can be. (It is also true that having the two temperatures be closer will cause less thermal energy to "leak" out.) Any change that makes the two temperatures closer will allow the refrigerator to use less energy to run.

Stop to Think 11.7: B. In this case, kinetic energy is transformed into potential energy; there is no entropy change. In the other cases, energy is transformed into thermal energy, meaning entropy increases.

Conservation Laws

In Part II we have discovered that we don't need to know all the details of an interaction to relate the properties of a system "before" the interaction to those "after" the interaction. We also found two important quantities, momentum and energy, that are often conserved. Momentum and energy are characteristics of a system.

Momentum and energy have conditions under which they are conserved. The total momentum $\vec{P}$ and the total energy E are conserved for an *isolated system*. Of course, not all systems are isolated. For both momentum and energy, it was useful to develop a *model* of a system interacting with its environment. Interactions within the system do not change $\vec{P}$ or E. The kinetic, potential, and thermal energies *within* the system can be transformed without changing E. Interactions between the system and the environment *do* change the system's momentum and energy. In particular:

- Impulse is the transfer of momentum to or from the system: $\Delta \vec{p} = \vec{J}$.

- Work is the transfer of energy to or from the system in a mechanical interaction: $\Delta E = W$.
- Heat is the energy transferred to or from the system in a thermal interaction: $\Delta E = Q$.

The laws of conservation of momentum and energy, when coupled with the laws of Newtonian mechanics of Part I, form a powerful set of tools for analyzing motion. But energy is a concept that can be used for much more than the study of motion; it can be used to analyze how your body uses food, how the sun shines, and a host of other problems.

The study of the transformation of energy from one form into another reveals certain limits. Thermal energy is different from other forms of energy. A transformation of energy from another form into thermal energy is *irreversible*. The study of heat and thermal energy thus led us to the discipline of thermodynamics, a subject we will take up further in Part III as we look at properties of matter.

KNOWLEDGE STRUCTURE II Conservation Laws

BASIC GOALS	How is the system "after" an interaction related to the system "before"? What quantities are conserved, and under what conditions? Why are some energy changes more efficient than others?

GENERAL PRINCIPLES	**Law of conservation of momentum** For an isolated system, $\vec{P}_f = \vec{P}_i$. **Law of conservation of energy** For an isolated system, there is no change in the system's energy:

$$\Delta K + \Delta U_g + \Delta U_s + \Delta E_{th} + \Delta E_{chem} + \cdots = 0$$

Energy can be exchanged with the environment as work or heat:

$$\Delta K + \Delta U_g + \Delta U_s + \Delta E_{th} + \Delta E_{chem} + \cdots = W + Q$$

Laws of thermodynamics First law: If only thermal energy changes, $\Delta E_{th} = W + Q$.
 Second law: The entropy of an isolated system always increases.

BASIC PROBLEM-SOLVING STRATEGY	Draw a visual overview for the system "before" and "after"; then use the conservation of momentum or energy equations to relate the two. If necessary, calculate impulse and/or work.

Momentum and impulse
In a collision, the total momentum

$$\vec{P} = \vec{p}_1 + \vec{p}_2 = m_1 \vec{v}_1 + m_2 \vec{v}_2$$

is the same before and after.

Before: m_1 ① $\xrightarrow{(v_{1x})_i}$ $\xleftarrow{(v_{2x})_i}$ ② m_2

After: $\xleftarrow{(v_{1x})_f}$ ① ② $\xrightarrow{(v_{2x})_f}$

A force can change the momentum of an object. The change is the **impulse:** $\Delta p_x = J_x$.

$J_x =$ area under force curve

Basic model of energy

Environment

Energy is *transformed* within the system.

System

$K \leftrightarrow U$

Work, heat

E_{chem}

E_{th}

Energy is *transferred* to or from the system from or to the environment.

Work $W = F_\parallel d$ is done by the component of a force parallel to a displacement.

Limitations on energy transfers and transformations
Thermal energy is random kinetic energy. Changing other forms of energy to thermal energy is **irreversible.** When transforming energy from one form into another, some may be "lost" as thermal energy. This limits efficiency:

$$\text{efficiency: } e = \frac{\text{what you get}}{\text{what you had to pay}}$$

A heat engine can convert thermal energy to useful work. The efficiency must be less than 100%.

Order Out of Chaos

The second law of thermodynamics specifies that "the future" is the direction of entropy increase. But, as we have seen, this doesn't mean that systems must invariably become more random. You don't need to look far to find examples of systems that spontaneously evolve to a state of greater order.

A snowflake is a perfect example. As water freezes, the random motion of water molecules is transformed into the orderly arrangement of a crystal. The entropy of the snowflake is less than that of the water vapor from which it formed. Has the second law of thermodynamics been turned on its head?

The entropy of the water molecules in the snowflake certainly decreases, but the water doesn't freeze as an isolated system. For it to freeze, heat energy must be transferred from the water to the surrounding air. The entropy of the air increases by *more* than the entropy of the water decreases. Thus the *total* entropy of the water + air system increases when a snowflake is formed, just as the second law predicts. If the system isn't isolated, its entropy can decrease without violating the second law as long as the entropy increases somewhere else.

Systems that become *more* ordered as time passes, and in which the entropy decreases, are called *self-organizing systems*. These systems can't be isolated. It is common in self-organizing systems to find a substantial flow of energy *through* the system. Your body takes in chemical energy from food, makes use of that energy, and then gives waste heat back to the environment. It is this energy flow that allows systems to develop a high degree of order and a very low entropy. The entropy of the environment undergoes a significant *increase* so as to let selected subsystems decrease their entropy and become more ordered.

Self-organizing systems don't violate the second law of thermodynamics, but this fact doesn't really explain their existence. If you toss a coin, no law of physics says that you can't get heads 100 times in a row—but you don't expect this to happen. Can we show that self-organization isn't just possible, but likely?

Let's look at a simple example. Suppose you heat a shallow dish of oil at the bottom, while holding the temperature of the top constant. When the temperature difference between the top and the bottom of the dish is small, heat is transferred from the bottom to the top by conduction. But convection begins when the temperature difference becomes large enough. The pattern of convection needn't be random, though; it can develop in a stable, highly ordered pattern, as we see in the figure. Convection is a much more efficient means of transferring energy than conduction, so the rate of transfer is *increased* as a result of the development of these ordered *convection cells*.

The development of the convection cells is an example of self-organization. The roughly 10^{23} molecules in the fluid had been moving randomly but now have begun behaving in a very orderly fashion. But there is more to the story. The convection cells transfer energy from the hot lower side of the dish to the cold upper side. This hot-to-cold energy transfer increases the entropy of the surrounding environment, as we have seen. In becoming more organized, the system has become more effective at transferring heat, resulting in a greater rate of entropy increase! Order has arisen out of disorder in the system, but the net result is a more rapid increase of the disorder of the universe.

Convection cells are thus a thermodynamically favorable form of order. We should expect this, because convection cells aren't confined to the laboratory. We see them in the sun, where they transfer energy from lower levels to the surface, and in the atmosphere of the earth, where they give rise to some of our most dramatic weather.

Self-organizing systems are a very active field of research in physical and biological sciences. The 1977 Nobel Prize in chemistry was awarded to the Belgian scientist Ilya Prigogine for his studies of *nonequilibrium thermodynamics,* the basic science underlying self-organizing systems. Prigogine and others have shown how energy flow through a system can, when the conditions are right, "bring order out of chaos." And this spontaneous ordering is not just possible—it can be probable. The existence and evolution of self-organizing systems, from thunderstorms to life on earth, might just be nature's preferred way of increasing entropy in the universe.

Convection cells in a shallow dish of oil heated from below (left) and in the sun (right).
In both, warmer fluid is rising (lighter color) and cooler fluid is sinking (darker color).

The following questions are related to the passage "Order Out of Chaos" on the previous page.

1. When water freezes to make a snowflake crystal, the entropy of the water
   A. Decreases.
   B. Increases.
   C. Does not change.
2. When thermal energy is transferred from a hot object to a cold object, the overall entropy
   A. Decreases.
   B. Increases.
   C. Does not change.

3. Do convection cells represent a reversible process?
   A. Yes, because they are orderly.
   B. No, because they transfer thermal energy from hot to cold.
   C. It depends on the type of convection cell.
4. In an isolated system far from thermal equilibrium, as time passes,
   A. The total energy stays the same; the total entropy stays the same.
   B. The total energy decreases; the total entropy increases.
   C. The total energy stays the same; the total entropy increases.
   D. The total energy decreases; the total entropy stays the same.

The following passages and associated questions are based on the material of Part II.

Big Air

A new generation of pogo sticks lets a rider bounce more than 2 meters off the ground by using elastic bands to store energy. When the pogo's plunger hits the ground, the elastic bands stretch as the pogo and rider come to rest. At the low point of the bounce, the stretched bands start to contract, pushing out the plunger and launching the rider into the air. For a total mass of 80 kg (rider plus pogo), a stretch of 0.40 m launches a rider 2.0 m above the starting point.

5. If you were to jump to the ground from a height of 2 meters, you'd likely injure yourself. But a pogo rider can do this repeatedly, bounce after bounce. How does the pogo stick make this possible?
   A. The elastic bands absorb the energy of the bounce, keeping it from hurting the rider.
   B. The elastic bands warm up as the rider bounces, absorbing dangerous thermal energy.
   C. The elastic bands simply convert the rider's kinetic energy to potential energy.
   D. The elastic bands let the rider come to rest over a longer time, meaning less force.
6. Assuming that the elastic bands stretch and store energy like a spring, how high would the 80 kg pogo and rider go for a stretch of 0.20 m?
   A. 2.0 m   B. 1.5 m   C. 1.0 m   D. 0.50 m
7. Suppose a much smaller rider (total mass of rider plus pogo of 40 kg) mechanically stretched the elastic bands of the pogo by 0.40 m, then got on the pogo and released the bands. How high would this unwise rider go?
   A. 8.0 m   B. 6.0 m   C. 4.0 m   D. 3.0 m
8. A pogo and rider of 80 kg total mass at the high point of a 2.0 m jump will drop 1.6 m before the pogo plunger touches the ground, slowing to a stop over an additional 0.40 m as the elastic bands stretch. What approximate average force does the pogo stick exert on the ground during the landing?
   A. 4000 N   B. 3200 N   C. 1600 N   D. 800 N

9. Riders can use fewer elastic bands, reducing the effective spring constant of the pogo. The maximum stretch of the bands is still 0.40 m. Reducing the number of bands will
   A. Reduce the force on the rider and give a lower jump height.
   B. Not change the force on the rider but give a lower jump height.
   C. Reduce the force on the rider but give the same jump height.
   D. Make no difference to the force on the rider or the jump height.

Testing Tennis Balls

Tennis balls are tested by being dropped from a height of 2.5 m onto a concrete floor. The 57 g ball hits the ground, compresses, then rebounds. A ball will be accepted for play if it rebounds to a height of about 1.4 m; it will be rejected if the bounce height is much more or much less than this.

10. Consider the sequence of energy transformations in the bounce. When the dropped ball is motionless on the floor, compressed, and ready to rebound, most of the energy is in the form of
    A. Kinetic energy.
    B. Gravitational potential energy.
    C. Thermal energy.
    D. Elastic potential energy.
11. If a ball is "soft," it will spend more time in contact with the floor and won't rebound as high as it is supposed to. The force on the floor of the "soft" ball is _____ the force on the floor of a "normal" ball.
    A. Greater than
    B. The same as
    C. Less than
12. Suppose a ball is dropped from 2.5 m and rebounds to 1.4 m.
    a. How fast is the ball moving just before it hits the floor?
    b. What is the ball's speed just after leaving the floor?
    c. What happens to the "lost" energy?
    d. If the time of the collision with the floor is 6.0 ms, what is the average force on the ball during the impact?

Squid Propulsion BIO

Squid usually move by using their fins, but they can utilize a form of "jet propulsion," ejecting water at high speed to rocket them backward, as shown in Figure II.1. A 4.0 kg squid can slowly draw in and then quickly eject 0.30 kg of water. The water is ejected in 0.10 s at a speed of 10 m/s. This gives the squid a quick burst of speed to evade predators or catch prey.

FIGURE II.1

13. What is the speed of the squid immediately after the water is ejected?
    A. 10 m/s
    B. 7.5 m/s
    C. 1.3 m/s
    D. 0.75 m/s
14. What is the squid's approximate acceleration in g?
    A. $10g$ B. $7.5g$ C. $1.0g$ D. $0.75g$
15. What is the average force on the water during the jet?
    A. 100 N   B. 30 N   C. 10 N   D. 3.0 N
16. This form of locomotion is speedy, but is it efficient? The energy that the squid expends goes two places: the kinetic energy of the squid and the kinetic energy of the water. Think about how to define "what you get" and "what you had to pay"; then calculate an efficiency for this particular form of locomotion. (You can ignore biomechanical efficiency for this problem.)

Teeing Off

A golf club has a lightweight flexible shaft with a heavy block of wood or metal (called the head of the club) at the end. A golfer making a long shot off the tee uses a driver, a club whose 300 g head is much more massive than the 46 g ball it will hit. The golfer swings the driver so that the club head is moving at 40 m/s just before it collides with the ball. The collision is so rapid that it can be treated as the collision of a moving 300 g mass (the club head) with a stationary 46 g mass (the ball); the shaft of the club and the golfer can be ignored. The collision takes 5.0 ms, and the ball leaves the tee with a speed of 69 m/s.

17. What is the change in momentum of the ball during the collision?
    A. 1.4 kg·m/s   B. 1.8 kg·m/s
    C. 3.2 kg·m/s   D. 5.1 kg·m/s
18. What is the speed of the club head immediately after the collision?
    A. 29 m/s   B. 25 m/s   C. 19 m/s   D. 11 m/s
19. Is this a perfectly elastic collision?
    A. Yes
    B. No
    C. There is insufficient information to make this determination.
20. If we define the kinetic energy of the club head before the collision as "what you paid" and the kinetic energy of the ball immediately after as "what you get," what is the efficiency of this energy transfer?
    A. 0.54   B. 0.46   C. 0.37   D. 0.27

Additional Integrated Problems

21. Football players measure their acceleration by seeing how fast they can sprint 40 yards (37 m). A zippy player can, from a standing start, run 40 yards in 4.1 s, reaching a top speed of about 11 m/s. For an 80 kg player, what is the average power output for this sprint?
    A. 300 W   B. 600 W   C. 900 W   D. 1200 W
22. The unit of horsepower was defined by considering the power output of a typical horse. Working-horse guidelines in the 1900s called for them to pull with a force equal to 10% of their body weight at a speed of 3.0 mph. For a typical working horse of 1200 lb, what power does this represent in W and in hp?
23. A 100 kg football player is moving at 6.0 m/s to the east; a 130 kg player is moving at 5.0 m/s to the west. They meet, each jumping into the air and grabbing the other player. While they are still in the air, which way is the pair moving, and how fast?
24. A swift blow with the hand can break a pine board. As the hand hits the board, the kinetic energy of the hand is transformed into elastic potential energy of the bending board; if the board bends far enough, it breaks. Applying a force to the center of a particular pine board deflects the center of the board by a distance that increases in proportion to the force. Ultimately the board breaks at an applied force of 800 N and a deflection of 1.2 cm.
    a. To break the board with a blow from the hand, how fast must the hand be moving? Use 0.50 kg for the mass of the hand.
    b. If the hand is moving this fast and comes to rest in a distance of 1.2 cm, what is the average force on the hand?
25. A child's sled has rails that slide with little friction across the snow. Logan has an old wooden sled with heavy iron rails that has a mass of 10 kg—quite a bit for a 30 kg child! Logan runs at 4.0 m/s and leaps onto the stationary sled and holds on tight as it slides forward. The impact time with the sled is 0.25 s.
    a. Immediately after Logan jumps on the sled, how fast is it moving?
    b. What was the force on the sled during the impact?
    c. How much energy was "lost" in the impact? Where did this energy go?

Properties of Matter

Individual bees do not have the ability to regulate their body temperature. But a colony of bees, working together, can very precisely regulate the temperature of their hive. How can the bees use the heat generated by their muscles, the structure of the hive, and the evaporation of water to achieve this control? In Part III, we will learn about the flows of matter and energy that drive such processes.

Beyond the Particle Model

The first 11 chapters of this book have made extensive use of the *particle model* in which we represent objects as point masses. The particle model is especially useful for describing how discrete objects move through space and how they interact with each other. Whether a ball is made of metal or wood is irrelevant to calculating its trajectory.

But there are many situations where the distinction between metal and wood is crucial. If you toss a metal ball and a wood ball into a pond, one sinks and the other floats. If you stir a pan on the stove with a metal spoon, it can quickly get too hot to hold unless it has a wooden handle.

Wood and metal have different physical properties. So do air and water. Our goal in Part III is to describe and understand the similarities and differences of different materials. To do so, we must go beyond the particle model and dig deeper into the nature of matter.

Macroscopic Physics

In Part III, we will be concerned with systems that are solids, liquids, or gases. Properties such as pressure, temperature, specific heat, and viscosity are characteristics of the system as a whole, not of the individual particles. Solids, liquids, and gases are often called *macroscopic* systems—the prefix "macro" (the opposite of "micro") meaning "large." We'll make sense of the behavior of these macroscopic properties by considering a microscopic view in which we think of these systems as collections of particle-like atoms. This "micro-to-macro" development will be a key piece of the following chapters.

In the coming chapters, we'll consider a wide range of practical questions, such as:

- How do the temperature and pressure of a system change when you heat it? Why do some materials respond quickly, others slowly?
- What are the mechanisms by which a system exchanges heat energy with its environment? Why does blowing on a cup of hot coffee cause it to cool off?
- Why are there three phases of matter—solids, liquids, gases? What happens during a phase change?
- Why do some objects float while others, with the same mass, sink? What keeps a massive steel ship afloat?
- What are the laws of motion of a flowing liquid? How do they differ from the laws governing the motion of a particle?

Both Newton's laws and the law of conservation of energy will remain important tools—they are, after all, the basic laws of physics—but we'll have to learn how they apply to macroscopic systems.

It should come as no surprise that an understanding of macroscopic systems and their properties is essential for understanding the world around us. Biological systems, from cells to ecosystems, are macroscopic systems exchanging energy with their environment. On a larger scale, energy transport on earth gives us weather, and the exchange of energy between the earth and space determines our climate.

12 Thermal Properties of Matter

This thermal image shows a person with warm hands holding a much cooler tarantula. Why do the hands radiate energy? And why does the tarantula radiate less?

LOOKING AHEAD ►►

The goal of Chapter 12 is to use the atomic model of matter to explain and explore many macroscopic phenomena associated with heat, temperature, and the properties of matter.

The Ideal Gas

We'll continue to develop a model of the ideal gas based on the motion of individual atoms or molecules.

Pressure is due to collisions of molecules with the inside surface of the ball. More molecules or faster molecules mean more pressure.

> **Looking Back ◄◄**
> 10.5 The nature of thermal energy
> 11.4 The ideal-gas model, the meaning of temperature

The Atomic Model

The central theme that runs through this chapter is the atomic model. We will explain the thermal properties of matter by modeling solids, liquids, and gases in terms of atoms and the interactions between atoms.

We can explain a wide range of physical phenomena in terms of this simple underlying model.

Thermal Expansion

When liquids and solids are heated, they expand because of the increased motion of their atoms or molecules.

In Alaska, the heating of normally cool railroad tracks in the summer sun makes them expand and may create "sun kinks."

Ideal-Gas Processes

The pressure, volume, and temperature of a gas are related. Changing one means changing one or both of the others.

A Styrofoam cup is made of gas bubbles in plastic. The cup on the left was lowered deep into the ocean, where the huge pressure compressed the bubbles and deformed the cup.

Changes on Heating and Cooling

Heat causes both changes in temperature and changes of **phase**— solids change to liquid, liquids to gas.

Molten rock cools and solidifies when it hits the ocean. This transfer of heat causes the ocean water to boil.

> **Looking Back ◄◄**
> 11.5 Heat and the first law of thermodynamics

Heat Transfer

We'll explore the mechanisms by which heat is transferred from one object to another.

Air heated by the kettle streams upward, an example of heat transfer by **convection**.

12.1 The Atomic Model of Matter

PhET: States of Matter
PhET: Gas Properties

We began exploring the concepts of thermal energy, temperature, and heat in Chapter 11, but many unanswered questions remain. How do the properties of matter depend on temperature? When you add heat to a system, by how much does its temperature change? And how is heat transferred to or from a system?

These are questions about the *macroscopic* state of systems, but we'll start our exploration by looking at a *microscopic* view, the atomic model that we've used to explain friction, elastic forces, and the nature of thermal energy. In this chapter, we'll use the atomic model to understand and explain the thermal properties of matter.

As you know, each element and most compounds can exist as a solid, liquid, or gas. These three **phases** of matter are familiar from everyday experience. An atomic view of the three phases is shown in FIGURE 12.1.

FIGURE 12.1 Atomic models of the three phases of matter: solid, liquid, and gas.

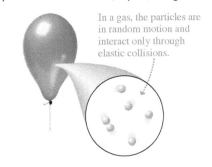

In a gas, the particles are in random motion and interact only through elastic collisions.

- A **gas** is a system in which each particle moves freely through space until, on occasion, it collides with another particle or the wall of its container.
- In a **liquid,** weak bonds permit motion while keeping the particles close together.
- A rigid **solid** has a definite shape and can be compressed or deformed only slightly, as we saw in Chapter 8. It consists of atoms connected by spring-like molecular bonds.

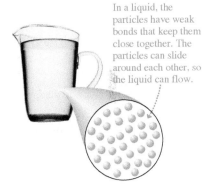

In a liquid, the particles have weak bonds that keep them close together. The particles can slide around each other, so the liquid can flow.

Our atomic model makes some simplifications that are worth noting. The basic particles of the gas in Figure 12.1 are drawn as simple spheres; no mention is made of the nature of the particles. The balloon might contain either helium (in which the basic particles are helium atoms) or air (in which the basic particles are nitrogen and oxygen molecules). A helium atom and a nitrogen molecule are quite different from each other, but many of the properties of the gas as a whole do not depend on the nature of the particles—a gas of helium atoms or oxygen molecules may behave identically. In such cases, we will simply refer to gas *particles,* which may be either atoms or molecules.

The basic particles in the liquid water in Figure 12.1 are water molecules. We ignore the structure of the molecules, so when we speak of the bonds that hold the particles in the liquid state, we are referring to the relatively weak intermolecular bonds among the water molecules, not the strong bonds between the hydrogen and oxygen atoms that form the molecules. The basic particles of the gold bars in Figure 12.1 are gold atoms. The bonds that hold these atoms together are the bonds that give the solid its structure. But there are solids composed of molecules that are held together by bonds between the molecules; water ice is one such example. In this case, the particles are the molecules, and the bonds that form the solid are the bonds between the molecules.

In a rigid solid, the particles are connected by relatively stiff spring-like bonds.

Atomic Mass and Atomic Mass Number

Before we see how the atomic model explains the thermal properties of matter, we need to remind you of some "atomic accounting." Recall that atoms of different elements have different masses. The mass of an atom is determined primarily by its most massive constituents: the protons and neutrons in its nucleus. The *sum* of the number of protons and the number of neutrons is the **atomic mass number** A:

$$A = \text{number of protons} + \text{number of neutrons}$$

A, which by definition is an integer, is written as a leading superscript on the atomic symbol. For example, the primary isotope of carbon, with six protons (which makes it carbon) and six neutrons, has $A = 12$ and is written ^{12}C. The radioactive isotope ^{14}C, used for carbon dating of archeological finds, contains six protons and eight neutrons.

TABLE 12.1 Some atomic mass numbers

Element	Symbol	A
Hydrogen	^{1}H	1
Helium	^{4}He	4
Carbon	^{12}C	12
Nitrogen	^{14}N	14
Oxygen	^{16}O	16
Neon	^{20}Ne	20
Aluminum	^{27}Al	27
Argon	^{40}Ar	40
Lead	^{207}Pb	207

The **atomic mass** scale is established by defining the mass of ^{12}C to be exactly 12 u, where u is the symbol for the *atomic mass unit*. That is, $m(^{12}C) = 12$ u. In kg, the atomic mass unit is

$$1 \text{ u} = 1.66 \times 10^{-27} \text{ kg}$$

Atomic masses are all very nearly equal to the integer atomic mass number A. For example, the mass of ^{1}H, with $A = 1$, is $m = 1.0078$ u. For our present purposes, it will be sufficient to use the integer atomic mass numbers as the values of the atomic mass. That is, we'll use $m(^1H) = 1$ u, $m(^4He) = 4$ u, and $m(^{16}O) = 16$ u. For molecules, the **molecular mass** is the sum of the atomic masses of the atoms that form the molecule. Thus the molecular mass of the diatomic molecule O_2, the constituent of oxygen gas, is $m(O_2) = 2m(^{16}O) = 32$ u.

NOTE ▶ An element's atomic mass number is *not* the same as its atomic number. The *atomic number*, which gives the element's position in the periodic table, is the number of protons. ◀

Table 12.1 lists the atomic mass numbers of some of the elements that we'll use for examples and homework problems. A complete periodic table, including atomic masses, is found in Appendix B.

The Definition of the Mole

TABLE 12.2 Monatomic and diatomic gases

Monatomic	Diatomic
Helium (He)	Hydrogen (H_2)
Neon (Ne)	Nitrogen (N_2)
Argon (Ar)	Oxygen (O_2)

One way to specify the amount of substance in a system is to give its mass. Another way, one connected to the number of atoms, is to measure the amount of substance in *moles*. **1 mole of substance, abbreviated 1 mol, is 6.02×10^{23} basic particles.**

The basic particle depends on the substance. Helium is a **monatomic gas,** meaning that the basic particle is the helium atom. Thus 6.02×10^{23} helium atoms are 1 mol of helium. But oxygen gas is a **diatomic gas** because the basic particle is the two-atom diatomic molecule O_2. 1 mol of oxygen gas contains 6.02×10^{23} *molecules* of O_2 and thus $2 \times 6.02 \times 10^{23}$ oxygen atoms. Table 12.2 lists the monatomic and diatomic gases that we will use for examples and problems.

The number of basic particles per mole of substance is called **Avogadro's number** N_A. The value of Avogadro's number is thus

$$N_A = 6.02 \times 10^{23} \text{ mol}^{-1}$$

The number n of moles in a substance containing N basic particles is

$$n = \frac{N}{N_A} \tag{12.1}$$

Moles of a substance in terms of the number of basic particles

The **molar mass** of a substance, M_{mol}, is the mass *in grams* of 1 mol of substance. To a good approximation, the numerical value of the molar mass equals the numerical value of the atomic or molecular mass. That is, the molar mass of He, with $m = 4$ u, is $M_{mol}(He) = 4$ g/mol, and the molar mass of diatomic O_2 is $M_{mol}(O_2) = 32$ g/mol.

You can use the molar mass to determine the number of moles. In one of the few instances where the proper units are *grams* rather than kilograms, the number of moles contained in a system of mass M consisting of atoms or molecules with molar mass M_{mol} is

$$n = \frac{M \text{ (in grams)}}{M_{mol}} \tag{12.2}$$

Moles of a substance in terms of its mass

One mole of helium, sulfur, copper, and mercury.

EXAMPLE 12.1   **Determining quantities of oxygen**

A system contains 100 g of oxygen. How many moles does it contain? How many molecules?

SOLVE The diatomic oxygen molecule O_2 has molar mass $M_{mol} = 32$ g/mol. From Equation 12.2,

$$n = \frac{100 \text{ g}}{32 \text{ g/mol}} = 3.1 \text{ mol}$$

Each mole contains N_A molecules, so the total number is $N = nN_A = 1.9 \times 10^{24}$ molecules.

FIGURE 12.2 There are 10^6 cm^3 in 1 m^3.

Subdivide the $1 \text{ m} \times 1 \text{ m} \times 1 \text{ m}$ cube into little cubes 1 cm on a side. You will get 100 subdivisions along each edge.

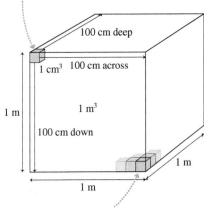

There are $100 \times 100 \times 100 = 10^6$ little 1 cm^3 cubes in the big 1 m^3 cube.

Volume

An important property that characterizes a macroscopic system is its volume V, the amount of space the system occupies. The SI unit of volume is m^3. Nonetheless, both cm^3 and, to some extent, liters (L) are widely used metric units of volume. In most cases, you *must* convert these to m^3 before doing calculations.

While it is true that 1 m = 100 cm, it is *not* true that $1 \text{ m}^3 = 100 \text{ cm}^3$. FIGURE 12.2 shows that the volume conversion factor is $1 \text{ m}^3 = 10^6 \text{ cm}^3$. A liter is 1000 cm^3, so $1 \text{ m}^3 = 10^3$ L. A milliliter (1 mL) is the same as 1 cm^3.

STOP TO THINK 12.1   Which system contains more atoms: 5 mol of helium ($A = 4$) or 1 mol of neon ($A = 20$)?

A. Helium.   B. Neon.   C. They have the same number of atoms.

12.2 The Atomic Model of an Ideal Gas

Solids and liquids are nearly incompressible because the atomic particles are in close contact with each other. Gases, in contrast, are highly compressible because the atomic particles are far apart. In Chapter 11, we introduced an atomic-level model of an *ideal gas,* reviewed in FIGURE 12.3. Our goal in this section is to further develop this model to understand the pressure of an ideal gas.

Molecular Speeds and Temperature

The atomic model of an ideal gas is based on random motion, so it's no surprise that the individual atoms in a gas are moving at different speeds. FIGURE 12.4 on the next page shows data from an experiment to measure the molecular speeds in nitrogen gas at 20°C. The results are presented as a histogram, a bar chart in which the height of the bar indicates what percentage of the molecules have a speed in the range of speeds shown below the bar. For example, 16% of the molecules have speeds in the range from 600 m/s to 700 m/s. The most probable speed, as judged from the tallest bar, is ≈ 500 m/s. This is quite fast: ≈ 1200 mph!

Because temperature is related to the average kinetic energy of the atoms, as we learned in Chapter 11, it will be useful to calculate the average kinetic energy for this distribution. An individual atom of mass m and velocity v has kinetic energy $K = \frac{1}{2}mv^2$. Recall that the average of a series of measurements is found by adding all the values and then dividing by the number of data points. Similarly, we can find the average kinetic energy by adding up all the kinetic energies of all the atoms and then dividing by the number of atoms:

$$K_{avg} = \frac{\sum \frac{1}{2}mv^2}{N} = \frac{1}{2}m\frac{\sum v^2}{N} = \frac{1}{2}m(v^2)_{avg} \qquad (12.3)$$

FIGURE 12.3 The ideal-gas model.

1. The gas is made up of a large number N of particles of mass m, each moving randomly.

2. The particles are quite far from each other and interact only rarely when they collide.

m

3. The collisions of the particles with each other (and with walls of the container) are elastic; no energy is lost in these collisions.

FIGURE 12.4 The distribution of molecular speeds in nitrogen gas at 20°C.

The height of a bar represents the percentage of molecules with speeds in the range on the horizontal axis.

The rms speed is 510 m/s.

N_2 molecules at 20°C

Speed range (m/s)

Martian airsicles The atmosphere of Mars is mostly carbon dioxide. At night, the temperature may drop so low that the molecules in the atmosphere will slow down enough to stick together—the atmosphere actually freezes. The frost on the surface in this image from the Viking 2 lander is composed partially of frozen carbon dioxide.

The quantity $\Sigma v^2/N$ is the sum of the values of v^2 for all the atoms divided by the number of atoms. By definition, this is average of the *squares* of all the individual speeds, which we've written $(v^2)_{avg}$.

The square root of this average is about how fast a typical atom in the gas is moving. Because we'll be taking the square root of the average, or mean, of the square of the speeds, we define the **root-mean-square speed** as

$$v_{rms} = \sqrt{(v^2)_{avg}} = \text{speed of a typical atom} \qquad (12.4)$$

The root-mean-square speed is often referred to as the *rms speed*. The rms speed isn't the average speed of atoms in the gas; it's the speed of an atom with the average kinetic energy. But the average speed and the rms speed are very nearly equal, so we'll interpret an rms speed as telling us the speed of a typical atom in the gas.

Rewriting Equation 12.3 in terms of v_{rms} gives the average kinetic energy per atom:

$$K_{avg} = \frac{1}{2}mv_{rms}^2 \qquad (12.5)$$

We learned in Chapter 11 that the temperature of a gas is related to the average kinetic energy of the atoms in the gas by

$$T = \frac{2}{3}\frac{K_{avg}}{k_B} \qquad (12.6)$$

where $k_B = 1.38 \times 10^{-23}$ J/K is Boltzmann's constant. Indeed, Equation 12.4 is really the definition of temperature for an ideal gas—temperature measures the average kinetic energy of the particles in a system. We can now relate the temperature to the speeds of the atoms if we substitute Equation 12.5 into Equation 12.6:

$$T = \frac{1}{3}\frac{mv_{rms}^2}{k_B} \qquad (12.7)$$

Solving Equation 12.7 for the rms speed of the atoms, we find that

$$v_{rms} = \sqrt{\frac{3k_B T}{m}} \qquad (12.8)$$

NOTE ▶ You must use absolute temperature, in kelvin, to compute rms speeds. ◀

We have been considering ideal gases made of atoms, but our results are equally valid for real gases made of either atoms (such as helium, He) or molecules (such as oxygen, O_2). At a given temperature, Equation 12.8 shows that the speed of atoms or molecules in a gas varies with the atomic or molecular mass. A gas with lighter atoms will have faster atoms, on average, than a gas with heavier atoms. The equation also shows that higher temperatures correspond to faster atomic or molecular speeds. The rms speed is proportional to the *square root* of the temperature. This is a new mathematical form that we will see again, so we will take a look at its properties.

Square-root relationships

Two quantities are said to have a **square-root relationship** if y is proportional to the square root of x. We write the mathematical relationship as

$$y = A\sqrt{x}$$

y is proportional to the square root of x

The graph of a square-root relationship is a parabola that has been rotated by 90°.

Increasing x by a factor of 4 increases y by a factor of 2.

$y = A\sqrt{x}$

Continued

SCALING If x has the initial value x_1, then y has the initial value y_1. Changing x from x_1 to x_2 changes y from y_1 to y_2. The ratio of y_2 to y_1 is

$$\frac{y_2}{y_1} = \frac{A\sqrt{x_2}}{A\sqrt{x_1}} = \sqrt{\frac{x_2}{x_1}}$$

which is the square root of the ratio of x_2 to x_1.

- If you increase x by a factor of 4, you increase y by a factor of $\sqrt{4} = 2$.
- If you decrease x by a factor of 9, you decrease y by a factor of $\sqrt{9} = 3$.

These examples illustrate a general rule:

Changing x by a factor of c changes y by a factor of $\sqrt{c}$.

Exercise 14 ✏

EXAMPLE 12.2 Speeds of air molecules

Most of the earth's atmosphere is the gas nitrogen, which consists of molecules, N_2. At the coldest temperature ever observed on earth, $-129°C$, what is the root-mean-square speed of the nitrogen molecules? Does the temperature at the earth's surface ever get high enough that a typical molecule is moving at twice this speed? (The highest temperature ever observed on earth was $58°C$.)

PREPARE You can use the periodic table to determine that the mass of a nitrogen atom is 14 u. A molecule consists of two atoms, so its mass is 28 u. Thus the molecular mass in SI units (i.e., kg) is

$$m = 28\ u \times \frac{1.66 \times 10^{-27}\ kg}{1\ u} = 4.6 \times 10^{-26}\ kg$$

The problem statement gives two temperatures we'll call T_1 and T_2; we need to express these in kelvin. The lowest temperature ever observed on earth is $T_1 = -129 + 273 = 144\ K$; the highest temperature is $T_2 = 58 + 273 = 331\ K$.

SOLVE We use Equation 12.8 to find v_{rms} for the nitrogen molecules at T_1:

$$v_{rms} = \sqrt{\frac{3k_B T_1}{m}} = \sqrt{\frac{3(1.38 \times 10^{-23}\ J/K)(144\ K)}{4.6 \times 10^{-26}\ kg}} = 360\ m/s$$

Because the rms speed is proportional to the square root of the temperature, doubling the rms speed would require increasing the temperature by a factor of 4. The ratio of the highest temperature ever recorded to the lowest temperature ever recorded is less than this:

$$\frac{T_2}{T_1} = \frac{331\ K}{144\ K} = 2.3$$

The temperature at the earth's surface is never high enough that nitrogen molecules move at twice the computed speed.

ASSESS We can use the square-root relationship to assess our computed result for the molecular speed. Figure 12.4 shows an rms speed of 510 m/s for nitrogen molecules at $20°C$, or 293 K. Temperature T_1 is approximately half of this, so we'd expect to compute a speed that is lower by about $1/\sqrt{2}$, which is what we found.

Pressure

Everyone has some sense of the concept of *pressure*. If you get a hole in your bicycle tire, the higher-pressure air inside comes squirting out. It's hard to get the lid off a vacuum-sealed jar because of the low pressure inside. But just what is pressure?

Let's take an atomic-scale view of pressure, defining it in terms of the motion of particles of a gas. Suppose we have a sample of gas in a container with rigid walls. As particles in the gas move around, they sometimes collide with and bounce off the walls, creating a force on the walls, as illustrated in FIGURE 12.5.

The force on a surface is proportional to the area. Doubling the surface area will double the number of collisions and thus double the force. Rather than the force itself, a more useful quantity is the force-to-area ratio F/A. This ratio is a property of the gas itself, independent of the surface, and it's what we call the gas **pressure**:

$$p = \frac{F}{A} \qquad (12.9)$$

Definition of pressure in a gas

You can see from Equation 12.9 that a gas exerts a force of magnitude

$$F = pA \qquad (12.10)$$

on a surface of area A. The force is *perpendicular* to the surface.

FIGURE 12.5 The pressure in a gas is due to the net force of the particles colliding with the walls.

There are an enormous number of collisions of particles against the wall every second.

Each collision exerts a force on the wall. The net force due to all the collisions causes the gas to have a pressure. The force of any one collision is incredibly small, but the number of collisions each second is exceedingly large, so the pressure can be considerable.

NOTE ▶ Pressure itself is *not* a force, even though we sometimes talk informally about "the force exerted by the pressure." The correct statement is that the *gas* exerts a force on a surface. ◀

From its definition, you can see that pressure has units of N/m². The SI unit of pressure is the **pascal**, defined as

$$1 \text{ pascal} = 1 \text{ Pa} = 1 \frac{\text{N}}{\text{m}^2}$$

This unit is named for the 17th-century French scientist Blaise Pascal, who was one of the first to study gases. A pascal is a very small pressure, so we usually see pressures in kilopascals, where 1 kPa = 1000 Pa.

The total force on the surface of your body due to the pressure of the atmosphere is over 40,000 pounds. Why doesn't this enormous force pushing in simply crush you? The key is that there is also a force pushing out. FIGURE 12.6a shows an empty plastic soda bottle. The bottle isn't a very sturdy structure, but the inward force due to the pressure of the atmosphere outside the bottle doesn't crush it because there is an equal pressure due to air inside the bottle that pushes out. The forces pushing on both sides are quite large, but they exactly balance and so there is no net force.

A net pressure force is exerted only where there's a pressure *difference* between the two sides of a surface. FIGURE 12.6b shows a surface of area A with a pressure difference $\Delta p = p_2 - p_1$ between the two sides. The net pressure force is

$$F_{\text{net}} = F_2 - F_1 = p_2 A - p_1 A = A(p_2 - p_1) = A \, \Delta p$$

This is the force that holds the lid on a vacuum-sealed jar, where the pressure inside is less than the pressure outside. To remove the lid, you have to exert a force greater than the force due to the pressure difference.

Decreasing the number of molecules in a container decreases the pressure because there are fewer collisions with the walls. The pressure in a completely empty container would be $p = 0$ Pa. This is called a *perfect vacuum*. A perfect vacuum cannot be achieved because it's impossible to remove every molecule from a region of space. In practice, a **vacuum** is an enclosed space in which $p \ll 1$ atm. Using $p = 0$ Pa is then a good approximation.

FIGURE 12.6 The net force depends on the pressure difference.

(a)

(b) Area A

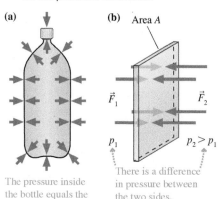

$\vec{F}_1$

$\vec{F}_2$

p_1

$p_2 > p_1$

The pressure inside the bottle equals the pressure outside, so there is no net force.

There is a difference in pressure between the two sides.

Measuring Pressure

The most important pressure for our daily lives is the pressure of the atmosphere. The pressure of the atmosphere varies with altitude and the weather, but the global average pressure at sea level, called the *standard atmosphere,* is

$$1 \text{ standard atmosphere} = 1 \text{ atm} = 101,300 \text{ Pa} = 101.3 \text{ kPa}$$

Just as we measured acceleration in units of g, we will often measure pressure in units of atm.

In the United States, pressure is often expressed in pounds per square inch, or psi. When you measure pressure in the tires on your car or bike, you probably use a gauge that reads in psi. The conversion factor is

$$1 \text{ atm} = 14.7 \text{ psi}$$

◀ **Too little pressure too fast** BIO This photo shows a rockfish, a popular game fish that can be caught at ocean depths up to 1000 ft. The great pressure at these depths is balanced by an equally large pressure inside the fish's swim bladder, a gas-filled organ that we will learn more about in Chapter 13. If the fish is hooked and rapidly raised to the lower pressure of the surface, the pressure inside the swim bladder is suddenly much greater than the pressure outside, causing the swim bladder to expand dramatically, damaging nearby organs. When reeled in from a great depth, these fish seldom survive.

Because the effects of pressure depend on pressure differences, most gauges measure not the actual or *absolute pressure* p but what is called the **gauge pressure**. The gauge pressure, denoted p_g, is the pressure *in excess* of atmospheric pressure; that is,

$$p_g = p - 1 \text{ atm}$$

You need to add 1 atm to the reading of a pressure gauge to find the absolute pressure p you need for doing most calculations in this chapter.

A tire-pressure gauge reads the gauge pressure p_g, not the absolute pressure p. Zero gauge pressure doesn't mean that there's no pressure inside the tire. It means that the pressure inside the tire is equal to atmospheric pressure. There's no pressure difference between the inside and the outside, and so the tire is flat.

EXAMPLE 12.3 **Finding the force due to a pressure difference**

Patients suffering from decompression sickness may be treated in a hyperbaric oxygen chamber filled with oxygen at greater than atmospheric pressure. A cylindrical chamber with flat end plates of diameter 0.75 m is filled with oxygen to a gauge pressure of 27 kPa. What is the resulting force on the end plate of the cylinder?

PREPARE There is a force on the end plate because of the pressure *difference* between the inside and outside. 27 kPa is the pressure in excess of 1 atm. If we assume the pressure outside is 1 atm, then 27 kPa is Δp, the pressure difference across the surface.

SOLVE The end plate has area $A = \pi(0.75 \text{ m}/2)^2 = 0.442 \text{ m}^2$. The pressure difference results in a net force

$$F_{net} = A \, \Delta p = (0.442 \text{ m}^2)(27{,}000 \text{ Pa}) = 12 \text{ kN}$$

ASSESS The area of the end plate is large, so we expect a large force. Our answer makes sense, although it is remarkable to think that this force results from the collisions of individual molecules with the plate. The large pressure force must be offset with an equally large force to keep the plate in place, so the end plate is fastened with stout bolts.

From Collisions to Pressure and the Ideal-Gas Law

We can use the fact that the pressure in a gas is due to the collisions of particles with the walls to make some qualitative predictions. FIGURE 12.7 presents a few such predictions.

FIGURE 12.7 Relating gas pressure to other variables.

Increasing the temperature of the gas means the particles move at higher speeds. They hit the walls more often and with more force, so there is more pressure.

Decreasing the volume of the container means more frequent collisions with the walls of the container, and thus more pressure.

Increasing the number of particles in the container means more frequent collisions with the walls of the container, and thus more pressure.

Based on the reasoning in Figure 12.7, we expect the following proportionalities:

- Pressure should be proportional to the temperature of the gas: $p \propto T$.
- Pressure should be inversely proportional to the volume of the container: $p \propto 1/V$.
- Pressure should be proportional to the number of gas particles: $p \propto N$.

In fact, careful experiments back up each of these predictions. It's not hard to do a quantitative extension of the qualitative treatment above that looks at the collisions with the walls and the resulting forces. This theoretical analysis leads to the same

Pumping up a bicycle tire adds more particles to the fixed volume of the tire, increasing the pressure.

proportionalities noted above, and ultimately produces a single equation that expresses these proportionalities:

$$p = C\frac{NT}{V}$$

The proportionality constant C is none other than Boltzmann's constant k_B, which allows us to write

$$pV = Nk_B T \qquad (12.11)$$

Ideal-gas law, version 1

Equation 12.11 is known as the **ideal-gas law.**

> NOTE ▶ When using the ideal-gas law, make sure that pressure p is the *absolute* pressure (in Pa) and temperature T is the *absolute* temperature (in K). ◀

The important point of the above discussion is that the ideal-gas law is more than just an empirical finding; it can be understood on the basis of the atomic model and an analysis of the forces in the collisions of particles in a gas with the walls of their container.

Equation 12.11 is written in terms of the number N of particles in the gas, whereas the ideal-gas law is stated in chemistry in terms of the number n of moles. But the change is easy to make. The number of particles is $N = nN_A$, so we can rewrite Equation 12.11 as

$$pV = nN_A k_B T = nRT \qquad (12.12)$$

Ideal-gas law, version 2

In this version of the equation, the proportionality constant—known as the *gas constant*—is

$$R = N_A k_B = 8.31 \text{ J/mol} \cdot \text{K}$$

The units may seem unusual, but the product of Pa and m^3, the units of pV, is equivalent to J.

> NOTE ▶ You may have learned to work gas problems using units of atmospheres and liters. To do so, you had a different numerical value of R that was expressed in those units. In physics we always work gas problems in SI units, so the above value of R is the one you need to use. ◀

We will go back and forth between solving problems in terms of moles and numbers of atoms, so the following equality will be useful:

$$Nk_B = nN_A k_B = nR \qquad (12.13)$$

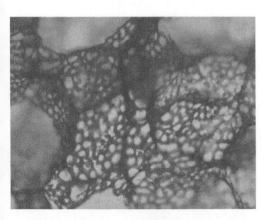

◀ **Gas exchange in the lungs** BIO When you draw a breath, how does the oxygen get into your bloodstream? The atomic model provides some insight. The picture is a highly magnified view of the alveoli, air sacs in the lungs, surrounded by capillaries, fine blood vessels. The thin membranes of the alveoli and the capillaries are permeable—small molecules can move across them. If a permeable membrane separates two regions of space having different concentrations of a molecule, the rapid motion of the molecules causes a net transport of molecules in the direction of lower concentration, as we might expect from the discussion of why heat flows from hot to cold in Chapter 11. This transport—entirely due to the motion of the molecules—is known as **diffusion**. In the lungs, the higher concentration of oxygen in the alveoli drives the diffusion of oxygen into the blood in the capillaries. At the same time, carbon dioxide diffuses from the blood into the alveoli. Diffusion is a rapid and effective means of transport in this case because the membranes are thin. Diffusion won't work to get oxygen from the lungs to other parts of the body, because diffusion is slow over large distances, so the oxygenated blood must be pumped throughout the body.

Let's review the meanings and the units of the various quantities in the ideal-gas law:

Number of moles in the
sample or container of gas

Absolute pressure, in
units of Pa

Gas constant, in units
of J/mol · K

$$pV = nRT$$

Volume of the sample or
container of gas, in units of m³

Temperature must be
expressed in K.

EXAMPLE 12.4 **Finding the volume of a mole**

What volume is occupied by 1 mole of an ideal gas at a pressure of 1.00 atm and a temperature of 0°C?

PREPARE The first step in ideal-gas law calculations is to convert all quantities to SI units:

$$p = 1.00 \text{ atm} = 101.3 \times 10^3 \text{ Pa}$$

$$T = 0 + 273 = 273 \text{ K}$$

SOLVE We use the ideal-gas law equation to compute

$$V = \frac{nRT}{p} = \frac{(1.00 \text{ mol})(8.31 \text{ J/mol} \cdot \text{K})(273 \text{ K})}{101.3 \times 10^3 \text{ Pa}} = 0.0224 \text{ m}^3$$

We recall from earlier in the chapter that 1.00 m³ = 1000 L, so we can write

$$V = 22.4 \text{ L}$$

ASSESS At this temperature and pressure, we find that the volume of 1 mole of a gas is 22.4 L, a result you might recall from chemistry. When we do calculations using gases, it will be useful to keep this volume in mind to see if our answers make physical sense.

NOTE ▶ The conditions of this example, 1 atm pressure and 0°C, are called *standard temperature and pressure,* abbreviated **STP**. They are a common reference point for many gas processes. ◀

STOP TO THINK 12.2 A sample of ideal gas is in a sealed container. The temperature of the gas and the volume of the container are both increased. What other properties of the gas necessarily change? (More than one answer may be correct.)

A. The rms speed of the gas atoms
B. The thermal energy of the gas
C. The pressure of the gas
D. The number of molecules of gas

12.3 Ideal-Gas Processes

This chapter is about the thermal properties of matter. What changes occur to matter as you change the temperature? We can use the ideal-gas law to make such deductions for gases because it provides a connection among the pressure, volume, and temperature of a gas. For example, suppose you measure the pressure in the tires on your car on a cold morning. How much will the tire pressure increase after the tires warm up in the sun and the temperature of the air in the tires has increased? We will solve this problem later in the chapter, but, for now, note these properties of this process:

■ The quantity of gas is fixed. No air is added to or removed from the tire. All of the processes we will consider will involve a fixed quantity of gas.
■ There is a well-defined initial state. The initial values of pressure, volume, and temperature will be designated p_i, V_i, and T_i.
■ There is a well-defined final state in which the pressure, volume, and temperature have values p_f, V_f, and T_f.

ActivPhysics: 8.4, 8.5, 8.6, 8.8, 8.9, 8.10, 8.11
PhET: Gas Properties
PhET: States of Matter

For gases in sealed containers, the number of moles (and the number of molecules) does not change. In that case, the ideal-gas law can be written as

$$\frac{pV}{T} = nR = \text{constant}$$

The values of the variables in the initial and final states are then related by

$$\frac{p_f V_f}{T_f} = \frac{p_i V_i}{T_i} \qquad (12.14)$$

Initial and final states for an ideal gas in a sealed container

This before-and-after relationship between the two states, reminiscent of a conservation law, will be valuable for many problems.

NOTE ▶ Because pressure and volume appear on both sides of the equation, this is a rare case of an equation for which we may use any units we wish, not just SI units. However, temperature *must* be in K. Unit-conversion factors for pressure and volume are multiplicative factors, and the same factor on both sides of the equation cancels. But the conversion from K to °C is an *additive* factor, and additive factors in the denominator don't cancel. ◀

pV Diagrams

It's useful to represent ideal-gas processes on a graph called a **pV diagram.** The important idea behind a *pV* diagram is that each point on the graph represents a single, unique state of the gas. This may seem surprising because a point on a graph specifies only the value of pressure and volume. But knowing *p* and *V*, and assuming that *n* is known for a sealed container, we can find the temperature from the ideal-gas law. Thus each point on a *pV* diagram actually represents a triplet of values (p, V, T) specifying the state of the gas.

For example, FIGURE 12.8a is a *pV* diagram showing three states of a system consisting of 1 mol of gas. The values of *p* and *V* can be read from the axes, then the temperature at that point calculated from the ideal-gas law. An ideal-gas process—a process that changes the state of the gas by, for example, heating it or compressing it—can be represented as a "trajectory" in the *pV* diagram. FIGURE 12.8b shows one possible process by which the gas of Figure 12.8a is changed from state 1 to state 3.

Constant-Volume Processes

Suppose you have a gas in the closed, rigid container shown in FIGURE 12.9a. Warming the gas will raise its pressure without changing its volume. This is an example of a **constant-volume process.** $V_f = V_i$ for a constant-volume process.

Because the value of *V* doesn't change, this process is shown as the vertical line i → f on the *pV* diagram of FIGURE 12.9b. **A constant-volume process appears on a pV diagram as a vertical line.**

FIGURE 12.8 The state of the gas and ideal-gas processes can be shown on a *pV* diagram.

(a) Each state of an ideal gas is represented as a point on a *pV* diagram.

(b) A process that changes the gas from one state to another is represented by a trajectory on a *pV* diagram.

FIGURE 12.9 A constant-volume process.

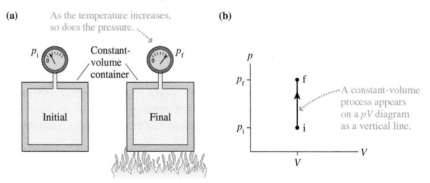

EXAMPLE 12.5 Computing tire pressure on a hot day

The pressure in a car tire is 30.0 psi on a cool morning when the air temperature is 0°C. After the day warms up and bright sun shines on the black tire, the temperature of the air inside the tire reaches 30°C. What is the tire pressure at this temperature?

PREPARE A tire is (to a good approximation) a sealed container with constant volume; this is a constant-volume process. The measured tire pressure is a gauge pressure, but the ideal-gas law requires an absolute pressure. We must correct for this. The initial pressure is

$$p_i = (p_g)_i + 1.00 \text{ atm} = 30.0 \text{ psi} + 14.7 \text{ psi} = 44.7 \text{ psi}$$

Temperatures must be in kelvin, so we convert:

$$T_i = 0°C + 273 = 273 \text{ K}$$

$$T_f = 30°C + 273 = 303 \text{ K}$$

SOLVE The gas is in a sealed container, so we can use the ideal-gas law as given in Equation 12.14 to solve for the final pressure. In this equation, we divide both sides by V_f, and then cancel the ratio of the two volumes, which is equal to 1 for this constant-volume process:

$$p_f = p_i \frac{V_i}{V_f} \frac{T_f}{T_i} = p_i \frac{T_f}{T_i}$$

The units for p_f will be the same as those for p_i, so we can keep the initial pressure in psi. The pressure at the higher temperature is

$$p_f = 44.7 \text{ psi} \times \frac{303 \text{ K}}{273 \text{ K}} = 49.6 \text{ psi}$$

This is an absolute pressure, but the problem asks for the measured pressure in the tire—a gauge pressure. Converting to gauge pressure gives

$$(p_g)_f = p_f - 1.00 \text{ atm} = 49.6 \text{ psi} - 14.7 \text{ psi} = 34.9 \text{ psi}$$

ASSESS The temperature has changed by 30 K, which is a bit more than 10% of the initial temperature, so we expect a large change in pressure. Our result seems reasonable, and it has practical implications: If you check the pressure in your tires when they are at a particular temperature, don't expect the pressure to be the same when conditions change!

Constant-Pressure Processes

Many gas processes take place at a constant, unchanging pressure. A constant-pressure process is also called an **isobaric process**. $p_f = p_i$ for an isobaric process.

One way to produce an isobaric process is shown in FIGURE 12.10a, where a gas is sealed in a cylinder by a lightweight, tight-fitting cap—a *piston*—that is free to slide up and down. In fact, the piston *will* slide up or down, compressing or expanding the gas inside, until it reaches the position at which $p_{gas} = p_{ext}$. That's the equilibrium position for the piston, the position at which the upward force $F_{gas} = p_{gas}A$, where A is the area of the face of the piston, exactly balances the downward force $F_{ext} = p_{ext}A$ due to the external pressure p_{ext}. The gas pressure in this situation is controlled by the external pressure p_{ext}. As long as the external pressure doesn't change, neither can the gas pressure inside the cylinder.

FIGURE 12.10 A constant-pressure (isobaric) process.

(a) In equilibrium, pressure must be the same on both sides of the piston.

Initial V_i — Final V_f

Moveable piston

Because the external pressure doesn't change, the gas pressure remains constant as the gas expands.

(b) An isobaric process appears on a pV diagram as a horizontal line.

Suppose we heat the gas in the cylinder. The gas pressure doesn't change because the pressure is controlled by the unchanging external pressure, not by the temperature. But as the temperature rises, the faster-moving atoms cause the gas to expand, pushing the piston outward. Because the pressure is always the same, this is an isobaric process, with a trajectory as shown in FIGURE 12.10b. **A constant-pressure process appears on a pV diagram as a horizontal line.**

EXAMPLE 12.6   **A constant-pressure compression**

A gas in a cylinder with a movable piston occupies 50.0 cm³ at 50°C. The gas is cooled at constant pressure until the temperature is 10°C. What is the final volume?

PREPARE This is a sealed container, so we can use Equation 12.14. The pressure of the gas doesn't change, so this is an isobaric process with $p_i/p_f = 1$.

The temperatures must be in kelvin, so we convert:

$$T_i = 50°C + 273 = 323 \text{ K}$$
$$T_f = 10°C + 273 = 283 \text{ K}$$

SOLVE We can use the ideal-gas law for a sealed container to solve for V_f:

$$V_f = V_i \frac{p_i}{p_f} \frac{T_f}{T_i} = 50.0 \text{ cm}^3 \times 1 \times \frac{283 \text{ K}}{323 \text{ K}} = 43.8 \text{ cm}^3$$

ASSESS In this example and the previous one, we have not converted pressure and volume units because these multiplicative factors cancel. But we did convert temperature to kelvin because this *additive* factor does *not* cancel.

Constant-Temperature Processes

FIGURE 12.11 A constant-temperature (isothermal) process.

(a)

(b)

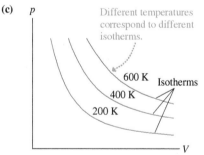

(c)

A constant-temperature process is also called an **isothermal process**. For an isothermal process $T_f = T_i$. One possible isothermal process is illustrated in FIGURE 12.11. A piston is being pushed down to compress a gas, but the gas cylinder is submerged in a large container of liquid that is held at a constant temperature. If the piston is pushed *slowly*, then heat-energy transfer through the walls of the cylinder will keep the gas at the same temperature as the surrounding liquid. This would be an *isothermal compression*. The reverse process, with the piston slowly pulled out, would be an *isothermal expansion*.

Representing an isothermal process on the pV diagram is a little more complicated than the two preceding processes because both p and V change. As long as T remains fixed, we have the relationship

$$p = \frac{nRT}{V} = \frac{\text{constant}}{V} \tag{12.15}$$

Because there is an inverse relationship between p and V, the graph of an isothermal process is a *hyperbola*.

The process shown as i → f in Figure 12.11b represents the *isothermal compression* shown in Figure 12.11a. An *isothermal expansion* would move in the opposite direction along the hyperbola. The graph of an isothermal process is known as an **isotherm**.

The location of the hyperbola depends on the value of T. If we use a higher constant temperature for the process in Figure 12.11a, the isotherm will move farther from the origin of the pV diagram. Figure 12.11c shows three isotherms for this process at three different temperatures. A gas undergoing an isothermal process will move along the isotherm for the appropriate temperature.

EXAMPLE 12.7   **Compressing air in the lungs**

A snorkeler takes a deep breath at the surface, filling his lungs with 4.0 L of air. He then descends to a depth of 5.0 m, where the pressure is 0.50 atm higher than at the surface. At this depth, what is the volume of air in the snorkeler's lungs?

PREPARE At the surface, the pressure of the air inside the snorkeler's lungs is 1.0 atm—it's atmospheric pressure at sea level. As he descends, the pressure inside his lungs must rise to match the pressure of the surrounding water, because the body can't sustain large pressure differences between inside and out. Further, the air stays at body temperature, making this an isothermal process with $T_f = T_i$.

SOLVE The ideal-gas law for a sealed container (the lungs) gives

$$V_f = V_i \frac{p_i}{p_f} \frac{T_f}{T_i} = 4.0\ \text{L} \times \frac{1.0\ \text{atm}}{1.5\ \text{atm}} = 2.7\ \text{L}$$

Notice that we didn't need to convert pressure to SI units. As long as the units are the same in the numerator and the denominator, they cancel.

ASSESS The air has a smaller volume at the greater pressure, as we would expect. The air inside your lungs does compress—significantly!—when you dive below the surface.

Thermodynamics of Ideal-Gas Processes

Chapter 11 introduced the first law of thermodynamics, and we saw that heat and work are just two different ways to add energy to a system. We've been considering the changes when we heat gases, but now we want to consider the other form of energy transfer—work.

When gases expand, they can do work by pushing against a piston. This is how the engine under the hood of your car works: When the spark plug fires in a cylinder in the engine, it ignites the gaseous fuel-air mixture inside. The hot gas expands, pushing the piston out and, through various mechanical linkages, turning the wheels of your car. Energy is transferred out of the gas as work; we say that the gas does work on the piston. Similarly, the gas in Figure 12.10a does work as it pushes on and moves the piston.

You learned in Chapter 10 that the work done by a constant force F in pushing an object a distance d is $W = Fd$. Let's apply this idea to a gas. **FIGURE 12.12a** shows a gas cylinder sealed at one end by a movable piston. Force $\vec{F}_{\text{gas}}$ is due to the gas pressure and has magnitude $F_{\text{gas}} = pA$. Force $\vec{F}_{\text{ext}}$, perhaps a force applied by a piston rod, is equal in magnitude and opposite in direction to $\vec{F}_{\text{gas}}$. The gas pressure would blow the piston out if the external force weren't there!

Suppose the gas expands at constant pressure, pushing the piston outward from x_i to x_f, a distance $d = x_f - x_i$, as shown in **FIGURE 12.12b**. As it does, the force due to the gas pressure does work

$$W_{\text{gas}} = F_{\text{gas}}d = (pA)(x_f - x_i) = p(x_f A - x_i A)$$

But $x_i A$ is the cylinder's initial volume V_i (recall that the volume of a cylinder is length times the area of the base), and $x_f A$ is the final volume V_f. Thus the work done is

$$W_{\text{gas}} = p(V_f - V_i) = p\ \Delta V \qquad (12.16)$$

Work done by a gas in an isobaric process

where ΔV is the *change* in volume.

Equation 12.16 has a particularly simple interpretation on a pV diagram. As **FIGURE 12.13a** shows, $p\ \Delta V$ is the "area under the pV graph" between V_i and V_f.

FIGURE 12.12 The expanding gas does work on the piston.

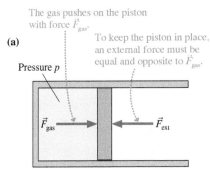

(a)

The gas pushes on the piston with force $\vec{F}_{\text{gas}}$.

To keep the piston in place, an external force must be equal and opposite to $\vec{F}_{\text{gas}}$.

Pressure p

$\vec{F}_{\text{gas}}$ $\vec{F}_{\text{ext}}$

(b)

As the piston moves a distance d, the gas does work $F_{\text{gas}}d$.

Piston area A

d

0 x_i x_f x

The gas volume changes by $\Delta V = dA$.

FIGURE 12.13 Calculating the work done in an ideal-gas process.

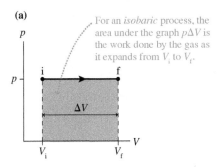

(a)

p

For an *isobaric* process, the area under the graph $p\Delta V$ is the work done by the gas as it expands from V_i to V_f.

p

i   f

ΔV

V_i V_f V

(b)

p

In general, the work done by a gas is the area under the graph between V_i and V_f.

i

f

$W_{\text{gas}} = $ area

V_i V_f V

Although we've shown this result only for an isobaric process, it turns out to be true for all ideal-gas processes. That is, as FIGURE 12.13b shows,

$$W_{\text{gas}} = \text{area under the } pV \text{ graph between } V_i \text{ and } V_f$$

There are a few things to clarify:

- In order for the gas to do work, its volume must change. No work is done in a constant-volume process.
- The simple relationship of Equation 12.16 applies only to constant-pressure processes. For any other ideal-gas process, you must use the geometry of the pV diagram to calculate the area under the graph.
- To calculate work, pressure must be in Pa and volume in m^3. The product of Pa (which is N/m^2) and m^3 is $N \cdot m$. But $1\ N \cdot m$ is $1\ J$—the unit of work and energy.
- W_{gas} is positive if the gas expands ($\Delta V > 0$). The gas does work by pushing against the piston. In this case, the work done is energy transferred out of the system, and the energy of the gas decreases. W_{gas} is negative if the piston compresses the gas ($\Delta V < 0$) because the force $\vec{F}_{\text{gas}}$ is opposite the displacement of the piston. Energy is transferred into the system as work, and the energy of the gas increases. We often say "work is done *on* the gas," but this just means that W_{gas} is negative.

In the first law of thermodynamics, $\Delta E_{\text{th}} = Q + W$, W is the work done by the environment—that is, by force $\vec{F}_{\text{ext}}$ acting on the system. But $\vec{F}_{\text{ext}}$ and $\vec{F}_{\text{gas}}$ are equal and opposite forces, as we noted above, so the work done by the environment is the negative of the work done by the gas: $W = -W_{\text{gas}}$. Consequently, the first law of thermodynamics can be written as

$$\Delta E_{\text{th}} = Q - W_{\text{gas}} \qquad (12.17)$$

In Chapter 11 we learned that the thermal energy of an ideal gas depends only on its temperature as $E_{\text{th}} = \frac{3}{2}Nk_BT$. Equation 12.13 tells us that Nk_B is equal to nR, so we can write the change in thermal energy of an ideal gas as

$$\Delta E_{\text{th}} = \frac{3}{2}Nk_B\ \Delta T = \frac{3}{2}nR\ \Delta T \qquad (12.18)$$

EXAMPLE 12.8   **Thermodynamics of an expanding gas**

A cylinder with a movable piston contains 0.016 mol of helium. A researcher expands the gas via the process illustrated in FIGURE 12.14. To achieve this, does she need to heat the gas? If so, how much heat energy must be added or removed?

FIGURE 12.14 pV diagram for Example 12.8.

PREPARE As the gas expands, it does work on the piston. Its temperature may change as well, implying a change in thermal energy. We can use the version of the first law of thermodynamics in Equation 12.17 to describe the energy changes in the gas. We'll first find the change in thermal energy by computing the temperature change, then calculate how much work is done by looking at

the area under the graph. Once we know W_{gas} and ΔE_{th}, we can use the first law to determine the sign and the magnitude of the heat—telling us whether heat energy goes in or out, and how much.

The graph tells us the pressure and the volume, so we can use the ideal-gas law to compute the temperature at the initial and final points. To do this we'll need the volumes in SI units. Reading the initial and final volumes on the graph and converting, we find

$$V_i = 100\ \text{cm}^3 \times \frac{1\ \text{m}^3}{10^6\ \text{cm}^3} = 1.0 \times 10^{-4}\ \text{m}^3$$

$$V_f = 300\ \text{cm}^3 \times \frac{1\ \text{m}^3}{10^6\ \text{cm}^3} = 3.0 \times 10^{-4}\ \text{m}^3$$

SOLVE The initial and final temperatures are found using the ideal-gas law:

$$T_i = \frac{p_iV_i}{nR} = \frac{(4.0 \times 10^5\ \text{Pa})(1.0 \times 10^{-4}\ \text{m}^3)}{(0.016\ \text{mol})(8.31\ \text{J/mol} \cdot \text{K})} = 300\ \text{K}$$

$$T_f = \frac{p_fV_f}{nR} = \frac{(2.0 \times 10^5\ \text{Pa})(3.0 \times 10^{-4}\ \text{m}^3)}{(0.016\ \text{mol})(8.31\ \text{J/mol} \cdot \text{K})} = 450\ \text{K}$$

The temperature increases, and so must the thermal energy. We can use Equation 12.18 to compute this change:

$$\Delta E_{th} = \frac{3}{2}(0.016 \text{ mol})(8.31 \text{ J/mol} \cdot \text{K})(450 \text{ K} - 300 \text{ K}) = 30 \text{ J}$$

The other piece of the puzzle is to compute the work done. We do this by finding the area under the graph for the process. FIGURE 12.15 shows that we can do this calculation by viewing the area as a triangle on top of a rectangle. Notice that the areas are in joules because they are the product of Pa and m³. The total work is

$$W_{gas} = \text{area of triangle} + \text{area of rectangle}$$

$$= 20 \text{ J} + 40 \text{ J} = 60 \text{ J}$$

Now we can use the first law as written in Equation 12.17 to find the heat:

$$Q = \Delta E_{th} + W_{gas} = 30 \text{ J} + 60 \text{ J} = 90 \text{ J}$$

FIGURE 12.15 The work done by the expanding gas is the total area under the graph.

Area of triangle:
$\frac{1}{2}(2.00 \times 10^5 \text{ Pa})(2.00 \times 10^{-4} \text{ m}^3)$
$= 20.0 \text{ J}$

Area of rectangle:
$(2.00 \times 10^5 \text{ Pa})(2.00 \times 10^{-4} \text{ m}^3)$
$= 40.0 \text{ J}$

This is a positive number, so—using the conventions introduced in Chapter 11—we see that 90 J of heat energy must be added to the gas.

ASSESS The gas does work—a loss of energy—but its temperature increases, so it makes sense that heat energy must be added.

Adiabatic Processes

You may have noticed that when you pump up a bicycle tire with a hand pump, the pump gets warm. We noted the reason for this in Chapter 11: When you press down on the handle of the pump, a piston in the pump's chamber compresses the gas. According to the first law of thermodynamics, doing work on the gas increases its thermal energy. So the gas temperature goes up, and heat is then transferred through the walls of the pump to your hand.

Now suppose you compress a gas in an insulated container, so that no heat is exchanged with the environment, or you compress a gas so quickly that there is no time for heat to be transferred. In either case, $Q = 0$. If a gas process has $Q = 0$, for either a compression or an expansion, we call this an **adiabatic process.**

An expanding gas does work, so $W_{gas} > 0$. If the expansion is adiabatic, meaning $Q = 0$, then the first law of thermodynamics as written in Equation 12.17 tells us that $\Delta E_{th} < 0$. Temperature is proportional to thermal energy, so the temperature will decrease as well. **An adiabatic expansion lowers the temperature of a gas.** If the gas is compressed, work is done on the gas ($W_{gas} < 0$). If the compression is adiabatic, the first law of thermodynamics implies that $\Delta E_{th} > 0$ and thus that the temperature increases. **An adiabatic compression raises the temperature of a gas.** Adiabatic processes allow you to use work, rather than heat, to change the temperature of a gas.

Adiabatic processes have many important applications. In the atmosphere, large masses of air moving across the planet exchange heat energy with their surroundings very slowly, so adiabatic expansions and compressions can lead to large and abrupt changes in temperature, as we see in the discussion of the Chinook wind.

▶ **Warm mountain winds** This image shows surface temperatures (in °F) in North America on a winter day. Notice the bright green area of unseasonably warm temperatures extending north and west from the center of the continent. On this day, a strong westerly wind, known as a Chinook wind, was blowing down off the Rocky Mountains, rapidly moving from high elevations (and low pressures) to low elevations (and higher pressures). The air was rapidly compressed as it descended. The compression was so rapid that no heat was exchanged with the environment, so this was an adiabatic process that significantly increased the air temperature.

CONCEPTUAL EXAMPLE 12.9 Adiabatic curves on a *pV* diagram

FIGURE 12.16 shows the *pV* diagram of a gas undergoing an isothermal compression from point 1 to point 2. Sketch how the *pV* diagram would look if the gas were compressed from point 1 to the same final pressure by a rapid adiabatic compression.

FIGURE 12.16 *pV* diagram for an isothermal compression.

REASON An adiabatic compression increases the temperature of the gas as the work done on the gas is transformed into thermal energy. Consequently, as seen in FIGURE 12.17, the curve of the

adiabatic compression cuts across the isotherms to end on a higher-temperature isotherm when the gas pressure reaches p_2.

FIGURE 12.17 *pV* diagram for an adiabatic compression.

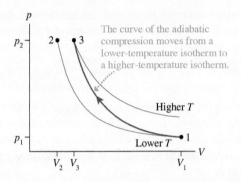

ASSESS In an isothermal compression, heat energy is transferred out of the gas so that the gas temperature stays the same. This heat transfer doesn't happen in an adiabatic compression, so we'd expect the gas to have a higher final temperature. In general, the temperature at the final point of an adiabatic compression is higher than at the starting point. Similarly, an adiabatic expansion ends on a lower-temperature isotherm.

STOP TO THINK 12.3 What is the ratio T_f/T_i for this process?

A. 1/4
B. 1/2
C. 1 (no change)
D. 2
E. 4
F. There is not enough information to decide.

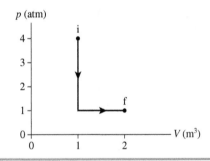

FIGURE 12.18 Increasing the temperature of a solid causes it to expand.

(a)

(b)

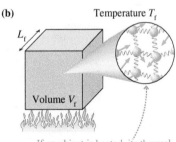

If an object is heated, its thermal energy increases. The atoms and molecules jiggle around at higher speeds and move farther apart.

12.4 Thermal Expansion

The bonds between atoms in solids and liquids mean that solids and liquids are much less compressible than gases, as we've noted. But raising the temperature of a solid or a liquid does produce a small, measurable change in volume. You've seen this principle at work if you've ever used a thermometer that contains mercury or alcohol (the kind with the red liquid) to measure a temperature. When you immerse the bulb of the thermometer in something warm, the liquid moves up the column for a simple reason: It expands. This **thermal expansion** underlies many practical phenomena.

FIGURE 12.18a shows a cube of material, initially at temperature T_i. The edge of the cube has length L_i, and the cube's volume is V_i. We then heat the cube, increasing its temperature to T_f, as shown in FIGURE 12.18b. The atoms now jiggle around faster, so the bonds are stretched. This increases the average distance between atoms, and so the cube's volume increases to V_f.

For most substances, the change in volume $\Delta V = V_f - V_i$ is linearly related to the change in temperature $\Delta T = T_f - T_i$ by

$$\Delta V = \beta V_i \,\Delta T \qquad (12.19)$$

Volume thermal expansion

Expanding spans A long steel bridge will slightly increase in length on a hot day and decrease on a cold day. Thermal expansion joints let the bridge's length change without causing the roadway to buckle.

The constant β is known as the **coefficient of volume expansion.** Its value depends on the nature of the bonds in a material; it can vary quite a bit from one substance to another. Because ΔT is measured in K, the units of β are K^{-1}.

As a solid's volume increases, each of its linear dimensions increases as well. We can write a similar expression for this linear thermal expansion. If an object of initial length L_i undergoes a temperature change ΔT, its length changes to L_f. The change in length, $\Delta L = L_f - L_i$, is given by

$$\Delta L = \alpha L_i \,\Delta T \qquad (12.20)$$

Linear thermal expansion

The constant α is the **coefficient of linear expansion.** Note that Equations 12.19 and 12.20 apply equally well to thermal *contractions,* in which case both ΔT and ΔV (or ΔL) are negative.

NOTE ▶ The expressions for thermal expansion are only approximate expressions that apply over a limited range of temperatures. They are what we call **empirical formulas;** they are a good fit to measured data, but they do not represent any underlying fundamental law. There are materials that do *not* closely follow Equations 12.19 and 12.20; water at low temperatures is one example, as we will see. ◄

Values of α and β for some common materials are listed in Table 12.3. The volume expansion of a liquid can be measured, but, because a liquid can change shape, we don't assign a coefficient of linear expansion to a liquid. Although α and β do vary slightly with temperature, the room-temperature values in Table 12.3 are adequate for all problems in this book. The values of α and β are very small, so the changes in length and volume, ΔL and ΔV, are a small fraction of the original length.

TABLE 12.3 Coefficients of linear and volume thermal expansion at 20°C

Substance	Linear α (K^{-1})	Volume β (K^{-1})
Aluminum	23×10^{-6}	69×10^{-6}
Glass	9×10^{-6}	27×10^{-6}
Iron or steel	12×10^{-6}	36×10^{-6}
Concrete	12×10^{-6}	36×10^{-6}
Ethyl alcohol		1100×10^{-6}
Water		210×10^{-6}
Air (and other gases)		3400×10^{-6}

EXAMPLE 12.10 **How much closer to space?**

The height of the Space Needle, a steel observation tower in Seattle, is 180 meters on a 0°C winter day. How much taller is it on a hot summer day when the temperature is 30°C?

PREPARE The steel expands because of an increase in temperature, which is

$$\Delta T = T_f - T_i = 30°C - 0°C = 30°C = 30 \text{ K}$$

SOLVE The coefficient of linear expansion is given in Table 12.3; we can use this value in Equation 12.20 to compute the increase in height:

$$\Delta L = \alpha L_i \,\Delta T = (12 \times 10^{-6} \text{ K}^{-1})(180 \text{ m})(30 \text{ K}) = 0.065 \text{ m}$$

ASSESS You don't notice buildings getting taller on hot days, so we expect the final answer to be small. The change is a small fraction of the height of the tower, as we expect. Our answer makes physical sense. Compared to 180 m, an expansion of 6.5 cm is not something you would easily notice—but it isn't negligible. The thermal expansion of structural elements in towers and bridges must be accounted for in the design to avoid damaging stresses. When designers failed to properly account for thermal stresses in the marble panels cladding the Amoco Building in Chicago, all 43,000 panels had to be replaced, at great cost.

Thermal expansion to the rescue If you have a stubborn lid on a glass jar, try this: Put the lid under very hot water for a short time. Heating the lid and the jar makes them both expand, but, as you can see from the data in Table 12.3, the steel lid—and the opening in the lid that fits over the glass jar—expands by more than the glass jar. The jar lid is now looser and can be more easily removed.

CONCEPTUAL EXAMPLE 12.11 **What happens to the hole?**

A metal plate has a circular hole in it. As the plate is heated, does the hole get larger or smaller?

REASON As the plate expands, you might think the hole would shrink (with the metal expanding into the hole). But suppose we took a metal plate and simply drew a circle where a hole could be cut. On heating, the plate and the marked area both expand, as we see in FIGURE 12.19. We could cut a hole on the marked line before or after heating; the size of the hole would be larger in the latter case. Therefore, the size of the hole must expand as the plate expands.

FIGURE 12.19 The thermal expansion of a hole.

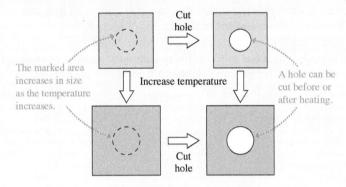

ASSESS This somewhat counterintuitive result has many practical applications, as you can see from the "Try It Yourself" exercise on loosening a jar lid.

Special Properties of Water and Ice

Water, the most important molecule for life, differs from other liquids in many important ways. If you cool a sample of water toward its freezing point of 0°C, you would expect its volume to decrease. FIGURE 12.20a shows a graph of the volume of a mole of water versus temperature. As the water is cooled, you can see that the volume indeed decreases—to a point. Once the water is cooled below 4°C, further cooling results in an *increase* in volume.

FIGURE 12.20 Variation of the volume of a mole of water with temperature.

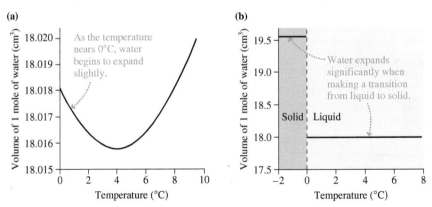

This anomalous behavior of water is a result of the charge distribution on the water molecules, which determines how nearby molecules interact with each other. As water approaches the freezing point, molecules begin to form clusters that are more strongly bound. Water molecules must actually get a bit farther apart to form such clusters, meaning the volume increases. Freezing the water results in an even greater increase in volume, as illustrated in FIGURE 12.20b.

This expansion on freezing has important consequences. In most materials, the solid phase is denser than the liquid phase, and so the solid material sinks. Because water *expands* as it freezes, ice is less dense than liquid water and floats. Not only do ice cubes float in your cold drink, but a lake freezes by forming ice on the top rather than at the bottom. This layer of ice then insulates the water below from much colder air above. Thus most lakes do not freeze solid, allowing aquatic life to survive even the harshest winters.

STOP TO THINK 12.4 An aluminum ring is tight around a solid iron rod. If we wish to loosen the ring to remove it from the rod, we should

A. Increase the temperature of the ring and rod.
B. Decrease the temperature of the ring and rod.

12.5 Specific Heat and Heat of Transformation

If you hold a glass of cold water in your hand, the heat from your hand will raise the temperature of the water. Similarly, the heat from your hand will melt an ice cube; this is what we will call a *phase change*. Increasing the temperature and changing the phase are two possible consequences of heating a system, and they form an important part of our understanding of the thermal properties of matter.

Video Tutor Demonstration   Video Tutor Demonstration

Specific Heat

Adding 4190 J of heat energy to 1 kg of water raises its temperature by 1 K. If you are fortunate enough to have 1 kg of gold, you need only 129 J of heat to raise its temperature by 1 K. The amount of heat that raises the temperature of 1 kg of a substance by 1 K is called the **specific heat** of that substance. The symbol for specific heat is c. Water has specific heat $c_{water} = 4190$ J/kg·K, and the specific heat of gold is $c_{gold} = 129$ J/kg·K. Specific heat depends only on the material from which an object is made. Table 12.4 lists the specific heats for some common liquids and solids.

If heat c is required to raise the temperature of 1 kg of a substance by 1 K, then heat Mc is needed to raise the temperature of mass M by 1 K and $Mc\,\Delta T$ is needed to raise the temperature of mass M by ΔT. In general, the heat needed to bring about a temperature change ΔT is

$$Q = Mc\,\Delta T \qquad (12.21)$$

Heat needed to produce a temperature change ΔT for mass M with specific heat c

TABLE 12.4 Specific heats of solids and liquids

Substance	c (J/kg·K)
Solids	
Lead	128
Gold	129
Copper	385
Iron	449
Aluminum	900
Water ice	2090
Mammalian body	3400
Liquids	
Mercury	140
Ethyl alcohol	2400
Water	4190

Q can be either positive (temperature goes up) or negative (temperature goes down).

Because $\Delta T = Q/Mc$, it takes more heat energy to change the temperature of a substance with a large specific heat than to change the temperature of a substance with a small specific heat. Water, with a very large specific heat, is slow to warm up and slow to cool down. This is fortunate for us. The large "thermal inertia" of water is essential for the biological processes of life.

Hurricane season At night, the large specific heat of water prevents the temperature of a body of water from dropping nearly as much as that of the surrounding air. Early in the morning, water vapor evaporating from a warm lake quickly condenses in the colder air above, forming mist. During the day, the opposite happens: The air becomes much warmer than the water. This lag between air and water temperatures is also at work at larger scales. Ocean temperatures in the northern hemisphere don't reach their maximum values until the late summer or early fall. This is why hurricanes, which are fueled by the energy in warm ocean water, happen in the fall but not the spring.

FIGURE 12.21 The temperature as a function of time as water is transformed from solid to liquid to gas.

(a)

(b)

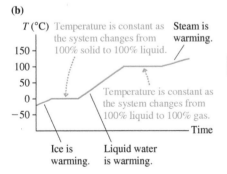

EXAMPLE 12.12 **Energy to run a fever**

A 70 kg student catches the flu, and his body temperature increases from 37.0°C (98.6°F) to 39.0°C (102.2°F). How much energy is required to raise his body's temperature?

PREPARE The increase in temperature requires the addition of energy. The change in temperature ΔT is 2.0°C, or 2.0 K.

SOLVE Raising the temperature of the body uses energy supplied internally from the chemical reactions of the body's metabolism, which transfer heat to the body. The specific heat of the body is given in Table 12.4 as 3400 J/kg · K. We can use Equation 12.21 to find the necessary heat energy:

$$Q = Mc\ \Delta T = (70\ \text{kg})(3400\ \text{J/kg} \cdot \text{K})(2.0\ \text{K}) = 4.8 \times 10^5\ \text{J}$$

ASSESS The body is mostly water, with a large specific heat, and the mass of the body is large, so we'd expect a large amount of energy to be necessary. Looking back to Chapter 11, we see that this is approximately the energy in a large apple, or the amount of energy required to walk 1 mile.

Phase Changes

The temperature inside the freezer compartment of a refrigerator is typically about −20°C. Suppose you remove a few ice cubes from the freezer and place them in a sealed container with a thermometer. Then, as in FIGURE 12.21a, you put a steady flame under the container. We'll assume that the heating is done slowly so that the inside of the container always has a single, uniform temperature.

FIGURE 12.21b shows the temperature as a function of time. After steadily rising from the initial −20°C, the temperature remains fixed at 0°C for an extended period of time. This is the interval of time during which the ice melts. As it's melting, the ice temperature is 0°C and the liquid water temperature is 0°C. Even though the system is being heated, the temperature doesn't begin to rise until all the ice has melted.

The atomic model can give us some insight into what is taking place. The thermal energy of a solid is the kinetic energy of the vibrating atoms plus the potential energy of stretched and compressed molecular bonds. If you heat a solid, at some point the thermal energy gets so large that the molecular bonds begin to break, allowing the atoms to move around—the solid begins to melt. Continued heating will produce further melting, as the energy is used to break more bonds. The temperature will not rise until all of the bonds are broken. If you wish to return the liquid to a solid, this energy must be removed.

NOTE ▶ In everyday language, the three phases of water are called *ice, water,* and *steam.* The term "water" implies the liquid phase. Scientifically, these are the solid, liquid, and gas phases of the compound called *water.* When we are working with different phases of water, we'll use the term "water" in the scientific sense of a collection of H_2O molecules. We'll say either *liquid* or *liquid water* to denote the liquid phase. ◀

CONCEPTUAL EXAMPLE 12.13 **Strategy for cooling a drink**

If you have a warm soda that you wish to cool, is it more effective to add 25 g of liquid water at 0°C or 25 g of water ice at 0°C?

REASON If you add liquid water at 0°C, heat will be transferred from the soda to the water, raising the temperature of the water and lowering that of the soda. If you add water ice at 0°C, heat first will be transferred from the soda to the ice to melt it, transforming the 0°C ice to 0°C liquid water, then will be transferred to the liquid water to raise its temperature. Thus more thermal energy will be removed from the soda, giving it a lower final temperature, if ice is used rather than liquid water.

ASSESS This makes sense because you know that this is what you do in practice. To cool a drink, you drop in an ice cube.

The temperature at which a solid becomes a liquid or, if the thermal energy is reduced, a liquid becomes a solid is called the **melting point** or the **freezing point.** Melting and freezing are *phase changes.* A system at the melting point is in **phase equilibrium,** meaning that any amount of solid can coexist with any amount of liquid. Raise the temperature ever so slightly and the entire system soon becomes liquid. Lower it slightly and it all becomes solid.

You can see another region of phase equilibrium of water in Figure 12.21b at 100°C. This is a phase equilibrium between the liquid phase and the gas phase, and any amount of liquid can coexist with any amount of gas at this temperature. As heat is added to the system, the temperature stays the same. The added energy is used to break bonds between the liquid molecules, allowing them to move into the gas phase. The temperature at which a gas becomes a liquid or a liquid becomes a gas is called the **condensation point** or the **boiling point.**

NOTE ▶ Liquid water becomes solid ice at 0°C, but that doesn't mean the temperature of ice is always 0°C. Ice reaches the temperature of its surroundings. If the air temperature in a freezer is −20°C, then the ice temperature is −20°C, Likewise, steam can be heated to temperatures above 100°C. That doesn't happen when you boil water on the stove because the steam escapes, but steam can be heated far above 100°C in a sealed container. ◀

Tin pest Some substances have multiple solid phases in which the atoms are arranged in lattices with different structures. Such substances can undergo a phase change between the solid phases; the atoms rearrange themselves, and the properties of the substance can change. The element tin slowly changes from the usual "white" phase to a brittle "gray" phase at low temperatures. The tin sample in this photo was chilled for one year; the resulting "tin pest" is quite obvious. Some historians speculate that this phase change destroyed the tin buttons on the coats of Napoleon's troops during their winter invasion of Russia in 1812, contributing to their defeat as they froze in the bitter cold.

CONCEPTUAL EXAMPLE 12.14 | **Fast or slow boil?**

You are cooking pasta on the stove; the water is at a slow boil. Will the pasta cook more quickly if you turn up the burner on the stove so that the water is at a fast boil?

REASON Water boils at 100°C; no matter how vigorously the water is boiling, the temperature is the same. It is the temperature of the water that determines how fast the cooking takes place.

Adding heat at a faster rate will make the water boil away more rapidly but will not change the temperature—and will not alter the cooking time.

ASSESS This result may seem counterintuitive, but you can try the experiment next time you cook pasta!

Heat of Transformation

In Figure 12.21b, the phase changes appeared as horizontal line segments on the graph. During these segments, heat is being transferred to the system but the temperature isn't changing. The thermal energy continues to increase during a phase change, but, as noted, the additional energy goes into breaking molecular bonds rather than speeding up the molecules. **A phase change is characterized by a change in thermal energy without a change in temperature.**

The amount of heat energy that causes 1 kg of a substance to undergo a phase change is called the **heat of transformation** of that substance. For example, laboratory experiments show that 333,000 J of heat are needed to melt 1 kg of ice at 0°C. The symbol for heat of transformation is L. The heat required for the entire system of mass M to undergo a phase change is

$$Q = ML \tag{12.22}$$

"Heat of transformation" is a generic term that refers to any phase change. Two particular heats of transformation are the **heat of fusion** L_f, the heat of transformation between a solid and a liquid, and the **heat of vaporization** L_v, the heat of transformation between a liquid and a gas. The heat needed for these phase changes is

$$Q = \begin{cases} \pm ML_f & \text{Heat needed to melt/freeze mass } M \\ \pm ML_v & \text{Heat needed to boil/condense mass } M \end{cases} \tag{12.23}$$

where the $\pm$ indicates that heat must be *added* to the system during melting or boiling but *removed* from the system during freezing or condensing. **You must explicitly include the minus sign when it is needed.**

Frozen frogs BIO It seems impossible, but common wood frogs survive the winter with much of their bodies frozen. When you dissolve substances in water, the freezing point lowers. Although the liquid water *between* cells in the frogs' bodies freezes, the water *inside* their cells remains liquid because of high concentrations of dissolved glucose. This prevents the cell damage that accompanies the freezing and subsequent thawing of tissues. When spring arrives, the frogs thaw and appear no worse for their winter freeze.

Lava—molten rock—undergoes a phase change from liquid to solid when it contacts liquid water; the transfer of heat to the water causes the water to undergo a phase change from liquid to gas.

Table 12.5 lists some heats of transformation. Notice that the heat of vaporization is always much higher than the heat of fusion, which our atomic model can explain. Melting breaks just enough molecular bonds to allow the system to lose rigidity and flow. Even so, the molecules in a liquid remain close together and loosely bonded. Vaporization breaks all bonds completely and sends the molecules flying apart. This process requires a larger increase in the thermal energy and thus a larger quantity of heat.

TABLE 12.5 Melting and boiling temperatures and heats of transformation at standard atmospheric pressure

Substance	T_m (°C)	L_f (J/kg)	T_b (°C)	L_v (J/kg)
Nitrogen (N_2)	−210	0.26×10^5	−196	1.99×10^5
Ethyl alcohol	−114	1.09×10^5	78	8.79×10^5
Mercury	−39	0.11×10^5	357	2.96×10^5
Water	0	3.33×10^5	100	22.6×10^5
Lead	328	0.25×10^5	1750	8.58×10^5

EXAMPLE 12.15 **Melting a popsicle**

A girl eats a 45 g frozen popsicle that was taken out of a −10°C freezer. How much energy does her body use to bring the popsicle up to body temperature?

PREPARE We can assume that the popsicle is pure water. Normal body temperature is 37°C. The specific heats of ice and liquid water are given in Table 12.4; the heat of fusion of water is given in Table 12.5.

SOLVE There are three parts to the problem: The popsicle must be warmed to 0°C, then melted, and then the resulting water must be warmed to body temperature. The heat needed to warm the frozen water by $\Delta T = 10°C = 10$ K to the melting point is

$$Q_1 = Mc_{ice} \Delta T = (0.045 \text{ kg})(2090 \text{ J/kg} \cdot \text{K})(10 \text{ K}) = 940 \text{ J}$$

Note that we use the specific heat of water ice, not liquid water, in this equation. Melting 45 g of ice requires heat

$$Q_2 = ML = (0.045 \text{ kg})(3.33 \times 10^5 \text{ J/kg}) = 15,000 \text{ J}$$

The liquid water must now be warmed to body temperature; this requires heat

$$Q_3 = Mc_{water} \Delta T = (0.045 \text{ kg})(4190 \text{ J/kg} \cdot \text{K})(37 \text{ K})$$
$$= 7000 \text{ J}$$

The total energy is the sum of these three values: $Q_{total} = 23,000$ J.

ASSESS More energy is needed to melt the ice than to warm the water, as we would expect. A commercial popsicle has 40 Calories, which is about 170 kJ. Roughly 15% of the chemical energy in this frozen treat is used to bring it up to body temperature!

Evaporation

Keeping your cool BIO Humans (and cattle and horses) have sweat glands, so we can perspire to moisten our skin, allowing evaporation to cool our bodies. Animals that do not perspire can also use evaporation to keep cool. Dogs, goats, rabbits, and even birds pant, evaporating water from their respiratory passages. Elephants spray water on their skin; other animals may lick their fur.

Water boils at 100°C. But individual molecules of water can move from the liquid phase to the gas phase at lower temperatures. This process is known as **evaporation**. Water evaporates as sweat from your skin at a temperature well below 100°C. We can use our atomic model to explain this.

In gases, we have seen that there is a variation in particle speeds. The same principle applies to water and other liquids. At any temperature, some molecules will be moving fast enough to go into the gas phase. And they will do so, carrying away thermal energy as they go. The molecules that leave the liquid are the ones that have the highest kinetic energy, so evaporation reduces the average kinetic energy (and thus the temperature) of the liquid left behind.

The evaporation of water, both from sweat and in moisture you exhale, is one of the body's methods of exhausting the excess heat of metabolism to the environment, allowing you to maintain a steady body temperature. The heat to evaporate a mass M of water is $Q = ML_v$, and this amount of heat is removed from your body. However, the heat of vaporization L_v is a little larger than the value for boiling. At a skin temperature of 30°C, the heat of vaporization of water is $L_v = 24 \times 10^5$ J/kg, or 6% higher than the value at 100°C in Table 12.5.

EXAMPLE 12.16 Computing heat loss by perspiration

The human body can produce approximately 30 g of perspiration per minute. At what rate is it possible to exhaust heat by the evaporation of perspiration?

SOLVE The evaporation of 30 g of perspiration at normal body temperature requires heat energy

$$Q = ML_v = (0.030 \text{ kg})(24 \times 10^5 \text{ J/kg}) = 7.2 \times 10^4 \text{ J}$$

This is the heat lost per minute; the rate of heat loss is

$$\frac{Q}{\Delta t} = \frac{7.2 \times 10^4 \text{ J}}{60 \text{ s}} = 1200 \text{ W}$$

ASSESS Given the metabolic power required for different activities, as listed in Chapter 11, this rate of heat removal is sufficient to keep the body cool even when exercising in hot weather—as long as the person drinks enough water to keep up this rate of perspiration.

STOP TO THINK 12.5 1 kg of barely molten lead, at 328°C, is poured into a large beaker holding liquid water right at the boiling point, 100°C. What is the mass of the water that will be boiled away as the lead solidifies?

A. 0 kg   B. <1 kg   C. 1 kg   D. >1 kg

12.6 Calorimetry

At one time or another you've probably put an ice cube into a hot drink to cool it quickly. You were engaged, in a trial-and-error way, in a practical aspect of heat transfer known as **calorimetry,** the quantitative measurement of the heat transferred between systems or evolved in reactions. You know that heat energy will be transferred from the hot drink into the cold ice cube, reducing the temperature of the drink, as shown in FIGURE 12.22.

Let's make this qualitative picture more precise. FIGURE 12.23 shows two systems that can exchange heat with each other but that are isolated from everything else. Suppose they start at different temperatures T_1 and T_2. As you know, heat energy will be transferred from the hotter to the colder system until they reach a common final temperature T_f. In the cooling coffee example of Figure 12.22, the coffee is system 1, the ice is system 2, and the insulating barrier is the mug.

The insulation prevents any heat energy from being transferred to or from the environment, so energy conservation tells us that any energy leaving the hotter system must enter the colder system. The concept is straightforward, but to state the idea mathematically we need to be careful with signs.

Let Q_1 be the energy transferred to system 1 as heat. Q_1 is positive if energy *enters* system 1, negative if energy *leaves* system 1. Similarly, Q_2 is the energy transferred to system 2. The fact that the systems are merely exchanging energy can be written as $|Q_1| = |Q_2|$. But Q_1 and Q_2 have opposite signs, so $Q_1 = -Q_2$. No energy is exchanged with the environment, so it makes more sense to write this relationship as

$$Q_{\text{net}} = Q_1 + Q_2 = 0 \qquad (12.24)$$

This idea is easily extended. No matter how many systems interact thermally, Q_{net} must equal zero.

> **NOTE** ▶ The signs are very important in calorimetry problems. ΔT is always $T_f - T_i$, so ΔT and Q are negative for any system whose temperature decreases. The proper sign of Q for any phase change must be supplied *by you,* depending on the direction of the phase change. ◀

FIGURE 12.22 Cooling hot coffee with ice.

FIGURE 12.23 Two systems interact thermally. In this particular example, where heat is being transferred from system 1 to system 2, $Q_2 > 0$ and $Q_1 < 0$.

Heat energy is transferred from system 1 to system 2. Energy conservation requires

$$|Q_1| = |Q_2|$$

Opposite signs mean that

$$Q_{\text{net}} = Q_1 + Q_2 = 0$$

PROBLEM-SOLVING
STRATEGY 12.1   Calorimetry problems

PREPARE Identify the individual interacting systems. Assume that they are isolated from the larger environment. List known information and identify what you need to find. Convert all quantities to SI units.

SOLVE The statement of energy conservation is

$$Q_{net} = Q_1 + Q_2 + \cdots = 0$$

- For systems that undergo a temperature change, $Q_{\Delta T} = Mc(T_f - T_i)$. Be sure to have the temperatures T_i and T_f in the correct order.
- For systems that undergo a phase change, $Q_{phase} = \pm ML$. Supply the correct sign by observing whether energy enters or leaves the system during the transition.
- Some systems may undergo a temperature change *and* a phase change. Treat the changes separately. The heat energy is $Q = Q_{\Delta T} + Q_{phase}$.

ASSESS The final temperature should be in the middle of the initial temperatures. A T_f that is higher or lower than all initial temperatures is an indication that something is wrong, usually a sign error.

EXAMPLE 12.17   **Using calorimetry to identify a metal**

200 g of an unknown metal is heated to 90.0°C, then dropped into 50.0 g of water at 20.0°C in an insulated container. The water temperature rises within a few seconds to 27.7°C, then changes no further. Identify the metal.

PREPARE The metal and the water interact thermally; there are no phase changes. We know all the initial and final temperatures. We will label the temperatures as follows: The initial temperature of the metal is T_m; the initial temperature of the water is T_w. The common final temperature is T_f. For water, $c_w = 4190$ J/kg·K is known from Table 12.4. Only the specific heat c_m of the metal is unknown.

SOLVE Energy conservation requires $Q_w + Q_m = 0$. Using $Q = Mc(T_f - T_i)$ for each, we have

$$Q_w + Q_m = M_w c_w (T_f - T_w) + M_m c_m (T_f - T_m) = 0$$

This is solved for the unknown specific heat:

$$c_m = \frac{-M_w c_w (T_f - T_w)}{M_m (T_f - T_m)}$$

$$= \frac{-(0.0500 \text{ kg})(4190 \text{ J/kg·K})(27.7°C - 20.0°C)}{(0.200 \text{ kg})(27.7°C - 90.0°C)}$$

$$= 129 \text{ J/kg·K}$$

Referring to Table 12.4, we find we have either 200 g of gold or, if we made an ever-so-slight experimental error, 200 g of lead!

ASSESS The temperature of the unknown metal changed much more than the temperature of the water. This means that the specific heat of the metal must be much less than that of water, which is exactly what we found.

EXAMPLE 12.18   **Calorimetry with a phase change**

Your 500 mL diet soda, with a mass of 500g, is at 20°C, room temperature, so you add 100 g of ice from the −20°C freezer. Does all the ice melt? If so, what is the final temperature? If not, what fraction of the ice melts? Assume that you have a well-insulated cup.

PREPARE We need to distinguish between two possible outcomes. If all the ice melts, then $T_f > 0°C$. It's also possible that the soda will cool to 0°C before all the ice has melted, leaving the ice and liquid in equilibrium at 0°C. We need to distinguish between these before knowing how to proceed. All the initial temperatures, masses, and specific heats are known. The final temperature of the combined soda + ice system is unknown.

SOLVE Let's first calculate the heat needed to melt all the ice and leave it as liquid water at 0°C. To do so, we must warm the ice by 20 K to 0°C, then change it to water. The heat input for this two-stage process is

This is the energy to raise the temperature of the ice from −20°C to 0°C. $\Delta T = 20$ K.   This is the energy to melt the ice once it reaches 0°C.

$$Q_{melt} = \overbrace{M_{ice} c_{ice} (20 \text{ K})} + \overbrace{M_{ice} L_f} = 37{,}000 \text{ J}$$

where L_f is the heat of fusion of water.

Q_{melt} is a *positive* quantity because we must *add* heat to melt the ice. Next, let's calculate how much heat energy will leave the 500 g soda if it cools all the way to 0°C:

$$Q_{cool} = M_{soda} c_{water} (-20 \text{ K}) = -42{,}000 \text{ J}$$

where $\Delta T = -20$ K because the temperature decreases. Because $|Q_{cool}| > Q_{melt}$, the soda has sufficient energy to melt all the ice. Hence the final state will be all liquid at $T_f > 0$. (Had we found

$|Q_{cool}| < Q_{melt}$, then the final state would have been an ice-liquid mixture at 0°C.)

Energy conservation requires $Q_{ice} + Q_{soda} = 0$. The heat Q_{ice} consists of three terms: warming the ice to 0°C, melting the ice to water at 0°C, then warming the 0°C water to T_f. The mass will still be M_{ice} in the last of these steps because it is the "ice system," but we need to use the specific heat of *liquid water*. Thus

$$Q_{ice} + Q_{soda} = [M_{ice}c_{ice}(20\text{ K}) + M_{ice}L_f$$
$$+ M_{ice}c_{water}(T_f - 0°C)]$$
$$+ M_{soda}c_{water}(T_f - 20°C) = 0$$

We've already done part of the calculation, allowing us to write

$$37{,}000\text{ J} + M_{ice}c_{water}(T_f - 0°C) + M_{soda}c_{water}(T_f - 20°C) = 0$$

Solving for T_f gives

$$T_f = \frac{20M_{soda}c_{water} - 37{,}000}{M_{ice}c_{water} + M_{soda}c_{water}} = 1.9°C$$

ASSESS A good deal of ice has been put in the soda, so it ends up being cooled nearly to the freezing point, as we might expect.

STOP TO THINK 12.6 1 kg of lead at 100°C is dropped into a container holding 1 kg of water at 0°C. Once the lead and water reach thermal equilibrium, the final temperature is

A. <50°C   B. 50°C   C. >50°C

12.7 Thermal Properties of Gases

Now it's time to turn back to gases. What happens when they are heated? Can we assign specific heats to gases as we did for solids and liquids? As we'll see, gases are harder to characterize than solids or liquids because the heat required to cause a specified temperature change depends on the *process* by which the gas changes state.

Just as for solids and liquids, heating a gas changes its temperature. But by how much? FIGURE 12.24 shows two isotherms on the pV diagram for a gas. Processes A and B, which start on the T_i isotherm and end on the T_f isotherm, have the *same* temperature change $\Delta T = T_f - T_i$, so we might expect them both to require the same amount of heat. But it turns out that process A, which takes place at constant volume, requires *less* heat than does process B, which occurs at constant pressure. The reason is that work is done in process B but not in process A.

It is useful to define two different versions of the specific heat of gases: one for constant-volume processes and one for constant-pressure processes. We will define these as *molar* specific heats because we usually do gas calculations using moles instead of mass. The quantity of heat needed to change the temperature of n moles of gas by ΔT is, for a constant-volume process,

$$Q = nC_V\,\Delta T \tag{12.25}$$

and for a constant-pressure process,

$$Q = nC_P\,\Delta T \tag{12.26}$$

C_V is the **molar specific heat at constant volume,** and C_P is the **molar specific heat at constant pressure.** Table 12.6 on the next page gives the values of C_V and C_P for some common gases. The units are J/mol · K. The values for air are essentially equal to those for N_2.

It's interesting that all the monatomic gases in Table 12.6 have the same values for C_P and for C_V. Why should this be? Monatomic gases are really close to ideal, so let's go back to our atomic model of the ideal gas. We know that the thermal energy of an ideal gas of N atoms is $E_{th} = \frac{3}{2}Nk_BT = \frac{3}{2}nRT$. If the temperature of an ideal gas changes by ΔT, its thermal energy changes by

$$\Delta E_{th} = \frac{3}{2}nR\,\Delta T \tag{12.27}$$

ActivPhysics: 8.7

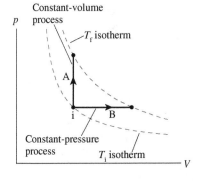
FIGURE 12.24 Processes A and B have the same ΔT and the same ΔE_{th}, but they require different amounts of heat.

TABLE 12.6 Molar specific heats
of gases (J/mol · K) at 20°C

Gas	C_P	C_V
Monatomic Gases		
He	20.8	12.5
Ne	20.8	12.5
Ar	20.8	12.5
Diatomic Gases		
H_2	28.7	20.4
N_2	29.1	20.8
O_2	29.2	20.9
Triatomic Gas		
Water vapor	33.3	25.0

If we keep the volume of the gas constant, so that no work is done, this energy change can come only from heat, so

$$Q = \frac{3}{2}nR\,\Delta T \tag{12.28}$$

Comparing Equation 12.28 with the definition of molar specific heat in Equation 12.25, we see that the molar specific heat at constant volume must be

$$C_V \text{ (monatomic gas)} = \frac{3}{2}R = 12.5 \text{ J/mol} \cdot \text{K} \tag{12.29}$$

This *predicted* value from the ideal-gas model is exactly the *measured* value of C_V for the monatomic gases in Table 12.6, a good check that the model we have been using is correct.

The molar specific heat at constant pressure is different. If you heat a gas in a sealed container so that there is no change in volume, then no work is done. But if you heat a sample of gas in a cylinder with a piston to keep it at constant pressure, the gas must expand, and it will do work as it expands. The expression for ΔE_{th} in Equation 12.27 is still valid, but now, according to the first law of thermodynamics, $Q = \Delta E_{th} + W_{gas}$. The work done by the gas in an isobaric process is $W_{gas} = p\,\Delta V$, so the heat required is

$$Q = \Delta E_{th} + W_{gas} = \frac{3}{2}nR\,\Delta T + p\,\Delta V \tag{12.30}$$

The ideal-gas law, $pV = nRT$, implies that if p is constant and only V and T change, then $p\,\Delta V = nR\,\Delta T$. Using this result in Equation 12.30, we find the heat needed to change the temperature by ΔT in a constant-pressure process is

$$Q = \frac{3}{2}nR\,\Delta T + nR\,\Delta T = \frac{5}{2}nR\,\Delta T$$

A comparison with the definition of molar specific heat shows that

$$C_P = \frac{5}{2}R = 20.8 \text{ J/mol} \cdot \text{K} \tag{12.31}$$

This is larger than C_V, as expected, and in perfect agreement for all the monatomic gases in Table 12.6.

EXAMPLE 12.19 **Work done by an expanding gas**

A typical weather balloon is made of a thin latex envelope that takes relatively little force to stretch, so the pressure inside the balloon is approximately equal to atmospheric pressure. The balloon is filled with a gas that is less dense than air, typically hydrogen or helium. Suppose a weather balloon filled with 180 mol of helium is waiting for launch on a cold morning at a high-altitude station. The balloon warms in the sun, which raises the temperature of the gas from 0°C to 30°C. As the balloon expands, how much work is done by the expanding gas?

PREPARE The work done is equal to $p\Delta V$, but we don't know the pressure (it's not sea level and we don't know the altitude) and we don't know the volume of the balloon. Instead, we'll use the first law of thermodynamics. We can rewrite Equation 12.17 as

$$W_{gas} = Q - \Delta E_{th}$$

The change in temperature of the gas is 30°C, so $\Delta T = 30$ K. We can compute how much heat energy is transferred to the balloon as it warms because this is a temperature change at constant

pressure, and we can compute how much the thermal energy of the gas increases because we know ΔT.

SOLVE The heat required to increase the temperature of the gas is given by Equation 12.26:

$$Q = nC_P\,\Delta T = (180\,\text{mol})(20.8 \text{ J/mol} \cdot \text{K})(30\,\text{K}) = 110 \text{ kJ}$$

The change in thermal energy depends on the change in temperature according to Equation 12.18:

$$E_{th} = \frac{3}{2}nR\,\Delta T = \frac{3}{2}(180 \text{ mol})(8.31 \text{ J/mol} \cdot \text{K})(30 \text{ K})$$
$$= 67 \text{ kJ}$$

The work done by the expanding balloon is just the difference between these two values:

$$W_{gas} = Q - \Delta E_{th} = 110 \text{ kJ} - 67 \text{ kJ} = 43 \text{ kJ}$$

ASSESS The numbers are large—it's a lot of heat and a large change in thermal energy—but it's a big balloon with a lot of gas, so this seems reasonable.

Now let's turn to the diatomic gases in Table 12.6. The molar specific heats are higher than for monatomic gases, and our atomic model explains why. The thermal energy of a monatomic gas consists exclusively of the translational kinetic energy of the atoms; heating a monatomic gas simply means that the atoms move faster. The thermal energy of a diatomic gas is more than just the translational energy, as shown in FIGURE 12.25. Heating a diatomic gas makes the molecules move faster, but it also causes them to rotate more rapidly. Energy goes into the translational kinetic energy of the molecules (thus increasing the temperature), but some goes into rotational kinetic energy. Because some of the added heat goes into rotation and not into translation, the specific heat of a diatomic gas is higher than that of a monatomic gas, as we see in Table 12.6. The table shows that water vapor, a triatomic gas, has an even higher specific heat, as we might expect.

FIGURE 12.25 Thermal energy of a diatomic gas.

The thermal energy of a diatomic gas is the sum of the translational kinetic energy of the molecules . . .

. . . plus the rotational kinetic energy of the molecules.

Heat Engines

Chapter 11 introduced the idea of a *heat engine,* a device that takes in heat energy from a hot reservoir, does useful work, and exhausts waste heat to a cold reservoir. Many real heat engines rely on gas processes, and we've now reached the point where we can examine heat engines more closely. A diagram of the (somewhat simplified) operation of a real heat engine, a two-stroke gasoline engine, is shown in FIGURE 12.26.

FIGURE 12.26 A simplified model of a gasoline engine.

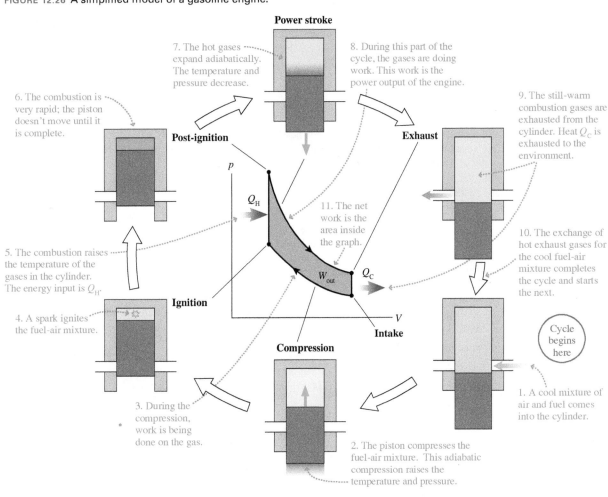

7. The hot gases expand adiabatically. The temperature and pressure decrease.

8. During this part of the cycle, the gases are doing work. This work is the power output of the engine.

6. The combustion is very rapid; the piston doesn't move until it is complete.

9. The still-warm combustion gases are exhausted from the cylinder. Heat Q_C is exhausted to the environment.

Post-ignition

Exhaust

Q_H

11. The net work is the area inside the graph.

5. The combustion raises the temperature of the gases in the cylinder. The energy input is Q_H.

W_{out}

Q_C

10. The exchange of hot exhaust gases for the cool fuel-air mixture completes the cycle and starts the next.

Ignition

4. A spark ignites the fuel-air mixture.

Intake

Compression

1. A cool mixture of air and fuel comes into the cylinder.

Cycle begins here

3. During the compression, work is being done on the gas.

2. The piston compresses the fuel-air mixture. This adiabatic compression raises the temperature and pressure.

NOTE ▶ It is common to use "gas" as shorthand for "gasoline." In this chapter, "gas" always refers to the state of matter. We will use "gasoline" or "fuel" to refer to the chemical energy source that you put in your tank. ◀

In this engine, the gases in the cylinder expand and contract in a repeating cycle as the piston moves back and forth. The cycle begins at the noted point with the introduction of gases (a mixture of air and fuel) into the cylinder. From this point, we can use our knowledge of gas processes to analyze the operation of the engine as it goes through its cycle. Figure 12.26 shows the connection between the operation of the engine and relevant points on the pV diagram of the gases in the engine's cylinder.

There are several important characteristics of this heat engine that apply generally to all heat engines:

- The sequence of processes forms a closed loop in the pV diagram. This must be true for the engine to go through its cycle over and over.
- Heat Q_H is taken in from a hot reservoir (in this case, from the burning fuel) at some point during the cycle. To bring the temperature back down at the end of the cycle, heat Q_C must be exhausted to a cold reservoir. This heat is carried out of the engine by the hot exhaust gases.
- The work done by the engine, W_{out}, is the area *inside* the closed loop on the pV diagram.
- Because the temperature returns to its starting point at the end of each cycle, there's no net change in thermal energy. Thus from energy conservation, $W_{out} = Q_H - Q_C$.

Work is the area inside the closed loop because of our earlier observation that the work done in a single process is the area under the graph. The work is negative for the compression, because ΔV is negative, and positive for the expansion. Thus the net work is the area under the upper curve *minus* the area under the lower curve, which is just the area inside the closed loop. This is true for all heat engines, not just the example shown here.

ActivPhysics: 8.12, 8.13, 8.14

EXAMPLE 12.20 **Finding the pressure and temperature in a gasoline engine**

At the start of a cycle in an internal combustion engine, 0.021 mol of air is introduced into the cylinder along with 0.018 g of gasoline. The adiabatic compression stroke raises the pressure to 17 atm and the temperature to 300°C. A spark then ignites the gasoline, which burns fully. What are the pressure and temperature immediately after ignition? (The combustion consumes oxygen but produces other gases; assume that the total number of moles of gas doesn't change.)

PREPARE Chapter 11 gives the energy content of gasoline as 44 kJ per gram, so we can figure out how much energy is liberated when the gas in the cylinder is burned. This combustion happens rapidly, so there is no time for the piston to move. The gas is heated at constant volume. The gas in the cylinder is mostly air, so we'll use $C_V = 20.8$ J/mol · K as the molar specific heat at constant volume.

SOLVE The energy released in the combustion of 0.018 g of gasoline is

$$Q = (44 \text{ kJ/g})(0.018 \text{ g}) = 790 \text{ J}$$

This heat is added to the air in the cylinder at constant volume, causing the temperature to increase by

$$\Delta T = \frac{Q}{nC_V} = \frac{790 \text{ J}}{(0.021 \text{ mol})(20.8 \text{ J/mol} \cdot \text{K})} = 1800°C$$

Thus igniting the fuel raises the temperature from $T_i = 300°C$ at the end of the compression stroke to $T_f = 2100°C$. The volume doesn't change, so the new pressure is

$$p_f = p_i \frac{V_i}{V_f} \frac{T_f}{T_i} = (17 \text{ atm})(1)\frac{2100 + 273}{300 + 273} = 70 \text{ atm}$$

ASSESS The pressure and temperature are both very large, but that's to be expected following an explosion in a confined volume. When you drive your car, a series of such explosions in your engine's cylinders provide the necessary force to move your car down the road. In a typical car moving at highway speeds, over 100 explosions are taking place under your hood each second.

12.8 Heat Transfer

You feel warmer when the sun is shining on you, colder when you are sitting on a cold concrete bench or when a stiff wind is blowing. This is due to the transfer of heat. Although we've talked about heat and heat transfers a lot in these last two chapters, we haven't said much about *how* heat is transferred from a hotter object to a colder object. There are four basic mechanisms, described in the table on the next page, by which objects exchange heat with other objects or their surroundings. Evaporation was treated in an earlier section; in this section we will consider the other mechanisms.

Heat-transfer mechanisms

When two objects are in direct physical contact, such as the soldering iron and the circuit board, heat is transferred by *conduction*. **Energy is transferred by direct contact.**

This special photograph shows air currents near a warm glass of water. Air near the glass is warmed and rises, taking thermal energy with it in a process known as *convection*. **Energy is transferred by the bulk motion of molecules with high thermal energy.**

The lamp shines on the lambs huddled below, warming them. The energy is transferred by infrared *radiation,* a form of electromagnetic waves. **Energy is transferred by electromagnetic waves.**

As we saw in an earlier section, the *evaporation* of liquid can carry away significant quantities of thermal energy. When you blow on a cup of cocoa, this increases the rate of evaporation, rapidly cooling it. **Energy is transferred by the removal of molecules with high thermal energy.**

Conduction

If you hold a metal spoon in a cup of hot coffee, the handle of the spoon soon gets warm. Thermal energy is transferred along the spoon from the coffee to your hand. The difference in temperature between the two ends drives this heat transfer by a process known as **conduction.** Conduction is the transfer of thermal energy directly through a physical material.

FIGURE 12.27 shows a copper rod placed between a hot reservoir (a fire) and a cold reservoir (a block of ice). We can use our atomic model to see how thermal energy is transferred along the rod by the interaction between atoms in the rod; fast-moving atoms at the hot end transfer energy to slower-moving atoms at the cold end.

Suppose we set up a series of experiments to measure the heat Q transferred through various rods. We would find the following trends in our data:

- Q increases if the temperature difference ΔT between the hot end and the cold end is increased.
- Q increases if the cross-section area A of the rod is increased.
- Q decreases if the length L of the rod is increased.
- Some materials (such as metals) transfer heat quite readily. Other materials (such as wood) transfer very little heat.

The final observation is one that is familiar to you: If you are stirring a pot of hot soup on the stove, you generally use a wood or plastic spoon rather than a metal one.

These experimental observations about heat conduction can be summarized in a single formula. If heat Q is transferred in a time interval Δt, the *rate* of heat transfer (joules per second) is $Q/\Delta t$. For a material of cross-section area A and length L, spanning a temperature difference ΔT, the rate of heat transfer is

$$\frac{Q}{\Delta t} = \left(\frac{kA}{L}\right)\Delta T \qquad (12.32)$$

Rate of conduction of heat across a temperature difference

FIGURE 12.27 **Conduction of heat in a solid rod.**

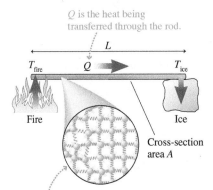

Q is the heat being transferred through the rod.

The particles on the left side of the rod are vibrating more vigorously than the particles on the right. The particles on the left transfer energy to the particles on the right via the bonds connecting them.

TABLE 12.7 Thermal conductivity values (measured at 20°C)

Material	k (W/m · K)
Diamond	1000
Silver	420
Copper	400
Iron	72
Stainless steel	14
Ice	1.7
Concrete	0.8
Plate glass	0.75
Skin	0.50
Muscle	0.46
Fat	0.21
Wood	0.2
Carpet	0.04
Fur, feathers	0.02–0.06
Air (27°C, 100 kPa)	0.026

Carpet or tile? If you walk around your house barefoot, you will notice that tile floors feel much colder than carpeted floors. The tile floor isn't really colder—the temperatures of all the floors in your house are nearly the same. But tile has a much higher thermal conductivity than carpet, so more heat will flow from your feet into the tile than into carpet. This causes the tile to feel colder.

Warm water (colored) moves by convection.

The quantity k, which characterizes whether the material is a good conductor of heat or a poor conductor, is called the **thermal conductivity** of the material. Because the heat transfer rate J/s is a *power,* measured in watts, the units of k are W/m · K. Values of k for some common materials are listed in Table 12.7; a larger number for k means a material is a better conductor of heat.

Good conductors of electricity, such as silver and copper, are usually good conductors of heat. Air, like all gases, is a poor conductor of heat because there are no bonds between adjacent atoms.

The weak bonds between molecules make most biological materials poor conductors of heat. Muscle is a better conductor than fat, so sea mammals have thick layers of fat for insulation. Land mammals insulate their bodies with fur, birds with feathers. Both fur and feathers trap a good deal of air, so their conductivity is similar to that of air, as Table 12.7 shows.

EXAMPLE 12.21 **Heat loss by conduction**

At the start of the section we noted that you "feel cold" when you sit on a cold concrete bench. "Feeling cold" really means that your body is losing a significant amount of heat. How significant? Suppose you are sitting on a 10°C concrete bench. You are wearing thin clothing that provides negligible insulation. In this case, most of the insulation that protects your body's core (temperature 37°C) from the cold of the bench is provided by a 1.0-cm-thick layer of fat on the part of your body that touches the bench. (The thickness varies from person to person, but this is a reasonable average value.) A good estimate of the area of contact with the bench is 0.10 m². Given these details, what is the heat loss by conduction?

PREPARE Heat is lost to the bench by conduction through the fat layer, so we can compute the rate of heat loss by using Equation 12.32. The thickness of the conducting layer is 0.010 m, the area is 0.10 m², and the thermal conductivity of fat is given in Table 12.7. The temperature difference is the difference between your body's core temperature (37°C) and the temperature of the bench (10°C), a difference of 27°C, or 27 K.

SOLVE We have all of the data we need to use Equation 12.32 to compute the rate of heat loss:

$$\frac{Q}{\Delta t} = \left(\frac{(0.21 \text{ W/m} \cdot \text{K})(0.10 \text{ m}^2)}{0.010 \text{ m}} \right)(27 \text{ K}) = 57 \text{ W}$$

ASSESS 57 W is more than half your body's resting power, which we learned in Chapter 11 is approximately 100 W. That's a significant loss, so your body will feel cold, a result that seems reasonable if you've ever sat on a cold bench for any length of time.

Convection

We noted that air is a poor conductor of heat. In fact, the data in Table 12.7 show that air has a thermal conductivity comparable to that of feathers. So why, on a cold day, will you be more comfortable if you are wearing a down jacket?

In conduction, faster-moving atoms transfer thermal energy to adjacent atoms. But in fluids such as water or air, there is a more efficient means to move energy: by transferring the faster-moving atoms themselves. When you place a pan of cold water on a burner on the stove, it's heated on the bottom. This heated water expands and becomes less dense than the water above it, so it rises to the surface while cooler, denser water sinks to take its place. This transfer of thermal energy by the motion of a fluid is known as **convection.**

Convection is usually the main mechanism for heat transfer in fluid systems. On a small scale, convection mixes the pan of water that you heat on the stove; on a large scale, convection is responsible for making the wind blow and ocean currents circulate. Air is a very poor thermal conductor, but it is very effective at transferring energy by convection. To use air for thermal insulation, it is necessary to trap the air in small pockets to limit convection. And that's exactly what feathers, fur, double-paned windows, and fiberglass insulation do. Convection is much more rapid in water than in air, which is why people can die of hypothermia in 65°F water but can live quite happily in 65°F air.

Radiation

You *feel* the warmth from the glowing red coals in a fireplace. On a cool day, you prefer to sit in the sun rather than the shade so that the sunlight keeps you warm. In both cases heat energy is being transferred to your body in the form of **radiation.**

Radiation consists of electromagnetic waves—a topic we will explore further in later chapters—that transfer energy from the object that emits the radiation to the object that absorbs it. Visible light, the red-to-violet colors of the rainbow, consists of electromagnetic waves, and objects that are hot enough to glow emit part of their radiation as visible light. We say these objects are "red hot" or, at a high enough temperature, "white hot." The white light from an incandescent lightbulb is radiation emitted by a thin wire filament that has been heated to a very high temperature by an electric current.

Electromagnetic waves of somewhat lower frequency are called *infrared radiation;* we can't see these waves, but we can sometimes sense them as "heat" as they are absorbed on our skin. Glowing objects emit part of their radiation as visible light but much of it as infrared radiation—the warmth that you feel from the glowing coals. Objects near room temperature, including your body, also radiate, but they emit nearly all of their radiation as infrared radiation. Thermal images, like the one of the teapot in FIGURE 12.28, are made with cameras having special infrared-sensitive detectors that allow them to "see" radiation that our eyes don't respond to.

NOTE ▶ The word "radiation" comes from "radiate," which means "to beam." You have likely heard the word used to refer to x rays and radioactive materials. This is not the sense we will use in this chapter. Here, we will use "radiation" to mean electromagnetic waves that "beam" from an object. ◀

Radiation is a significant part of the energy balance that keeps your body at the proper temperature. Radiation from the sun or from warm, nearby objects is absorbed by your skin, increasing your body's thermal energy. At the same time, your body radiates energy away. You can change your body temperature by absorbing more radiation (sitting next to a fire) or by emitting more radiation (taking off your hat and scarf to expose more skin).

The energy radiated by an object shows a strong dependence on temperature. In Figure 12.28, the hot teapot glows much more brightly than the cooler hand. In the photo that opened the chapter, the person's warm hands emit quite a bit more energy than the cooler spider. We can quantify the dependence of radiated energy on temperature. If heat energy Q is radiated in a time interval Δt by an object with surface area A and absolute temperature T, the *rate* of heat transfer $Q/\Delta t$ (joules per second) is found to be

$$\frac{Q}{\Delta t} = e\sigma A T^4 \tag{12.33}$$

Rate of heat transfer by radiation at temperature T (Stefan's law)

Quantities in this equation are defined as follows:

- e is the **emissivity** of a surface, a measure of the effectiveness of radiation. The value of e ranges from 0 to 1. Human skin is a very effective radiator at body temperature, with $e = 0.97$, regardless of skin color.

A feather coat BIO Penguins are birds and thus have feathers, even though they do not fly. The feathers are more obvious on this penguin chick than on the adults. A penguin's short, dense feathers serve a different role than the flight feathers of other birds: They trap air to provide thermal insulation. The feathers are equipped with muscles at the base of the shafts to flatten them and eliminate these air pockets; otherwise, the penguins would be too buoyant to swim underwater.

FIGURE 12.28 A thermal image of a teapot.

 PhET: Blackbody Spectrum
PhET: The Greenhouse Effect

Global heat transfer This satellite image shows radiation emitted by the waters of the ocean off the east coast of the United States. You can clearly see the warm waters of the Gulf Stream, a large-scale convection that transfers heat to northern latitudes. The satellite "sees" the radiation from the earth, so this radiation must readily pass through the atmosphere into space. In fact, the *only* means by which the earth as a whole can reduce its thermal energy is by radiation, because there is no conduction or convection in the vacuum of space. This has consequences for the energy balance of the earth, as we consider in a section on the greenhouse effect at the end of Part III.

- T is the absolute temperature in kelvin.
- A is the surface area in m^2.
- σ is a constant known as the Stefan-Boltzmann constant, with the value $\sigma = 5.67 \times 10^{-8}$ W/m$^2 \cdot$ K^4.

Notice the very strong fourth-power dependence on temperature. Doubling the absolute temperature of an object increases the radiant heat transfer by a factor of 16!

The amount of energy radiated by an animal can be surprisingly large. An adult human with bare skin in a room at a comfortable temperature has a skin temperature of approximately 33°C, or 306 K. A typical value for the skin's surface area is 1.8 m^2. With these values and the emissivity of skin noted above, we can calculate the rate of heat transfer via radiation from the skin:

$$\frac{Q}{\Delta t} = e\sigma A T^4 = (0.97)\left(5.67 \times 10^{-8}\,\frac{\text{W}}{\text{m}^2 \cdot \text{K}^4}\right)(1.8\text{ m}^2)(306\text{ K})^4 = 870\text{ W}$$

As we learned in Chapter 11, the body at rest generates approximately 100 W of thermal energy. If the body radiated energy at 870 W, it would quickly cool. At this rate of emission, the body temperature would drop by 1°C every 7 minutes! Clearly, there must be some mechanism to balance this emitted radiation, and there is: the radiation *absorbed* by the body.

When you sit in the sun, your skin warms due to the radiation you absorb. Even if you are not in the sun, you are absorbing the radiation emitted by the objects surrounding you. Suppose an object at temperature T is surrounded by an environment at temperature T_0. The *net* rate at which the object radiates heat energy—that is, radiation emitted minus radiation absorbed—is

$$\frac{Q_{\text{net}}}{\Delta t} = e\sigma A(T^4 - T_0^4) \qquad (12.34)$$

This makes sense. An object should have no net energy transfer by radiation if it's in thermal equilibrium ($T = T_0$) with its surroundings. Note that the emissivity e appears for absorption as well; objects that are good emitters are also good absorbers.

EXAMPLE 12.22 **Determining energy loss by radiation for the body**

A person with a skin temperature of 33°C is in a room at 24°C. What is the net rate of heat transfer by radiation?

PREPARE Body temperature is $T = 33 + 273 = 306$ K; the temperature of the room is $T_0 = 24 + 273 = 297$ K.

SOLVE The net radiation rate, given by Equation 12.34, is

$$\frac{Q_{\text{net}}}{\Delta t} = e\sigma A(T^4 - T_0^4)$$

$$= (0.97)\left(5.67 \times 10^{-8}\,\frac{\text{W}}{\text{m}^2 \cdot \text{K}^4}\right)(1.8\text{ m}^2)[(306\text{ K})^4 - (297\text{ K})^4] = 98\text{ W}$$

ASSESS This is a reasonable value, roughly matching your resting metabolic power. When you are dressed (little convection) and sitting on wood or plastic (little conduction), radiation is your body's primary mechanism for dissipating the excess thermal energy of metabolism.

The infrared radiation emitted by a dog is captured in this image. His cool nose and paws radiate much less energy than the rest of his body.

STOP TO THINK 12.7 Suppose you are an astronaut in the vacuum of space, hard at work in your sealed spacesuit. The only way that you can transfer heat to the environment is by

A. Conduction.   B. Convection.   C. Radiation.   D. Evaporation.

Breathing in cold air

On a cold day, breathing costs your body energy; as the cold air comes into contact with the warm tissues of your lungs, the air warms due to heat transferred from your body. The thermal image of the person inflating a balloon in FIGURE 12.29 shows that exhaled air is quite a bit warmer than the surroundings.

FIGURE 12.29 A thermal image of a person blowing up a balloon on a cold day.

FIGURE 12.30 shows this process for a frosty $-10°C$ (14°F) day. The inhaled air warms to nearly the temperature of the interior of your body, 37°C. When you exhale, some heat is retained by the body, but most is lost; the exhaled air is still about 30°C.

FIGURE 12.30 Breathing warms the air.

Outside air
$T = -10°C$

Exhaled air
$T = 30°C$

Your lungs hold several liters of air, but only a small part of the air is exchanged during each breath. A typical person takes 12 breaths each minute, with each breath drawing in 0.50 L of outside air. If the air warms up from $-10°C$ to 30°C, what is the volume of the air exhaled with each breath? What fraction of your body's resting power goes to warming the air? (Note that gases are exchanged as you breathe—oxygen to carbon dioxide—but to a good approximation the number of atoms, and thus the number of moles, stays the same.) Consider only the energy required to warm the air, not the energy lost to evaporation from the tissues of the lungs.

PREPARE There are two parts to the problem, which we'll solve in two different ways. First, we need to figure out the volume of exhaled air. When your body warms the air, its temperature increases, so its volume will increase as well. The initial and final states represented in Figure 12.30 are at atmospheric pressure, so we can treat this change as an isobaric (constant-pressure) process. We'll need the absolute temperatures of the initial and final states:

$$T_i = -10°C + 273 = 263 \text{ K}$$

$$T_f = 30°C + 273 = 303 \text{ K}$$

Next, we'll determine how much heat energy is required to raise the temperature of the air. Because the initial and final pressures are the same, we'll do this by computing the heat needed to raise the temperature of a gas at constant pressure. The change in temperature is $+40°C$, so we can use $\Delta T = 40$ K. Air is a mix of nitrogen and oxygen with a small amount of other gases. C_P for nitrogen and oxygen is the same to two significant figures, so we will assume the gas has $C_P = 29$ J/mol·K.

SOLVE The change in volume of the air in your lungs is a constant-pressure process. 0.50 L of air is breathed in; this is V_f. When the temperature increases, so does the volume. The gas isn't in a sealed container, but we are considering the same "parcel" of gas before and after, so we can use the ideal-gas law to find the volume after the temperature increase:

$$V_f = V_i \frac{p_i T_f}{p_f T_i} = (0.50 \text{ L}) \times 1 \times \frac{303 \text{ K}}{263 \text{ K}} = 0.58 \text{ L}$$

The volume increases by a little over 10%, from 0.50 L to 0.58 L.

Now we can move on to the second part: determining the energy required. We'll need the number of moles of gas, which we can compute from the ideal-gas law:

$$n = \frac{pV}{RT} = \frac{(101.3 \times 10^3 \text{ Pa})(0.50 \times 10^{-3} \text{ m}^3)}{(8.31 \text{ J/mol·K})(263 \text{ K})} = 0.023 \text{ mol}$$

In doing this calculation, we used 1 m³ = 1000 L to convert the 0.50 L volume to m³. Now we can compute the heat needed to warm one breath, using Equation 12.26:

$$Q(\text{one breath}) = nC_P \Delta T = (0.023 \text{ mol})(29 \text{ J/mol·K})(40 \text{ K})$$
$$= 27 \text{ J}$$

If you take 12 breaths a minute, a single breath takes 1/12 of a minute, or 5.0 s. Thus the heat power your body supplies to warm the incoming air is

$$P = \frac{Q}{\Delta t} = \frac{27 \text{ J}}{5.0 \text{ s}} = 5.4 \text{ W}$$

At rest, your body typically uses 100 W, so this is just over 5% of your body's resting power. You breathe in a good deal of air each minute and warm it by quite a bit, but the specific heat of air is small enough that the energy required is reasonably modest.

ASSESS The air expands slightly and a small amount of energy goes into heating it. If you've been outside on a cold day, you know that neither change is dramatic, so this final result seems reasonable. The energy loss is noticeable but reasonably modest; other forms of energy loss are more important when you are outside on a cold day.

SUMMARY

The goal of Chapter 12 has been to use the atomic model of matter to explain and explore many macroscopic phenomena associated with heat, temperature, and the properties of matter.

GENERAL PRINCIPLES

Atomic Model

We model matter as being made of simple basic particles. The relationship of these particles to each other defines the phase.

 Gas Liquid Solid

The atomic model explains thermal expansion, specific heat, and heat transfer.

Atomic Model of a Gas

Macroscopic properties of gases can be explained in terms of the atomic model of the gas. The speed of the particles is related to the temperature:

 p, V, T

$$v_{rms} = \sqrt{\frac{3k_B T}{m}}$$

The collisions of particles with each other and with the walls of the container determine the pressure.

Ideal-Gas Law

The ideal gas law relates the pressure, volume, and temperature in a sample of gas. We can express the law in terms of the number of atoms or the number of moles in the sample:

$$pV = Nk_B T$$

$$pV = nRT$$

For a gas process in a sealed container,

$$\frac{p_i V_i}{T_i} = \frac{p_f V_f}{T_f}$$

IMPORTANT CONCEPTS

Effects of heat transfer

A system that is heated can either change temperature or change phase.

The **specific heat** c of a material is the heat required to raise 1 kg by 1 K.

$$Q = Mc\,\Delta T$$

The **heat of transformation** is the energy necessary to change the phase of 1 kg of a substance. Heat is added to change a solid to a liquid or a liquid to a gas; heat is removed to reverse these changes.

$$Q = \begin{cases} \pm ML_f & \text{(melt/freeze)} \\ \pm ML_v & \text{(boil/condense)} \end{cases}$$

The **molar specific heat** of a gas depends on the process.

For a constant-volume process: $Q = nC_V\,\Delta T$
For a constant-pressure process: $Q = nC_P\,\Delta T$

Mechanisms of heat transfer

An object can transfer heat to other objects or to its environment:

Conduction is the transfer of heat by direct physical contact.

$$\frac{Q}{\Delta t} = \left(\frac{kA}{L}\right)\Delta T$$

Convection is the transfer of heat by the motion of a fluid.

Radiation is the transfer of heat by electromagnetic waves.

$$\frac{Q}{\Delta t} = e\sigma AT^4$$

A *pV* (pressure-volume) diagram is a useful means of looking at a process involving a gas.

A **constant-volume** process has no change in volume.

An **isobaric** process happens at a constant pressure.

An **isothermal** process happens at a constant temperature.

An **adiabatic** process involves no transfer of heat; the temperature changes.

The work done by a gas is the area under the graph.

APPLICATIONS

Thermal expansion Objects experience an increase in volume and an increase in length when their temperature changes:

$$\Delta V = \beta V_i\,\Delta T \qquad \Delta L = \alpha L_i\,\Delta T$$

Calorimetry When two or more systems interact thermally, they come to a common final temperature determined by

$$Q_{net} = Q_1 + Q_2 + Q_3 + \cdots = 0$$

The number of **moles** is

$$n = \frac{M\text{ (in grams)}}{M_{mol}}$$

QUESTIONS

Conceptual Questions

1. Which has more mass, a mole of Ne gas or a mole of N_2 gas?

2. If you launch a projectile upward with a high enough speed, its kinetic energy is sufficient to allow it to escape the earth's gravity—it will go up and not come back down. Given enough time, hydrogen and helium gas atoms in the earth's atmosphere will escape, so these elements are not present in our atmosphere. Explain why hydrogen and helium atoms have the necessary speed to escape but why other elements, such as oxygen and nitrogen, do not.

3. You may have noticed that latex helium balloons tend to shrink rather quickly; a balloon filled with air lasts a lot longer. Balloons shrink because gas diffuses out of them. The rate of diffusion is faster for smaller particles and for particles of higher speed. Diffusion is also faster when there is a large difference in concentration between two sides of a membrane. Given these facts, explain why an air-filled balloon lasts longer than a helium balloon.

4. If you buy a sealed bag of potato chips in Miami and drive with it to Denver, where the atmospheric pressure is lower, you will find that the bag gets very "puffy." Explain why.

5. If you double the typical speed of the molecules in a gas, by what factor does the pressure change? Give a simple explanation why the pressure changes by this factor.

6. Two gases have the same number of molecules per cubic meter (N/V) and the same rms speed. The molecules of gas 2 are more massive than the molecules of gas 1.
   a. Do the two gases have the same pressure? If not, which is larger?
   b. Do the two gases have the same temperature? If not, which is larger?

7. a. Which contains more particles, a mole of helium gas or a mole of oxygen gas? Explain.
   b. Which contains more particles, a gram of helium gas or a gram of oxygen gas? Explain.

8. You have 100 g of aluminum and 100 g of lead.
   a. Which contains a larger number of moles? Explain.
   b. Which contains more atoms? Explain.

9. Suppose you could suddenly increase the speed of every atom in a gas by a factor of 2.
   a. Does the thermal energy of the gas change? If so, by what factor? If not, why not?
   b. Does the molar specific heat change? If so, by what factor? If not, why not?

10. A gas cylinder contains 1.0 mol of helium at a temperature of 20°C. A second identical cylinder contains 1.0 mol of neon at 20°C. The helium atoms are moving with a higher average speed, but the gas pressure in the two containers is the same. Explain how this is possible.

11. A gas is in a sealed container. By what factor does the gas pressure change if

a. The volume is doubled and the temperature is tripled?
b. The volume is halved and the temperature is tripled?

12. A gas is in a sealed container. By what factor does the gas temperature change if
   a. The volume is doubled and the pressure is tripled?
   b. The volume is halved and the pressure is tripled?

13. What is the maximum amount of work that a gas can do during a constant-volume process?

14. You need to precisely measure the dimensions of a large wood panel for a construction project. Your metal tape measure was left outside for hours in the sun on a hot summer day, and now the tape is so hot it's painful to pick up. How will your measurements differ from those taken by your coworker, whose tape stayed in the shade? Explain.

15. Your car's radiator is made of steel and is filled with water. You fill the radiator to the very top with cold water, then drive off without remembering to replace the cap. As the water and the steel radiator heat up, will the level of water drop or will it rise and overflow? Explain.

16. Materials A and B have equal densities, but A has a larger specific heat than B. You have 100 g cubes of each material. Cube A, initially at 0°C, is placed in good thermal contact with cube B, initially at 200°C. The cubes are inside a well-insulated container where they don't interact with their surroundings. Is their final temperature greater than, less than, or equal to 100°C? Explain.

17. Two containers hold equal masses of nitrogen gas at equal temperatures. You supply 10 J of heat to container A while not allowing its volume to change, and you supply 10 J of heat to container B while not allowing its pressure to change. Afterward, is temperature T_A greater than, less than, or equal to T_B? Explain.

18. You need to raise the temperature of a gas by 10°C. To use the smallest amount of heat energy, should you heat the gas at constant pressure or at constant volume? Explain.

19. A sample of ideal gas is in a cylinder with a movable piston. 600 J of heat is added to the gas in an isothermal process. As the gas expands, pushing against the piston, how much work does it do?

20. A student is heating chocolate in a pan on the stove. He uses a cooking thermometer to measure the temperature of the chocolate and sees it varies as shown in Figure Q12.20. Describe what is happening to the chocolate in each of the three portions of the graph.

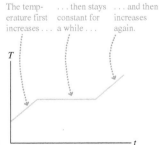

FIGURE Q12.20

21. If you bake a cake at high elevation, where atmospheric pressure is lower than at sea level, you will need to adjust the recipe. You will need to cook the cake for a longer time, and you will need to add less baking powder. (Baking powder is a leavening agent. As it heats, it releases gas bubbles that cause the cake to rise.) Explain why those adjustments are necessary.

22. The specific heat of aluminum is higher than that of iron. 1 kg blocks of iron and aluminum are heated to 100°C, and each is then dropped into its own 1 L beaker of 20°C water. Which beaker will end up with the warmer water? Explain.

23. A student is asked to sketch a pV diagram for a gas that goes through a cycle consisting of (a) an isobaric expansion, (b) a constant-volume reduction in temperature, and (c) an isothermal process that returns the gas to its initial state. The student draws the diagram shown in Figure Q12.23. What, if anything, is wrong with the student's diagram?

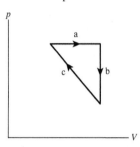

FIGURE Q12.23

24. If you have two spoons of the same size, one silver and one stainless steel, there is a quick test to tell which is which. Hold the end of a spoon in each hand, then lower them both into a cup of very hot water. One spoon will feel hot first. Is that the silver spoon or the stainless steel spoon? Explain.

25. If you live somewhere with cold, clear nights, you may have noticed some mornings when there was frost on open patches of ground but not under trees. This is because the ground under trees does not get as cold as open ground. Explain how tree cover keeps the ground under trees warmer.

Multiple-Choice Questions

26. | A tire is inflated to a gauge pressure of 35 psi. The absolute pressure in the tire is
    A. Less than 35 psi.
    B. Equal to 35 psi.
    C. Greater than 35 psi.

27. | The number of atoms in a container is increased by a factor of 2 while the temperature is held constant. The pressure
    A. Decreases by a factor of 4.
    B. Decreases by a factor of 2.
    C. Stays the same.
    D. Increases by a factor of 2.
    E. Increases by a factor of 4.

28. ‖ A gas is compressed by an isothermal process that decreases its volume by a factor of 2. In this process, the pressure
    A. Does not change.
    B. Increases by a factor of less than 2.
    C. Increases by a factor of 2.
    D. Increases by a factor of more than 2.

29. ‖‖ A gas is compressed by an adiabatic process that decreases its volume by a factor of 2. In this process, the pressure
    A. Does not change.
    B. Increases by a factor of less than 2.
    C. Increases by a factor of 2.
    D. Increases by a factor of more than 2.

30. | Suppose you do a calorimetry experiment to measure the specific heat of a penny. You take a number of pennies, measure their mass, heat them to a known temperature, and then drop them into a container of water at a known temperature. You then deduce the specific heat of a penny by measuring the temperature change of the water. Unfortunately, you didn't realize that you dropped one penny on the floor while transferring them to the water. This will
    A. Cause you to underestimate the specific heat.
    B. Cause you to overestimate the specific heat.
    C. Not affect your calculation of specific heat.

31. | A cup of water is heated with a heating coil that delivers 100 W of heat. In one minute, the temperature of the water rises by 20°C. What is the mass of the water?
    A. 72 g   B. 140 g
    C. 720 g   D. 1.4 kg

32. | Three identical beakers each hold 1000 g of water at 20°C. 100 g of liquid water at 0°C is added to the first beaker, 100 g of ice at 0°C is added to the second beaker, and the third beaker gets 100 g of aluminum at 0°C. The contents of which container end up at the lowest final temperature?
    A. The first beaker.
    B. The second beaker.
    C. The third beaker.
    D. All end up at the same temperature.

33. ‖‖‖ 100 g of ice at 0°C and 100 g of steam at 100°C interact thermally in a well-insulated container. The final state of the system is
    A. An ice-water mixture at 0°C.
    B. Water at a temperature between 0°C and 50°C.
    C. Water at 50°C.
    D. Water at a temperature between 50°C and 100°C.
    E. A water-steam mixture at 100°C.

34. | Suppose the 600 W of radiation emitted in a microwave oven is absorbed by 250 g of water in a very lightweight cup. Approximately how long will it take to heat the water from 20°C to 80°C?
    A. 50 s   B. 100 s
    C. 150 s   D. 200 s

35. ‖ 40,000 J of heat is added to 1.0 kg of ice at −10°C. How much ice melts?
    A. 0.012 kg   B. 0.057 kg
    C. 0.12 kg   D. 1.0 kg

36. ‖ Steam at 100°C causes worse burns than liquid water at
BIO 100°C. This is because
    A. The steam is hotter than the water.
    B. Heat is transferred to the skin as steam condenses.
    C. Steam has a higher specific heat than water.
    D. Evaporation of liquid water on the skin causes cooling.

PROBLEMS

Section 12.1 The Atomic Model of Matter

1. | Which contains the most moles: 10 g of hydrogen gas, 100 g of carbon, or 50 g of lead?

2. ‖‖ How many grams of water (H_2O) have the same number of oxygen atoms as 1.0 mol of oxygen gas?

3. ‖‖ How many atoms of hydrogen are in 100 g of hydrogen peroxide (H_2O_2)?

4. ‖ How many cubic millimeters (mm^3) are in 1 L?

5. ‖ A box is 200 cm wide, 40 cm deep, and 3.0 cm high. What is its volume in m^3?

Section 12.2 The Atomic Model of an Ideal Gas

6. ‖‖ Dry ice is frozen carbon dioxide. If you have 1.0 kg of dry ice, what volume will it occupy if you heat it enough to turn it into a gas at a temperature of 20°C?

7. | What is the absolute pressure of the air in your car's tires, in psi, when your pressure gauge indicates they are inflated to 35.0 psi? Assume you are at sea level.

8. ‖‖ Total lung capacity of a typical adult is approximately 5.0 L. BIO Approximately 20% of the air is oxygen. At sea level and at an average body temperature of 37°C, how many moles of oxygen do the lungs contain at the end of an inhalation?

9. ‖‖ Many cultures around the world still use a simple weapon BIO called a blowgun, a tube with a dart that fits tightly inside. A sharp breath into the end of the tube launches the dart. When exhaling forcefully, a healthy person can supply air at a gauge pressure of 6.0 kPa. What force does this pressure exert on a dart in a 1.5-cm-diameter tube?

10. ‖ When you stifle a sneeze, you can damage delicate tissues BIO because the pressure of the air that is not allowed to escape may rise by up to 45 kPa. If this extra pressure acts on the inside of your 8.4-mm-diameter eardrum, what is the outward force?

11. ‖‖ 7.5 mol of helium are in a 15 L cylinder. The pressure gauge on the cylinder reads 65 psi. What are (a) the temperature of the gas in °C and (b) the average kinetic energy of a helium atom?

12. ‖ Mars has an atmosphere composed almost entirely of carbon dioxide, with an average temperature of –63°C. What is the rms speed of a molecule in Mars's atmosphere?

13. ‖ 3.0 mol of gas at a temperature of −120°C fills a 2.0 L container. What is the gas pressure?

14. | 265 m/s is a typical cruising speed for a jet airliner. At what temperature (in °C) do the molecules of nitrogen gas have an rms speed of 265 m/s?

15. ‖‖ 10 g of liquid water is placed in a flexible bag, the air is excluded, and the bag is sealed. It is then placed in a microwave oven where the water is boiled to make steam at 100°C. What is the volume of the bag after all the water has boiled? Assume that the pressure inside the bag is equal to atmospheric pressure.

Section 12.3 Ideal-Gas Processes

16. ‖ A cylinder contains 3.0 L of oxygen at 300 K and 2.4 atm. The gas is heated, causing a piston in the cylinder to move outward. The heating causes the temperature to rise to 600 K and the volume of the cylinder to increase to 9.0 L. What is the final gas pressure?

17. ‖‖ A gas with initial conditions p_i, V_i, and T_i expands isothermally until $V_f = 2V_i$. What are (a) T_f and (b) p_f?

18. ‖‖ 0.10 mol of argon gas is admitted to an evacuated 50 cm^3 container at 20°C. The gas then undergoes heating at constant volume to a temperature of 300°C.
   a. What is the final pressure of the gas?
   b. Show the process on a pV diagram. Include a proper scale on both axes.

19. | 0.10 mol of argon gas is admitted to an evacuated 50 cm^3 container at 20°C. The gas then undergoes an isobaric heating to a temperature of 300°C.
   a. What is the final volume of the gas?
   b. Show the process on a pV diagram. Include a proper scale on both axes.

20. ‖‖ 0.10 mol of argon gas is admitted to an evacuated 50 cm^3 container at 20°C. The gas then undergoes an isothermal expansion to a volume of 200 cm^3.
   a. What is the final pressure of the gas?
   b. Show the process on a pV diagram. Include a proper scale on both axes.

21. ‖ 0.0040 mol of gas undergoes the process shown in Figure P12.21.
   a. What type of process is this?
   b. What are the initial and final temperatures?

FIGURE P12.21   **FIGURE P12.22**

22. ‖‖ 0.0040 mol of gas follows the hyperbolic trajectory shown in Figure P12.22.
   a. What type of process is this?
   b. What are the initial and final temperatures?
   c. What is the final volume V_f?

23. ‖ A gas with an initial temperature of 900°C undergoes the process shown in Figure P12.23.
   a. What type of process is this?
   b. What is the final temperature?
   c. How many moles of gas are there?

FIGURE P12.23   **FIGURE P12.24**

24. ‖‖ How much work is done on the gas in the process shown in Figure P12.24?

25. ‖ It is possible to make a thermometer by sealing gas in a rigid container and measuring the absolute pressure. Such a constant-volume gas thermometer is placed in an ice-water bath at 0.00°C. After reaching thermal equilibrium, the gas pressure is recorded as 55.9 kPa. The thermometer is then placed in contact with a sample of unknown temperature. After the thermometer reaches a new equilibrium, the gas pressure is 65.1 kPa. What is the temperature of this sample?

26. ‖ A 1.0 cm³ air bubble is released from the sandy bottom of a warm, shallow sea, where the gauge pressure is 1.5 atm. The bubble rises slowly enough that the air inside remains at the same constant temperature as the water.
   a. What is the volume of the bubble as it reaches the surface?
   b. As the bubble rises, is heat energy transferred from the water to the bubble or from the bubble to the water? Explain.

27. ‖ A weather balloon rises through the atmosphere, its volume expanding from 4.0 m³ to 12 m³ as the temperature drops from 20°C to −10°C. If the initial gas pressure inside the balloon is 1.0 atm, what is the final pressure?

Section 12.4 Thermal Expansion

28. ‖‖ A straight rod consists of a 1.2-cm-long piece of aluminum attached to a 2.0-cm-long piece of steel. By how much will the length of this rod change if its temperature is increased from 20°C to 40°C?

29. ‖ The length of a steel beam increases by 0.73 mm when its temperature is raised from 22°C to 35°C. What is the length of the beam at 22°C?

30. ‖ Older railroad tracks in the U.S. are made of 12-m-long pieces of steel. When the tracks are laid, gaps are left between the sections to prevent buckling when the steel thermally expands. If a track is laid at 16°C, how large should the gaps be if the track is not to buckle when the temperature is as high as 50°C?

31. ‖‖‖ The temperature of an aluminum disk is increased by 120°C. By what percentage does its volume increase?

Section 12.5 Specific Heat and Heat of Transformation

32. ‖‖ How much energy must be removed from a 200 g block of ice to cool it from 0°C to −30°C?

33. ‖‖‖ How much heat is needed to change 20 g of mercury at 20°C into mercury vapor at the boiling point?

34. ‖ a. 100 J of heat energy are transferred to 20 g of mercury. By how much does the temperature increase?
   b. How much heat is needed to raise the temperature of 20 g of water by the same amount?

35. ‖ The maximum amount of water an adult in temperate
BIO climates can perspire in one hour is typically 1.8 L. However, after several weeks in a tropical climate the body can adapt, increasing the maximum perspiration rate to 3.5 L/h. At what rate, in watts, is energy being removed when perspiring that rapidly? Assume all of the perspired water evaporates. At body temperature, the heat of vaporization of water is $L_v = 24 \times 10^5$ J/kg.

36. ‖ Alligators and other reptiles don't use enough metabolic
BIO energy to keep their body temperatures constant. They cool off at night and must warm up in the sun in the morning. Suppose a

300 kg alligator with an early-morning body temperature of 25°C is absorbing radiation from the sun at a rate of 1200 W. How long will the alligator need to warm up to a more favorable 30°C? (Assume that the specific heat of the reptilian body is the same as that of the mammalian body.)

37. ‖ When air is inhaled, it quickly becomes saturated with water
BIO vapor as it passes through the moist upper airways. When breathing dry air, about 25 mg of water are exhaled with each breath. At 12 breaths/min, what is the rate of energy loss due to evaporation? Express your answer in both watts and Calories per day. At body temperature, the heat of vaporization of water is $L_v = 24 \times 10^5$ J/kg.

38. ‖‖‖ It is important for the body to have mechanisms to effectively
BIO cool itself; if not, moderate exercise could easily increase body temperatures to dangerous levels. Suppose a 70 kg man runs on a treadmill for 30 min, using a metabolic power of 1000 W. Assume that all of this power goes to thermal energy in the body. If he couldn't perspire or otherwise cool his body, by how much would his body temperature rise during this exercise?

39. ‖‖‖ What minimum heat is needed to bring 100 g of water at 20°C to the boiling point and completely boil it away?

Section 12.6 Calorimetry

40. ‖‖‖ 30 g of copper pellets are removed from a 300°C oven and immediately dropped into 100 mL of water at 20°C in an insulated cup. What will the new water temperature be?

41. ‖‖‖ A copper block is removed from a 300°C oven and dropped into 1.00 kg of water at 20.0°C. The water quickly reaches 25.5°C and then remains at that temperature. What is the mass of the copper block?

42. ‖‖‖ A 750 g aluminum pan is removed from the stove and plunged into a sink filled with 10.0 kg of water at 20.0°C. The water temperature quickly rises to 24.0°C. What was the initial temperature of the pan?

43. ‖ A 500 g metal sphere is heated to 300°C, then dropped into a beaker containing 4.08 kg of mercury at 20.0°C. A short time later the mercury temperature stabilizes at 99.0°C. Identify the metal.

44. ‖ Brewed coffee is often too hot to drink right away. You can cool it with an ice cube, but this dilutes it. Or you can buy a device that will cool your coffee without dilution—a 200 g aluminum cylinder that you take from your freezer and place in a mug of hot coffee. If the cylinder is cooled to −20°C, a typical freezer temperature, and then dropped into a large cup of coffee (essentially water, with a mass of 500 g) at 85°C, what is the final temperature of the coffee?

45. ‖‖‖‖ Marianne really likes coffee, but on summer days she doesn't want to drink a hot beverage. If she is served 200 mL of coffee at 80°C in a well-insulated container, how much ice at 0°C should she add to obtain a final temperature of 30°C?

46. ‖ If a person has a dangerously high fever, submerging her in
BIO ice water is a bad idea, but an ice pack can help to quickly bring her body temperature down. How many grams of ice at 0°C will be melted in bringing down a 60 kg patient's fever from 40°C to 39°C?

Section 12.7 Thermal Properties of Gases

47. | A container holds 1.0 g of argon at a pressure of 8.0 atm.
    a. How much heat is required to increase the temperature by 100°C at constant volume?
    b. How much will the temperature increase if this amount of heat energy is transferred to the gas at constant pressure?

48. ‖ A container holds 1.0 g of oxygen at a pressure of 8.0 atm.
    a. How much heat is required to increase the temperature by 100°C at constant pressure?
    b. How much will the temperature increase if this amount of heat energy is transferred to the gas at constant volume?

49. | What is the temperature change of 1.0 mol of a monatomic gas if its thermal energy is increased by 1.0 J?

50. ‖ The temperature of 2.0 g of helium is increased at constant volume by ΔT. What mass of oxygen can have its temperature increased by the same amount at constant volume using the same amount of heat?

51. ‖‖ How much work is done per cycle by a gas following the pV trajectory of Figure P12.51?

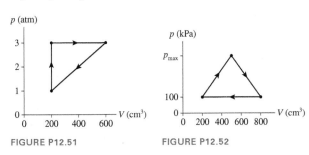

FIGURE P12.51   FIGURE P12.52

52. ‖‖ A gas following the pV trajectory of Figure P12.52 does 60 J of work per cycle. What is p_{max}?

Section 12.8 Heat Transfer

53. ‖‖ A 1.8-cm-thick wood floor covers a 4.0 m × 5.5 m room. The subfloor on which the flooring sits is at a temperature of 16.2°C, while the air in the room is at 19.6°C. What is the rate of heat conduction through the floor?

54. ‖‖‖ A copper-bottomed kettle, its bottom 24 cm in diameter and 3.0 mm thick, sits on a burner. The kettle holds boiling water, and energy flows into the water from the kettle bottom at 800 W. What is the temperature of the bottom surface of the kettle?

55. ‖‖‖ What is the greatest possible rate of energy transfer by radiation from a metal cube 2.0 cm on a side that is at 700°C? Its emissivity is 0.20.

56. ‖ What is the greatest possible rate of energy transfer by radiation for a 5.0-cm-diameter sphere that is at 100°C?

57. ‖ Seals may cool themselves by
    BIO using *thermal windows,* patches on their bodies with much higher than average surface temperature. Suppose a seal has a 0.030 m² thermal window at a temperature of 30°C. If the seal's surroundings are a frosty −10°C, what is the net rate of energy loss by radiation? Assume an emissivity equal to that of a human.

58. ‖ Electronics and inhabitants of the International Space Station generate a significant amount of thermal energy that the station must get rid of. The only way that the station can exhaust thermal energy is by radiation, which it does using thin, 1.8-m-by-3.6-m panels that have a working temperature of about 6°C. How much power is radiated from each panel? Assume that the panels are in the shade so that the absorbed radiation will be negligible. Assume that the emissivity of the panels is 1.0. **Hint:** Don't forget that the panels have two sides!

59. ‖ The glowing filament in a lamp is radiating energy at a rate of 60 W. At the filament's temperature of 1500°C, the emissivity is 0.23. What is the surface area of the filament?

60. ‖‖ If you lie on the ground at night with no cover, you get cold
    BIO rather quickly. Much of this is due to energy loss by radiation. At night in a dry climate, the temperature of the sky can drop to −40°C. If you are lying on the ground with thin clothing that provides little insulation, the surface temperature of your skin and clothes will be about 30°C. Estimate the net rate at which your body loses energy by radiation to the night sky under these conditions. **Hint:** What area should you use?

General Problems

61. ‖ A rigid container holds 2.0 mol of gas at a pressure of 1.0 atm and a temperature of 30°C.
    a. What is the container's volume?
    b. What is the pressure if the temperature is raised to 130°C?

62. ‖ A 15-cm-diameter compressed-air tank is 50 cm tall. The pressure at 20°C is 150 atm.
    a. How many moles of air are in the tank?
    b. What volume would this air occupy at STP?

63. ‖‖ A 10-cm-diameter cylinder of helium gas is 30 cm long and at 20°C. The pressure gauge reads 120 psi.
    a. How many helium atoms are in the cylinder?
    b. What is the mass of the helium?

64. ‖ Party stores sell small tanks containing 30 g of helium gas. If you use such a tank to fill 0.010 m³ foil balloons (which don't stretch, and so have an internal pressure that is very close to atmospheric pressure), how many balloons can you expect to fill?

65. ‖‖‖ Suppose you take and hold a deep breath on a chilly day,
    BIO inhaling 3.0 L of air at 0°C. Assume that air pressure is 1.0 atm.
    a. How much heat must your body supply to warm the air to your internal body temperature of 37°C?
    b. How much does the air's volume increase as it is warmed?

66. ‖ On average, each person in the industrialized world is responsible for the emission of 10,000 kg of carbon dioxide (CO_2) every year. This includes CO_2 that you generate directly, by burning fossil fuels to operate your car or your furnace, as well as CO_2 generated on your behalf by electric generating stations and manufacturing plants. CO_2 is a greenhouse gas that contributes to global warming. If you were to store your yearly CO_2 emissions in a cube at STP, how long would each edge of the cube be?

67. ‖‖ On a cool morning, when the temperature is 15°C, you measure the pressure in your car tires to be 30 psi. After driving 20 mi on the freeway, the temperature of your tires is 45°C. What pressure will your tire gauge now show?

68. ‖ Suppose you inflate your car tires to 35 psi on a 20°C day. Later, the temperature drops to 0°C. What is the pressure in your tires now?

69. | The volume in a constant-*pressure* gas thermometer is directly proportional to the absolute temperature. A constant-pressure thermometer is calibrated by adjusting its volume to 1000 mL while it is in contact with a reference cell at 0.01°C. The volume increases to 1638 mL when the thermometer is placed in contact with a sample. What is the sample's temperature in °C?

70. ‖ A compressed-air cylinder is known to fail if the pressure exceeds 110 atm. A cylinder that was filled to 25 atm at 20°C is stored in a warehouse. Unfortunately, the warehouse catches fire and the temperature reaches 950°C. Does the cylinder explode?

71. ‖ A rigid sphere has a valve that can be opened or closed. The sphere with the valve open is placed in boiling water in a room where the air pressure is 1.0 atm. After a long period of time has elapsed, the valve is closed. What will be the pressure inside the sphere if it is then placed in (a) a mixture of ice and water and (b) an insulated box filled with dry ice, which is at −78.5°C?

72. ‖‖ 80 J of work are done on the gas in the process shown in Figure P12.72. What is V_f in cm^3?

FIGURE P12.72   FIGURE P12.73

73. ‖‖ How much work is done by the gas in the process shown in Figure P12.73?

74. ‖ 0.10 mol of gas undergoes the process $1 \rightarrow 2$ shown in Figure P12.74.
    a. What are temperatures T_1 and T_2?
    b. What type of process is this?
    c. The gas undergoes constant-volume heating from point 2 until the pressure is restored to the value it had at point 1. What is the final temperature of the gas?

FIGURE P12.74

75. ‖ 10 g of dry ice (solid CO_2) is placed in a 10,000 cm^3 container, then all the air is quickly pumped out and the container sealed. The container is warmed to 0°C, a temperature at which CO_2 is a gas.
    a. What is the gas pressure? Give your answer in atm.
    The gas then undergoes an isothermal compression until the pressure is 3.0 atm, immediately followed by an isobaric compression until the volume is 1000 cm^3.
    b. What is the final temperature of the gas?
    c. Show the process on a pV diagram.

76. ‖‖ A large freshwater fish has a swim bladder with a volume of BIO $5.0 \times 10^{-4} m^3$. The fish descends from a depth where the absolute pressure is 3.0 atm to deeper water where the swim bladder is compressed to 60% of its initial volume. As the fish descends, the gas pressure in the swim bladder is always equal to the water pressure, and the temperature of the gas remains at the internal temperature of the fish's body. To adapt to its new location, the fish must add gas to reinflate its swim bladder to the original volume. This takes energy to accomplish. What's the minimum amount of work required to expand the swim bladder back to its original volume?

77. ‖‖ A 5.0-m-diameter garden pond holds 5.9×10^3 kg of water. Solar energy is incident on the pond at an average rate of 400 W/m². If the water absorbs all the solar energy and does not exchange energy with its surroundings, how many hours will it take to warm from 15°C to 25°C?

78. ‖‖‖ 0.030 mol of an ideal monatomic gas undergoes an adiabatic compression that raises its temperature from 10°C to 50°C. How much work is done on the gas to compress it?

79. ‖‖‖ 0.15 mol of an ideal monatomic gas undergoes an adiabatic expansion, cooling from 20°C to −10°C. How much work is done by the gas during the expansion?

80. ‖‖ Susan, whose mass is 68 kg, climbs 59 m to the top of the
BIO Cape Hatteras lighthouse.
INT a. During the climb, by how much does her potential energy increase?
    b. For a typical efficiency of 25%, what metabolic energy does she require to complete the climb?
    c. When exercising, the body must perspire and use other mechanisms to cool itself to avoid potentially dangerous increases on body temperature. If we assume that Susan doesn't perspire or otherwise cool herself and that all of the "lost" energy goes into increasing her body temperature, by how much would her body temperature increase during this climb?

81. ‖‖ A typical nuclear reactor generates 1000 MW of electric energy. In doing so, it produces "waste heat" at a rate of 2000 MW, and this heat must be removed from the reactor. Many reactors are sited next to large bodies of water so that they can use the water for cooling. Consider a reactor where the intake water is at 18°C. State regulations limit the temperature of the output water to 30°C so as not to harm aquatic organisms. How many kilograms of cooling water have to be pumped through the reactor each minute?

82. ‖‖ A 68 kg woman cycles at a constant 15 km/h. All of the meta-
BIO bolic energy that does not go to forward propulsion is converted
INT to thermal energy in her body. If the only way her body has to keep cool is by evaporation, how many kilograms of water must she lose to perspiration each hour to keep her body temperature constant?

83. ‖‖ A 1200 kg car traveling at 60 mph quickly brakes to a halt.
INT The kinetic energy of the car is converted to thermal energy of the disk brakes. The brake disks (one per wheel) are iron disks with a mass of 4.0 kg. Estimate the temperature rise in each disk as the car stops.

84. ‖‖ A 5000 kg African elephant
BIO has a resting metabolic rate of
INT 2500 W. On a hot day, the ele-
phant's environment is likely to be nearly the same temperature as the animal itself, so cooling by radiation is not effective. The only plausible way to keep cool is by evaporation, and elephants spray water on their body to accomplish this. If this is the only possible means of cooling, how many kilograms of water per hour must be evaporated from an elephant's skin to keep it at a constant temperature?

85. ‖‖ Suppose you drop a water balloon from a height of 10 m. If
INT the balloon doesn't break on impact, its kinetic energy will be converted to thermal energy. Estimate the temperature rise of the water. Is this likely to be noticeable?

86. ‖ What is the maximum mass of lead you could melt with 1000 J of heat, starting from 20°C?

87. ‖ An experiment measures the temperature of a 200 g substance while steadily supplying heat to it. Figure P12.87 shows the results of the experiment. What are (a) the specific heat of the liquid phase and (b) the heat of vaporization?

FIGURE P12.87

88. ‖‖ 10 g of aluminum at 200°C and 20 g of copper are dropped into 50 cm³ of ethyl alcohol at 15°C. The temperature quickly comes to 25°C. What was the initial temperature of the copper?

89. ‖ A 100 g ice cube at −10°C is placed in an aluminum cup whose initial temperature is 70°C. The system comes to an equilibrium temperature of 20°C. What is the mass of the cup?

90. ‖ A 50.0 g thermometer is used to measure the temperature of 200 g of water. The specific heat of the thermometer, which is mostly glass, is 750 J/kg·K, and it reads 20.0°C while lying on the table. After being completely immersed in the water, the thermometer's reading stabilizes at 71.2°C. What was the actual water temperature before it was measured?

91. ‖‖ Your 300 mL cup of coffee is too hot to drink when served at 90°C. What is the mass of an ice cube, taken from a −20°C freezer, that will cool your coffee to a pleasant 60°C?

92. ‖ A gas is compressed from 600 cm³ to 200 cm³ at a constant pressure of 400 kPa. At the same time, 100 J of heat energy is transferred out of the gas. What is the change in thermal energy of the gas during this process?

93. ‖‖ An expandable cube, initially 20 cm on each side, contains 3.0 g of helium at 20°C. 1000 J of heat energy are transferred to this gas. What are (a) the final pressure if the process is at constant volume and (b) the final volume if the process is at constant pressure?

94. ‖‖ 0.10 mol of a monatomic gas follows the process shown in Figure P12.94.
    a. How much heat energy is transferred to or from the gas during process $1 \rightarrow 2$?
    b. How much heat energy is transferred to or from the gas during process $2 \rightarrow 3$?
    c. What is the total change in thermal energy of the gas?

FIGURE P12.94   FIGURE P12.95

95. ‖ A monatomic gas follows the process $1 \rightarrow 2 \rightarrow 3$ shown in Figure P12.95. How much heat is needed for (a) process $1 \rightarrow 2$ and (b) process $2 \rightarrow 3$?

96. ‖ What are (a) the heat Q_H extracted from the hot reservoir and
INT (b) the efficiency for a heat engine described by the pV diagram of Figure P12.96?

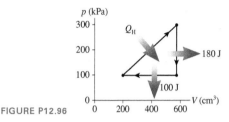

FIGURE P12.96

97. ‖ The top layer of your goose down sleeping bag has a thickness of 5.0 cm and a surface area of 1.0 m². When the outside temperature is −20°C, you lose 25 Cal/h by heat conduction through the bag (which remains at a cozy 35°C inside). Assume that you're sleeping on an insulated pad that eliminates heat conduction to the ground beneath you. What is the thermal conductivity of the goose down?

98. ‖‖ Suppose you go outside in your fiber-filled jacket on a windless but very cold day. The thickness of the jacket is 2.5 cm, and it covers 1.1 m² of your body. The purpose of fiber- or down-filled jackets is to trap a layer of air, and it's really the air layer that provides the insulation. If your skin temperature is 34°C while the air temperature is −20°C, at what rate is heat being conducted through the jacket and away from your body?

99. ‖‖ Two thin, square copper plates are radiating energy at the same rate. The edge length of plate 2 is four times that of plate 1. What is the ratio of absolute temperatures T_1/T_2 of the plates?

100. ‖ The surface area of an adult human is about 1.8 m². Suppose
BIO a person with a skin temperature of 34°C is standing with bare skin in a room where the air is 25°C but the walls are 17°C.
    a. There is a "dead-air" layer next to your skin that acts as insulation. If the dead-air layer is 5.0 mm thick, what is the person's rate of heat loss by conduction?
    b. What is the person's net radiation loss to the walls? The emissivity of skin is 0.97.
    c. Does conduction or radiation contribute more to the total rate of energy loss?
    d. If the person is metabolizing food at a rate of 155 W, does the person feel comfortable, chilly, or too warm?

Passage Problems

Thermal Properties of the Oceans

Seasonal temperature changes in the ocean only affect the top layer of water, to a depth of 500 m or so. This "mixed" layer is thermally isolated from the cold, deep water below. The average temperature of this top layer of the world's oceans, which has area 3.6×10^8 km², is approximately 17°C.

In addition to seasonal temperature changes, the oceans have experienced an overall warming trend over the last century that is expected to continue as the earth's climate changes. A warmer ocean means a larger volume of water; the oceans will rise. Suppose the average temperature of the top layer of the world's oceans were to increase from a temperature T_i to a temperature T_f. The area of the oceans will not change, as this is fixed by the size of the ocean basin, so any thermal expansion of the water will cause the water level to rise, as shown in Figure P12.101. The original volume is the product of the original depth and the surface area, $V_i = Ad_i$. The change in volume is given by $\Delta V = A\, \Delta d$.

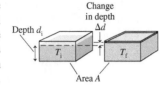

Depth d_i Change in depth Δd

T_i T_f

Area A

FIGURE P12.101

101. | If the top 500 m of ocean water increased in temperature from 17°C to 18°C, what would be the resulting rise in ocean height?
   A. 0.11 m   B. 0.22 m
   C. 0.44 m   D. 0.88 m

102. | Approximately how much energy would be required to raise the temperature of the top layer of the oceans by 1°C? (1 m³ of water has a mass of 1000 kg.)
   A. 1×10^{24} J   B. 1×10^{21} J
   C. 1×10^{18} J   D. 1×10^{15} J

103. | Water's coefficient of expansion varies with temperature. For water at 2°C, an increase in temperature of 1°C would cause the volume to
   A. Increase.   B. Stay the same.   C. Decrease.

104. | The ocean is mostly heated from the top, by light from the sun. The warmer surface water doesn't mix much with the colder deep ocean water. This lack of mixing can be ascribed to a lack of
   A. Conduction.
   B. Convection.
   C. Radiation.
   D. Evaporation.

STOP TO THINK ANSWERS

Stop to Think 12.1: A. Both helium and neon are monatomic gases, where the basic particles are atoms. 5 mol of helium contain 5 times as many atoms as 1 mol of neon, though both samples have the same mass.

Stop to Think 12.2: A, B. An increase in temperature means that the atoms have a larger average kinetic energy and will thus have a larger rms speed. Because the thermal energy of the gas is simply the total kinetic energy of the atoms, this must increase as well. The pressure *could* change, but it's not required; T and V could increase by the same factor, which would keep p constant. The container is sealed, so the number of molecules does not change.

Stop to Think 12.3: B. The product pV/T is constant. During the process, pV decreases by a factor of 2, so T must decrease by a factor of 2 as well.

Stop to Think 12.4: A. The thermal expansion coefficients of aluminum are greater than those of iron. Heating the rod and the ring will expand the outer diameter of the rod and the inner diameter of the ring, but the ring's expansion will be greater.

Stop to Think 12.5: B. To solidify the lead, heat must be removed; this heat boils the water. The heat of vaporization of water is 10 times the heat of fusion of lead, so much less than 1 kg of water vaporizes as 1 kg of lead solidifies.

Stop to Think 12.6: A. The lead cools and the water warms as heat is transferred from the lead to the water. The specific heat of water is much larger than that of lead, so the temperature change of the water is much less than that of the lead.

Stop to Think 12.7: C. With a sealed suit and no matter around you, there is no way to transfer heat to the environment except by radiation.

13 Fluids

The 20,000 pound boat floats while the 130 pound diver sinks. What determines whether an object floats or sinks?

LOOKING AHEAD ▶

The goal of Chapter 13 is to understand the static and dynamic properties of fluids.

Pressure in Fluids

The pressure in a **fluid**—a gas or a liquid—exerts a force on the fluid's container as well as on all parts of the fluid itself.

The pressure in a liquid increases with depth. The high pressure at the base of this water tower allows water to be distributed throughout the city.

> **Looking Back ◀◀**
> 5.1 Equilibrium
> 12.3 Pressure in gases

Measuring Pressure

Pressure is measured by the force it exerts on a known area. An important kind of pressure gauge is the **manometer.**

Blood pressure can be measured by the height of the mercury in this manometer.

Buoyancy

Why do some objects float while others sink? You'll learn that the **buoyant force**, the upward force of a fluid on an immersed object, is described by a simple but powerful concept called **Archimedes' principle.**

Teams from across the country compete in the annual National Concrete Canoe Competition. You'll learn how such a heavy object can stay afloat.

Fluid Dynamics

The volume of a moving fluid is conserved. This requires flowing fluids to speed up as they squeeze through a narrow section of a tube.

You'll learn why holding your thumb over the end of a hose makes the water come out faster.

> **Looking Back ◀◀**
> 4.6, 5.2 Newton's second law
> 10.2 Work
> 10.6 Conservation of energy

In studying moving fluids, we'll use many of the same ideas we used for studying the motion of particles: Newton's laws and conservation of energy.

Moving fluids can exert large forces on objects. **Bernoulli's equation**, a statement of conservation of energy applied to fluids, gives us a way to calculate pressures and forces due to moving fluids.

You'll learn how forces due to the motion of fluids can be enough to lift a massive airplane or lift the roof off a house during a hurricane.

Viscosity

You know from experience that some liquids, such as water, flow freely while others, like honey, are hard to pour. Honey has a much higher **viscosity** than water. You'll learn how viscosity affects the flow of fluids.

13.1 Fluids and Density

A **fluid** is simply a substance that flows. Because they flow, fluids take the shape of their container rather than retaining a shape of their own. You may think that gases and liquids are quite different, but both are fluids, and their similarities are often more important than their differences.

As you learned in Chapter 12, a gas, as shown in FIGURE 13.1a, is a system in which each molecule moves freely through space until, on occasion, it collides with another molecule or with the wall of the container. The gas you are most familiar with is air, a mixture of mostly nitrogen and oxygen molecules. Gases are *compressible;* that is, the volume of a gas is easily increased or decreased, a consequence of the "empty space" between the molecules in a gas.

Liquids are more complicated than either gases or solids. Liquids, like solids, are essentially *incompressible.* This property tells us that the molecules in a liquid, as in a solid, are about as close together as they can get without coming into contact with each other. At the same time, a liquid flows and deforms to fit the shape of its container. The fluid nature of a liquid tells us that the molecules are free to move around.

Together, these observations suggest the model of a liquid shown in FIGURE 13.1b. Here you see a system in which the molecules are loosely held together by weak molecular bonds. The bonds are strong enough that the molecules never get far apart but not strong enough to prevent the molecules from sliding around each other.

Density

An important parameter that characterizes a macroscopic system is its *density.* Suppose you have several blocks of copper, each of different size. Each block has a different mass m and a different volume V. Nonetheless, all the blocks are copper, so there should be some quantity that has the *same* value for all the blocks, telling us, "This is copper, not some other material." The most important such parameter is the *ratio* of mass to volume, which we call the **mass density** ρ (lowercase Greek rho):

$$\rho = \frac{m}{V} \qquad (13.1)$$

Mass density of an object of mass m and volume V

Conversely, an object of mass density ρ and volume V has mass

$$m = \rho V \qquad (13.2)$$

The SI units of mass density are kg/m³. Nonetheless, units of g/cm³ are widely used. You need to convert these to SI units before doing most calculations. You must convert both the grams to kilograms and the cubic centimeters to cubic meters. The net result is the conversion factor

$$1 \text{ g/cm}^3 = 1000 \text{ kg/m}^3$$

The mass density is independent of the object's size. That is, mass and volume are parameters that characterize a *specific piece* of some substance—say, copper—whereas mass density characterizes the substance itself. All pieces of copper have the same mass density, which differs from the mass density of almost any other substance. Thus mass density allows us to talk about the properties of copper in general without having to refer to any specific piece of copper.

The mass density is usually called simply "the density" if there is no danger of confusion. However, we will meet other types of density as we go along, and sometimes it is important to be explicit about which density you are using. Table 13.1 provides a short list of the mass densities of various fluids. Notice the enormous difference between the densities of gases and liquids. Gases have lower densities because the molecules in gases are farther apart than in liquids. Also, the density of a

FIGURE 13.1 Simple atomic-level models of gases and liquids.

(a) A gas

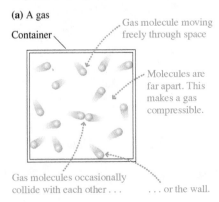

Container — Gas molecule moving freely through space

Molecules are far apart. This makes a gas compressible.

Gas molecules occasionally collide with each other . . . . . . or the wall.

(b) A liquid

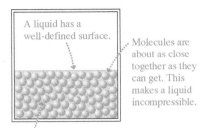

A liquid has a well-defined surface.

Molecules are about as close together as they can get. This makes a liquid incompressible.

Molecules make weak bonds with each other that keep them close together. But the molecules can slide around each other, allowing the liquid to flow and conform to the shape of its container.

TABLE 13.1 Densities of fluids at 1 atm pressure

Substance	ρ (kg/m³)
Helium gas (20°C)	0.166
Air (20°C)	1.20
Air (0°C)	1.28
Gasoline	680
Ethyl alcohol	790
Oil (typical)	900
Water	1000
Seawater	1030
Blood (whole)	1060
Glycerin	1260
Mercury	13,600

liquid varies only slightly with temperature because its molecules are always nearly in contact. The density of a gas, such as air, has a larger variation with temperature because it's easy to change the already large distance between the molecules.

What does it *mean* to say that the density of gasoline is 680 kg/m³? Recall in Chapter 1 we discussed the meaning of the word "per." We found that it meant "for each," so that 2 miles per hour means you travel 2 miles *for each* hour that passes. In the same way, saying that the density of gasoline is 680 kg per cubic meter means that there are 680 kg of gasoline *for each* 1 cubic meter of the liquid. If we have 2 m³ of gasoline, each will have a mass of 680 kg, so the total mass will be 2 × 680 kg = 1360 kg. The product ρV is the number of cubic meters times the mass of each cubic meter—that is, the total mass of the object.

PhET: Gas Properties
PhET: States of Matter

EXAMPLE 13.1   **Weighing the air in a living room**

What is the mass of air in a living room with dimensions 4.0 m × 6.0 m × 2.5 m?

PREPARE Table 13.1 gives air density at a temperature of 20°C, which is about room temperature.

SOLVE The room's volume is

$$V = (4.0\text{ m}) \times (6.0\text{ m}) \times (2.5\text{ m}) = 60\text{ m}^3$$

The mass of the air is

$$m = \rho V = (1.20\text{ kg/m}^3)(60\text{ m}^3) = 72\text{ kg}$$

ASSESS This is perhaps more mass—about that of an adult person—than you might have expected from a substance that hardly seems to be there. For comparison, a swimming pool this size would contain 60,000 kg of water.

STOP TO THINK 13.1   A piece of glass is broken into two pieces of different size. Rank in order, from largest to smallest, the mass densities of pieces 1, 2, and 3.

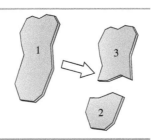

13.2 Pressure

In Chapter 12, you learned how a gas exerts a force on the walls of its containers. Liquids also exert forces on the walls of their containers, as shown in FIGURE 13.2, where a force $\vec{F}$ due to the liquid pushes against a small area A of the wall. Just as for a gas, we define the pressure at this point in the fluid to be the ratio of the force to the area on which the force is exerted:

$$p = \frac{F}{A} \tag{13.3}$$

This is the same as Equation 12.9 of Chapter 12. Recall also from Chapter 12 that the SI unit of pressure, the pascal, is defined as

$$1\text{ pascal} = 1\text{ Pa} = 1\ \frac{\text{N}}{\text{m}^2}$$

It's important to realize that the force due to a fluid's pressure pushes not only on the walls of its container, but on *all* parts of the fluid itself. If you punch holes in a container of water, the water spurts out from the holes, as in FIGURE 13.3. It is the force due to the pressure of the water behind each hole that pushes the water forward through the holes.

FIGURE 13.2 The fluid presses against area A with force $\vec{F}$.

The fluid pushes with force $\vec{F}$ against area A.

FIGURE 13.3 Pressure pushes the water *sideways,* out of the holes.

To measure the pressure at any point within a fluid we can use the simple pressure-measuring device shown in FIGURE 13.4a. Because the spring constant k and the area A are known, we can determine the pressure by measuring the compression of the spring. Once we've built such a device, we can place it in various liquids and gases to learn about pressure. FIGURE 13.4b shows what we can learn from simple experiments.

FIGURE 13.4 Learning about pressure.

(a) Piston attached to spring

Vacuum; no fluid force is exerted on the piston from this side.

1. The fluid exerts force $\vec{F}$ on a piston with surface area A.

2. The force compresses the spring. Because the spring constant k is known, we can use the spring's compression to find F.

3. Because A is known, we can find the pressure from $p = F/A$.

(b) Pressure-measuring device in fluid

1. There is pressure *everywhere* in a fluid, not just at the bottom or at the walls of the container.

2. The pressure at a given depth in the fluid is the same whether you point the pressure-measuring device up, down, or sideways. The fluid pushes up, down, and sideways with equal strength.

3. In a *liquid*, the pressure increases rapidly with depth below the surface. In a *gas*, the pressure is nearly the same at all points (at least in laboratory-size containers).

The first statement in Figure 13.4b emphasizes again that pressure exists at *all* points within a fluid, not just at the walls of the container. You may recall that tension exists at *all* points in a string, not only at its ends where it is tied to an object. We understood tension as the different parts of the string *pulling* against each other. Pressure is an analogous idea, except that the different parts of a fluid are *pushing* against each other.

Video Tutor Demonstration

Pressure in Liquids

If you introduce a liquid into a container, the force of gravity pulls the liquid down, causing it to fill the bottom of the container. It is this force of gravity—that is, the weight of the liquid—that is responsible for the pressure in a liquid. Pressure increases with depth in a liquid because the liquid below is being squeezed by all the liquid above, including any other liquid floating on the first liquid, as well as the pressure of the air above the liquid.

We'd like to determine the pressure at a depth d below the surface of the liquid. We will assume that the liquid is at rest; flowing liquids will be considered later in this chapter. The darker shaded cylinder of liquid in FIGURE 13.5 extends from the surface to depth d. This cylinder, like the rest of the liquid, is in static equilibrium with $\vec{F}_{net} = \vec{0}$. Several forces act on this cylinder: its weight mg, a downward force $p_0 A$ due to the pressure p_0 at the surface of the liquid, an upward force pA due to the liquid beneath the cylinder pushing up on the bottom of the cylinder, and inward-directed forces due to the liquid pushing in on the sides of the cylinder. The forces due to the liquid pushing on the cylinder are a consequence of our earlier observation that different parts of a fluid push against each other. Pressure p, the pressure at the bottom of the cylinder, is what we're trying to find.

The horizontal forces cancel each other. The upward force balances the two downward forces, so

$$pA = p_0 A + mg \qquad (13.4)$$

The liquid is a cylinder of cross-section area A and height d. Its volume is $V = Ad$ and its mass is $m = \rho V = \rho A d$. Substituting this expression for the mass of the liquid into Equation 13.4, we find that the area A cancels from all terms. The pressure at depth d in a liquid is then

$$p = p_0 + \rho g d \qquad (13.5)$$

Pressure of a liquid with density ρ at depth d

FIGURE 13.5 Measuring the pressure at depth d in a liquid.

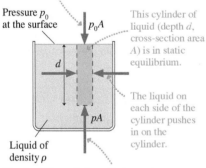

Whatever is above the liquid pushes down on the top of the cylinder.

Pressure p_0 at the surface

$p_0 A$

This cylinder of liquid (depth d, cross-section area A) is in static equilibrium.

d

The liquid on each side of the cylinder pushes in on the cylinder.

pA

Liquid of density ρ

The liquid beneath the cylinder pushes up on the cylinder. The pressure at depth d is p.

pA

mg $p_0 A$

$\vec{F}_{net} = \vec{0}$

Free-body diagram of the column of liquid. The horizontal forces cancel and are not shown.

Because of our assumption that the fluid is at rest, the pressure given by Equation 13.5 is called the **hydrostatic pressure.** The fact that g appears in Equation 13.5 reminds us that the origin of this pressure is the gravitational force on the fluid.

As expected, $p = p_0$ at the surface, where $d = 0$. Pressure p_0 is usually due to the air or other gas above the liquid. For a liquid that is open to the air at sea level, $p_0 = 1$ atm $= 101.3$ kPa, as we learned in Section 12.2. In other situations, p_0 might be the pressure due to a piston or a closed surface pushing down on the top of the liquid.

NOTE ▶ Equation 13.5 assumes that the fluid is *incompressible;* that is, its density ρ doesn't increase with depth. This is an excellent assumption for liquids, but not a good one for a gas. Equation 13.5 should not be used for calculating the pressure of a gas. Gas pressure is found with the ideal-gas law. ◀

EXAMPLE 13.2 **The pressure on a submarine**

A submarine cruises at a depth of 300 m. What is the pressure at this depth? Give the answer in both pascals and atmospheres.

SOLVE The density of seawater, from Table 13.1, is $\rho = 1030$ kg/m³. At the surface, $p_0 = 1$ atm $= 101.3$ kPa. The pressure at depth $d = 300$ m is found from Equation 13.5 to be

$$p = p_0 + \rho g d$$

$$= (1.013 \times 10^5 \text{ Pa}) + (1030 \text{ kg/m}^3)(9.80 \text{ m/s}^2)(300 \text{ m})$$

$$= 3.13 \times 10^6 \text{ Pa}$$

Converting the answer to atmospheres gives

$$p = (3.13 \times 10^6 \text{ Pa}) \times \frac{1 \text{ atm}}{1.013 \times 10^5 \text{ Pa}} = 30.9 \text{ atm}$$

ASSESS The pressure deep in the ocean is very great. The research submarine *Alvin,* shown in the left photo, can safely dive as deep

as 4500 m, where the pressure is over 450 atm! Its viewports are over 3.5 inches thick to withstand this pressure. As shown in the right photo, each viewport is tapered, with its larger face toward the sea. The water pressure then pushes the viewports firmly into their conical seats, helping to seal them tightly.

According to Equation 13.5, the hydrostatic pressure in a liquid depends on only the depth and the pressure at the surface. This observation has some important implications. FIGURE 13.6a shows two connected tubes. It's certainly true that the larger volume of liquid in the wide tube weighs more than the liquid in the narrow tube. You might think that this extra weight would push the liquid in the narrow tube higher than in the wide tube. But it doesn't. If d_1 were larger than d_2, then, according to the hydrostatic pressure equation, the pressure at the bottom of the narrow tube would be higher than the pressure at the bottom of the wide tube. This *pressure difference* would cause the liquid to *flow* from right to left until the heights were equal.

Thus a first conclusion: **A connected liquid in hydrostatic equilibrium rises to the same height in all open regions of the container.** This is the familiar observation that "water seeks its own level."

FIGURE 13.6b shows two connected tubes of different shape. The conical tube holds more liquid above the dotted line, so you might think that $p_1 > p_2$. But it isn't. Both points are at the same depth; thus $p_1 = p_2$. You can arrive at the same conclusion by thinking about the pressure at the bottoms of the tubes. If p_1 were greater than p_2, the pressure at the bottom of the left tube would be greater than the pressure at the bottom of the right tube. This would cause the liquid to flow until the pressures were equal. Thus a second conclusion: **In hydrostatic equilibrium, the pressure is the same at all points on a horizontal line through a connected liquid of a single kind.** (When the liquid is not the same kind at different points on the line, the pressure need not be the same.)

NOTE ▶ Both of these conclusions are restricted to liquids in hydrostatic equilibrium. The situation is entirely different for flowing fluids, as we'll see later on. ◀

FIGURE 13.6 Some properties of a liquid in hydrostatic equilibrium are not what you might expect.

(a)

Is this possible?

(b)

Is $p_1 > p_2$?

Video Tutor Demonstration

EXAMPLE 13.3 **Pressure in a closed tube**

Water fills the tube shown in FIGURE 13.7. What is the pressure at the top of the closed tube?

FIGURE 13.7 A bent tube closed at one end.

100 cm

Closed

40 cm

PREPARE This is a liquid in hydrostatic equilibrium. The closed tube is not an open region of the container, so the water cannot

rise to an equal height. Nevertheless, the pressure is still the same at all points on a horizontal line. In particular, the pressure at the top of the closed tube equals the pressure in the open tube at the height of the dotted line. Assume $p_0 = 1$ atm.

SOLVE A point 40 cm above the bottom of the open tube is at a depth of 60 cm. The pressure at this depth is

$$p = p_0 + \rho g d$$
$$= (1.01 \times 10^5 \text{ Pa}) + (1000 \text{ kg/m}^3)(9.80 \text{ m/s}^2)(0.60 \text{ m})$$
$$= 1.07 \times 10^5 \text{ Pa} = 1.06 \text{ atm}$$

ASSESS The water in the open tube *pushes* the water in the closed tube up against the top of the tube. Consequently, in accordance with Newton's third law, the top of the tube *presses down on the liquid* with a force of magnitude $F = pA$. This explains why the pressure at the top of the closed tube is greater than atmospheric pressure.

We can draw one more conclusion from the hydrostatic pressure equation $p = p_0 + \rho g d$. If we change the pressure at the surface to $p_1 = p_0 + \Delta p$, so that Δp is the *change* in pressure, then the pressure at a point at a depth d becomes

$$p' = p_1 + \rho g d = (p_0 + \Delta p) + \rho g d = (p_0 + \rho g d) + \Delta p = p + \Delta p$$

That is, the pressure at depth d changes by the same amount as it did at the surface. This idea was first recognized by Blaise Pascal (the same Pascal for whom the pressure unit is named) and is called *Pascal's principle:*

Pascal's principle If the pressure at one point in an incompressible fluid is changed, the pressure at every other point in the fluid changes by the same amount.

For example, if we compress the air above the open tube in Example 13.3 to a pressure of 1.50 atm, an increase of 0.50 atm, the pressure at the top of the closed tube will increase to 1.56 atm.

STOP TO THINK 13.2 Water is slowly poured into the container until the water level has risen into tubes 1, 2, and 3. The water doesn't overflow from any of the tubes. How do the water depths in the three columns compare to each other?

A. $d_1 > d_2 > d_3$
B. $d_1 < d_2 < d_3$
C. $d_1 = d_2 = d_3$
D. $d_1 = d_2 > d_3$
E. $d_1 = d_2 < d_3$

FIGURE 13.8 Atmospheric pressure and density.

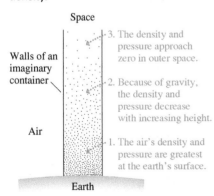

Atmospheric Pressure

We live at the bottom of a "sea" of air that extends up many kilometers. As FIGURE 13.8 shows, there is no well-defined top to the atmosphere; it just gets less and less dense with increasing height until reaching zero in the vacuum of space. Nonetheless, 99% of the air in the atmosphere is below about 30 km.

If we recall that a gas like air is quite compressible, we can see why the atmosphere becomes less dense with increasing altitude. In a liquid, pressure increases with depth because of the weight of the liquid above. The same holds true for the air in the atmosphere, but because the air is compressible, the weight of the air above compresses the air below, increasing its density. At high altitudes there is very little air above to push down, so the density is less.

We learned in Chapter 12 that the global average sea-level pressure, the *standard atmosphere,* is 1 atm = 101,300 Pa. The standard atmosphere, usually referred to simply as "atmospheres," is a commonly used unit of pressure. But it is not an SI unit, so you must convert atmospheres to pascals before doing most calculations with pressure.

> **NOTE** ▶ Unless you happen to live right at sea level, the atmospheric pressure around you is not exactly 1 atm. A pressure gauge must be used to determine the actual atmospheric pressure. For simplicity, this textbook will always assume that the pressure of the air is $p_{atmos} = 1$ atm unless stated otherwise. ◀

Atmospheric pressure varies not only with altitude, but also with changes in the weather. Large-scale regions of low-pressure air are created at the equator, where hot air rises and flows to the north and south temperate zones. There the air falls, creating high-pressure zones. Local winds and weather are largely determined by presence and movement of air masses of differing pressure. You may have seen weather maps like the one shown in FIGURE 13.9 on the evening news. The letters H and L denote regions of high and low atmospheric pressure.

FIGURE 13.9 High- and low-pressure zones on a weather map.

13.3 Measuring and Using Pressure

The pressure in a fluid is measured with a *pressure gauge,* which is often a device very similar to that shown in Figure 13.4. The fluid pushes against a spring, and the displacement of the spring is indicated on a scale. The familiar tire-pressure gauge shown in FIGURE 13.10 works in the same way. The pressure p_{tire} exerts a force $p_{tire}A$ on the front area A of the piston, while atmospheric pressure exerts a force $p_{atmos}A$ on the back of the piston. Thus the *net* pressure force on the piston is $(p_{tire} - p_{atmos})A$. This force compresses the spring until equilibrium is reached. Thus the movement of the scale depends not on the absolute pressure in the tire, but on the *difference* between the tire pressure and atmospheric pressure. This type of gauge measures the *gauge pressure* $p_g = p_{tire} - p_{atmos}$, an idea introduced in Chapter 12.

FIGURE 13.10 A tire gauge measures the difference between the tire's pressure and atmospheric pressure.

Piston — This fixed disk holds the end of the spring. The scale can slide through it.

The piston is not attached to the scale.

Spring

Scale

p_{tire}

Tire valve

The difference between p_{tire} and p_{atmos} pushes the piston forward against the spring.

p_{atmos}

When the gauge is removed from the tire, the spring pushes the piston back, but the scale remains out where it can be read easily.

Solving Hydrostatic Problems

We now have enough information to formulate a set of rules for working with hydrostatic problems.

> **TACTICS BOX 13.1** Hydrostatics
>
> ❶ **Draw a picture.** Show open surfaces, pistons, boundaries, and other features that affect pressure. Include height and area measurements and fluid densities. Identify the points at which you need to find the pressure.
> ❷ **Determine the pressure p_0 at surfaces.**
> ■ **Surface open to the air:** $p_0 = p_{atmos}$, usually 1 atm.
> ■ **Surface in contact with a gas:** $p_0 = p_{gas}$.
> ■ **Closed surface:** $p_0 = F/A$, where F is the force that the surface, such as a piston, exerts on the fluid.
> ❸ **Use horizontal lines.** The pressure in a connected fluid (of one kind) is the same at any point along a horizontal line.
> ❹ **Allow for gauge pressure.** Pressure gauges read $p_g = p - 1$ atm.
> ❺ **Use the hydrostatic pressure equation:** $p = p_0 + \rho g d$.

Exercises 5–7

Manometers and Barometers

Gas pressure is sometimes measured with a device called a *manometer*. A manometer, shown in FIGURE 13.11, is a U-shaped tube connected to the gas at one end and open to the air at the other end. The tube is filled with a liquid—often mercury—of density ρ. The liquid is in static equilibrium. A scale allows the user to measure the height h of the right side of the liquid above the left side.

Steps 1–3 from Tactics Box 13.1 lead to the conclusion that the pressures p_1 and p_2 must be equal. Pressure p_1, at the surface on the left, is simply the gas pressure: $p_1 = p_{gas}$. Pressure p_2 is the hydrostatic pressure at depth $d = h$ in the liquid on the right: $p_2 = 1$ atm $+ \rho gh$. Equating these two pressures gives

$$p_{gas} = 1 \text{ atm} + \rho gh \qquad (13.6)$$

NOTE ▶ The height h has a *positive* value when the liquid is *higher* on the right than on the left ($p_{gas} > 1$ atm) and a *negative* value when the liquid is *lower* on the right than on the left ($p_{gas} < 1$ atm). ◀

Another important pressure-measuring instrument is the *barometer*, which is used to measure atmospheric pressure p_{atmos}. FIGURE 13.12a shows a glass tube, sealed at the bottom, that has been completely filled with a liquid. If we temporarily seal the top end, we can invert the tube and place it in a beaker of the same liquid. When the temporary seal is removed, some, but not all, of the liquid runs out, leaving a liquid column in the tube that is a height h above the surface of the liquid in the beaker. This device, shown in FIGURE 13.12b, is a barometer. What does it measure? And why doesn't *all* the liquid in the tube run out?

We can analyze the barometer much as we did the manometer. Point 1 in Figure 13.12b is open to the atmosphere, so $p_1 = p_{atmos}$. The pressure at point 2 is the pressure due to the weight of the liquid in the tube plus the pressure of the gas above the liquid. But in this case there is no gas above the liquid! Because the tube had been completely full of liquid when it was inverted, the space left behind when the liquid ran out is essentially a vacuum, with $p_0 = 0$. Thus pressure p_2 is simply ρgh.

Because points 1 and 2 are on a horizontal line, and the liquid is in hydrostatic equilibrium, the pressures at these two points must be equal. Equating these two pressures gives

$$p_{atmos} = \rho gh \qquad (13.7)$$

Thus we can measure the atmosphere's pressure by measuring the height of the liquid column in a barometer.

Equation 13.7 shows that the liquid height is $h = p_{atmos}/\rho g$. If a barometer were made using water, with $\rho = 1000$ kg/m^3, the liquid column would be more than 10 m high, which is impractical. Instead, mercury, with its high density of 13,600 kg/m^3, is usually used. The average air pressure at sea level causes a column of mercury in a mercury barometer to stand 760 mm above the surface. We can then use Equation 13.7 to find that the average atmospheric pressure is

$$p_{atmos} = \rho_{Hg}gh = (13{,}600 \text{ kg/m}^3)(9.80 \text{ m/s}^2)(0.760 \text{ m})$$

$$= 1.013 \times 10^5 \text{ Pa} = 101.3 \text{ kPa}$$

This is the value given earlier as "1 standard atmosphere."

Because of the importance of mercury-filled barometers in measuring pressure, the height of a column of mercury in millimeters is a common unit of pressure. From our discussion of barometers, 760 millimeters of mercury (abbreviated "mm Hg") corresponds to a pressure of 1 atm.

FIGURE 13.11 A manometer is used to measure gas pressure.

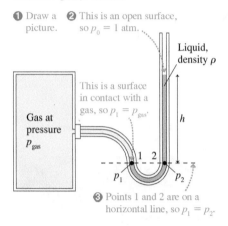

① Draw a picture.
② This is an open surface, so $p_0 = 1$ atm.
Liquid, density ρ
This is a surface in contact with a gas, so $p_1 = p_{gas}$.
Gas at pressure p_{gas}
h
1   2
p_1 p_2
③ Points 1 and 2 are on a horizontal line, so $p_1 = p_2$.

FIGURE 13.12 A barometer.

(a) Seal and invert tube.

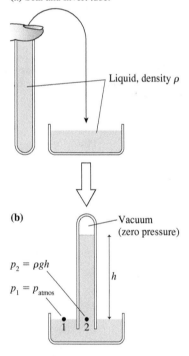

Liquid, density ρ

(b)
Vacuum (zero pressure)
$p_2 = \rho gh$
$p_1 = p_{atmos}$
h
1   2

| EXAMPLE 13.4 | Pressure in a tube with two liquids |

A U-shaped tube is closed at one end; the other end is open to the atmosphere. Water fills the side of the tube that includes the closed end, while oil, floating on the water, fills the side of the tube open to the atmosphere. The two liquids do not mix. The height of the oil above the point where the two liquids touch is 75 cm, while the height of the closed end of the tube above this point is 25 cm. What is the gauge pressure at the closed end?

FIGURE 13.13 A tube containing two different liquids.

PREPARE Following the steps in Tactics Box 13.1, we start by drawing the picture shown in FIGURE 13.13. We know that the pressure at the open surface of the oil is $p_0 = 1$ atm. Pressures p_1 and p_2 are the same because they are on a horizontal line that connects two points in the *same* fluid. (The pressure at point A is *not* equal to p_3, even though point A and the closed end are on the same horizontal line, because the two points are in *different* fluids.)

We can apply the hydrostatic pressure equation twice: once to find the pressure p_1 by its known depth below the open end at pressure p_0, and again to find the pressure p_3 at the closed end once we know p_2 a distance d below it. We'll need the densities of water and oil, which are found in Table 13.1 to be $\rho_w = 1000$ kg/m^3 and $\rho_o = 900$ kg/m^3.

SOLVE The pressure at point 1, 75 cm below the open end, is

$$p_1 = p_0 + \rho_o g h$$
$$= 1 \text{ atm} + (900 \text{ kg/m}^3)(9.8 \text{ m/s}^2)(0.75 \text{ m})$$
$$= 1 \text{ atm} + 6600 \text{ Pa}$$

(We will keep $p_0 = 1$ atm separate in this result because we'll eventually need to subtract exactly 1 atm to calculate the gauge pressure.) We can also use the hydrostatic pressure equation to find

$$p_2 = p_3 + \rho_w g d$$
$$= p_3 + (1000 \text{ kg/m}^3)(9.8 \text{ m/s}^2)(0.25 \text{ m})$$
$$= p_3 + 2500 \text{ Pa}$$

But we know that $p_2 = p_1$, so

$$p_3 = p_2 - 2500 \text{ Pa} = p_1 - 2500 \text{ Pa}$$
$$= 1 \text{ atm} + 6600 \text{ Pa} - 2500 \text{ Pa}$$
$$= 1 \text{ atm} + 4100 \text{ Pa}$$

The gauge pressure at point 3, the closed end of the tube, is $p_3 - 1$ atm or 4100 Pa.

ASSESS The oil's open surface is 50 cm higher than the water's closed surface. Their densities are not too different, so we expect a pressure difference of roughly $\rho g(0.50 \text{ m}) = 5000$ Pa. This is not too far from our answer, giving us confidence that it's correct.

Pressure Units

In practice, pressure is measured in a number of different units. This plethora of units and abbreviations has arisen historically as scientists and engineers working on different subjects (liquids, high-pressure gases, low-pressure gases, weather, etc.) developed what seemed to them the most convenient units. These units continue in use through tradition, so it is necessary to become familiar with converting back and forth among them. Table 13.2 gives the basic conversions.

TABLE 13.2 Pressure units

Unit	Abbreviation	Conversion to 1 atm	Uses
pascal	Pa	101.3 kPa	SI unit: 1 Pa = 1 N/m^2 used in most calculations
atmosphere	atm	1 atm	general
millimeters of mercury	mm Hg	760 mm Hg	gases and barometric pressure
inches of mercury	in	29.92 in	barometric pressure in U.S. weather forecasting
pounds per square inch	psi	14.7 psi	U.S. engineering and industry

FIGURE 13.14 Blood pressure during one cycle of a heartbeat.

Blood Pressure

The last time you had a medical checkup, the doctor may have told you something like, "Your blood pressure is 120 over 80." What does that mean?

About every 0.8 s, assuming a pulse rate of 75 beats per minute, your heart "beats." The heart muscles contract and push blood out into your aorta. This contraction, like squeezing a balloon, raises the pressure in your heart. The pressure increase, in accordance with Pascal's principle, is transmitted through all your arteries.

FIGURE 13.14 is a pressure graph showing how blood pressure changes during one cycle of the heartbeat. The medical condition of *high blood pressure* usually means that your maximum (*systolic*) blood pressure is higher than necessary for blood circulation. The high pressure causes undue stress and strain on your entire circulatory system, often leading to serious medical problems. Low blood pressure can cause you to faint if you stand up quickly because the pressure isn't adequate to pump the blood up to your brain.

As shown in FIGURE 13.15, blood pressure is measured with a cuff that goes around your arm. The doctor or nurse pressurizes the cuff, places a stethoscope over the artery in your arm, then slowly releases the pressure while watching a pressure gauge. Initially, the cuff squeezes the artery shut and cuts off the blood flow. When the cuff pressure drops below the systolic pressure, the pressure pulse during each beat of your heart forces the artery open briefly and a squirt of blood goes through. The doctor or nurse records the pressure when he or she hears the blood start to flow. This is your systolic pressure.

This pulsing of the blood through your artery lasts until the cuff pressure reaches the diastolic pressure. Then the artery remains open continuously and the blood flows smoothly. This transition is easily heard in the stethoscope, and the doctor or nurse records your base or *diastolic* pressure.

Blood pressure is measured in millimeters of mercury. And it is a gauge pressure, the pressure in excess of 1 atm. A fairly typical blood pressure of a healthy young adult is 120/80, meaning that the systolic pressure is $p_g = 120$ mm Hg (absolute pressure $p = 880$ mm Hg) and the diastolic pressure is 80 mm Hg.

FIGURE 13.15 Measuring blood pressure with a manometer.

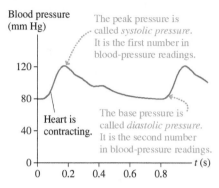

CONCEPTUAL EXAMPLE 13.5 **Blood pressure and the height of the arm**

In Figure 13.15, the patient's arm is held at about the same height as her heart. Why?

REASON The hydrostatic pressure of a fluid varies with height. Although flowing blood is not in hydrostatic equilibrium, it is still true that blood pressure increases with the distance below the heart and decreases above it. Because the upper arm when held beside the body is at the same height as the heart, the pressure here is the same as the pressure at the heart. If the patient held her arm straight up, the pressure cuff would be a distance $d \approx 25$ cm above her heart and the pressure would be *less* than the pressure at the heart by $\Delta p = \rho_{\text{blood}} gd \approx 20$ mm Hg.

ASSESS 20 mm Hg is a substantial fraction of the average blood pressure. Measuring pressure above or below heart level could lead to a misdiagnosis of the patient's condition.

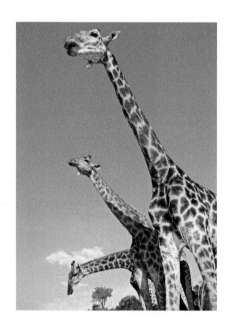

◀ **Pressure at the top** BIO A giraffe's head is some 2.5 m above its heart, compared to a distance of only about 30 cm for humans. To pump blood this extra height requires a blood pressure at the giraffe's heart that is some 170 mm Hg higher than a human's, making its blood pressure more than twice as high as a human's.

13.4 Buoyancy

A rock, as you know, sinks like a rock. Wood floats on the surface of a lake. A penny with a mass of a few grams sinks, but a massive steel aircraft carrier floats. How can we understand these diverse phenomena?

An air mattress floats effortlessly on the surface of a swimming pool. But if you've ever tried to push an air mattress underwater, you know it is nearly impossible. As you push down, the water pushes up. This upward force of a fluid is called the **buoyant force.**

The basic reason for the buoyant force is easy to understand. FIGURE 13.16 shows a cylinder submerged in a liquid. The pressure in the liquid increases with depth, so the pressure at the bottom of the cylinder is greater than at the top. Both cylinder ends have equal area, so force $\vec{F}_{up}$ is greater than force $\vec{F}_{down}$. (Remember that pressure forces push in *all* directions.) Consequently, the pressure in the liquid exerts a *net upward force* on the cylinder of magnitude $F_{net} = F_{up} - F_{down}$. This is the buoyant force.

The submerged cylinder illustrates the idea in a simple way, but the result is not limited to cylinders or to liquids. Suppose we isolate a parcel of fluid of arbitrary shape and volume by drawing an imaginary boundary around it, as shown in FIGURE 13.17a. This parcel is in static equilibrium. Consequently, the parcel's weight force pulling it down must be balanced by an upward force. The upward force, which is exerted on this parcel of fluid by the surrounding fluid, is the buoyant force $\vec{F}_B$. The buoyant force matches the weight of the fluid: $F_B = w$.

Now imagine that we could somehow remove this parcel of fluid and instantaneously replace it with an object having exactly the same shape and size, as shown in FIGURE 13.17b. Because the buoyant force is exerted by the *surrounding* fluid, and the surrounding fluid hasn't changed, the buoyant force on this new object is *exactly the same* as the buoyant force on the parcel of fluid that we removed.

When an object (or a portion of an object) is immersed in a fluid, it *displaces* fluid that would otherwise fill that region of space. This fluid is called the **displaced fluid.** The displaced fluid's volume is exactly the volume of the portion of the object that is immersed in the fluid. Figure 13.17 leads us to conclude that the magnitude of the upward buoyant force matches the weight of this displaced fluid.

This idea was first recognized by the ancient Greek mathematician and scientist Archimedes, perhaps the greatest scientist of antiquity, and today we know it as *Archimedes' principle:*

> **Archimedes' principle** A fluid exerts an upward buoyant force $\vec{F}_B$ on an object immersed in or floating on the fluid. The magnitude of the buoyant force equals the weight of the fluid displaced by the object.

Suppose the fluid has density ρ_f and the object displaces a volume V_f of fluid. The mass of the displaced fluid is then $m_f = \rho_f V_f$ and so its weight is $w_f = \rho_f V_f g$. Thus Archimedes' principle in equation form is

$$F_B = \rho_f V_f g \tag{13.8}$$

NOTE ▶ It is important to distinguish the density and volume of the displaced fluid from the density and volume of the object. To do so, we'll use subscript f for the fluid and o for the object. ◀

FIGURE 13.16 The buoyant force arises because the fluid pressure at the bottom of the cylinder is greater than at the top.

The net force of the fluid on the cylinder is the buoyant force $\vec{F}_B$.

Increasing pressure

$\vec{F}_{down}$

$\vec{F}_{net} = \vec{F}_B$

$\vec{F}_{up}$

$F_{up} > F_{down}$ because the pressure is greater at the bottom. Hence the fluid exerts a net upward force.

FIGURE 13.17 The buoyant force on an object is the same as the buoyant force on the fluid it displaces.

(a) Imaginary boundary around a parcel of fluid

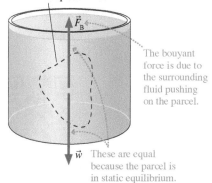

$\vec{F}_B$

The buoyant force is due to the surrounding fluid pushing on the parcel.

$\vec{w}$ These are equal because the parcel is in static equilibrium.

(b) Real object with same size and shape as the parcel of fluid

$\vec{F}_B$

The buoyant force on the object is the same as on the parcel of fluid because the *surrounding* fluid has not changed.

EXAMPLE 13.6   **Is the crown gold?**

Legend has it that Archimedes was asked by King Hiero of Syracuse to determine whether a crown was of pure gold or had been adulterated with a lesser metal by an unscrupulous goldsmith. It was this problem that led him to the principle that bears his name. In a modern version of his method, a crown weighing 8.30 N is suspended underwater from a string. The tension in the string is measured to be 7.81 N. Is the crown pure gold?

PREPARE To discover whether the crown is pure gold, we need to determine its density ρ_o and compare it to the known density of gold. **FIGURE 13.18** shows the forces acting on the crown. In addition to the familiar tension and weight forces, the water exerts an upward buoyant force on the crown. The size of the buoyant force is given by Archimedes' principle.

FIGURE 13.18 The forces acting on the submerged crown.

SOLVE Because the crown is in static equilibrium, its acceleration and the net force on it are zero. Newton's second law then reads

$$\sum F_y = F_B + T - w_o = 0$$

from which the buoyant force is

$$F_B = w_o - T = 8.30 \text{ N} - 7.81 \text{ N} = 0.49 \text{ N}$$

According to Archimedes' principle, $F_B = \rho_f V_f\, g$, where V_f is the volume of the fluid displaced. Here, where the crown is completely submerged, the volume of the fluid displaced is equal to the volume V_o of the crown. Now the crown's weight is $w_o = m_o g = \rho_o V_o g$, so its volume is

$$V_o = \frac{w_o}{\rho_o g}$$

Inserting this volume into Archimedes' principle gives

$$F_B = \rho_f V_o g = \rho_f \left(\frac{w_o}{\rho_o g} \right) g = \frac{\rho_f}{\rho_o} w_o$$

or, solving for ρ_0,

$$\rho_o = \frac{\rho_f w_o}{F_B} = \frac{(1000 \text{ kg/m}^3)(8.30 \text{ N})}{0.49 \text{ N}} = 17{,}000 \text{ kg/m}^3$$

The crown's density is considerably lower than that of pure gold, which is 19,300 kg/m³. The crown is not pure gold.

ASSESS For an object made of a dense material such as gold, the buoyant force is small compared to its weight.

Class Video

Float or Sink?

If you *hold* an object underwater and then release it, it rises to the surface, sinks, or remains "hanging" in the water. How can we predict which it will do? Whether it heads for the surface or the bottom depends on whether the upward buoyant force F_B on the object is larger or smaller than the downward weight force w_o.

The magnitude of the buoyant force is $\rho_f V_f g$. The weight of a uniform object, such as a block of steel, is simply $\rho_o V_o g$. But a compound object, such as a scuba diver, may have pieces of varying density. If we define the **average density** to be $\rho_{avg} = m_o/V_o$, the weight of a compound object can be written as $w_o = \rho_{avg} V_o g$.

Comparing $\rho_f V_f g$ to $\rho_{avg} V_o g$, and noting that $V_f = V_o$ for an object that is fully submerged, we see that an object floats or sinks depending on whether the fluid density ρ_f is larger or smaller than the object's average density ρ_{avg}. If the densities are equal, the object is in static equilibrium and hangs motionless. This is called **neutral buoyancy**. These conditions are summarized in Tactics Box 13.2.

◄ **Submersible scales** BIO In Example 13.6, we saw how the density of an object could be determined by weighing it both underwater and in air. This idea is the basis of an accurate method for determining a person's percentage of body fat. Fat has a lower density than lean muscle or bone, so a lower overall body density implies a greater proportion of body fat. To determine a person's density, he is first weighed in air and then lowered completely into water and weighed again. Standard tables accurately relate body density to fat percentage.

MP

TACTICS BOX 13.2 Finding whether an object floats or sinks

❶ Object sinks

❷ Object floats

❸ Object has neutral buoyancy

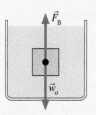

An object sinks if it weighs more than the fluid it displaces—that is, if its average density is greater than the density of the fluid:

$$\rho_{avg} > \rho_f$$

An object rises to the surface if it weighs less than the fluid it displaces—that is, if its average density is less than the density of the fluid:

$$\rho_{avg} < \rho_f$$

An object hangs motionless if it weighs exactly the same as the fluid it displaces—that is, if its average density equals the density of the fluid:

$$\rho_{avg} = \rho_f$$

Exercises 10–12

For example, steel is denser than water, so a chunk of steel sinks. Oil is less dense than water, so oil floats on water. Fish use *swim bladders* filled with air and scuba divers use weighted belts to adjust their average density to match the water. Both are examples of neutral buoyancy.

If you release a block of wood underwater, the net upward force causes the block to shoot to the surface. Then what? To understand floating, let's begin with a *uniform* object such as the block shown in FIGURE 13.19. This object contains nothing tricky, like indentations or voids. Because it's floating, it must be the case that $\rho_o < \rho_f$.

Now that the object is floating, it's in static equilibrium. Thus, the upward buoyant force, given by Archimedes' principle, exactly balances the downward weight of the object; that is,

$$F_B = \rho_f V_f g = w_o = \rho_o V_o g \qquad (13.9)$$

For a floating object, the volume of the displaced fluid is *not* the same as the volume of the object. In fact, we can see from Equation 13.9 that the volume of fluid displaced by a floating object of uniform density is

$$V_f = \frac{\rho_o}{\rho_f} V_o \qquad (13.10)$$

which is *less* than V_o because $\rho_o < \rho_f$.

NOTE ▶ Equation 13.10 applies only to *uniform* objects. It does not apply to boats, hollow spheres, or other objects of nonuniform composition. ◀

FIGURE 13.19 A floating object is in static equilibrium.

An object of density ρ_o and volume V_o is floating on a fluid of density ρ_f.

Fluid, density ρ_f

The submerged volume of the object is equal to the volume V_f of displaced fluid.

▶ **Hidden depths** You've probably heard it said that "90% of an iceberg is underwater." Equation 13.10 is the basis for that statement. Most icebergs break off glaciers and are fresh-water ice with a density of 917 kg/m³. The density of seawater is 1030 kg/m³. Thus

$$V_f = \frac{917 \text{ kg/m}^3}{1030 \text{ kg/m}^3} V_o = 0.89 V_o$$

V_f, the volume of the displaced water, is also the volume of the iceberg that is underwater. You can see that, indeed, 89% of the volume of an iceberg is underwater.

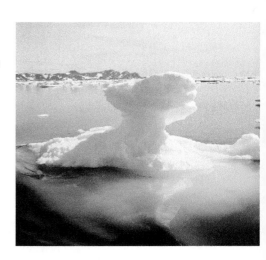

CONCEPTUAL EXAMPLE 13.7 **Which has the greater buoyant force?**

A block of iron sinks to the bottom of a vessel of water while a block of wood of the *same size* floats. On which is the buoyant force greater?

REASON The buoyant force is equal to the volume of water displaced. The iron block is completely submerged, so it displaces a volume of water equal to its own volume. The wood block floats, so it displaces only the fraction of its volume that is under water, which is *less* than its own volume. The buoyant force on the iron block is therefore greater than on the wood block.

ASSESS This result may seem counterintuitive, but remember that the iron block sinks because of its high density, while the wood block floats because of its low density. A smaller buoyant force is sufficient to keep it floating.

EXAMPLE 13.8 **Measuring the density of an unknown liquid**

You need to determine the density of an unknown liquid. You notice that a block floats in this liquid with 4.6 cm of the side of the block submerged. When the block is placed in water, it also floats but with 5.8 cm submerged. What is the density of the unknown liquid?

PREPARE Assume that the block is an object of uniform composition. FIGURE 13.20 shows the block as well as the cross-section area A and submerged lengths h_u in the unknown liquid and h_w in water.

FIGURE 13.20 A block floating in two liquids.

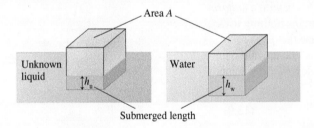

Submerged length

SOLVE The block is floating, so Equation 13.10 applies. The block displaces volume $V_u = Ah_u$ of the unknown liquid. Thus

$$V_u = Ah_u = \frac{\rho_0}{\rho_u} V_0$$

Similarly, the block displaces volume $V_w = Ah_w$ of the water, leading to

$$V_w = Ah_w = \frac{\rho_0}{\rho_w} V_0$$

Because there are two fluids, we've used subscripts w for water and u for the unknown in place of the fluid subscript f. The product $\rho_0 V_0$ appears in both equations. In the first $\rho_0 V_0 = \rho_u Ah_u$, and in the second $\rho_0 V_0 = \rho_w Ah_w$. Equating the right-hand sides gives

$$\rho_u Ah_u = \rho_w Ah_w$$

The area A cancels, and the density of the unknown liquid is

$$\rho_u = \frac{h_w}{h_u}\rho_w = \frac{5.8 \text{ cm}}{4.6 \text{ cm}}1000 \text{ kg/m}^3 = 1300 \text{ kg/m}^3$$

ASSESS Comparison with Table 13.1 shows that the unknown liquid is likely to be glycerin.

FIGURE 13.21 How a boat floats.

As the boat settles into the water, the water displaced, and hence the buoyant force, increases.

The boat's constant weight is that of the thin steel hull.

The boat floats in equilibrium when its weight and the buoyant force are equal.

Boats and Balloons

A chunk of steel sinks, so how does a steel-hulled boat float? As we've seen, an object floats if the upward buoyant force—the weight of the displaced water—balances the weight of the object. A boat is really a large hollow shell whose weight is determined by the volume of steel in the hull. As FIGURE 13.21 shows, the volume of water displaced by a shell is *much* larger than the volume of the hull itself. As a boat settles into the water, it sinks until the weight of the displaced water exactly matches the boat's weight. It is then in static equilibrium, so it floats at that level.

The concept of buoyancy and flotation applies to all fluids, not just liquids. An object immersed in a gas such as air feels a buoyant force as well. Because the density of air is so low, this buoyant force is generally negligible. Nonetheless, even though the buoyant force due to air is small, an object will float in air if it weighs less than the air that it displaces. This is why a floating balloon cannot be filled with regular air. If it were, then the weight of the air inside it would equal the weight of the air it displaced, so that it would have no net upward force on it. Adding in the weight of the balloon itself would then lead to a net downward force. For a balloon to float, it must be filled with a gas that has a *lower* density than that of air. The following example illustrates how this works.

EXAMPLE 13.9 How big does a balloon need to be?

What diameter must a helium-filled balloon have to float with neutral buoyancy? The mass of the empty balloon is 2.0 g.

PREPARE We'll model the balloon as a sphere. The balloon will float when its weight—the weight of the empty balloon plus the helium—equals the weight of the air it displaces. The densities of air and helium are given in Table 13.1.

SOLVE The volume of the balloon is $V_{balloon}$. Its weight is

$$w_{balloon} = m_{balloon} g + \rho_{He} V_{balloon} g$$

where $m_{balloon}$ is the mass of the empty balloon. The weight of the displaced air is

$$w_{air} = \rho_{air} V_{air} g = \rho_{air} V_{ballon} g$$

where we noted that the volume of the displaced air is the volume of the balloon. The balloon will float when these two forces are equal, or when

$$\rho_{air} V_{balloon} g = m_{balloon} g + \rho_{He} V_{balloon} g$$

The g cancels, and we can solve for the volume of the balloon:

$$V_{balloon} = \frac{m_{balloon}}{\rho_{air} - \rho_{He}} = \frac{2.0 \times 10^{-3}\ kg}{1.28\ kg/m^3 - 0.17\ kg/m^3} = 1.8 \times 10^{-3}\ m^3$$

A sphere has volume $V = (4\pi/3)r^3$. Thus the balloon's radius is

$$r = \left(\frac{3V_{balloon}}{4\pi}\right)^{\frac{1}{3}} = \left(\frac{3 \times (1.8 \times 10^{-3}\ m^3)}{4\pi}\right)^{\frac{1}{3}} = 0.075\ m$$

The diameter of the balloon is twice this, or 15 cm.

ASSESS This example shows why a helium balloon will no longer float once its volume falls below a certain value.

STOP TO THINK 13.3 An ice cube is floating in a glass of water that is filled entirely to the brim. When the ice cube melts, the water level will

A. Fall.   B. Stay the same.   C. Rise, causing the water to spill.

Hot air rising A hot-air balloon is filled with a low-density gas: hot air! You learned in Chapter 12 that gases expand upon heating, thus lowering their density. The air at the top of a hot-air balloon is surprisingly hot—about 100°C, the temperature of boiling water. Using the ideal-gas law, you should be able to show that the density of 100°C air is only 79% that of room-temperature air at 20°C. A burst of flame lowers the density of the air and thus the balloon's weight. The balloon rises when its weight becomes less than the weight of the cooler air it has displaced.

 PhET: Balloons and Buoyancy

 Class Video

13.5 Fluids in Motion

The wind blowing through your hair, a white-water river, and oil gushing from an oil well are examples of fluids in motion. We've focused thus far on fluid statics, but it's time to turn our attention to fluid *dynamics*.

Fluid flow is a complex subject. Many aspects of fluid flow, especially turbulence and the formation of eddies, are still not well understood and are areas of current research. We will avoid these difficulties by using a simplified *model* of an *ideal* fluid. Our model can be expressed in three assumptions about the fluid:

1. The fluid is *incompressible.* This is a very good assumption for liquids, but it also holds reasonably well for a moving gas, such as air. For instance, even when a 100 mph wind slams into a wall, its density changes by only about 1%.
2. The flow is *steady.* That is, the fluid velocity at each point in the fluid is constant; it does not fluctuate or change with time. Flow under these conditions is called **laminar flow,** and it is distinguished from *turbulent flow.*
3. The fluid is *nonviscous.* Water flows much more easily than cold pancake syrup because the syrup is a very viscous liquid. Viscosity is resistance to flow, and assuming a fluid is nonviscous is analogous to assuming the motion of a particle is frictionless. Gases have very low viscosity, and even many liquids are well approximated as being nonviscous.

Later, in Section 13.7, we'll relax assumption 3 and consider the effects of viscosity.

FIGURE 13.22 Rising smoke changes from laminar flow to turbulent flow.

Turbulent flow

Laminar flow

FIGURE 13.23 Flow speed changes through a tapered tube.

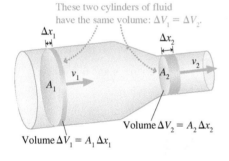

These two cylinders of fluid have the same volume: $\Delta V_1 = \Delta V_2$.

Δx_1

Δx_2

v_1

v_2

A_1

A_2

Volume $\Delta V_2 = A_2 \Delta x_2$

Volume $\Delta V_1 = A_1 \Delta x_1$

FIGURE 13.24 The speed of the water is inversely proportional to the diameter of the stream.

(a) Reducing the diameter with a nozzle causes the speed to increase.

(b)

An increasing speed causes the diameter to decrease.

The rising smoke in FIGURE 13.22 begins as laminar flow, recognizable by the smooth contours, but at some point undergoes a transition to turbulent flow. A laminar-to-turbulent transition is not uncommon in fluid flow. Our model of fluids can be applied to the laminar flow, but not to the turbulent flow.

The Equation of Continuity

Consider a fluid flowing through a tube—oil through a pipe or blood through an artery. If the tube's diameter changes, as happens in FIGURE 13.23, what happens to the speed of the fluid?

When you squeeze a toothpaste tube, the volume of toothpaste that emerges matches the amount by which you reduce the volume of the tube. An *incompressible* fluid flowing through a rigid tube or pipe acts the same way. Fluid is neither created nor destroyed within the tube, and there's no place to store any extra fluid introduced into the tube. If volume V enters the tube during some interval of time Δt, then an equal volume of fluid must leave the tube.

To see the implications of this idea, suppose all the molecules of the fluid in Figure 13.23 are moving forward with speed v_1 at a point where the cross-section area is A_1. Farther along the tube, where the cross-section area is A_2, their speed is v_2. During an interval of time Δt, the molecules in the wider section move forward a distance $\Delta x_1 = v_1 \Delta t$ and those in the narrower section move $\Delta x_2 = v_2 \Delta t$. Because the fluid is incompressible, the volumes ΔV_1 and ΔV_2 must be equal; that is,

$$\Delta V_1 = A_1 \Delta x_1 = A_1 v_1 \Delta t = \Delta V_2 = A_2 \Delta x_2 = A_2 v_2 \Delta t \qquad (13.11)$$

Dividing both sides of the equation by Δt gives the **equation of continuity**:

$$v_1 A_1 = v_2 A_2 \qquad (13.12)$$

The equation of continuity relating the speed v of an incompressible fluid to the cross-section area A of the tube in which it flows

Equations 13.11 and 13.12 say that **the volume of an incompressible fluid entering one part of a tube or pipe must be matched by an equal volume leaving downstream.**

An important consequence of the equation of continuity is that **flow is faster in narrower parts of a tube, slower in wider parts.** You're familiar with this conclusion from many everyday observations. The garden hose shown in FIGURE 13.24a squirts farther after you put a nozzle on it. This is because the narrower opening of the nozzle gives the water a higher exit speed. Water flowing from the faucet shown in FIGURE 13.24b picks up speed as it falls. As a result, the flow tube "necks down" to a smaller diameter.

The *rate* at which fluid flows through the tube—volume per second—is $\Delta V/\Delta t$. This is called the **volume flow rate Q**. We can see from Equation 13.11 that

$$Q = \frac{\Delta V}{\Delta t} = vA \qquad (13.13)$$

The SI units of Q are m³/s, although in practice Q may be measured in cm³/s, liters per minute, or, in the United States, gallons per minute and cubic feet per minute. Another way to express the meaning of the equation of continuity is to say that **the volume flow rate is constant at all points in a tube.**

EXAMPLE 13.10 Speed of water through a hose

A garden hose has an inside diameter of 16 mm. The hose can fill a 10 L bucket in 20 s.

a. What is the speed of the water out of the end of the hose?
b. What diameter nozzle would cause the water to exit with a speed 4 times greater than the speed inside the hose?

PREPARE Water is essentially incompressible, so the equation of continuity applies.

SOLVE

a. The volume flow rate is $Q = \Delta V/\Delta t = (10 \text{ L})/(20 \text{ s}) = 0.50$ L/s. To convert this to SI units, recall that $1 \text{ L} = 1000 \text{ mL} = 10^3 \text{ cm}^3 = 10^{-3} \text{ m}^3$. Thus $Q = 5.0 \times 10^{-4} \text{ m}^3/\text{s}$. We can find the speed of the water from Equation 13.13:

$$v = \frac{Q}{A} = \frac{Q}{\pi r^2} = \frac{5.0 \times 10^{-4} \text{ m}^3/\text{s}}{\pi (0.0080 \text{ m})^2} = 2.5 \text{ m/s}$$

b. The quantity $Q = vA$ remains constant as the water flows through the hose and then the nozzle. To increase v by a factor of 4, A must be reduced by a factor of 4. The cross-section area depends on the square of the diameter, so the area is reduced by a factor of 4 if the diameter is reduced by a factor of 2. Thus the necessary nozzle diameter is 8 mm.

Class Video

EXAMPLE 13.11 Blood flow in capillaries

The volume flow rate of blood leaving the heart to circulate throughout the body is about 5 L/min for a person at rest. All this blood eventually must pass through the smallest blood vessels, the capillaries. Microscope measurements show that a typical capillary is 6 μm in diameter and 1 mm long, and the blood flows through it at an average speed of 1 mm/s.

a. Estimate the total number of capillaries in the body.
b. Estimate the total surface area of all the capillaries.

The various lengths and areas are shown in FIGURE 13.25.

FIGURE 13.25 A capillary (not to scale).

Cross-section area A_{cap}

Surface area

$2r \approx 6 \text{ } \mu$m

$L \approx 1 \text{ mm}$

PREPARE We can use the equation of continuity: The 5 L of blood passing through the heart each minute must be the total flow through all the capillaries combined.

SOLVE

a. We'll start by converting Q to SI units:

$$Q = 5\frac{\text{L}}{\text{min}} \times \frac{1 \text{ m}^3}{1000 \text{ L}} \times \frac{1 \text{ min}}{60 \text{ s}} = 8 \times 10^{-5} \text{ m}^3/\text{s}$$

to one-significant-figure accuracy. Then the total cross-section area of all the capillaries together is

$$A_{total} = \frac{Q}{v} = \frac{8 \times 10^{-5} \text{ m}^3/\text{s}}{0.001 \text{ m/s}} = 0.08 \text{ m}^2$$

The cross-section area of each capillary is $A_{cap} = \pi r^2$, so the total number of capillaries is approximately

$$N = \frac{A_{total}}{A_{cap}} = \frac{0.08 \text{ m}^2}{\pi (3 \times 10^{-6} \text{ m})^2} = 3 \times 10^9$$

b. The surface area of one capillary is

$$A = \text{circumference of capillary} \times \text{length}$$
$$= 2\pi rL = 2\pi (3 \times 10^{-6} \text{ m})(0.001 \text{ m}) = 2 \times 10^{-8} \text{ m}^2$$

so the total surface area of all the capillaries is about

$$A_{surface} = NA = (3 \times 10^9)(2 \times 10^{-8} \text{ m}) = 60 \text{ m}^2$$

ASSESS The number of capillaries is huge, and the total surface area is about the area of a two-car garage. As we saw in Chapter 12, oxygen and nutrients move from the blood into cells by the slow process of diffusion. Only by having this large surface area available for diffusion can the required rate of gas and nutrient exchange be attained.

FIGURE 13.26 Smoke reveals the laminar air flow around a car in a wind tunnel.

Streamline

Representing Fluid Flow: Streamlines and Fluid Elements

Representing the flow of fluid is more complicated than representing the motion of a point particle because fluid flow is the collective motion of a vast number of particles. FIGURE 13.26 gives us an idea of one possible fluid-flow representation. Here smoke is being used to help engineers visualize the air flow around a car in a wind tunnel. The smoothness of the flow tells us this is laminar flow. But notice also how the individual smoke trails retain their identity. They don't cross or get mixed together. Each smoke trail represents a *streamline* in the fluid.

Imagine that we could inject a tiny colored drop of water into a stream of water undergoing laminar flow. Because the flow is steady and the water is incompressible, this colored drop would maintain its identity as it flowed along. The path or trajectory followed by this "particle of fluid" is called a **streamline**. Smoke particles mixed with the air allow you to see the streamlines in the wind-tunnel photograph of Figure 13.26. FIGURE 13.27 illustrates three important properties of streamlines.

FIGURE 13.27 Particles in a fluid move along streamlines.

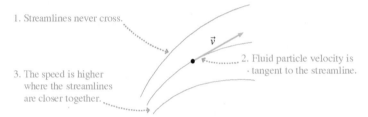

1. Streamlines never cross.

$\vec{v}$

2. Fluid particle velocity is tangent to the streamline.

3. The speed is higher where the streamlines are closer together.

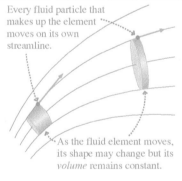

FIGURE 13.28 Motion of a fluid element.

Every fluid particle that makes up the element moves on its own streamline.

As the fluid element moves, its shape may change but its *volume* remains constant.

As we study the motion of a fluid, it is often also useful to consider a small *volume* of fluid, a volume containing many particles of fluid. Such a volume is called a **fluid element**. FIGURE 13.28 shows two important properties of a fluid element. Unlike a particle, a fluid element has an actual shape and volume. Although the shape of a fluid element may change as it moves, the equation of continuity requires that its volume remain constant. The progress of a fluid element as it moves along streamlines and changes shape is another very useful representation of fluid motion.

STOP TO THINK 13.4

2   8

10

?   4

Flows in cm³/s

The figure shows volume flow rates (in cm³/s) for all but one tube. What is the volume flow rate through the unmarked tube? Is the flow direction in or out?

FIGURE 13.29 A motion diagram of a fluid element moving through a narrowing tube.

A fluid element coasts at steady speed through the constant-diameter segments of the tube.

$\vec{a}$

$\vec{v}_1$ $\vec{v}_2$

As a fluid element flows through the tapered section, it speeds up. Because it is accelerating, there must be a force acting on it.

13.6 Fluid Dynamics

The equation of continuity describes a moving fluid but doesn't tell us anything about *why* the fluid is in motion. To understand the dynamics, consider the ideal fluid moving from left to right through the tube shown in FIGURE 13.29. The fluid moves at a steady speed v_1 in the wider part of the tube. In accordance with the equation of continuity, its speed is a higher, but steady, v_2 in the narrower part of the tube. If we follow a fluid element through the tube, we see that it undergoes an *acceleration* from v_1 to v_2 in the tapered section of the tube.

In the absence of friction, Newton's first law tells us that a particle will coast forever at a steady speed. An ideal fluid is nonviscous and thus analogous to a particle moving without friction. This means a fluid element moving through the constant-diameter sections of the tube in Figure 13.29 requires no force to "coast" at steady speed. On the other hand, a fluid element moving through the tapered section of the tube accelerates, speeding up from v_1 to v_2. According to Newton's second law, there must be a net force acting on this fluid element to accelerate it.

What is the origin of this force? There are no external forces, and the horizontal motion rules out gravity. Instead, the fluid element is pushed from both ends by the *surrounding fluid*—that is, by *pressure forces*. The fluid element with cross-section area A in FIGURE 13.30 has a higher pressure on its left side than on its right. Thus the force $F_L = p_L A$ of the fluid pushing on its left side—a force pushing to the right—is greater than the force $F_R = p_R A$ of the fluid on its right side. The net force, which points from the higher-pressure side of the element to the lower-pressure side, is

$$F_{net} = F_L - F_R = (p_L - p_R)A = A\,\Delta p$$

In other words, there's a net force on the fluid element, causing it to change speed, if and only if there's a pressure *difference* Δp between the two faces.

Thus, in order to accelerate the fluid elements in Figure 13.29 through the neck, the pressure p_1 in the wider section of the tube must be higher than the pressure p_2 in the narrower section. When the pressure is changing from one point in a fluid to another, we say that there is a **pressure gradient** in that region. We can also say that pressure forces are caused by pressure gradients, so **an ideal fluid accelerates wherever there is a pressure gradient.**

As a result, **the pressure is higher at a point along a streamline where the fluid is moving slower, lower where the fluid is moving faster.** This property of fluids was discovered in the 18th century by the Swiss scientist Daniel Bernoulli and is called the **Bernoulli effect.**

NOTE ▶ It is important to realize that it is the change in pressure from high to low that *causes* the fluid to speed up. A high fluid speed doesn't *cause* a low pressure any more than a fast-moving particle causes the force that accelerated it. ◀

This relationship between pressure and fluid speed can be used to measure the speed of a fluid with a device called a *Venturi tube*. FIGURE 13.31 shows a simple Venturi tube suitable for a flowing liquid. The high pressure at point 1, where the fluid is moving slowly, causes the fluid to rise in the vertical pipe to a total height d_1. Because there's no vertical motion of the fluid, we can use the hydrostatic pressure equation to find that the pressure at point 1 is $p_1 = p_0 + \rho g d_1$. At point 3, on the same streamline, the fluid is moving faster and the pressure is lower; thus the fluid in the vertical pipe rises to a lower height d_3. The pressure *difference* is $\Delta p = \rho g(d_1 - d_3)$, so the pressure difference across the neck of the pipe can be found by measuring the difference in heights of the fluid. We'll see later in this section how to relate this pressure difference to the increase of speed.

FIGURE 13.30 The net force on a fluid element due to pressure points from high to low pressure.

Higher-pressure side   Lower-pressure side

$\vec{F}_L$ $\vec{F}_R$

Area A $\vec{F}_{net}$

Because $F = pA$, the force on the higher-pressure side is larger than that on the lower-pressure side.

FIGURE 13.31 A Venturi tube measures flow speeds of a fluid.

d_1 d_2 d_3 d_4

1   v_1 2   3 v_2 4

Slower-moving fluid, higher pressure   Faster-moving fluid, lower pressure

Note that the fluid height d_1 is the same as d_2, and d_3 is the same as d_4. For an ideal fluid, with no viscosity, no pressure difference is needed to keep the fluid moving at a constant speed, as it does in both the large- and small-diameter sections of the tube. In the next section we'll see how this result changes for a viscous fluid.

1. Hold strip at lower edge of bottom lip, just touching lip.

1 inch × 8 inch strip of notebook paper

2. Pucker lips and blow hard straight out over the top of the strip.

Blowing up Try the experiment in the figure. You might expect the strip to be pushed *down* by the force of your breath, but you'll find that the strip actually *rises*. Your breath moving over the curved strip is similar to wind blowing over a hill, and Bernoulli's effect likewise predicts a zone of lower pressure above the strip that causes it to rise.

Applications of the Bernoulli Effect

Many important applications of the Bernoulli effect can be understood by considering the flow of air over a hill, as shown in FIGURE 13.32. Far to the left, away from the hill, the wind blows at a constant speed, so its streamlines are equally spaced. But as the air moves over the hill, the hill forces the streamlines to bunch together so that the air speeds up. According to the Bernoulli effect, there exists a zone of *low pressure* at the crest of the hill, where the air is moving the fastest.

Using these ideas, we can understand *lift*, the upward force on the wing of a moving airplane that makes flight possible. FIGURE 13.33 shows an airplane wing, seen in cross section, for an airplane flying to the left. The figure is drawn in the reference frame of the airplane, so that the wing appears stationary and the air flows past it to the right. The shape of the wing is such that, just as for the hill in Figure 13.32, the

FIGURE 13.32 Wind speeds up as it crests a hill.

The pressure is p_{atmos} where the streamlines are undisturbed.

p_{atmos}

Streamlines

The streamlines bunch together as the wind goes over the hill.

The higher air speed here is accompanied by a region of lower pressure.

FIGURE 13.33 Air flow over a wing generates lift by creating unequal pressures above and below.

As the air squeezes over the top of the wing, it speeds up. There is a region of low pressure associated with this faster-moving air.

$\vec{F}_{lift}$

The pressure is higher below the wing where the air is moving more slowly. The high pressure below and the low pressure above result in a net upward lift force.

streamlines of the air must squeeze together as they pass over the wing. This increased speed is, by the Bernoulli effect, accompanied by a region of low pressure above the wing. The air speed below the wing is actually slowed, so that there's a region of high pressure below. This high pressure pushes up on the wing, while the low-pressure air above it presses down, but less strongly. The result is a net upward force—the lift.

The Bernoulli effect also explains how hurricanes destroy the roofs of houses. The roofs are not "blown" off; they are *lifted* off by pressure differences caused by the Bernoulli effect. FIGURE 13.34 shows that the situation is similar to that for the hill and the airplane wing. The pressure difference causing the lift force is not very large—but the force is proportional to the *area* of the roof, which, being very large, can produce a lift force large enough to separate the roof from its supporting walls.

FIGURE 13.34 How high winds lift roofs off.

The wind speeds up as it squeezes over the rooftop. This implies a low-pressure zone above the roof.

The pressure inside the house is atmospheric pressure, which is higher. The result is a net upward force on the roof.

Smaller, slightly curved hill gives a low pressure.

Taller, sharply curved hill gives an even lower pressure.

The pressure difference between the two ends pushes air through the burrow.

Nature's air conditioning Prairie dogs ventilate their underground burrows with the same aerodynamic forces and pressures that give airplanes lift. The two entrances to their burrows are surrounded by mounds, one higher than the other. When the wind blows across these mounds, the pressure is reduced at the top, just as for an airplane's wing. The taller mound, with its greater curvature, has the lower pressure of the two entrances. Air then is pushed through the burrow toward this lower-pressure side.

Bernoulli's Equation

We've seen that a pressure gradient causes a fluid to accelerate horizontally. Not surprisingly, gravity can also cause a fluid to speed up or slow down if the fluid changes elevation. These are the key ideas of fluid dynamics. Now we would like to make these ideas quantitative by finding a numerical relationship for pressure, height, and the speed of a fluid. We can do so by applying the statement of conservation of mechanical energy you learned in Chapter 10,

$$\Delta K + \Delta U = W$$

where U is the gravitational potential energy and W is the work done by other forces—in this case, pressure forces. Recall that we're still considering ideal fluids, with no friction or viscosity, so there's no dissipation of energy to thermal energy.

FIGURE 13.35a shows fluid flowing through a tube. The tube narrows from cross-section area A_1 to area A_2 as it bends uphill. Let's concentrate on the large volume of the fluid that is shaded in Figure 13.35a. **This moving segment of fluid will be our system for the purpose of applying conservation of energy.**

To use conservation of energy, we need to draw a before-and-after overview. The "before" situation is shown in FIGURE 13.35b. A short time Δt later, the system has moved along the tube a bit, as shown in the "after" drawing of FIGURE 13.35c. Because the tube is not of uniform diameter, the two ends of the fluid system do not move the same distance during Δt: The lower end moves distance Δx_1, while the upper end moves Δx_2. Thus the system moves *out of* a cylindrical volume $\Delta V_1 = A_1 \Delta x_1$ at the lower end and *into* a volume $\Delta V_2 = A_2 \Delta x_2$ at the upper end. The equation of continuity tells us that these two volumes must be the same, so $A_1 \Delta x_1 = A_2 \Delta x_2 = \Delta V$.

From the "before" situation to the "after" situation, the system *loses* the kinetic and potential energy it originally had in the volume ΔV_1 but *gains* the kinetic and potential energy in the volume ΔV_2 that it later occupies. (The energy it has in the region between these two small volumes is unchanged.) Let's find the kinetic energy in each of these small volumes. The mass of fluid in each cylinder is $m = \rho \, \Delta V$, where ρ is the density of the fluid. The kinetic energies of the two small volumes 1 and 2 are then

$$K_1 = \frac{1}{2}\rho \underbrace{\Delta V}_{m} v_1^2 \quad \text{and} \quad K_2 = \frac{1}{2}\rho \underbrace{\Delta V}_{m} v_2^2$$

Thus the net *change* in kinetic energy is

$$\Delta K = K_2 - K_1 = \frac{1}{2}\rho \, \Delta V v_2^2 - \frac{1}{2}\rho \, \Delta V v_1^2$$

Similarly, the net change in the gravitational potential energy of our fluid system is

$$\Delta U = U_2 - U_1 = \rho \, \Delta V g y_2 - \rho \, \Delta V g y_1$$

The final piece of our conservation of energy treatment is the work done on the system by the rest of the fluid. As the fluid system moves, positive work is done on it by the force $\vec{F}_1$ due to the pressure p_1 of the fluid to the left of the system, while negative work is done on the system by the force $\vec{F}_2$ due to the pressure p_2 of the fluid to the right of the system. The positive work is

$$W_1 = F_1 \, \Delta x_1 = (p_1 A_1) \, \Delta x_1 = p_1(A_1 \, \Delta x_1) = p_1 \, \Delta V$$

Similarly the negative work is

$$W_2 = -F_2 \, \Delta x_2 = -(p_2 A_2) \, \Delta x_2 = -p_2(A_2 \, \Delta x_2) = -p_2 \, \Delta V$$

FIGURE 13.35 An ideal fluid flowing through a tube.

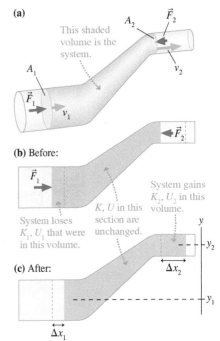

(a)

This shaded volume is the system.

(b) Before:

System loses K_1, U_1 that were in this volume.

K, U in this section are unchanged.

System gains K_2, U_2 in this volume.

(c) After:

Living under pressure BIO When plaque builds up in major arteries, such as the carotid artery that supplies the head, dangerous drops in blood pressure can result. *Doppler ultrasound,* which you'll study in Chapter 15, uses sound waves to produce images of the interior of the body, and can detect the velocity of flowing blood. The image above shows the blood flow through a carotid artery with significant plaque buildup; yellow indicates a higher blood velocity than red. Once the velocities are known at two points along the flow, Bernoulli's equation can be used to deduce the corresponding pressure drop.

Thus the *net* work done on the system is

$$W = W_1 + W_2 = p_1\,\Delta V - p_2\,\Delta V = (p_1 - p_2)\,\Delta V$$

We can now use these expressions for ΔK, ΔU, and W to write the energy equation as

$$\underbrace{\frac{1}{2}\rho\,\Delta Vv_2^2 - \frac{1}{2}\rho\,\Delta Vv_1^2}_{\Delta K} + \underbrace{\rho\,\Delta Vgy_2 - \rho\,\Delta Vgy_1}_{\Delta U} = \underbrace{(p_1 - p_2)\,\Delta V}_{W}$$

The ΔV's cancel, and we can rearrange the remaining terms to get **Bernoulli's equation:**

$$p_2 + \frac{1}{2}\rho v_2^2 + \rho gy_2 = p_1 + \frac{1}{2}\rho v_1^2 + \rho gy_1 \qquad (13.14)$$

Bernoulli's equation relating pressure p, speed v, and height y
at any two points along a streamline in an ideal fluid

Video Tutor
Demonstration

Equation 13.14, a quantitative statement of the ideas we developed earlier in this section, is really nothing more than a statement about work and energy. Using Bernoulli's equation is very much like using the law of conservation of energy. Rather than identifying a "before" and "after," you want to identify two points on a streamline. As the following example shows, Bernoulli's equation is often used in conjunction with the equation of continuity.

EXAMPLE 13.12 **Pressure in an irrigation system**

Water flows through the pipes shown in FIGURE 13.36. The water's speed through the lower pipe is 5.0 m/s, and a pressure gauge reads 75 kPa. What is the reading of the pressure gauge on the upper pipe?

FIGURE 13.36 The water pipes of an irrigation system.

PREPARE Treat the water as an ideal fluid obeying Bernoulli's equation. Consider a streamline connecting point 1 in the lower pipe with point 2 in the upper pipe.

SOLVE Bernoulli's equation, Equation 13.14, relates the pressures, fluid speeds, and heights at points 1 and 2. It is easily solved for the pressure p_2 at point 2:

$$p_2 = p_1 + \frac{1}{2}\rho v_1^2 - \frac{1}{2}\rho v_2^2 + \rho gy_1 - \rho gy_2$$

$$= p_1 + \frac{1}{2}\rho(v_1^2 - v_2^2) + \rho g(y_1 - y_2)$$

All quantities on the right are known except v_2, and that is where the equation of continuity will be useful. The cross-section areas and water speeds at points 1 and 2 are related by

$$v_1A_1 = v_2A_2$$

from which we find

$$v_2 = \frac{A_1}{A_2}v_1 = \frac{r_1^2}{r_2^2}v_1 = \frac{(0.030\text{ m})^2}{(0.020\text{ m})^2}(5.0\text{ m/s}) = 11.25\text{ m/s}$$

The pressure at point 1 is $p_1 = 75\text{ kPa} + 1\text{ atm} = 176{,}300\text{ Pa}$. We can now use the above expression for p_2 to calculate $p_2 = 105{,}900\text{ Pa}$. This is the absolute pressure; the pressure gauge on the upper pipe will read

$$p_2 = 105{,}900\text{ Pa} - 1\text{ atm} = 4.6\text{ kPa}$$

ASSESS Reducing the pipe size decreases the pressure because it makes $v_2 > v_1$. Gaining elevation also reduces the pressure.

STOP TO THINK 13.5   Rank in order, from highest to lowest, the liquid heights h_1 to h_4 in tubes 1 to 4. The air flow is from left to right.

13.7 Viscosity and Poiseuille's Equation

Thus far, the only thing we've needed to know about a fluid is its density. It is the density that determines how the pressure in a static fluid increases with depth, and density appears in Bernoulli's equation for the motion of a fluid. But you know from everyday experience that another property of fluids is often crucial in determining how fluids flow. The densities of honey and water are not too different, but there's a huge difference in the way honey and water pour. The honey is much "thicker." This property of a fluid, which measures its resistance to flow, is called **viscosity**. A very viscous fluid flows slowly when poured and is difficult to force through a pipe or tube. The viscous nature of fluids is of key importance in understanding a wide range of real-world applications, from blood flow to the flight of birds to throwing a curveball.

An ideal fluid, with no viscosity, will "coast" at constant speed through a constant-diameter tube with no change in pressure. That's why the fluid heights are the same in the first and second pressure-measuring columns on the Venturi tube of Figure 13.31. But as FIGURE 13.37 shows, any real fluid requires a *pressure difference* between the ends of a tube to keep the fluid moving at constant speed. The size of the pressure difference depends on the viscosity of the fluid. Think about how much harder you have to suck on a straw to drink a thick milkshake than to drink water or to pull air through the straw.

FIGURE 13.37 A viscous fluid needs a pressure difference to keep it moving. Compare this to Figure 13.31, which showed an ideal fluid.

The pressure drops between points 1 and 2. In this region, the pressure gradient causes the fluid to speed up. The pressure drops between points 3 and 4.

In these regions, a pressure gradient is needed simply to keep the fluid moving with constant speed.

FIGURE 13.38 The pressure difference needed to keep the fluid flowing is proportional to the fluid's viscosity.

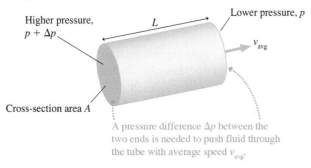

Higher pressure, $p + \Delta p$

Lower pressure, p

L

v_{avg}

Cross-section area A

A pressure difference Δp between the two ends is needed to push fluid through the tube with average speed v_{avg}.

FIGURE 13.38 shows a viscous fluid flowing with a constant average speed v_{avg} through a tube of length L and cross-section area A. Experiments show that the pressure difference needed to keep the fluid moving is proportional to v_{avg} and to L and inversely proportional to A. We can write

$$\Delta p = 8\pi\eta \frac{Lv_{avg}}{A} \tag{13.15}$$

where $8\pi\eta$ is the constant of proportionality and η (lowercase Greek eta) is called the **coefficient of viscosity** (or just the *viscosity*). (The 8π enters the equation from the technical definition of viscosity, which need not concern us.)

Equation 13.15 makes sense. A more viscous fluid needs a larger pressure difference to push it through the tube; an ideal fluid, with $\eta = 0$, will keep flowing without any

TABLE 13.3 Viscosities of fluids

Fluid	$\eta\,(\text{Pa}\cdot\text{s})$
Air (20°C)	1.8×10^{-5}
Water (20°C)	1.0×10^{-3}
Water (40°C)	0.7×10^{-3}
Water (60°C)	0.5×10^{-3}
Whole blood (37°C)	2.5×10^{-3}
Motor oil (−30°C)	3×10^{5}
Motor oil (40°C)	0.07
Motor oil (100°C)	0.01
Honey (15°C)	600
Honey (40°C)	20

pressure difference. We can also see from Equation 13.15 that the units of viscosity are $\text{N} \cdot \text{s/m}^2$ or, equivalently, $\text{Pa} \cdot \text{s}$. Table 13.3 gives values of η for some common fluids. Note that the viscosity of many liquids decreases *very* rapidly with temperature. Cold oil hardly flows at all, but hot oil pours almost like water.

Poiseuille's Equation

Viscosity has a profound effect on how a fluid moves through a tube. FIGURE 13.39a shows that in an ideal fluid, all fluid particles move with the same speed v, the speed that appears in the equation of continuity. For a viscous fluid, FIGURE 13.39b shows that the fluid moves fastest in the center of the tube. The speed decreases as you move away from the center of the tube until reaching zero on the walls of the tube. That is, the layer of fluid in contact with the tube doesn't move at all. Whether it be water through pipes or blood through arteries, the fact that the fluid at the outer edges "lingers" and barely moves allows deposits to build on the inside walls of a tube.

FIGURE 13.39 Viscosity alters the velocities of the fluid particles.

(a) Ideal fluid

The velocity is the same at all points in the tube.

(b) Viscous fluid

The velocity is maximum at the center of the tube. It decreases away from the center.

The velocity is zero on the walls of the tube.

Although we can't characterize the flow of a viscous liquid by a single flow speed v, we can still define the *average* flow speed. Suppose a fluid with viscosity η flows through a circular pipe with radius R and cross-section area $A = \pi R^2$. From Equation 13.15, a pressure difference Δp between the ends of the pipe causes the fluid to flow with average speed

$$v_{\text{avg}} = \frac{R^2}{8\eta L}\,\Delta p \qquad (13.16)$$

The average flow speed is directly proportional to the pressure difference; for the fluid to flow twice as fast, you would need to double the pressure difference between the ends of the pipe.

Equation 13.13 defined the volume flow rate $Q = \Delta V/\Delta t$ and found that $Q = vA$ for an ideal fluid. For viscous flow, where v isn't constant throughout the fluid, we simply need to replace v with the average speed v_{avg} found in Equation 13.16. Using $A = \pi R^2$ for a circular tube, we see that a pressure difference Δp causes a volume flow rate

$$Q = v_{\text{avg}}A = \frac{\pi R^4 \Delta p}{8\eta L} \qquad (13.17)$$

Poiseuille's equation for viscous flow through a tube of radius R and length L

This result is called **Poiseuille's equation** after the French scientist Jean Poiseuille (1797–1869) who first performed this calculation.

One surprising result of Poiseuille's equation is the very strong dependence of the flow on the tube's radius; the volume flow rate is proportional to the *fourth* power of R. If you double the radius of a tube, the flow rate will increase by a factor of $2^4 = 16$. This strong radius dependence comes from two factors. First, the flow rate depends on the area of the tube, which is proportional to R^2; larger tubes carry more fluid. Second, the average speed is faster in a larger tube because the center of the tube, where the flow is fastest, is farther from the "drag" exerted by the wall. As we've seen, the average speed is also proportional to R^2. These two terms combine to give the R^4 dependence.

CONCEPTUAL EXAMPLE 13.13 **Blood pressure and cardiovascular disease**

Cardiovascular disease is a narrowing of the arteries due to the buildup of plaque deposits on the interior walls. Magnetic resonance imaging, which you'll learn about in Chapter 24, can create exquisite three-dimensional images of the internal structure of the body. Shown are the carotid arteries that supply blood to the head, with a dangerous narrowing—a *stenosis*—indicated by the arrow.

If a section of an artery has narrowed by 8%, not nearly as much as the stenosis shown, by what percentage must the blood-pressure difference between the ends of the narrowed section increase to keep blood flowing at the same rate?

REASON According to Poiseuille's equation, the pressure difference Δp must increase to compensate for a decrease in the artery's radius R if the blood flow rate Q is to remain unchanged. If we write Poiseuille's equation as

$$R^4 \Delta p = \frac{8\eta L Q}{\pi}$$

we see that the product $R^4 \Delta p$ must remain unchanged if the artery is to deliver the same flow rate. Let the initial artery radius and pressure difference be R_i and Δp_i. Disease decreases the radius by 8%, meaning that $R_f = 0.92R_i$. The requirement

$$R_i^4 \Delta p_i = R_f^4 \Delta p_f$$

can be solved for the new pressure difference:

$$\Delta p_f = \frac{R_i^4}{R_f^4} \Delta p_i = \frac{R_i^4}{(0.92R_i)^4} \Delta p_i = 1.4 \, \Delta p_i$$

The pressure difference must increase by 40% to maintain the flow.

ASSESS Because the flow rate depends on R^4, even a small change in radius requires a large change in Δp to compensate. Either the person's blood pressure must increase, which is dangerous, or he or she will suffer a significant reduction in blood flow. For the stenosis shown in the image, the reduction in radius is much greater than 8%, and the pressure difference will be large and very dangerous.

EXAMPLE 13.14 **Pressure drop along a capillary**

In Example 13.11 we examined blood flow through a capillary. Using the numbers from that example, calculate the pressure "drop" from one end of a capillary to the other.

PREPARE Example 13.11 gives enough information to determine the flow rate through a capillary. We can then use Poiseuille's equation to calculate the pressure difference between the ends.

SOLVE The measured volume flow rate leaving the heart was given as 5 L/min = 8×10^{-5} m³/s. This flow is divided among all the capillaries, which we found to number $N = 3 \times 10^9$. Thus the flow rate through each capillary is

$$Q_{cap} = \frac{Q_{heart}}{N} = \frac{8 \times 10^{-5} \text{ m}^3/\text{s}}{3 \times 10^9} = 2.7 \times 10^{-14} \text{ m}^3/\text{s}$$

Solving Poiseuille's equation for Δp, we get

$$\Delta p = \frac{8\eta L Q_{cap}}{\pi R^4} = \frac{8(2.5 \times 10^{-3} \text{ Pa} \cdot \text{s})(0.001 \text{ m})(2.7 \times 10^{-14} \text{ m}^3/\text{s})}{\pi (3 \times 10^{-6} \text{ m})^4} = 2100 \text{ Pa}$$

Converting to mm of mercury, the units of blood pressure, the pressure drop across the capillary is $\Delta p = 16$ mm Hg.

ASSESS The average blood pressure provided by the heart (the average of the systolic and diastolic pressures) is about 100 mm Hg. A physiology textbook will tell you that the pressure has decreased to 35 mm by the time blood enters the capillaries, and it exits from capillaries into the veins at 17 mm. Thus the pressure drop across the capillaries is 18 mm Hg. Our calculation, based on the laws of fluid flow and some simple estimates of capillary size, is in almost perfect agreement with measured values.

A viscous fluid flows through the pipe shown. The three marked segments are of equal length. Across which segment is the pressure difference the greatest?

A   B   C

INTEGRATED EXAMPLE 13.15   **An intravenous transfusion**

At the hospital, a patient often receives fluids via an intravenous (IV) infusion. A bag of the fluid is held at a fixed height above the patient's body. The fluid then travels down a large-diameter, flexible tube to a catheter—a short tube with a small diameter—inserted into the patient's vein.

1.0 L of saline solution, with a density of 1020 kg/m³ and a viscosity of 1.1×10^{-3} Pa·s, is to be infused into a patient in 8.0 h. The catheter is 30 mm long and has an inner diameter of 0.30 mm. The pressure in the patient's vein is 20 mm Hg. How high above the patient should the bag be positioned to get the desired flow rate?

PREPARE FIGURE 13.40 shows a sketch of the situation, defines variables, and lists the known information. We're concerned with the flow of a viscous fluid. According to Poiseuille's equation, the flow rate depends inversely on the fourth power of a tube's radius. We are told that the tube from the elevated bag to the catheter has a large diameter, while the diameter of the catheter is small. Thus, we expect the flow rate to be determined entirely by the flow through the narrow catheter; the wide tube has a negligible effect on the rate.

FIGURE 13.40 Visual overview of an IV transfusion.

To use Poiseuille's equation for the catheter, we need the pressure difference Δp between the ends of the catheter. We know the pressure on the end of the catheter in the patient's vein is $p_v = 20$ mm Hg or, converting to SI units using Table 13.2,

$$p_v = 20 \text{ mm Hg} \times \frac{101 \times 10^3 \text{ Pa}}{760 \text{ mm Hg}} = 2700 \text{ Pa}$$

This is a gauge pressure, the pressure in excess of 1 atm. The pressure on the fluid side of the catheter is due to the hydrostatic pressure of the saline solution filling the bag and the flexible tube leading to the catheter. This pressure is given by the hydrostatic pressure equation $p = p_0 + \rho g d$, where d is the "depth" of the catheter below the bag. Thus we'll use Δp to find d.

SOLVE The desired volume flow rate is

$$Q = \frac{\Delta V}{\Delta t} = \frac{1.0 \text{ L}}{8.0 \text{ h}} = 0.125 \text{ L/h}$$

Converting to SI units using $1.0 \text{ L} = 1.0 \times 10^{-3} \text{ m}^3$, we have

$$Q = 0.125 \, \frac{\text{L}}{\text{h}} \times \frac{1.0 \times 10^{-3} \text{ m}^3}{\text{L}} \times \frac{1 \text{ h}}{3600 \text{ s}} = 3.5 \times 10^{-8} \text{ m}^3/\text{s}$$

Poiseuille's equation for viscous fluid flow is

$$Q = \frac{\pi R^4 \Delta p}{8 \eta L}$$

Thus the pressure difference needed between the ends of the tube to produce the desired flow rate Q is

$$\Delta p = \frac{8 \eta L Q}{\pi R^4}$$

$$= \frac{8(1.1 \times 10^{-3} \text{ Pa·s})(0.030 \text{ m})(3.5 \times 10^{-8} \text{ m}^3/\text{s})}{\pi (1.5 \times 10^{-4} \text{ m})^4}$$

$$= 5800 \text{ Pa}$$

Now Δp is the difference between the fluid pressure p_f at one end of the catheter and the vein pressure p_v at the other end: $\Delta p = p_f - p_v$. We know p_v, so

$$p_f = p_v + \Delta p = 2700 \text{ Pa} + 5800 \text{ Pa} = 8500 \text{ Pa}$$

This pressure, like the vein pressure, is a gauge pressure. The true hydrostatic pressure at the catheter is $p = 1 \text{ atm} + 8500 \text{ Pa}$. But the hydrostatic pressure in the fluid is

$$p = p_0 + \rho g d = 1 \text{ atm} + \rho g d$$

We see that $\rho g d = 8500$ Pa. Solving for d, we find the required elevation of the bag above the patient's arm:

$$d = \frac{p_f}{\rho g} = \frac{8500 \text{ Pa}}{(1020 \text{ kg/m}^3)(9.8 \text{ m/s}^2)} = 0.85 \text{ m}$$

ASSESS This height of about a meter seems reasonable for the height of an IV bag. In practice, the bag can be raised or lowered to adjust the fluid flow rate.

SUMMARY

The goal of Chapter 13 has been to understand the static and dynamic properties of fluids.

GENERAL PRINCIPLES

Fluid Statics

Gases

- Freely moving particles
- Compressible
- Pressure mainly due to particle collisions with walls

Liquids

- Loosely bound particles
- Incompressible
- Pressure due to the weight of the liquid
- Hydrostatic pressure at depth d is $p = p_0 + \rho g d$
- The pressure is the same at all points on a horizontal line through a liquid (of one kind) in hydrostatic equilibrium

Fluid Dynamics

Ideal-fluid model

- Incompressible
- Smooth, laminar flow
- Nonviscous

Density ρ

Equation of continuity

Volume flow rate $Q = \dfrac{\Delta V}{\Delta t} = v_1 A_1 = v_2 A_2$

Bernoulli's equation is a statement of energy conservation:

$$p_1 + \frac{1}{2}\rho v_1^2 + \rho g y_1 = p_2 + \frac{1}{2}\rho v_2^2 + \rho g y_2$$

Poiseuille's equation governs viscous flow through a tube:

$$Q = v_{\text{avg}} A = \frac{\pi R^4 \Delta p}{8\eta L}$$

IMPORTANT CONCEPTS

Density $\rho = m/V$, where m is mass and V is volume.

Pressure $p = F/A$, where F is force magnitude and A is the area on which the force acts.

- Pressure exists at all points in a fluid.
- Pressure pushes equally in all directions.
- Gauge pressure $p_g = p - 1$ atm.

Viscosity η is the property of a fluid that makes it resist flowing.

Representing fluid flow

Streamlines are the paths of individual fluid particles.

The velocity of a fluid particle is tangent to its streamline. $\vec{v}$

The speed is higher where the streamlines are closer together.

Fluid elements contain a fixed volume of fluid. Their shape may change as they move.

Every fluid particle that makes up the element moves on its own streamline.

APPLICATIONS

Buoyancy is the upward force of a fluid on an object immersed in the fluid.

Archimedes' principle: The magnitude of the buoyant force equals the weight of the fluid displaced by the object.

Sink: $\quad \rho_{\text{avg}} > \rho_f \quad F_B < w_o$

Float: $\quad \rho_{\text{avg}} < \rho_f \quad F_B > w_o$

Neutrally buoyant: $\rho_{\text{avg}} = \rho_f \quad F_B = w_o$

Barometers measure atmospheric pressure. Atmospheric pressure is related to the height of the liquid column by $p_{\text{atmos}} = \rho g h$.

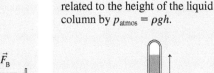

Manometers measure pressure. The pressure at the closed end of the tube is $p = 1$ atm $+ \rho g h$.

These two points are at the same pressure p.

Problem difficulty is labeled as | (straightforward) to ||||| (challenging). Problems labeled INT integrate significant material from earlier chapters; BIO are of biological or medical interest.

For homework assigned on MasteringPhysics, go to www.masteringphysics.com

Scan this QR code to launch a Video Tutor Solution that will help you solve problems for this chapter.

QUESTIONS

Conceptual Questions

1. Which has the greater density, 1 g of mercury or 1000 g of water?

2. A 1×10^{-3} m^3 chunk of material has a mass of 3 kg.
   a. What is the material's density?
   b. Would a 2×10^{-3} m^3 chunk of the same material have the same mass? Explain.
   c. Would a 2×10^{-3} m^3 chunk of the same material have the same density? Explain.

3. You are given an irregularly shaped chunk of material and asked to find its density. List the *specific* steps that you would follow to do so.

4. Object 1 has an irregular shape. Its density is 4000 kg/m^3.
   a. Object 2 has the same shape and dimensions as object 1, but it is twice as massive. What is the density of object 2?
   b. Object 3 has the same mass and the same *shape* as object 1, but its size in all three dimensions is twice that of object 1. What is the density of object 3?

5. BIO When you get a blood transfusion the bag of blood is held above your body, but when you donate blood the collection bag is held below. Why is this?

6. BIO To explore the bottom of a 10-m-deep lake, your friend Tom proposes to get a long garden hose, put one end on land and the other in his mouth for breathing underwater, and descend into the depths. Susan, who overhears the conversation, reacts with horror and warns Tom that he will not be able to inhale when he is at the lake bottom. Why is Susan so worried?

7. Rank in order, from largest to smallest, the pressures at A, B, and C in Figure Q13.7. Explain.

8. Refer to Figure Q13.7. Rank in order, from largest to smallest, the pressures at D, E, and F. Explain.

9. Cylinders A and B contain liquids. The pressure p_A at the bottom of A is higher than the pressure p_B at the bottom of B. Is the ratio p_A/p_B of the absolute pressures larger, smaller, or equal to the ratio of the gauge pressures? Explain.

FIGURE Q13.7

10. In Figure Q13.10, A and B are rectangular tanks full of water. They have equal heights and equal side lengths (the dimension into the page), but different widths.

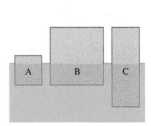

FIGURE Q13.10

   a. Compare the forces the water exerts on the bottoms of the tanks. Is F_A larger, smaller, or equal to F_B? Explain.
   b. Compare the forces the water exerts on the sides of the tanks. Is F_A larger, smaller, or equal to F_B? Explain.

11. Helium-filled weather balloons are spherical when they reach very high altitudes. However, they are only partially inflated with helium before they are released. Explain why this is done.

12. Water expands when heated. Suppose a beaker of water is heated from 10°C to 90°C. Does the pressure at the bottom of the beaker increase, decrease, or stay the same? Explain.

13. In Figure Q13.13, is p_A larger, smaller, or equal to p_B? Explain.

14. A beaker of water rests on a scale. A metal ball is then lowered into the beaker using a string tied to the ball. The ball doesn't touch the sides or bottom of the beaker, and no water spills from the beaker. Does the scale reading decrease, increase, or stay the same? Explain.

FIGURE Q13.13

15. Rank in order, from largest to smallest, the densities of objects A, B, and C in Figure Q13.15. Explain.

FIGURE Q13.15   **FIGURE Q13.16**

16. Objects A, B, and C in Figure Q13.16 have the same volume. Rank in order, from largest to smallest, the sizes of the buoyant forces F_A, F_B, and F_C on A, B, and C. Explain.

17. Refer to Figure Q13.16. Now A, B, and C have the same density, but still have the masses given in the figure. Rank in order, from largest to smallest, the sizes of the buoyant forces on A, B, and C. Explain.

18. When you stand on a bathroom scale, it reads 700 N. Suppose a giant vacuum cleaner sucks half the air out of the room, reducing the pressure to 0.5 atm. Would the scale reading increase, decrease, or stay the same? Explain.

19. Suppose you stand on a bathroom scale that is on the bottom of a swimming pool. The water comes up to your waist. Does the scale read more, less, or the same as your true weight? Explain.

20. When you place an egg in water, it sinks. If you add salt to the water, after some time the egg floats. Explain.

21. Submerged submarines contain tanks filled with water. To rise to the surface, compressed air is used to force the water out of the tanks. Explain why this works.

22. Fish can adjust their buoyancy with an organ called the *swim* BIO *bladder.* The swim bladder is a flexible gas-filled sac; the fish can increase or decrease the amount of gas in the swim bladder so that it stays neutrally buoyant—neither sinking nor floating. Suppose the fish is neutrally buoyant at some depth and then goes deeper. What needs to happen to the volume of air in the swim bladder? Will the fish need to add or remove gas from the swim bladder to maintain its neutral buoyancy?

23. Figure Q13.23 shows two identical beakers filled to the same height with water. Beaker B has a plastic sphere floating in it. Which beaker, with all its contents, weighs more? Or are they equal? Explain.

FIGURE Q13.23

24. A tub of water, filled to the brim, sits on a scale. Then a floating block of wood is placed in the tub, pushing some water over the rim. The water that overflows immediately runs off the scale. What happens to the reading of the scale?

25. Ships A and B have the same height and the same mass. Their cross-section profiles are shown in Figure Q13.25. Does one ship ride higher in the water (more height above the water line) than the other? If so, which one? Explain.

FIGURE Q13.25

26. Gas flows through a pipe, as shown in Figure Q13.26. The pipe's constant outer diameter is shown; you can't see into the pipe to know how the inner diameter changes.

FIGURE Q13.26

Rank in order, from largest to smallest, the gas speeds v_1 to v_3 at points 1, 2, and 3. Explain.

27. Liquid flows through a pipe as shown in Figure Q13.27. The pipe's constant outer diameter is shown; you can't see into the pipe to know how the inner diameter changes.

FIGURE Q13.27

Rank in order, from largest to smallest, the flow speeds v_1 to v_3 at points 1, 2, and 3. Explain.

28. A liquid with negligible viscosity flows through the pipe shown in Figure Q13.28. This is an overhead view.
   a. Rank in order, from largest to smallest, the flow speeds v_1 to v_4 at points 1 to 4. Explain.
   b. Rank in order, from largest to smallest, the pressures p_1 to p_4 at points 1 to 4. Explain.

FIGURE Q13.28

FIGURE Q13.29

29. Wind blows over the house shown in Figure Q13.29. A window on the ground floor is open. Is there an air flow through the house? If so, does the air flow in the window and out the chimney, or in the chimney and out the window? Explain.

30. Two pipes have the same inner cross-section area. One has a circular cross section and the other has a rectangular cross section with its height one-tenth its width. Through which pipe, if either, would it be easier to pump a viscous liquid? Explain.

Multiple-Choice Questions

31. | Figure Q13.31 shows a 100 g block of copper ($\rho = 8900 \text{ kg/m}^3$) and a 100 g block of aluminum ($\rho = 2700 \text{ kg/m}^3$) connected by a massless string that runs over two massless, frictionless pulleys. The two blocks exactly balance, since they have the same mass. Now suppose that the whole system is submerged in water. What will happen?
   A. The copper block will fall, the aluminum block will rise.
   B. The aluminum block will fall, the copper block will rise.
   C. Nothing will change.
   D. Both blocks will rise.

Copper   Aluminum

FIGURE Q13.31

32. | Masses A and B rest on very light pistons that enclose a fluid, as shown in Figure Q13.32. There is no friction between the pistons and the cylinders they fit inside. Which of the following is true?
   A. Mass A is greater.   B. Mass B is greater.
   C. Mass A and mass B are the same.

FIGURE Q13.32

33. | If you dive underwater, you notice an uncomfortable pres-BIO sure on your eardrums due to the increased pressure. The human eardrum has an area of about 70 mm^2 (7×10^{-5} m^2), and it can sustain a force of about 7 N without rupturing. If your body had no means of balancing the extra pressure (which, in reality, it does), what would be the maximum depth you could dive without rupturing your eardrum?
   A. 0.3 m   B. 1 m   C. 3 m   D. 10 m

34. ‖ An 8.0 lb bowling ball has a diameter of 8.5 inches. When lowered into water, this ball will
   A. Float.   B. Sink.   C. Have neutral buoyancy.

35. | A basketball has a mass of 0.50 kg and a volume of 8.0×10^{-3} m^3. What is the magnitude of the net force on a basketball when it is fully submerged in water?
   A. 4.9 N   B. 74 N   C. 78 N   D. 83 N

36. | An object floats in water, with 75% of its volume submerged. What is its approximate density?
   A. 250 kg/m^3 B. 750 kg/m^3
   C. 1000 kg/m^3 D. 1250 kg/m^3

37. | A syringe is being used to squirt water as shown in Figure Q13.37. The water is ejected from the nozzle at 10 m/s. At what speed is the plunger of the syringe being depressed?

FIGURE Q13.37

   A. 0.01 m/s B. 0.1 m/s   C. 1 m/s   D. 10 m/s

38. ‖ Water flows through a 4.0-cm-diameter horizontal pipe at a speed of 1.3 m/s. The pipe then narrows down to a diameter of 2.0 cm. Ignoring viscosity, what is the pressure difference between the wide and narrow sections of the pipe?
    A. 850 Pa   B. 3400 Pa   C. 9300 Pa
    D. 12,700 Pa   E. 13,500 Pa

39. ‖ A 15-m-long garden hose has an inner diameter of 2.5 cm. One end is connected to a spigot; 20°C water flows from the other end at a rate of 1.2 L/s. What is the gauge pressure at the spigot end of the hose?
    A. 1900 Pa   B. 2700 Pa   C. 4200 Pa
    D. 5800 Pa   E. 7300 Pa

PROBLEMS

Section 13.1 Fluids and Density

1. ‖ A 100 mL beaker holds 120 g of liquid. What is the liquid's density in SI units?

2. ‖ Containers A and B have equal volumes. Container A holds helium gas at 1.0 atm pressure and 20°C. Container B is completely filled with a liquid whose mass is 7600 times the mass of helium gas in container A. Identify the liquid in B.

3. ‖ Air enclosed in a sphere has density $\rho = 1.4$ kg/m³. What will the density be if the radius of the sphere is halved, compressing the air within?

4. ‖ Air enclosed in a cylinder has density $\rho = 1.4$ kg/m³.
    a. What will be the density of the air if the length of the cylinder is doubled while the radius is unchanged?
    b. What will be the density of the air if the radius of the cylinder is halved while the length is unchanged?

5. ‖ a. 50 g of gasoline are mixed with 50 g of water. What is the average density of the mixture?
    b. 50 cm³ of gasoline are mixed with 50 cm³ of water. What is the average density of the mixture?

6. ‖ Ethyl alcohol has been added to 200 mL of water in a container that has a mass of 150 g when empty. The resulting container and liquid mixture has a mass of 512 g. What volume of alcohol was added to the water?

7. ‖ The average density of the body of a fish is 1080 kg/m³. To keep
    BIO from sinking, the fish increases its volume by inflating an internal air bladder, known as a swim bladder, with air. By what percent must the fish increase its volume to be neutrally buoyant in fresh water? Use the Table 13.1 value for the density of air at 20°C.

Section 13.2 Pressure

8. ‖ The deepest point in the ocean is 11 km below sea level, deeper than Mt. Everest is tall. What is the pressure in atmospheres at this depth?

9. ‖ a. What volume of water has the same mass as 8.0 m³ of ethyl alcohol?
    b. If this volume of water completely fills a cubic tank, what is the pressure at the bottom?

10. ‖ A 1.0-m-diameter vat of liquid is 2.0 m deep. The pressure at the bottom of the vat is 1.3 atm. What is the mass of the liquid in the vat?

11. ‖ A 35-cm-tall, 5.0-cm-diameter cylindrical beaker is filled to its brim with water. What is the downward force of the water on the bottom of the beaker?

12. ‖ The gauge pressure at the bottom of a cylinder of liquid is $p_g = 0.40$ atm. The liquid is poured into another cylinder with twice the radius of the first cylinder. What is the gauge pressure at the bottom of the second cylinder?

13. ‖ A research submarine has a 20-cm-diameter window 8.0 cm thick. The manufacturer says the window can withstand forces up to 1.0×10^6 N. What is the submarine's maximum safe depth in seawater? The pressure inside the submarine is maintained at 1.0 atm.

14. ‖ The highest that George can suck water up a very long straw
    BIO is 2.0 m. (This is a typical value.) What is the lowest pressure that he can maintain in his mouth?

15. ‖ The two 60-cm-diameter cylinders in Figure P13.15, closed at one end, open at the other, are joined to form a single cylinder, then the air inside is removed.

    a. How much force does the atmosphere exert on the flat end of each cylinder?
    b. Suppose the upper cylinder is bolted to a sturdy ceiling. How many 100 kg football players would need to hang from the lower cylinder to pull the two cylinders apart?

    FIGURE P13.15

Section 13.3 Measuring and Using Pressure

16. ‖ What is the gas pressure inside the box shown in Figure P13.16?

FIGURE P13.16   FIGURE P13.17

17. ‖ The container shown in Figure P13.17 is filled with oil. It is open to the atmosphere on the left.
    a. What is the pressure at point A?
    b. What is the pressure difference between points A and B? Between points A and C?

18. ‖ Glycerin is poured into an open U-shaped tube until the height in both sides is 20 cm. Ethyl alcohol is then poured into one arm until the height of the alcohol column is 20 cm. The two liquids do not mix. What is the difference in height between the top surface of the glycerin and the top surface of the alcohol?

19. ‖ A U-shaped tube, open to the air on both ends, contains mercury. Water is poured into the left arm until the water column is 10.0 cm deep. How far upward from its initial position does the mercury in the right arm rise?

20. | What is the height of a water barometer at atmospheric pressure?

21. ||| Postural hypotension is the occurrence of low (systolic)
BIO blood pressure when standing up too quickly from a reclined position, causing fainting or lightheadedness. For most people, a systolic pressure less than 90 mm Hg is considered low. If the blood pressure in your brain is 120 mm when you are lying down, what would it be when you stand up? Assume that your brain is 40 cm from your heart and that $\rho = 1060$ kg/m³ for your blood. Note: Normally, your blood vessels constrict and expand to keep your brain blood pressure stable when you change your posture.

Section 13.4 Buoyancy

22. || A 6.00-cm-diameter sphere with a mass of 89.3 g is neutrally buoyant in a liquid. Identify the liquid.

23. ||| A cargo barge is loaded in a saltwater harbor for a trip up a freshwater river. If the rectangular barge is 3.0 m by 20.0 m and sits 0.80 m deep in the harbor, how deep will it sit in the river?

24. || A 10 cm × 10 cm × 10 cm wood block with a density of 700 kg/m³ floats in water.
    a. What is the distance from the top of the block to the water if the water is fresh?
    b. If it's seawater?

25. || What is the tension in the string in Figure P13.25?

100 cm³ of aluminum, density $\rho_{Al} = 2700$ kg/m³

Ethyl alcohol

FIGURE P13.25

26. | A 10 cm × 10 cm × 10 cm block of steel ($\rho_{steel} = 7900$ kg/m³) is suspended from a spring scale. The scale is in newtons.
    a. What is the scale reading if the block is in air?
    b. What is the scale reading after the block has been lowered into a beaker of oil and is completely submerged?

27. ||| Styrofoam has a density of 300 kg/m³. What is the maximum mass that can hang without sinking from a 50-cm-diameter Styrofoam sphere in water? Assume the volume of the mass is negligible compared to that of the sphere.

28. |||| Calculate the buoyant force due to the surrounding air on a man weighing 800 N. Assume his average density is the same as that of water.

Section 13.5 Fluids in Motion

29. ||| River Pascal with a volume flow rate of 5.0×10^5 L/s joins with River Archimedes, which carries 10.0×10^5 L/s, to form the Bernoulli River. The Bernoulli River is 150 m wide and 10 m deep. What is the speed of the water in the Bernoulli River?

30. || Water flowing through a 2.0-cm-diameter pipe can fill a 300 L bathtub in 5.0 min. What is the speed of the water in the pipe?

31. |||| A pump is used to empty a 6000 L wading pool. The water exits the 2.5-cm-diameter hose at a speed of 2.1 m/s. How long will it take to empty the pool?

32. || A 1.0-cm-diameter pipe widens to 2.0 cm, then narrows to 0.50 cm. Liquid flows through the first segment at a speed of 4.0 m/s.
    a. What are the speeds in the second and third segments?
    b. What is the volume flow rate through the pipe?

Section 13.6 Fluid Dynamics

33. || What does the top pressure gauge in Figure P13.33 read?

FIGURE P13.33   **FIGURE P13.34**

34. |||| The 3.0-cm-diameter water line in Figure P13.34 splits into two 1.0-cm-diameter pipes. All pipes are circular and at the same elevation. At point A, the water speed is 2.0 m/s and the gauge pressure is 50 kPa. What is the gauge pressure at point B?

35. ||| A rectangular trough, 2.0 m long, 0.60 m wide, and 0.45 m deep, is completely full of water. One end of the trough has a small drain plug right at the bottom edge. When you pull the plug, at what speed does water emerge from the hole?

Section 13.7 Viscosity and Poiseuille's Equation

36. ||||| What pressure difference is required between the ends of a 2.0-m-long, 1.0-mm-diameter horizontal tube for 40°C water to flow through it at an average speed of 4.0 m/s?

37. ||||| Water flows at 0.25 L/s through a 10-m-long garden hose 2.5 cm in diameter that is lying flat on the ground. The temperature of the water is 20°C. What is the gauge pressure of the water where it enters the hose?

38. || Figure P13.38 shows a water-filled syringe with a 4.0-cm-long needle. What is the gauge pressure of the water at the point P, where the needle meets the wider chamber of the syringe?

FIGURE P13.38

General Problems

39. || The density of gold is 19,300 kg/m³. 197 g of gold is shaped into a cube. What is the length of each edge?

40. || The density of copper is 8920 kg/m³. How many moles are in
INT a 2.0 cm × 2.0 cm × 2.0 cm cube of copper?

41. ||| The density of aluminum is 2700 kg/m³. How many atoms
INT are in a 2.0 cm × 2.0 cm × 2.0 cm cube of aluminum?

42. || A 50-cm-thick layer of oil floats on a 120-cm-thick layer of water. What is the pressure at the bottom of the water layer?

43. |||| An oil layer floats on 85 cm of water in a tank. The absolute pressure at the bottom of the tank is 112.0 kPa. How thick is the oil?

44. || The little Dutch boy saved Holland by sticking his finger in the leaking dike. If the water level was 2.5 m above his finger, *estimate* the force of the water on his finger.

45. ‖ a. In Figure P13.45, how much force does the fluid exert on the end of the cylinder at A?
    b. How much force does the fluid exert on the end of the cylinder at B?

FIGURE P13.45

46. ‖‖ A friend asks you how much pressure is in your car tires. You know that the tire manufacturer recommends 30 psi, but it's been a while since you've checked. You can't find a tire gauge in the car, but you do find the owner's manual and a ruler. Fortunately, you've just finished taking physics, so you tell your friend, "I don't know, but I can figure it out." From the owner's manual you find that the car's mass is 1500 kg. It seems reasonable to assume that each tire supports one-fourth of the weight. With the ruler you find that the tires are 15 cm wide and the flattened segment of the tire in contact with the road is 13 cm long. What answer will you give your friend?

47. ‖‖ A diver 50 m deep in 10°C fresh water exhales a 1.0-cm-diameter bubble. What is the bubble's diameter just as it reaches the surface of the lake, where the water temperature is 20°C?
    Hint: Assume that the air bubble is always in thermal equilibrium with the surrounding water.

48. ‖ A 6.0-cm-tall cylinder floats in water with its axis perpendicular to the surface. The length of the cylinder above water is 2.0 cm. What is the cylinder's mass density?

49. ‖ A sphere completely submerged in water is tethered to the bottom with a string. The tension in the string is one-third the weight of the sphere. What is the density of the sphere?

50. ‖ You need to determine the density of a ceramic statue. If you suspend it from a spring scale, the scale reads 28.4 N. If you then lower the statue into a tub of water so that it is completely submerged, the scale reads 17.0 N. What is the density?

51. ‖ A 5.0 kg rock whose density is 4800 kg/m³ is suspended by a string such that half of the rock's volume is under water. What is the tension in the string?

52. ‖ A flat slab of styrofoam, with a density of 32 kg/m³, floats on a lake. What minimum volume must the slab have so that a 40 kg boy can sit on the slab without it sinking?

53. ‖‖‖ A 2.0 mL syringe has an inner diameter of 6.0 mm, a needle inner diameter of 0.25 mm, and a plunger pad diameter (where you place your finger) of 1.2 cm. A nurse uses the syringe to inject medicine into a patient whose blood pressure is 140/100. Assume the liquid is an ideal fluid.
    a. What is the minimum force the nurse needs to apply to the syringe?
    b. The nurse empties the syringe in 2.0 s. What is the flow speed of the medicine through the needle?

54. ‖ A child's water pistol shoots water through a 1.0-mm-diameter hole. If the pistol is fired horizontally 70 cm above the ground, a squirt hits the ground 1.2 m away. What is the volume flow rate during the squirt? Ignore air resistance.

55. ‖ The leaves of a tree lose water to the atmosphere via the process of *transpiration*. A particular tree loses water at the rate of 3×10^{-8} m³/s; this water is replenished by the upward flow of sap through vessels in the trunk. This tree's trunk contains about 2000 vessels, each 100 μm in diameter. What is the speed of the sap flowing in the vessels?

56. ‖ A hurricane wind blows across a 6.00 m × 15.0 m flat roof at a speed of 130 km/h.
    a. Is the air pressure above the roof higher or lower than the pressure inside the house? Explain.
    b. What is the pressure difference?
    c. How much force is exerted on the roof? If the roof cannot withstand this much force, will it "blow in" or "blow out"?

57. ‖‖‖‖ Water flows from the pipe shown in Figure P13.57 with a speed of 4.0 m/s.
    a. What is the water pressure as it exits into the air?
    b. What is the height h of the standing column of water?

FIGURE P13.57   10 cm²

58. ‖‖‖‖ Air flows through the tube shown in Figure P13.58. Assume that air is an ideal fluid.
    a. What are the air speeds v_1 and v_2 at points 1 and 2?
    b. What is the volume flow rate?

FIGURE P13.58   **FIGURE P13.59**

59. ‖‖‖ Air flows through the tube shown in Figure P13.59 at a rate of 1200 cm³/s. Assume that air is an ideal fluid. What is the height h of mercury in the right side of the U-tube?

60. ‖‖‖ Water flows at 5.0 L/s through a horizontal pipe that narrows smoothly from 10 cm diameter to 5.0 cm diameter. A pressure gauge in the narrow section reads 50 kPa. What is the reading of a pressure gauge in the wide section?

61. ‖‖‖ The mercury manometer shown in Figure P13.61 is attached to a gas cell. The mercury height h is 120 mm when the cell is placed in an ice-water mixture. The mercury height drops to 30 mm when the device is carried into an industrial freezer. What is the freezer temperature?

FIGURE P13.61

    Hint: The right tube of the manometer is much narrower than the left tube. What reasonable assumption can you make about the gas volume?

62. ⫴ Figure P13.62 shows a section of a long tube that narrows near its open end to a diameter of 1.0 mm. Water at 20°C flows out of the open end at 0.020 L/s. What is the gauge pressure at point P, where the diameter is 4.0 mm?

FIGURE P13.62

63. ‖ Smoking tobacco is bad for your circulatory health. In an
BIO attempt to maintain the blood's capacity to deliver oxygen, the body increases its red blood cell production, and this increases the viscosity of the blood. In addition, nicotine from tobacco causes arteries to constrict.

For a nonsmoker, with blood viscosity of 2.5×10^{-3} Pa · s, normal blood flow requires a pressure difference of 8.0 mm Hg between the two ends of an artery. If this person were to smoke regularly, his blood viscosity would increase to 2.7×10^{-3} Pa · s, and the arterial diameter would constrict to 90% of its normal value. What pressure difference would be needed to maintain the same blood flow?

64. ⫴ A stiff, 10-cm-long tube with an inner diameter of 3.0 mm is attached to a small hole in the side of a tall beaker. The tube sticks out horizontally. The beaker is filled with 20°C water to a level 45 cm above the hole, and it is continually topped off to maintain that level. What is the volume flow rate through the tube?

Passage Problems

Blood Pressure and Blood Flow   BIO

The blood pressure at your heart is approximately 100 mm Hg. As blood is pumped from the left ventricle of your heart, it flows through the aorta, a single large blood vessel with a diameter of about 2.5 cm. The speed of blood flow in the aorta is about 60 cm/s. Any change in pressure as blood flows in the aorta is due to the change in height: the vessel is large enough that viscous drag is not a major factor. As the blood moves through the circulatory system, it flows into successively smaller and smaller blood vessels until it reaches the capillaries. Blood flows in the capillaries at the much lower speed of approximately 0.7 mm/s. The diameter of capillaries and other small blood vessels is so small that viscous drag is a major factor.

65. | There is a limit to how long your neck can be. If your neck were too long, no blood would reach your brain! What is the maximum height a person's brain could be above his heart, given the noted pressure and assuming that there are no valves or supplementary pumping mechanisms in the neck? The density of blood is 1060 kg/m³.
    A. 0.97 m   B. 1.3 m   C. 9.7 m   D. 13 m

66. | Because the flow speed in your capillaries is much less than in the aorta, the total cross-section area of the capillaries considered together must be much larger than that of the aorta. Given the flow speeds noted, the total area of the capillaries considered together is equivalent to the cross-section area of a single vessel of approximately what diameter?
    A. 25 cm   B. 50 cm   C. 75 cm   D. 100 cm

67. | Suppose that in response to some stimulus a small blood vessel narrows to 90% its original diameter. If there is no change in the pressure across the vessel, what is the ratio of the new volume flow rate to the original flow rate?
    A. 0.66   B. 0.73   C. 0.81   D. 0.90

68. | Sustained exercise can increase the blood flow rate of the heart by a factor of 5 with only a modest increase in blood pressure. This is a large change in flow. Although several factors come into play, which of the following physiological changes would most plausibly account for such a large increase in flow with a small change in pressure?
    A. A decrease in the viscosity of the blood
    B. Dilation of the smaller blood vessels to larger diameters
    C. Dilation of the aorta to larger diameter
    D. An increase in the oxygen carried by the blood

STOP TO THINK ANSWERS

Stop to Think 13.1: $\rho_1 = \rho_2 = \rho_3$. Density depends only on what the object is made of, not how big the pieces are.

Stop to Think 13.2: C. These are all open tubes, so the liquid rises to the same height in all three despite their different shapes.

Stop to Think 13.3: B. The weight of the displaced water equals the weight of the ice cube. When the ice cube melts and turns into water, that amount of water will exactly fill the volume that the ice cube is now displacing.

Stop to Think 13.4: 1 cm³/s out. The fluid is incompressible, so the sum of what flows in must match the sum of what flows out. 13 cm³/s is known to be flowing in while 12 cm³/s flows out. An additional 1 cm³/s must flow out to achieve balance.

Stop to Think 13.5: $h_2 > h_4 > h_3 > h_1$. The liquid level is higher where the pressure is lower. The pressure is lower where the flow speed is higher. The flow speed is highest in the narrowest tube, zero in the open air.

Stop to Think 13.6: A. All three segments have the same volume flow rate Q. According to Poiseuille's equation, the segment with the smallest radius R has the greatest pressure difference Δp.

Properties of Matter

The goal of Part III has been to understand macroscopic systems and their properties. We've introduced no new fundamental laws in these chapters. Instead, we've broadened and extended the scope of Newton's laws and the law of conservation of energy. In many ways, Part III has focused on *applications* of the general principles introduced in Parts I and II.

That matter exists in three phases—solids, liquids, gases—is perhaps the most basic fact about macroscopic systems. We looked at an atomic-level picture of the three phases of matter, and we also found a connection between *heat* and *phase changes.* Both liquids and gases are *fluids,* and we spent quite a bit of time investigating the properties of fluids, ranging from pressure and the ideal-gas law to buoyancy, fluid flow, and Bernoulli's equation.

Along the way, we introduced *mechanical properties of* matter, such as density and viscosity, and *thermal properties,*

such as thermal-expansion coefficients and specific heats. You should now be able to use these properties to figure out what happens when you heat a system, whether an object will float, and how fast a fluid flows. These are all very practical, useful things to know, with many applications to the world around us.

Last, but not least, we discovered that many *macroscopic* properties are determined by the *microscopic* motions of atoms and molecules. For example, we found that the ideal-gas law is based on the idea that gas pressure is due to the collisions of atoms with the walls of the container. Similarly, regularities in the specific heats of gases were explained on the basis of how atoms and molecules share the thermal energy of a system. Atoms are important, even if we can't see them or follow their individual motions.

KNOWLEDGE STRUCTURE III Properties of Matter

BASIC GOAL How can we describe the macroscopic flows of energy and matter in heat transfer and fluid flow?

GENERAL PRINCIPLES Phases of matter

Gas: Particles are freely moving. Thermal energy is kinetic energy of motion of particles. Pressure is due to collisions of particles with walls of container.

Liquid: Particles are loosely bound, but flow is possible. Heat is transferred by convection and conduction. Pressure is due to gravity.

Solid: Particles are joined by spring-like bonds. Increasing temperature causes expansion. Heat is transferred by conduction only.

Heat must be added to change a solid to a liquid and a liquid to a gas. Heat must be removed to reverse these changes.

Ideal-gas processes

We can graph processes on a pV diagram. Work by the gas is the area under the graph.

For a gas process in a sealed container, the ideal-gas law relates values of pressure, volume, and temperature:

$$\frac{p_i V_i}{T_i} = \frac{p_f V_f}{T_f}$$

- Constant-volume process $V = \text{constant}$
- Isothermal process $T = \text{constant}$
- Isobaric process $p = \text{constant}$
- Adiabatic process $Q = 0$

Heat and heat transfer

The **specific heat** c of a material is the heat required to raise the temperature of 1 kg by 1 K:

$$Q = Mc\,\Delta T$$

When two or more systems interact thermally, they come to a common final temperature determined by

$$Q_{net} = Q_1 + Q_2 + Q_3 + \cdots = 0$$

Conduction transfers heat by direct physical contact.
Convection transfers heat by the motion of a fluid.
Radiation transfers heat by electromagnetic waves.

Fluid statics

Archimedes' principle: The magnitude of the buoyant force equals the weight of the fluid displaced by the object.

An object sinks if it is more dense than the fluid in which it is submerged; if it is less dense, it floats.

Pressure increases with depth in a liquid. The pressure at depth d is

$$p = p_0 + \rho g d$$

Fluid flow Ideal fluid flow is laminar, incompressible, and nonviscous. The **equation of continuity** is

$$v_1 A_1 = v_2 A_2$$

Bernoulli's equation is

$$p_1 + \tfrac{1}{2}\rho v_1^2 + \rho g y_1 =$$
$$p_2 + \tfrac{1}{2}\rho v_2^2 + \rho g y_2$$

Size and Life

Physicists look for simple models and general principles that underlie and explain diverse physical phenomena. In the first 13 chapters of this book, you've seen that just a handful of general principles and laws can be used to solve a wide range of problems. Can this approach have any relevance to a subject like biology? It may seem surprising, but there *are* general "laws of biology" that apply, with quantitative accuracy, to organisms as diverse as elephants and mice.

Let's look at an example. An elephant uses more metabolic power than a mouse. This is not surprising, as an elephant is quite a bit bigger. But recasting the data shows an interesting trend. When we looked at the energy required to raise the temperature of different substances, we considered *specific heat*. The "specific" meant that we considered the heat required for 1 kilogram. For animals, rather than metabolic rate, we can look at the *specific metabolic rate,* the metabolic power used *per kilogram* of tissue. If we factor out the mass difference between a mouse and an elephant, are their specific metabolic powers the same?

In fact, the specific metabolic rate varies quite a bit among mammals, as the graph of specific metabolic rate versus mass shows. But there is an interesting trend: All of the data points lie on a single smooth curve. In other words, there really is a biological *law* we can use to predict a mammal's metabolic rate knowing only its mass M. In particular, the specific metabolic rate is proportional to $M^{-0.25}$. Because a 4000 kg elephant is 160,000 times more massive than a 25 g mouse, the mouse's specific metabolic power is $(160,000)^{0.25} = 20$ times that of the elephant. A law that shows how a property scales with the size of a system is called a *scaling law*.

A similar scaling law holds for birds, reptiles, and even bacteria. Why should a single simple relationship hold true for organisms that range in size from a single cell to a 100 ton blue whale? Interestingly, no one knows for sure. It is a matter of current research to find out just what this and other scaling laws tell us about the nature of life.

Perhaps the metabolic-power scaling law is a result of heat transfer. In Chapter 12, we noted that all metabolic energy used by an animal ends up as heat, which must be transferred to the environment. A 4000 kg elephant has 160,000 times the mass of a 25 g mouse, but it has only about 3,000 times the surface area. The heat transferred to the environment depends on the surface area; the more surface area, the greater the rate of heat transfer. An elephant with a mouse-sized metabolism simply wouldn't be able to dissipate heat fast enough—it would quickly overheat and die.

If heat dissipation were the only factor limiting metabolism, we can show that the specific metabolic rate should scale as $M^{-0.33}$, quite different from the $M^{-0.25}$ scaling observed. Clearly, another factor is at work. Exactly what underlies the $M^{-0.25}$ scaling is still a matter of debate, but some recent analysis suggests the scaling is due to limitations not of heat transfer but of fluid flow. Cells in mice, elephants, and all mammals receive nutrients and oxygen for metabolism from the bloodstream. Because the minimum size of a capillary is about the same for all mammals, the structure of the circulatory system must vary from animal to animal. The human aorta has a diameter of about 1 inch; in a mouse, the diameter is approximately 1/20th of this. Thus a mouse has fewer levels of branching to smaller and smaller blood vessels as we move from the aorta to the capillaries. The smaller blood vessels in mice mean that viscosity is more of a factor throughout the circulatory system. The circulatory system of a mouse is quite different from that of an elephant.

A model of specific metabolic rate based on blood-flow limitations predicts a $M^{-0.25}$ law, exactly as observed. The model also makes other testable predictions. For example, the model predicts that the smallest possible mammal should have a body mass of about 1 gram—exactly the size of the smallest shrew. Even smaller animals have different types of circulatory systems; in the smallest animals, nutrient transport is by diffusion alone. But the model can be extended to predict that the specific metabolic rate for these animals will follow a scaling law similar to that for mammals, exactly as observed. It is too soon to know if this model will ultimately prove to be correct, but it's indisputable that there are large-scale regularities in biology that follow mathematical relationships based on the laws of physics.

Specific metabolic rate as a function of body mass follows a simple scaling law.

PART III PROBLEMS

The following questions are related to the passage "Size and Life" on the previous page. BIO

1. A typical timber wolf has a mass of 40 kg, a typical jackrabbit a mass of 2.5 kg. Given the scaling law presented in the passage, we'd expect the specific metabolic rate of the jackrabbit to be higher by a factor of
   A. 2   B. 4   C. 8   D. 16
2. A typical timber wolf has a mass of 40 kg, a typical jackrabbit a mass of 2.5 kg. Given the scaling law presented in the passage, we'd expect the wolf to use _____ times more energy than a jackrabbit in the course of a day.
   A. 2   B. 4   C. 8   D. 16
3. Given the data of the graph, approximately how much energy, in Calories, would a 200 g rat use during the course of a day?
   A. 10   B. 20   C. 100   D. 200
4. All other things being equal, species that inhabit cold climates tend to be larger than related species that inhabit hot climates. For instance, the Alaskan hare is the largest North American hare, with a typical mass of 5.0 kg, double that of a jackrabbit. A likely explanation is that

A. Larger animals have more blood flow, allowing for better thermoregulation.
B. Larger animals need less food to survive than smaller animals.
C. Larger animals have larger blood volumes than smaller animals.
D. Larger animals lose heat less quickly than smaller animals.

5. The passage proposes that there are quantitative "laws" of biology that have their basis in physical principles, using the scaling of specific metabolic rate with body mass as an example. Which of the following regularities among animals might also be an example of such a "law"?
   A. As a group, birds have better color vision than mammals.
   B. Reptiles have a much lower specific metabolic rate than mammals.
   C. Predators tend to have very good binocular vision; prey animals tend to be able to see over a very wide angle.
   D. Jump height varies very little among animals. Nearly all animals, ranging in size from a flea to a horse, have a maximum vertical leap that is quite similar.

The following passages and associated questions are based on the material of Part III.

Keeping Your Cool BIO

A 68 kg cyclist is pedaling down the road at 15 km/h, using a total metabolic power of 480 W. A certain fraction of this energy is used to move the bicycle forward, but the balance ends up as thermal energy in his body, which he must get rid of to keep cool. On a very warm day, conduction, convection, and radiation transfer little energy, and so he does this by perspiring, with the evaporation of water taking away the excess thermal energy.

6. If the cyclist reaches his 15 km/h cruising speed by rolling down a hill, what is the approximate height of the hill?
   A. 22 m   B. 11 m   C. 2 m   D. 1 m
7. As he cycles at a constant speed on level ground, at what rate is chemical energy being converted to thermal energy in his body, assuming a typical efficiency of 25% for the conversion of chemical energy to the mechanical energy of motion?
   A. 480 W   B. 360 W   C. 240 W   D. 120 W
8. To keep from overheating, the cyclist must get rid of the excess thermal energy generated in his body. If he cycles at this rate for 2 hours, how many liters of water must he perspire, to the nearest 0.1 liter?
   A. 0.4 L   B. 0.9 L   C. 1.1 L   D. 1.4 L
9. Being able to exhaust this thermal energy is very important. If he isn't able to get rid of any of the excess heat, by how much will the temperature of his body increase in 10 minutes of riding, to the nearest 0.1°C?
   A. 0.3°C   B. 0.6°C   C. 0.9°C   D. 1.2°C

Weather Balloons

The data used to generate weather forecasts are gathered by hundreds of weather balloons launched from sites throughout the world. A typical balloon is made of latex and filled with hydrogen.

A packet of sensing instruments (called a *radiosonde*) transmits information back to earth as the balloon rises into the atmosphere.

At the beginning of its flight, the average density of the weather balloon package (total mass of the balloon plus cargo divided by their volume) is less than the density of the surrounding air, so the balloon rises. As it does, the density of the surrounding air decreases, as shown in Figure III.1. The balloon will rise to the point at which the buoyant force of the air exactly balances its weight. This would not be very high if the balloon couldn't expand. However, the latex envelope of the balloon is very thin and very stretchy, so the balloon can, and does, expand, allowing the volume to increase by a factor of 100 or more. The expanding balloon displaces an ever-larger volume of the lower-density air, keeping the buoyant force greater than the weight force until the balloon rises to an altitude of 40 km or more.

FIGURE III.1

440

10. A balloon launched from sea level has a volume of approximately 4 m³. What is the approximate buoyant force on the balloon?
   A. 50 N   B. 40 N
   C. 20 N   D. 10 N

11. A balloon launched from sea level with a volume of 4 m³ will have a volume of about 12 m³ on reaching an altitude of 10 km. What is the approximate buoyant force now?
   A. 50 N   B. 40 N
   C. 20 N   D. 10 N

12. The balloon expands as it rises, keeping the pressures inside and outside the balloon approximately equal. If the balloon rises slowly, heat transfers will keep the temperature inside the same as the outside air temperature. A balloon with a volume of 4.0 m³ is launched at sea level, where the atmospheric pressure is 100 kPa and the temperature is 15°C. It then rises slowly to a height of 5500 m, where the pressure is 50 kPa and the temperature is –20°C. What is the volume of the balloon at this altitude?
   A. 5.0 m³   B. 6.0 m³
   C. 7.0 m³   D. 8.0 m³

13. If the balloon rises quickly, so that no heat transfer is possible, the temperature inside the balloon will drop as the gas expands. If a 4.0 m³ balloon is launched at a pressure of 100 kPa and rapidly rises to a point where the pressure is 50 kPa, the volume of the balloon will be
   A. Greater than 8.0 m³
   B. 8.0 m³
   C. Less than 8.0 m³

14. At the end of the flight, the radiosonde is dropped and falls to earth by parachute. Suppose the parachute achieves its terminal speed at a height of 30 km. As it descends into the atmosphere, how does the terminal speed change?
   A. It increases.
   B. It stays the same.
   C. It decreases.

Passenger Balloons

Long-distance balloon flights are usually made using a hot-air-balloon/helium-balloon hybrid. The balloon has a sealed, flexible chamber of helium gas that expands or contracts to keep the helium pressure approximately equal to the air pressure outside. The helium chamber sits on top of an open (that is, air can enter or leave), constant-volume chamber of propane-heated air. Assume that the hot air and the helium are kept at a constant temperature by burning propane.

15. A balloon is launched at sea level, where the air pressure is 100 kPa. The helium has a volume of 1000 m³ at this altitude. What is the volume of the helium when the balloon has risen to a height where atmospheric pressure is 33 kPa?
   A. 330 m³   B. 500 m³   C. 1000 m³   D. 3000 m³

16. A balloon is launched at sea level, where the air pressure is 100 kPa. The density in the hot-air chamber is 1.0 kg/m³. What is the density of the air when the balloon has risen to a height where the atmospheric pressure is 33 kPa?
   A. 3.0 kg/m³
   B. 1.0 kg/m³
   C. 0.66 kg/m³
   D. 0.33 kg/m³

17. A balloon is at a height of 5.0 km and is descending at a constant rate. The buoyancy force is directed _____; the drag force is directed _____.
   A. Up, up
   B. Up, down
   C. Down, up
   D. Down, down

Additional Integrated Problems

18. When you exhale, all of the air in your lungs must exit
BIO through the trachea. If you exhale through your nose, this air subsequently leaves through your nostrils. The area of your nostrils is less than that of your trachea. How does the speed of the air in the trachea compare to that in the nostrils?

19. Sneezing requires an increase in pressure of the air in the lungs;
BIO a typical sneeze might result in an extra pressure of 7.0 kPa. Estimate how much force this exerts on the diaphragm, the large muscle at the bottom of the ribcage.

20. A 20 kg block of aluminum sits on the bottom of a tank of water. How much force does the block exert on the bottom of the tank?

21. We've seen that fish can control their buoyancy through the
BIO use of a swim bladder, a gas-filled organ inside the body. You can assume that the gas pressure inside the swim bladder is roughly equal to the external water pressure. A fish swimming at a particular depth adjusts the volume of its swim bladder to give it neutral buoyancy. If the fish swims upward or downward, the changing water pressure causes the bladder to expand or contract. Consequently, the fish must adjust the quantity of gas to restore the original volume and thus reestablish neutral buoyancy. Consider a large, 7.0 kg striped bass with a volume of 7.0 L. When neutrally buoyant, 7.0% of the fish's volume is taken up by the swim bladder. Assume a body temperature of 15°C.
   a. How many moles of air are in the swim bladder when the fish is at a depth of 80 ft?
   b. What will the volume of the swim bladder be if the fish ascends to a 50 ft depth without changing the quantity of gas?
   c. To return the swim bladder to its original size, how many moles of gas must be added?

Oscillations and Waves

Wolves are social animals, and they howl to communicate over distances of several miles with other members of their pack. How are such sounds made? How do they travel through the air? And how are other wolves able to hear these sounds from such a great distance?

Motion That Repeats Again and Again

Up to this point in the book, we have generally considered processes that have a clear starting and ending point, such as a car accelerating from rest to a final speed, or a solid being heated from an initial to a final temperature. In Part IV, we begin to consider processes that are *periodic*—they repeat. A child on a swing, a boat bobbing on the water, and even the repetitive bass beat of a rock song are *oscillatory motions* that happen over and over without a starting or ending point. The *period*, the time for one cycle of the motion, will be a key parameter for us to consider as we look at oscillatory motion.

Our first goal will be to develop the language and tools needed to describe oscillations, ranging from the swinging of the bob of a pendulum clock to the bouncing of a car on its springs. Once we understand oscillations, we will extend our analysis to consider oscillations that travel—*waves*.

The Wave Model

We've had great success modeling the motion of complex objects as the motion of one or more particles. We were even able to explain the macroscopic properties of matter, such as pressure and temperature, in terms of the motion of the atomic particles that comprise all matter.

Now it's time to explore another way of looking at nature, the *wave model*. Familiar examples of waves include

- Ripples on a pond.
- The sound of thunder.
- The swaying ground of an earthquake.
- A vibrating guitar string.
- The colors of a rainbow.

Despite the great diversity of types and sources of waves, there is a single, elegant physical theory that is capable of describing them all. Our exploration of wave phenomena will call upon water waves, sound waves, and light waves for examples, but our goal will be to emphasize the unity and coherence of the ideas that are common to *all* types of waves. As was the case with the particle model, we will use the wave model to explain a wide range of phenomena.

When Waves Collide

The collision of two particles is a dramatic event. Energy and momentum are transferred as the two particles head off in different directions. Something much gentler happens when two waves come together—the two waves pass through each other unchanged. Where they overlap, we get a *superposition* of the two waves. We will finish our discussion of waves by analyzing the standing waves that result from the superposition of two waves traveling in opposite directions. The physics of standing waves will allow us to understand how your vocal tract can produce such a wide range of sounds, and how your ears are able to analyze them.

14 Oscillations

A gibbon swings below a branch, moving forward by pivoting about one handhold and then the next. How does an understanding of oscillatory motion allow us to analyze the swinging motion of a gibbon—and the walking motion of other animals?

LOOKING AHEAD ▶

The goal of Chapter 14 is to understand systems that oscillate with simple harmonic motion.

Simple Harmonic Motion

A cart attached to a spring oscillates back and forth. A graph of its motion is sinusoidal. This is a special kind of motion called **simple harmonic motion.**

Oscillation

An understanding of simple harmonic motion will build on many topics from past chapters.

> **Looking Back ◀◀**
> 3.8 Period and frequency
> 6.2 Velocity and acceleration in circular motion
> 8.3 Springs and restoring forces
> 10.1 and 10.6 Energy transformations and the conservation of energy

Spring Systems

Oscillations occur in any system having a restoring force that pushes the system back toward an equilibrium position.

A person bouncing up and down on elastic cords and the swaying of a tall building in the wind are both examples of simple harmonic motion.

An oscillation is characterized by the **period** (the time for one oscillation) and the **amplitude** (the size of the oscillation).

Pendulum Systems

A mass swinging on the end of a rod or a cord is a **pendulum** —and another example of simple harmonic motion. Its motion is mathematically the same as that of a mass on a spring.

The period of a pendulum is determined by the pendulum length and the strength of gravity; the amplitude doesn't affect the period. This makes a pendulum the ideal basis for a clock.

Damping and Resonance

As time goes on, oscillating systems may lose energy. This **damping** results in a slow decay of the oscillation.

The pendulum swings back and forth, tracing a pattern in the sand. The drag from the sand makes each oscillation smaller than the last.

The tuning fork oscillates at a particular frequency. There is one particular spot on a membrane in the inner ear that also oscillates at this exact frequency.

We'll see that the concept of **resonance** explains how your ear can distinguish different frequencies.

14.1 Equilibrium and Oscillation

Consider a marble that is free to roll inside a spherical bowl, as shown in FIGURE 14.1. The marble has an **equilibrium position** at the bottom of the bowl where it will rest with no net force on it. If you push the marble away from equilibrium, the marble's weight leads to a net force directed back toward the equilibrium position. We call this a **restoring force** because it acts to restore equilibrium. The magnitude of this restoring force increases if the marble is moved farther away from the equilibrium position.

If you pull the marble to the side and release it, it doesn't just roll back to the bottom of the bowl and stay put. It keeps on moving, rolling up and down each side of the bowl, repeatedly moving through its equilibrium position, as we see in FIGURE 14.2. We call such repetitive motion an **oscillation.** This oscillation is a result of an interplay between the restoring force and the marble's inertia, something we will see in all of the oscillations we consider.

We'll start our description by noting the most important fact about oscillatory motion: It repeats. Any oscillation is characterized by a *period,* the time for the motion to repeat. We met the concepts of period and frequency when we studied circular motion in Chapter 6. As a starting point then, let's review these ideas and see how they apply to oscillatory motion.

Frequency and Period

An electrocardiogram (ECG), such as the one shown in FIGURE 14.3, is a record of the electrical signals of the heart as it beats. We will explore the ECG in some detail in Chapter 21. Although the shape of a typical ECG is rather complex, notice that it has a *repeating pattern.* For this or any oscillation, the time to complete one full cycle is called the **period** of the oscillation. Period is given the symbol T.

An equivalent piece of information is the number of cycles, or oscillations, completed per second. If the period is $\frac{1}{10}$ s, then the oscillator can complete 10 cycles in 1 second. Conversely, an oscillation period of 10 s allows only $\frac{1}{10}$ of a cycle to be completed per second. In general, T seconds per cycle implies that $1/T$ cycles will be completed each second. The number of cycles per second is called the **frequency** f of the oscillation. The relationship between frequency and period is therefore

$$f = \frac{1}{T} \quad \text{or} \quad T = \frac{1}{f} \tag{14.1}$$

The units of frequency are **hertz,** abbreviated Hz. By definition,

$$1 \text{ Hz} = 1 \text{ cycle per second} = 1 \text{ s}^{-1}$$

We will frequently deal with very rapid oscillations and make use of the units shown in Table 14.1.

NOTE ▶ Uppercase and lowercase letters *are* important. 1 MHz is 1 megahertz = 10^6 Hz, but 1 mHz is 1 millihertz = 10^{-3} Hz! ◀

EXAMPLE 14.1 **Frequency and period of a radio station**

An FM radio station broadcasts an oscillating radio wave at a frequency of 100 MHz. What is the period of the oscillation?

SOLVE The frequency f of oscillations in the radio transmitter is 100 MHz = 1.0×10^8 Hz. The period is the inverse of the frequency; hence,

$$T = \frac{1}{f} = \frac{1}{1.0 \times 10^8 \text{ Hz}} = 1.0 \times 10^{-8} \text{ s} = 10 \text{ ns}$$

FIGURE 14.1 Equilibrium and restoring forces for a ball in a bowl.

When the ball is displaced from equilibrium . . .

$\vec{n}$ $\vec{F}_{\text{net}}$ $\vec{F}_{\text{net}}$

$\vec{w}$ $\vec{F}_{\text{net}}$

Equilibrium position

. . . a free-body diagram shows a net restoring force.

The farther away from equilibrium, the greater the net force.

FIGURE 14.2 The motion of a ball rolling in a bowl.

When the ball is moved from equilibrium and released, a restoring force pulls it back toward equilibrium . . .

$\vec{F}_{\text{net}}$ $\vec{F}_{\text{net}}$

$\vec{v}$

. . . but inertia causes the ball to continue moving to the other side . . .

. . . where the restoring force is directed back toward equilibrium. The ball reverses direction and continues oscillating.

FIGURE 14.3 An electrocardiogram has a well-defined period.

Successive beats of the heart produce approximately the same signal.

Period T

Voltage across chest

0   1   2   3

Time (s)

TABLE 14.1 Common units of frequency

Frequency	Period
10^3 Hz = 1 kilohertz = 1 kHz	1 ms
10^6 Hz = 1 megahertz = 1 MHz	1 μs
10^9 Hz = 1 gigahertz = 1 GHz	1 ns

Oscillatory Motion

Let's return to the marble in the bowl and describe its motion in more detail. We'll start by making a graph of the motion, with positions to the right of equilibrium positive and positions to the left of equilibrium negative. FIGURE 14.4 shows a series of "snapshots" of the motion and the corresponding points on the graph. This graph has the form of a *cosine function*. A graph or a function that has the form of a sine or cosine function is called **sinusoidal.** A sinusoidal oscillation is called **simple harmonic motion,** often abbreviated SHM.

FIGURE 14.4 Constructing a position-versus-time graph for a marble rolling in a bowl.

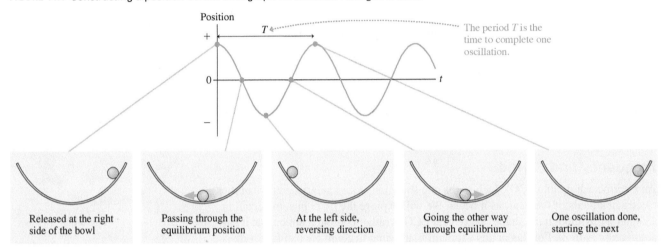

| Released at the right side of the bowl | Passing through the equilibrium position | At the left side, reversing direction | Going the other way through equilibrium | One oscillation done, starting the next |

A marble rolling in the bottom of a bowl undergoes simple harmonic motion, as does a car bouncing up and down on its springs. SHM is very common, but we'll find that most cases of SHM can be modeled as one of two simple systems: a mass oscillating on a spring or a pendulum swinging back and forth. The following table shows two examples.

Examples of simple harmonic motion

Oscillating system		Related real-world example	
Mass on a spring	The mass oscillates back and forth due to the restoring force of the spring. The period depends on the mass and the stiffness of the spring.	Vibrations in the ear	Sound waves entering the ear cause the oscillation of a membrane in the cochlea. The vibration can be modeled as a mass on a spring. The period of oscillation of a segment of the membrane depends on mass (the thickness of the membrane) and stiffness (the rigidity of the membrane).
Pendulum	The mass oscillates back and forth due to the restoring gravitational force. The period depends on the length of the pendulum and the free-fall acceleration g.	Motion of legs while walking	The motion of a walking animal's legs can be modeled as pendulum motion. The rate at which the legs swing depends on the length of the legs and the free-fall acceleration g.

STOP TO THINK 14.1 Two oscillating systems have periods T_1 and T_2, with $T_1 < T_2$. How are the frequencies of the two systems related?

A. $f_1 < f_2$ B. $f_1 = f_2$ C. $f_1 > f_2$

14.2 Linear Restoring Forces and Simple Harmonic Motion

Simple harmonic motion can occur when a system has a restoring force that pushes it back toward equilibrium. We will begin our study with a very simple system, analyzing it in detail before moving on to other oscillatory systems.

FIGURE 14.5 shows a glider that rides with very little friction on an air track. There is a spring connecting the glider to the end of the track. When the spring is neither stretched nor compressed, the net force on the glider is zero. The glider just sits there—this is the equilibrium position.

If the glider is now displaced from this equilibrium position by Δx, the spring exerts a force back toward equilibrium—a restoring force. In Section 8.3, we found that the spring force is given by Hooke's law: $(F_{sp})_x = -k\,\Delta x$, where k is the spring constant. (Recall that a "stiffer" spring has a larger value of k.) If we set the origin of our coordinate system at the equilibrium position, the displacement from equilibrium Δx is equal to x; thus the spring force can be written as $(F_{sp})_x = -kx$.

The net force on the glider is simply the spring force, so we can write

$$(F_{net})_x = -kx \qquad (14.2)$$

The negative sign tells us that this is a restoring force because the force is in the direction opposite the displacement. If we pull the cart to the right (x is positive), the force is to the left (negative)—back toward equilibrium.

This is a **linear restoring force**; that is, **the net force is toward the equilibrium position and is proportional to the distance from equilibrium.**

Motion of a Mass on a Spring

If we pull the air-track glider of Figure 14.5 a short distance to the right and release it, it will oscillate back and forth. FIGURE 14.6 shows actual data from an experiment in which the position of a glider was measured 20 times every second. This is a position-versus-time graph that has been rotated 90° from its usual orientation in order for the x-axis to match the motion of the glider.

The object's maximum displacement from equilibrium is called the **amplitude** A of the motion. The object's position oscillates between $x = -A$ and $x = +A$.

NOTE ▶ When interpreting a graph, notice that the amplitude is the distance from equilibrium to the maximum, *not* the distance from the minimum to the maximum. ◀

The graph of the position is sinusoidal, so this is simple harmonic motion. **Oscillation about an equilibrium position with a linear restoring force is always simple harmonic motion.** There are many other circumstances in which a linear restoring force exists, and we will see simple harmonic motion in these cases as well.

Vertical Mass on a Spring

FIGURE 14.7 on the following page shows a block of mass m hanging from a spring with spring constant k. Will this mass-spring system have the same simple harmonic

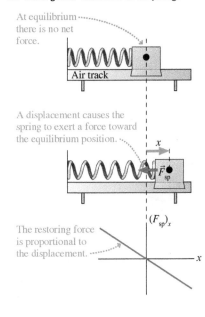

FIGURE 14.5 The restoring force on an air-track glider attached to a spring.

At equilibrium there is no net force.

A displacement causes the spring to exert a force toward the equilibrium position.

The restoring force is proportional to the displacement.

$(F_{net})_x$

p.37
PROPORTIONAL

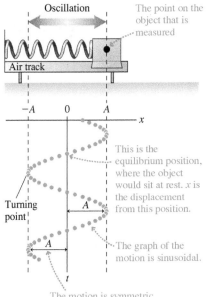

FIGURE 14.6 An experiment showing the oscillation of an air-track glider.

Oscillation

The point on the object that is measured

Air track

$-A$ 0 A

This is the equilibrium position, where the object would sit at rest. x is the displacement from this position.

Turning point

The graph of the motion is sinusoidal.

The motion is symmetric about the equilibrium position. Maximum distance to the left and to the right is A.

FIGURE 14.7 The equilibrium position of a mass on a vertical spring.

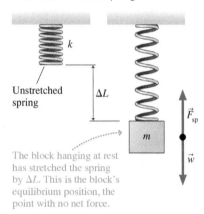

Unstretched spring

ΔL

$\vec{F}_{sp}$

m

$\vec{w}$

The block hanging at rest has stretched the spring by ΔL. This is the block's equilibrium position, the point with no net force.

FIGURE 14.8 Displacing the block from its equilibrium position produces a restoring force.

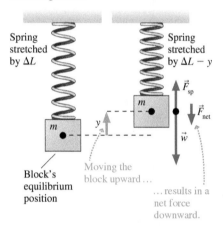

Spring stretched by ΔL

Spring stretched by $\Delta L - y$

$\vec{F}_{sp}$

m

$\vec{F}_{net}$

m

y

$\vec{w}$

Block's equilibrium position

Moving the block upward …

…results in a net force downward.

Class Video

Pendulum motion at the playground.

motion as the horizontal system we just saw, or will gravity add an additional complication? An important fact to notice is that the equilibrium position of the block is *not* where the spring is at its unstretched length. At the equilibrium position of the block, where it hangs motionless, the spring has stretched by ΔL.

Finding ΔL is a static-equilibrium problem in which the upward spring force balances the downward weight force of the block. The y-component of the spring force is given by Hooke's law:

$$(F_{sp})_y = k\,\Delta L \tag{14.3}$$

Newton's first law for the block in equilibrium is

$$(F_{net})_y = (F_{sp})_y + w_y = k\,\Delta L - mg = 0 \tag{14.4}$$

from which we can find

$$\Delta L = \frac{mg}{k} \tag{14.5}$$

This is the distance the spring stretches when the block is attached to it.

Suppose we now displace the block from this equilibrium position, as shown in **FIGURE 14.8**. We've placed the origin of the y-axis at the block's equilibrium position in order to be consistent with our analyses of oscillations throughout this chapter. If the block moves upward, as in the figure, the spring gets shorter compared to its equilibrium length, but the spring is still *stretched* compared to its unstretched length in Figure 14.7. When the block is at position y, the spring is stretched by an amount $\Delta L - y$ and hence exerts an *upward* spring force $F_{sp} = k(\Delta L - y)$. The net force on the block at this point is

$$(F_{net})_y = (F_{sp})_y + w_y = k(\Delta L - y) - mg = (k\,\Delta L - mg) - ky \tag{14.6}$$

But $k\,\Delta L - mg = 0$, from Equation 14.4, so the net force on the block is

$$(F_{net})_y = -ky \tag{14.7}$$

Equation 14.7 for a mass hung from a spring has the same form as Equation 14.2 for the horizontal spring, where we found $(F_{net})_x = -kx$. That is, the restoring force for vertical oscillations is identical to the restoring force for horizontal oscillations. **The role of gravity is to determine where the equilibrium position is, but it doesn't affect the restoring force for displacement from the equilibrium position.** Because it has a linear restoring force, **a mass on a vertical spring oscillates with simple harmonic motion.** The motion has the same form as that of the air-track glider.

The Pendulum

The chapter opened with a picture of a gibbon, whose body swings back and forth below a tree branch. The motion of the gibbon is essentially that of a **pendulum,** a mass suspended from a pivot point by a light string or rod. A pendulum oscillates about its equilibrium position, but is this simple harmonic motion? To answer this question, we need to examine the restoring force on the pendulum. If the restoring force is linear, the motion will be simple harmonic.

FIGURE 14.9a shows a mass m attached to a string of length L and free to swing back and forth. The pendulum's position can be described by either the arc of length s or the angle θ, both of which are zero when the pendulum hangs straight down. Because angles are measured counterclockwise, s and θ are positive when the pendulum is to the right of center, negative when it is to the left.

Two forces are acting on the mass: the string tension $\vec{T}$ and the weight $\vec{w}$. The motion is along a circular arc. We choose a coordinate system on the mass with one axis along the radius of the circle and the other tangent to the circle. We divide the forces into tangential components, parallel to the motion (denoted with a subscript t), and components directed toward the center of the circle. These are shown on the free-body diagram of FIGURE 14.9b.

The mass must move along a circular arc, as noted. As Figure 14.9b shows, the net force in this direction is the tangential component of the weight:

$$(F_{net})_t = \sum F_t = w_t = -mg\sin\theta \qquad (14.8)$$

This is the restoring force pulling the mass back toward the equilibrium position.

This equation becomes much simpler if we restrict the pendulum's oscillations to *small angles* of about 10° (0.17 rad) or less. For such small angles, if the angle θ is in radians, it turns out that

$$\sin\theta \approx \theta$$

This result, which applies only when the angle is in radians, is called the **small-angle approximation**.

> NOTE ▶ You can check this approximation on your calculator. Put your calculator in radian mode, enter some values that are less than 0.17 rad, take the sine, and see what you get. ◀

Recall from Chapter 6 that the angle is related to the arc length by $\theta = s/L$. Using this and the small-angle approximation, we can write the restoring force as

$$(F_{net})_t = -mg\sin\theta \approx -mg\theta = -mg\frac{s}{L} = -\left(\frac{mg}{L}\right)s \qquad (14.9)$$

The net force is directed toward the equilibrium position, and it is linearly proportional to the displacement s from equilibrium. In other words, **the force on a pendulum is a linear restoring force for small angles, so the pendulum will undergo simple harmonic motion.**

Whenever there is a linear restoring force, there can be simple harmonic motion. There are many examples beyond the few we have considered so far, such as sloshing water in a cup or the vibration of a bridge or a building swaying in the wind. We will see these and other examples in the coming sections.

STOP TO THINK 14.2 A ball is hung from a rope, making a pendulum. When it is pulled 5° to the side, the restoring force is 1.0 N. What will be the magnitude of the restoring force if the ball is pulled 10° to the side?

A. 0.5 N   B. 1.0 N   C. 1.5 N   D. 2.0 N

14.3 Describing Simple Harmonic Motion

Now that we know what *causes* simple harmonic motion, we can continue to develop graphical and mathematical descriptions. If we do this for one system, we can adapt the description to any system. The details will vary, but the basic form of the motion will stay the same.

Let's look in detail at one period of the oscillation of a mass on a vertical spring. As we saw in the preceding section, the mass has an equilibrium position at which the net force is zero. If the mass is displaced from equilibrium, a linear restoring force causes the mass to undergo simple harmonic motion. In the table on the next page we present snapshots of the motion together with graphs of the position, velocity, and acceleration.

FIGURE 14.9 Describing the motion of and force on a pendulum.

(a)

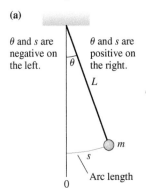

θ and s are negative on the left.

θ and s are positive on the right.

θ

L

m

s

0   Arc length

(b)

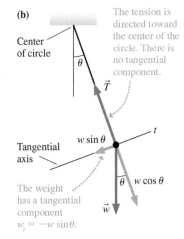

Center of circle

The tension is directed toward the center of the circle. There is no tangential component.

$\vec{T}$

θ

t

$w\sin\theta$

Tangential axis

The weight has a tangential component $w_t = -w\sin\theta$.

θ $w\cos\theta$

$\vec{w}$

 PhET: Pendulum Lab

 ActivPhysics: 9.1, 9.2, 9.5

Details of oscillatory motion

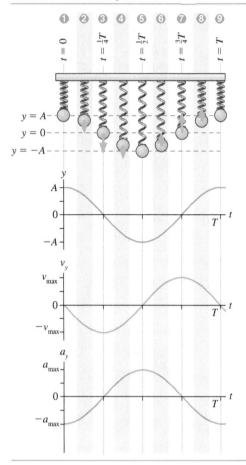

A mass is suspended from a vertical spring with an equilibrium position at $y = 0$. The mass is then lifted upward by a distance A and released. We measure position with respect to the equilibrium position, with positive positions above the equilibrium point, negative below.

❶ The mass starts at its maximum positive displacement, $y = A$. The velocity is zero at the instant the mass is released, but the acceleration is negative because there is a net downward force.

❷ The mass is now moving downward, so the velocity is negative and the distance from equilibrium is decreasing. As the mass nears equilibrium, the restoring force, and thus the magnitude of the acceleration, decreases.

❸ At this time the mass is at the equilibrium position, so the net force—and thus the acceleration—is zero. The speed is at a maximum, but the velocity is negative because the motion is downward.

❹ The velocity is still negative but its magnitude is decreasing, so the acceleration is positive.

❺ At this time, the mass has reached the lowest point of its motion, with $y = -A$. This is a **turning point** of the motion. The velocity is zero. The spring is at its maximum extension, so there is a net upward force and the acceleration is positive.

❻ The mass has begun moving upward; the velocity is positive, and the acceleration is positive.

❼ The mass is passing through the equilibrium position again, but in the opposite direction. The acceleration is zero because there is no net force; the upward velocity is positive.

❽ The mass continues moving upward. The velocity is positive but its magnitude is decreasing, so the acceleration is negative.

❾ The mass is now back at its starting position. This is another turning point; the mass is at rest but will soon begin moving downward, and the whole cycle will repeat.

There are three general points to note about the description of simple harmonic motion in the table above:

■ The graphs are for an oscillation in which the object just happened to be at $y = A$ at $t = 0$. You can certainly imagine a different set of *initial conditions,* with the object at $y = -A$ or somewhere in the middle of an oscillation. But even if an oscillation begins at a different position, it will certainly pass through the $y = A$ position and we can simply choose to set $t = 0$ at this instant.

■ The position, velocity, and acceleration graphs are all sinusoidal functions. The graphs all have the same general shape. We'll return to this point later.

■ If we did a series of experiments on this system, we would find that **the frequency does not depend on the amplitude of the motion;** small oscillations and large oscillations have the same period. This is a key feature of simple harmonic motion that we will explore in more detail later in the chapter. Keep in mind that all these features of the motion of a mass on a spring also apply to other examples of simple harmonic motion.

Now that we have a complete graphical description of the motion, let's develop a mathematical description.

The position-versus-time graph in the above table is a cosine curve. We can write the object's position as

$$x(t) = A \cos\left(\frac{2\pi t}{T}\right) \tag{14.10}$$

where the notation $x(t)$ indicates that the position x is a *function* of time t. Because $\cos(2\pi \text{ rad}) = \cos(0 \text{ rad})$, we see that the position at time $t = T$ is the same as the position at $t = 0$. In other words, this is a cosine function with period T. We can write Equation 14.10 in an alternative form. Because the oscillation frequency is $f = 1/T$, we can write

$$x(t) = A\cos(2\pi ft) \tag{14.11}$$

NOTE ▶ The argument $2\pi ft$ of the cosine function is in *radians*. That will be true throughout this chapter. Don't forget to set your calculator to radian mode before working oscillation problems. ◀

Just as the position graph was a cosine function, the velocity graph is an upside-down sine function with the same period T. The velocity v_x, which is a function of time, can be written as

$$v_x(t) = -v_{max}\sin\left(\frac{2\pi t}{T}\right) = -v_{max}\sin(2\pi ft) \tag{14.12}$$

NOTE ▶ v_{max} is the maximum *speed* and thus is inherently a *positive* number. The minus sign in Equation 14.12 is needed to turn the sine function upside down. ◀

How about the acceleration? As we saw earlier in Equation 14.2, the restoring force that causes the mass to oscillate with simple harmonic motion is $(F_{net})_x = -kx$. Using Newton's second law, we see that this force causes an acceleration

$$a_x = \frac{(F_{net})_x}{m} = -\frac{k}{m}x \tag{14.13}$$

Acceleration is proportional to the position x, but with a minus sign. Consequently we expect the acceleration-versus-time graph to be an inverted form of the position-versus-time graph. This is, indeed, what we find; the acceleration-versus-time graph in the table on the previous page is clearly an upside-down cosine function with the same period T. We can write the acceleration as

$$a_x(t) = -a_{max}\cos\left(\frac{2\pi t}{T}\right) = -a_{max}\cos(2\pi ft) \tag{14.14}$$

In this and coming chapters, we will use sine and cosine functions extensively, so we will summarize some of the key aspects of mathematical relationships using these functions.

Keeping the beat The metal rod in a metronome swings back and forth, making a loud click each time it passes through the center. This is simple harmonic motion, so the motion repeats, cycle after cycle, with the same period. Musicians use this steady click to help them keep a steady beat. The photo—a long exposure—shows another interesting aspect of the motion: You can see the rod most clearly at those points where it was momentarily at rest—at each end of its swing.

⊓⊔ Sinusoidal relationships   (MP)

A quantity that oscillates in time and can be written

$$x = A\sin\left(\frac{2\pi t}{T}\right)$$

or

$$x = A\cos\left(\frac{2\pi t}{T}\right)$$

is called a **sinusoidal function** with **period** T. The argument of the functions, $2\pi t/T$, is in radians.

The graphs of both functions have the same shape, but they have different initial values at $t = 0$ s.

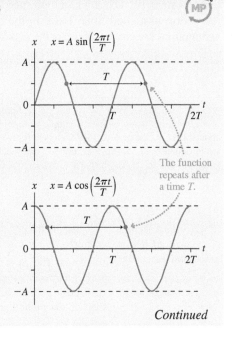

The function repeats after a time T.

Continued

LIMITS If x is a sinusoidal function, then x is:

- *Bounded*—it can take only values between A and $-A$.
- *Periodic*—it repeats the same sequence of values over and over again. Whatever value x has at time t, it has the same value at $t + T$.

SPECIAL VALUES The function x has special values at certain times:

	$t = 0$	$t = \frac{1}{4}T$	$t = \frac{1}{2}T$	$t = \frac{3}{4}T$	$t = T$
$x = A\sin(2\pi t/T)$	0	A	0	$-A$	0
$x = A\cos(2\pi t/T)$	A	0	$-A$	0	A

Exercise 6

EXAMPLE 14.2   **Motion of a glider on a spring**

An air-track glider oscillates horizontally on a spring at a frequency of 0.50 Hz. Suppose the glider is pulled to the right of its equilibrium position by 12 cm and then released. Where will the glider be 1.0 s after its release? What is its velocity at this point?

PREPARE The glider undergoes simple harmonic motion with amplitude 12 cm. The frequency is 0.50 Hz, so the period is $T = 1/f = 2.0$ s. The glider is released at maximum extension from the equilibrium position, meaning that we can take this point to be $t = 0$.

SOLVE 1.0 s is exactly half the period. As the graph of the motion in FIGURE 14.10 shows, half a cycle brings the glider to its left turning point, 12 cm to the left of the equilibrium position. The velocity at this point is zero.

FIGURE 14.10 Position-versus-time graph for the glider.

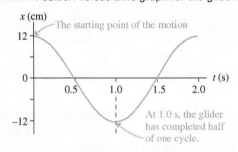

ASSESS Drawing a graph was an important step that helped us make sense of the motion.

We were able to determine the velocity in Example 14.2 because $t = 1.0$ s was a turning point where the instantaneous velocity was zero. To determine the velocity at other points, we need to know v_{max} and use Equation 14.12. How does v_{max} depend on other variables of the motion? Basic reasoning about the motion tells us a few things. A large amplitude implies a high speed because the glider moves a large distance. A small period implies a high speed as well because the glider must complete its motion in a short time. Later in the chapter we will show that both of these assumptions are correct, and that the maximum speed is

$$v_{max} = 2\pi f A = \frac{2\pi A}{T} \tag{14.15}$$

◀ **Small bird, fast wings** BIO As this rufous hummingbird flaps its wings, the motion of the wing tips is approximately simple harmonic. The frequency of the motion is about 45 Hz, so the period of the wingbeat is only a few hundredths of a second. As we see in Equation 14.15, this short period means that the tips of the hummingbird's tiny wings are moving at a high speed—over 15 m/s, or nearly 35 mph!

EXAMPLE 14.3   **Analyzing the motion of a hanging toy**

A classic children's toy consists of a wooden animal suspended from a spring. If you lift the toy up by 10 cm and let it go, it will gently bob up and down, completing 4 oscillations in 10 seconds.

a. What is the oscillation frequency?
b. When does the toy first reach its maximum speed, and what is this speed?

c. What are the position and velocity 4.0 s after you release the toy?

PREPARE The toy is a mass on a vertical spring, so it undergoes simple harmonic motion. The toy begins its motion at its maximum positive displacement of 10 cm, or 0.10 m; this is the amplitude of the motion. Because the toy is released at maximum positive displacement, we can set the moment of release as $t = 0$ s. The toy completes 4 oscillations in 10 seconds, so the period is 1/4 of 10 seconds, or $T = 2.5$ s. FIGURE 14.11 shows the first two cycles of the oscillation.

FIGURE 14.11 A position graph for the spring toy.

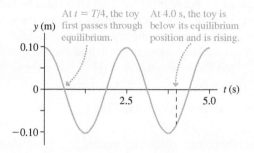

SOLVE a. The period is 2.5 s, so the frequency is

$$f = \frac{1}{T} = \frac{1}{2.5\text{ s}} = 0.40 \text{ oscillation/s} = 0.40 \text{ Hz}$$

b. Figure 14.11 shows that the toy first passes through the equilibrium position at $t = T/4 = (2.5 \text{ s})/4 = 0.62$ s. This is

a point of maximum speed, with the value given by Equation 14.15:

$$v_{max} = 2\pi f A = 2\pi(0.40 \text{ Hz})(0.10\text{ m}) = 0.25 \text{ m/s}$$

c. 4.0 s after release is $t = 4.0$ s. Figure 14.11 shows that the toy is below the equilibrium position and rising at this time, so we expect that the position is negative and the velocity is positive. We can use Equations 14.11 and 14.12 to find the position and velocity at this time:

$$\begin{aligned} y(t = 4.0 \text{ s}) &= A \cos(2\pi f t) \\ &= (0.10 \text{ m})\cos[2\pi(0.40 \text{ Hz})(4.0 \text{ s})] \\ &= -0.081 \text{ m} \end{aligned}$$

$$\begin{aligned} v_y(t = 4.0 \text{ s}) &= -v_{max} \sin(2\pi f t) \\ &= -(0.25 \text{ m/s})\sin[2\pi(0.40 \text{ Hz})(4.0 \text{ s})] \\ &= 0.15 \text{ m/s} \end{aligned}$$

Note that your calculator *must* be in radian mode to do calculations like these.

ASSESS Our calculations for $t = 4.0$ s show that the toy is below the equilibrium position and moving upward, just as we expected from the graph in Figure 14.11. Drawing the graph provided a good check on our work.

Connection to Uniform Circular Motion

Both circular motion and simple harmonic motion are motions that repeat. Many of the concepts we have used for describing simple harmonic motion were introduced in our study of circular motion. We will use the close connection between the two to extend our knowledge of the kinematics of circular motion to simple harmonic motion.

We can demonstrate the relationship between circular and simple harmonic motion with a simple experiment. Suppose a turntable has a small ball glued to the edge. As FIGURE 14.12a shows, we can make a "shadow movie" of the ball by projecting a light past the ball and onto a screen. The ball's shadow oscillates back and forth as the turntable rotates.

If you place a real object on a real spring directly below the shadow, as shown in FIGURE 14.12b, and if you adjust the turntable to have the same period as the spring, you will find that the shadow's motion exactly matches the simple harmonic motion of the object on the spring. **Uniform circular motion projected onto one dimension is simple harmonic motion.**

We can show why the projection of circular motion is simple harmonic motion by considering the particle in FIGURE 14.13 on the next page. As in Chapter 6, we can locate the particle by the angle ϕ measured counterclockwise from the x-axis. Projecting the ball's shadow onto a screen in Figure 14.12a is equivalent to observing just the x-component of the particle's motion. Figure 14.13 shows that the x-component, when the particle is at angle ϕ, is

$$x = A\cos\phi$$

If the particle starts from $\phi_0 = 0$ at $t = 0$, its angle at a later time t is

$$\phi = \omega t$$

where ω is the particle's *angular velocity,* as defined in Chapter 6. Recall that the angular velocity is related to the frequency f by

$$\omega = 2\pi f$$

FIGURE 14.12 A projection of the circular motion of a rotating ball matches the SHM of an object on a spring.

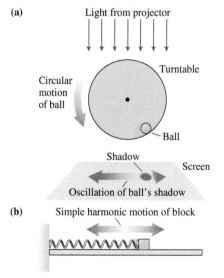

FIGURE 14.13 **A particle in uniform circular motion with radius _A_ and angular velocity _ω_.**

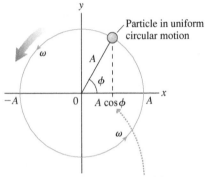

The _x_-component of the particle's position describes the position of the ball's shadow.

TRY IT YOURSELF

SHM in your microwave It's possible to do something like the turntable demonstration right at home. Place a tall (microwave safe) glass or cup filled with water on the outside edge of the turntable in your microwave oven. Start the oven. The turntable will rotate, moving the cup in a circle. Stand in front of the oven with your eyes level with the cup. Watch the cup, paying attention to the side-to-side motion. This motion is the horizontal component of the circular motion, and so it is simple harmonic motion.

The particle's _x_-component can therefore be expressed as

$$x(t) = A\cos(2\pi f t) \qquad (14.16)$$

This is identical to Equation 14.11 for the position of a mass on a spring! **The _x_-component of a particle in uniform circular motion is simple harmonic motion.**

We can use this correspondence to deduce more details. FIGURE 14.14 is the same motion we looked at in Figure 14.13, but here we've shown the velocity vector (tangent to the circle) and the acceleration vector (a centripetal acceleration pointing to the center of the circle). The magnitude of the velocity vector is the particle's speed. Recall from Chapter 6 that the speed of a particle in circular motion with radius _A_ and frequency _f_ is $v = 2\pi f A$. Thus the _x_-component of the velocity vector, which is pointing in the negative _x_-direction, is

$$v_x = -v\sin\phi = -(2\pi f)A\sin(2\pi f t)$$

FIGURE 14.14 **Projection of the velocity and acceleration vectors.**

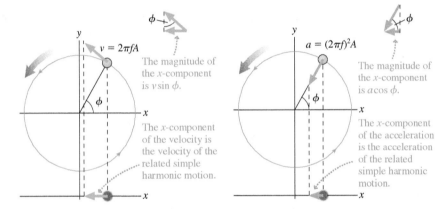

According to the correspondence between circular motion and simple harmonic motion, this is the velocity of an object in simple harmonic motion. This is, indeed, exactly Equation 14.12, which we deduced from the graph of the motion, if we define the maximum speed, as we did in Equation 14.15, to be

$$v_{max} = 2\pi f A = \frac{2\pi A}{T}$$

Similarly, the magnitude of the acceleration vector is the centripetal acceleration $a = v^2/A = (2\pi f)^2 A$. The _x_-component of the acceleration vector, which is the acceleration for simple harmonic motion, is

$$a_x = -a\cos\phi = -(2\pi f)^2 A\cos(2\pi f t)$$

The maximum acceleration is

$$a_{max} = (2\pi f)^2 A \qquad (14.17)$$

We can now summarize our findings for the position, velocity, and acceleration of an object in simple harmonic motion:

$$x(t) = A\cos(2\pi f t)$$
$$v_x(t) = -(2\pi f)A\sin(2\pi f t) \qquad (14.18)$$
$$a_x(t) = -(2\pi f)^2 A\cos(2\pi f t)$$

_x, v_x, and a_x_
p.453

SINUSOIDAL

Position, velocity, and acceleration for an object in simple harmonic motion with frequency _f_ and amplitude _A_

Any simple harmonic motion follows these equations. **If you know the amplitude and the frequency, the motion is completely specified.**

| EXAMPLE 14.4 | Measuring the sway of a tall building |

The John Hancock Center in Chicago is 100 stories high. Strong winds can cause the building to sway, as is the case with all tall buildings. On particularly windy days, the top of the building is known to oscillate with an amplitude of 40 cm ($\approx$16 in) and a period of 7.7 s. What are the maximum speed and acceleration of the top of the building?

PREPARE We will assume that the oscillation of the building is simple harmonic motion with amplitude $A = 0.40$ m. The frequency can be computed from the period:

$$f = \frac{1}{T} = \frac{1}{7.7 \text{ s}} = 0.13 \text{ Hz}$$

SOLVE We can use Equations 14.15 and 14.17 for the maximum velocity and acceleration to compute:

$$v_{max} = 2\pi fA = 2\pi(0.13 \text{ Hz})(0.40 \text{ m}) = 0.33 \text{ m/s}$$

$$a_{max} = (2\pi f)^2 A = [2\pi(0.13 \text{ Hz})]^2(0.40 \text{ m}) = 0.27 \text{ m/s}^2$$

In terms of the free-fall acceleration, the maximum acceleration is $a_{max} = 0.027g$.

ASSESS The free-fall acceleration is quite small, as you would expect; if it were large, building occupants would certainly complain! Even if they don't notice the motion directly, office workers on high floors of high buildings may experience a bit of nausea when the oscillations are large because the acceleration affects the equilibrium organ in the inner ear.

STOP TO THINK 14.3 The figures show four identical oscillators at different points in their motion. Which is moving fastest at the time shown?

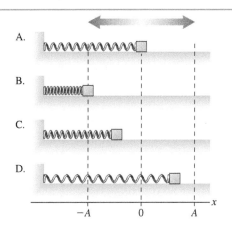

14.4 Energy in Simple Harmonic Motion

A bungee jumper falls, increasing in speed, until the elastic cords attached to his ankles start to stretch. The kinetic energy of his motion is transformed into the elastic potential energy of the cords. Once the cords reach their maximum stretch, his velocity reverses. He rises as the elastic potential energy of the cords is transformed back into kinetic energy. If he keeps bouncing (simple harmonic motion), this transformation happens again and again.

This interplay between kinetic and potential energy is very important to understanding simple harmonic motion. The five diagrams in FIGURE 14.15a on the next page show the position and velocity of a mass on a spring at successive points in time.

The object begins at rest, with the spring at a maximum extension; the kinetic energy is zero, and the potential energy is a maximum. As the spring contracts, the object speeds up until it reaches the center point of its oscillation, the equilibrium point. At this point, the potential energy is zero and the kinetic energy is a maximum. As the object continues to move, it slows down as it compresses the

Elastic cords lead to the up-and-down motion of a bungee jump.

FIGURE 14.15 Energy transformations for a mass on a spring.

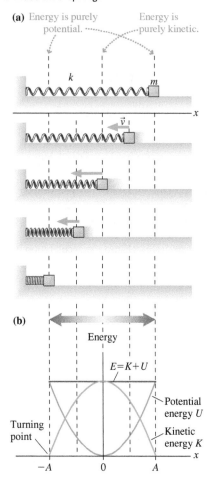

(a) Energy is purely potential. Energy is purely kinetic.

k

m

x

$\vec{v}$

(b)

Energy

$E = K + U$

Potential energy U

Turning point

Kinetic energy K

x

$-A$ 0 A

spring. Eventually, it reaches the turning point, where its instantaneous velocity is zero. At this point, the kinetic energy is zero and the potential energy is again a maximum.

Now we'll specify that the object has mass m, the spring has spring constant k, and the motion takes place on a frictionless surface. You learned in Chapter 10 that the elastic potential energy of a spring stretched by a distance x from its equilibrium position is

$$U = \frac{1}{2}kx^2 \qquad (14.19)$$

The potential energy is zero at the equilibrium position and is a maximum when the spring is at its maximum extension or compression. There is no energy loss to thermal energy, so conservation of energy for this system can be written

$$E = K + U = \frac{1}{2}mv^2 + \frac{1}{2}kx^2 = \text{constant} \qquad (14.20)$$

FIGURE 14.15b shows a graph of the potential energy, kinetic energy, and total energy for the object as it moves. You can see that, as the object goes through its motion, energy is transformed from potential to kinetic and then back to potential. At maximum displacement, with $x = \pm A$ and $v_x = 0$, the energy is purely potential, so the potential energy has its maximum value:

$$E(\text{at } x = \pm A) = U_{\text{max}} = \frac{1}{2}kA^2 \qquad (14.21)$$

At $x = 0$, where $v_x = \pm v_{\text{max}}$, the energy is purely kinetic, so the kinetic energy has its maximum value:

$$E(\text{at } x = 0) = K_{\text{max}} = \frac{1}{2}m(v_{\text{max}})^2 \qquad (14.22)$$

CONCEPTUAL EXAMPLE 14.5   **Energy changes for a playground swing**

You are at the park, undergoing simple harmonic motion on a swing. Describe the changes in energy that occur during one cycle of the motion, starting from when you are at the farthest forward point, motionless and just about to swing backward.

REASON The motion of the swing is that of a pendulum, with you playing the role of the pendulum bob. The energy at different points of the motion is illustrated in FIGURE 14.16. When you are motionless and at the farthest forward point, you are raised up; you have potential energy. As you swing back, your potential energy decreases and your kinetic energy increases, reaching a maximum when the swing is at the lowest point. The swing continues to move backward; you rise up, transforming kinetic energy into potential energy. The process then reverses as you move forward.

ASSESS This description matches the experience of anyone who has been on a swing. You know that you are momentarily motionless at the highest points, and that the motion is fastest at the lowest point.

FIGURE 14.16 Energy at different points of the motion of a swing.

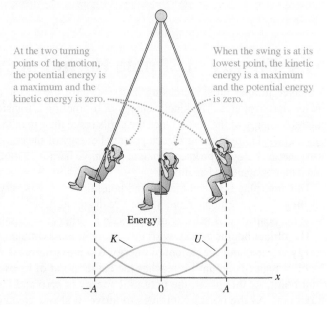

At the two turning points of the motion, the potential energy is a maximum and the kinetic energy is zero.

When the swing is at its lowest point, the kinetic energy is a maximum and the potential energy is zero.

Energy

K U

x

$-A$ 0 A

Finding the Frequency for Simple Harmonic Motion

Now that we have an energy description of simple harmonic motion, we can use what we know about energy to deduce other details of the motion. Let's return to the mass on a spring of Figure 14.15. The graph in Figure 14.15b shows energy being transformed back and forth between kinetic and potential energy. At the turning points, the energy is purely potential; at the equilibrium point, the energy is purely kinetic. Because the total energy doesn't change, the maximum kinetic energy given in Equation 14.22 must be equal to the maximum potential energy given in Equation 14.21:

$$\frac{1}{2}m(v_{max})^2 = \frac{1}{2}kA^2 \qquad (14.23)$$

By solving Equation 14.23 for the maximum speed, we can see that it is related to the amplitude by

$$v_{max} = \sqrt{\frac{k}{m}}A \qquad (14.24)$$

Earlier we found that

$$v_{max} = 2\pi fA \qquad (14.25)$$

Comparing Equations 14.24 and 14.25, we see that the frequency, and thus the period, of an oscillating mass on a spring is determined by the spring constant k and the object's mass m:

$$f = \frac{1}{2\pi}\sqrt{\frac{k}{m}} \quad \text{and} \quad T = 2\pi\sqrt{\frac{m}{k}} \qquad (14.26)$$

Frequency and period of SHM
for mass m on a spring with spring constant k

$\sqrt{\frac{k}{m}}$ p.37 PROPORTIONAL

We can make two observations about these equations:

- **The frequency and period of simple harmonic motion are determined by the physical properties of the oscillator.** The frequency and period of a mass on a spring are determined by (1) the mass and (2) the stiffness of the spring, as shown in FIGURE 14.17. This dependence of frequency and period on a force term and an inertia term will also apply to other oscillators.
- **The frequency and period of simple harmonic motion do not depend on the amplitude A.** A small oscillation and a large oscillation have the same frequency and period.

CONCEPTUAL EXAMPLE 14.6 **Changing mass, changing period**

An astronaut measures her mass each day using the Body Mass Measurement Device on the Space Shuttle, as described at right. During an 8-day flight, her mass steadily decreases. How does this change the frequency of her oscillatory motion on the device?

REASON The period and frequency of a mass-spring system depend on the mass of the object and the spring constant. The spring constant of the device won't change, so the only change that matters is the change in the astronaut's mass. Equation 14.26 shows that the frequency is proportional to $\sqrt{k/m}$, so a decrease in her mass will cause an increase in the frequency. The oscillation will be a bit more rapid.

ASSESS This makes sense. The force of the spring—which causes the oscillation—is the same, but the mass to be accelerated is less. We expect a higher frequency.

Now that we have a complete description of simple harmonic motion in one system, we will summarize the details in a Tactics Box on the next page, showing how to use this information to solve oscillation problems.

FIGURE 14.17 Frequency dependence on mass and spring stiffness.

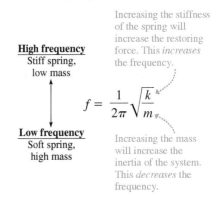

Increasing the stiffness of the spring will increase the restoring force. This *increases* the frequency.

High frequency
Stiff spring, low mass

Low frequency
Soft spring, high mass

$$f = \frac{1}{2\pi}\sqrt{\frac{k}{m}}$$

Increasing the mass will increase the inertia of the system. This *decreases* the frequency.

Measuring mass in space Astronauts on extended space flights monitor their mass to track the effects of weightlessness on their bodies. But because they are weightless, they can't just hop on a scale! Instead, they use an ingenious device in which an astronaut sitting on a platform oscillates back and forth due to the restoring force of a spring. The astronaut is the moving mass in a mass-spring system, so a measurement of the period of the motion allows a determination of an astronaut's mass.

ActivPhysics: 9.3, 9.4, 9.6, 9.7, 9.8, 9.9

TACTICS
BOX 14.1   Identifying and analyzing simple harmonic motion

❶ If the net force acting on a particle is a linear restoring force, the motion is simple harmonic motion around the equilibrium position.

❷ The position, velocity, and acceleration as a function of time are given in Equations 14.18. The equations are given here in terms of x, but they can be written in terms of y, θ, or some other variable if the situation calls for it.

❸ The amplitude A is the maximum value of the displacement from equilibrium. The maximum speed and the maximum magnitude of the acceleration are $v_{max} = 2\pi f A$ and $a_{max} = (2\pi f)^2 A$.

❹ The frequency f (and hence the period $T = 1/f$) depends on the physical properties of the particular oscillator, but f does *not* depend on A.

For a mass on a spring, the frequency is given by $f = \dfrac{1}{2\pi}\sqrt{\dfrac{k}{m}}$.

❺ The sum of potential energy plus kinetic energy is constant. As the oscillation proceeds, energy is transformed from kinetic into potential energy and then back again.

Exercise 11 ✎

EXAMPLE 14.7   Finding the frequency of an oscillator

A spring has an unstretched length of 10.0 cm. A 25 g mass is hung from the spring, stretching it to a length of 15.0 cm. If the mass is pulled down and released so that it oscillates, what will be the frequency of the oscillation?

PREPARE The spring provides a linear restoring force, so the motion will be simple harmonic, as noted in Tactics Box 14.1.

FIGURE 14.18 Visual overview of a mass suspended from a spring.

The oscillation frequency depends on the spring constant, which we can determine from the stretch of the spring. FIGURE 14.18 gives a visual overview of the situation.

SOLVE When the mass hangs at rest, after stretching the spring to 15 cm, the net force on it must be zero. Thus the magnitude of the upward spring force equals the downward weight, giving $k\Delta L = mg$. The spring constant is thus

$$k = \frac{mg}{\Delta L} = \frac{(0.025 \text{ kg})(9.8 \text{ m/s}^2)}{0.050 \text{ m}} = 4.9 \text{ N/m}$$

Now that we know the spring constant, we can compute the oscillation frequency:

$$f = \frac{1}{2\pi}\sqrt{\frac{k}{m}} = \frac{1}{2\pi}\sqrt{\frac{4.9 \text{ N/m}}{0.025 \text{ kg}}} = 2.2 \text{ Hz}$$

ASSESS 2.2 Hz is 2.2 oscillations per second. This seems like a reasonable frequency for a mass on a spring. A frequency in the kHz range (thousands of oscillations per second) would have been suspect!

EXAMPLE 14.8   Weighing DNA molecules

It has recently become possible to "weigh" individual DNA molecules by measuring the influence of their mass on a nanoscale oscillator. FIGURE 14.19 shows a thin rectangular cantilever etched out of silicon. The cantilever has a mass of 3.7×10^{-16} kg. If pulled down and released, the end of the cantilever vibrates with simple harmonic motion,

FIGURE 14.19 A nanoscale cantilever.

moving up and down like a diving board after a jump. When the end of the cantilever is bathed with DNA molecules whose ends have been modified to bind to a surface, one or more molecules may attach to the end of the cantilever. The addition of their mass causes a very slight—but measurable—decrease in the oscillation frequency.

A vibrating cantilever of mass M can be modeled as a simple block of mass $\frac{1}{3}M$ attached to a spring. (The factor of $\frac{1}{3}$ arises from the moment of inertia of a bar pivoted at one end: $I = \frac{1}{3}ML^2$.) Neither the mass nor the spring constant can be determined very accurately—perhaps only to two significant figures—but the oscillation frequency can be measured with very high precision simply by counting the oscillations. In one experiment, the cantilever was initially vibrating at exactly 12 MHz. Attachment of a DNA molecule caused the frequency to decrease by 50 Hz. What was the mass of the DNA molecule?

PREPARE We will model the cantilever as a block of mass $m = \frac{1}{3} M = 1.2 \times 10^{-16}$ kg oscillating on a spring with spring constant k. When the mass increases to $m + m_{DNA}$, the oscillation frequency decreases from $f_0 = 12,000,000$ Hz to $f_1 = 11,999,950$ Hz.

SOLVE The oscillation frequency of a mass on a spring is given by Equation 14.26. Addition of mass doesn't change the spring constant, so solving this equation for k allows us to write

$$k = m(2\pi f_0)^2 = (m + m_{DNA})(2\pi f_1)^2$$

The 2π terms cancel, and we can rearrange this equation to give

$$\frac{m + m_{DNA}}{m} = 1 + \frac{m_{DNA}}{m} = \left(\frac{f_0}{f_1}\right)^2 = \left(\frac{12,000,000 \text{ Hz}}{11,999,950 \text{ Hz}}\right)^2$$
$$= 1.0000083$$

Subtracting 1 from both sides gives

$$\frac{m_{DNA}}{m} = 0.0000083$$

and thus

$$m_{DNA} = 0.0000083m = (0.0000083)(1.2 \times 10^{-16} \text{ kg})$$
$$= 1.0 \times 10^{-21} \text{ kg} = 1.0 \times 10^{-18} \text{ g}$$

ASSESS This is a reasonable mass for a DNA molecule. It's a remarkable technical achievement to be able to measure a mass this small. With a slight further improvement in sensitivity, scientists will be able to determine the number of base pairs in a strand of DNA simply by weighing it!

> **EXAMPLE 14.9**   **Slowing a mass with a spring collision**

A 1.5 kg mass slides across a horizontal, frictionless surface at a speed of 2.0 m/s until it collides with and sticks to the free end of a spring with spring constant 50 N/m. The spring's other end is anchored to a wall. How far has the spring compressed when the mass is, at least for an instant, at rest? How much time does it take for the spring to compress to this point?

PREPARE This is a collision problem, but we can solve it using the tools of simple harmonic motion. FIGURE 14.20 gives a visual overview of the problem. The motion is along the x-axis. We have set $x = 0$ at the uncompressed end of the spring, which is the point of collision. Once the mass hits and sticks, it will start oscillating with simple harmonic motion. The position-versus-time graph shows that the motion of the mass until it stops is $\frac{1}{4}$ of a cycle of simple harmonic motion—though the starting point is different from our usual choice. During this quarter cycle of motion, the kinetic energy of the mass is transformed into the potential energy of the compressed spring.

SOLVE Conservation of energy tells us that the potential energy of the spring when fully compressed is equal to the initial kinetic energy of the mass, so we write

$$\frac{1}{2}m(v_x)_i^2 = \frac{1}{2}kx_f^2$$

The final position of the mass is

$$x_f = (v_x)_i \sqrt{\frac{m}{k}} = (2.0 \text{ m/s}) \sqrt{\frac{1.5 \text{ kg}}{50 \text{ N/m}}} = 0.35 \text{ m}$$

This is the compression of the spring.

Because the compression is $\frac{1}{4}$ of a cycle of simple harmonic motion, the time needed to stop the mass is $t_f = \frac{1}{4}T$. The period is computed using Equation 14.26, so we write

$$t_f = \frac{1}{4}T = \frac{1}{4}2\pi \sqrt{\frac{m}{k}} = \frac{\pi}{2}\sqrt{\frac{1.5 \text{ kg}}{50 \text{ N/m}}} = 0.27 \text{ s}$$

This is the time required for the spring to compress.

ASSESS Interestingly, the time needed to stop the mass does not depend on its initial velocity or on the distance the spring compresses. The motion is simple harmonic; thus the period depends only on the stiffness of the spring and the mass, not on the details of the motion.

FIGURE 14.20 Visual overview for the mass-spring collision.

The spring compresses by x_f as the mass comes to rest.

The mass is instantaneously at rest when the spring reaches maximum compression.

The graph is the start of a sine function, and the motion is $\frac{1}{4}$ of a cycle of SHM.

The mass would, after stopping, reverse direction and continue the cycle of SHM.

Automobile collision times When a car hits a stationary barrier, it takes approximately 0.1 s to come to rest, regardless of the initial speed, something we can understand with a simple model of the collision. The crumpling of the front of a car during a collision is quite complex, but for many cars the force is approximately proportional to the displacement during the compression of the front of the car. As long as we consider only this initial compression, we can model the body of the car as a mass and the front of the car as a spring. With this model, the collision is similar to that of Example 14.9, and, as in the example, the time for the car to come to rest does not depend on the initial speed.

ActivPhysics: 9.10, 9.11, 9.12

FIGURE 14.21 A simple pendulum.

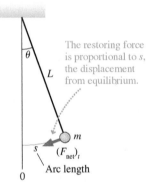

Many real-world collisions (such as a pole vaulter landing on a foam pad) involve a moving object that is stopped by an elastic object. In other cases (such as a bouncing rubber ball) the object itself is elastic. The time of the collision is reasonably constant, independent of the speed of the collision, for the reasons noted in the above example.

STOP TO THINK 14.4 Four mass-spring systems have masses and spring constants shown here. Rank in order, from highest to lowest, the frequencies of the oscillations.

A. [spring k, mass $4m$]

B. [spring $\frac{1}{2}k$, mass m]

C. [spring k, mass $2m$]

D. [spring $2k$, mass m]

14.5 Pendulum Motion

As we've already seen, a simple pendulum—a mass at the end of a string or a rod that is free to pivot—is another system that exhibits simple harmonic motion. Everything we have learned about the mass on a spring can be applied to the pendulum as well.

In the first part of the chapter, we looked at the restoring force in the pendulum. For a pendulum of length L displaced by an arc length s, as in FIGURE 14.21, the tangential restoring force is

$$(F_{net})_t = -\frac{mg}{L}s \qquad (14.27)$$

NOTE ▶ Recall that this equation holds only for small angles. ◀

This linear restoring force has exactly the same form as the net force in a mass-spring system, but with the constants mg/L in place of the constant k. Given this, we can quickly deduce the essential features of pendulum motion by replacing k, wherever it occurs in the oscillating spring equations, with mg/L.

- The oscillation of a pendulum is simple harmonic motion; the equations of motion can be written for the arc length or the angle:

$$s(t) = A\cos(2\pi ft) \qquad \text{or} \qquad \theta(t) = \theta_{max}\cos(2\pi ft)$$

- The frequency can be obtained from the equation for the frequency of the mass on a spring by substituting mg/L in place of k:

$$f = \frac{1}{2\pi}\sqrt{\frac{g}{L}} \qquad \text{and} \qquad T = 2\pi\sqrt{\frac{L}{g}} \qquad (14.28)$$

Frequency of a pendulum of length L with free-fall acceleration g

- As for a mass on a spring, the frequency does not depend on the amplitude. Note also that **the frequency, and hence the period, is independent of the mass.** It depends only on the length of the pendulum.

◀ **Pendulum prospecting** The period of a pendulum clock does not depend on the amplitude, but it does depend on the strength of gravity. Soon after Christiaan Huygens built an accurate pendulum clock in 1656 (the photo shows a replica), Jean Richer discovered that the clock ran more slowly near the equator. Richer correctly surmised that this was due to the weaker gravity near the equator because of the greater distance from the center of the earth. In later years, more accurate pendulums were built that could detect much smaller variations in gravity—small enough that they could sense the presence of dense mineral deposits or low-density strata containing petroleum.

Galileo was the first person to study the pendulum in detail. He realized that the pendulum's fixed frequency would serve as the basis of an accurate clock. Pendulum clocks were the most accurate timepieces available until well into the 20th century.

EXAMPLE 14.10   Designing a pendulum for a clock

A grandfather clock is designed so that one swing of the pendulum in either direction takes 1.00 s. What is the length of the pendulum?

PREPARE   One period of the pendulum is two swings, so the period is $T = 2.00$ s.

SOLVE   The period is independent of the mass and depends only on the length. From Equation 14.28,

$$T = \frac{1}{f} = 2\pi\sqrt{\frac{L}{g}}$$

Solving for L, we find

$$L = g\left(\frac{T}{2\pi}\right)^2 = (9.80 \text{ m/s}^2)\left(\frac{2.00 \text{ s}}{2\pi}\right)^2 = 0.993 \text{ m}$$

ASSESS   A pendulum clock with a "tick" or "tock" each second requires a long pendulum of about 1 m—which is why these clocks were originally known as "tall case clocks."

Physical Pendulums and Locomotion

In Chapter 6, we computed maximum walking speed using the ideas of circular motion. We can also model the motion of your legs during walking as pendulum motion. When you walk, you push off with your rear leg and then let it swing forward for the next stride. At normal, comfortable walking speeds, you use very little force to bring your leg forward. Your leg swings forward under the influence of gravity—like a pendulum.

Try this: Stand on one leg, and gently swing your free leg back and forth. There is a certain frequency at which it will naturally swing. This is your leg's pendulum frequency. Now, try swinging your leg at twice this frequency. You can do it, but it is very difficult. The muscles that move your leg back and forth aren't very strong because under normal circumstances they don't need to apply much force.

A pendulum, like your leg, whose mass is distributed along its length is known as a **physical pendulum.** The motion of a physical pendulum is similar to that of a simple pendulum, but its frequency depends on the distribution of mass.

FIGURE 14.22 shows a simple pendulum and a physical pendulum of the same length. The position of the center of gravity of the physical pendulum is at a distance d from the pivot.

What will be the frequency of a physical pendulum? This is really a rotational motion problem similar to those we considered in Chapter 7. We would expect the frequency to depend on the moment of inertia and the distance to the center of gravity as follows:

- The moment of inertia I is a measure of an object's resistance to rotation. Increasing the moment of inertia while keeping other variables equal should cause the frequency to decrease. In an expression for the frequency of the physical pendulum, we would expect I to appear in the denominator.
- When the pendulum is pushed to the side, a gravitational torque pulls it back. The greater the distance d of the center of gravity from the pivot point, the greater the torque. Increasing this distance while keeping the other variables constant should cause the frequency to increase. In an expression for the frequency of the physical pendulum, we would expect d to appear in the numerator.

FIGURE 14.22   A simple pendulum and a physical pendulum of equal length.

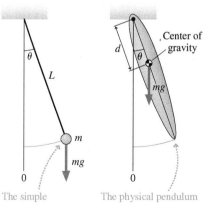

The simple pendulum is a small mass m at the end of a light rod of length L.

The physical pendulum is an extended object with mass m, length L, and moment of inertia I.

A careful analysis of the motion of the physical pendulum produces a result for the frequency that matches these expectations:

$$f = \frac{1}{2\pi}\sqrt{\frac{mgd}{I}} \qquad (14.29)$$

Frequency of a physical pendulum of mass m,
moment of inertia I, with center of gravity distance d from the pivot

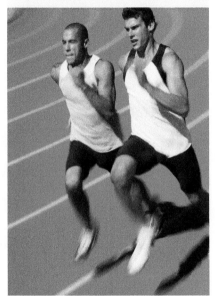

How do you hold your arms? You maintain your balance when walking or running by moving your arms back and forth opposite the motion of your legs. You hold your arms so that the natural period of their pendulum motion matches that of your legs. At a normal walking pace, your arms are extended and naturally swing at the same period as your legs. When you run, your gait is more rapid. To decrease the period of the pendulum motion of your arms to match, you bend them at the elbows, shortening their effective length and increasing the natural frequency of oscillation. To test this for yourself, try running fast with your arms fully extended. It's quite awkward!

EXAMPLE 14.11 **Finding the frequency of a swinging leg**

A student in a biomechanics lab measures the length of his leg, from hip to heel, to be 0.90 m. What is the frequency of the pendulum motion of the student's leg? What is the period?

PREPARE We can model a human leg reasonably well as a rod of uniform cross section, pivoted at one end (the hip). Recall from Chapter 7 that the moment of inertia of a rod pivoted about its end is $\frac{1}{3}mL^2$. The center of gravity of a uniform leg is at the midpoint, so $d = L/2$.

SOLVE The frequency of a physical pendulum is given by Equation 14.29. Before we put in numbers, we will use symbolic relationships and simplify:

$$f = \frac{1}{2\pi}\sqrt{\frac{mgd}{I}} = \frac{1}{2\pi}\sqrt{\frac{mg(L/2)}{\frac{1}{3}mL^2}} = \frac{1}{2\pi}\sqrt{\frac{3}{2}\frac{g}{L}}$$

The expression for the frequency is similar to that for the simple pendulum, but with an additional numerical factor of 3/2 inside the square root. The numerical value of the frequency is

$$f = \frac{1}{2\pi}\sqrt{\left(\frac{3}{2}\right)\left(\frac{9.8 \text{ m/s}^2}{0.90 \text{ m}}\right)} = 0.64 \text{ Hz}$$

The period is

$$T = \frac{1}{f} = 1.6 \text{ s}$$

ASSESS Notice that we didn't need to know the mass of the leg to find the period. The period of a physical pendulum does not depend on the mass, just as it doesn't for the simple pendulum. The period depends only on the *distribution* of mass. When you walk, swinging your free leg forward to take another stride corresponds to half a period of this pendulum motion. For a period of 1.6 s, this is 0.80 s. For a normal walking pace, one stride in just under one second sounds about right.

As you walk, your legs do swing as physical pendulums as you bring them forward. The frequency is fixed by the length of your legs and their distribution of mass; it doesn't depend on amplitude. Consequently, you don't increase your walking speed by taking more rapid steps—changing the frequency is quite difficult. You simply take longer strides, changing the amplitude but not the frequency.

Gibbons and other apes move through the forest canopy by a hand-over-hand swinging motion called *brachiation*. In this motion, the body swings under a pivot point where a hand grips a tree branch, a clear example of pendulum motion. A brachiating ape will increase its speed by taking bigger swings; it does this by "pumping" the swinging motion, much as you do when increasing your amplitude on a playground swing. But because the period of the pendulum motion is fixed, a brachiating gibbon can only go so fast. At some point a maximum speed is reached, and gibbons and other apes break into a different gait, launching themselves from branch to branch through the air.

STOP TO THINK 14.5   A pendulum clock is made with a metal rod. It keeps perfect time at a temperature of 20°C. At a higher temperature, the metal rod lengthens. How will this change the clock's timekeeping?

A. The clock will run fast; the dial will be ahead of the actual time.
B. The clock will keep perfect time.
C. The clock will run slow; the dial will be behind the actual time.

14.6 Damped Oscillations

A real pendulum clock must have some energy input; otherwise, the oscillation of the pendulum would slowly decrease in amplitude due to air resistance. If you strike a bell, the oscillation will soon die away as energy is lost to sound waves in the air and dissipative forces within the metal of the bell.

All real oscillators do run down—some very slowly but others quite quickly—as their mechanical energy is transformed into the thermal energy of the oscillator and its environment. An oscillation that runs down and stops is called a **damped oscillation.**

For a pendulum, the main energy loss is due to air resistance, which we called the *drag force* in Chapter 4. When we learned about the drag force, we noted that it depends on velocity: The faster the motion, the bigger the drag force. For this reason, the decrease in amplitude of an oscillating pendulum will be fastest at the start of the motion. For a pendulum or other oscillator with modest damping, we end up with a graph of motion like that in FIGURE 14.23a. The maximum displacement, x_{max}, decreases with time. As the oscillation decays, the *rate* of the decay decreases; the difference between successive peaks is less.

If we plot a smooth curve that connects the peaks of successive oscillations (we call such a curve an *envelope*), we get the dotted line shown in FIGURE 14.23b. It's possible, using calculus, to show that x_{max} decreases with time as

$$x_{max}(t) = Ae^{-t/\tau} \tag{14.30}$$

where $e \approx 2.718$ is the base of the natural logarithm and A is the *initial* amplitude. This steady decrease of x_{max} with time is called an **exponential decay.**

The constant τ (lowercase Greek tau) in Equation 14.30 is called the **time constant.** After one time constant has elapsed—that is, at $t = \tau$—the maximum displacement x_{max} has decreased to

$$x_{max}(\text{at } t = \tau) = Ae^{-1} = \frac{A}{e} \approx 0.37A$$

In other words, the oscillation has decreased after one time constant to about 37% of its initial value. The time constant τ measures the "characteristic time" during which damping causes the amplitude of the oscillation to decay away. An oscillation that decays quickly has a small time constant, whereas a "lightly damped" oscillator, which decays very slowly, has a large time constant.

Because we will see exponential decay again, we will look at it in more detail.

FIGURE 14.23 The motion of a damped oscillator.

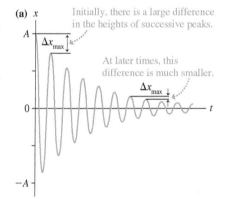

(a) Initially, there is a large difference in the heights of successive peaks.

At later times, this difference is much smaller.

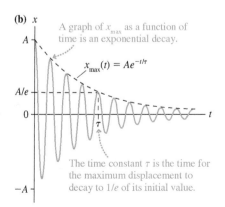

(b) A graph of x_{max} as a function of time is an exponential decay.

$x_{max}(t) = Ae^{-t/\tau}$

The time constant τ is the time for the maximum displacement to decay to $1/e$ of its initial value.

Exponential decay

Exponential decay occurs when a quantity y is proportional to the number e taken to the power $-t/\tau$. The quantity τ is known as the **time constant**. We write this mathematically as

$$y = Ae^{-t/\tau}$$

y is proportional to $e^{-t/\tau}$

SCALING Whenever t increases by one time constant, y decreases by a factor of $1/e$. For instance:

- At time $t = 0$, $y = A$.
- Increasing time to $t = \tau$ reduces y to A/e.
- A further increase to $t = 2\tau$ reduces y by another factor of $1/e$ to A/e^2.

Generally, we can say:

At $t = n\tau$, y has the value A/e^n.

LIMITS As t becomes large, y becomes very small and approaches zero.

Exercises 14–17

y starts with initial value A.

$y = Ae^{-t/\tau}$

y has decreased to 37% of its initial value.

Because t appears as the ratio t/τ, the important time intervals are τ, 2τ, and so on.

Damping smoothes the ride A car's wheels are attached to the car's body with springs so that the wheels can move up and down as the car moves over an uneven road. The car-spring system is a simple harmonic oscillator with a typical period of just under 1 second. You don't want the car to continue bouncing after hitting a bump, so a shock absorber provides damping. The time constant for the damping is about the same length as the period, so that the oscillation damps quickly.

Different Amounts of Damping

The damped oscillation shown in Figure 14.23 continues for a long time. The amplitude isn't zero after one time constant, or two, or three. . . . Mathematically, the oscillation never ceases, though the amplitude will eventually be so small as to be undetectable. For practical purposes, we can speak of the time constant τ as the *lifetime* of an oscillation—a measure of about how long it takes to decay. The best way to measure the relative size of the time constant is to compare it to the period. If $\tau \gg T$, the oscillation persists for many, many periods and the amplitude decrease from cycle to cycle is quite small. The oscillation of a bell after it is struck has $\tau \gg T$; the sound continues for a long time. Other oscillatory systems have very short time constants, as noted in the description of a car's suspension.

EXAMPLE 14.12   **Finding a clock's decay time**

The pendulum in a grandfather clock has a period of 1.00 s. If the clock's driving spring is allowed to run down, damping due to friction will cause the pendulum to slow to a stop. If the time constant for this decay is 300 s, how long will it take for the pendulum's swing to be reduced to half its initial amplitude?

PREPARE The time constant of 300 s is much greater than the 1.00 s period, so this is an example of modest damping as described by Equation 14.30.

SOLVE Equation 14.30 gives an expression for the decay of the maximum displacement of a damped harmonic oscillator:

$$x_{max}(t) = Ae^{-t/\tau}$$

As noted in Tactics Box 14.1, we can write this equation equally well in terms of the pendulum's angle in a straightforward manner:

$$\theta_{max}(t) = \theta_i e^{-t/\tau}$$

where θ_i is the initial angle of swing. At some time t, the time we wish to find, the amplitude has decayed to half its initial value. At this time,

$$\theta_{max}(t) = \theta_i e^{-t/\tau} = \frac{1}{2}\theta_i$$

The θ_i cancels, giving $e^{-t/\tau} = \frac{1}{2}$.

To solve this for t, we take the natural logarithm of both sides and use the logarithm property $\ln(e^a) = a$:

$$\ln(e^{-t/\tau}) = -\frac{t}{\tau} = \ln\left(\frac{1}{2}\right) = -\ln 2$$

In the last step we used the property $\ln(1/b) = -\ln b$. Now we can solve for t:

$$t = \tau \ln 2$$

The time constant was specified as $\tau = 300$ s, so

$$t = (300 \text{ s})(0.693) = 208 \text{ s}$$

It will take 208 s, or about 3.5 min, for the oscillations to decay by half after the spring has run down.

ASSESS The time is less than the time constant, which makes sense. The time constant is the time for the amplitude to decay to 37% of its initial value; we are looking for the time to decay to 50% of its initial value, which should be a shorter time. The time to decay to $\frac{1}{2}$ of the initial amplitude, $t = \tau \ln 2$, could be called the *half-life.* We will see this expression again when we work with radioactivity, another example of an exponential decay.

STOP TO THINK 14.6 Rank in order, from largest to smallest, the time constants τ_A to τ_D of the decays in the figures. The scales on all the graphs are the same.

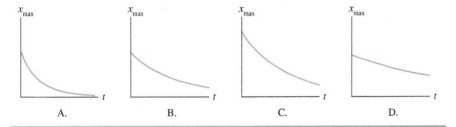

A.   B.   C.   D.

14.7 Driven Oscillations and Resonance

If you jiggle a cup of water, the water sloshes back and forth. This is an example of an oscillator (the water in the cup) subjected to a periodic external force (from your hand). This motion is called a **driven oscillation.**

We can give many examples of driven oscillations. The electromagnetic coil on the back of a loudspeaker cone provides a periodic magnetic force to drive the cone back and forth, causing it to send out sound waves. Earthquakes cause the surface of the earth to move back and forth; this motion causes buildings to oscillate, possibly producing damage or collapse.

Consider an oscillating system that, when left to itself, oscillates at a frequency f_0. We will call this the **natural frequency** of the oscillator. f_0 is simply the frequency of the system if it is displaced from equilibrium and released.

Suppose that this system is now subjected to a *periodic* external force of frequency f_{ext}. This frequency, which is called the **driving frequency,** is completely independent of the oscillator's natural frequency f_0. Somebody or something in the environment selects the frequency f_{ext} of the external force, causing the force to push on the system f_{ext} times every second. The external force causes the oscillation of the system, so it will oscillate at f_{ext}, the driving frequency, not at its natural frequency f_0.

Let's return to the example of the cup of water. If you nudge the cup, you will notice that the water sloshes back and forth at a particular frequency; this is the natural frequency f_0. Now shake the cup at some frequency; this is the driving frequency f_{ext}. As you shake the cup, the oscillation amplitude of the water depends very sensitively on the frequency f_{ext} of your hand. If the driving frequency is near the natural frequency of the system, the oscillation amplitude may become so large that water splashes out of the cup.

Any driven oscillator will show a similar dependence of amplitude on the driving frequency. Suppose a mass on a spring has a natural frequency $f_0 = 2$ Hz. We can use an external force to push and pull on the mass at frequency f_{ext}, measure the amplitude of the resulting oscillation, and then repeat this over and over for many different driving frequencies. A graph of amplitude versus driving frequency, such as the one in FIGURE 14.24, is called the oscillator's **response curve.**

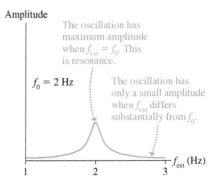

Serious sloshing Water in a cup has a natural frequency at which it will slosh back and forth. The same is true of larger bodies of water. Water in Canada's Bay of Fundy would naturally move into or out of the bay with a period of 12 hours. This is nearly equal to the period of the tidal force of the moon; the two daily high tides are 12.5 hours apart. This *resonance,* a close match between the bay's natural frequency and the moon's driving frequency, produces a huge tidal amplitude. Low tide can be as much as 16 m below high tide, leaving boats high and dry.

FIGURE 14.24 The response curve shows the amplitude of a driven oscillator at frequencies near its natural frequency $f_0 = 2$ Hz.

FIGURE 14.25 The response curve becomes taller and narrower as the damping is reduced.

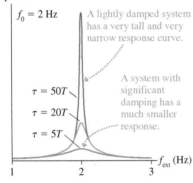

Amplitude

A lightly damped system has a very tall and very narrow response curve.

$f_0 = 2$ Hz

A system with significant damping has a much smaller response.

$\tau = 50T$
$\tau = 20T$
$\tau = 5T$

f_{ext} (Hz)

At the right and left edges of Figure 14.24, the driving frequency is substantially different from the oscillator's natural frequency. The system oscillates, but its amplitude is very small. The system simply does not respond well to a driving frequency that differs much from f_0. As the driving frequency gets closer and closer to the natural frequency, the amplitude of the oscillation rises dramatically. After all, f_0 is the frequency at which the system "wants" to oscillate, so it is quite happy to respond to a driving frequency near f_0. Hence the amplitude reaches a maximum when the driving frequency matches the system's natural frequency: $f_{ext} = f_0$. This large-amplitude response to a driving force whose frequency matches the natural frequency of the system is a phenomenon called **resonance.** Within the context of driven oscillations, the natural frequency f_0 is often called the **resonance frequency.**

The amplitude can become exceedingly large when the frequencies match, especially if there is very little damping. FIGURE 14.25 shows the response curve of the oscillator of Figure 14.24 with different amounts of damping. Three different graphs are plotted, each with a different time constant for damping. The three graphs have damping that ranges from $\tau = 50T$ (very little damping) to $\tau = 5T$ (significant damping).

◀ Simple harmonic music A typical wine glass has a natural frequency of oscillation and a very small amount of damping. A tap on the rim of the glass causes it to "ring" like a bell. The time constant is hundreds of times longer than the period, so the sound will persist for several seconds. If you moisten your finger and slide it gently around the rim of the glass, it will stick and slip in quick succession. With some practice you can match the stick-slip to the frequency of oscillation of the glass. The resulting resonance creates a large amplitude and thus a very loud sound. You can tune the oscillation frequency by adding water, turning a set of glasses into an unusual musical instrument.

CONCEPTUAL EXAMPLE 14.13 **Fixing an unwanted resonance**

Railroad cars have a natural frequency at which they rock side to side. This can lead to problems on certain stretches of track that have bumps where the rails join. If the joints alternate sides, with a bump on the left rail and then on the right, a train car moving down the track is bumped one way and then the other. In some cases, bumps have caused rocking with amplitude large enough to derail the train. A train moving down the track at a certian speed is experiencing a large amplitude of oscillation due to alternating joints in the track. How can the driver correct this potentially dangerous situation?

REASON The large amplitude of oscillation is produced by a resonance, a match between the frequency at which the train car rocks back and forth and the frequency at which the car hits the bumps. To eliminate this resonance, the driver must either reduce the speed of the train—decreasing the driving frequency—or increase the speed of the train—thus increasing the driving frequency.

ASSESS It's perhaps surprising that increasing the speed of the train could produce a smoother ride. But increasing the frequency at which the train hits the bumps will eliminate the match with the natural rocking frequency just as surely as decreasing the speed.

Resonance and Hearing

Resonance in a system means that certain frequencies produce a large response and others do not. The phenomenon of resonance is responsible for the frequency discrimination of the ear.

As we will see in the next chapter, sound is a vibration in air. FIGURE 14.26 on the next page provides an overview of the structures by which sound waves that enter the ear produce vibrations in the cochlea, the coiled, fluid-filled, sound-sensing organ of the inner ear.

FIGURE 14.26 The structures of the ear.

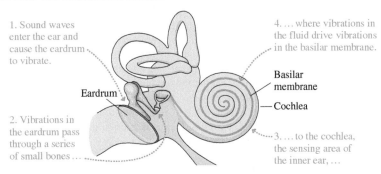

1. Sound waves enter the ear and cause the eardrum to vibrate.

4. … where vibrations in the fluid drive vibrations in the basilar membrane.

Eardrum

Basilar membrane

Cochlea

2. Vibrations in the eardrum pass through a series of small bones …

3. … to the cochlea, the sensing area of the inner ear, …

FIGURE 14.27 shows a very simplified model of the cochlea. As a sound wave travels down the cochlea, it causes a large-amplitude vibration of the basilar membrane at the point where the membrane's natural oscillation frequency matches the sound frequency—a resonance. Lower-frequency sound causes a response farther from the stapes. Sensitive hair cells on the membrane sense the vibration and send nerve signals to your brain. The fact that different frequencies produce maximal response at different positions allows your brain to very accurately determine frequency because a small shift in frequency causes a detectable change in the position of the maximal response. People with no musical training can listen to two notes and easily determine which is at a higher pitch.

We now know a bit about how your ear responds to the vibration of a sound wave—but how does this vibration get from a source to your ear? This is a topic we will consider in the next chapter, when we look at *waves,* oscillations that travel.

FIGURE 14.27 Resonance plays a role in determining the frequencies of sounds we hear.

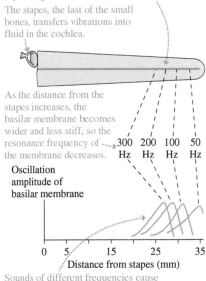

To analyze the cochlea, we imagine the spiral structure unrolled, with the basilar membrane separating two fluid-filled chambers.

The stapes, the last of the small bones, transfers vibrations into fluid in the cochlea.

As the distance from the stapes increases, the basilar membrane becomes wider and less stiff, so the resonance frequency of the membrane decreases.

300 Hz   200 Hz   100 Hz   50 Hz

Oscillation amplitude of basilar membrane

Distance from stapes (mm)

Sounds of different frequencies cause different responses in the basilar membrane.

INTEGRATED EXAMPLE 14.14   Springboard diving

Flexible diving boards designed for large deflections are called springboards. If a diver jumps up and lands on the end of the board, the resulting deflection of the diving board produces a linear restoring force that launches him into the air. But if the diver simply bobs up and down on the end of the board, we can effectively model his motion as that of a mass oscillating on a spring.

A light and flexible springboard deflects by 15 cm when a 65 kg diver stands on its end. He then jumps and lands on the end of the board, depressing it by a total of 25 cm, after which he moves up and down with the oscillations of the end of the board.

a. What is the frequency of the oscillation?
b. What is the maximum speed of his up-and-down motion?

Suppose the diver then drives the motion of the board with his legs, gradually increasing the amplitude of the oscillation. At some point the oscillation becomes large enough that his feet leave the board.

c. What is the amplitude of the oscillation when the diver just becomes airborne at one point of the cycle? What is the acceleration at this point?
d. A diver leaving a springboard can achieve a much greater height than a diver jumping from a fixed platform. Use energy concepts to explain how the spring of the board allows a greater vertical jump.

PREPARE We will model the diver on the board as a mass on a spring. As we've seen, the oscillation frequency is determined by the spring constant and the mass. The mass of the diver is given; we can determine the spring constant from the deflection of the springboard when the diver stands on the end.

FIGURE 14.28 is a sketch of the oscillation that will help us visualize the motion. The equilibrium position, with the diver standing motionless on the end of the board, corresponds to a deflection of 15 cm. When the diver jumps on the board, the total deflection is 25 cm, which means a deflection of an additional 10 cm beyond the equilibrium position, so 10 cm is the amplitude of the subsequent oscillation. When the board rises, it won't bend beyond its undeflected position, so the maximum possible amplitude is 15 cm.

FIGURE 14.28 Position-versus-time graph for the springboard.

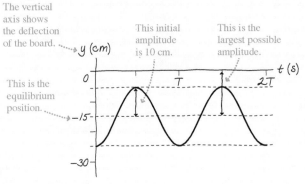

The vertical axis shows the deflection of the board.

This initial amplitude is 10 cm.

This is the largest possible amplitude.

This is the equilibrium position.

Continued

NOTE ▶ We've started the graph at the lowest point of the motion. Because we'll use only the equations for the maximum values of the speed and the acceleration, not the full equations that describe the motion, the exact starting point isn't critical. ◀

SOLVE a. FIGURE 14.29 shows the forces on the diver as he stands motionless at the end of the board. The net force on him is zero, $\vec{F}_{net} = \vec{F}_{sp} + \vec{w} = \vec{0}$, so the two forces have equal magnitudes and we can write

$$F_{sp} = w$$

A linear restoring force means that the board obeys Hooke's law for a spring: $F_{sp} = k\Delta y$, where k is the spring constant. Thus the equilibrium equation is

$$k\Delta y = mg$$

Solving for the spring constant, we find

$$k = \frac{mg}{\Delta y} = \frac{(65 \text{ kg})(9.8 \text{ m/s}^2)}{0.15 \text{ m}} = 4.2 \times 10^3 \text{ N/m}$$

FIGURE 14.29 Forces on a springboard diver at rest at the end of the board.

The deflection of the board produces a restoring force like that of a spring.

In equilibrium, the force due to the spring of the board is equal to the weight force.

The frequency of the oscillation depends on the diver's mass and the spring constant of the board:

$$f = \frac{1}{2\pi}\sqrt{\frac{k}{m}} = \frac{1}{2\pi}\sqrt{\frac{4.2 \times 10^3 \text{ N/m}}{65 \text{ kg}}} = 1.3 \text{ Hz}$$

b. The maximum speed of the oscillation is given by Equation 14.15:

$$v_{max} = 2\pi f A = 2\pi(1.3 \text{ Hz})(0.10 \text{ m}) = 0.82 \text{ m/s}$$

c. We can see from Figure 14.28 that an amplitude of 15 cm returns the board to its undeflected position. At this point, the board exerts no upward force—no supporting normal force—on the diver, so the diver loses contact with the board. (His apparent weight becomes zero.) The acceleration at this point in the motion has the maximum possible magnitude but is negative because the acceleration graph is an upside-down version of the position graph. For a 15 cm oscillation amplitude, the acceleration at this point is computed using Equation 14.17:

$$a = -a_{max} = -(2\pi f)^2 A = [2\pi(1.3 \text{ Hz})]^2(0.15 \text{ m})$$
$$= -10 \text{ m/s}^2$$

d. The maximum jump height from a fixed platform is determined by the maximum speed at which a jumper leaves the ground. During a jump, chemical energy in the muscles is transformed into kinetic energy. This kinetic energy is transformed into potential energy as the jumper rises, back into kinetic energy as he falls, then into thermal energy as he hits the ground. The springboard recaptures and stores this kinetic energy rather than letting it degrade to thermal energy; a diver can jump up once and land on the board, storing the energy of his initial jump as elastic potential energy of the bending board. Then, as the board rebounds, turning the stored energy back into kinetic energy, the diver can push off from this moving platform, transforming even more chemical energy and thus further increasing his kinetic energy. This allows the diver to get "two jumps worth" of chemical energy in a single jump.

ASSESS The answer to part c, -10 m/s^2 is very close to $a = -g$; only rounding errors in early steps kept our result from being exactly $a = -g$. This is to be expected. We learned in earlier chapters that an object loses contact with a surface—like a car coming off the track in a loop-the-loop—when its apparent weight becomes zero: $w_{app} = 0$. And in Chapter 5 we found that the apparent weight of an object in vertical motion becomes zero when $a = -g$—that is, when it enters free fall. This correspondence is a good check on our work; because part c has the answer we expect, we have confidence in our earlier steps.

SUMMARY

The goal of Chapter 14 has been to understand systems that oscillate with simple harmonic motion.

GENERAL PRINCIPLES

Restoring Forces

SHM occurs when a **linear restoring force** acts to return a system to an equilibrium position.

Mass on spring

$(F_{net})_x = -kx$

The frequency of a mass on a spring depends on the mass and the spring constant:

$$f = \frac{1}{2\pi}\sqrt{\frac{k}{m}}$$

Pendulum

$$(F_{net})_t = -\left(\frac{mg}{L}\right)s$$

The frequency of a pendulum depends on the length and the free-fall acceleration:

$$f = \frac{1}{2\pi}\sqrt{\frac{g}{L}}$$

Energy

If there is no friction or dissipation, kinetic and potential energies are alternately transformed into each other in SHM, with the sum of the two conserved.

$$E = \frac{1}{2}mv_x^2 + \frac{1}{2}kx^2$$
$$= \frac{1}{2}mv_{max}^2$$
$$= \frac{1}{2}kA^2$$

IMPORTANT CONCEPTS

Oscillation

An **oscillation** is a repetitive motion about an equilibrium position. The **amplitude** A is the maximum displacement from equilibrium. The period T is the time for one cycle. We may also characterize an oscillation by its frequency f.

Simple Harmonic Motion (SHM)

SHM is an oscillation that is described by a sinusoidal function. All systems that undergo SHM can be described by the same functional forms.

Position-versus-time is a cosine function.

Velocity-versus-time is an inverted sine function.

Acceleration-versus-time is an inverted cosine function.

$x(t) = A\cos(2\pi ft)$

$x_{max} = A$

$v_x(t) = -v_{max}\sin(2\pi ft)$

$v_{max} = 2\pi fA$

$a_x(t) = -a_{max}\cos(2\pi ft)$

$a_{max} = (2\pi f)^2 A$

APPLICATIONS

Damping

Simple harmonic motion with damping (due to drag) decreases in amplitude over time. The **time constant** τ determines how quickly the amplitude decays.

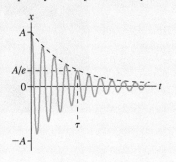

Resonance

A system that oscillates has a **natural frequency** of oscillation f_0. **Resonance** occurs if the system is driven with a frequency f_{ext} that matches this natural frequency. This may produce a large amplitude of oscillation.

Physical pendulum

A **physical pendulum** is a pendulum with mass distributed along its length. The frequency depends on the position of the center of gravity and the moment of inertia.

The motion of legs during walking can be described using a physical pendulum model.

$$f = \frac{1}{2\pi}\sqrt{\frac{mgd}{I}}$$

Problem difficulty is labeled as | (straightforward) to ||| (challenging). Problems labeled INT integrate significant material from earlier chapters; BIO are of biological or medical interest.

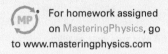
For homework assigned on MasteringPhysics, go to www.masteringphysics.com

Scan this QR code to launch a **Video Tutor Solution** that will help you solve problems for this chapter.

QUESTIONS

Conceptual Questions

1. Give three real-world examples of *oscillatory* motion. (Note that circular motion is similar to, but not the same as oscillatory motion.)
2. A person's heart rate is given in beats per minute. Is this a period or a frequency?
3. Figure Q14.3 shows the position-versus-time graph of a particle in SHM.
   a. At what time or times is the particle moving to the right at maximum speed?
   b. At what time or times is the particle moving to the left at maximum speed?
   c. At what time or times is the particle instantaneously at rest?

FIGURE Q14.3

4. A block oscillating on a spring has an amplitude of 20 cm. What will be the amplitude if the maximum kinetic energy is doubled?
5. A block oscillating on a spring has a maximum speed of 20 cm/s. What will be the block's maximum speed if the amplitude of the oscillation is doubled?
6. A block oscillating on a spring has a maximum kinetic energy of 2.0 J. What will be the maximum kinetic energy if the amplitude is doubled? Explain.
7. A block oscillating on a spring has a maximum speed of 30 cm/s. What will be the block's maximum speed if the initial elongation of the spring is doubled?
8. For the graph in Figure Q14.8, determine the frequency *f* and the oscillation amplitude *A*.

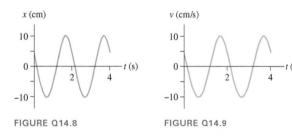

FIGURE Q14.8   **FIGURE Q14.9**

9. For the graph in Figure Q14.9, determine the frequency *f* and the oscillation amplitude *A*.

10. A block oscillating on a spring has period $T = 2.0$ s.
    a. What is the period if the block's mass is doubled?
    b. What is the period if the value of the spring constant is quadrupled?
    c. What is the period if the oscillation amplitude is doubled while m and k are unchanged?
    Note: You do not know values for either m or k. Do *not* assume any particular values for them. The required analysis involves thinking about ratios.
11. A pendulum on Planet X, where the value of g is unknown, oscillates with a period of 2.0 s. What is the period of this pendulum if:
    a. Its mass is doubled?
    b. Its length is doubled?
    c. Its oscillation amplitude is doubled?
    Note: You do not know the values of m, L, or g, so do not assume any specific values.
12. BIO Flies flap their wings at frequencies much too high for pure muscle action. A hypothesis for how they achieve these high frequencies is that the flapping of their wings is the driven oscillation of a mass-spring system. One way to test this is to trim a fly's wings. If the oscillation of the wings can be modeled as a mass-spring system, how would this change the frequency of the wingbeats?
13. As we saw in Chapter 6, the free-fall acceleration is slightly less in Denver than in Miami. If a pendulum clock keeps perfect time in Miami, will it run fast or slow in Denver? Explain.
14. If you want to play a tune on wine glasses, you'll need to adjust the oscillation frequencies by adding water to the glasses. This changes the mass that oscillates (more water means more mass) but not the restoring force, which is determined by the stiffness of the glass itself. If you need to raise the frequency of a particular glass, should you add water or remove water?
15. BIO Sprinters push off from the ball of their foot, then bend their knee to bring their foot up close to the body as they swing their leg forward for the next stride. Why is this an effective strategy for running fast?
16. BIO Gibbons move through the trees by swinging from successive handholds, as we have seen. To increase their speed, gibbons may bring their legs close to their bodies. How does this help them move more quickly?
17. Describe the difference between the time constant τ and the period T. Don't just *name* them; say what is different about the physical concepts that they represent.

18. What is the difference between the driving frequency and the natural frequency of an oscillator?

19. Humans have a range of hearing of approximately 20 Hz to
BIO 20 kHz. Mice have auditory systems similar to humans, but all of the physical elements are smaller. Given this, would you expect mice to have a higher or lower frequency range than humans? Explain.

20. A person driving a truck on a "washboard" road, one with regularly spaced bumps, notices an interesting effect: When the truck travels at low speed, the amplitude of the vertical motion of the car is small. If the truck's speed is increased, the amplitude of the vertical motion also increases, until it becomes quite unpleasant. But if the speed is increased yet further, the amplitude decreases, and at high speeds the amplitude of the vertical motion is small again. Explain what is happening.

21. We've seen that stout tendons in the legs of hopping kangaroos
BIO store energy. When a kangaroo lands, much of the kinetic energy of motion is converted to elastic energy as the tendons stretch, returning to kinetic energy when the kangaroo again leaves the ground. If a hopping kangaroo increases its speed, it spends more time in the air with each bounce, but the contact time with the ground stays approximately the same. Explain why you would expect this to be the case.

Multiple-Choice Questions

22. | A spring has an unstretched length of 20 cm. A 100 g mass hanging from the spring stretches it to an equilibrium length of 30 cm.
   a. Suppose the mass is pulled down to where the spring's length is 40 cm. When it is released, it begins to oscillate. What is the amplitude of the oscillation?
   A. 5.0 cm   B. 10 cm   C. 20 cm   D. 40 cm
   b. For the data given above, what is the frequency of the oscillation?
   A. 0.10 Hz   B. 0.62 Hz   C. 1.6 Hz   D. 10 Hz
   c. Suppose this experiment were done on the moon, where the free-fall acceleration is approximately 1/6 of that on the earth. How would this change the frequency of the oscillation?
   A. The frequency would decrease.
   B. The frequency would increase.
   C. The frequency would stay the same.

23. | Figure Q14.23 represents the motion of a mass on a spring.
   a. What is the period of this oscillation?
   A. 12 s   B. 24 s   C. 36 s
   D. 48 s   E. 50 s

   b. What is the amplitude of the oscillation?
   A. 1.0 cm   B. 2.5 cm   C. 4.5 cm
   D. 5.0 cm   E. 9.0 cm
   c. What is the position of the mass at time $t = 30$ s?
   A. −4.5 cm   B. −2.5 cm   C. 0.0 cm
   D. 4.5 cm   E. 30 cm
   d. When is the first time the velocity of the mass is zero?
   A. 0 s   B. 2 s   C. 8 s
   D. 10 s   E. 13 s
   e. At which of these times does the kinetic energy have its maximum value?
   A. 0 s   B. 8 s   C. 13 s
   D. 26 s   E. 30 s

24. | A ball of mass m oscillates on a spring with spring constant $k = 200$ N/m. The ball's position is $x = (0.350 \text{ m})\cos(15.0t)$, with t measured in seconds.
   a. What is the amplitude of the ball's motion?
   A. 0.175 m   B. 0.350 m   C. 0.700 m
   D. 7.50 m   E. 15.0 m
   b. What is the frequency of the ball's motion?
   A. 0.35 Hz   B. 2.39 Hz   C. 5.44 Hz
   D. 6.28 Hz   E. 15.0 Hz
   c. What is the value of the mass m?
   A. 0.45 kg   B. 0.89 kg   C. 1.54 kg
   D. 3.76 kg   E. 6.33 kg
   d. What is the total mechanical energy of the oscillator?
   A. 1.65 J   B. 3.28 J   C. 6.73 J
   D. 10.1 J   E. 12.2 J
   e. What is the ball's maximum speed?
   A. 0.35 m/s   B. 1.76 m/s   C. 2.60 m/s
   D. 3.88 m/s   E. 5.25 m/s

25. ‖ If you carry heavy weights in your hands, how will this affect the natural frequency at which your arms swing back and forth?
   A. The frequency will increase.
   B. The frequency will stay the same.
   C. The frequency will decrease.

26. | A heavy brass ball is used to make a pendulum with a period of 5.5 s. How long is the cable that connects the pendulum ball to the ceiling?
   A. 4.7 m   B. 6.2 m
   C. 7.5 m   D. 8.7 m

27. | Suppose you travel to the moon, and you take with you two timepieces: a pendulum clock and a wristwatch that runs with a wheel and a mainspring. (The wheel and spring work, essentially, like a mass on a spring, but the wheel rotates back and forth rather than moving up and down.) Which will keep good time on the moon?
   A. Only the pendulum clock
   B. Only the wristwatch
   C. Both timepieces
   D. Neither timepiece

28. | Very loud sounds can damage hearing by injuring the
BIO vibration-sensing hair cells on the basilar membrane. Suppose a person has injured hair cells on a segment of the basilar membrane close to the stapes. What type of sound is most likely to have produced this particular pattern of damage?
   A. Loud music with a mix of different frequencies
   B. A very loud, high-frequency sound
   C. A very loud, low-frequency sound

FIGURE Q14.23

PROBLEMS

Section 14.1 Equilibrium and Oscillation

Section 14.2 Linear Restoring Forces and Simple Harmonic Motion

1. | When a guitar string plays the note "A," the string vibrates at 440 Hz. What is the period of the vibration?

2. | In the aftermath of an intense earthquake, the earth as a whole "rings" with a period of 54 minutes. What is the frequency (in Hz) of this oscillation?

3. | In taking your pulse, you count 75 heartbeats in 1 min. What
BIO are the period (in s) and frequency (in Hz) of your heart's oscillations?

4. || Make a table with 3 columns and 8 rows. In row 1, label the columns θ (°), θ (rad), and $\sin\theta$. In the left column, starting in row 2, write 0, 2, 4, 6, 8, 10, and 12.
   a. Convert each of these angles, in degrees, to radians. Put the results in column 2. Show four decimal places.
   b. Calculate the sines. Put the results, showing four decimal places, in column 3.
   c. What is the first angle for which θ and $\sin\theta$ differ by more than 0.0010?
   d. Over what range of angles does the small-angle approximation appear to be valid?

5. | A heavy steel ball is hung from a cord to make a pendulum. The ball is pulled to the side so that the cord makes a 5° angle with the vertical. Holding the ball in place takes a force of 20 N. If the ball is pulled farther to the side so that the cord makes a 10° angle, what force is required to hold the ball?

Section 14.3 Describing Simple Harmonic Motion

6. || An air-track glider attached to a spring oscillates between the 10 cm mark and the 60 cm mark on the track. The glider completes 10 oscillations in 33 s. What are the (a) period, (b) frequency, (c) amplitude, and (d) maximum speed of the glider?

7. ||| An air-track glider is attached to a spring. The glider is pulled to the right and released from rest at $t = 0$ s. It then oscillates with a period of 2.0 s and a maximum speed of 40 cm/s.
   a. What is the amplitude of the oscillation?
   b. What is the glider's position at $t = 0.25$ s?

8. | What are the (a) amplitude and (b) frequency of the oscillation shown in Figure P14.8?

FIGURE P14.8

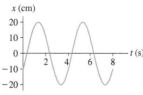

FIGURE P14.9

9. | What are the (a) amplitude and (b) frequency of the oscillation shown in Figure P14.9?

10. | An object in simple harmonic motion has an amplitude of 6.0 cm and a frequency of 0.50 Hz. Draw a position graph showing two cycles of the motion.

11. | During an earthquake, the top of a building oscillates with an amplitude of 30 cm at 1.2 Hz. What are the magnitudes of (a) the maximum displacement, (b) the maximum velocity, and (c) the maximum acceleration of the top of the building?

12. || Some passengers on an ocean cruise may suffer from motion sickness as the ship rocks back and forth on the waves. At one position on the ship, passengers experience a vertical motion of amplitude 1 m with a period of 15 s.
   a. To one significant figure, what is the maximum acceleration of the passengers during this motion?
   b. What fraction is this of g?

13. || A passenger car traveling down a rough road bounces up and down at 1.3 Hz with a maximum vertical acceleration of 0.20 m/s², both typical values. What are the (a) amplitude and (b) maximum speed of the oscillation?

14. ||| The New England Merchants Bank Building in Boston is 152 m high. On windy days it sways with a frequency of 0.17 Hz, and the acceleration of the top of the building can reach 2.0% of the free-fall acceleration, enough to cause discomfort for occupants. What is the total distance, side to side, that the top of the building moves during such an oscillation?

Section 14.4 Energy in Simple Harmonic Motion

15. ||| a. When the displacement of a mass on a spring is $\frac{1}{2}A$, what fraction of the mechanical energy is kinetic energy and what fraction is potential energy?
   b. At what displacement, as a fraction of A, is the energy half kinetic and half potential?

16. ||| A 1.0 kg block is attached to a spring with spring constant 16 N/m. While the block is sitting at rest, a student hits it with a hammer and almost instantaneously gives it a speed of 40 cm/s. What are
   a. The amplitude of the subsequent oscillations?
   b. The block's speed at the point where $x = \frac{1}{2}A$?

17. | A block attached to a spring with unknown spring constant oscillates with a period of 2.00 s. What is the period if
   a. The mass is doubled?
   b. The mass is halved?
   c. The amplitude is doubled?
   d. The spring constant is doubled?
   Parts a to d are independent questions, each referring to the initial situation.

18. || A 200 g air-track glider is attached to a spring. The glider is pushed 10.0 cm against the spring, then released. A student with a stopwatch finds that 10 oscillations take 12.0 s. What is the spring constant?

19. ||| The position of a 50 g oscillating mass is given by $x(t) = (2.0 \text{ cm})\cos(10t)$, where t is in seconds. Determine:
   a. The amplitude.
   b. The period.
   c. The spring constant.
   d. The maximum speed.
   e. The total energy.
   f. The velocity at $t = 0.40$ s.

20. ‖ A 200 g mass attached to a horizontal spring oscillates at a frequency of 2.0 Hz. At one instant, the mass is at $x = 5.0$ cm and has $v_x = -30$ cm/s. Determine:
    a. The period.
    b. The amplitude.
    c. The maximum speed.
    d. The total energy.
21. ‖ A 507 g mass oscillates with an amplitude of 10.0 cm on a spring whose spring constant is 20.0 N/m. Determine:
    a. The period.
    b. The maximum speed.
    c. The total energy.
22. ‖‖ A 300 g oscillator has a speed of 95.4 cm/s when its displacement is 3.00 cm and 71.4 cm/s when its displacement is 6.00 cm. What is the oscillator's maximum speed?

Section 14.5 Pendulum Motion

23. ‖ A mass on a string of unknown length oscillates as a pendulum with a period of 4.00 s. What is the period if
    a. The mass is doubled?
    b. The string length is doubled?
    c. The string length is halved?
    d. The amplitude is halved?
    Parts a to d are independent questions, each referring to the initial situation.
24. ‖‖ A 200 g ball is tied to a string. It is pulled to an angle of 8.00° and released to swing as a pendulum. A student with a stopwatch finds that 10 oscillations take 12.0 s. How long is the string?
25. ‖ The angle of a pendulum is given by $\theta(t) = (0.10 \text{ rad})\cos(5t)$, where t is in seconds. Determine:
    a. The amplitude.
    b. The frequency.
    c. The length of the string.
    d. The angle at $t = 2.0$ s.
26. ‖ It is said that Galileo discovered a basic principle of the pendulum—that the period is independent of the amplitude—by using his pulse to time the period of swinging lamps in the cathedral as they swayed in the breeze. Suppose that one oscillation of a swinging lamp takes 5.5 s. How long is the lamp chain?
27. ‖ The free-fall acceleration on the moon is 1.62 m/s². What is the length of a pendulum whose period on the moon matches the period of a 2.00-m-long pendulum on the earth?
28. ‖ Astronauts on the first trip to Mars take along a pendulum that has a period on earth of 1.50 s. The period on Mars turns out to be 2.45 s. What is the Martian free-fall acceleration?
29. ‖‖ A building is being knocked down with a wrecking ball, which is a big metal sphere that swings on a 10-m-long cable. You are (unwisely!) standing directly beneath the point from which the wrecking ball is hung when you notice that the ball has just been released and is swinging directly toward you. How much time do you have to move out of the way?
30. ‖‖ Interestingly, there have been several studies using cadavers
    BIO to determine the moment of inertia of human body parts by letting them swing as a pendulum about a joint. In one study, the center of gravity of a 5.0 kg lower leg was found to be 18 cm from the knee. When pivoted at the knee and allowed to swing, the oscillation frequency was 1.6 Hz. What was the moment of inertia of the lower leg?
31. ‖‖ A pendulum clock keeps time by the swinging of a uniform solid rod pivoted at one end. The angular position of the rod is given by $\theta(t) = (0.175 \text{ rad})\sin(\pi t)$, where t is in seconds.
    a. What is the angular position of the rod at $t = 0.250$ s?
    b. What is the period of oscillation?
    c. How long is the rod?

32. ‖‖ You and your friends find a rope that hangs down 15 m from a high tree branch right at the edge of a river. You find that you can run, grab the rope, and swing out over the river. You run at 2.0 m/s and grab the rope, launching yourself out over the river. How long must you hang on if you want to stay dry?
33. ‖ A thin, circular hoop with a radius of 0.22 m is hanging from its rim on a nail. When pulled to the side and released, the hoop swings back and forth as a physical pendulum. The moment of inertia of a hoop for a rotational axis passing through its edge is $I = 2MR^2$. What is the period of oscillation of the hoop?
34. ‖‖‖ An elephant's legs have a
    BIO reasonably uniform cross section from top to bottom, and they are quite long, pivoting high on the animal's body. When an elephant moves at a walk, it uses very little energy to bring its legs forward, sim- ply allowing them to swing like pendulums. For fluid walking motion, this time should be half the time for a complete stride; as soon as the right leg finishes swinging forward, the elephant plants the right foot and begins swinging the left leg forward.
    a. An elephant has legs that stretch 2.3 m from its shoulders to the ground. How much time is required for one leg to swing forward after completing a stride?
    b. What would you predict for this elephant's stride frequency? That is, how many steps per minute will the elephant take?

Section 14.6 Damped Oscillations

35. ‖ The amplitude of an oscillator decreases to 36.8% of its initial value in 10.0 s. What is the value of the time constant?
36. ‖ Calculate and draw an accurate displacement graph from $t = 0$ s to $t = 10$ s of a damped oscillator having a frequency of 1.0 Hz and a time constant of 4.0 s.
37. ‖ A small earthquake starts a lamppost vibrating back and forth. The amplitude of the vibration of the top of the lamppost is 6.5 cm at the moment the quake stops, and 8.0 s later it is 1.8 cm.
    a. What is the time constant for the damping of the oscillation?
    b. What was the amplitude of the oscillation 4.0 s after the quake stopped?
38. ‖ When you drive your car over a bump, the springs connecting the wheels to the car compress. Your shock absorbers then damp the subsequent oscillation, keeping your car from bouncing up and down on the springs. Figure P14.38 shows real data for a car driven over a bump. Estimate the frequency and the time constant for this damped oscillation.

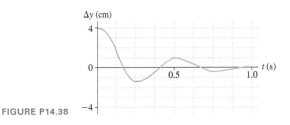

FIGURE P14.38

Section 14.7 Driven Oscillations and Resonance

39. ‖ A 25 kg child sits on a 2.0-m-long rope swing. You are going to give the child a small, brief push at regular intervals. If you want to increase the amplitude of her motion as quickly as possible, how much time should you wait between pushes?

40. ‖ Your car rides on springs, so it will have a natural frequency of oscillation. Figure P14.40 shows data for the amplitude of motion of a car driven at different frequencies. The car is driven at 20 mph over a washboard road with bumps spaced 10 feet apart; the resulting ride is quite bouncy. Should the driver speed up or slow down for a smoother ride?

FIGURE P14.40

41. ‖ Vision is blurred if the head is vibrated at 29 Hz because the
BIO vibrations are resonant with the natural frequency of the eyeball held by the musculature in its socket. If the mass of the eyeball is 7.5 g, a typical value, what is the effective spring constant of the musculature attached to the eyeball?

General Problems

42. ‖ A spring has an unstretched length of 12 cm. When an 80 g ball is hung from it, the length increases by 4.0 cm. Then the ball is pulled down another 4.0 cm and released.
   a. What is the spring constant of the spring?
   b. What is the period of the oscillation?
   c. Draw a position-versus-time graph showing the motion of the ball for three cycles of the oscillation. Let the equilibrium position of the ball be $y = 0$. Be sure to include appropriate units on the axes so that the period and the amplitude of the motion can be determined from your graph.

43. ‖ A 0.40 kg ball is suspended from a spring with spring constant 12 N/m. If the ball is pulled down 0.20 m from the equilibrium position and released, what is its maximum speed while it oscillates?

44. ‖ A spring is hanging from the ceiling. Attaching a 500 g mass to the spring causes it to stretch 20.0 cm in order to come to equilibrium.
   a. What is the spring constant?
   b. From equilibrium, the mass is pulled down 10.0 cm and released. What is the period of oscillation?
   c. What is the maximum speed of the mass? At what position or positions does it have this speed?

45. ‖ A spring with spring constant 15.0 N/m hangs from the ceiling. A ball is suspended from the spring and allowed to come to rest. It is then pulled down 6.00 cm and released. If the ball makes 30 oscillations in 20.0 s, what are its (a) mass and (b) maximum speed?

46. ‖ A spring is hung from the ceiling. When a coffee mug is attached to its end, the spring stretches 2.0 cm before reaching its new equilibrium length. The mug is then pulled down slightly and released. What is the frequency of oscillation?

47. ‖ On your first trip to Planet X you happen to take along a 200 g mass, a 40.0-cm-long spring, a meter stick, and a stopwatch. You're curious about the free-fall acceleration on Planet X, where ordinary tasks seem easier than on earth, but you can't find this information in your Visitor's Guide. One night you suspend the spring from the ceiling in your room and hang the mass from it. You find that the mass stretches the spring by 31.2 cm. You then pull the mass down 10.0 cm and release it. With the stopwatch you find that 10 oscillations take 14.5 s. Can you now satisfy your curiosity?

48. ‖ An object oscillating on a spring has the velocity graph shown in Figure P14.48. Draw a velocity graph if the following changes are made.
   a. The amplitude is doubled and the frequency is halved.
   b. The amplitude and spring constant are kept the same, but the mass is quadrupled.
   Parts a and b are independent questions, each starting from the graph shown.

FIGURE P14.48   FIGURE P14.49

49. ‖ The two graphs in Figure P14.49 are for two different vertical mass-spring systems.
   a. What is the frequency of system A? What is the first time at which the mass has maximum speed while traveling in the upward direction?
   b. What is the period of system B? What is the first time at which the mechanical energy is all potential?
   c. If both systems have the same mass, what is the ratio k_A/k_B of their spring constants?

50. ‖ As we've seen, astronauts measure their mass by measuring the
BIO period of oscillation when sitting in a chair connected to a spring. The Body Mass Measurement Device on Skylab, a 1970s space station, had a spring constant of 606 N/m. The empty chair oscillated with a period of 0.901 s. What is the mass of an astronaut who oscillates with a period of 2.09 s when sitting in the chair?

51. ‖‖ A 100 g ball attached to a spring with spring constant 2.50 N/m oscillates horizontally on a frictionless table. Its velocity is 20.0 cm/s when $x = -5.00$ cm.
   a. What is the amplitude of oscillation?
   b. What is the speed of the ball when $x = 3.00$ cm?

52. ‖ The ultrasonic transducer used in a medical ultrasound imag-
BIO ing device is a very thin disk ($m = 0.10$ g) driven back and forth in SHM at 1.0 MHz by an electromagnetic coil.
   a. The maximum restoring force that can be applied to the disk without breaking it is 40,000 N. What is the maximum oscillation amplitude that won't rupture the disk?
   b. What is the disk's maximum speed at this amplitude?

53. ‖ A compact car has a mass of 1200 kg. Assume that the car has one spring on each wheel, that the springs are identical, and that the mass is equally distributed over the four springs.
   a. What is the spring constant of each spring if the empty car bounces up and down 2.0 times each second?
   b. What will be the car's oscillation frequency while carrying four 70 kg passengers?

54. ‖ Four people with a combined mass of 300 kg are riding in a 1100 kg car. When they drive down a washboard road with bumps spaced 5.0 m apart, they notice that the car bounces up and down with a maximum amplitude when the car is traveling at 6.0 m/s. The driver stops the car and everyone exits the vehicle. How much does the car rise up on its springs?

55. ‖ A 500 g air-track glider attached to a spring with spring constant 10 N/m is sitting at rest on a frictionless air track. A 250 g glider is pushed toward it from the far end of the track at a speed of 120 cm/s. It collides with and sticks to the 500 g glider. What are the amplitude and period of the subsequent oscillations?

56. ‖‖ A 1.00 kg block is attached to a horizontal spring with spring constant 2500 N/m. The block is at rest on a frictionless surface. A 10.0 g bullet is fired into the block, in the face opposite the spring, and sticks.
    a. What was the bullet's speed if the subsequent oscillations have an amplitude of 10.0 cm?
    b. Could you determine the bullet's speed by measuring the oscillation frequency? If so, how? If not, why not?

57. ‖‖‖ Figure P14.57 shows two springs, each with spring constant 20 N/m, connecting a 2.5 kg block to two walls. The block slides on a frictionless surface. If the block is displaced from equilibrium, it will undergo simple harmonic motion. What is the frequency of that motion?

FIGURE P14.57

58. ‖ Bungee Man is a superhero who does super deeds with the help of Super Bungee cords. The Super Bungee cords act like ideal springs no matter how much they are stretched. One day, Bungee Man stopped a school bus that had lost its brakes by hooking one end of a Super Bungee to the rear of the bus as it passed him, planting his feet, and holding on to the other end of the Bungee until the bus came to a halt. (Of course, he then had to quickly release the Bungee before the bus came flying back at him.) The mass of the bus, including passengers, was 12,000 kg, and its speed was 21.2 m/s. The bus came to a stop in 50.0 m.
    a. What was the spring constant of the Super Bungee?
    b. How much time after the Super Bungee was attached did it take the bus to stop?

59. ‖‖‖ Two 50 g blocks are held 30 cm above a table. As shown in Figure P14.59, one of them is just touching a 30-cm-long spring. The blocks are released at the same time. The block on the left hits the table at exactly the same instant as the block on the right first comes to an instantaneous rest. What is the spring constant?

30 cm
FIGURE P14.59

60. ‖ The earth's free-fall acceleration varies from 9.78 m/s² at the equator to 9.83 m/s² at the poles. A pendulum whose length is precisely 1.000 m can be used to measure g. Such a device is called a *gravimeter*.
    a. How long do 100 oscillations take at the equator?
    b. How long do 100 oscillations take at the north pole?
    c. Suppose you take your gravimeter to the top of a high mountain peak near the equator. There you find that 100 oscillations take 201 s. What is g on the mountain top?

61. ‖‖‖ A pendulum clock has a heavy bob supported on a very thin steel rod that is 1.00000 m long at 20°C.
    a. To 6 significant figures, what is the clock's period? Assume that g is 9.80 m/s² exactly.
    b. To 6 significant figures, what is the period if the temperature increases by 10°C?
    c. The clock keeps perfect time at 20°C. At 30°C, after how many hours will the clock be off by 1.0 s?

62. ‖‖‖ A pendulum consists of a massless, rigid rod with a mass at one end. The other end is pivoted on a frictionless pivot so that it can turn through a complete circle. The pendulum is inverted,

so the mass is directly above the pivot point, then released. The speed of the mass as it passes through the lowest point is 5.0 m/s. If the pendulum later undergoes small-amplitude oscillations at the bottom of the arc, what will the frequency be?

63. ‖ Two side-by-side pendulum clocks have heavy bobs at the ends of rigid, very lightweight arms. One pendulum has a 38.8-cm-long rod, the other a 24.8-cm-long rod. Each clock makes one tick for each complete swing of its pendulum.
    a. Determine the frequencies and periods of the two clocks.
    b. Because the two pendulums have different frequencies, their ticks are usually "out of step." However, you notice that they do get back into step (tick at the same instant) at regular intervals. How much time elapses between such events?
    c. The getting-into-step phenomenon is, itself, periodic. What is the frequency of this phenomenon? Can you see a relationship between its frequency and the frequencies of the two clocks?

64. ‖‖‖ Orangutans can move by brachiation, swinging like a pendulum beneath successive handholds. If an orangutan has arms that are 0.90 m long and repeatedly swings to a 20° angle, taking one swing immediately after another, estimate how fast it is moving in m/s.

65. ‖ The 15 g head of a bobble-head doll oscillates in SHM at a frequency of 4.0 Hz.
    a. What is the spring constant of the spring on which the head is mounted?
    b. Suppose the head is pushed 2.0 cm against the spring, then released. What is the head's maximum speed as it oscillates?
    c. The amplitude of the head's oscillations decreases to 0.50 cm in 4.0 s. What is the head's time constant?

66. ‖ An oscillator with a mass of 500 g and a period of 0.50 s has an amplitude that decreases by 2.0% during each complete oscillation. If the initial amplitude is 10 cm, what will be the amplitude after 25 oscillations?

67. ‖‖‖ An infant's toy has a 120 g wooden animal hanging from a spring. If pulled down gently, the animal oscillates up and down with a period of 0.50 s. His older sister pulls the spring a bit more than intended. She pulls the animal 30 cm below its equilibrium position, then lets go. The animal flies upward and detaches from the spring right at the animal's equilibrium position. If the animal does not hit anything on the way up, how far above its equilibrium position will it go?

68. ‖‖‖ A jellyfish can propel itself with jets of water pushed out of its bell, a flexible structure on top of its body. The elastic bell and the water it contains function as a mass-spring system, greatly increasing efficiency. Normally, the jellyfish emits one jet right after the other, but we can get some insight into the jet system by looking at a single jet thrust. Figure P14.68 shows a graph of the motion of one point in the wall of the bell for such a single jet; this is the pattern of a damped oscillation. The spring constant for the bell can be estimated to be 1.2 N/m.
    a. What is the period for the oscillation?
    b. Estimate the effective mass participating in the oscillation. This is the mass of the bell itself plus the mass of the water.
    c. Consider the peaks of positive displacement in the graph. By what factor does the amplitude decrease over one period? Given this, what is the time constant for the damping?

FIGURE P14.68

69. ⦀ A 200 g oscillator in a vacuum chamber has a frequency of 2.0 Hz. When air is admitted, the oscillation decreases to 60% of its initial amplitude in 50 s. How many oscillations will have been completed when the amplitude is 30% of its initial value?

70. ⦀ While seated on a tall bench, extend your lower leg a small
BIO amount and then let it swing freely about your knee joint, with no muscular engagement. It will oscillate as a damped pendulum. Figure P14.70 is a graph of the lower leg angle versus time in such an experiment. Estimate (a) the period and (b) the time constant for this oscillation.

FIGURE P14.70

71. ⦀ A 2.0 kg block oscillates up and down on a spring with spring constant 220 N/m. Its initial amplitude is 15 cm. If the time constant for damping of the oscillation is 3.0 s, how much mechanical energy has been dissipated from the block-spring system after 6.0 s?

72. ⦀ In Chapter 10, we saw that the Achilles tendon will stretch
BIO and then rebound, storing and returning energy during a step. We can model this motion as that of a mass on a spring. This is far from a perfect model, but it does give some insight. If a 60 kg person stands on a low wall with her full weight on the ball of one foot and the heel free to move, the stretch of the Achilles tendon will cause her center of gravity to lower by about 2.5 mm.
   a. What is the spring constant of her Achilles tendon?
   b. If she bounces a little, what is her oscillation period?
   c. When walking or running, the tendon spring begins to stretch as the ball of the foot takes the weight of a stride, transforming kinetic energy into elastic potential energy. Ideally, the cycle of the motion will have advanced so that potential energy has just finished being converted back to kinetic energy as the foot leaves the ground. What fraction of an oscillation period should the time between landing and liftoff correspond to? Given the period you calculated above, what is this time?
   d. Sprinters running a short race keep their foot in contact with the ground for about 0.10 s, some of which corresponds to the heel strike and subsequent rolling forward of the foot. Given this, does the answer to part c make sense?

Passage Problems

Web Spiders and Oscillations

All spiders have special organs that make them exquisitely sensitive to vibrations. Web spiders detect vibrations of their web to determine what has landed in their web, and where.

In fact, spiders carefully adjust the tension of strands to "tune" their web. Suppose an insect lands and is trapped in a web. The silk of the web serves as the spring in a spring-mass system while the body of the insect is the mass. The frequency of oscillation depends on the restoring force of the web and the mass of the insect. Spiders respond more quickly to larger—and therefore more valuable—prey, which they can distinguish by the web's oscillation frequency.

Suppose a 12 mg fly lands in the center of a horizontal spider's web, causing the web to sag by 3.0 mm.

73. ⎸ Assuming that the web acts like a spring, what is the spring constant of the web?
   A. 0.039 N/m   B. 0.39 N/m
   C. 3.9 N/m   D. 39 N/m

74. ⎸ Modeling the motion of the fly on the web as a mass on a spring, at what frequency will the web vibrate when the fly hits it?
   A. 0.91 Hz   B. 2.9 Hz   C. 9.1 Hz   D. 29 Hz

75. ⎸ If the web were vertical rather than horizontal, how would the frequency of oscillation be affected?
   A. The frequency would be higher.
   B. The frequency would be lower.
   C. The frequency would be the same.

76. ⎸ Spiders are more sensitive to oscillations at higher frequencies. For example, a low-frequency oscillation at 1 Hz can be detected for amplitudes down to 0.1 mm, but a high-frequency oscillation at 1 kHz can be detected for amplitudes as small as 0.1 μm. For these low- and high-frequency oscillations, we can say that
   A. The maximum acceleration of the low-frequency oscillation is greater.
   B. The maximum acceleration of the high-frequency oscillation is greater.
   C. The maximum accelerations of the two oscillations are approximately equal.

STOP TO THINK ANSWERS

Stop to Think 14.1: C. The frequency is inversely proportional to the period, so a shorter period implies a higher frequency.

Stop to Think 14.2: D. The restoring force is proportional to the displacement. If the displacement from equilibrium is doubled, the force is doubled as well.

Stop to Think 14.3: A. The maximum speed occurs when the mass passes through its equilibrium position.

Stop to Think 14.4: $f_D > f_C = f_B > f_A$. The frequency is determined by the ratio of k to m.

Stop to Think 14.5: C. The increase in length will cause the frequency to decrease and thus the period will increase. The time between ticks will increase, so the clock will run slow.

Stop to Think 14.6: $\tau_D > \tau_B = \tau_C > \tau_A$. The time constant is the time to decay to 37% of the initial height. The time constant is independent of the initial height.

15 Traveling Waves and Sound

This bat's ears are much more prominent than its eyes. It would appear that hearing is a much more important sense than sight for bats. How does a bat use sound waves to locate prey?

LOOKING AHEAD ▶

The goal of Chapter 15 is to learn the basic properties of traveling waves.

The Wave Model

A **wave** is a disturbance traveling through a medium.

The wave propagates, but the particles of the medium don't. Here the coils of a stretched spring simply move up and back down as the wave passes.

Wave Properties

A few basic quantities can describe any type of wave.

This train of ocean waves is periodic. How fast do the waves move? That's the wave **speed**. What is the distance between successive wave crests? That's the **wavelength**. How many waves strike the beach each minute? That's the **frequency**.

The description of wave motion is closely related to that of simple harmonic motion.

> **Looking Back** ◀◀
> Section 14.3 Description of simple harmonic motion

Types of Waves

Our model can describe any type of wave, from ocean waves to vibrating strings, but two types of waves are especially important: **sound** and **light.**

Displaying the sound waves from a tuning fork clearly shows their periodic nature.

Visible light comes in a range of wavelengths corresponding to the colors of the rainbow.

Energy and Intensity

All waves carry energy. How much? That's a question of **intensity.** Your ears are sensitive to sounds over a remarkable range of intensities, so we use the logarithmic **decibel** scale for sound intensity level.

A lens focuses sunlight onto a small area, increasing the intensity.

Doppler Effect

The frequency and wavelength of waves are shifted when there is relative motion between the source and the observer of waves. We call this the **Doppler effect.**

Radar waves shift in frequency when they reflect from a moving vehicle; the higher the speed, the bigger the shift.

15.1 The Wave Model

The *particle model* that we have been using since Chapter 1 allowed us to simplify the treatment of motion of complex objects by considering them to be particles. Balls, cars, and rockets obviously differ from one another, but the general features of their motions are well described by treating them as particles. As we saw in Chapter 3, a ball or a rock or a car flying through the air will undergo the same motion. The particle model helps us understand this underlying simplicity.

In this chapter we will introduce the basic properties of waves with a **wave model** that emphasizes those aspects of wave behavior common to all waves. Although sound waves, water waves, and radio waves are clearly different, the wave model will allow us to understand many of the important features they share.

The wave model is built around the idea of a **traveling wave,** which is an organized disturbance that travels with a well-defined wave speed. This definition seems straightforward, but several new terms must be understood to gain a complete understanding of the concept of a traveling wave.

FIGURE 15.1 Ripples on a pond are a traveling wave.

The disturbance is the rippling of the water's surface.

The water is the medium.

Mechanical Waves

Mechanical waves are waves that involve the motion of a substance through which they move, the **medium.** For example, the medium of a water wave is the water, the medium of a sound wave is the air, and the medium of a wave on a stretched string is the string.

As a wave passes through a medium, the atoms that make up the medium are displaced from equilibrium, much like pulling a spring away from its equilibrium position. This is a **disturbance** of the medium. The water ripples of FIGURE 15.1 are a disturbance of the water's surface.

A wave disturbance is created by a *source.* The source of a wave might be a rock thrown into water, your hand plucking a stretched string, or an oscillating loudspeaker cone pushing on the air. Once created, the disturbance travels outward through the medium at the **wave speed** *v*. This is the speed with which a ripple moves across the water or a pulse travels down a string.

The disturbance propagates through the medium, and a wave does transfer *energy,* but **the medium as a whole does not travel!** The ripples on the pond (the disturbance) move outward from the splash of the rock, but there is no outward flow of water. Likewise, the particles of a string oscillate up and down but do not move in the direction of a pulse traveling along the string. **A wave transfers energy, but it does not transfer any material or substance outward from the source.**

You may have been at a sporting event in which spectators do "The Wave." The wave moves around the stadium, but the spectators (the medium, in this case) stay right where they are. This is a clear example of the principle that a wave does not transfer any material.

Electromagnetic and Matter Waves

Mechanical waves require a medium, but there are waves that do not. Two important types of such waves are electromagnetic waves and matter waves.

Electromagnetic waves are waves of an *electromagnetic field.* Electromagnetic waves are very diverse, including visible light, radio waves, microwaves, and x rays. Electromagnetic waves require no material medium and can travel through a vacuum; light can travel through space, though sound cannot. At this point, we have not defined what an "electromagnetic field" is, so we won't worry about the precise nature of what is "waving" in electromagnetic waves. The wave model can describe many of the important aspects of these waves without a detailed description of their exact nature. We'll look more closely at electromagnetic waves in Chapter 25, once we have a full understanding of electric and magnetic fields.

One of the most significant discoveries of the 20th century was that material particles, such as electrons and atoms, have wave-like characteristics. We will learn how a full description of matter at an atomic scale requires an understanding of such **matter waves** in Chapter 28.

Transverse and Longitudinal Waves

Most waves fall into two general classes: *transverse* and *longitudinal*. For mechanical waves, these terms describe the relationship between the motion of the particles that carry the wave and the motion of the wave itself.

Two types of wave motion

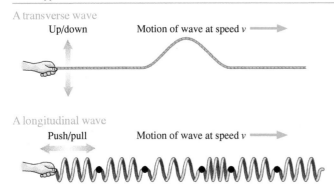

A transverse wave
Up/down   Motion of wave at speed v →

For mechanical waves, a **transverse wave** is a wave in which the particles in the medium move *perpendicular* to the direction in which the wave travels. Shaking the end of a stretched string up and down creates a wave that travels along the string in a horizontal direction while the particles that make up the string oscillate vertically.

A longitudinal wave
Push/pull   Motion of wave at speed v →

In a **longitudinal wave,** the particles in the medium move *parallel* to the direction in which the wave travels. Here we see a chain of masses connected by springs. If you give the first mass in the chain a sharp push, a disturbance travels down the chain by compressing and expanding the springs.

The rapid motion of the earth's crust during an earthquake can produce a disturbance that travels through the earth. The two most important types of earthquake waves are S waves (which are transverse) and P waves (which are longitudinal), as shown in FIGURE 15.2. The longitudinal P waves are faster, but the transverse S waves are more destructive. Residents of a city a few hundred kilometers from an earthquake will feel the resulting P waves as much as a minute before the S waves, giving them a crucial early warning.

FIGURE 15.2 **Different types of earthquake waves.**

The passage of a P wave expands and compresses the ground. The motion is parallel to the direction of travel of the wave.

Motion of wave →
P wave
Motion of ground

The passage of an S wave moves the ground up and down. The motion is perpendicular to the direction of travel of the wave.

Motion of wave →
S wave

Motion of ground

STOP TO THINK 15.1 Spectators at a sporting event do "The Wave," as shown in the photo on the preceding page. Is this a transverse or longitudinal wave?

15.2 Traveling Waves

When you drop a pebble in a pond, waves travel outward. But how does this happen? How does a mechanical wave travel through a medium? In answering this question, we must be careful to distinguish the motion of the wave from the motion of the particles that make up the medium. The wave itself is not a particle, so we cannot apply Newton's laws to the wave. However, we can use Newton's laws to examine how the medium responds to a disturbance.

Waves on a String

FIGURE 15.3 shows a transverse *wave pulse* traveling to the right along a stretched string. Imagine watching a little dot on the string as a wave pulse passes by. As the pulse approaches from the left, the string near the dot begins to curve. Once the string

Class Video

FIGURE 15.3 **The motion of a string as a wave passes.**

$\vec{T}$
$\vec{F}_{net}$
$\vec{T}$
Wave →

As the wave reaches this point, the curvature of the string leads to a net force that pulls the string upward.

$\vec{T}$
$\vec{T}$ $\vec{F}_{net}$
Wave →

After the peak has passed, the curvature of the string leads to a net force that pulls the string downward.

curves, the tension forces pulling on a small segment of string no longer cancel each other. As the wave passes, the curvature of the string leads to a net force that first pulls each little piece of the string up and then, after the pulse passes, back down. Each point on the string moves perpendicular to the motion of the wave, so **a wave on a string is a transverse wave.**

No new physical principles are required to understand how this wave moves. The motion of a pulse along a string is a direct consequence of the tension acting on the segments of the string. An external force may have been required to create the pulse, but **once started, the pulse continues to move because of the internal dynamics of the medium.**

Sound Waves

FIGURE 15.4 A sound wave produced by a loudspeaker.

Next, let's see how a sound wave in air is created using a loudspeaker. When the loudspeaker cone in FIGURE 15.4a moves forward, it compresses the air in front of it, as shown in FIGURE 15.4b. The *compression* is the disturbance that travels forward through the air. This is much like the sharp push on the end of the chain of springs on the preceding page, so **a sound wave is a longitudinal wave.** We usually think of sound waves as traveling in air, but sound can travel through any gas, through liquids, and even through solids. A wave similar to that in Figure 15.4b is produced if you hit the end of a metal rod with a hammer.

(a)

The loudspeaker cone moves in and out in response to electrical signals.

The motion of a wave on a string is determined by the internal dynamics of the string. Similarly, the motion of a sound wave in air is determined by the physics of gases that we explored in Chapter 12. Once created, the wave in Figure 15.4b will propagate forward; its motion is entirely determined by the properties of the air.

Wave Speed Is a Property of the Medium

(b)
The loudspeaker receives an electrical pulse and pushes out sharply. This creates a compression of the air.

Compression

v_{sound}

Speaker

Molecules

This compression is the disturbance. It travels at the wave speed v_{sound}.

The above discussions of waves on a string and sound waves in air show that the motion of these waves depends on the properties of the medium. A full analysis of these waves would lead to the important and somewhat surprising conclusion that **the wave speed does not depend on the shape or size of the pulse, how the pulse was generated, or how far it has traveled.**

What properties of a string determine the speed of waves traveling along the string? The only likely candidates are the string's mass, length, and tension. Because a pulse doesn't travel faster on a longer and thus more massive string, neither the total mass m nor the total length L is important. Instead, the speed depends on the mass-to-length *ratio*, which is called the **linear density** μ of the string:

$$\mu = \frac{m}{L} \tag{15.1}$$

Linear density characterizes the *type* of string we are using. A fat string has a larger value of μ than a skinny string made of the same material. Similarly, a steel wire has a larger value of μ than a plastic string of the same diameter.

How does the speed of a wave on a string vary with the tension and the linear density? Using what we know about forces and motion, we can make some predictions:

- A string with a greater tension responds more rapidly, so the wave will move at a higher speed. **Wave speed increases with increasing tension.**
- A string with a greater linear density has more inertia. It will respond less rapidly, so the wave will move at a lower speed. **Wave speed decreases with increasing linear density.**

Lateral line organ

◀ **Sensing water waves** BIO The African clawed frog has a hunting strategy similar to that of many spiders: It sits and waits for prey to come to it. Like a spider, the frog detects prey animals by the vibrations they cause—not in a web, but in the water. The frog has an array of sensors called the lateral line organ on each side of its body. This organ, highlighted in the photo at left, detects oscillations of the water due to passing waves. The frog can determine where the waves come from and what type of animal made them, and thus whether a strike is called for.

A full analysis of the motion of the string leads to an expression for the speed of a wave that shows both of these trends:

$$v_{\text{string}} = \sqrt{\frac{T_s}{\mu}} \qquad (15.2)$$

Wave speed on a stretched string with tension T_s and linear density μ

The subscript s on the symbol T_s for the string's tension will distinguish it from the symbol T for the *period* of oscillation.

Every point on a wave pulse travels with the speed given by Equation 15.2. You can increase the wave speed either by *increasing* the string's tension (make it tighter) or by *decreasing* the string's linear density (make it skinnier). We'll examine the implications for stringed musical instruments in Chapter 16.

ActivPhysics: 10.2

EXAMPLE 15.1   When does the spider sense its lunch?

All spiders are very sensitive to vibrations. An orb spider will sit at the center of its large, circular web and monitor radial threads for vibrations created when an insect lands. Assume that these threads are made of silk with a linear density of 1.0×10^{-5} kg/m under a tension of 0.40 N. If an insect lands in the web 30 cm from the spider, how long will it take for the spider to find out?

PREPARE When the insect hits the web, a wave pulse will be transmitted along the silk fibers. The speed of the wave depends on the properties of the silk.

SOLVE First, we determine the speed of the wave:

$$v = \sqrt{\frac{T_s}{\mu}} = \sqrt{\frac{0.40 \text{ N}}{1.0 \times 10^{-5} \text{ kg/m}}} = 200 \text{ m/s}$$

The time for the wave to travel a distance $d = 30$ cm to reach the spider is

$$\Delta t = \frac{d}{v} = \frac{0.30 \text{ m}}{200 \text{ m/s}} = 1.5 \text{ ms}$$

ASSESS Spider webs are made of very light strings under significant tension, so the wave speed is quite high and we expect a short travel time—important for the spider to quickly respond to prey caught in the web. Our answer makes sense.

What properties of a gas determine the speed of a sound wave traveling through the gas? It seems plausible that the speed of a sound pulse is related to the speed with which the molecules of the gas move—faster molecules should mean a faster sound wave. In Chapter 12, we found that the typical speed of an atom of mass m, the root-mean-square speed, is

$$v_{\text{rms}} = \sqrt{\frac{3k_B T}{m}}$$

where k_B is Boltzmann's constant and T the absolute temperature in kelvin. A thorough analysis finds that the sound speed is slightly less than this rms speed, but has the same dependence on the temperature and the molecular mass:

$$v_{\text{sound}} = \sqrt{\frac{\gamma k_B T}{m}} = \sqrt{\frac{\gamma R T}{M}} \qquad (15.3)$$

Sound speed in a gas at temperature T

In Equation 15.3 M is the molar mass (kg per mol) and γ is a constant that depends on the gas: $\gamma = 1.67$ for monatomic gases such as helium, $\gamma = 1.40$ for diatomic

ActivPhysics: 10.3

TABLE 15.1 The speed of sound

Medium	Speed (m/s)
Air (0°C)	331
Air (20°C)	343
Helium (0°C)	970
Ethyl alcohol	1170
Water	1480
Human tissue (ultrasound)	1540
Lead	1200
Aluminum	5100
Granite	6000
Diamond	12,000

gases such as nitrogen and oxygen, and $\gamma \approx 1.3$ for a triatomic gas such as carbon dioxide or water vapor.

Certain trends in Equation 15.3 are worth mentioning:

- The speed of sound in air (and other gases) increases with temperature. **For calculations in this chapter, you can use the speed of sound in air at 20°C, 343 m/s, unless otherwise specified.**
- At a given temperature, the speed of sound increases as the molecular mass of the gas decreases. Thus the speed of sound in room-temperature helium is faster than that in room-temperature air.
- The speed of sound doesn't depend on the pressure or the density of the gas.

Table 15.1 lists the speeds of sound in various materials. The bonds between atoms in liquids and solids result in higher sound speeds in these phases of matter. Generally, sound waves travel faster in liquids than in gases, and faster in solids than in liquids. The speed of sound in a solid depends on its density and stiffness. Light, stiff solids (such as diamond) transmit sound at very high speeds. The sound speed is much lower in dense, soft solids such as lead.

EXAMPLE 15.2   **The speed of sound on Mars**

On a typical Martian morning, the very thin atmosphere (which is almost entirely carbon dioxide) is a frosty $-100°C$. What is the speed of sound? At what approximate temperature would the speed be double this value?

PREPARE Equation 15.3 gives the speed of sound in terms of the molar mass and the absolute temperature. If we assume that the atmosphere is composed of pure CO_2, the molar mass is the sum of the molar masses of the constituents: 12 g/mol for C and 16 g/mol for each O, giving $M = 12 + 16 + 16 = 44$ g/mol $= 0.044$ kg/mol. The absolute temperature is $T = 173$ K. Carbon dioxide is a triatomic gas, so $\gamma = 1.3$.

SOLVE The speed of sound with the noted conditions is

$$v_{sound} = \sqrt{\frac{\gamma RT}{M}} = \sqrt{\frac{(1.3)(8.31 \text{ J/mol})(173 \text{ K})}{0.044 \text{ kg/mol}}} = 210 \text{ m/s}$$

Rather than do a separate calculation to determine the temperature required for the higher speed, we can make an argument using proportionality. The speed is proportional to the square root of the temperature, so doubling the speed requires an increase in the temperature by a factor of 4 to about 690 K, or about 420°C.

ASSESS The speed of sound doesn't depend on pressure, so even though the atmosphere is "thin" we needn't adjust our calculation. The speed of sound is lower for heavier molecules and colder temperatures, so we expect that the speed of sound on Mars, with its cold, carbon-dioxide atmosphere, will be lower than that on earth, just as we found.

Electromagnetic waves, such as light, travel at a much higher speed than do mechanical waves. As we'll discuss in Chapter 25, all electromagnetic waves travel at the same speed in a vacuum. We call this speed the **speed of light,** which we represent with the symbol c. The value of the speed of light in a vacuum is

$$v_{light} = c = 3.00 \times 10^8 \text{ m/s} \tag{15.4}$$

This is almost one million times the speed of sound in air! At this speed, light could circle the earth 7.5 times in one second.

> **NOTE** ▶ The speed of electromagnetic waves is lower when they travel through a material, but this value for the speed of light in a vacuum is also good for electromagnetic waves traveling through air. ◀

EXAMPLE 15.3   **How far away was the lightning?**

During a thunderstorm, you see a flash from a lightning strike. 8.0 seconds later, you hear the crack of the thunder. How far away did the lightning strike?

PREPARE Two different kinds of waves are involved, with very different wave speeds. The flash of the lightning generates light waves; these will travel from the point of the strike to your position essentially instantaneously. (It takes light about 5 μs to travel

1 mile—not something you will notice.) The strike also generates sound waves that you hear as thunder; these travel much more slowly. The delay between the flash and the thunder is the time it takes for the sound wave to travel.

SOLVE We will assume that the speed of sound has its room temperature (20°C) value of 343 m/s. During the time between seeing the flash and hearing the thunder, the sound travels a distance

$$d = v \, \Delta t = (343 \text{ m/s})(8.0 \text{ s}) = 2.7 \times 10^3 \text{ m} = 2.7 \text{ km}$$

ASSESS This seems reasonable. As you know from casual observations of lightning storms, an 8-second delay between the flash of the lightning and the crack of the thunder means a strike that is close but not too close. A few km seems reasonable.

Distance to a lightning strike Sound travels approximately 1 km in 3 s, or 1 mi in 5s. When you see a lightning flash, start counting seconds. When you hear the thunder, stop counting. Divide the result by 3, and you will have the approximate distance to the lightning strike in kilometers; divide by 5 and you will have the approximate distance in miles.

STOP TO THINK 15.2 Suppose you shake the end of a stretched string to produce a wave. Which of the following actions would increase the speed of the wave down the string? There may be more than one correct answer; if so, give all that are correct.

A. Move your hand up and down more quickly as you generate the wave.
B. Move your hand up and down a greater distance as you generate the wave.
C. Use a heavier string of the same length, under the same tension.
D. Use a lighter string of the same length, under the same tension.
E. Stretch the string tighter to increase the tension.
F. Loosen the string to decrease the tension.

15.3 Graphical and Mathematical Descriptions of Waves

Now that we know a bit about waves and how they travel, it's time to develop our understanding further by describing waves with graphs and equations.

Describing waves and their motion takes a bit more thought than describing particles and their motion. Until now, we have been concerned with quantities, such as position and velocity, that depend only on time. We can write these, as we did in Chapter 14, as $x(t)$ or $v(t)$, indicating that x and v are *functions* of the time variable t. Functions of the single variable t are all right for a particle, because a particle is in only one place at a time, but a wave is not localized. It is spread out through space at each instant of time. We need a function that tells us what a wave is doing at an instant of time (when) at a particular point in space (where). We need a function that depends on *both* position and time.

NOTE ▶ The analysis that follows is for a wave on a string, which is easy to visualize, but the results apply to any traveling wave. ◀

Snapshot and History Graphs

When we considered the motion of particles, we developed a graphical description before the mathematical description. We'll follow a similar approach for waves. Consider the wave pulse shown moving along a stretched string in FIGURE 15.5. (We will consider somewhat artificial triangular and square-shaped wave pulses in this section to clearly show the edges of the pulse.) The graph shows the string's displacement y at a particular instant of time t_1 as a function of position x along the string. This is a "snapshot" of the wave, much like what you might make with a camera whose shutter is opened briefly at t_1. A graph that shows the wave's displacement as a function of position at a single instant of time is called a **snapshot graph.** For a wave on a string, a snapshot graph is literally a picture of the wave at this instant.

As the wave moves, we can take more snapshots. FIGURE 15.6 shows a sequence of snapshot graphs as the wave of Figure 15.5 continues to move. These are like successive

FIGURE 15.5 A snapshot graph of a wave pulse on a string.

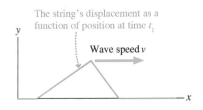

FIGURE 15.6 A sequence of snapshot graphs shows the wave in motion.

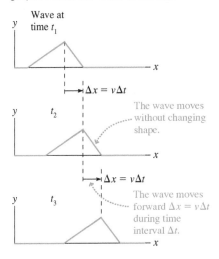

FIGURE 15.7 Constructing a history graph.

(a) Snapshot graphs

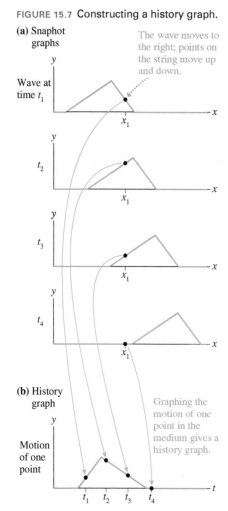

The wave moves to the right; points on the string move up and down.

Wave at time t_1

x_1

t_2

x_1

t_3

x_1

t_4

x_1

(b) History graph

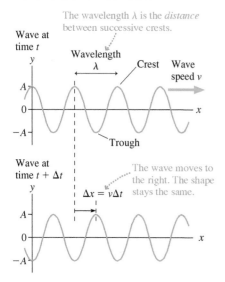

Motion of one point

Graphing the motion of one point in the medium gives a history graph.

t_1 t_2 t_3 t_4

FIGURE 15.8 Snapshot graphs show the motion of a sinusoidal wave.

The wavelength λ is the *distance* between successive crests.

Wave at time t

Wavelength λ

Crest   Wave speed v

A

0

$-A$

Trough

Wave at time $t + \Delta t$

$\Delta x = v \Delta t$

The wave moves to the right. The shape stays the same.

A

0

$-A$

frames from a video, reminiscent of the sequences of pictures we saw in Chapter 1. The wave pulse moves forward a distance $\Delta x = v\, \Delta t$ during each time interval Δt; that is, the wave moves with constant speed.

A snapshot graph shows the motion of the *wave,* but that's only half the story. Now we want to consider the motion of the *medium.* For the wave of Figure 15.5 we can construct a different type of graph, as shown in FIGURE 15.7. Figure 15.7a shows four snapshot graphs of the wave as it travels. In each of the graphs we've placed a dot at a particular point on the string carrying the wave. As the wave travels horizontally, the dot moves vertically; this is a transverse wave. We can use information from these graphs to construct the graph in Figure 15.7b, which shows the motion of this one point on the string. We call this a **history graph** because it shows the history—the time evolution—of this particular point in the medium.

Take a close look at the history graph. The snapshot graphs show the steeper edge of the wave on the right; the history graph has the steeper edge on the left. Careful thought tells why. The history graph isn't a picture of the wave—it's a record of the motion of one point in the medium. As the wave moves toward the dot, the steep leading edge of the wave causes the dot to rise quickly. On the displacement-versus-time history graph, *earlier* times (smaller values of t) are to the *left* and *later* times (larger t) to the *right*. The rapid rise when the wave hits the dot is at an early time, and so appears on the left side of the Figure 15.7b history graph.

Sinusoidal Waves

Waves can come in many different shapes, but for the mathematical description of wave motion we will focus on a particular shape, the **sinusoidal wave.** This is the type of wave produced by a source that oscillates with simple harmonic motion. For example, a loudspeaker cone that oscillates in SHM radiates a sinusoidal sound wave. The sinusoidal electromagnetic waves broadcast by television and FM radio stations are generated by electrons oscillating back and forth in the antenna wire with SHM.

The pair of snapshot graphs in FIGURE 15.8 show two successive views of a string carrying a sinusoidal wave, revealing the motion of the wave as it moves to the right. We define the **amplitude** A of the wave to be the maximum value of the displacement. The crests of the wave—the high points—have displacement $y_{crest} = A$, and the troughs—the low points—have displacement $y_{trough} = -A$. Because the wave is produced by a source undergoing SHM, which is periodic, the wave is periodic as well. As you move from left to right along the "frozen" wave in the top snapshot graph of Figure 15.8, the disturbance repeats itself over and over. The distance spanned by one cycle of the motion is called the **wavelength** of the wave. Wavelength is symbolized by λ (lowercase Greek lambda) and, because it is a length, it is measured in units of meters. The wavelength is shown in Figure 15.8 as the distance between two crests, but it could equally well be the distance between two troughs. As time passes, the wave moves to the right; comparing the two snapshot graphs in Figure 15.8 makes this motion apparent.

The snapshot graphs of Figure 15.8 show that the wave, at one instant in time, is a sinusoidal function of the distance x along the wave, with wavelength λ. At the time represented by the top graph of Figure 15.8, the displacement is given by

$$y(x) = A \cos\left(2\pi \frac{x}{\lambda}\right) \tag{15.5}$$

Next, let's look at the motion of a point in the medium as this wave passes. FIGURE 15.9 shows a history graph for a point in a string as the sinusoidal wave of Figure 15.8 passes by. This graph has exactly the same shape as the snapshot graphs of Figure 15.8—it's a sinusoidal function—but the meaning of the graph is different; it shows the motion of one point in the medium. This graph is identical to the graphs you worked with in Chapter 14 because **each point in the medium oscillates with simple harmonic motion as the wave passes.** The *period T* of the wave, shown on the graph, is the time interval to complete one cycle of the motion.

NOTE ▶ Wavelength is the spatial analog of period. The period T is the *time* in which the disturbance at a single point in space repeats itself. The wavelength λ is the *distance* in which the disturbance at one instant of time repeats itself. ◀

The period is related to the wave *frequency* by $T = 1/f$, exactly as in SHM. Because each point on the string oscillates up and down in SHM with period T, we can describe the motion of a point on the string with the familiar expression

$$y(t) = A \cos\left(2\pi \frac{t}{T}\right) \tag{15.6}$$

NOTE ▶ As in Chapter 14, the argument of the cosine function is in radians. Make sure that your calculator is in radian mode before starting a calculation with the trigonometric equations in this chapter. ◀

Equation 15.5 gives the displacement as a function of position at one instant in time, and Equation 15.6 gives the displacement as a function of time at one point in space. How can we combine these two to form a single expression that is a complete description of the wave? As we'll verify, a wave traveling to the right is described by the equation

$$y(x, t) = A \cos\left(2\pi\left(\frac{x}{\lambda} - \frac{t}{T}\right)\right) \tag{15.7}$$

Displacement of a traveling wave moving to the right with amplitude A, wavelength λ, and period T

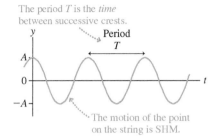
p.453

SINUSOIDAL

The notation $y(x, t)$ indicates that the displacement y is a function of the *two* variables x and t. We must specify both where (x) and when (t) before we can calculate the displacement of the wave.

We can understand why this expression describes a wave traveling to the right by looking at FIGURE 15.10. In the figure, we have graphed Equation 15.7 at five instants of time, each separated by one-quarter of the period T, to make five snapshot graphs. The crest marked with the arrow represents one point on the wave. As the time t increases, so does the position x of this point—the wave moves to the right. One full period has elapsed between the first graph and the last. During this time, the wave has moved by one wavelength. And, as the wave has passed, each point in the medium has undergone one complete oscillation.

For a wave traveling to the left, we have a slightly different form:

$$y(x, t) = A\cos\left(2\pi\left(\frac{x}{\lambda} + \frac{t}{T}\right)\right) \tag{15.8}$$

Displacement of a traveling wave moving to the left

NOTE ▶ A wave moving to the right (the $+x$-direction) has a $-$ in the expression, while a wave moving to the left (the $-x$-direction) has a $+$. Remember that the sign is *opposite* the direction of travel. ◀

FIGURE 15.9 A history graph shows the motion of a point on a string carrying a sinusoidal wave.

The period T is the *time* between successive crests.

The motion of the point on the string is SHM.

FIGURE 15.10 Equation 15.7 graphed at intervals of one-quarter of the period. This is a traveling wave moving to the right.

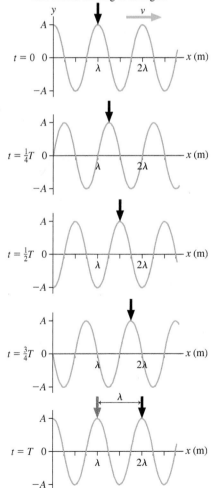

During a time interval of exactly one period, the crest has moved forward exactly one wavelength.

EXAMPLE 15.4 Determining the rise and fall of a boat

A boat is moving to the right at 5.0 m/s with respect to the water. An ocean wave is moving to the left, opposite the motion of the boat. The waves have 2.0 m between the top of the crests and the bottom of the troughs. The period of the waves is 8.3 s, and their wavelength is 110 m. At one instant, the boat sits on a crest of the wave. 20 s later, what is the vertical displacement of the boat?

PREPARE We begin with the visual overview, as in FIGURE 15.11. Let $t = 0$ be the instant the boat is on the crest, and draw a snapshot graph of the traveling wave at that time. Because the wave is traveling to the left, we will use Equation 15.8 to represent the wave. The boat begins at a crest of the wave, so we see that the boat can start the problem at $x = 0$.

FIGURE 15.11 Visual overview for the boat.

Known
$A = 1.0$ m, $\lambda = 110$ m, $T = 8.3$ s
$t_i = 0$ s, $t_f = 20$ s, $v_{boat} = 5.0$ m/s
$x_i = 0$ m, $y_i = A = 1.0$ m

Find
y_f

The distance between the high and low points of the wave is 2.0 m; the amplitude is half this, so $A = 1.0$ m. The wavelength and period are given in the problem.

SOLVE The boat is moving to the right at 5.0 m/s. At $t_f = 20$ s the boat is at position

$$x_f = (5.0 \text{ m/s})(20 \text{ s}) = 100 \text{ m}$$

We need to find the wave's displacement at this position and time. Substituting known values for amplitude, wavelength, and period into Equation 15.8, for a wave traveling to the left, we obtain the following equation for the wave:

$$y(x, t) = (1.0 \text{ m}) \cos\left(2\pi\left(\frac{x}{110 \text{ m}} + \frac{t}{8.3 \text{ s}}\right)\right)$$

At $t_f = 20$ s and $x_f = 100$ m, the boat's displacement on the wave is

$$y_f = y(\text{at } 100 \text{ m}, 20 \text{ s}) = (1.0 \text{ m}) \cos\left(2\pi\left(\frac{100 \text{ m}}{110 \text{ m}} + \frac{20 \text{ s}}{8.3 \text{ s}}\right)\right)$$

$$= -0.42 \text{ m}$$

ASSESS The final displacement is negative—meaning the boat is in a trough of a wave, not underwater. Don't forget that your calculator must be in radian mode when you make your final computation!

The Fundamental Relationship for Sinusoidal Waves

ActivPhysics: 10.1 (MP)

In Figure 15.10, one critical observation is that the wave crest marked by the arrow has moved one full wavelength between the first graph and the last. That is, **during a time interval of exactly one period T, each crest of a sinusoidal wave travels forward a distance of exactly one wavelength λ.** Because speed is distance divided by time, the wave speed must be

$$v = \frac{\text{distance}}{\text{time}} = \frac{\lambda}{T} \quad (15.9)$$

Using $f = 1/T$, it is customary to write Equation 15.9 in the form

$$v = \lambda f \quad (15.10)$$

Relationship between velocity, wavelength, and frequency for sinusoidal waves

Although Equation 15.10 has no special name, it is *the* fundamental relationship for sinusoidal waves. When using it, keep in mind the *physical* meaning that a wave moves forward a distance of one wavelength during a time interval of one period.

We will frequently see problems in which we are given two of the variables in Equation 15.10 but we need to find the third, as in the following example.

EXAMPLE 15.5 Writing the equation for a wave

A sinusoidal wave with an amplitude of 1.5 cm and a frequency of 100 Hz travels at 200 m/s in the positive *x*-direction. Write the equation for the wave's displacement as it travels.

PREPARE The problem statement gives the following characteristics of the wave: $A = 1.5$ cm $= 0.015$ m, $v = 200$ m/s, and $f = 100$ Hz.

SOLVE To write the equation for the wave, we need the amplitude, the wavelength, and the period. The amplitude was given in the problem statement. We can use the fundamental relationship for sinusoidal waves to find the wavelength:

$$\lambda = \frac{v}{f} = \frac{200 \text{ m/s}}{100 \text{ Hz}} = 2.0 \text{ m}$$

The period can be calculated from the frequency:

$$T = \frac{1}{f} = \frac{1}{100 \text{ Hz}} = 0.010 \text{ s}$$

With these values in hand, we can write the equation for the wave's displacement using Equation 15.7:

$$y(x, t) = (0.015 \text{ m}) \cos\left(2\pi\left(\frac{x}{2.0 \text{ m}} - \frac{t}{0.010 \text{ s}} \right) \right)$$

ASSESS If the speed of a wave is known, you can use the fundamental relationship for sinusoidal waves to find the wavelength if you are given the frequency, or the frequency if you are given the wavelength. You'll often need to do this in the early stages of problems that you solve.

STOP TO THINK 15.3 Three waves travel to the right with the same speed. Which wave has the highest frequency?

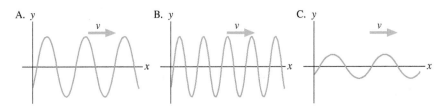

15.4 Sound and Light Waves

PhET: Sound
PhET: Radio Waves and
Electromagnetic Fields

Think about how you are experiencing the world right now. Chances are, your senses of sight and sound are hard at work, detecting and interpreting light and sound waves from the world around you. Because these waves are so important to us, we'll spend some time exploring their properties.

Sound Waves

We saw in Figure 15.4 how a loudspeaker creates a sound wave. If the loudspeaker cone moves with simple harmonic motion, it will create a sinusoidal sound wave, as illustrated in FIGURE 15.12. Each time the cone moves forward, it moves the air molecules closer together, creating a region of higher pressure. A half cycle later, as the cone moves backward, the air has room to expand and the pressure decreases. These regions of higher and lower pressure are called **compressions** and **rarefactions**, respectively.

As Figure 15.12 suggests, it is often most convenient and informative to think of a sound wave as a pressure wave. As the graph of the pressure shows, the pressure oscillates sinusoidally around the atmospheric pressure p_{atmos}. This is a snapshot graph of the wave at one instant of time, and the distance between two adjacent crests (two points of maximum compression) is the wavelength λ.

When the wave reaches your ear, the oscillating pressure causes your eardrums to vibrate. This vibration is transferred through your inner ear to the cochlea, where it is sensed, as we learned in Chapter 14. Humans with normal hearing are able to detect sinusoidal sound waves with frequencies between about 20 Hz and 20,000 Hz, or 20 kHz. Low frequencies are perceived as a "low pitch" bass note, while high frequencies are heard as a "high pitch" treble note.

FIGURE 15.12 A sound wave is a pressure wave.

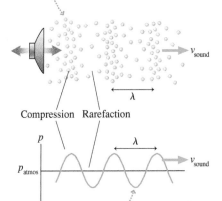

The loudspeaker cone moves back and forth, creating regions of higher and lower pressure—compressions and rarefactions.

The sound wave is a pressure wave. Compressions are crests; rarefactions are troughs.

Range of wavelengths of sound

What are the wavelengths of sound waves at the limits of human hearing and at the midrange frequency of 500 Hz? Notes sung by human voices are near 500 Hz, as are notes played by striking keys near the center of a piano keyboard.

PREPARE We will do our calculation at room temperature, 20°C, so we will use $v = 343$ m/s for the speed of sound.

SOLVE We can solve for the wavelengths given the fundamental relationship $v = f\lambda$:

$f = 20$ Hz: $\qquad \lambda = \dfrac{v}{f} = \dfrac{343 \text{ m/s}}{20 \text{ Hz}} = 17$ m

$f = 500$ Hz: $\qquad \lambda = \dfrac{v}{f} = \dfrac{343 \text{ m/s}}{500 \text{ Hz}} = 0.69$ m

$f = 20$ kHz: $\qquad \lambda = \dfrac{v}{f} = \dfrac{343 \text{ m/s}}{20 \times 10^3 \text{ Hz}} = 0.017 \text{ m} = 1.7$ cm

ASSESS The wavelength of a 20 kHz note is a small 1.7 cm. At the other extreme, a 20 Hz note has a huge wavelength of 17 m! A wave moves forward one wavelength during a time interval of one period, and a wave traveling at 343 m/s can move 17 m during the $\frac{1}{20}$ s period of a 20 Hz note.

TABLE 15.2 Range of hearing for animals

Animal	Range of hearing (Hz)
Elephant	<5–12,000
Owl	200–12,000
Human	20–20,000
Dog	30–45,000
Mouse	1000–90,000
Bat	2000–100,000
Porpoise	75–150,000

Short wavelengths mean sharper images
Light doesn't travel very far in any but the clearest water. To navigate through and investigate their surroundings, vessels at sea can create images using sound instead of light, sending out sound waves and detecting and analyzing the reflections. This image of a shipwreck on the ocean bottom was made from the surface with 600 kHz ultrasound. This high frequency gave a very short wavelength of just under a quarter of a centimeter, making for very sharp outlines and fine details in the image.

It is well known that dogs are sensitive to high frequencies that humans cannot hear. Other animals also have quite different ranges of hearing than humans; some examples are listed in Table 15.2.

Elephants communicate over great distances with vocalizations at frequencies far too low for us to hear. These low-frequency sounds are transmitted with less energy loss than high-frequency sounds, allowing elephants to hear each other from over 6 km away—important for these social animals that may forage over very large areas.

There are animals that use frequencies well above the range of our hearing as well. High-frequency sounds are useful for *echolocation*—emitting a pulse of sound and listening for its reflection. Bats, which generally feed at night, rely much more on their hearing than their sight. They find and catch insects by echolocation, emitting loud chirps whose reflections are detected by their large, sensitive ears. The frequencies that they use are well above the range of our hearing; we call such sound **ultrasound.** Why do bats and other animals use high frequencies for this purpose?

In Chapter 19, we will look at the *resolution* of optical instruments. The finest detail that your eye—or any optical instrument—can detect is limited by the wavelength of light. Shorter wavelengths allow for the imaging of smaller details.

The same limitations apply to the acoustic image of the world made by bats. In order to sense fine details of their surroundings, bats must use sound of very short wavelength (and thus high frequency). A 50 kHz chirp from a little brown bat has a wavelength of just over half a centimeter, allowing the bat to precisely locate an insect that reflects it. Other animals that use echolocation, such as porpoises, also produce and sense high-frequency sounds.

Sound travels very well though tissues in the body, and the reflections of sound waves from different tissues can be used to create an image of the body's interior. The fine details necessary for a clinical diagnosis require the short wavelengths of ultrasound. X rays create very good images of bones; ultrasound is used for creating images of soft tissues. It is also useful in cases where the radiation exposure of x rays should be avoided. You have certainly seen ultrasound images taken during pregnancy, where the use of x rays is clearly undesirable.

Ultrasonic frequencies in medicine

To make a sufficiently detailed ultrasound image of a fetus in its mother's uterus, a physician has decided that a wavelength of 0.50 mm is needed. What frequency is required?

Computer processing of an ultrasound image shows fine detail.

PREPARE The speed of ultrasound in the body is given in Table 15.1 as 1540 m/s.

SOLVE We can use the fundamental relationship among speed, wavelength, and frequency to calculate

$$f = \frac{v}{\lambda} = \frac{1540 \text{ m/s}}{0.50 \times 10^{-3} \text{ m}} = 3.1 \times 10^6 \text{ Hz} = 3.1 \text{ MHz}$$

ASSESS This is a reasonable result. Clinical ultrasound uses frequencies in the range of 1–20 MHz. Lower frequencies have greater penetration; higher frequencies (and thus shorter wavelengths) show finer detail.

Light and Other Electromagnetic Waves

A light wave is an electromagnetic wave, an oscillation of the electromagnetic field. Other electromagnetic waves, such as radio waves, microwaves, and ultraviolet light, have the same physical characteristics as light waves even though we cannot sense them with our eyes. As we saw earlier, all electromagnetic waves, regardless of wavelength or frequency, travel through vacuum (or air) with the same speed: $c = 3.00 \times 10^8$ m/s.

The wavelengths of light are extremely short. Visible light is an electromagnetic wave with a wavelength (in air) of roughly 400 nm $(=400 \times 10^{-9} \text{ m})$ to 700 nm $(=700 \times 10^{-9} \text{ m})$. Each wavelength is perceived as a different color. Longer wavelengths, in the 600–700 nm range, are seen as orange or red light; shorter wavelengths, in the 400–500 nm range, are seen as blue or violet light.

FIGURE 15.13 shows that the visible spectrum is a small slice out of the much broader **electromagnetic spectrum.** We will have much more to say about light and the rest of the electromagnetic spectrum in future chapters.

FIGURE 15.13 The electromagnetic spectrum from 10^6 Hz to 10^{18} Hz.

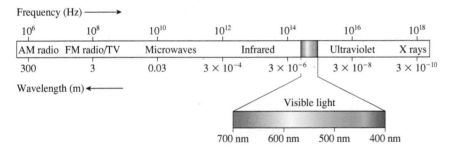

EXAMPLE 15.8   Finding the frequency of microwaves

The wavelength of microwaves in a microwave oven is 12 cm. What is the frequency of the waves?

PREPARE Microwaves are electromagnetic waves, so their speed is the speed of light, $c = 3.00 \times 10^8$ m/s.

SOLVE Using the fundamental relationship for sinusoidal waves, we find

$$f = \frac{v}{\lambda} = \frac{3.00 \times 10^8 \text{ m/s}}{0.12 \text{ m}} = 2.5 \times 10^9 \text{ Hz} = 2.5 \text{ GHz}$$

ASSESS This is a high frequency, but the speed of the waves is also very high, so our result seems reasonable.

We've just used the same equation to describe ultrasound and microwaves, which brings up a remarkable point: The wave model we've been developing applies equally well to all types of waves. Features such as wavelength, frequency, and speed are characteristics of waves in general. At this point we don't yet know any details about electromagnetic fields, yet we can use the wave model to say some significant things about the properties of electromagnetic waves.

It's also interesting to note that the 2.5 GHz frequency of microwaves in an oven we found in Example 15.8 is similar to the frequencies of other devices you use each day. Many cordless phones work at a frequency of 2.4 GHz, and cell phones at just under 2.0 GHz. Although these frequencies are not very different from those of the waves that heat your food in a microwave oven, the *intensity* is much less—which brings us to the topic of the next section.

15.5 Energy and Intensity

A traveling wave transfers energy from one point to another. The sound wave from a loudspeaker sets your eardrum into motion. Light waves from the sun warm the earth and, if focused with a lens, can start a fire. The *power* of a wave is the rate, in joules per second, at which the wave transfers energy. As you learned in Chapter 10, power is measured in watts. A person singing or shouting as loud as possible is emitting energy in the form of sound waves at a rate of about 1 W, or 1 J/s. A 25 W lightbulb emits about 1 W of visible light, with the other 24 W of power being emitted as heat, or infrared radiation, rather than as visible light. In this section, we will learn how to characterize the power of waves. A first step in doing so is to understand how waves change as they spread out.

Circular, Spherical, and Plane Waves

Suppose you were to take a photograph of ripples spreading on a pond. If you mark the location of the *crests* on the photo, your picture would look like FIGURE 15.14a. The lines that locate the crests are called **wave fronts,** and they are spaced precisely one wavelength apart. A wave like this is called a **circular wave.** It is a two-dimensional wave that spreads across a surface.

Although the wave fronts are circles, you would hardly notice the curvature if you observed a small section of the wave front very far away from the source. The wave fronts would appear to be parallel lines, still spaced one wavelength apart and traveling at speed v as in FIGURE 15.14b.

Many waves of interest, such as sound waves or light waves, move in three dimensions. For example, loudspeakers and lightbulbs emit **spherical waves.** The crests of the wave form a series of concentric, spherical shells separated by the wavelength λ. In essence, the waves are three-dimensional ripples. It will still be useful to draw wave-front diagrams such as Figure 15.14a, but now the circles are slices through the spherical shells locating the wave crests.

If you observe a spherical wave very far from its source, the small piece of the wave front that you can see is a little patch on the surface of a very large sphere. If the radius of the sphere is sufficiently large, you will not notice the curvature and this little patch of the wave front appears to be a plane. FIGURE 15.15 illustrates the idea of a **plane wave.**

The better to hear you with BIO The great grey owl has its ears on the front of its face, hidden behind its facial feathers. Its round face works like a radar dish, collecting the energy of sound waves and "funneling" it into the ears. Collecting sound over a large area in this manner allows owls to sense very quiet sounds. Having ears on the front of the face allows them to precisely determine the source of sounds as well, an asset for a bird of prey. These owls can hear—and locate—mice moving underneath a thick blanket of snow.

FIGURE 15.14 The wave fronts of a circular or spherical wave.

(a)

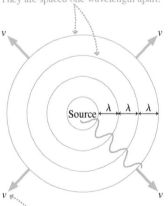

Wave fronts are the crests of the wave. They are spaced one wavelength apart.

Source

The circular wave fronts move outward from the source at speed v.

(b)

Very far away from the source, small sections of the wave fronts appear to be straight lines.

FIGURE 15.15 A plane wave.

Very far from the source, small segments of spherical wave fronts appear to be planes. The wave is cresting at every point in these planes.

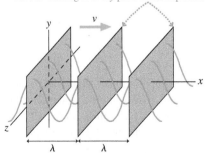

Power, Energy, and Intensity

Imagine doing two experiments with a lightbulb that emits 2 W of visible light. In the first, you hang the bulb in the center of a room and allow the light to illuminate the walls. In the second experiment, you use mirrors and lenses to "capture" the bulb's light and focus it onto a small spot on one wall. (This is what a projector does.) The energy emitted by the bulb is the same in both cases, but, as you know, the light is much brighter when focused onto a small area. We would say that the focused light is more *intense* than the diffuse light that goes in all directions. Similarly, a loudspeaker that beams its sound forward into a small area produces a louder sound in that area than a speaker of equal power that radiates the sound in all directions. Quantities such as brightness and loudness depend not only on the rate of energy transfer, or power, but also on the *area* that receives that power.

FIGURE 15.16 shows a wave impinging on a surface of area a. The surface is perpendicular to the direction in which the wave is traveling. This might be a real physical surface, such as your eardrum or a solar cell, but it could equally well be a mathematical surface in space that the wave passes right through. If the wave has power P, we define the **intensity** I of the wave as

$$I = \frac{P}{a} \qquad (15.11)$$

The SI units of intensity are W/m². Because intensity is a power-to-area ratio, a wave focused onto a small area has a higher intensity than a wave of equal power that is spread out over a large area.

NOTE ▶ In this chapter we will use a for area to avoid confusion with amplitude, for which we use the symbol A. ◀

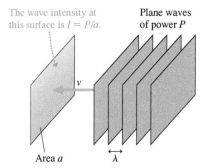

FIGURE 15.16 Plane waves of power P impinge on area a.

The wave intensity at this surface is $I = P/a$.

Plane waves of power P

v

Area a

λ

EXAMPLE 15.9 | **The intensity of a laser beam**

A bright, tightly focused laser pointer emits 1.0 mW of light power into a beam that is 1.0 mm in diameter. What is the intensity of the laser beam?

SOLVE The light waves of the laser beam pass through a circle of diameter 1.0 mm. The intensity of the laser beam is

$$I = \frac{P}{a} = \frac{P}{\pi r^2} = \frac{0.0010 \text{ W}}{\pi (0.00050 \text{ m})^2} = 1300 \text{ W/m}^2$$

ASSESS This intensity is roughly equal to the intensity of sunlight at noon on a summer day. Such a high intensity for a low-power source may seem surprising, but the area is very small, so the energy is packed into a tiny spot. You know that the light from a laser pointer won't burn you but you don't want the beam to shine into your eye, so an intensity similar to that of sunlight seems reasonable.

Sound from a loudspeaker and light from a lightbulb become less intense as you get farther from the source. This is because spherical waves spread out to fill larger and larger volumes of space. To conserve energy, the wave's amplitude must decrease with increasing distance r.

If a source of spherical waves radiates uniformly in all directions, then, as FIGURE 15.17 shows, the power at distance r is spread uniformly over the surface of a sphere of radius r. The surface area of a sphere is $a = 4\pi r^2$, so the intensity of a uniform spherical wave is

$$I = \frac{P_{\text{source}}}{4\pi r^2} \qquad (15.12)$$

Intensity at distance r of a spherical wave from a source of power P_{source}

I

p. 186

r

INVERSE-SQUARE

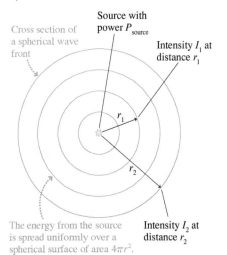

FIGURE 15.17 A source emitting uniform spherical waves.

Cross section of a spherical wave front

Source with power P_{source}

Intensity I_1 at distance r_1

r_1

r_2

The energy from the source is spread uniformly over a spherical surface of area $4\pi r^2$.

Intensity I_2 at distance r_2

The inverse-square dependence of r is really just a statement of energy conservation. The source emits energy at the rate of P joules per second. The energy is spread over a larger and larger area as the wave moves outward. Consequently, the *energy per area* must decrease in proportion to the surface area of a sphere.

If the intensity at distance r_1 is $I_1 = P_{source}/4\pi r_1^2$ and the intensity at r_2 is $I_2 = P_{source}/4\pi r_2^2$, then you can see that the intensity *ratio* is

$$\frac{I_1}{I_2} = \frac{r_2^2}{r_1^2} \tag{15.13}$$

You can use Equation 15.13 to compare the intensities at two distances from a source without needing to know the power of the source.

NOTE ▶ Wave intensities are strongly affected by reflections and absorption. Equations 15.12 and 15.13 apply to situations such as the light from a star and the sound from a firework exploding high in the air. Indoor sound does *not* obey a simple inverse-square law because of the many reflecting surfaces. ◀

EXAMPLE 15.10   **Intensity of sunlight on Mars**

The intensity of sunlight on earth is roughly 1300 W/m² at noon on a summer day. Mars orbits at a distance from the sun approximately 1.5 times that of earth. Assuming similar absorption of energy by the Martian atmosphere, what would you predict for the intensity of sunlight at noon during the Martian summer?

PREPARE We aren't given the power emitted by the sun or the distances from the sun to earth and to Mars, but we can solve this problem by using the ratios of distances and intensities.

SOLVE According to Equation 15.13,

$$I_{Mars} = I_{earth}\frac{r_{earth}^2}{r_{Mars}^2} = (1300 \text{ W/m}^2)\left(\frac{1}{1.5}\right)^2 = 580 \text{ W/m}^2$$

ASSESS The intensity of sunlight is quite a bit less on Mars than on earth, as we would expect, given the much greater distance of Mars from the sun.

STOP TO THINK 15.4 A plane wave, a circular wave, and a spherical wave all have the same intensity. Each of the waves travels the same distance. Afterward, which wave has the highest intensity?

A. The plane wave   B. The circular wave   C. The spherical wave

---

15.6 Loudness of Sound

Ten guitars playing in unison sound only about twice as loud as one guitar. 100 trumpets playing together seem to you only four times as loud as a soloist. Generally, **increasing the sound intensity by a factor of 10 results in an increase in perceived loudness by a factor of approximately 2.** Thus your ears are sensitive over a very wide range of intensities. The difference in intensity between the quietest sound you can detect and the loudest you can safely hear is a factor of 1,000,000,000,000! A normal conversation has 10,000 times the sound intensity of a whisper, but it sounds only about 16 times as loud.

The loudness of sound is measured by a quantity called the **sound intensity level.** Because of the wide range of intensities we can hear, and the fact that the difference in perceived loudness is much less than the actual difference in intensity, the sound intensity level is measured on a *logarithmic scale*. In this section we will explain what this means. The units of sound intensity level (i.e., of loudness) are *decibels,* a word you have likely heard.

◀ **The loudest animal in the world** BIO The blue whale is the largest animal in the world, up to 30 m (about 100 ft) long, weighing 150,000 kg or more. It is also the loudest. At close range in the water, the 10–30 second calls of the blue whale would be intense enough to damage tissues in your body. Blue whales produce sound with a larynx, much as humans do, but at much lower frequencies of 10–40 Hz that can travel great distances in water. Their loud, low-frequency calls can be heard by other whales hundreds of miles away.

The Decibel Scale

There is a lower limit to the intensity of sound that a human can hear. The exact value varies among individuals and varies with frequency, but an average value for the lowest-intensity sound that can be heard in an extremely quiet room is

$$I_0 = 1.0 \times 10^{-12} \, \text{W/m}^2$$

This intensity is called the *threshold of hearing*. A sound wave can have lower intensity than this, but you won't be able to perceive it.

It's convenient and logical to place the zero of our loudness scale at the threshold of hearing. All other sounds can then be referenced to this intensity. To create a loudness scale, we define the *sound intensity level,* expressed in **decibels** (dB), as

$$\beta = (10 \, \text{dB}) \log_{10}\left(\frac{I}{I_0}\right) \qquad (15.14)$$

Sound intensity level in decibels for a sound of intensity *I*

Quiet as a mouse 0 dB is the lower limit of human hearing, but other animals can hear quieter sounds. The harvest mouse has an especially well-developed sense of hearing and will detect and respond to sounds down to −10 dB, making it hard for predators to sneak up on it.

β is the lowercase Greek letter beta. The decibel is named after Alexander Graham Bell, inventor of the telephone. Sound intensity level is actually dimensionless, since it's formed from the ratio of two intensities, so decibels are actually just a *name* to remind us that we're dealing with an intensity *level* rather than a true intensity.

Equation 15.14 takes the base-10 logarithm of the intensity ratio I/I_0. As a reminder, logarithms work like this:

If you express a number as a power of 10 . . . . . . the logarithm is the exponent.

$$\log_{10}(1000) = \log_{10}(10^3) = 3$$

Right at the threshold of hearing, where $I = I_0$, the sound intensity level is

$$\beta = (10 \, \text{dB}) \log_{10}\left(\frac{I_0}{I_0}\right) = (10 \, \text{dB}) \log_{10}(1) = (10 \, \text{dB}) \log_{10}(10^0) = 0 \, \text{dB}$$

The threshold of hearing corresponds to 0 dB, as we wanted.

Table 15.3 lists the intensities and sound intensity levels for a number of typical sounds. Notice that the sound intensity level increases by 10 dB each time the actual intensity increases by a factor of 10. For example, the sound intensity level increases from 70 dB to 80 dB when the sound intensity increases from $10^{-5} \, \text{W/m}^2$ to $10^{-4} \, \text{W/m}^2$. A 20 dB increase in the sound intensity level means a factor of 100 increase in intensity; 30 dB a factor of 1000. We found earlier that sound is perceived as "twice as loud" when the intensity increases by a factor of 10. In terms of decibels, we can say that the apparent loudness of a sound doubles with each 10 dB increase in the sound intensity level.

The range of sounds in Table 15.3 is very wide; the top of the scale, 130 dB, represents 10 trillion times the intensity of the quietest sound you can hear. Vibrations of this intensity will injure the delicate sensory apparatus of the ear and cause pain. Exposure to less intense sounds also is not without risk. A fairly short exposure to 120 dB can cause damage to the hair cells in the ear, but lengthy exposure to sound intensity levels of over 85 dB can produce damage as well.

TABLE 15.3 Intensity and sound intensity levels of common environmental sounds

Sound	β (dB)	I (W/m²)
Threshold of hearing	0	1.0×10^{-12}
Person breathing, at 3 m	10	1.0×10^{-11}
A whisper, at 1 m	20	1.0×10^{-10}
Classroom during test, no talking	30	1.0×10^{-9}
Residential street, no traffic	40	1.0×10^{-8}
Quiet restaurant	50	1.0×10^{-7}
Normal conversation, at 1 m	60	1.0×10^{-6}
Busy traffic	70	1.0×10^{-5}
Vacuum cleaner, for user	80	1.0×10^{-4}
Niagara Falls, at viewpoint	90	1.0×10^{-3}
Pneumatic hammer, at 2 m	100	0.010
Home stereo at max volume	110	0.10
Rock concert	120	1.0
Threshold of pain	130	10

◀ **Hearing hairs** BIO This electron microscope picture shows the hair cells in the cochlea of the ear that are responsible for sensing sound. Each cell has a curved row of tiny hairs, which give your ears their remarkable sensitivity. Even very tiny vibrations transmitted into the fluid of the cochlea deflect the hairs, triggering a response in the cells. Motion of the basilar membrane by as little as 0.5 nm, about 5 atomic diameters, can produce an electrical response in the hair cells. With this remarkable sensitivity, it is no wonder that loud sounds can damage these structures.

EXAMPLE 15.11 **Finding the loudness of a shout**

A person shouting at the top of his lungs emits about 1.0 W of energy as sound waves. What is the sound intensity level 1.0 m from such a person?

PREPARE We will assume that the shouting person emits a spherical sound wave, in which case the intensity decreases according to Equation 15.12.

SOLVE At a distance of 1.0 m, the sound intensity is

$$I = \frac{P}{4\pi r^2} = \frac{1.0 \text{ W}}{4\pi(1.0 \text{ m})^2} = 0.080 \text{ W/m}^2$$

Thus the sound intensity level is

$$\beta = (10 \text{ dB})\log_{10}\left(\frac{0.080 \text{ W/m}^2}{1.0 \times 10^{-12} \text{ W/m}^2}\right) = 110 \text{ dB}$$

ASSESS This is quite loud (compare with values in Table 15.3), as you might expect.

NOTE ▶ In calculating the sound intensity level, be sure to use the $\log_{10}$ button on your calculator, not the natural logarithm button. On many calculators, $\log_{10}$ is labeled LOG and the natural logarithm is labeled LN. ◀

Equation 15.14 allows us to compute the sound intensity level β from the intensity I. We can do the reverse, finding an intensity from the sound intensity level, by taking the inverse of the $\log_{10}$ function. Recall, from the definition of the base-10 logarithm, that $10^{\log(x)} = x$. Applying this to Equation 15.14, we find

$$I = (1.0 \times 10^{-12} \text{ W/m}^2)10^{(\beta/10 \text{ dB})} \qquad (15.15)$$

EXAMPLE 15.12 **How far away can you hear a conversation?**

The sound intensity level 1.0 m from a person talking in a normal conversational voice is 60 dB. Suppose you are outside, 100 m from the person speaking. If it is a very quiet day with minimal background noise, will you be able to hear him or her?

PREPARE We know how sound intensity changes with distance, but not sound intensity level, so we need to break this problem into three steps. First, we will convert the sound intensity level at 1.0 m into intensity, using Equation 15.15. Second, we will compute the intensity at a distance of 100 m, using Equation 15.13. Finally, we will convert this result back to a sound intensity level, using Equation 15.14, so that we can judge the loudness.

SOLVE The sound intensity level of a normal conversation at 1.0 m is 60 dB. The intensity is

$$I(1 \text{ m}) = (1.0 \times 10^{-12} \text{ W/m}^2)10^{(60 \text{ dB/10 dB})}$$

$$= 1.0 \times 10^{-6} \text{ W/m}^2$$

The intensity at 100 m can be found using Equation 15.13:

$$\frac{I(100 \text{ m})}{I(1 \text{ m})} = \frac{(1 \text{ m})^2}{(100 \text{ m})^2}$$

$$I(100 \text{ m}) = I(1 \text{ m})(1.0 \times 10^{-4}) = 1.0 \times 10^{-10} \text{ W/m}^2$$

This intensity corresponds to a sound intensity level

$$\beta = (10 \text{ dB})\log_{10}\left(\frac{1.0 \times 10^{-10} \text{ W/m}^2}{1.0 \times 10^{-12} \text{ W/m}^2}\right) = 20 \text{ dB}$$

This is above the threshold for hearing—about the level of a whisper—so it could be heard on a very quiet day.

ASSESS The sound is well within what the ear can detect. However, normal background noise is rarely less than 40 dB, which would make the conversation difficult to decipher. Our result thus seems reasonable based on experience. The sound is at a level that can theoretically be detected, but it will be much quieter than the ambient level of sound, so it's not likely to be noticed.

15.7 The Doppler Effect and Shock Waves

In this final section, we will look at sounds from moving objects and for moving observers. You've likely noticed that the pitch of an ambulance's siren drops as it goes past you. A higher pitch suddenly becomes a lower pitch. This change in frequency, which is due to the motion of the ambulance, is called the *Doppler effect*. A more dramatic effect happens when an object moves faster than the speed of sound. The crack of a whip is a *shock wave* produced when the tip moves at a *supersonic* speed. These examples—and much of this section—concern sound waves, but the phenomena we will explore apply generally to all waves.

Sound Waves from a Moving Source

FIGURE 15.18a shows a source of sound waves moving away from Pablo and toward Nancy at a steady speed v_s. The subscript s indicates that this is the speed of the source, not the speed of the waves. The source is emitting sound waves of frequency f_0 as it travels. Part a of the figure is a motion diagram showing the positions of the source at times $t = 0$, T, $2T$, and $3T$, where $T = 1/f_0$ is the period of the waves.

After a wave crest leaves the source, its motion is governed by the properties of the medium. The motion of the source cannot affect a wave that has already been emitted. Thus each circular wave front in FIGURE 15.18b is centered on the point from which it was emitted. You can see that the wave crests are bunched up in the direction in which the source is moving and are stretched out behind it. The distance between one crest and the next is one wavelength, so the wavelength λ_+ that Nancy measures is *less* than the wavelength $\lambda_0 = v/f_0$ that would be emitted if the source were at rest. Similarly, λ_- behind the source is larger than λ_0.

These crests move through the medium at the wave speed v. Consequently, the frequency $f_+ = v/\lambda_+$ detected by the observer whom the source is approaching is *higher* than the frequency f_0 emitted by the source. Similarly, $f_- = v/\lambda_-$ detected behind the source is *lower* than frequency f_0. This change of frequency when a source moves

Catching a wave on the sun SOHO (the **S**olar and **H**eliospheric **O**bservatory) is a satellite studying the sun. The instrument on the satellite responsible for images like this measures the Doppler effect of light emitted from the surface of the sun. If the surface is rising toward the satellite, the light is shifted to higher frequencies; these positions are shown darker on the image. If the surface is falling, the light is shifted to lower frequencies and is shown lighter. This series of images of the sun's surface shows a wave produced by the disruption of a solar flare. This wave is similar to the wave from an earthquake on earth, but 20 times as fast and carrying 40,000 times as much energy as a typical earthquake wave.

FIGURE 15.18 A motion diagram showing the wave fronts emitted by a source as it moves to the right at speed v_s.

(a) Motion of the source

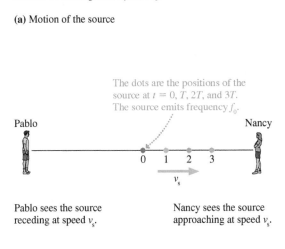

The dots are the positions of the source at $t = 0$, T, $2T$, and $3T$. The source emits frequency f_0.

Pablo

Nancy

v_s

Pablo sees the source receding at speed v_s.

Nancy sees the source approaching at speed v_s.

(b) Snapshot at time $3T$

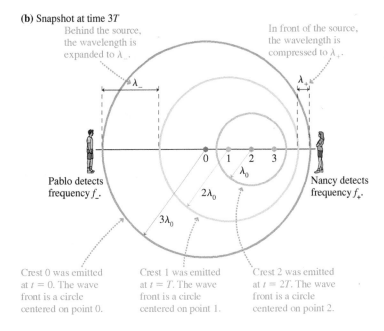

Behind the source, the wavelength is expanded to λ_-.

In front of the source, the wavelength is compressed to λ_+.

λ_-

λ_+

Pablo detects frequency f_-.

Nancy detects frequency f_+.

λ_0

$2\lambda_0$

$3\lambda_0$

Crest 0 was emitted at $t = 0$. The wave front is a circle centered on point 0.

Crest 1 was emitted at $t = T$. The wave front is a circle centered on point 1.

Crest 2 was emitted at $t = 2T$. The wave front is a circle centered on point 2.

ActivPhysics: 10.8, 10.9

relative to an observer is called the **Doppler effect.** A quantitative analysis based on this information would show that the frequency heard by a stationary observer depends on whether the observer sees the source approaching or receding:

$$f_+ = \frac{f_0}{1 - v_s/v}$$

Observed frequency of a wave of speed v emitted from a source approaching at speed v_s

$$f_- = \frac{f_0}{1 + v_s/v}$$

(15.16)

Observed frequency of a wave of speed v emitted from a source receding at speed v_s

As expected, $f_+ > f_0$ (the frequency is higher) for an approaching source because the denominator is less than 1, and $f_- < f_0$ (the frequency is lower) for a receding source.

EXAMPLE 15.13 **How fast are the police driving?**

A police siren has a frequency of 550 Hz as the police car approaches you, 450 Hz after it has passed you and is moving away. How fast are the police traveling?

PREPARE The siren's frequency is altered by the Doppler effect. The frequency is f_+ as the car approaches and f_- as it moves away. We can write two equations for these frequencies and solve for the speed of the police car, v_s.

SOLVE Because our goal is to find v_s, we rewrite Equations 15.16 as

$$f_0 = \left(1 + \frac{v_s}{v}\right)f_- \quad \text{and} \quad f_0 = \left(1 - \frac{v_s}{v}\right)f_+$$

Subtracting the second equation from the first, we get

$$0 = f_- - f_+ + \frac{v_s}{v}(f_- + f_+)$$

Now we can solve for the speed v_s:

$$v_s = \frac{f_+ - f_-}{f_+ + f_-}v = \frac{100 \text{ Hz}}{1000 \text{ Hz}}343 \text{ m/s} = 34 \text{ m/s}$$

ASSESS This is pretty fast (about 75 mph) but reasonable for a police car speeding with the siren on.

A Stationary Source and a Moving Observer

Suppose the police car in Example 15.13 is at rest while you drive toward it at 34 m/s. You might think that this is equivalent to having the police car move toward you at 34 m/s, but there is an important difference. Mechanical waves move through a medium, and the Doppler effect depends not just on how the source and the observer move with respect to each other but also on how they move with respect to the medium. The frequency heard by an observer moving at speed v_0 relative to a stationary source emitting frequency f_0 is given by

$$f_+ = \left(1 + \frac{v_0}{v}\right)f_0$$

Doppler effect for an observer approaching a source

(15.17)

$$f_- = \left(1 - \frac{v_0}{v}\right)f_0$$

Doppler effect for an observer receding from a source

A quick calculation shows that the frequency of the police siren as you approach it at 34 m/s is 545 Hz, not the 550 Hz you heard as it approached you at 34 m/s.

The Doppler Effect for Light Waves

If a source of light waves is receding from you, the wavelength λ_- that you detect is longer than the wavelength λ_0 emitted by the source. Because the wavelength is shifted toward the red end of the visible spectrum, the longer wavelengths of light, this effect is called the **red shift**. Similarly, the light you detect from a source moving toward you is **blue shifted** to shorter wavelengths. For objects moving at normal speeds, this is a small effect; you won't see a Doppler shift of the flashing light of the police car in the above example! But for objects moving at very high speeds, the Doppler effect is significant.

In the 1920s, an analysis of the spectra of many distant galaxies showed that they *all* had a distinct red shift—all distant galaxies are moving away from us. How can we make sense of this observation? The astronomer Edwin Hubble concluded that the galaxies of the universe are *all* moving apart from each other. Extrapolating backward in time brings us to a point when all the matter of the universe—and even space itself, according to the theory of relativity—began rushing out of a primordial fireball. Many observations and measurements since have given support to the idea that the universe began in a *Big Bang* about 14 billion years ago.

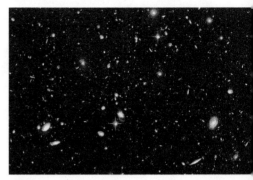

The greater the distance to a galaxy, the faster it moves away from us. This photo shows galaxies at distances of up to 12 billion light years. The great distances imply large red shifts, making the light from the most distant galaxies appear distinctly red.

Frequency Shift on Reflection from a Moving Object

A wave striking a barrier or obstacle can *reflect* and travel back toward the source of the wave, a process we will examine more closely in the next chapter. For sound, the reflected wave is called an *echo*. A bat is able to determine the distance to a flying insect by measuring the time between the emission of an ultrasonic chirp and the detection of the echo from the insect. But if the bat is to catch the insect, it's just as important to know where the insect is going—its velocity. The bat can figure this out by noting the *frequency shift* in the reflected wave, another application of the Doppler effect.

Suppose a sound wave of frequency f_0 travels toward a moving object. The object would see the wave's frequency Doppler shifted to a higher frequency f_+, as given by Equation 15.17. The wave reflected back toward the sound source by the moving object is also Doppler shifted to a higher frequency because, to the source, the reflected wave is coming from a moving object. Thus the echo from a moving object is "double Doppler shifted." If the object's speed v_o is much lower than the wave speed v ($v_o \ll v$), the frequency *shift* of waves reflected from a moving object is

$$\Delta f = \pm 2 f_0 \frac{v_o}{v} \qquad (15.18)$$

Frequency shift of waves reflected from an object moving at speed v_o

The + case is for objects moving toward the source of sound, the − for objects moving away. Notice that there is no shift (i.e., the reflected wave has the same frequency as the emitted wave) when the reflecting object is at rest.

The *Doppler blood flow meter* is an important application of the frequency shift of waves reflected from moving objects. If an ultrasound emitter is pressed against the skin, the sound waves reflect off tissues in the body. In most cases, the frequency of the reflected wave is the same as that of the emitted wave. However, some of the sound waves reflect from blood cells moving through arteries toward or away from the emitter. The moving blood cells produce a frequency shift Δf in the reflected wave. By measuring Δf, doctors can determine blood flow speeds in an entirely noninvasive manner.

Frequency shift on reflection is observed for all types of waves. Radar units emit pulses of radio waves and observe the reflected waves. The time between the emission of a pulse and its return gives an object's position. The change in frequency of the returned pulse gives the object's speed. This is the principle behind the radar guns used by traffic police, as well as the Doppler radar images you have seen in weather reports.

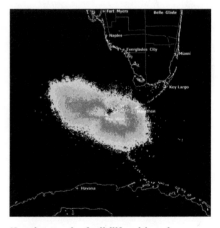

Keeping track of wildlife with radar Doppler radar is tuned to measure only those reflected radio waves that have a frequency shift, eliminating reflections from stationary objects and showing only objects in motion. Televised Doppler radar images of storms are made using radio waves reflected from moving water droplets. But this Doppler radar image of an area off the tip of Florida was made on a clear night with no rain. The blue and green patch isn't a moving storm, it's a moving flock of birds. Migratory birds frequently move at high altitudes at night, so Doppler radar is an excellent tool for analyzing their movements.

EXAMPLE 15.14 **Ultrasound frequency to measure blood flow**

A biomedical engineer is designing a Doppler blood flow meter to measure blood flow in an artery where a typical flow speed is known to be 0.60 m/s. What ultrasound frequency should she use to produce a frequency shift of 1500 Hz when this flow is detected?

SOLVE We can rewrite Equation 15.18 to calculate the frequency of the emitter:

$$f_0 = \left(\frac{\Delta f}{2}\right)\left(\frac{v}{v_{\text{blood}}}\right)$$

The values on the right side are all known. Thus the required ultrasound frequency is

$$f_0 = \left(\frac{1500 \text{ Hz}}{2}\right)\left(\frac{1540 \text{ m/s}}{0.60 \text{ m/s}}\right) = 1.9 \text{ MHz}$$

ASSESS Doppler units to measure blood flow in deep tissues actually work at about 2.0 MHz, so our answer is reasonable.

If we add a frequency-shift measurement to an ultrasound imaging unit, like the one in Example 15.7, we have a device—called *Doppler ultrasound*—that can show not only structure but also motion. *Doppler ultrasound* is a very valuable tool in cardiology because an image can reveal the motion of the heart muscle and the blood in the chambers of the heart in addition to the structure of the heart itself.

Shock Waves

When sound waves are emitted by a moving source, the frequency is shifted, as we have seen. Now, let's look at what happens when the source speed v_s exceeds the wave speed v and the source "outruns" the waves it produces.

Earlier in this section, in Figure 15.18, we looked at a motion diagram of waves emitted by a moving source. **FIGURE 15.19** is the same diagram, but in this case the source is moving faster than the waves. This motion causes the waves to overlap. (Compare Figure 15.19 to Figure 15.18.) The amplitudes of the overlapping waves add up to produce a very large amplitude wave—a **shock wave.**

Anything that moves faster than the speed of sound in air will create a shock wave. The speed of sound was broken on land in 1997 by a British team driving the Thrust SCC in Nevada's Black Rock Desert. **FIGURE 15.20a** shows the shock waves produced during a **supersonic** (faster than the speed of sound) run. You can see the distortion of the view of the landscape behind the car where the waves add to produce regions of high pressure. This shock wave travels along with the car. If the car went by you, the passing of the shock wave would produce a **sonic boom,** the distinctive loud sound you may have heard when a supersonic aircraft passes. The crack of a whip is a sonic boom as well, though on a much smaller scale.

FIGURE 15.19 Waves emitted by a source traveling faster than the speed of the waves in a medium.

The source of waves is moving to the right at v_s. The positions at times $t = 0, t = T, t = 2T, \ldots$ are marked.

At each point, the source emits a wave that spreads out. A snapshot is taken at $t = 7T$.

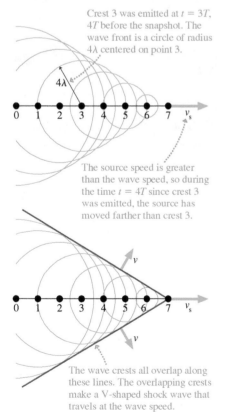

Crest 3 was emitted at $t = 3T$, $4T$ before the snapshot. The wave front is a circle of radius 4λ centered on point 3.

The source speed is greater than the wave speed, so during the time $t = 4T$ since crest 3 was emitted, the source has moved farther than crest 3.

The wave crests all overlap along these lines. The overlapping crests make a V-shaped shock wave that travels at the wave speed.

FIGURE 15.20 Extreme and everyday examples of shock waves.

Shock waves are not necessarily an extreme phenomenon. A boat (or even a duck!) can easily travel faster than the speed of the water waves it creates; the resulting wake, with its characteristic "V" shape as shown in FIGURE 15.20b, is really a shock wave.

STOP TO THINK 15.5   Amy and Zack are both listening to the source of sound waves that is moving to the right. Compare the frequencies each hears.

A. $f_{Amy} > f_{Zack}$
B. $f_{Amy} = f_{Zack}$
C. $f_{Amy} < f_{Zack}$

Amy f_0 Zack

INTEGRATED EXAMPLE 15.15   Shaking the ground

Earthquakes are dramatic slips of the earth's crust. You may feel the waves generated by an earthquake even if you're some distance from the *epicenter*, the point where the slippage occurs. Earthquake waves are usually complicated, but some of the long-period waves shake the ground with motion that is approximately simple harmonic motion. FIGURE 15.21 shows the vertical position of the ground recorded at a distant monitoring station following an earthquake that hit Japan in 2003. This particular wave traveled with a speed of 3500 m/s.

a. Was the wave transverse or longitudinal?
b. What were the wave's frequency and wavelength?
c. What were the maximum speed and the maximum acceleration of the ground during this earthquake wave?
d. Intense earthquake waves produce accelerations greater than free-fall acceleration of gravity. How does this wave compare?

FIGURE 15.21 The vertical motion of the ground during the passage of an earthquake wave.

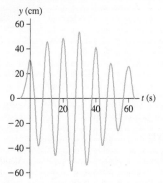

be 0.50 m (it varies, but this is a reasonable average over a few cycles). Because the ground was in simple harmonic motion, the traveling wave was a sinusoidal wave. Consequently, we can use the fundamental relationships for sinusoidal waves to relate the wavelength, frequency, and speed.

SOLVE

a. The graph shows the *vertical* motion of the ground. This motion of the ground—the medium—was perpendicular to the horizontal motion of the wave traveling along the ground, so this was a transverse wave.

b. We can see from the graph that 6 cycles of the oscillation took 60 seconds, so the period was $T = 10$ s. The period of the wave was the same as that of the point on the ground, 10 s; thus the frequency was $f = 1/T = 1/10$ s $= 0.10$ Hz. The speed of the wave was 3500 m/s, so the wavelength was

$$\lambda = \frac{v}{f} = \frac{3500 \text{ m/s}}{0.10 \text{ Hz}} = 35,000 \text{ m} = 35 \text{ km}$$

c. The motion of the ground was simple harmonic motion with frequency 0.10 Hz and amplitude 0.50 m. We can compute the maximum speed and acceleration using relationships from Chapter 14:

$$v_{max} = 2\pi f A = (2\pi)(0.10 \text{ Hz})(0.50 \text{ m}) = 0.31 \text{ m/s}$$

$$a_{max} = (2\pi f)^2 A = [2\pi(0.10 \text{ Hz})]^2(0.50 \text{ m}) = 0.20 \text{ m/s}^2$$

d. This was a reasonably gentle earthquake wave, with an acceleration of the ground quite small compared to the free-fall acceleration of gravity:

$$a_{max}(\text{in units of } g) = \frac{0.20 \text{ m/s}^2}{9.8 \text{ m/s}^2} = 0.020g$$

PREPARE There are two different but related parts to the solution: analyzing the motion of the ground, and analyzing the motion of the wave. The graph in Figure 15.21 is a history graph; it's a record of the motion of one point of the medium—the ground. The graph is approximately sinusoidal, so we can model the motion of the ground as simple harmonic motion. If we look at the middle portion of the wave, we can estimate the amplitude to

ASSESS The wavelength is quite long, as we might expect for such a fast wave with a long period. Given the relatively small amplitude and long period, it's no surprise that the maximum speed and acceleration are relatively modest. You'd certainly feel the passage of this wave, but it wouldn't knock buildings down. This value is less than the acceleration for the sway of the top of the building in Example 14.4 in Chapter 14!

SUMMARY

The goal of Chapter 15 has been to learn the basic properties of traveling waves.

GENERAL PRINCIPLES

The Wave Model

This model is based on the idea of a traveling wave, which is an organized disturbance traveling at a well-defined **wave speed** v.

- In transverse waves the particles of the medium move *perpendicular* to the direction in which the wave travels.

- In longitudinal waves the particles of the medium move *parallel* to the direction in which the wave travels.

A wave transfers energy, but there is no material or substance transferred.

Mechanical waves require a material **medium.** The speed of the wave is a property of the medium, not the wave. The speed does not depend on the size or shape of the wave.

- For a **wave on a string,** the string is the medium.

$$v_{string} = \sqrt{\frac{T_s}{\mu}}$$

- A **sound wave** is a wave of compressions and rarefactions of a medium such as air.

In a gas:

$$v_{sound} = \sqrt{\frac{\gamma RT}{M}}$$

Electromagnetic waves are waves of the electromagnetic field. They do not require a medium. All electromagnetic waves travel at the same speed in a vacuum, $c = 3.00 \times 10^8$ m/s.

IMPORTANT CONCEPTS

Graphical representation of waves

A snapshot graph is a picture of a wave at one instant in time. For a periodic wave, the **wavelength** λ is the distance between crests.

Fixed t:

A history graph is a graph of the displacement of one point in a medium versus time. For a periodic wave, the **period** T is the time between crests.

Fixed x:

Mathematical representation of waves

Sinusoidal waves are produced by a source moving with simple harmonic motion. The equation for a sinusoidal wave is a function of position and time:

$$y(x, t) = A\cos\left(2\pi\left(\frac{x}{\lambda} \pm \frac{t}{T}\right)\right)$$

+: wave travels to left
−: wave travels to right

For sinusoidal and other periodic waves:

$$T = \frac{1}{f} \qquad v = f\lambda$$

The intensity of a wave is the ratio of the power to the area:

$$I = \frac{P}{A}$$

For a **spherical wave** the power decreases with the surface area of the spherical **wave fronts:**

$$I = \frac{P_{source}}{4\pi r^2}$$

APPLICATIONS

The loudness of a sound is given by the sound intensity level. This is a logarithmic function of intensity and is in units of **decibels.**

- The usual **reference level** is the quietest sound that can be heard:

$$I_0 = 1.0 \times 10^{-12} \text{ W/m}^2$$

- The sound intensity level in dB is computed relative to this value:

$$\beta = (10 \text{ dB})\log_{10}\left(\frac{I}{I_0}\right)$$

- A sound at the reference level corresponds to 0 dB.

The Doppler effect is a shift in frequency when there is relative motion of a wave source (frequency f_0, wave speed v) and an observer.

Moving source, stationary observer:

Receding source:

$$f_- = \frac{f_0}{1 + v_s/v}$$

Approaching source:

$$f_+ = \frac{f_0}{1 - v_s/v}$$

Moving observer, stationary source:

Approaching the source:

$$f_+ = \left(1 + \frac{v_o}{v}\right)f_0$$

Moving away from the source:

$$f_- = \left(1 - \frac{v_o}{v}\right)f_0$$

Reflection from a moving object:

For $v_o \ll v$, $\Delta f = \pm 2f_0\frac{v_o}{v}$

When an object moves faster than the wave speed in a medium, a shock wave is formed.

Problem difficulty is labeled as | (straightforward) to |||| (challenging). Problems labeled INT integrate significant material from earlier chapters; BIO are of biological or medical interest.

For instructor-assigned homework, go to www.masteringphysics.com

Scan this QR code to launch a Video Tutor Solution that will help you solve problems for this chapter.

QUESTIONS

Conceptual Questions

1. a. In your own words, define what a *transverse wave* is.
   b. Give an example of a wave that, from your own experience, you know is a transverse wave. What observations or evidence tells you this is a transverse wave?

2. a. In your own words, define what a *longitudinal wave* is.
   b. Give an example of a wave that, from your own experience, you know is a longitudinal wave. What observations or evidence tells you this is a longitudinal wave?

3. The wave pulses shown in Figure Q15.3 travel along the same string. Rank in order, from largest to smallest, their wave speeds v_1, v_2, and v_3. Explain.

FIGURE Q15.3

4. Is it ever possible for one sound wave in air to overtake and pass another? Explain.

5. A wave pulse travels along a string at a speed of 200 cm/s. What will be the speed if:
   a. The string's tension is doubled?
   b. The string's mass is quadrupled (but its length is unchanged)?
   c. The string's length is quadrupled (but its mass is unchanged)?
   d. The string's mass and length are both quadrupled?
   Note that parts a–d are independent and refer to changes made to the original string.

6. An ultrasonic range finder sends out a pulse of ultrasound and measures the time between the emission of the pulse and the return of an echo from an object. This time is used to determine the distance to the object. To get good accuracy from the device, a user must enter the air temperature in the room. Why is this?

7. A thermostat on the wall of your house keeps track of the air temperature. This simple approach is of little use in the large volume of a covered sports stadium, but there are systems that determine an average temperature of the air in a stadium by measuring the time delay between the emission of a pulse of sound on one side of the stadium and its detection on the other. Explain how such a system works.

8. When water freezes, the density decreases and the bonds between molecules become stronger. Do you expect the speed of sound to be greater in liquid water or in water ice?

9. Figure Q15.9 shows a history graph of the motion of one point on a string as a wave traveling to the left passes by. Sketch a snapshot graph for this wave.

FIGURE Q15.9

10. Figure Q15.10 shows a history graph *and* a snapshot graph for a wave pulse on a string. They describe the same wave from two perspectives.
    a. In which direction is the wave traveling? Explain.
    b. What is the speed of this wave?

FIGURE Q15.10

11. Rank in order, from largest to smallest, the wavelengths λ_1 to λ_3 for sound waves having frequencies $f_1 = 100$ Hz, $f_2 = 1000$ Hz, and $f_3 = 10,000$ Hz. Explain.

12. Explain why there is a factor of 2π in Equation 15.5.

13. BIO Bottlenose dolphins use echolocation pulses with a frequency of about 100 kHz, higher than the frequencies used by most bats. Why might you expect these water-dwelling creatures to use higher echolocation frequencies than bats?

14. A laser beam has intensity I_0.
    a. What is the intensity, in terms of I_0, if a lens focuses the laser beam to 1/10 its initial diameter?
    b. What is the intensity, in terms of I_0, if a lens defocuses the laser beam to 10 times its initial diameter?

15. Sound wave A delivers 2 J of energy in 2 s. Sound wave B delivers 10 J of energy in 5 s. Sound wave C delivers 2 mJ of energy in 1 ms. Rank in order, from largest to smallest, the sound powers P_A, P_B, and P_C of these three waves. Explain.

16. When you want to "snap" a towel, the best way to wrap the towel is so that the end that you hold and shake is thick, and the far end is thin. When you shake the thick end, a wave travels down the towel. How does wrapping the towel in a tapered shape help make for a good snap?
    Hint: Think about the speed of the wave as it moves down the towel.

17. The volume control on your stereo is likely designed so that each time you turn it by one click, the loudness increases by a certain number of dB. Does each click increase the output power by a fixed amount as well?

18. A bullet can travel at a speed of over 1000 m/s. When a bullet is fired from a rifle, the actual firing makes a distinctive sound, but people at a distance may hear a second, different sound that is even louder. Explain the source of this sound.

19. You are standing at $x = 0$ m, listening to seven identical sound sources described by Figure Q15.19. At $t = 0$ s, all seven are at $x = 343$ m and moving as shown below. The sound from all seven will reach your ear at $t = 1$ s. Rank in order, from highest to lowest, the seven frequencies f_1 to f_7 that you hear at $t = 1$ s. Explain.

1 ☼⟶ 50 m/s, speeding up
2 ☼⟶ 50 m/s, steady speed
3 ☼⟶ 50 m/s, slowing down
4 ☼ At rest
50 m/s, speeding up ⟵☼ 5
50 m/s, steady speed ⟵☼ 6
FIGURE Q15.19 50 m/s, slowing down ⟵☼ 7

Multiple-Choice Questions

20. ❘ Denver, Colorado, has an oldies station that calls itself "KOOL 105." This means that they broadcast radio waves at a frequency of 105 MHz. Suppose that they decide to describe their station by its wavelength (in meters), instead of by its frequency. What name would they now use?
    A. KOOL 0.35
    B. KOOL 2.85
    C. KOOL 3.5
    D. KOOL 285

21. ❘ What is the frequency of blue light with a wavelength of 400nm?
    A. 1.33×10^3 Hz
    B. 7.50×10^{12} Hz
    C. 1.33×10^{14} Hz
    D. 7.50×10^{14} Hz

22. ❘ Ultrasound can be used to deliver energy to tissues for ther-
    BIO apy. It can penetrate tissue to a depth approximately 200 times its wavelength. What is the approximate depth of penetration of ultrasound at a frequency of 5.0 MHz?
    A. 0.29 mm
    B. 1.4 cm
    C. 6.2 cm
    D. 17 cm

23. ❘ A sinusoidal wave traveling on a string has a period of 0.20 s, a wavelength of 32 cm, and an amplitude of 3 cm. The speed of this wave is
    A. 0.60 cm/s.
    B. 6.4 cm/s.
    C. 15 cm/s.
    D. 160 cm/s.

24. ❘❘ Two strings of different linear density are joined together and pulled taut. A sinusoidal wave on these strings is traveling to the right, as shown in Figure Q15.24. When the wave goes across the boundary from string 1 to string 2, the frequency is unchanged. What happens to the velocity?

String 1 | String 2
FIGURE Q15.24

    A. The velocity increases.
    B. The velocity stays the same.
    C. The velocity decreases.

25. ❘❘ You stand at $x = 0$ m, listening to a sound that is emitted at frequency f_0. Figure Q15.25 shows the frequency you hear during a four-second interval. Which of the following describes the motion of the sound source?

FIGURE Q15.25

    A. It moves from left to right and passes you at $t = 2$ s.
    B. It moves from right to left and passes you at $t = 2$ s.
    C. It moves toward you but doesn't reach you. It then reverses direction at $t = 2$ s.
    D. It moves away from you until $t = 2$ s. It then reverses direction and moves toward you but doesn't reach you.

PROBLEMS

Section 15.1 The Wave Model

Section 15.2 Traveling Waves

1. ❘❘ The wave speed on a string under tension is 200 m/s. What is the speed if the tension is doubled?

2. ❘❘ The wave speed on a string is 150 m/s when the tension is 75.0 N. What tension will give a speed of 180 m/s?

3. ❘❘ A wave travels along a string at a speed of 280 m/s. What will be the speed if the string is replaced by one made of the same material and under the same tension but having twice the radius?

4. ❘❘ The back wall of an auditorium is 26.0 m from the stage. If you are seated in the middle row, how much time elapses between a sound from the stage reaching your ear directly and the same sound reaching your ear after reflecting from the back wall?

5. ❘❘❘❘ A hammer taps on the end of a 4.00-m-long metal bar at room temperature. A microphone at the other end of the bar picks up two pulses of sound, one that travels through the metal and one that travels through the air. The pulses are separated in time by 11.0 ms. What is the speed of sound in this metal?

6. ❘❘ In an early test of sound propagation through the ocean, an underwater explosion of 1 pound of dynamite in the Bahamas was detected 3200 km away on the coast of Africa. How much time elapsed between the explosion and the detection?

Section 15.3 Graphical and Mathematical Descriptions of Waves

7. ❘❘ Figure P15.7 is a snapshot graph of a wave at $t = 0$ s. Draw the history graph for this wave at $x = 6$ m, for $t = 0$ s to 6 s.

FIGURE P15.7   **FIGURE P15.8**

8. ❘❘ Figure P15.8 is a snapshot graph of a wave at $t = 2$ s. Draw the history graph for this wave at $x = 0$ m, for $t = 0$ s to 8 s.

9. ‖ Figure P15.9 is a history graph at $x = 0$ m of a wave moving to the right at 1 m/s. Draw a snapshot graph of this wave at $t = 1$ s.

FIGURE P15.9

FIGURE P15.10

10. ‖ Figure P15.10 is a history graph at $x = 2$ m of a wave moving to the left at 1 m/s. Draw the snapshot graph of this wave at $t = 0$ s.

11. | A sinusoidal wave has period 0.20 s and wavelength 2.0 m. What is the wave speed?

12. | A sinusoidal wave travels with speed 200 m/s. Its wavelength is 4.0 m. What is its frequency?

13. ‖ The motion detector used in a physics lab sends and receives 40 kHz ultrasonic pulses. A pulse goes out, reflects off the object being measured, and returns to the detector. The lab temperature is 20°C.
   a. What is the wavelength of the waves emitted by the motion detector?
   b. How long does it take for a pulse that reflects off an object 2.5 m away to make a round trip?

14. | The displacement of a wave traveling in the positive x-direction is $y(x, t) = (3.5 \text{ cm})\cos(2.7x - 92t)$, where x is in m and t is in s. What are the (a) frequency, (b) wavelength, and (c) speed of this wave?

15. ‖ The displacement of a wave traveling in the negative x-direction is $y(x, t) = (5.2 \text{ cm})\cos(5.5x + 72t)$, where x is in m and t is in s. What are the (a) frequency, (b) wavelength, and (c) speed of this wave?

16. ‖ A traveling wave has displacement given by $y(x, t) = (2.0 \text{ cm}) \times \cos(2\pi x - 4\pi t)$, where x is measured in cm and t in s.
   a. Draw a snapshot graph of this wave at $t = 0$ s.
   b. On the same set of axes, use a dotted line to show the snapshot graph of the wave at $t = 1/8$ s.
   c. What is the speed of the wave?

17. | Figure P15.17 is a snapshot graph of a wave at $t = 0$ s. What are the amplitude, wavelength, and frequency of this wave?

FIGURE P15.17

FIGURE P15.18

18. | Figure P15.18 is a history graph at $x = 0$ m of a wave moving to the right at 2 m/s. What are the amplitude, frequency, and wavelength of this wave?

19. ‖ A boat is traveling at 4.0 m/s in the same direction as an ocean wave of wavelength 30 m and speed 6.8 m/s. If the boat is on the crest of a wave, how much time will elapse until the boat is next on a crest?

20. ‖ In the deep ocean, a water wave with wavelength 95 m travels at 12 m/s. Suppose a small boat is at the crest of this wave, 1.2 m above the equilibrium position. What will be the vertical position of the boat 5.0 s later?

Section 15.4 Sound and Light Waves

21. | A dolphin emits ultrasound at 100 kHz and uses the timing of
   BIO reflections to determine the position of objects in the water. What is the wavelength of this ultrasound?

22. ‖ a. What is the wavelength of a 2.0 MHz ultrasound wave traveling through aluminum?
   b. What frequency of electromagnetic wave would have the same wavelength as the ultrasound wave of part a?

23. | a. At 20°C, what is the frequency of a sound wave in air with a wavelength of 20 cm?
   b. What is the frequency of an electromagnetic wave with a wavelength of 20 cm?
   c. What would be the wavelength of a sound wave in water that has the same frequency as the electromagnetic wave of part b?

24. ‖ a. What is the frequency of blue light that has a wavelength of 450 nm?
   b. What is the frequency of red light that has a wavelength of 650 nm?

25. ‖ a. Telephone signals are often transmitted over long distances by microwaves. What is the frequency of microwave radiation with a wavelength of 3.0 cm?
   b. Microwave signals are beamed between two mountaintops 50 km apart. How long does it take a signal to travel from one mountaintop to the other?

26. ‖ a. An FM radio station broadcasts at a frequency of 101.3 MHz. What is the wavelength?
   b. What is the frequency of a sound source that produces the same wavelength in 20°C air?

Section 15.5 Energy and Intensity

27. ‖ Sound is detected when a sound wave causes the eardrum
   BIO to vibrate (see Figure 14.26). Typically, the diameter of the
   INT eardrum is about 8.4 mm in humans. When someone speaks to you in a normal tone of voice, the sound intensity at your ear is approximately 1.0×10^{-6} W/m². How much energy is delivered to your eardrum each second?

28. ‖ At a rock concert, the sound intensity 1.0 m in front of the
   BIO bank of loudspeakers is 0.10 W/m². A fan is 30 m from the
   INT loudspeakers. Her eardrums have a diameter of 8.4 mm. How much sound energy is transferred to each eardrum in 1.0 second?

29. ‖ The intensity of electromagnetic waves from the sun is 1.4 kW/m² just above the earth's atmosphere. Eighty percent of this reaches the surface at noon on a clear summer day. Suppose you model your back as a 30 cm × 50 cm rectangle. How many joules of solar energy fall on your back as you work on your tan for 1.0 hr?

30. ‖ The sun emits electromagnetic waves with a power of 4.0×10^{26} W. Determine the intensity of electromagnetic waves from the sun just outside the atmospheres of (a) Venus, (b) Mars, and (c) Saturn. Refer to the table of astronomical data inside the back cover.

31. ‖ A large solar panel on a spacecraft in Earth orbit produces 1.0 kW of power when the panel is turned toward the sun. What power would the solar cell produce if the spacecraft were in orbit around Saturn, 9.5 times as far from the sun?

32. ‖ Solar cells convert the energy of incoming light to electric energy; a good quality cell operates at an efficiency of 15%. Each person in the United States uses energy (for lighting, heating, transportation, etc.) at an average rate of 11 kW. Although

sunlight varies with season and time of day, solar energy falls on the United States at an average intensity of 200 W/m². Assuming you live in an average location, what total solar-cell area would you need to provide all of your energy needs with energy from the sun?

33. ‖ LASIK eye surgery uses pulses of laser light to shave off tis-
BIO sue from the cornea, reshaping it. A typical LASIK laser emits a 1.0-mm-diameter laser beam with a wavelength of 193 nm. Each laser pulse lasts 15 ns and contains 1.0 mJ of light energy.
   a. What is the power of one laser pulse?
   b. During the very brief time of the pulse, what is the intensity of the light wave?

Section 15.6 Loudness of Sound

34. ‖ What is the sound intensity level of a sound with an intensity of 3.0×10^{-6} W/m²?

35. ‖‖ What is the sound intensity of a whisper at a distance of 2.0 m, in W/m²? What is the corresponding sound intensity level in dB?

36. ‖ You hear a sound at 65 dB. What is the sound intensity level if the intensity of the sound is doubled?

37. ‖ The sound intensity from a jack hammer breaking concrete is 2.0 W/m² at a distance of 2.0 m from the point of impact. This is sufficiently loud to cause permanent hearing damage if the operator doesn't wear ear protection. What are (a) the sound intensity and (b) the sound intensity level for a person watching from 50 m away?

38. ‖‖ A concert loudspeaker suspended high off the ground emits 35 W of sound power. A small microphone with a 1.0 cm² area is 50 m from the speaker. What are (a) the sound intensity and (b) the sound intensity level at the position of the microphone?

39. ‖ A rock band playing an outdoor concert produces sound at 120 dB 5.0 m away from their single working loudspeaker. What is the sound intensity level 35 m from the speaker?

40. ‖‖ Your ears are sensitive to differences in pitch, but they are
BIO not very sensitive to differences in intensity. You are not capable of detecting a difference in sound intensity level of less than 1 dB. By what factor does the sound intensity increase if the sound intensity level increases from 60 dB to 61 dB?

Section 15.7 The Doppler Effect and Shock Waves

41. ‖ An opera singer in a convertible sings a note at 600 Hz while cruising down the highway at 90 km/hr. What is the frequency heard by
   a. A person standing beside the road in front of the car?
   b. A person standing beside the road behind the car?

42. ‖ An osprey's call is a distinct whistle at 2200 Hz. An osprey
BIO calls while diving at you, to drive you away from her nest. You hear the call at 2300 Hz. How fast is the osprey approaching?

43. ‖ A whistle you use to call your hunting dog has a frequency of 21 kHz, but your dog is ignoring it. You suspect the whistle may not be working, but you can't hear sounds above 20 kHz. To test it, you ask a friend to blow the whistle, then you hop on your bicycle. In which direction should you ride (toward or away from your friend) and at what minimum speed to know if the whistle is working?

44. ‖ A friend of yours is loudly singing a single note at 400 Hz while driving toward you at 25.0 m/s on a day when the speed of sound is 340 m/s.
   a. What frequency do you hear?
   b. What frequency does your friend hear if you suddenly start singing at 400 Hz?

45. ‖‖ While anchored in the middle of a lake, you count exactly three waves hitting your boat every 10 s. You raise anchor and start motoring slowly in the same direction the waves are going. When traveling at 1.5 m/s, you notice that exactly two waves are hitting the boat from behind every 10 s. What is the speed of the waves on the lake?

46. ‖‖‖ A Doppler blood flow unit emits ultrasound at 5.0 MHz.
BIO What is the frequency shift of the ultrasound reflected from blood moving in an artery at a speed of 0.20 m/s?

General Problems

47. ‖ You're watching a carpenter pound a nail. He hits the nail twice a second, but you hear the sound of the strike when his hammer is fully raised. What is the minimum distance from you to the carpenter? Assume the air temperature is 20°C.

48. ‖ A 2.50 kHz sound wave is transmitted through an aluminum rod.
   a. What is its wavelength in the aluminum?
   b. What is the sound wave's frequency when it passes into the air?
   c. What is its wavelength in air?

49. ‖ Oil explorers set off explosives to make loud sounds, then listen for the echoes from underground oil deposits. Geologists suspect that there is oil under 500-m-deep Lake Physics. It's known that Lake Physics is carved out of a granite basin. Explorers detect a weak echo 0.94 s after exploding dynamite at the lake surface. If it's really oil, how deep will they have to drill into the granite to reach it?

50. ‖ A 2.0-m-long string is under 20 N of tension. A pulse travels the length of the string in 50 ms. What is the mass of the string?

51. ‖ A stout cord is stretched between two fixed supports. You
INT vigorously shake one end of the string and send a sinusoidal wave of wavelength 4.0 m along it at 16 m/s. The amplitude of the motion is 2.0 cm. What are the maximum speed and maximum acceleration of a point on the string as the wave passes?

52. ‖ A female orb spider has a mass of 0.50 g. She is suspended
BIO from a tree branch by a 1.1 m length of 0.0020-mm-diameter
INT silk. Spider silk has a density of 1300 kg/m³. If you tap the branch and send a vibration down the thread, how long does it take to reach the spider?

53. ‖ Andy (mass 80 kg) uses a 3.0-m-long rope to pull Bob (mass
INT 60 kg) across the floor ($\mu_k = 0.20$) at a constant speed of 1.0 m/s. Bob signals to Andy to stop by "plucking" the rope, sending a wave pulse forward along the rope. The pulse reaches Andy 150 ms later. What is the mass of the rope?

54. ‖ If a bungee cord is stretched horizontally to a length of 2.5 m, the tension in the cord is 2.1 N. A transverse pulse on the cord travels from one end to the other in 0.80 s. If the cord is stretched to a length of 3.5 m, the pulse takes the same time of 0.80 s to travel from one end to the other. What is the tension in the cord when it is stretched to this length?

55. ‖ String 1 in Figure P15.55 has linear density 2.0 g/m and string 2 has linear density 4.0 g/m. A student sends pulses in both directions by quickly pulling up on the knot,

FIGURE P15.55

then releasing it. What should the string lengths L_1 and L_2 be if the pulses are to reach the ends of the strings simultaneously?

56. ‖ In 2003, an earthquake in Japan generated 1.1 Hz waves that
INT traveled outward at 7.0 km/s. 200 km to the west, seismic instruments recorded a maximum acceleration of 0.25g along the east-west axis.

a. How much time elapsed between the earthquake and the first detection of the waves?
b. Was this a transverse or a longitudinal wave?
c. What was the wavelength?
d. What was the maximum horizontal displacement of the ground as the wave passed?

57. ⫿ A coyote can locate a sound source with good accuracy by
BIO comparing the arrival times of a sound wave at its two ears. Suppose a coyote is listening to a bird whistling at 1000 Hz. The bird is 3.0 m away, directly in front of the coyote's right ear. The coyote's ears are 15 cm apart.
a. What is the distance between the bird and the coyote's left ear?
b. What is the difference in the arrival time of the sound at the left ear and the right ear?
c. What is the ratio of this time difference to the period of the sound wave?
Hint: You are looking for the difference between two numbers that are nearly the same. What does this near equality imply about the necessary precision during intermediate stages of the calculation?

58. ⫿ An earthquake produces longitudinal P waves that travel outward at 8000 m/s and transverse S waves that move at 4500 m/s. A seismograph at some distance from the earthquake records the arrival of the S waves 2.0 min after the arrival of the P waves. How far away was the earthquake? You can assume that the waves travel in straight lines, although actual seismic waves follow more complex routes.

59. ⫿ One way to monitor global warming is to measure the average temperature of the ocean. Researchers are doing this by measuring the time it takes sound pulses to travel underwater over large distances. At a depth of 1000 m, where ocean temperatures hold steady near 4°C, the average sound speed is 1480 m/s. It's known from laboratory measurements that the sound speed increases 4.0 m/s for every 1.0°C increase in temperature. In one experiment, where sounds generated near California are detected in the South Pacific, the sound waves travel 8000 km. If the smallest time change that can be reliably detected is 1.0 s, what is the smallest change in average temperature that can be measured?

60. ⫿ Figure P15.60 shows two snapshot graphs taken 10 ms apart, with the blue curve being the first snapshot. What are the (a)wavelength, (b) speed, (c) frequency, and (d) amplitude of this wave?

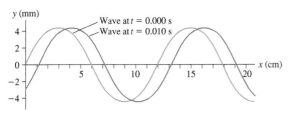

FIGURE P15.60

61. ⫿ Low-frequency vertical oscillations are one possible cause of
BIO motion sickness, with 0.3 Hz having the strongest effect. Your boat is bobbing in place at just the right frequency to cause you the maximum discomfort.
a. How much time elapses between two waves hitting the ship?
b. If the wave crests appear to be about 30 m apart, what would you estimate to be the speed of the waves?

62. ⫿ A wave on a string is described by $y(x, t) = (3.0 \text{ cm}) \times \cos[2\pi(x/(2.4 \text{ m}) + t/(0.20 \text{ s}))]$, where x is in m and t in s.
a. In what direction is this wave traveling?
b. What are the wave speed, frequency, and wavelength?
c. At $t = 0.50$ s, what is the displacement of the string at $x = 0.20$ m?

63. ⎮ Write the y-equation for a wave traveling in the negative x-direction with wavelength 50 cm, speed 4.0 m/s, and amplitude 5.0 cm.

64. ⎮ Write the y-equation for a wave traveling in the positive x-direction with frequency 200 Hz, speed 400 m/s, and amplitude 0.010 mm.

65. ⎮ A wave is described by the expression $y(x, t) = (3.0 \text{ cm}) \times \cos(1.5x - 50t)$, where x is in m and t is in s.
a. Draw an accurate snapshot graph of this wave.
b. What is the speed of the wave and in what direction is it traveling?

66. ⫿ A point on a string undergoes simple harmonic motion as a
INT sinusoidal wave passes. When a sinusoidal wave with speed 24 m/s, wavelength 30 cm, and amplitude of 1.0 cm passes, what is the maximum speed of a point on the string?

67. ⫿ A simple pendulum is
INT made by attaching a small cup of sand with a hole in the bottom to a 1.2-m-long string. The pendulum is mounted on the back of a small motorized

FIGURE P15.67

car. As the car drives forward, the pendulum swings from side to side and leaves a trail of sand as shown in Figure P15.67. How fast was the car moving?

68. ⫿ a. A typical 100 W lightbulb produces 4.0 W of visible light. (The other 96 W are dissipated as heat and infrared radiation.) What is the light intensity on a wall 2.0 m away from the lightbulb?
b. A krypton laser produces a cylindrical red laser beam 2.0 mm in diameter with 2.0 W of power. What is the light intensity on a wall 2.0 m away from the laser?

69. ⫿ An AM radio station broadcasts with a power of 25 kW at a frequency of 920 kHz. Estimate the intensity of the radio wave at a point 10 km from the broadcast antenna.

70. ⫿ The earth's average distance from the sun is 1.50×10^{11} m. At this distance, the intensity of radiation from the sun is 1.38 kW/m². The earth's radius is 6.37×10^6 m. What is the total solar power received by the earth? (For comparison, total human power consumption is roughly 10^{13} W.)

71. ⫿ Lasers can be used to drill or cut material. One such laser generates a series of high-intensity pulses rather than a continuous beam of light. Each pulse contains 500 mJ of energy and lasts 10 ns. The laser fires 10 such pulses per second.
a. What is the *peak power* of the laser light? The peak power is the power output during one of the 10 ns pulses.
b. What is the average power output of the laser? The average power is the total energy delivered per second.
c. A lens focuses the laser beam to a 10-μm-diameter circle on the target. During a pulse, what is the light intensity on the target?
d. The intensity of sunlight at the surface of the earth at midday is about 1100 W/m². What is the ratio of the laser intensity on the target to the intensity of the midday sun?

72. ⫿ The quietest sound you can hear is 0 dB. Estimate the diame-
BIO ter of your ear canal and compute an approximate area. At 0 dB, how much sound power is "captured" by one ear? (Ignore any focusing of energy by the pinna, the external folds of your ear.)

73. ‖ The sound intensity 50 m from a wailing tornado siren is 0.10 W/m^2.
    a. What is the sound intensity level?
    b. In a noisy neighborhood, the weakest sound likely to be heard over background noise is 60 dB. Estimate the maximum distance at which the siren can be heard.

74. ‖ A harvest mouse can detect sounds as quiet as -10 dB. Suppose you are sitting in a field on a very quiet day while a harvest mouse sits nearby at the entrance to its nest. A very gentle breeze causes a leaf 1.5 m from your head to rustle, generating a faint sound right at the limit of your ability to hear it. The sound of the rustling leaf is also right at the threshold of hearing of the harvest mouse. How far is the harvest mouse from the leaf?

75. ‖‖ A speaker at an open-air concert emits 600 W of sound power, radiated equally in all directions.
    a. What is the intensity of the sound 5.0 m from the speaker?
    b. What sound intensity level would you experience there if you did not have any protection for your ears?
    c. Earplugs you can buy in the drugstore have a noise reduction rating of 23 decibels. If you are wearing those earplugs but your friend Phil is not, how far from the speaker should Phil stand to experience the same loudness as you?

76. ‖ A bat locates insects by emitting ultrasonic "chirps" and then listening for echoes. The lowest-frequency chirp of a big brown bat is 26 kHz. How fast would the bat have to fly, and in what direction, for you to just barely be able to hear the chirp at 20 kHz?

77. ‖ A physics professor demonstrates the Doppler effect by tying a 600 Hz sound generator to a 1.0-m-long rope and whirling it around her head in a horizontal circle at 100 rpm. What are the highest and lowest frequencies heard by a student in the classroom? Assume the room temperature is 20°C.

78. ‖ Ocean waves with wavelength 1.2 m and period 1.5 s are moving past a pier. A boy runs along the pier, in the direction opposite to the motion of the wave, at 3.5 m/s. How many wave crests pass the boy each second?

79. ‖ A source of sound moves toward you at speed v_s and away from Jane, who is standing on the other side of it. You hear the sound at twice the frequency as Jane. What is the speed of the source? Assume that the speed of sound is 340 m/s.

80. ‖‖ When the heart pumps blood into the aorta, the *pressure gradient*—the difference between the blood pressure inside the heart and the blood pressure in the artery—is an important diagnostic measurement. A direct measurement of the pressure gradient is difficult, but an indirect determination can be made by measuring the Doppler shift of reflected ultrasound. Blood is

essentially at rest in the heart; when it leaves and enters the aorta, it speeds up significantly and—according to Bernoulli's equation—the pressure must decrease. A doctor using ultrasound of 2.5 MHz measures a 6000 Hz frequency shift as the ultrasound reflects from blood ejected from the heart.
    a. What is the speed of the blood in the aorta?
    b. What is the difference in blood pressure between the inside of the heart and the aorta? Assume that the patient is lying down and that there is no difference in height as the blood moves from the heart into the aorta.

Passage Problems

Echolocation BIO

As discussed in the chapter, many species of bats find flying insects by emitting pulses of ultrasound and listening for the reflections. This technique is called **echolocation**. Bats possess several adaptations that allow them to echolocate very effectively.

81. | Although we can't hear them, the ultrasonic pulses are very loud. In order not to be deafened by the sound they emit, bats can temporarily turn off their hearing. Muscles in the ear cause the bones in their middle ear to separate slightly, so that they don't transmit vibrations to the inner ear. After an ultrasound pulse ends, a bat can hear an echo from an object a minimum of 1 m away. Approximately how much time after a pulse is emitted is the bat ready to hear its echo?
    A. 0.5 ms　　B. 1 ms　　C. 3 ms　　D. 6 ms

82. | Bats are sensitive to very small changes in frequency of the reflected waves. What information does this allow them to determine about their prey?
    A. Size　　B. Speed　　C. Distance　　D. Species

83. | Some bats have specially shaped noses that they use to focus the ultrasound pulses in the forward direction. Why is this useful?
    A. They are not distracted by echoes from several directions.
    B. The energy of the pulse is concentrated in a smaller area, so the intensity is larger.
    C. The pulse goes forward only, so it doesn't affect the bat's hearing.

84. | Some bats utilize a sound pulse with a rapidly decreasing frequency. A decreasing-frequency pulse has
    A. Decreasing wavelength.
    B. Decreasing speed.
    C. Increasing wavelength.
    D. Increasing speed.

STOP TO THINK ANSWERS

Stop to Think 15.1: Transverse. The wave moves horizontally through the crowd, but individual spectators move up and down, transverse to the motion of the wave.

Stop to Think 15.2: D, E. Shaking your hand faster or farther will change the shape of the wave, but this will not change the wave speed; the speed is a property of the medium. Changing the linear density of the string or its tension will change the wave speed. To increase the speed, you must decrease the linear density or increase the tension.

Stop to Think 15.3: B. All three waves have the same speed, so the frequency is highest for the wave that has the shortest wave-

length. (Imagine the three waves moving to the right; the one with the crests closest together has the crests passing by most rapidly.)

Stop to Think 15.4: A. The plane wave does not spread out, so its intensity will be constant. The other two waves spread out, so their intensity will decrease.

Stop to Think 15.5: C. The source is moving toward Zack, so he observes a higher frequency. The source is moving away from Amy, so she observes a lower frequency.

16 Superposition and Standing Waves

The didgeridoo is a simple musical instrument played by aboriginal tribes in Australia. It consists of a hollow tube that is open at both ends. How can the player get a wide range of notes out of such a simple device?

LOOKING AHEAD ▶

The goal of Chapter 16 is to use the idea of superposition to understand the phenomena of interference and standing waves.

Superposition

Traveling waves can pass through each other. As they do, their displacements add together. This is the **principle of superposition.**

The surface of the water supports multiple waves. It looks like the waves simply stack on top of each other, which, in fact, they do.

> **Looking Back** ◀◀
> 15.2–15.3 The fundamental properties of traveling waves

Standing Waves

Traveling waves bounce back and forth between the ends of a string that is clamped at both ends. The superposition of these reflected waves makes the string vibrate up and down. We call this a **standing wave.**

Standing waves occur only as well-defined patterns called **modes,** each with its own distinctive frequency. These are the **resonant modes** of the medium. Some points on the wave, called **nodes,** do not oscillate at all.

> **Looking Back** ◀◀
> 14.7 The principle of resonance

Constructive and Destructive Interference

Two waves on a string each displace the string upward. Where the two waves overlap, the displacement is twice that of the individual waves. This is **constructive interference.**

Noise-canceling headphones create a sound wave that is inverted from the ambient sound. When the waves are added, they cancel, producing a much smaller wave. This is **destructive interference.**

Music and Speech

Standing waves on the strings of the guitar allow it to produce different musical notes. The frequency is determined by the length, mass, and tension of the string.

A tube can support a standing wave as well—a standing sound wave. We'll see how to calculate the possible standing waves and how these determine the notes a wind instrument can produce.

Your vocal system also depends on standing waves. A vibration of your vocal cords is amplified by the resonances of the tube of your vocal tract. We'll see how these elements work together to make speech.

> **Looking Back** ◀◀
> 15.4 The nature of sound waves

16.1 The Principle of Superposition

FIGURE 16.1a shows two baseball players, Alan and Bill, at batting practice. Unfortunately, someone has turned the pitching machines so that pitching machine A throws baseballs toward Bill while machine B throws toward Alan. If two baseballs are launched at the same time and with the same speed, they collide at the crossing point and bounce away. Two baseballs cannot occupy the same point of space at the same time.

FIGURE 16.1 Two baseballs cannot pass through each other. Two waves can.

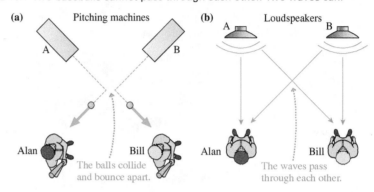

(a) Pitching machines
A   B
Alan   Bill
The balls collide and bounce apart.

(b) Loudspeakers
A   B
Alan   Bill
The waves pass through each other.

FIGURE 16.2 Two wave pulses on a stretched string pass through each other.

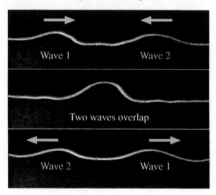

Wave 1   Wave 2

Two waves overlap

Wave 2   Wave 1

But unlike baseballs, sound waves *can* pass directly through each other. In FIGURE 16.1b, Alan and Bill are listening to the stereo system in the locker room after practice. Both hear the music quite well, without distortion or missing sound, so the sound wave that travels from speaker A toward Bill must pass through the wave traveling from speaker B toward Alan, with no effect on either. This is a basic property of waves.

What happens to the medium at a point where two waves are present simultaneously? What is the displacement of the medium at this point? FIGURE 16.2 shows a sequence of photos of two wave pulses traveling along a stretched string. In the first photo, the waves are approaching each other. In the second, the waves overlap, and the displacement of the string is larger than it was for either of the individual waves. A careful measurement would reveal that the displacement is the sum of the displacements of the two individual waves. In the third frame, the waves have passed through each other and continue on as if nothing had happened.

This result is not limited to stretched strings; the outcome is the same whenever two waves of any type pass through each other. This is known as the *principle of superposition:*

> **Principle of superposition** When two or more waves are *simultaneously* present at a single point in space, the displacement of the medium at that point is the sum of the displacements due to each individual wave.

FIGURE 16.3 The superposition of two waves on a string as they pass through each other.

1 m/s   1 m/s
$t = 0$ s
x (m)
0 1 2 3 4 5 6 7
Two waves approach each other.

$t = 1$ s
x (m)
0 1 2 3 4 5 6 7

$t = 2$ s
x (m)
0 1 2 3 4 5 6 7
The net displacement is the point-by-point summation of the individual waves.

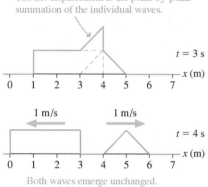

$t = 3$ s
x (m)
0 1 2 3 4 5 6 7

1 m/s   1 m/s
$t = 4$ s
x (m)
0 1 2 3 4 5 6 7
Both waves emerge unchanged.

To use the principle of superposition you must know the displacement that each wave would cause if it traveled through the medium alone. Then you go through the medium *point by point* and add the displacements due to each wave *at that point* to find the net displacement at that point. The outcome will be different at each point in the medium because the displacements are different at each point.

Let's illustrate this principle with an idealized example. FIGURE 16.3 shows five snapshot graphs taken 1 s apart of two waves traveling at the same speed (1 m/s) in opposite directions along a string. The displacement of each wave is shown as a dotted line. The solid line is the sum *at each point* of the two displacements at that point. This is the displacement that you would actually observe as the two waves pass through each other.

Constructive and Destructive Interference

The superposition of two waves is often called **interference**. The displacements of the waves in Figure 16.3 are both positive, so the total displacement of the medium where they overlap is larger than it would be due to either of the waves separately. We call this **constructive interference.**

FIGURE 16.4 shows another series of snapshot graphs of two counterpropagating waves, but this time one has a negative displacement. The principle of superposition still applies, but now the displacements are opposite each other. The displacement of the medium where the waves overlap is *less* than it would be due to either of the waves separately. We call this **destructive interference.**

In the series of graphs in Figure 16.4 the displacement of the medium at $x = 3.5$ m is always zero. The positive displacement of the wave traveling to the right and the negative displacement of the wave traveling to the left always exactly cancel at this spot. The complete cancellation at one point of two waves traveling in opposite directions is something we will see again. When the displacements of the waves cancel, where does the energy of the wave go? We know that the waves continue on unchanged after their interaction, so no energy is dissipated. Consider the graph at $t = 1.5$ s. There is no net displacement at any point of the medium at this instant, but the *string is moving rapidly*. The energy of the waves hasn't vanished—it is in the form of the kinetic energy of the medium.

FIGURE 16.4 Two waves with opposite displacements produce destructive interference.

Two waves approach each other.

The leading edges of the waves meet, and the displacements offset each other at this point.

At this moment, the net displacement of the medium is zero.

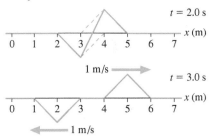

Both waves emerge unchanged.

STOP TO THINK 16.1 Two pulses on a string approach each other at speeds of 1 m/s. What is the shape of the string at $t = 6$ s?

Approaching waves at $t = 0$ s

A.

C.

B.

D.

▶ **Breaking stones with sound** BIO As we saw in Chapter 15, waves carry energy. The energy of high-intensity ultrasonic waves can be used to break up kidney stones so that they can be cleared from the body, a technique known as *shock wave lithotripsy*. This machine uses two generators, each of which produces ultrasonic waves. The two waves, which enter the body at different points, are directed so that they overlap and produce constructive interference at the position of a stone. This allows the individual waves to have lower intensity, minimizing tissue damage as they pass through the body, while still providing a region of high intensity right where it is needed.

16.2 Standing Waves

When you pluck a guitar string or a rubber band stretched between your fingers, you create waves. But how is this possible? There isn't really anywhere for the waves to go, because the string or the rubber band is held between two fixed ends. FIGURE 16.5 shows a strobe photograph of waves on a stretched elastic cord. This is a wave, though it may not look like one, because it doesn't "travel" either right or left. Waves that are "trapped" between two boundaries, like those in the photo or on a guitar

FIGURE 16.5 The motion of a standing wave on a string.

string, are what we call *standing waves.* **Individual points on the string oscillate up and down, but the wave itself does not travel.** It is called a **standing wave** because the crests and troughs "stand in place" as it oscillates. As we'll see, a standing wave isn't a totally new kind of wave; it is simply the superposition of two traveling waves moving in opposite directions.

Superposition Creates a Standing Wave

Suppose we have a string on which two sinusoidal waves of equal wavelength and amplitude travel in opposite directions, as in FIGURE 16.6a. When the waves meet, the displacement of the string will be a superposition of these two waves. FIGURE 16.6b shows nine snapshot graphs, at intervals of $\frac{1}{8}T$, of the two waves as they move through each other. The red and orange dots identify particular crests of each of the waves to help you see that the red wave is traveling to the right and the orange wave to the left. At *each point,* the net displacement of the medium is found by adding the red displacement and the orange displacement. The resulting blue wave is the superposition of the two traveling waves.

FIGURE 16.6 Two sinusoidal waves traveling in opposite directions.

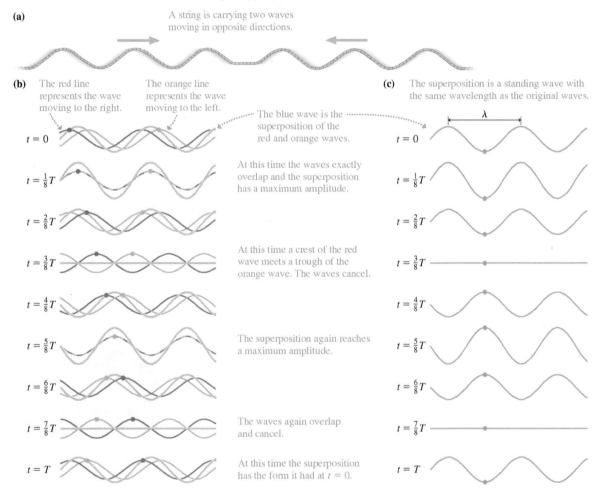

(a) A string is carrying two waves moving in opposite directions.

(b) The red line represents the wave moving to the right. The orange line represents the wave moving to the left.

The blue wave is the superposition of the red and orange waves.

$t = 0$

$t = \frac{1}{8}T$ At this time the waves exactly overlap and the superposition has a maximum amplitude.

$t = \frac{2}{8}T$

$t = \frac{3}{8}T$ At this time a crest of the red wave meets a trough of the orange wave. The waves cancel.

$t = \frac{4}{8}T$

$t = \frac{5}{8}T$ The superposition again reaches a maximum amplitude.

$t = \frac{6}{8}T$

$t = \frac{7}{8}T$ The waves again overlap and cancel.

$t = T$ At this time the superposition has the form it had at $t = 0$.

(c) The superposition is a standing wave with the same wavelength as the original waves.

λ

$t = 0$

$t = \frac{1}{8}T$

$t = \frac{2}{8}T$

$t = \frac{3}{8}T$

$t = \frac{4}{8}T$

$t = \frac{5}{8}T$

$t = \frac{6}{8}T$

$t = \frac{7}{8}T$

$t = T$

FIGURE 16.6c shows just the superposition of the two waves. This is the wave that you would actually observe in the medium. The blue dot shows that the wave in Figure 16.6c is moving neither right nor left. The superposition of the two counterpropagating traveling waves is a standing wave. Notice that the wavelength of the standing wave, the distance between two crests or two troughs, is the same as the wavelengths of the two traveling waves that combine to produce it.

Nodes and Antinodes

In FIGURE 16.7 we have superimposed the nine snapshot graphs of Figure 16.6c into a single graphical representation of this standing wave. The graphs at different times overlap, much as the photos of the string at different times in the strobe photograph of Figure 16.5. The motion of individual points on the standing wave is now clearly seen. A striking feature of a standing-wave pattern is points that *never move!* These points, which are spaced $\lambda/2$ apart, are called **nodes.** Halfway between the nodes are points where the particles in the medium oscillate with maximum displacement. These points of maximum amplitude are called **antinodes,** and you can see that they are also spaced $\lambda/2$ apart. This means that **the wavelength of a standing wave is** *twice* **the distance between successive nodes or successive antinodes.**

It seems surprising and counterintuitive that some particles in the medium have no motion at all. This happens for the same reason we saw in Figure 16.4: The two waves exactly offset each other at that point. Look carefully at the two traveling waves in Figure 16.6b. You will see that the nodes occur at points where at *every instant* of time the displacements of the two traveling waves have equal magnitudes but *opposite signs.* Thus the superposition of the displacements at these points is always zero—they are points of destructive interference. The antinodes have large displacements. They correspond to points where the two displacements have equal magnitudes and the *same sign* at all times. Constructive interference at these points gives a displacement twice that of each individual wave.

The intensity of a wave is largest at points where it oscillates with maximum amplitude. FIGURE 16.8 shows that the points of maximum intensity along the standing wave occur at the antinodes; the intensity is zero at the nodes. For a standing sound wave, the loudness varies from zero (no sound) at the nodes to a maximum at the antinodes and then back to zero. The key idea is that **the intensity is maximum at points of constructive interference and zero at points of destructive interference.**

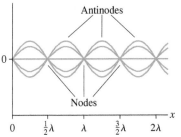

FIGURE 16.7 Superimposing multiple snapshot graphs of a standing wave clearly shows the nodes and antinodes.

The nodes and antinodes are spaced $\lambda/2$ apart.

FIGURE 16.8 Intensity of a standing wave.

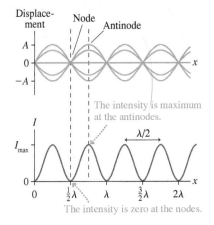

| EXAMPLE 16.1 | Setting up a standing wave |

Two children hold an elastic cord at each end. Each child shakes her end of the cord 2.0 times per second, sending waves at 3.0 m/s toward the middle, where the two waves combine to create a standing wave. What is the distance between adjacent nodes?

SOLVE The distance between adjacent nodes is $\lambda/2$. The wavelength, frequency, and speed are related as $v = f\lambda$, as we saw in Chapter 15, so the wavelength is

$$\lambda = \frac{v}{f} = \frac{3.0 \text{ m/s}}{2.0 \text{ Hz}} = 1.5 \text{ m}$$

The distance between adjacent nodes is $\lambda/2$ and thus is 0.75 m.

16.3 Standing Waves on a String

The oscillation of a guitar string is a standing wave. A standing wave is naturally produced on a string when both ends are fixed (i.e., tied down), as in the case of a guitar string or the string in the photo of Figure 16.5. We also know that a standing wave is produced when there are two counterpropagating traveling waves. But you don't shake both ends of a guitar string to produce the standing wave! How do we actually get two traveling waves on a string with both ends fixed? Before we can answer this question, we need a brief explanation of what happens when a traveling wave encounters a boundary or a discontinuity.

ActivPhysics: 10.4, 10.5, 10.6
PhET: Wave on a String

Reflections

We know that light reflects from mirrors; it can also reflect from the surface of a pond or from a pane of glass. As we saw in Chapter 15, sound waves reflect as well;

FIGURE 16.9 A wave reflects when it encounters a boundary.

The reflected pulse is inverted and its amplitude is unchanged.

that's how an echo is produced. To understand reflections, we'll look at waves on a string, but the results will be completely general and can be applied to other waves as well.

Suppose we have a string that is attached to a wall or other fixed support, as in **FIGURE 16.9**. The wall is what we will call a *boundary*—it's the end of the medium. When the pulse reaches this boundary, it reflects, moving away from the wall. *All* the wave's energy is reflected; hence **the amplitude of a wave reflected from a boundary is unchanged.** Figure 16.9 shows that the amplitude doesn't change when the pulse reflects, but the pulse is inverted.

Waves also reflect from what we will call a *discontinuity,* a point where there is a change in the properties of the medium. **FIGURE 16.10a** shows a discontinuity where a string with a large linear density connects with a string with a small linear density. The tension is the same in both strings, so the wave speed is slower on the left, faster on the right. Whenever a wave encounters a discontinuity, some of the wave's energy is *transmitted* forward and some is reflected. Because energy must be conserved, both the transmitted and the reflected pulses have a smaller amplitude than the initial pulse in this case.

TRY IT YOURSELF

Through the glass darkly A piece of window glass is a discontinuity to a light wave, so it both transmits and reflects light. To verify this, look at the windows in a brightly lit room at night. The small percentage of the interior light that reflects from windows is more intense than the light coming in from outside, so reflection dominates and the windows show a mirror-like reflection of the room. Now turn out the lights. With no more reflected interior light you will be able to see the transmitted light from outside.

FIGURE 16.10 The reflection of a wave at a discontinuity.

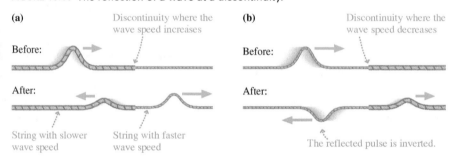

In **FIGURE 16.10b**, an incident wave encounters a discontinuity at which the wave speed decreases. Once again, some of the wave's energy is transmitted and some is reflected.

In Figure 16.10a, the reflected pulse is right-side up. The string on the right is light and provides little resistance, so the junction moves up and down as the pulse passes. This motion of the string is like the original "snap" of the string that started the pulse, so the reflected pulse has the same orientation as the original pulse. In Figure 16.10b, the string on the right is more massive, so it looks more like the fixed boundary in Figure 16.9 and the reflected pulse is again inverted.

Creating a Standing Wave

Now that we understand reflections, let's create a standing wave. **FIGURE 16.11** shows a string of length L that is tied at $x = 0$ and $x = L$. This string has *two* boundaries where reflections can occur. If you wiggle the string in the middle, sinusoidal waves travel outward in both directions and soon reach the boundaries, where they reflect. The reflections at the ends of the string cause two waves of *equal amplitude and wavelength* to travel in opposite directions along the string. As we've just seen, these are the conditions that cause a standing wave!

What kind of standing waves might develop on the string? There are two conditions that must be met:

- Because the string is fixed at the ends, the displacements at $x = 0$ and $x = L$ must be zero at all times. Stated another way, we require nodes at both ends of the string.
- We know that standing waves have a spacing of $\lambda/2$ between nodes. This means that the nodes must be equally spaced.

FIGURE 16.11 Reflections at the two boundaries cause a standing wave on the string.

Wiggle the string in the middle.

Two waves move away from the middle.

$x = 0$ The reflected waves travel through each other. This creates a standing wave. $x = L$

FIGURE 16.12 shows the first three possible waves that meet these conditions. These are called the standing-wave **modes** of the string. To help quantify the possible waves, we can assign a **mode number** m to each. The first wave in Figure 16.12, with a node at each end, has mode number $m = 1$. The next wave is $m = 2$, and so on.

> NOTE ▶ Figure 16.12 shows only the first three modes, for $m = 1$, $m = 2$, and $m = 3$. But there are many more modes, for all possible values of m. ◀

The distance between adjacent nodes is $\lambda/2$, so the different modes have different wavelengths. For the first mode in Figure 16.12, the distance between nodes is the length of the string, so we can write

$$\lambda_1 = 2L$$

The subscript identifies the mode number; in this case $m = 1$. For $m = 2$, the distance between nodes is $L/2$; this means that $\lambda_2 = L$. Generally, for any mode m the wavelength is given by the following equation:

$$\lambda_m = \frac{2L}{m} \qquad m = 1, 2, 3, 4, \ldots \qquad (16.1)$$

Wavelengths of standing-wave modes of a string of length L

These are the only possible wavelengths for standing waves on the string. **A standing wave can exist on the string *only* if its wavelength is one of the values given by Equation 16.1.**

> NOTE ▶ Other wavelengths, which would be perfectly acceptable wavelengths for a traveling wave, cannot exist as a *standing* wave of length L because they do not meet the constraint of having a node at each end of the string. ◀

If standing waves are possible only for certain wavelengths, then only specific oscillation frequencies are allowed. Because $\lambda f = v$ for a sinusoidal wave, the oscillation frequency corresponding to wavelength λ_m is

$$f_m = \frac{v}{\lambda_m} = \frac{v}{2L/m} = m\left(\frac{v}{2L}\right) \qquad m = 1, 2, 3, 4, \ldots \qquad (16.2)$$

Frequencies of standing-wave modes of a string of length L

FIGURE 16.13 shows the first three modes with their wavelengths and frequencies. You can see that **the mode number m is equal to the number of antinodes of the standing wave.** You can therefore tell a string's mode of oscillation by counting the number of antinodes (*not* the number of nodes).

In Chapter 14, we looked at the concept of *resonance*. A mass on a spring has a certain frequency at which it "wants" to oscillate. If the system is driven at its resonance frequency, it will develop a large amplitude of oscillation. A stretched string will support standing waves, meaning it has a series of frequencies at which it "wants" to oscillate: the frequencies of the different standing-wave modes. We can call these **resonant modes,** or more simply, **resonances.** A small oscillation of a stretched string at a frequency near one of its resonant modes will cause it to develop a standing wave with a large amplitude. FIGURE 16.14 shows photographs of the first four standing-wave modes on a string, corresponding to four different driving frequencies.

> NOTE ▶ When we draw standing-wave modes, as in Figure 16.13, we usually show only the *envelope* of the wave, the greatest extent of the motion of the string. The string's motion is actually continuous and goes through all intermediate positions as well, as we see from the time-exposure photographs of standing waves in Figure 16.14. ◀

FIGURE 16.12 The first three possible standing waves on a string of length L.

The simplest standing wave has one node at each end, and no more.

The next possible standing wave we can make has an additional node in the center.

The third possible standing wave has two nodes in addition to the nodes at the end.

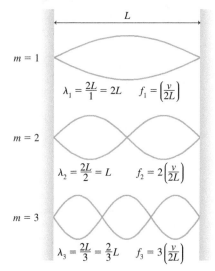

FIGURE 16.13 Possible standing waves of a string fixed at both ends.

$m = 1$

$$\lambda_1 = \frac{2L}{1} = 2L \qquad f_1 = \left(\frac{v}{2L}\right)$$

$m = 2$

$$\lambda_2 = \frac{2L}{2} = L \qquad f_2 = 2\left(\frac{v}{2L}\right)$$

$m = 3$

$$\lambda_3 = \frac{2L}{3} = \frac{2}{3}L \qquad f_3 = 3\left(\frac{v}{2L}\right)$$

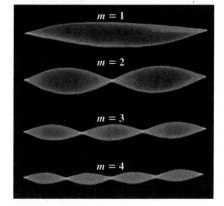

FIGURE 16.14 Resonant modes of a stretched string.

$m = 1$

$m = 2$

$m = 3$

$m = 4$

The Fundamental and the Higher Harmonics

The sequence of possible frequencies for a standing wave on a string has an interesting pattern that is worth exploring. The first mode has frequency

$$f_1 = \frac{v}{2L} \qquad (16.3)$$

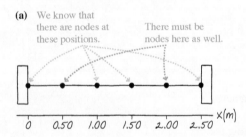

We call this the **fundamental frequency** of the string. All of the other modes have frequencies that are multiples of this fundamental frequency. We can rewrite Equation 16.2 in terms of the fundamental frequency as

$$f_m = mf_1 \qquad m = 1, 2, 3, 4, \ldots \qquad (16.4)$$

The allowed standing-wave frequencies are all integer multiples of the fundamental frequency. This sequence of possible frequencies is called a set of **harmonics.** The fundamental frequency f_1 is also known as the *first harmonic,* the $m = 2$ wave at frequency f_2 is called the *second harmonic,* the $m = 3$ wave is called the *third harmonic,* and so on. The frequencies above the fundamental frequency, the harmonics with $m = 2, 3, 4, \ldots$, are referred to as the **higher harmonics.**

EXAMPLE 16.2 **Identifying harmonics on a string**

A 2.50-m-long string vibrates as a 100 Hz standing wave with nodes at 1.00 m and 1.50 m from one end of the string and at no points in between these two. Which harmonic is this? What is the string's fundamental frequency? And what is the speed of the traveling waves on the string?

PREPARE We begin with the visual overview in FIGURE 16.15, in which we sketch this particular standing wave and note the known and unknown quantities. We set up an x-axis with one end

FIGURE 16.15 A visual overview of the string.

(a) We know that there are nodes at these positions. There must be nodes here as well.

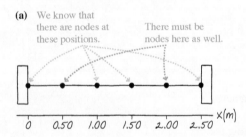

(b) The mode with nodes at these positions looks like this.

Known
$L = 2.50 \text{ m}$
$f_m = 100 \text{ Hz}$

Find
m, f_1, v

of the string at $x = 0$ m and the other end at $x = 2.50$ m. The ends of the string are nodes, and there are nodes at 1.00 m and 1.50 m as well, with no nodes in between. We know that standing-wave nodes are equally spaced, so there must be other nodes on the string, as shown in Figure 16.15a. Figure 16.15b is a sketch of the standing-wave mode with this node structure.

SOLVE We count the number of antinodes of the standing wave to deduce the mode number; this is mode $m = 5$. This is the fifth harmonic. The frequencies of the harmonics are given by $f_m = mf_1$, so the fundamental frequency is

$$f_1 = \frac{f_5}{5} = \frac{100 \text{ Hz}}{5} = 20 \text{ Hz}$$

The wavelength of the fundamental mode is $\lambda_1 = 2L = 2(2.50 \text{ m}) = 5.00$ m, so can find the wave speed using the fundamental relationship for sinusoidal waves:

$$v = f_1\lambda_1 = (20 \text{ Hz})(5.00 \text{ m}) = 100 \text{ m/s}$$

ASSESS We can calculate the speed of the wave using any possible mode, which gives us a way to check our work. The distance between successive nodes is $\lambda/2$. Figure 16.15 shows that the nodes are spaced by 0.50 m, so the wavelength of the $m = 5$ mode is 1.00 m. The frequency of this mode is 100 Hz, so we calculate

$$v = f_5\lambda_5 = (100 \text{ Hz})(1.00 \text{ m}) = 100 \text{ m/s}$$

This is the same speed that we calculated earlier, which gives us confidence in our results.

Stringed Musical Instruments

Think about stringed musical instruments, such as the guitar, the piano, and the violin. These instruments all have strings that are fixed at both ends and tightened to create tension. A disturbance is generated on the string by plucking, striking, or bowing. Regardless of how it is generated, the disturbance creates standing waves on the string. Understanding the sound of a stringed musical instrument means understanding standing waves.

In Chapter 15, we saw that the speed of a wave on a stretched string depended on T_s, the tension in the string, and μ, the linear density, as $v = \sqrt{T_s/\mu}$. Combining this with Equation 16.3, we find that the fundamental frequency of a stretched string is

$$f_1 = \frac{v}{2L} = \frac{1}{2L}\sqrt{\frac{T_s}{\mu}} \qquad (16.5)$$

When you pluck or bow a string, you initially excite a wide range of frequencies. However, resonance sees to it that the only frequencies to persist are those of the possible standing waves. The string will support a wave of the fundamental frequency f_1 plus waves of all the higher harmonics f_2, f_3, f_4, and so on. Your brain interprets the sound as a musical note of frequency f_1; the higher harmonics determine the *tone quality*, a concept we will explore later in the chapter.

NOTE ▶ In Equation 16.5, v is the wave speed *on the string,* not the speed of sound in air. ◀

For instruments like the guitar or the violin, the strings are all the same length and under approximately the same tension. Were that not the case, the neck of the instrument would tend to twist toward the side of higher tension. The strings have different frequencies because they differ in linear density. The lower-pitched strings are "fat" while the higher-pitched strings are "skinny." This difference changes the frequency by changing the wave speed. Small adjustments are then made in the tension to bring each string to the exact desired frequency.

Standing waves on a bridge This photo shows the Tacoma Narrows suspension bridge on the day in 1940 when it experienced a catastrophic oscillation that led to its collapse. Aerodynamic forces caused the amplitude of a particular resonant mode of the bridge to increase dramatically until the bridge failed. In this photo, the red line shows the original line of the deck of the bridge. You can clearly see the large amplitude of the oscillation and the node at the center of the span.

CONCEPTUAL EXAMPLE 16.3 Tuning and playing a guitar

A guitar has strings of a fixed length. Plucking a string makes a particular musical note. A player can make other notes by pressing the string against frets, metal bars on the neck of the guitar, as shown in FIGURE 16.16. The fret becomes the new end of the string, making the effective length shorter.

FIGURE 16.16 Guitar frets.

a. A guitar player plucks a string to play a note. He then presses down on a fret to make the string shorter. Does the new note have a higher or lower frequency?

b. The frequency of one string is too low. (Musically, we say the note is "flat.") How must the tension be adjusted to bring the string to the right frequency?

REASON

a. The fundamental frequency, the note we hear, is $f_1 = (1/2L)\sqrt{T_s/\mu}$. Because f_1 is inversely proportional to L, decreasing the string length increases the frequency.

b. Because f is proportional to the square root of T_s, the player must increase the tension to increase the fundamental frequency.

ASSESS If you watch someone play a guitar, you can see that he or she plays higher notes by moving the fingers to shorten the strings.

EXAMPLE 16.4 Setting the tension in a guitar string

The fifth string on a guitar plays the musical note A, at a frequency of 110 Hz. On a typical guitar, this string is stretched between two fixed points 0.640 m apart, and this length of string has a mass of 2.86 g. What is the tension in the string?

PREPARE Strings sound at their fundamental frequency, so 110 Hz is f_1.

SOLVE The linear density of the string is

$$\mu = \frac{m}{L} = \frac{2.86 \times 10^{-3}\text{ kg}}{0.640\text{ m}} = 4.47 \times 10^{-3}\text{ kg/m}$$

We can rearrange Equation 16.5 for the fundamental frequency to solve for the tension in terms of the other variables:

$$T_s = (2Lf_1)^2\mu = [2(0.640\text{ m})(110\text{ Hz})]^2 (4.47 \times 10^{-3}\text{ kg/m})$$

$$= 88.6\text{ N}$$

ASSESS If you have ever strummed a guitar, you know that the tension is quite large, so this result seems reasonable. If each of the guitar's six strings has approximately the same tension, the total force on the neck of the guitar is a bit more than 500 N.

PhET: Wave Interference

FIGURE 16.17 A laser contains a standing light wave between two parallel mirrors.

Laser cavity

Standing light wave

Full reflector

Laser beam

Partial reflector

Standing Electromagnetic Waves

The standing-wave descriptions we've found for a vibrating string are valid for any transverse wave, including an electromagnetic wave. For example, standing light waves can be established between two parallel mirrors that reflect the light back and forth. The mirrors are boundaries, analogous to the boundaries at the ends of a string. In fact, this is exactly how a laser works. The two facing mirrors in FIGURE 16.17 form what is called a *laser cavity.*

Because the mirrors act exactly like the points to which a string is tied, the light wave must have a node at the surface of each mirror. (To allow some of the light to escape the laser cavity and form the *laser beam,* one of the mirrors lets some of the light through. This doesn't affect the node.)

Microwave modes A microwave oven uses a type of electromagnetic wave—microwaves, with a wavelength of about 12 cm—to heat food. The inside walls of a microwave oven are reflective to microwaves, so we have the correct conditions to set up a standing wave. This isn't a good thing! A standing wave has high intensity at the antinodes and low intensity at the nodes, so your oven has hot spots and cold spots, as we see in this thermal image showing the interior of an oven with a thin layer of water that has been "cooked" for a short time. A turntable in a microwave oven keeps the food moving so that no part of your dinner remains at a node or an antinode.

EXAMPLE 16.5   Finding the mode number for a laser

A helium-neon laser emits light of wavelength $\lambda = 633$ nm. A typical cavity for such a laser is 15.0 cm long. What is the mode number of the standing wave in this cavity?

PREPARE Because a light wave is a transverse wave, Equation 16.1 for λ_m applies to a laser as well as a vibrating string.

SOLVE The standing light wave in a laser cavity has a mode number m that is roughly

$$m = \frac{2L}{\lambda} = \frac{2 \times 0.150 \text{ m}}{633 \times 10^{-9} \text{ m}} = 474,000$$

ASSESS The wavelength of light is very short, so we'd expect the nodes to be closely spaced. A high mode number seems reasonable.

STOP TO THINK 16.2 A standing wave on a string is shown. Which of the modes shown below (on the same string) has twice the frequency of the original wave?

Original standing wave

A.   B.   C.   D.

Class Video

16.4 Standing Sound Waves

Wind instruments like flutes, trumpets, and didgeridoos work very differently from stringed instruments. The player blows air into one end of a tube, producing standing waves of sound that make the notes we hear. In this section, we will look at the properties of such standing sound waves.

Recall that a sound wave is a longitudinal pressure wave. The air molecules oscillate back and forth parallel to the direction in which the wave is traveling, creating *compressions* (regions of higher pressure) and *rarefactions* (regions of lower pressure). Consider a sound wave confined to a long, narrow column of air, such as the air in a tube. A wave traveling down the tube eventually reaches the end, where it encounters the atmospheric pressure of the surrounding environment. This is a discontinuity, much like the small rope meeting the big rope in Figure 16.10b. Part of the wave's energy is transmitted out into the environment, allowing you to hear the sound, and part is reflected back into the tube. Reflections at both ends of the tube create waves traveling both directions inside the tube, and their superposition, like that of the reflecting waves on a string, is a standing wave.

We start by looking at a sound wave in a tube open at both ends. What kind of standing waves can exist in such a tube? Because the ends of the tube are open to the atmosphere, the pressure at the ends is fixed at atmospheric pressure and cannot vary. This is analogous to a stretched string that is fixed at the end. As a result, **the open end of a column of air must be a node of the pressure wave.**

FIGURE 16.18a shows a column of air open at both ends. We call this an *open-open tube*. Whereas the antinodes of a standing wave on a string are points where the string oscillates with maximum displacement, the antinodes of a standing sound wave are where the pressure has the largest variation, creating, alternately, the maximum compression and the maximum rarefaction. In Figure 16.18a, the air molecules squeeze together on the left side of the tube. Then, in FIGURE 16.18b, half a cycle later, the air molecules squeeze together on the right side. The varying density creates a variation in pressure across the tube, as the graphs show. FIGURE 16.18c combines the information of Figures 16.18a and 16.18b into a graph of the pressure of the standing sound wave in the tube.

As the standing wave oscillates, the air molecules "slosh" back and forth along the tube with the wave frequency, alternately pushing together (maximum pressure at the antinode) and pulling apart (minimum pressure at the antinode). This makes sense, because sound is a longitudinal wave in which the air molecules oscillate parallel to the tube.

NOTE ▶ The variation in pressure from atmospheric pressure in a real standing sound wave is much smaller than Figure 16.18 implies. When we display graphs of the pressure in sound waves, we won't generally graph the pressure p. Instead, we will graph Δp, the variation from atmospheric pressure. ◀

Many musical instruments, such as a flute, can be modeled as open-open tubes. The flutist blows across one end to create a standing wave inside the tube, and a note of this frequency is emitted from both ends of the flute. The possible standing waves in tubes, like standing waves on strings, are resonances of the system. A gentle puff of air across the mouthpiece of a flute can cause large standing waves at these resonant frequencies.

Other instruments work differently from the flute. A trumpet or a clarinet is a column of air open at the bell end but *closed* by the player's lips at the mouthpiece. To be complete in our treatment of sound waves in tubes, we need to consider tubes that are closed at one or both ends. At a closed end, the air molecules can alternately rush toward the wall, creating a compression, and then rush away from the wall, leaving a rarefaction. Thus **a closed end of an air column is an antinode of pressure.**

FIGURE 16.19 shows graphs of the first three standing-wave modes of a tube open at both ends (an *open-open tube*), a tube closed at both ends (a *closed-closed tube*), and a tube open at one end but closed at the other (an *open-closed tube*), all with the same length L. These are graphs of the pressure wave, with a node at open ends and an antinode at closed ends. The standing wave in the closed-closed tube looks like the wave in the open-open tube except that the positions of the nodes and antinodes are interchanged. In both cases there are m half-wavelength segments between the

FIGURE 16.18 The $m = 2$ standing sound wave inside an open-open column of air.

(a) At one instant

(b) Half a cycle later

The shift between compression and rarefaction means a motion of molecules along the tube.

(c) At the ends of the tube, the pressure is equal to atmospheric pressure. These are nodes.

At the antinodes, each cycle sees a change from compression to rarefaction and back to compression.

FIGURE 16.19 The first three standing sound wave modes in columns of air with different ends. These graphs show the pressure variation in the tube.

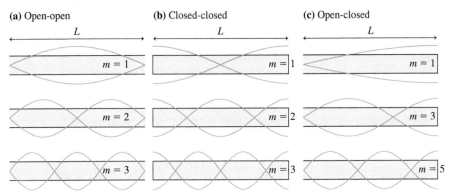

ends; thus the wavelengths and frequencies of an open-open tube and a closed-closed tube are the same as those of a string tied at both ends:

$$\lambda_m = \frac{2L}{m}$$
$$f_m = m\left(\frac{v}{2L}\right) = mf_1 \qquad m = 1, 2, 3, 4, \dots \qquad (16.6)$$

Wavelengths and frequencies of standing sound wave modes
in an open-open or closed-closed tube

The open-closed tube is different, as we can see from Figure 16.19. The $m = 1$ mode has a node at one and an antinode at the other, and so has only one-quarter of a wavelength in a tube of length L. The $m = 1$ wavelength is $\lambda_1 = 4L$, twice the $m = 1$ wavelength of an open-open or a closed-closed tube. Consequently, **the fundamental frequency of an open-closed tube is half that of an open-open or a closed-closed tube of the same length.**

The wavelength of the next mode of the open-closed tube is $4L/3$. Because this is $1/3$ of λ_1, we assign $m = 3$ to this mode. The wavelength of the subsequent mode is $4L/5$, so this is $m = 5$. In other words, an open-closed tube allows only odd-numbered modes. Consequently, the possible wavelengths and frequencies are

$$\lambda_m = \frac{4L}{m}$$
$$f_m = m\left(\frac{v}{4L}\right) = mf_1 \qquad m = 1, 3, 5, 7, \dots \qquad (16.7)$$

Wavelengths and frequencies of standing sound wave modes
in an open-closed tube

Fiery interference In this apparatus, a speaker at one end of the metal tube emits a sinusoidal wave. The wave reflects from the other end, which is closed, to make a counter-propagating wave and set up a standing sound wave in the tube. The tube is filled with propane gas that exits through small holes on top. The burning propane allows us to easily discern the nodes and the antinodes of the standing sound wave. An exciting demonstration—but one you shouldn't try yourself!

NOTE ▶ Because sound is a pressure wave, the graphs of Figure 16.19 are *not* "pictures" of the wave as they are for a string wave. The graphs show the pressure variation versus position x. The tube itself is shown merely to indicate the location of the open and closed ends, but the diameter of the tube is *not* related to the amplitude of the wave. ◀

We are now in a position to suggest the following problem-solving strategy, not just for sound waves, but for any standing wave.

PROBLEM-SOLVING
STRATEGY 16.1   **Standing waves**

PREPARE
- For sound waves, determine what sort of pipe or tube you have: open-open, closed-closed, or open-closed.
- For string or light waves, the ends will be fixed points.
- Determine known values: length of the tube or string, frequency, wavelength, positions of nodes or antinodes.
- It may be useful to sketch a visual overview, including a picture of the relevant mode.

SOLVE For a string, the allowed frequencies and wavelengths are given by Equations 16.1 and 16.2. For sound waves in an open-open or closed-closed tube, the allowed frequencies and wavelengths are given by Equation 16.6; for an open-closed tube, by Equation 16.7.

ASSESS Does your final answer seem reasonable? Is there another way to check on your results? For example, the frequency times the wavelength for any mode should equal the wave speed—you can check to see that it does.

EXAMPLE 16.6 **Resonances of the ear canal**

The eardrum, which transmits vibrations to the sensory organs of your ear, lies at the end of the ear canal. As FIGURE 16.20 shows, the ear canal in adults is about 2.5 cm in length. What frequency standing waves can occur within the ear canal that are within the range of human hearing? The speed of sound in the warm air of the ear canal is 350 m/s.

FIGURE 16.20 The anatomy of the ear.

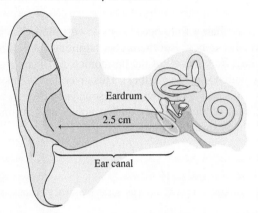

PREPARE We proceed according to the steps in Problem-Solving Strategy 16.1. We can treat the ear canal as an open-closed tube: open to the atmosphere at the external end, closed by the eardrum at the other end. The possible standing-wave modes appear as in Figure 16.19c. The length of the tube is 2.5 cm.

SOLVE Equation 16.7 gives the allowed frequencies in an open-closed tube. We are looking for the frequencies in the range 20 Hz–20,000 Hz. The fundamental frequency is

$$f_1 = \frac{v}{4L} = \frac{350 \text{ m/s}}{4(0.025 \text{ m})} = 3500 \text{ Hz}$$

The higher harmonics are odd multiples of this frequency:

$$f_3 = 3(3500 \text{ Hz}) = 10,500 \text{ Hz}$$

$$f_5 = 5(3500 \text{ Hz}) = 17,500 \text{ Hz}$$

These three modes lie within the range of human hearing; higher modes are greater than 20,000 Hz.

ASSESS The ear canal is short, so we expect the resonant frequencies to be high; our answers seem reasonable.

How important are the resonances of the ear canal calculated in Example 16.6? In Chapter 15, you learned about the decibel scale for measuring loudness of sound. In fact, your ears have varying sensitivity to sounds of different frequencies. FIGURE 16.21 shows a curve of *equal perceived loudness,* the sound intensity level (in dB) required to give the *impression* of equal loudness for sinusoidal waves of the noted frequency. Lower values mean that your ear is more sensitive at that frequency. In general, the curve decreases to about 1000 Hz, the frequency at which your hearing is most acute, then slowly rises at higher frequencies. However, this general trend is punctuated by two dips in the curve, showing two frequencies at which a quieter sound produces the same perceived loudness. As you can see, these two dips correspond to the resonances f_1 and f_3 of the ear canal. Incoming sounds at these frequencies produce a larger oscillation, resulting in an increased sensitivity to these frequencies.

FIGURE 16.21 A curve of equal perceived loudness.

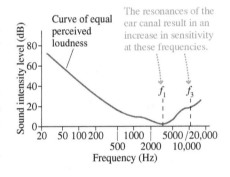

Wind Instruments

With a wind instrument, blowing into the mouthpiece creates a standing sound wave inside a tube of air. The player changes the notes by using her fingers to cover holes or open valves, changing the effective length of the tube. The first open hole becomes a node because the tube is open to the atmosphere at that point. The fact that the holes are on the side, rather than literally at the end, makes very little difference. The length of the tube determines the standing-wave resonances, and thus the musical note that the instrument produces.

Many wind instruments have a "buzzer" at one end of the tube, such as a vibrating reed on a saxophone or clarinet, or the musician's vibrating lips on a trumpet or trombone. Buzzers like these generate a continuous range of frequencies rather than single notes, which is why they sound like a "squawk" if you play on just the mouthpiece without the rest of the instrument. When the buzzer is connected to the body of the instrument, most of those frequencies cause little response. But the frequencies from the buzzer that match the resonant frequencies of the instrument cause the buildup of large amplitudes at these frequencies—standing-wave resonances. The combination of these frequencies makes the musical note that we hear.

Truly classical music The oldest known musical instruments are bone flutes from burial sites in central China. The flutes in the photo are up to 9000 years old and are made from naturally hollow bones from crowned cranes. The positions of the holes determine the frequencies that the flutes can produce. Soon after the first flutes were created, the design was standardized so that different flutes would play the same notes—including the notes in the modern Chinese musical scale.

CONCEPTUAL EXAMPLE 16.7 **Comparing the flute and the clarinet**

A flute and a clarinet have about the same length, but the lowest note that can be played on the clarinet is much lower than the lowest note that can be played on the flute. Why is this?

REASON A flute is an open-open tube; the frequency of the fundamental mode is $f_1 = v/2L$. A clarinet is open at one end, but the player's lips and the reed close it at the other end. The clarinet is thus an open-closed tube with a fundamental frequency $f_1 = v/4L$.

This is about half the fundamental frequency of the flute, so the lowest note on the clarinet has a much lower pitch. In musical terms, it's about an octave lower than the flute.

ASSESS A quick glance at Figure 16.19 shows that the wavelength of the lowest mode of the open-closed tube is longer than that of the open-open tube, so we expect a lower frequency for the clarinet.

A clarinet has a lower pitch than a flute because its lowest mode has a longer wavelength and thus a lower frequency. But the higher harmonics are different as well. An open-open tube like a flute has all of the harmonics; an open-closed tube like a clarinet has only those with odd mode numbers. This gives the two instruments a very different tone quality—it's easy to distinguish the sound of a flute from that of a clarinet. We'll explore this connection between the harmonics an instrument produces and its tone quality in the next section.

EXAMPLE 16.8 **The importance of warming up**

Wind instruments have an adjustable joint to change the tube length. Players know that they may need to adjust this joint to stay in tune—that is, to stay at the correct frequency. To see why, suppose a "cold" flute plays the note A at 440 Hz when the air temperature is 20°C.

a. How long is the tube? At 20°C, the speed of sound in air is 343 m/s.
b. As the player blows air through the flute, the air inside the instrument warms up. Once the air temperature inside the flute has risen to 32°C, increasing the speed of sound to 350 m/s, what is the frequency?
c. At the higher temperature, how must the length of the tube be changed to bring the frequency back to 440 Hz?

SOLVE A flute is an open-open tube with fundamental frequency $f_1 = v/2L$.

a. At 20°C, the length corresponding to 440 Hz is

$$L = \frac{v}{2f} = \frac{343 \text{ m/s}}{2(440 \text{ Hz})} = 0.390 \text{ m}$$

b. As the speed of sound increases, the frequency changes to

$$f_1(\text{at } 32°C) = \frac{350 \text{ m/s}}{2(0.390 \text{ m})} = 449 \text{ Hz}$$

c. To bring the flute back into tune, the length must be increased to give a frequency of 440 Hz with a speed of 350 m/s. The new length is

$$L = \frac{v}{2f_1} = \frac{350 \text{ m/s}}{2(440 \text{ Hz})} = 0.398 \text{ m}$$

Thus the flute must be increased in length by 8 mm.

ASSESS A small change in the absolute temperature produces a correspondingly small change in the speed of sound. We expect that this will require a small change in length, so our answer makes sense.

STOP TO THINK 16.3 A tube that is open at both ends supports a standing wave with harmonics at 300 Hz and 400 Hz, with no harmonics between. What is the fundamental frequency of this tube?

A. 50 Hz B. 100 Hz C. 150 Hz D. 200 Hz E. 300 Hz

16.5 Speech and Hearing

When you hear a particular note played on a guitar, it sounds very different from the same note played on a trumpet. And you have perhaps been to a lecture in which the speaker talked at essentially the same pitch the entire time—but you could still understand what was being said. Clearly, there is more to your brain's perception of sound than pitch alone. How do you tell the difference between a guitar and a trumpet? How do you distinguish between an "oo" vowel sound and an "ee" vowel sound at the same pitch?

The Frequency Spectrum

To this point, we have pictured sound waves as sinusoidal waves, with a well-defined frequency. In fact, most of the sounds that you hear are not pure sinusoidal waves. Most sounds are a mix, or superposition, of different frequencies. For example, we have seen how certain standing-wave modes are possible on a stretched string. When you pluck a string on a guitar, you generally don't excite just one standing-wave mode—you simultaneously excite many different modes.

If you play the note "middle C" on a guitar, the fundamental frequency is 262 Hz. There will be a standing wave at this frequency, but there will also be standing waves at the frequencies 524 Hz, 786 Hz, 1048 Hz, . . . , all the higher harmonics predicted by Equation 16.4.

FIGURE 16.22a is a bar chart showing all the frequencies present in the sound of the vibrating guitar string. The height of each bar shows the relative intensity of that harmonic. The fundamental frequency has the highest intensity, but many other harmonics have significant intensities as well. A bar chart showing the relative intensities of the different frequencies is called the **frequency spectrum** of the sound.

When your brain interprets the mix of frequencies from the guitar in Figure 16.22a, it identifies the fundamental frequency as the *pitch*. 262 Hz corresponds to middle C, so you will identify the pitch as middle C, even though the sound consists of many different frequencies. Your brain uses the higher harmonics to determine the **tone quality,** which is also called the *timbre*. The tone quality—and therefore the higher harmonics—is what makes a middle C played on a guitar sound quite different from a middle C played on a trumpet. The frequency spectrum of a trumpet would show a very different pattern of the relative intensities of the higher harmonics, and this different mix of higher harmonics gives the trumpet a different sound.

The actual sound wave produced by a guitar playing middle C is shown in FIGURE 16.22b. The sound wave is periodic, with a period of 3.82 ms that corresponds to the 262 Hz fundamental frequency. But the wave doesn't have a simple sinusoidal shape; it is more complex. **The higher harmonics don't change the period of the sound wave; they change only its shape.** The sound wave of a trumpet playing middle C would also have a 3.82 ms period, but its shape would be entirely different.

FIGURE 16.22 The frequency spectrum and a graph of the sound wave of a guitar playing a note with fundamental frequency 262 Hz.

(a)

(b)

The vertical axis is the change in pressure from atmospheric pressure due to the sound wave.

CONCEPTUAL EXAMPLE 16.9	Playing the didgeridoo

The didgeridoo, a musical instrument developed by aboriginal Australians, is deceptively simple. It consists of a tube (a eucalyptus stem or branch hollowed out by termites) of $1\frac{1}{2}$m or more in length. The player presses his lips against the end and blows air through his lips as with a trumpet. He may also make sounds with his vocal cords. Skilled players can make a wide variety of sounds. How is this possible with such a simple instrument?

REASON Because the lips seal one end, a didgeridoo has the resonances of an open-closed tube, given by Equation 16.7. The instrument can therefore produce many different frequencies. Changing the vibration of the lips and the sounds from the vocal cords can change the mix of standing-wave modes that are produced, leading to very different sounds.

Vowels and Formants

Try this: Keep your voice at the same pitch and say the "ee" sound, as in "beet," then the "oo" sound, as in "boot." Pay attention to how you reshape your mouth as you

One instrument, many sounds A synthesizer can be adjusted to sound like a flute, a clarinet, a trumpet, a piano—or any other musical instrument. The keys on a synthesizer determine what fundamental frequency to produce. The other controls adjust the mix of higher harmonics to match the frequency spectrum of various musical instruments, effectively mimicking their sounds.

FIGURE 16.23 The frequency spectrum from the vocal cords, and after passing through the vocal tract.

(a) Frequencies from the vocal cords

When you speak, your vocal cords produce a mix of frequencies.

(b) Actual spoken frequencies (vowel sound "ee")

When you form your vocal tract to make a certain vowel sound, it increases the amplitudes of certain frequencies and suppresses others.

The broad peaks at which amplification occurs are due to filtering by the formants.

First formant

Second formant

Saying "ah" BIO Why, during a throat exam, does a doctor ask you to say "ah"? This particular vowel sound is formed by opening the mouth and the back of the throat wide—giving a clear view of the tissues of the throat.

move back and forth between the two sounds. The two vowel sounds are at the same pitch, and thus have the same period, but they sound quite different. The difference in sound arises from the difference in the higher harmonics, just as for musical instruments. As you speak, you adjust the properties of your vocal tract to produce different mixes of harmonics that make the "ee," "oo," "ah," and other vowel sounds.

Speech begins with the vibration of your vocal cords, stretched bands of tissue in your throat. The vibration is similar to that of a wave on a stretched string. In ordinary speech, the average fundamental frequency for adult males and females is about 150 Hz and 250 Hz, respectively, but you can change the vibration frequency by changing the tension of your vocal cords. That's how you make your voice higher or lower as you sing.

Your vocal cords produce a mix of different frequencies as they vibrate—the fundamental frequency and a rich mixture of higher harmonics. If you put a microphone in your throat and measured the sound waves right at your vocal cords the frequency spectrum would appear as in FIGURE 16.23a.

There is more to the story though. Before reaching the opening of your mouth, sound from your vocal cords must pass through your vocal tract—a series of hollow cavities including your throat, mouth, and nose. The vocal tract acts like a series of tubes, and, as in any tube, certain frequencies will set up standing-wave resonances. The rather broad standing-wave resonances of the vocal tract are called **formants.** Harmonics of your vocal cords at or near the formant frequencies will be amplified; harmonics far from a formant will be suppressed. FIGURE 16.23b shows the formants of an adult male making an "ee" sound. The filtering of the vocal cord harmonics by the formants is clear.

You can change the shape and frequencies of the formants, and thus the sound you make, by changing the shape and length of your vocal tract. You do this by changing your mouth opening and the shape and position of your tongue. The first two formants for an "ee" sound are at roughly 270 Hz and 2300 Hz, but for an "oo" sound they are 300 Hz and 870 Hz. The much lower second formant of the "oo" emphasizes midrange frequencies, making a "calming" sound, while the more strident sound of "ee" comes from enhancing the higher frequencies.

CONCEPTUAL EXAMPLE 16.10 **High-frequency hearing loss**

As you age, your hearing sensitivity will decrease. This decrease is not uniform; for most people, the loss of sensitivity is greater for higher frequencies. The loss of sensitivity at high frequencies may make it difficult to understand what others are saying. Why is this?

REASON It is the high-frequency components of speech that allow us to distinguish different vowel sounds. A decrease in sensitivity to these higher frequencies makes it more difficult to make such distinctions.

ASSESS This result makes sense. In Figure 16.23b, the lowest frequency is less than 200 Hz, but the second formant is over 2000 Hz. There's a big difference between what we hear as the pitch of someone's voice and the frequencies we use to interpret speech.

STOP TO THINK 16.4 These sound waves represent notes played on different musical instruments. Which has the highest pitch?

16.6 The Interference of Waves from Two Sources

Perhaps you have seen headphones that offer "active noise reduction." When you turn on the headphones, they produce sound that somehow *cancels* noise from the external environment. How does adding sound to a system make it quieter?

We began the chapter by noting that waves, unlike particles, can pass through each other. Where they do, the principle of superposition tells us that the displacement of the medium is the sum of the displacements due to each wave acting alone. Consider the two loudspeakers in FIGURE 16.24, both emitting sound waves with the same frequency. In Figure 16.24a, sound from loudspeaker 2 passes loudspeaker 1, then two overlapped sound waves travel to the right along the *x*-axis. What sound is heard at the point indicated with the dot? And what about at the dot in Figure 16.24b, where the speakers are side by side? These are two cases we will consider in this section. Although we'll use sound waves for our discussion, the results are general and apply to all waves. In Chapter 17, we will use these ideas to study the interference of light waves.

Interference Along a Line

FIGURE 16.25 shows traveling waves from two loudspeakers spaced exactly one wavelength apart. The graphs are slightly displaced from each other so that you can see what each wave is doing, but the *physical situation* is one in which the waves are traveling *on top of* each other. We assume that the two speakers emit sound waves of identical frequency f, wavelength λ, and amplitude A.

At every point along the line, the net sound pressure wave will be the sum of the pressures from the individual waves. That's the principle of superposition. Because the two speakers are separated by one wavelength, the two waves are aligned crest-to-crest and trough-to-trough. Waves aligned this way are said to be **in phase;** waves that are in phase march along "in step" with each other. The superposition is a traveling wave with wavelength λ and twice the amplitude of the individual waves. This is constructive interference.

> NOTE ▶ Textbook pictures can be misleading because they're frozen in time. The net sound wave in Figure 16.25 is a *traveling* wave, moving to the right with the speed of sound v. It differs from the two individual waves only by having twice the amplitude. This is not a standing wave with nodes and antinodes that remain in one place. ◀

If d_1 and d_2 are the distances from loudspeakers 1 and 2 to a point at which we want to know the combined sound wave, their difference $\Delta d = d_2 - d_1$ is called the **path-length difference.** It is the *extra* distance traveled by wave 2 on the way to the point where the two waves are combined. In Figure 16.25, we see that constructive interference results from a path-length difference $\Delta d = \lambda$. But increasing Δd by an additional λ would produce exactly the same result, so we will also have constructive interference for $\Delta d = 2\lambda$, $\Delta d = 3\lambda$, and so on. In other words, **two waves will be in phase and will produce constructive interference any time their path-length difference is a whole number of wavelengths.**

In FIGURE 16.26, the two speakers are separated by half a wavelength. Now the crests of one wave align with the troughs of the other, and the waves march along "out of step" with each other. We say that the two waves are **out of phase.** When two waves are out of phase, they are equal and opposite at every point. Consequently, the sum of the two waves is zero *at every point*. This is destructive interference.

The destructive interference of Figure 16.26 results from a path-length difference $\Delta d = \frac{1}{2}\lambda$. Again, increasing Δd by an additional λ would produce a picture that looks exactly the same, so we will also have destructive interference for $\Delta d = 1\frac{1}{2}\lambda$, $\Delta d = 2\frac{1}{2}\lambda$, and so on. That is, **two waves will be out of phase and will produce destructive interference any time their path-length difference is a whole number of wavelengths plus half a wavelength.**

FIGURE 16.24 Interference of waves from two sources.

(a) Two sound waves overlapping along a line

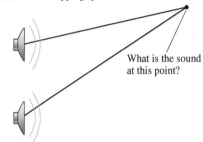

Speaker 2   Speaker 1   What is the sound at this point?

(b) Two overlapping spherical sound waves

What is the sound at this point?

FIGURE 16.25 Constructive interference of two waves traveling along the *x*-axis.

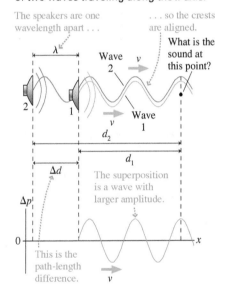

The speakers are one wavelength apart . . . . . . so the crests are aligned.

What is the sound at this point?

Wave 2 v

Wave 1 v

d_2

d_1

Δd

The superposition is a wave with larger amplitude.

Δp

0 ——— x

This is the path-length difference. v

FIGURE 16.26 Destructive interference of two waves traveling along the *x*-axis.

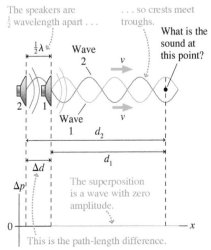

The speakers are $\frac{1}{2}$ wavelength apart . . . . . . so crests meet troughs.

What is the sound at this point?

Wave 2 v

Wave 1 v d_2

d_1

Δd

The superposition is a wave with zero amplitude.

Δp

0 ——— x

This is the path-length difference.

Summing up, for two identical sources of waves, constructive interference occurs when the path-length difference is

$$\Delta d = m\lambda \qquad m = 0, 1, 2, 3, \ldots \tag{16.8}$$

and destructive interference occurs when the path-length difference is

$$\Delta d = \left(m + \frac{1}{2} \right)\lambda \qquad m = 0, 1, 2, 3, \ldots \tag{16.9}$$

NOTE ▶ The path-length difference needed for constructive or destructive interference depends on the wavelength and hence the frequency. If one particular frequency interferes destructively, another may not. ◀

The path-length difference is not necessarily the distance between the speakers, as we see in the next example. It is simply the difference in the distances traveled by the two waves.

EXAMPLE 16.11   Is the sound loud or quiet? Part I

Two loudspeakers 42.0 m apart and facing each other emit identical 115 Hz sinusoidal sound waves. Susan is walking along a line between the speakers. As she walks, she finds herself moving through loud and quiet spots. If Susan stands 19.5 m from one speaker, is she standing at a quiet spot or a loud spot? Assume that the speed of sound is 345 m/s.

PREPARE As Susan walks along the line between the speakers, she moves between points of constructive interference (loud spots) and destructive interference (quiet spots). Is her current position one of constructive or destructive interference? This will depend on the path-length difference. We start with a visual overview of the situation in FIGURE 16.27.

FIGURE 16.27 Visual overview of loudspeakers.

Known
$f = 115$ Hz
$v = 345$ m/s

Find
$\Delta d = d_2 - d_1$

SOLVE At Susan's position, the distances the two waves travel to reach her are

$$d_1 = 19.5 \text{ m} \qquad d_2 = 42.0 \text{ m} - 19.5 \text{ m} = 22.5 \text{ m}$$

At the point where the two waves reach Susan and interfere, their path-length difference is

$$\Delta d = d_2 - d_1 = 3.0 \text{ m}$$

To know if we have constructive or destructive interference, we need to compare this with the wavelength:

$$\lambda = \frac{v}{f} = \frac{345 \text{ m/s}}{115 \text{ Hz}} = 3.0 \text{ m}$$

Because the path-length difference is exactly one wavelength, Susan is standing at a point of constructive interference; that is, she is standing at a loud spot.

ASSESS There's a nice way that we can check to see that our answer makes sense. As you'll recall from earlier in the chapter, two counterpropagating waves create a standing wave. In this case, the conditions for constructive and destructive interference are the same as the conditions for antinodes and nodes, respectively, that we found earlier. Susan is at an antinode of the standing wave. The ideas of interference give us a different perspective on standing waves.

FIGURE 16.28 Opposite waves cancel.

At each position, the wave from speaker 2 is opposite that from speaker 1.

Speaker 1

Speaker 2

Δp

The superposition is thus a wave with zero amplitude at all points.

The analysis above assumed that the two loudspeakers were emitting identical waves. Another interesting and important case of interference, illustrated in FIGURE 16.28, occurs when one loudspeaker emits a sound wave that is *the exact inverse* of the wave from the other speaker. If the speakers are side by side, so that $\Delta d = 0$, the superposition of these two waves will result in destructive interference; they will completely cancel. This destructive interference does not require the waves to have any particular frequency or any particular shape.

Headphones with *active noise reduction* use this technique. A microphone on the outside of the headphones measures ambient sound. A circuit inside the headphones produces an inverted version of the microphone signal and sends it to the headphone speakers. The ambient sound and the inverted version of the sound from the speakers arrive at the ears together and interfere destructively, reducing the sound intensity. In this case, *adding* sound results in a *lower* overall intensity inside the headphones!

Interference of Spherical Waves

Interference along a line illustrates the idea of interference, but it's not very realistic. In practice, sound waves from a loudspeaker or light waves from a lightbulb spread out as spherical waves. FIGURE 16.29 shows a wave-front diagram for a spherical wave. Recall that the wave fronts represent the *crests* of the wave and are spaced by the wavelength λ. Halfway between two wave fronts is a trough of the wave. What happens when two spherical waves overlap? For example, imagine two loudspeakers emitting identical waves radiating sound in all directions. FIGURE 16.30 shows the wave fronts of the two waves. This is a static picture, of course, so you have to imagine the wave fronts spreading out as new circular rings are born at the speakers. The waves overlap as they travel, and, as was the case in one dimension, this causes interference.

Consider a particular point like that marked by the red dot in Figure 16.30. The two waves each have a crest at this point, so there is constructive interference here. But at other points, such as that marked by the black dot, a crest overlaps a trough, so this is a point of destructive interference.

Notice—simply by counting the wave fronts—that the red dot is three wavelengths from speaker 2 ($r_2 = 3\lambda$) but only two wavelengths from speaker 1 ($r_1 = 2\lambda$). The path-length difference of the two waves arriving at the red dot is $\Delta r = r_2 - r_1 = \lambda$. That is, the wave from speaker 2 has to travel one full wavelength more than the wave from speaker 1, so the waves are in phase (crest aligned with crest) and interfere constructively. You should convince yourself that Δr is a *whole number of wavelengths* at every point where two wave fronts intersect.

Similarly, the path-length difference at the black dot, where the interference is destructive, is $\Delta r = \frac{1}{2}\lambda$. As with interference along a line, destructive interference results when the path-length difference is a whole number of wavelengths plus half a wavelength.

Thus the general rule for determining whether there is constructive or destructive interference at any point is the same for spherical waves as for waves traveling along a line. For identical sources, constructive interference occurs when the path-length difference is

$$\Delta r = m\lambda \qquad m = 0, 1, 2, 3, \ldots \qquad (16.10)$$

Destructive interference occurs when the path-length difference is

$$\Delta r = \left(m + \frac{1}{2}\right)\lambda \qquad m = 0, 1, 2, 3, \ldots \qquad (16.11)$$

The conditions for constructive and destructive interference are the same for spherical waves as for waves along a line. And the treatment we have seen for sound waves can be applied to any wave, as we have noted. For any two wave sources, the following Tactics Box sums up how to determine if the interference at a point is constructive or destructive.

TACTICS BOX 16.1 Identifying constructive and destructive interference (MP)

❶ Identify the path length from each source to the point of interest. Compute the path-length difference $\Delta r = |r_2 - r_1|$.

❷ Find the wavelength, if it is not specified.

❸ If the path-length difference is a whole number of wavelengths ($\lambda, 2\lambda, 3\lambda, \ldots$), crests are aligned with crests and there is constructive interference.

❹ If the path-length difference is a whole number of wavelengths plus a half wavelength ($1\frac{1}{2}\lambda, 2\frac{1}{2}\lambda, 3\frac{1}{2}\lambda, \ldots$), crests are aligned with troughs and there is destructive interference.

Exercises 9,10 ✐

NOTE ▶ Keep in mind that interference is determined by Δr, the path-length *difference*, not by r_1 or r_2. ◀

FIGURE 16.29 A spherical wave.

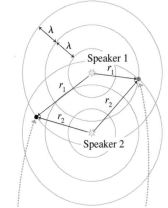

The wave fronts are crests, separated by λ.

Troughs are halfway between wave fronts.

Source

λ

v

r

This graph shows the crests and troughs of the wave.

FIGURE 16.30 The overlapping wave patterns of two sources.

Two sources emit identical spherical waves.

λ

λ

Speaker 1

r_1

r_1

r_2

r_2

r_2

Speaker 2

Destructive interference occurs where a crest overlaps a trough.

Constructive interference occurs where two crests overlap.

EXAMPLE 16.12 **Is the sound loud or quiet? Part II**

Two speakers are 3.0 m apart and play identical tones of frequency 170 Hz. Sam stands directly in front of one speaker at a distance of 4.0 m. Is this a loud spot or a quiet spot? Assume that the speed of sound in air is 340 m/s.

PREPARE FIGURE 16.31 shows a visual overview of the situation, showing the positions of and path lengths from each speaker.

FIGURE 16.31 Visual overview of two speakers.

SOLVE Following the steps in Tactics Box 16.1, we first compute the path-length difference. r_1, r_2, and the distance between the speakers form a right triangle, so we can use the Pythagorean theorem to find

$$r_2 = \sqrt{(4.0 \text{ m})^2 + (3.0 \text{ m})^2} = 5.0 \text{ m}$$

Thus the path-length difference is

$$\Delta r = r_2 - r_1 = 1.0 \text{ m}$$

Next, we compute the wavelength:

$$\lambda = \frac{v}{f} = \frac{340 \text{ m/s}}{170 \text{ Hz}} = 2.0 \text{ m}$$

The path-length difference is $\frac{1}{2}\lambda$, so this is a point of destructive interference. Sam is at a quiet spot.

Taming and tuning exhaust noise It's possible to use destructive interference to cut automobile exhaust noise using a device called a *resonator*. The wide section of pipe at the end of the exhaust system is a tube with one closed end. A sound wave enters the tube, reflects from the end, and reenters the exhaust pipe. If the length of the tube is just right, the reflected wave will be out of phase with the sound wave in the pipe, producing destructive interference. The resonator is tuned to eliminate the loudest frequencies from the engine, but other frequencies will produce constructive interference, enhancing them and giving the exhaust a certain "note."

So far, we have looked at interference only at particular points. What can we say about the overall pattern of points at which we have constructive or destructive interference? For instance, the red dot in Figure 16.30 is only one point where $\Delta r = \lambda$; you should be able to locate several more. Taken together, all the points with $\Delta r = \lambda$ form a curved line along which constructive interference is occurring. Another curved line of constructive interference connects all the points at which $\Delta r = 2\lambda$, another connects the $\Delta r = 3\lambda$ points, and so on. These lines, shown as red lines in FIGURE 16.32, are called **antinodal lines**. They are analogous to the antinodes of a standing wave—hence the name. An antinode is a *point* of constructive interference; for spherical waves, oscillation at maximum amplitude occurs along a continuous *line*. To understand this idea better, imagine the static picture of Figure 16.32 evolving with time. As the wave fronts expand, the *intersection point* of two rings moves outward along one of the red lines.

FIGURE 16.32 The points of constructive and destructive interference fall along antinodal and nodal lines.

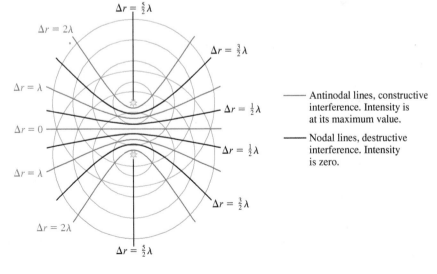

Similarly, we can connect together points where Δr is a multiple of λ plus $\frac{1}{2}\lambda$. The black dot in Figure 16.30 is just one of many points with $\Delta r = \frac{1}{2}\lambda$. Together, these points of destructive interference form a **nodal line** along which the displacement is always zero. The nodal lines in Figure 16.32 are shown in black.

You are regularly exposed to sound from two separated sources: stereo speakers. When you walk across a room in which a stereo is playing, why don't you hear a pattern of loud and soft sounds as you cross antinodal and nodal lines? First, we don't listen to single frequencies. Music is a complex sound wave with many frequencies, but only one frequency at a time satisfies the condition for constructive or destructive interference. Most of the sound frequencies are not affected. Second, reflections of sound waves from walls and furniture make the situation much more complex than the idealized two-source picture in Figure 16.32. Sound wave interference can be heard, but it takes careful selection of a pure tone and a room with no hard, reflecting surfaces. Interference that's rather tricky to demonstrate with sound waves is easy to produce with light waves, as we'll see in the next chapter.

The two water waves overlap, leading to patterns of constructive and destructive interference.

> **STOP TO THINK 16.5** These speakers emit identical sound waves with a wavelength of 1.0 m. At the point indicated, is the interference constructive, destructive, or something in between?

16.7 Beats

Thus far we have looked at the superposition of waves from sources having the same frequency. We can also use the principle of superposition to investigate a phenomenon that is easily demonstrated with two sources of slightly *different* frequencies.

Suppose two sinusoidal waves are traveling toward your ear, as shown in FIGURE 16.33. The two waves have the same amplitude but slightly different frequencies: The red wave has a slightly higher frequency (and thus a slightly shorter wavelength) than the orange wave. This slight difference causes the waves to combine in a manner that alternates between constructive and destructive interference. Their superposition, drawn in blue below the two waves, is a wave whose amplitude shows

ActivPhysics: 10.7

FIGURE 16.33 The superposition of two sound waves with slightly different frequencies.

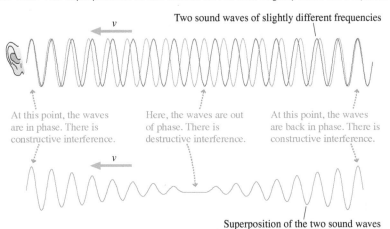

Two sound waves of slightly different frequencies

At this point, the waves are in phase. There is constructive interference.

Here, the waves are out of phase. There is destructive interference.

At this point, the waves are back in phase. There is constructive interference.

Superposition of the two sound waves

a periodic variation. As the waves reach your ear, you will hear a single tone whose intensity is *modulated*. That is, the sound goes up and down in volume, loud, soft, loud, soft, . . . , making a distinctive sound pattern called **beats**.

Suppose the two waves have frequencies f_1 and f_2 that differ only slightly, so that $f_1 \approx f_2$. A complete mathematical analysis would show that the air oscillates against your eardrum at frequency

$$f_{osc} = \frac{1}{2}(f_1 + f_2)$$

This is the *average* of f_1 and f_2, and it differs little from either since the two frequencies are nearly equal. Further, the intensity of the sound is modulated at a frequency called the *beat frequency*:

$$f_{beat} = |f_1 - f_2| \qquad (16.12)$$

The beat frequency is the *difference* between the two individual frequencies.

FIGURE 16.34 is a history graph of the wave at the position of your ear. You can see both the sound wave oscillation at frequency f_{osc} and the much slower intensity oscillation at frequency f_{beat}. Frequency f_{osc} determines the pitch you hear, while f_{beat} determines the frequency of the loud-soft-loud modulations of the sound intensity.

Musicians can use beats to tune their instruments. If one flute is properly tuned at 440 Hz but another plays at 438 Hz, the flutists will hear two loud-soft-loud beats per second. The second flutist is "flat" and needs to shorten her flute slightly to bring the frequency up to 440 Hz.

Many measurement devices use beats to determine an unknown frequency by comparing it to a known frequency. For example, Chapter 15 described a Doppler blood flow meter that used the Doppler shift of ultrasound reflected from moving blood to determine its speed. The meter determines this very small frequency shift by combining the emitted wave and the reflected wave and measuring the resulting beat frequency. The beat frequency is equal to the shift in frequency on reflection, exactly what is needed to determine the blood speed. Another example of using beats to make a measurement is given in the following example.

FIGURE 16.34 The modulated sound of beats.

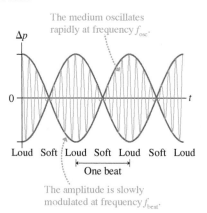

The medium oscillates rapidly at frequency f_{osc}.

Loud Soft Loud Soft Loud Soft Loud
|← One beat →|

The amplitude is slowly modulated at frequency f_{beat}.

EXAMPLE 16.13 **Detecting bats using beats**

The little brown bat is a common bat species in North America. It emits echolocation pulses at a frequency of 40 kHz, well above the range of human hearing. To allow observers to "hear" these bats, the bat detector shown in **FIGURE 16.35** combines the bat's sound wave at frequency f_1 with a wave of frequency f_2 from a tunable oscillator. The resulting beat frequency is isolated with a filter, then amplified and sent to a loudspeaker. To what frequency should the tunable oscillator be set to produce an audible beat frequency of 3 kHz?

SOLVE The beat frequency is $f_{beat} = |f_1 - f_2|$, so the oscillator frequency and the bat frequency need to *differ* by 3 kHz. An oscillator frequency of either 37 kHz or 43 kHz will work nicely.

FIGURE 16.35 The operation of a bat detector.

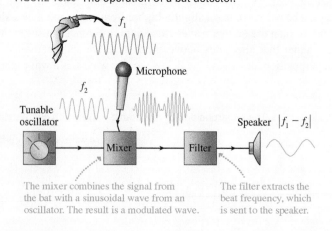

The mixer combines the signal from the bat with a sinusoidal wave from an oscillator. The result is a modulated wave.

The filter extracts the beat frequency, which is sent to the speaker.

STOP TO THINK 16.6 You hear three beats per second when two sound tones are generated. The frequency of one tone is known to be 610 Hz. The frequency of the other is

A. 604 Hz   B. 607 Hz   C. 613 Hz
D. 616 Hz   E. Either A or D   F. Either B or C

The sounds of the human vocal system result from the interplay of two different oscillations: the oscillation of the vocal cords and the standing-wave resonances of the vocal tract. A dog's vocalizations are

Class Video

based on similar principles, but the canine vocal tract is quite a bit simpler than that of a human. When a dog growls or howls, the shape of the vocal tract is essentially a tube closed at the larynx and open at the lips.

All dogs growl at a low pitch because the fundamental frequency of the vocal cords is quite low. But the growls of small dogs and big dogs differ because they have very different formants. The frequency of the formants is determined by the length of the vocal tract, and the vocal-tract length is a pretty good measure of the size of a dog. A larger dog has a longer vocal tract and a correspondingly lower-frequency formant, which sends an important auditory message to other dogs.

The masses of two different dogs and the frequencies of their formants are given in Table 16.1.

a. What is the approximate vocal-tract length of these two dogs? Assume that the speed of sound is 350 m/s at a dog's body temperature.

b. Growls aren't especially loud; at a distance of 1.0 m, a dog's growl is about 60 dB—the same as normal conversation. What is the acoustic power emitted by a 60 dB growl?

c. The lower-pitched growl of the Doberman will certainly sound more menacing, but which dog's 60 dB growl sounds louder to a human? **Hint:** Assume that most of the acoustic energy is at frequencies near the first formant; then look at the curve of equal perceived loudness in Figure 16.21.

TABLE 16.1 Mass and acoustic data for two growling dogs

Breed	Mass (kg)	First formant (Hz)	Second formant (Hz)
West Highland Terrier (Westie)	8.0	650	1950
Doberman	38	350	1050

PREPARE FIGURE 16.36 shows an idealized model of a dog's vocal tract as an open-closed tube. The formants will correspond to the standing-wave resonances of this system. The first two modes are shown in the figure. The first formant corresponds to

FIGURE 16.36 A model of the canine vocal tract.

Lips   Larynx

L

$m = 1$; the second formant corresponds to $m = 3$ because an open-closed tube has only odd harmonics. The frequencies of the

formants will allow us to determine the length of the tube that produces them.

For the question about loudness, we can determine the sound intensity from the sound intensity level. Knowing the distance, we can use this value to determine the emitted acoustic power.

SOLVE a. We can use the frequency of the first formant to find the length of the vocal tract. Recall that the standing-wave frequencies of an open-closed tube are given by

$$f_m = m\frac{v}{4L} \qquad m = 1, 3, 5, \ldots$$

Rearranging this to solve for L, with $m = 1$, we find

$$L(\text{Westie}) = m\frac{v}{4f_m} = (1)\frac{350 \text{ m/s}}{4(650 \text{ Hz})} = 0.13 \text{ m}$$

$$L(\text{Doberman}) = m\frac{v}{4f_m} = (1)\frac{350 \text{ m/s}}{4(350 \text{ Hz})} = 0.25 \text{ m}$$

The length is greater for the Doberman, as we would predict, given the relative masses of the dogs.

b. Equation 15.15 lets us compute the sound intensity for a given sound intensity level:

$$I = (1.0 \times 10^{-12} \text{ W/m}^2)10^{(\beta/10\text{dB})}$$

$$= (1.0 \times 10^{-12} \text{ W/m}^2)10^{(60 \text{ dB}/10\text{dB})} = 1.0 \times 10^{-6} \text{ W/m}^2$$

This is the intensity at a distance of 1.0 m. The sound spreads out in all directions, so we can use Equation 15.12, $I = P_{\text{source}}/4\pi r^2$, to compute the power of the source:

$$P_{\text{source}} = I \cdot 4\pi r^2 = (1.0 \times 10^{-6} \text{ W/m}^2) \cdot 4\pi(1.0 \text{ m})^2 = 13 \text{ }\mu\text{W}$$

A growl may sound menacing, but that's not because of its power!

c. Figure 16.21 is a curve of equal perceived loudness. The curve steadily decreases until reaching ≈3500 Hz, so the acoustic power needed to produce the same sensation of loudness decreases with frequency up to this point. That is, below 3500 Hz your ear is more sensitive to higher frequencies than to lower frequencies. Much of the acoustic power of a dog growl is concentrated at the frequencies of the first two formants. The Westie's growl has its energy at higher frequencies than that of the Doberman, so the Westie's growl will sound louder—though the lower formants of the Doberman's growl will make it sound more formidable.

ASSESS The lengths of the vocal tract that we calculated—13 cm (5 in) for a small terrier and 25 cm (10 in) for a Doberman—seem reasonable given the size of the dogs. We can also check our work by looking at the second formant, corresponding to $m = 3$; using this harmonic in the second expression in Equation 16.7, we find

$$L(\text{Westie}) = m\frac{v}{4f_m} = (3)\frac{350 \text{ m/s}}{4(1950 \text{ Hz})} = 0.13 \text{ m}$$

$$L(\text{Doberman}) = m\frac{v}{4f_m} = (3)\frac{350 \text{ m/s}}{4(1050 \text{ Hz})} = 0.25 \text{ m}$$

This exact match to our earlier calculations gives us confidence in our model and in our results.

SUMMARY

The goal of Chapter 16 has been to use the idea of superposition to understand the phenomena of interference and standing waves.

GENERAL PRINCIPLES

Principle of Superposition

The displacement of a medium when more than one wave is present is the sum of the displacements due to each individual wave.

Interference

In general, the superposition of two or more waves into a single wave is called interference.

Constructive interference occurs when crests are aligned with crests and troughs with troughs. We say the waves are in phase. It occurs when the path-length difference Δd is a whole number of wavelengths.

Destructive interference occurs when crests are aligned with troughs. We say the waves are out of phase. It occurs when the path-length difference Δd is a whole number of wavelengths plus half a wavelength.

IMPORTANT CONCEPTS

Standing Waves

Two identical traveling waves moving in opposite directions create a standing wave.

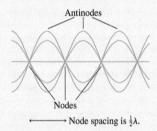

Node spacing is $\frac{1}{2}\lambda$.

The boundary conditions determine which standing-wave frequencies and wavelengths are allowed. The allowed standing waves are **modes** of the system.

A standing wave on a string has a node at each end. Possible modes:

$$\lambda_m = \frac{2L}{m} \qquad f_m = m\left(\frac{v}{2L}\right) = mf_1$$

$$m = 1, 2, 3, \ldots$$

A standing sound wave in a tube can have different boundary conditions: open-open, closed-closed, or open-closed.

Open-open

$$f_m = m\left(\frac{v}{2L}\right)$$

$$m = 1, 2, 3, \ldots$$

Closed-closed

$$f_m = m\left(\frac{v}{2L}\right)$$

$$m = 1, 2, 3, \ldots$$

Open-closed

$$f_m = m\left(\frac{v}{4L}\right)$$

$$m = 1, 3, 5, \ldots$$

APPLICATIONS

Beats (loud-soft-loud-soft modulations of intensity) are produced when two waves of slightly different frequencies are superimposed.

Loud Soft Loud Soft Loud Soft Loud

$$f_{\text{beat}} = |f_1 - f_2|$$

Standing waves are multiples of a **fundamental frequency,** the frequency of the lowest mode. The higher modes are the higher **harmonics.**

For sound, the fundamental frequency determines the perceived **pitch;** the higher harmonics determine the **tone quality.**

Our vocal cords create a range of harmonics. The mix of higher harmonics is changed by our vocal tract to create different vowel sounds.

QUESTIONS

Conceptual Questions

1. Light can pass easily through water and through air, but light will reflect from the surface of a lake. What does this tell you about the speed of light in air and in water?

2. Ocean waves are partially reflected from the entrance to a harbor, where the depth of the water is suddenly less. What does this tell you about the speed of waves in water of different depths?

3. A string has an abrupt change in linear density at its midpoint so that the speed of a pulse on the left side is 2/3 of that on the right side.
   a. On which side is the linear density greater? Explain.
   b. From which side would you start a pulse so that its reflection from the midpoint would not be inverted? Explain.

4. A guitarist finds that the frequency of one of her strings is too low by 1.4%. Should she increase or decrease the tension of the string? Explain.

5. BIO Certain illnesses inflame your vocal cords, causing them to swell. How does this affect the pitch of your voice? Explain.

6. Figure Q16.6 shows a standing wave on a string that is oscillating at frequency f_0. How many antinodes will there be if the frequency is doubled to $2f_0$? Explain.

FIGURE Q16.6

7. Figure Q16.7 shows a standing sound wave in a tube of air that is open at both ends.
   a. Which mode (value of m) standing wave is this?
   b. Is the air vibrating horizontally or vertically?

FIGURE Q16.7

8. A typical flute is about 66 cm long. A piccolo is a very similar instrument, though it is smaller, with a length of about 32 cm. How does the pitch of a piccolo compare to that of a flute?

9. Some pipes on a pipe organ are open at both ends, others are closed at one end. For pipes that play low-frequency notes, there is an advantage to using pipes that are closed at one end. What is the advantage?

10. A flute player tunes her instrument when the air (and the flute) is cold. As she plays, the flute and the air inside it warm up. Both the changing speed of sound in the air inside and the thermal expansion of the flute affect the frequency of the sound wave produced by the flute. After some time, she finds that her playing is "sharp"—the frequencies are too high. Which change produced this effect: the warming of the air or the warming of the body of the flute?

11. BIO A friend's voice sounds different over the telephone than it does in person. This is because telephones do not transmit frequencies over about 3000 Hz. 3000 Hz is well above the normal frequency of speech, so why does eliminating these high frequencies change the sound of a person's voice?

12. Suppose you were to play a trumpet after breathing helium, in which the speed of sound is much greater than in air. Would the pitch of the instrument be higher or lower than normal, or would it be unaffected by being played with helium inside the tube rather than air?

13. If you pour liquid in a tall, narrow glass, you may hear sound with a steadily rising pitch. What is the source of the sound, and why does the pitch rise as the glass fills?

14. BIO When you speak after breathing helium, in which the speed of sound is much greater than in air, your voice sounds quite different. The frequencies emitted by your vocal cords do not change since they are determined by the mass and tension of your vocal cords. So what *does* change when your vocal tract is filled with helium rather than air?

15. BIO Sopranos can sing notes at very high frequencies—over 1000 Hz. When they sing such high notes, it can be difficult to understand the words they are singing. Use the concepts of harmonics and formants to explain this.

16. When you hit a baseball with a bat, the bat flexes and then vibrates. We can model this vibration as a transverse standing wave. The modes of this standing wave are similar to the modes of a stretched string, but with one important difference: The ends of the bat are antinodes instead of nodes, because the ends of the bat are free to move. The modes thus look like the modes of a stretched string with antinodes replacing nodes and nodes replacing antinodes. If the ball hits the bat near an antinode of a standing-wave mode, the bat will start oscillating in this mode. The batter holds the bat at one end, which is also an antinode, so a large vibration of the bat causes an unpleasant vibration in the batter's hands. This can be avoided if the ball hits the bat at what players call the "sweet spot," which is a node of the standing-wave pattern. The first standing-wave mode of a vibrating bat is the $m = 2$ mode. Sketch the appearance of this vibrational mode of the bat, then estimate the approximate distance of the sweet spot (as a fraction of the bat's length) from the end of the bat.

17. BIO If a cold gives you a stuffed-up nose, it changes the way your voice sounds, even if your vocal cords are not affected. Explain why this is so.

18. BIO A small boy and a grown woman both speak at approximately the same pitch. Nonetheless, it's easy to tell which is which from listening to the sounds of their voices. How are you able to make this determination?

19. Figure Q16.19 shows wave fronts of a circular wave. Are the displacements at the following pairs of positions *in phase* or *out of phase?* Explain.

   a. A and B   b. C and D   c. E and F

FIGURE Q16.19

Multiple-Choice Questions

Questions 20 through 22 refer to the snapshot graph Figure Q16.20.

FIGURE Q16.20

20. | At $t = 1$ s, what is the displacement y of the string at $x = 7$ cm?
   A. −1.0 mm   B. 0 mm   C. 0.5 mm
   D. 1.0 mm   E. 2.0 mm

21. | At $x = 3$ cm, what is the earliest time that y will equal 2 mm?
   A. 0.5 s   B. 0.7 s   C. 1.0 s
   D. 1.5 s   E. 2.5 s

22. | At $t = 1.5$ s, what is the value of y at $x = 10$ cm?
   A. −2.0 mm   B. −1.0 mm   C. −0.5 mm
   D. 0 mm   E. 1.0 mm

23. || Two sinusoidal waves with the same amplitude A and frequency f travel in opposite directions along a long string. You stand at one point and watch the string. The maximum displacement of the string at that point is
   A. A B. $2A$ C. 0
   D. There is not enough information to decide.

24. | A student in her physics lab measures the standing-wave modes of a tube. The lowest frequency that makes a resonance is 20 Hz. As the frequency is increased, the next resonance is at 60 Hz. What will be the next resonance after this?
   A. 80 Hz   B. 100 Hz   C. 120 Hz   D. 180 Hz

25. | An organ pipe is tuned to exactly 384 Hz when the temperature in the room is 20°C. Later, when the air has warmed up to 25°C, the frequency is
   A. Greater than 384 Hz.
   B. 384 Hz.
   C. Less than 384 Hz.

26. || Two guitar strings made of the same type of wire have the same length. String 1 has a higher pitch than string 2. Which of the following is true?
   A. The wave speed of string 1 is greater than that of string 2.
   B. The tension in string 2 is greater than that in string 1.
   C. The wavelength of the lowest standing-wave mode on string 2 is longer than that on string 1.
   D. The wavelength of the lowest standing-wave mode on string 1 is longer than that on string 2.

27. | The frequency of the lowest standing-wave mode on a 1.0-m-long string is 20 Hz. What is the wave speed on the string?
   A. 10 m/s   B. 20 m/s   C. 30 m/s   D. 40 m/s

28. | Suppose you pluck a string on a guitar and it produces the note A at a frequency of 440 Hz. Now you press your finger down on the string against one of the frets, making this point the new end of the string. The newly shortened string has 4/5 length of the full string. When you pluck the string, its frequency will be
   A. 350 Hz   B. 440 Hz   C. 490 Hz   D. 550 Hz

PROBLEMS

Section 16.1 The Principle of Superposition

1. | Figure P16.1 is a snapshot graph at $t = 0$ s of two waves on a taut string approaching each other at 1 m/s. Draw six snapshot graphs, stacked vertically, showing the string at 1 s intervals from $t = 1$ s to $t = 6$ s.

FIGURE P16.1

2. || Figure P16.2 is a snapshot graph at $t = 0$ s of two waves approaching each other at 1 m/s. Draw four snapshot graphs, stacked vertically, showing the string at $t = 2, 4, 6,$ and 8 s.

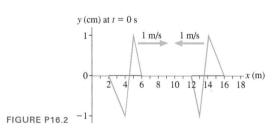

FIGURE P16.2

3. ‖ Figure P16.3a is a snapshot graph at $t = 0$ s of two waves on a string approaching each other at At what time was the snapshot graph in Figure P16.3b taken?

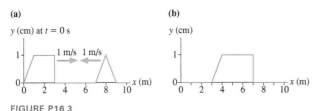

FIGURE P16.3

Section 16.2 Standing Waves

Section 16.3 Standing Waves on a String

4. ‖‖ Figure P16.4 is a snapshot graph at $t = 0$ s of a pulse on a string moving to the right at 1 m/s. The string is fixed at $x = 5$ m. Draw a history graph spanning the time interval $t = 0$ s to $t = 10$ s for the location $x = 3$ m on the string.

FIGURE P16.4

5. ‖‖ At $t = 0$ s, a small "upward" (positive y) pulse centered at $x = 6.0$ m is moving to the right on a string with fixed ends at $x = 0.0$ m and $x = 10.0$ m. The wave speed on the string is 4.0 m/s. At what time will the string next have the same appearance that it did at $t = 0$ s?

6. ‖‖ You are holding one end of an elastic cord that is fastened to a wall 3.0 m away. You begin shaking the end of the cord at 3.5 Hz, creating a continuous sinusoidal wave of wavelength 1.0 m. How much time will pass until a standing wave fills the entire length of the string?

7. ‖‖ A 2.0-m-long string is fixed at both ends and tightened until the wave speed is 40 m/s. What is the frequency of the standing wave shown in Figure P16.7?

FIGURE P16.7   FIGURE P16.8

8. ‖ Figure P16.8 shows a standing wave oscillating at 100 Hz on a string. What is the wave speed?

9. ‖ A bass guitar string is 89 cm long with a fundamental frequency of 30 Hz. What is the wave speed on this string?

10. ‖‖ The fundamental frequency of a guitar string is 384 Hz. What is the fundamental frequency if the tension in the string is halved?

11. ‖ a. What are the three longest wavelengths for standing waves on a 240-cm-long string that is fixed at both ends?
    b. If the frequency of the second-longest wavelength is 50.0 Hz, what is the frequency of the third-longest wavelength?

12. ‖ A 121-cm-long, 4.00 g string oscillates in its $m = 3$ mode with a frequency of 180 Hz and a maximum amplitude of 5.00 mm. What are (a) the wavelength and (b) the tension in the string?

13. ‖ A guitar string with a linear density of 2.0 g/m is stretched between supports that are 60 cm apart. The string is observed to form a standing wave with three antinodes when driven at a frequency of 420 Hz. What are (a) the frequency of the fifth harmonic of this string and (b) the tension in the string?

14. ‖ A violin string has a standard length of 32.8 cm. It sounds the musical note A (440 Hz) when played without fingering. How far from the end of the string should you place your finger to play the note C (523 Hz)?

15. ‖ The lowest note on a grand piano has a frequency of 27.5 Hz. The entire string is 2.00 m long and has a mass of 400 g. The vibrating section of the string is 1.90 m long. What tension is needed to tune this string properly?

Section 16.4 Standing Sound Waves

16. ‖ The lowest frequency in the audible range is 20 Hz. (a) What are the lengths of (a) the shortest open-open tube and (b) the shortest open-closed tube needed to produce this frequency?

17. ‖ The contrabassoon is the wind instrument capable of sounding the lowest pitch in an orchestra. It is folded over several times to fit its impressive 18 ft length into a reasonable size instrument.
    a. If we model the instrument as an open-closed tube, what is its fundamental frequency? The sound speed inside is 350 m/s because the air is warmed by the player's breath.
    b. The actual fundamental frequency of the contrabassoon is 27.5 Hz, which should be different from your answer in part a. This means the model of the instrument as an open-closed tube is a bit too simple. But if you insist on using that model, what is the "effective length" of the instrument?

18. ‖ Figure P16.18 shows a standing sound wave in an 80-cm-long tube. The tube is filled with an unknown gas. What is the speed of sound in this gas?

$f = 500$ Hz

80 cm

FIGURE P16.18

19. ‖ What are the three longest wavelengths for standing sound waves in a 121-cm-long tube that is (a) open at both ends and (b) open at one end, closed at the other?

20. ‖ The lowest pedal note on a large pipe organ has a fundamental frequency of 16 Hz. This extreme bass note is more felt as a rumble than heard with the ears. What is the length of the open-closed pipe that makes that note?

21. ‖ The fundamental frequency of an open-open tube is 1500 Hz INT when the tube is filled with 0°C helium. What is its frequency when filled with 0°C air?

22. ‖ *Parasaurolophus* was a BIO dinosaur whose distinguishing feature was a hollow crest on the head. The 1.5-m-long hollow tube in the crest had connections to the nose and throat, leading some investigators to hypothesize that the tube was a resonant chamber for vocalization. If you model the tube as an open-closed system, what are the first three resonant frequencies?

23. ‖ A drainage pipe running under a freeway is 30.0 m long. Both ends of the pipe are open, and wind blowing across one end causes the air inside to vibrate.
    a. If the speed of sound on a particular day is 340 m/s, what will be the fundamental frequency of air vibration in this pipe?
    b. What is the frequency of the lowest harmonic that would be audible to the human ear?
    c. What will happen to the frequency in the later afternoon as the air begins to cool?
24. ‖ Although the vocal tract is quite complicated, we can make a
    BIO simple model of it as an open-closed tube extending from the opening of the mouth to the diaphragm, the large muscle separating the abdomen and the chest cavity. What is the length of this tube if its fundamental frequency equals a typical speech frequency of 200 Hz? Assume a sound speed of 350 m/s. Does this result for the tube length seem reasonable, based on observations on your own body?
25. ‖‖ A child has an ear canal that is 1.3 cm long. At what sound
    BIO frequencies in the audible range will the child have increased hearing sensitivity?

Section 16.5 Speech and Hearing

26. ‖ The first formant of your vocal system can be modeled as the
    BIO resonance of an open-closed tube, the closed end being your vocal cords and the open end your lips. Estimate the frequency of the first formant from the graph of Figure 16.23, and then estimate the length of the tube of which this is a resonance. Does your result seem reasonable?
27. ‖‖ Deep-sea divers often breathe a mixture of helium and oxy-
    BIO gen to avoid the complications of breathing high-pressure
    INT nitrogen. At great depths the mix is almost entirely helium, which has the side effect of making the divers' voices sound very odd. Breathing helium doesn't affect the frequency at which the vocal cords vibrate, but it does affect the frequencies of the formants. The text gives the frequencies of the first two formants for an "ee" vowel sound as 270 and 2300 Hz. What will these frequencies be for a helium-oxygen mixture in which the speed of sound at body temperature is 750 m/s?

Section 16.6 The Interference of Waves from Two Sources

28. ‖‖ Two loudspeakers in a 20°C room emit 686 Hz sound waves along the x-axis. What is the smallest distance between the speakers for which the interference of the sound waves is destructive?
29. ‖‖ Two loudspeakers emit sound waves along the x-axis. The sound has maximum intensity when the speakers are 20 cm apart. The sound intensity decreases as the distance between the speakers is increased, reaching zero at a separation of 30 cm.
    a. What is the wavelength of the sound?
    b. If the distance between the speakers continues to increase, at what separation will the sound intensity again be a maximum?
30. ‖‖ Two identical loudspeakers separated by distance d emit 170 Hz sound waves along the x-axis. As you walk along the axis, away from the speakers, you don't hear anything even though both speakers are on. What are three possible values for d? Assume a sound speed of 340 m/s.

31. ‖ Figure P16.31 shows the circular wave fronts emitted by two sources. Make a table with rows labeled P, Q, and R and columns labeled r_1, r_2, Δr, and C/D. Fill in the table for points P, Q, and R, giving the distances as multiples of λ and indicating, with a C or a D, whether the interference at that point is constructive or destructive.

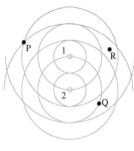

FIGURE P16.31

32. ‖‖ Two identical loudspeakers 2.0 m apart are emitting 1800 Hz sound waves into a room where the speed of sound is 340 m/s. Is the point 4.0 m directly in front of one of the speakers, perpendicular to the plane of the speakers, a point of maximum constructive interference, perfect destructive interference, or something in between?

Section 16.7 Beats

33. ‖ Two strings are adjusted to vibrate at exactly 200 Hz. Then the tension in one string is increased slightly. Afterward, three beats per second are heard when the strings vibrate at the same time. What is the new frequency of the string that was tightened?
34. ‖ A flute player hears four beats per second when she compares her note to a 523 Hz tuning fork (the note C). She can match the frequency of the tuning fork by pulling out the "tuning joint" to lengthen her flute slightly. What was her initial frequency?

General Problems

35. ‖ The fundamental frequency of a standing wave on a 1.0-m-long string is 440 Hz. What would be the wave speed of a pulse moving along this string?
36. ‖‖ In addition to producing images, ultrasound can be used to
    BIO heat tissues of the body for therapeutic purposes. When a sound
    INT wave hits the boundary between soft tissue and air, or between soft tissue and bone, most of the energy is reflected; only 0.11% is transmitted. This means that standing waves can be set up in the body, creating excess thermal energy in the tissues at an antinode. Suppose 0.75 MHz ultrasound is directed through a layer of tissue with a bone 0.50 cm below the surface. Will standing waves be created? Explain.
37. ‖‖ An 80-cm-long steel string with a linear density of 1.0 g/m is
    INT under 200 N tension. It is plucked and vibrates at its fundamental frequency. What is the wavelength of the sound wave that reaches your ear in a 20°C room?
38. ‖‖ Tendons are, essentially, elastic cords stretched between
    BIO two fixed ends; as such, they can support standing waves.
    INT These resonances can be undesirable. The Achilles tendon connects the heel with a muscle in the calf. A woman has a 20-cm-long tendon with a cross-section area of 110 mm². The density of tendon tissue is 1100 kg/m³. For a reasonable tension of 500 N, what will be the resonant frequencies of her Achilles tendon?
39. ‖ A string, stretched between two fixed posts, forms standing-wave resonances at 325 Hz and 390 Hz. What is the largest possible value of its fundamental frequency?

40. ||| Spiders may "tune" strands of their webs to give enhanced
BIO response at frequencies corresponding to the frequencies at which
INT desirable prey might struggle. Orb web silk has a typical diameter
of 0.0020 mm, and spider silk has a density of 1300 kg/m³. To
give a resonance at 100 Hz, to what tension must a spider adjust
a 12-cm-long strand of silk?

41. ||| A violinist places her finger so that the vibrating section of a
INT 1.0 g/m string has a length of 30 cm, then she draws her bow
across it. A listener nearby in a 20°C room hears a note with a
wavelength of 40 cm. What is the tension in the string?

42. || A particularly beautiful note reaching your ear from a rare
INT Stradivarius violin has a wavelength of 39.1 cm. The room is
slightly warm, so the speed of sound is 344 m/s. If the string's
linear density is 0.600 g/m and the tension is 150 N, how long is
the vibrating section of the violin string?

43. || A heavy piece of hanging sculpture is suspended by a 90-cm-
INT long, 5.0 g steel wire. When the wind blows hard, the wire
hums at its fundamental frequency of 80 Hz. What is the mass
of the sculpture?

44. | An experimenter finds that standing waves on a 0.80-m-long
string, fixed at both ends, occur at 24 Hz and 32 Hz, but at no
frequencies in between.
   a. What is the fundamental frequency?
   b. What is the wave speed on the string?
   c. Draw the standing-wave pattern for the string at 32 Hz.

45. ||| Astronauts visiting Planet X have a 2.5-m-long string whose
INT mass is 5.0 g. They tie the string to a support, stretch it horizontally over a pulley 2.0 m away, and hang a 1.0 kg mass on
the free end. Then the astronauts begin to excite standing
waves on the string. Their data show that standing waves exist
at frequencies of 64 Hz and 80 Hz, but at no frequencies in
between. What is the value of g, the free-fall acceleration, on
Planet X?

46. |||| A 75 g bungee cord has an equilibrium length of 1.2 m. The
INT cord is stretched to a length of 1.8 m, then vibrated at 20 Hz.
This produces a standing wave with two antinodes. What is the
spring constant of the bungee cord?

47. |||| A 2.5-cm-diameter steel cable
(with density 7900 kg/m³) that
is part of the suspension system
for a footbridge stretches 14 m
between the tower and the
ground. After walking over the
bridge, a hiker finds that the
cable is vibrating in its funda-
mental mode with a period of 0.40 s. What is the tension in
the cable?

48. || Lake Erie is prone to
remarkable *seiches*—standing
waves that slosh water back
and forth in the lake basin from
the west end at Toledo to the
east end at Buffalo. Figure
P16.48 shows smoothed data for the displacement from normal
water levels along the lake at the high point of one particular
seiche. 3 hours later the water was at normal levels throughout
the basin; 6 hours later the water was high in Toledo and low in
Buffalo.
   a. What is the wavelength of this standing wave?
   b. What is the frequency?
   c. What is the wave speed?

FIGURE P16.48

49. || A steel wire is used to
INT stretch a spring, as shown in
Figure P16.49. An oscillating
magnetic field drives the steel
wire back and forth. A standing
wave with three antinodes is created when the spring is stretched
8.0 cm. What stretch of the spring produces a standing wave
with two antinodes?

FIGURE P16.49

50. || Just as you are about to step into a nice hot bath, a small
earthquake rattles your bathroom. Immediately afterward, you
notice that the water in the tub is oscillating. The water in the
center seems to be motionless while the water at the two ends
alternately rises and falls, like a seesaw. You happen to know
that your bathtub is 1.4 m long, and you count 10 complete
oscillations of the water in 20 s.
   a. What is the wavelength of this standing wave?
   b. What is the speed of the waves that are reflecting back and
      forth inside the tub to create the standing wave?

51. ||| A microwave generator can
produce microwaves at any frequency between 10 GHz and
20 GHz. As Figure P16.51
shows, the microwaves are
aimed, through a small hole, into a "microwave cavity" that
consists of a 10-cm-long cylinder with reflective ends.
   a. Which frequencies between 10 GHz and 20 GHz will create
      standing waves in the microwave cavity?
   b. For which of these frequencies is the cavity midpoint an
      antinode?

FIGURE P16.51

52. || An open-open organ pipe is 78.0 cm long. An open-closed
pipe has a fundamental frequency equal to the third harmonic of
the open-open pipe. How long is the open-closed pipe?

53. ||| A carbon-dioxide laser emits infrared light with a wavelength
INT of 10.6 μm.
   a. What is the length of a tube that will oscillate in the
      m = 100,000 mode?
   b. What is the frequency?
   c. Imagine a pulse of light bouncing back and forth between
      the ends of the tube. How many round trips will the pulse
      make in each second?

54. ||| In 1866, the German scientist Adolph Kundt developed a
technique for accurately measuring the speed of sound in various gases. A long glass tube, known today as a Kundt's tube,
has a vibrating piston at one end and is closed at the other. Very
finely ground particles of cork are sprinkled in the bottom of
the tube before the piston is inserted. As the vibrating piston
is slowly moved forward, there are a few positions that cause
the cork particles to collect in small, regularly spaced piles
along the bottom. Figure P16.54 shows an experiment in which
the tube is filled with pure oxygen and the piston is driven at
400 Hz.

FIGURE P16.54

   a. Do the cork particles collect at standing-wave nodes or
      antinodes?
      Hint: Consider the appearance of the ends of the tube.
   b. What is the speed of sound in oxygen?

55. ‖ A 40-cm-long tube has a 40-cm-long insert that can be pulled in and out, as shown in Figure P16.55. A vibrating tuning fork is held next to the tube. As the insert is slowly pulled out, the sound from the tuning fork creates standing waves in the tube when the total length L is 42.5 cm, 56.7 cm, and 70.9 cm. What is the frequency of the tuning fork? The air temperature is 20°C.

FIGURE P16.55

56. ‖‖ A 1.0-m-tall vertical tube is filled with 20°C water. A tuning fork vibrating at 580 Hz is held just over the top of the tube as the water is slowly drained from the bottom. At what water heights, measured from the bottom of the tube, will there be a standing sound wave in the air at the top of the tube?

57. ‖ A 50-cm-long wire with a mass of 1.0 g and a tension of 440 N passes across the open end of an open-closed tube of air. The wire, which is fixed at both ends, is bowed at the center so as to vibrate at its fundamental frequency and generate a sound wave. Then the tube length is adjusted until the fundamental frequency of the tube is heard. What is the length of the tube? Assume the speed of sound is 340 m/s.

58. ‖‖ A 25-cm-long wire with a linear density of 20 g/m passes across the open end of an 85-cm-long open-closed tube of air. If the wire, which is fixed at both ends, vibrates at its fundamental frequency, the sound wave it generates excites the second vibrational mode of the tube of air. What is the tension in the wire? Assume the speed of sound is 340 m/s.

59. ‖‖ Two loudspeakers located along the x-axis as shown in Figure P16.59 produce sounds of equal frequency. Speaker 1 is at the origin, while the location of speaker 2 can be varied by a remote control wielded by the listener. He notices maxima in the sound intensity when speaker 2 is located at $x = 0.75$ m and 1.00 m, but at no points in between. What is the frequency of the sound? Assume the speed of sound is 340 m/s.

FIGURE P16.59

60. ‖‖ You are standing 2.50 m directly in front of one of the two loudspeakers shown in Figure P16.60. They are 3.00 m apart and both are playing a 686 Hz tone in phase. As you begin to walk directly away from the speaker, at what distances from the speaker do you hear a *minimum* sound intensity? The room temperature is 20°C.

FIGURE P16.60

61. ‖ FM station KCOM ("All commercials, all the time") transmits simultaneously, at a frequency of 99.9 MHz, from two broadcast towers placed precisely 31.5 m apart along a north-south line.
   a. What is the wavelength of KCOM's transmissions?

b. Suppose you stand 90.0 m due east of the point halfway between the two towers with your portable FM radio. Will you receive a strong or weak signal at this position? Why?

c. You then stand 90.0 m due north of the northern tower with your radio. Will you receive a strong or weak signal at this position? Why?

62. ‖‖ Two loudspeakers, 4.0 m apart and facing each other, play identical sounds of the same frequency. You stand halfway between them, where there is a maximum of sound intensity. Moving from this point toward one of the speakers, you encounter a minimum of sound intensity when you have moved 0.25 m.
   a. What is the frequency of the sound?
   b. If the frequency is then increased while you remain 0.25 m from the center, what is the first frequency for which that location will be a maximum of sound intensity?

63. ‖‖ Two radio antennas are separated by 2.0 m. Both broadcast identical 750 MHz waves. If you walk around the antennas in a circle of radius 10 m, how many maxima will you detect?

64. ‖ Certain birds produce vocalizations consisting of two distinct frequencies that are not harmonically related—that is, the two frequencies are not harmonics of a common fundamental frequency. These two frequencies must be produced by two different vibrating structures in the bird's vocal tract.
   a. Wood ducks have been observed to make a call with approximately equal intensities at 850 Hz and 1200 Hz. The membranes that produce the vocalizations do not seem to vibrate at frequencies less than 500 Hz. Given this limitation, could these two frequencies be higher harmonics of a lower-frequency fundamental?
   b. If we model the duck's vocal tract as an open-closed tube, what length has a fundamental frequency equal to the lower of the two frequencies in part a?

65. ‖ Piano tuners tune pianos by listening to the beats between the harmonics of two different strings. When properly tuned, the note A should have the frequency 440 Hz and the note E should be at 659 Hz. The tuner can determine this by listening to the beats between the third harmonic of the A and the second harmonic of the E.
   a. A tuner first tunes the A string very precisely by matching it to a 440 Hz tuning fork. She then strikes the A and E strings simultaneously and listens for beats between the harmonics. What beat frequency indicates that the E string is properly tuned?
   b. The tuner starts with the tension in the E string a little low, then tightens it. What is the frequency of the E string when she hears four beats per second?

66. ‖ A flutist assembles her flute in a room where the speed of sound is 342 m/s. When she plays the note A, it is in perfect tune with a 440 Hz tuning fork. After a few minutes, the air inside her flute has warmed to where the speed of sound is 346 m/s.
   a. How many beats per second will she hear if she now plays the note A as the tuning fork is sounded?
   b. How far does she need to extend the "tuning joint" of her flute to be in tune with the tuning fork?

67. ‖‖ A student waiting at a stoplight notices that her turn signal, which has a period of 0.85 s, makes one blink exactly in sync with the turn signal of the car in front of her. The blinker of the car ahead then starts to get ahead, but 17 s later the two are exactly in sync again. What is the period of the blinker of the other car?

68. ⫿ Musicians can use beats to tune their instruments. One flute is properly tuned and plays the musical note A at exactly 440 Hz. A second player sounds the same note and hears that her instrument is slightly "flat" (i.e., at too low a frequency). Playing at the same time as the first flute, she hears two loud-soft-loud beats per second. Must she shorten or lengthen her flute, and by how much, to bring it into tune? Assume a speed of sound of 350 m/s.

69. ⫿ INT Police radars determine speed by measuring the Doppler shift of radio waves reflected by a moving vehicle. They do so by determining the beat frequency between the reflected wave and the 10.5 GHz emitted wave. Some units can be calibrated by using a tuning fork; holding a vibrating fork in front of the unit causes the display to register a speed corresponding to the vibration frequency. A tuning fork is labeled "55 mph." What is the frequency of the tuning fork?

70. ⫿ BIO INT A Doppler blood flow meter emits ultrasound at a frequency of 5.0 MHz. What is the beat frequency between the emitted waves and the waves reflected from blood cells moving away from the emitter at 0.15 m/s?

71. ⏐ BIO INT An ultrasound unit is being used to measure a patient's heartbeat by combining the emitted 2.0 MHz signal with the sound waves reflected from the moving tissue of one point on the heart. The beat frequency between the two signals has a maximum value of 520 Hz. What is the maximum speed of the heart tissue?

Passage Problems

Harmonics and Harmony

You know that certain musical notes sound good together—harmonious—whereas others do not. This harmony is related to the various harmonics of the notes.

The musical notes C (262 Hz) and G (392 Hz) make a pleasant sound when played together; we call this consonance. As Figure P16.72 shows, the harmonics of the two notes are either far from each other or very close to each other (within a few Hz). This is the key to consonance: harmonics that are spaced either far apart or very close. The close harmonics have a beat frequency of a few Hz that is perceived as pleasant. If the harmonics of two notes are close but not too close, the rather high beat frequency between the two is quite unpleasant. This is what we hear as dissonance. Exactly how much a difference is maximally dissonant is a matter of opinion, but harmonic separations of 30 or 40 Hz seem to be quite unpleasant for most people.

FIGURE P16.72

72. ⏐ What is the beat frequency between the second harmonic of G and the third harmonic of C?
    A. 1 Hz   B. 2 Hz   C. 4 Hz   D. 6 Hz

73. ⏐ Would a G-flat (frequency 370 Hz) and a C played together be consonant or dissonant?
    A. Consonant
    B. Dissonant

74. ⏐ An organ pipe open at both ends is tuned so that its fundamental frequency is a G. How long is the pipe?
    A. 43 cm   B. 87 cm   C. 130 cm   D. 173 cm

75. ⏐ If the C were played on an organ pipe that was open at one end and closed at the other, which of the harmonic frequencies in Figure 16.72 would be present?
    A. All of the harmonics in the figure would be present.
    B. 262, 786, and 1310 Hz
    C. 524, 1048, and 1572 Hz
    D. 262, 524, and 1048 Hz

STOP TO THINK ANSWERS

Stop to Think 16.1: C. The figure shows the two waves at $t = 6$ s and their superposition. The superposition is the *point-by-point* addition of the displacements of the two individual waves.

```
          ___
         /   \\
        / \\ / \\
_____/__\\X/__\_____ x (m)
 0  2  4  6  8  10 12 14 16 18 20
```

Stop to Think 16.2: C. Standing-wave frequencies are $f_m = mf_1$. The original wave has frequency $f_2 = 2f_1$ because it has two antinodes. The wave with frequency $2f_2 = 4f_1$ is the $m = 4$ mode with four antinodes.

Stop to Think 16.3: B. 300 Hz and 400 Hz are not f_1 and f_2 because 400 Hz ≠ 2 × 300 Hz. Instead, both are multiples of the fundamental frequency. Because the difference between them is 100 Hz, we see that $f_3 = 3 \times 100$ Hz and $f_4 = 4 \times 100$ Hz. Thus $f_1 = 100$ Hz.

Stop to Think 16.4: D. Highest pitch, or highest frequency, corresponds to the shortest period. For a complex wave, the period is the time required for the entire wave pattern to repeat.

Stop to Think 16.5: Constructive interference. The path-length difference is $\Delta r = 1.0$ m $= \lambda$. Interference is constructive when the path-length difference is a whole number of wavelengths.

Stop to Think 16.6: F. The beat frequency is the difference between the two frequencies.

Oscillations and Waves

As we have studied oscillations and waves, one point we have emphasized is the *unity* of the basic physics. The mathematics of oscillation describes the motion of a mass on a spring or the motion of a gibbon swinging from a branch. The same theory of waves works for string waves and sound waves and light waves. A few basic ideas enable us to understand a wide range of physical phenomena.

The physics of oscillations and waves is not quite as easily summarized as the physics of particles. Newton's laws and the conservation laws are two very general sets of principles about particles, principles that allowed us to develop the powerful problem-solving strategies of Parts I and II. The knowledge structure of oscillations and waves, shown below, rests more heavily on *phenomena* than on general principles. This knowledge structure doesn't contain a problem-solving strategy or a wide range of general principles, but is instead a logical grouping of the major topics you studied. This is a different way of structuring knowledge, but it still provides you with a mental framework for analyzing and thinking about wave problems.

The physics of oscillations and waves will be with us for the rest of the book. Part V is an exploration of optics, beginning with a detailed study of light as a wave. In Part VI, we will study the nature of electromagnetic waves in more detail. Finally, in Part VII, we will see that matter has a wave nature. There, the wave ideas we have developed in Part IV will lead us into the exciting world of quantum physics, finishing with some quite remarkable insights about the nature of light and matter.

KNOWLEDGE STRUCTURE IV Oscillations and Waves

BASIC GOALS	How can we describe oscillatory motion? How does a wave travel through a medium?	What are the distinguishing features of waves? What happens when two waves meet?	

GENERAL PRINCIPLES Simple harmonic motion occurs when a linear restoring force acts to return a system to equilibrium.
The period of simple harmonic motion depends on physical properties of the system but not the amplitude.
All sinusoidal waves, whether water waves, sound waves, or light waves, have the same functional form.
When two waves meet, they pass through each other, combining where they overlap by superposition.

Simple harmonic motion

$$x(t) = A\cos(2\pi ft)$$

$$v_x(t) = -v_{max}\sin(2\pi ft)$$
$$v_{max} = 2\pi fA$$

$$a_x(t) = -a_{max}\cos(2\pi ft)$$
$$a_{max} = (2\pi f)^2 A$$

The frequency of a mass on a spring depends on the spring constant and the mass:

$$f = \frac{1}{2\pi}\sqrt{\frac{k}{m}}$$

The frequency of a pendulum depends on the length and the free-fall acceleration:

$$f = \frac{1}{2\pi}\sqrt{\frac{g}{L}}$$

Traveling waves

All traveling waves are described by the same equation:

$$y = A\cos\left(2\pi\left(\frac{x}{\lambda} \pm \frac{t}{T}\right)\right)$$

+: wave travels to left
−: wave travels to right

The wave speed depends on the properties of the medium.

$$v_{string} = \sqrt{\frac{T_s}{\mu}}$$

The speed, wavelength, period, and frequency of a wave are related.

$$T = \frac{1}{f} \qquad v = f\lambda$$

Superposition and interference

The superposition of two waves is the sum of the displacements of the two individual waves.

Constructive interference occurs when crests are aligned with crests and troughs with troughs. Constructive interference occurs when the path-length difference is a whole number of wavelengths.

Destructive interference occurs when crests are aligned with troughs. Destructive interference occurs when the path-length difference is a whole number of wavelengths plus half a wavelength.

Standing waves

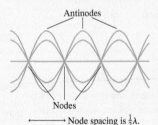

Antinodes

Nodes

Node spacing is $\frac{1}{2}\lambda$.

Standing waves are due to the superposition of two traveling waves moving in opposite directions.

The boundary conditions determine which standing-wave frequencies and wavelengths are allowed. The allowed standing waves are modes of the system.

For a string of length L, the modes have wavelength and frequency

$$\lambda_m = \frac{2L}{m} \qquad f_m = m\left(\frac{v_{string}}{2L}\right) = mf_1 \qquad m = 1, 2, 3, 4, \ldots$$

Waves in the Earth and the Ocean

In December 2004, a large earthquake off the coast of Indonesia produced a devastating water wave, called a *tsunami,* that caused tremendous destruction thousands of miles away from the earthquake's epicenter. The tsunami was a dramatic illustration of the energy carried by waves.

It was also a call to action. Many of the communities hardest hit by the tsunami were struck hours after the waves were generated, long after seismic waves from the earthquake that passed through the earth had been detected at distant recording stations, long after the possibility of a tsunami was first discussed. With better detection and more accurate models of how a tsunami is formed and how a tsunami propagates, the affected communities could have received advance warning. The study of physics may seem an abstract undertaking with few practical applications, but on this day a better scientific understanding of these waves could have averted tragedy.

Let's use our knowledge of waves to explore the properties of a tsunami. In Chapter 15, we saw that a vigorous shake of one end of a rope causes a pulse to travel

One frame from a computer simulation of the Indian Ocean tsunami three hours after the earthquake that produced it. The disturbance propagating outward from the earthquake is clearly seen, as are wave reflections from the island of Sri Lanka.

along it, carrying energy as it goes. The earthquake that produced the Indian Ocean tsunami of 2004 caused a sudden upward displacement of the seafloor that produced a corresponding rise in the surface of the ocean. This was the *disturbance* that produced the tsunami, very much like a quick shake on the end of a rope. The resulting wave propagated through the ocean, as we see in the figure.

This simulation of the tsunami looks much like the ripples that spread when you drop a pebble into a pond. But there is a big difference—the scale. The fact that you can see the individual waves on this diagram that spans 5000 km is quite revealing. To show up so clearly, the individual wave pulses must be very wide—up to hundreds of kilometers from front to back.

A tsunami is actually a "shallow water wave," even in the deep ocean, because the depth of the ocean is much less than the width of the wave. Consequently, a tsunami travels differently than normal ocean waves. In Chapter 15 we learned that wave speeds are fixed by the properties of the medium. That is true for normal ocean waves, but the great width of the wave causes a tsunami to "feel the bottom." Its wave speed is determined by the depth of the ocean: The greater the depth, the greater the speed. In the deep ocean, a tsunami travels at hundreds of kilometers per hour, much faster than a typical ocean wave. Near shore, as the ocean depth decreases, so does the speed of the wave.

The height of the tsunami in the open ocean was about half a meter. Why should such a small wave—one that ships didn't even notice as it passed—be so fearsome? Again, it's the *width* of the wave that matters. Because a tsunami is the wave motion of a considerable mass of water, great energy is involved. As the front of a tsunami wave nears shore, its speed decreases, and the back of the wave moves faster than the front. Consequently, the width decreases. The water begins to pile up, and the wave dramatically increases in height.

The Indian Ocean tsunami had a height of up to 15 m when it reached shore, with a width of up to several kilometers. This tremendous mass of water was still moving at high speed, giving it a great deal of energy. A tsunami reaching the shore isn't like a typical wave that breaks and crashes. It is a kilometers-wide wall of water that moves onto the shore and just keeps on coming. In many places, the water reached 2 km inland.

The impact of the Indian Ocean tsunami was devastating, but it was the first tsunami for which scientists were able to use satellites and ocean sensors to make planet-wide measurements. An analysis of the data has helped us better understand the physics of these ocean waves. We won't be able to stop future tsunamis, but with a better knowledge of how they are formed and how they travel, we will be better able to warn people to get out of their way.

PART IV PROBLEMS

The following questions are related to the passage "Waves in the Earth and the Ocean" on the previous page.

1. Rank from fastest to slowest the following waves according to their speed of propagation:
   A. An earthquake wave   B. A tsunami
   C. A sound wave in air   D. A light wave
2. The increase in height as a tsunami approaches shore is due to
   A. The increase in frequency as the wave approaches shore.
   B. The increase in speed as the wave approaches shore.
   C. The decrease in speed as the wave approaches shore.
   D. The constructive interference with the wave reflected from shore.
3. In the middle of the Indian Ocean, the tsunami referred to in the passage was a train of pulses approximating a sinusoidal wave with speed 200 m/s and wavelength 150 km. What was the approximate period of these pulses?
   A. 1 min   B. 3 min
   C. 5 min   D. 15 min

4. If a train of pulses moves into shallower water as it approaches a shore,
   A. The wavelength increases.
   B. The wavelength stays the same.
   C. The wavelength decreases.
5. The tsunami described in the passage produced a very erratic pattern of damage, with some areas seeing very large waves and nearby areas seeing only small waves. Which of the following is a possible explanation?
   A. Certain areas saw the wave from the primary source, others only the reflected waves.
   B. The superposition of waves from the primary source and reflected waves produced regions of constructive and destructive interference.
   C. A tsunami is a standing wave, and certain locations were at nodal positions, others at antinodal positions.

The following passages and associated questions are based on the material of Part IV.

Deep-Water Waves

Water waves are called *deep-water waves* when the depth of the water is much greater than the wavelength of the wave. The speed of deep-water waves depends on the wavelength as follows:

$$v = \sqrt{\frac{g\lambda}{2\pi}}$$

Suppose you are on a ship at rest in the ocean, observing the crests of a passing sinusoidal wave. You estimate that the crests are 75 m apart.

6. Approximately how much time elapses between one crest reaching your ship and the next?
   A. 3 s
   B. 5 s
   C. 7 s
   D. 12 s
7. The captain starts the engines and sails directly opposite the motion of the waves at 4.5 m/s. Now how much time elapses between one crest reaching your ship and the next?
   A. 3 s
   B. 5 s
   C. 7 s
   D. 12 s
8. In the deep ocean, a longer-wavelength wave travels faster than a shorter-wavelength wave. Thus, a higher-frequency wave travels _____ a lower-frequency wave.
   A. Faster than
   B. At the same speed as
   C. Slower than

Attenuation of Ultrasound   BIO

Ultrasound is absorbed in the body; this complicates the use of ultrasound to image tissues. The intensity of a beam of ultrasound decreases by a factor of 2 after traveling a distance of 40 wavelengths. Each additional travel of 40 wavelengths results in a decrease by another factor of 2.

9. A beam of 1.0 MHz ultrasound begins with an intensity of 1000 W/m^2. After traveling 12 cm through tissue with no significant reflection, the intensity is about
   A. 750 W/m^2 B. 500 W/m^2
   C. 250 W/m^2 D. 125 W/m^2
10. A physician is making an image with ultrasound of initial intensity 1000 W/m^2. When the frequency is set to 1.0 MHz, the intensity drops to 500 W/m^2 at a certain depth in the patient's body. What will be the intensity at this depth if the physician changes the frequency to 2.0 MHz?
    A. 750 W/m^2 B. 500 W/m^2
    C. 250 W/m^2 D. 125 W/m^2
11. A physician is using ultrasound to make an image of a patient's heart. Increasing the frequency will provide
    A. Better penetration and better resolution.
    B. Less penetration but better resolution.
    C. More penetration but worse resolution.
    D. Less penetration and worse resolution.
12. A physician is using Doppler ultrasound to measure the motion of a patient's heart. The device measures the beat frequency between the emitted and the reflected waves. Increasing the frequency of the ultrasound will
    A. Increase the beat frequency.
    B. Not affect the beat frequency.
    C. Decrease the beat frequency.

Measuring the Speed of Sound

A student investigator is measuring the speed of sound by looking at the time for a brief, sinusoidal pulse from a loudspeaker to travel down a tube, reflect from the closed end, and reach a microphone. The apparatus is shown in Figure IV.1a; typical data recorded by the microphone are graphed in Figure IV.1b. The first pulse is the sound directly from the loudspeaker; the second pulse is the reflection from the closed end. A portion of the returning wave reflects from the open end of the tube and makes another round trip before being detected by the microphone; this is the third pulse seen in the data.

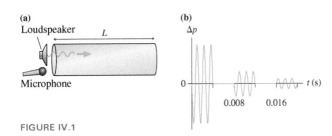

FIGURE IV.1

13. What was the approximate frequency of the sound wave used in this experiment?
   A. 250 Hz
   B. 500 Hz
   C. 750 Hz
   D. 1000 Hz
14. What can you say about the reflection of sound waves at the ends of a tube?
   A. Sound waves are inverted when reflected both from open and closed tube ends.
   B. Sound waves are inverted when reflected from a closed end, not inverted when reflected from an open end.
   C. Sound waves are inverted when reflected from an open end, not inverted when reflected from a closed end.
   D. Sound waves are not inverted when reflected either from open or closed tube ends.
15. What was the approximate length of the tube?
   A. 0.35 m
   B. 0.70 m
   C. 1.4 m
   D. 2.8 m
16. An alternative technique to determine sound speed is to measure the frequency of a standing wave in the tube. What is the wavelength of the lowest resonance of this tube?
   A. $L/2$
   B. L
   C. $2L$
   D. $4L$

In the Swing

A rope swing is hung from a tree right at the edge of a small creek. The rope is 5.0 m long; the creek is 3.0 m wide.

17. You sit on the swing, and your friend gives you a gentle push so that you swing out over the creek. How long will it be until you swing back to where you started?
   A. 4.5 s   B. 3.4 s
   C. 2.2 s   D. 1.1 s
18. Now you switch places with your friend, who has twice your mass. You give your friend a gentle push so that he swings out over the creek. How long will it be until he swings back to where he started?
   A. 4.5 s   B. 3.4 s
   C. 2.2 s   D. 1.1 s
19. Your friend now pushes you over and over, so that you swing higher and higher. At some point you are swinging all the way across the creek—at the top point of your arc you are right above the opposite side. How fast are you moving when you get back to the lowest point of your arc?
   A. 6.3 m/s   B. 5.4 m/s
   C. 4.4 m/s   D. 3.1 m/s

Additional Integrated Problems

20. BIO The jumping gait of the kangaroo is efficient because energy is stored in the stretch of stout tendons in the legs; the kangaroo literally bounces with each stride. We can model the bouncing of a kangaroo as the bouncing of a mass on a spring. A 70 kg kangaroo hits the ground, the tendons stretch to a maximum length, and the rebound causes the kangaroo to leave the ground approximately 0.10 s after its feet first touch.
   a. Modeling this as the motion of a mass on a spring, what is the period of the motion?
   b. Given the kangaroo mass and the period you've calculated, what is the spring constant?
   c. If the kangaroo speeds up, it must bounce higher and farther with each stride, and so must store more energy in each bounce. How does this affect the time and the amplitude of each bounce?
21. BIO A brand of earplugs reduces the sound intensity level by 27 dB. By what factor do these earplugs reduce the acoustic intensity?
22. BIO Sperm whales, just like bats, use echolocation to find prey. A sperm whale's vocal system creates a single sharp click, but the emitted sound consists of several equally spaced clicks of decreasing intensity. Researchers use the time interval between the clicks to estimate the size of the whale that created them. Explain how this might be done.
   Hint: The head of a sperm whale is complex, with air pockets at either end.

Mathematics Review

Algebra

Using exponents:

$$a^{-x} = \frac{1}{a^x} \qquad a^x a^y = a^{(x+y)} \qquad \frac{a^x}{a^y} = a^{(x-y)} \qquad (a^x)^y = a^{xy}$$

$$a^0 = 1 \qquad a^1 = a \qquad a^{1/n} = \sqrt[n]{a}$$

Fractions:

$$\left(\frac{a}{b}\right)\left(\frac{c}{d}\right) = \frac{ac}{bd} \qquad \frac{a/b}{c/d} = \frac{ad}{bc} \qquad \frac{1}{1/a} = a$$

Logarithms:

Natural (base e) logarithms: If $a = e^x$, then $\ln(a) = x$ $\qquad \ln(e^x) = x \qquad\qquad e^{\ln(x)} = x$

Base 10 logarithms: If $a = 10^x$, then $\log_{10}(a) = x \qquad \log_{10}(10^x) = x \qquad 10^{\log_{10}(x)} = x$

The following rules hold for both natural and base 10 algorithms:

$$\ln(ab) = \ln(a) + \ln(b) \qquad\qquad \ln\left(\frac{a}{b}\right) = \ln(a) - \ln(b) \qquad \ln(a^n) = n\ln(a)$$

The expression $\ln(a + b)$ cannot be simplified.

Linear equations: The graph of the equation $y = ax + b$ is a straight line. a is the slope of the graph. b is the y-intercept.

Proportionality: To say that y is proportional to x, written $y \propto x$, means that $y = ax$, where a is a constant. Proportionality is a special case of linearity. A graph of a proportional relationship is a straight line that passes through the origin. If $y \propto x$, then

$$\frac{y_1}{y_2} = \frac{x_1}{x_2}$$

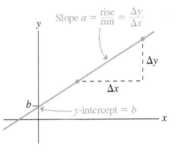

Quadratic equation: The quadratic equation $ax^2 + bx + c = 0$ has the two solutions $x = \dfrac{-b \pm \sqrt{b^2 - 4ac}}{2a}$.

Geometry and Trigonometry

Area and volume:

Rectangle

$A = ab$

Triangle

$A = \frac{1}{2}ab$

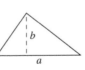

Circle

$C = 2\pi r$

$A = \pi r^2$

Rectangular box

$V = abc$

Right circular cylinder

$V = \pi r^2 l$

Sphere

$A = 4\pi r^2$

$V = \frac{4}{3}\pi r^3$

Arc length and angle: The angle θ in radians is defined as $\theta = s/r$.

The arc length that spans angle θ is $s = r\theta$.

2π rad $= 360°$

Right triangle: Pythagorean theorem $c = \sqrt{a^2 + b^2}$ or $a^2 + b^2 = c^2$

$$\sin\theta = \frac{b}{c} = \frac{\text{far side}}{\text{hypotenuse}} \qquad \theta = \sin^{-1}\left(\frac{b}{c}\right)$$

$$\cos\theta = \frac{a}{c} = \frac{\text{adjacent side}}{\text{hypotenuse}} \qquad \theta = \cos^{-1}\left(\frac{a}{c}\right)$$

$$\tan\theta = \frac{b}{a} = \frac{\text{far side}}{\text{adjacent side}} \qquad \theta = \tan^{-1}\left(\frac{b}{a}\right)$$

In general, if it is known that sine of an angle θ is x, so $x = \sin\theta$, then we can find θ by taking the *inverse sine* of x, denoted $\sin^{-1} x$. Thus $\theta = \sin^{-1} x$. Similar relations apply for cosines and tangents.

General triangle: $\alpha + \beta + \gamma = 180° = \pi$ rad

Identities:

$\tan\alpha = \dfrac{\sin\alpha}{\cos\alpha}$ $\qquad\qquad \sin^2\alpha + \cos^2\alpha = 1$

$\sin(-\alpha) = -\sin\alpha$ $\qquad\qquad \cos(-\alpha) = \cos\alpha$

$\sin(2\alpha) = 2\sin\alpha\cos\alpha$ $\qquad\qquad \cos(2\alpha) = \cos^2\alpha - \sin^2\alpha$

Expansions and Approximations

Binomial approximation: $(1 + x)^n \approx 1 + nx$ if $x \ll 1$

Small-angle approximation: If $\alpha \ll 1$ rad, then $\sin\alpha \approx \tan\alpha \approx \alpha$ and $\cos\alpha \approx 1$.

The small-angle approximation is excellent for $\alpha < 5°$ (≈ 0.1 rad) and generally acceptable up to $\alpha \approx 10°$.

Periodic Table of Elements

Legend: Atomic number — 27, Symbol — Co, Atomic mass — 58.9

Transition elements — groups 3–12
Inner transition elements — Lanthanides and Actinides

Group	1	2	3	4	5	6	7	8	9	10	11	12	13	14	15	16	17	18
Period 1	1 H 1.0																	2 He 4.0
Period 2	3 Li 6.9	4 Be 9.0											5 B 10.8	6 C 12.0	7 N 14.0	8 O 16.0	9 F 19.0	10 Ne 20.2
Period 3	11 Na 23.0	12 Mg 24.3											13 Al 27.0	14 Si 28.1	15 P 31.0	16 S 32.1	17 Cl 35.5	18 Ar 39.9
Period 4	19 K 39.1	20 Ca 40.1	21 Sc 45.0	22 Ti 47.9	23 V 50.9	24 Cr 52.0	25 Mn 54.9	26 Fe 55.8	27 Co 58.9	28 Ni 58.7	29 Cu 63.5	30 Zn 65.4	31 Ga 69.7	32 Ge 72.6	33 As 74.9	34 Se 79.0	35 Br 79.9	36 Kr 83.8
Period 5	37 Rb 85.5	38 Sr 87.6	39 Y 88.9	40 Zr 91.2	41 Nb 92.9	42 Mo 95.9	43 Tc 96.9	44 Ru 101.1	45 Rh 102.9	46 Pd 106.4	47 Ag 107.9	48 Cd 112.4	49 In 114.8	50 Sn 118.7	51 Sb 121.8	52 Te 127.6	53 I 126.9	54 Xe 131.3
Period 6	55 Cs 132.9	56 Ba 137.3	71 Lu 175.0	72 Hf 178.5	73 Ta 180.9	74 W 183.9	75 Re 186.2	76 Os 190.2	77 Ir 192.2	78 Pt 195.1	79 Au 197.0	80 Hg 200.6	81 Tl 204.4	82 Pb 207.2	83 Bi 209.0	84 Po 209.0	85 At 210.0	86 Rn 222.0
Period 7	87 Fr 223.0	88 Ra 226.0	103 Lr 262.1	104 Rf 261	105 Db 262	106 Sg 263	107 Bh 264	108 Hs 269	109 Mt 268	110 Ds 271	111 Rg 272							

Lanthanides 6

57 La 138.9	58 Ce 140.1	59 Pr 140.9	60 Nd 144.2	61 Pm 144.9	62 Sm 150.4	63 Eu 152.0	64 Gd 157.3	65 Tb 158.9	66 Dy 162.5	67 Ho 164.9	68 Er 167.3	69 Tm 168.9	70 Yb 173.0

Actinides 7

89 Ac 227.0	90 Th 232.0	91 Pa 231.0	92 U 238.0	93 Np 237.0	94 Pu 239.1	95 Am 241.1	96 Cm 244.1	97 Bk 249.1	98 Cf 252.1	99 Es 257.1	100 Fm 257.1	101 Md 258.1	102 No 259.1

Inner transition elements

APPENDIX C

ActivPhysics OnLine™ Activities www.masteringphysics.com

The following list gives the activity numbers and titles of the ActivPhysics activities available in the Pearson eText and the Study Area of MasteringPhysics, followed by the corresponding textbook page references.

APPENDIX C

PhET Simulations www.masteringphysics.com

The following list gives the titles of the PhET simulations available in the Pearson eText and in the Study Area of MasteringPhysics, with the corresponding textbook section and page references.

*Indicates an associated tutorial available in the MasteringPhysics Item Library

Video Resources (MP) www.masteringphysics.com

The following lists describe the videos available in the Pearson eText and in the Study Area of MasteringPhysics, with the corresponding textbook section and page references.

Class Videos

Video Tutor Solutions

Video Tutor Demonstrations

Atomic and Nuclear Data

Atomic Number (Z)	Element	Symbol	Mass Number (A)	Atomic Mass (u)	Percent Abundance	Decay Mode	Half-Life $t_{1/2}$
0	(Neutron)	n	1	1.008 665		β^-	10.4 min
1	Hydrogen	H	1	1.007 825	99.985	stable	
	Deuterium	D	2	2.014 102	0.015	stable	
	Tritium	T	3	3.016 049		β^-	12.33 yr
2	Helium	He	3	3.016 029	0.000 1	stable	
			4	4.002 602	99.999 9	stable	
			6	6.018 886		β^-	0.81 s
3	Lithium	Li	6	6.015 121	7.50	stable	
			7	7.016 003	92.50	stable	
			8	8.022 486		β^-	0.84 s
4	Beryllium	Be	9	9.012 174	100	stable	
			10	10.013 534		β^-	1.5×10^6 yr
5	Boron	B	10	10.012 936	19.90	stable	
			11	11.009 305	80.10	stable	
			12	12.014 352		β^-	0.020 2 s
6	Carbon	C	10	10.016 854		β^+	19.3 s
			11	11.011 433		β^+	20.4 min
			12	12.000 000	98.90	stable	
			13	13.003 355	1.10	stable	
			14	14.003 242		β^-	5 730 yr
			15	15.010 599		β^-	2.45 s
7	Nitrogen	N	12	12.018 613		β^+	0.011 0 s
			13	13.005 738		β^+	9.96 min
			14	14.003 074	99.63	stable	
			15	15.000 108	0.37	stable	
			16	16.006 100		β^-	7.13 s
			17	17.008 450		β^-	4.17 s
8	Oxygen	O	15	15.003 065		β^+	122 s
			16	15.994 915	99.76	stable	
			17	16.999 132	0.04	stable	
			18	17.999 160	0.20	stable	
			19	19.003 577		β^-	26.9 s
9	Fluorine	F	18	18.000 937		β^+	109.8 min
			19	18.998 404	100	stable	
			20	19.999 982		β^-	11.0 s
10	Neon	Ne	19	19.001 880		β^+	17.2 s
			20	19.992 435	90.48	stable	
			21	20.993 841	0.27	stable	
			22	21.991 383	9.25	stable	
17	Chlorine	Cl	35	34.968 853	75.77	stable	
			36	35.968 307		β^-	3.0×10^5 yr
			37	36.965 903	24.23	stable	

Atomic Number (Z)	Element	Symbol	Mass Number (A)	Atomic Mass (u)	Percent Abundance	Decay Mode	Half-Life $t_{1/2}$
18	Argon	Ar	36	35.967 547	0.34	stable	
			38	37.962 732	0.06	stable	
			39	38.964 314		β^-	269 yr
			40	39.962 384	99.60	stable	
			42	41.963 049		β^-	33 yr
19	Potassium	K	39	38.963 708	93.26	stable	
			40	39.964 000	0.01	β^+	1.28×10^9 yr
			41	40.961 827	6.73	stable	
26	Iron	Fe	54	54.939 613	5.9	stable	
			56	55.934 940	91.72	stable	
			57	56.935 396	2.1	stable	
			58	57.933 278	0.28	stable	
			60	59.934 072		β^-	1.5×10^6 yr
27	Cobalt	Co	59	58.933 198	100	stable	
			60	59.933 820		β^-	5.27 yr
38	Strontium	Sr	84	83.913 425	0.56%	stable	
			86	85.909 262	9.86%	stable	
			87	86.908 879	7.00%	stable	
			88	87.905 614	82.58%	stable	
			89	88.907 450		β^-	50.53 days
			90	89.907 738		β^-	27.78 yr
53	Iodine	I	127	126.904 474	100	stable	
			129	128.904 984		β^-	1.6×10^7 yr
			131	130.906 124		β^-	8 days
54	Xenon	Xe	128	127.903 531	1.9	stable	
			129	128.904 779	26.4	stable	
			130	129.903 509	4.1	stable	
			131	130.905 069	21.2	stable	
			132	131.904 141	26.9	stable	
			133	132.905 906		β^-	5.4 days
			134	133.905 394	10.4	stable	
			136	135.907 215	8.9	stable	
55	Cesium	Cs	133	132.905 436	100	stable	
			137	136.907 078		β^-	30 yr
82	Lead	Pb	204	203.973 020	1.4	stable	
			206	205.974 440	24.1	stable	
			207	206.975 871	22.1	stable	
			208	207.976 627	52.4	stable	
			210	209.984 163		α, β^-	22.3 yr
			211	210.988 734		β^-	36.1 min
83	Bismuth	Bi	209	208.980 374	100	stable	
			211	210.987 254		α	2.14 min
			215	215.001 836		β^-	7.4 min
86	Radon	Rn	219	219.009 477		α	3.96 s
			220	220.011 369		α	55.6 s
			222	222.017 571		α, β^-	3.823 days

Atomic Number (Z)	Element	Symbol	Mass Number (A)	Atomic Mass (u)	Percent Abundance	Decay Mode	Half-Life $t_{1/2}$
88	Radium	Ra	223	223.018 499		α	11.43 days
			224	224.020 187		α	3.66 days
			226	226.025 402		α	1 600 yr
			228	228.031 064		β^-	5.75 yr
90	Thorium	Th	227	227.027 701		α	18.72 days
			228	228.028 716		α	1.913 yr
			229	229.031 757		α	7 300 yr
			230	230.033 127		α	75.000 yr
			231	231.036 299		α, β^-	25.52 hr
			232	232.038 051	100	α	1.40×10^{10} yr
			234	234.043 593		β^-	24.1 days
92	Uranium	U	233	233.039 630		α	1.59×10^5 yr
			234	234.040 946		α	2.45×10^5 yr
			235	235.043 924	0.72	α	7.04×10^8 yr
			236	236.045 562		α	2.34×10^7 yr
			238	238.050 784	99.28	α	4.47×10^9 yr
93	Neptunium	Np	237	237.048 168		α	2.14×10^6 yr
			238	238.050 946		β^-	2.12 days
			239	239.052 939		β^-	2.36 days
94	Plutonium	Pu	238	238.049 555		α	87.7 yr
			239	239.052 157		α	2.412×10^4 yr
			240	240.053 808		α	6 560 yr
			242	242.058 737		α	3.73×10^6 yr
			244	244.064 200		α	8.1×10^7 yr
95	Americium	Am	241	241.056 823		α	432.21 yr
			243	243.061 375		α	73.070 yr

Answers

Answers to odd-numbered multiple-choice questions

21. C
23. A
25. B
27. D

Answers to odd-numbered problems

1.

Skid begins   Stops

3.
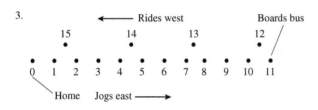

5. −22 m
7. 800 m east of starting point
9. Bike, ball, cat, toy car
11. −1.0 m/s
13. 15 s
15. a. 0.20 m b. 20 m/s c. 27 m/s
17. 1 km/ks < 1 cm/ms < 1 mm/μs
19. a. 3 b. 4 c. 5 d. 3
21. 3.81×10^2 m
23. 4.2×10^{-8} m/s
25. 1.2×10^{-9} m/s or 4.4 μm/h
27. 3.3 km
29. 10 m
31. 38 km
33. 50 yd at 32°
35.

37.

39. **Pictorial representation**

Motion diagram

47. 12 in/ns
49. 43 mph
51. 3.0×10^4 ms
53. 40 ms
55. a.

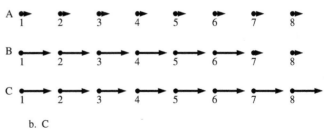

   b. C
   c. A
57. a. AB and CD b. All segments c. AB and CD
59. 30 m
61. 12 min
63. B
65. A

Chapter 2

Answers to odd-numbered multiple-choice questions

15. C
17. C
19. D
21. B
23. B
25. A

Answers to odd-numbered problems

1. b.

5. a. 8 s
   b.

7. a.

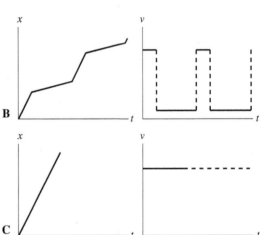

   b. 14 m
9. 2.5 m/s, 0 m/s, −10 m/s
11. a. Beth   b. 20 min
13. 4.3 min
15. a. 15 m   b. 90 m
17. a.

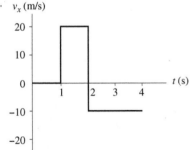

   b. Yes, at t = 2 s

19. a. 26 m, 28 m, 26 m   b Yes, at t = 3 s
21.

23. a. Positive   b. Negative   c. Negative
25. 6.1 m/s², 2.5 m/s², 1.5 m/s²
27. a. 36 m/s²   b. 0.22 m
29. 26 m/s
31. 1 mi
33. Yes
35. a. 5 m   b. 22 m/s
37. 10.0 s
39. 0.31 m
41. a. Both magnitudes and directions are equal   b. Equal
43. a. 33 m   b. 25 m/s
45. a. 3.0 s   b. 15 m/s   c. $(v_1)_f$ = 31 m/s $(v_2)_f$ = 35 m/s
47.

49. 57 mph
51. b.

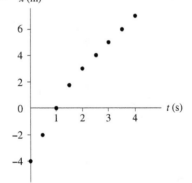

   c. 4 m   d. 4 m   e. 4 m/s   f. 2 m/s   g. −2 m/s²

53. a. 180 mph b. 2.3 m/s² c. 35 s d. No
55. 8.7 y
57. a. ≈1.0 cm b. 35 m/s² c. 0.84 m/s
59. a. 1000 m/s² b. 1.0 ms c. 5.1 cm
61. 33 m/s²
63. a. 24 m/s b. 4.5 s
65. 12 m/s
67. 110 m
69. a. 4.1 s b. Same
71. a. 4.0 s b. 16 m
73. a. 100 m
   b.
75. B
77. B

Chapter 3

Answers to odd-numbered multiple-choice questions
17. B
19. D
21. a. D b. A c. C d. A
23. a. C b. D
25. B
27. D

Answers to odd-numbered problems
7. 12 m/s
9. 87 m/s
11. a. $d_x = 71$ m, $d_y = -71$ m b. $v_x = 280$ m/s, $v_y = 100$ m/s
   c. $a_x = 0.0$ m/s², $d_y = -5.0$ m/s²
13. a. $v = 45$ m/s, $\theta = 63°$ b. $a = 6.3$ m/s², $\theta = 288°$
15. 5.0 km, 24° counterclockwise from $+x$-axis
17. 530 m
19. 1.3 s
21. Ball 1: 5 m/s; Ball 2: −15 m/s
23. 2.0 km/h
25. a. 22° b. 400 m
27. a.   d. 10 m
29. 71 m
31. a. 64 ms b. 780 m/s
33. a. 15 s b. 330 m c. 280 m

35. a. 90 rev/s b. 11 ms
37. a. 170 rev/s; 6.0 ms b. 63 m/s c. 6,700 g
39. a. 4.0 m/s² b. 32 m/s²
41. 27 m
43. a. $\vec{D} = (8, 7)$ c. $D = \sqrt{113}$, $\theta = \tan^{-1}(7/8) = 41°$
45. a. $\vec{B} = (-2, 2)$ b. $B = 2\sqrt{2}$, $\theta = 135°$
47. a. 4.3 m b. 5.5 m
49. 7.5 m
51. 46 min
53. a. 64 m b. 7.1 s
55. No
57. a. 39 mi b. 20 mph
59. 41° south of west
61. a. 7° south of east b. 2 h, 29 min
63. a. $(v_x)_0 = 2.0$ m/s $(v_y)_0 = 4.0$ m/s
      $(v_x)_1 = 2.0$ m/s $(v_y)_0 = 2.0$ m/s
      $(v_x)_2 = 2.0$ m/s $(v_y)_0 = 0.0$ m/s
      $(v_x)_3 = 2.0$ m/s $(v_y)_0 = -2.0$ m/s
   b. 2.0 m/s² c. 63°
65. a. $v = L\sqrt{g/2h}$ b. 6.0 m/s c. Yes, it is reasonable
67. 6.0 m
69. Yes, by 1.0 m
71. 3.5 s
73. a. 6.1 m/s b. 1.8 m
75. 11 mph
77. a. 2.9 m/s², 0.30g b. 57 mph
79. B
81. C

Chapter 4

Answers to odd-numbered multiple-choice questions
21. C
23. A
25. D
27. A
29. B

Answers to odd-numbered problems
1. First is rear-end; second is head on
5.
7. Weight, tension force by rope
9. Weight, normal force by ground, kinetic friction force by ground
11. Weight, normal force by ground, kinetic friction force by ground
13. $m_1 = 0.08$ kg and $m_3 = 0.50$ kg
15. a. 2.4 m/s² b. 0.60 m/s²
17. a. 16 m/s² b. 4.0 m/s² c. 8.0 m/s² d. 32 m/s²
19. 2.5 m/s²
21. 0.25 kg
23. 7.5×10^2 N
25. 0.02 m/s²
29.

Force identification	Free-body diagram

35.

Force identification   **Free-body diagram**

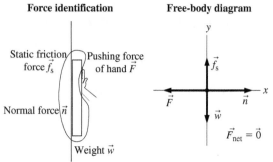

39. **Motion diagram**   41. **Motion diagram**

43.   45.

47.   49.

53.

55.

59.

61.

63.

67. a.

b. Greater
69. C
71. C

Chapter 5

Answers to odd-numbered multiple-choice questions
21. D
23. a. B   b. D
25. a. C   b. B
27. C
29. C
31. D

Answers to odd-numbered problems
1. $T_1 = 87$ N $T_2 = 50$ N
3. 110 N
5. 270 N

7. 170 kg

9.

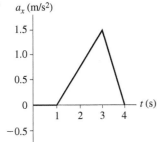

11. $a_x = 1.0 \text{ m/s}^2$ $a_y = 0.0 \text{ m/s}^2$
13. a. 0.0 N   b. 0.0 N   c. 250 N
15. 9800 N, toward the rear
17. a. 539 N   b. 89.1 N, 55.0 kg
19. a. 780 N   b. 1600 N
21. a. 780 N   b. 1100 N
23. a. 5.9 N   b. 5.1 N
25. 0.25
27. 140 m
29. a.

                            c. 4.9 m/s²   d. 2.9 m/s²

31. a. 68 N   b. 610 N
33. 170 m/s
35. a. 6.0 N   b. 10 N
37. a. 20 N   b. 21 N
39. a. 1.0 N   b. 50 N
41. a. 530 N   b. 5300 N
43. $F_{net}(1 \text{ s}) = 8 \text{ N}$ $F_{net}(4 \text{ s}) = 0 \text{ N}$ $F_{net}(7 \text{ s}) = -12 \text{ N}$
45. a. 490 N   b. 740 N
47. a. 2.0×10^4 m/s²   b. 2800 N   c. 2800 N   d. Forehead no, cheek yes
49. a. 230 N   b. 0.20 m/s
51. a. 3.96 N   b. 2.32 N
53. a. 1.3 m/s²   b. 2.0 m/s²
55. 60 m
57. a. 9.8 m/s²   b. −9.8 m/s²   c. 20 m/s²   d. 2.5 m/s   e. 31 cm
59. a. 17 m/s   b. 230 m
61. Stay at rest
63. 1.9×10^5 N
65. $T_1 = 17 \text{ N}$ $T_2 = 27 \text{ N}$
67. 27°
69. a. −5g   b. 3g
71. 0.93 m/s², down
73. 3.7 cm
81. A
83. D

Chapter 6

Answers to odd-numbered multiple-choice questions
21. D
23. C
25. B
27. A

29. D
31. D
33. D

Answers to odd-numbered problems
1. a. $\theta = \pi/2$ b. $\theta = 0$ c. $\theta = 4\pi/3$
3. 1.7×10^{-3} rad/s
5. a. 1.3 rad, 72°   b. 4×10^{-5} rad/s
7. 3.0 rad
9. a. 25 rad   b. −5 rad/s
11. 3.9 m/s
13. a. 20 s   b. 2.5 m/s
15. $v = 5.7$ m/s $a = 110$ m/s²
17. $T_3 > T_1 = T_4 > T_2$
19. 9400 N, toward center, static friction
21. a. 1700 m/s²   b. 240 N
23. 12 m/s
25. 20 m/s
27. 1.6 m/s²
29. 1/2
31. 6.00×10^{-4}
33. a. 3.53×10^{22} N   b. 1.99×10^{20} N   c. 0.564%
35. 1600 d
37. 92 min, 7700 m/s
39. 4.2 h
43. North pole, by 2.5 N
45. 5.5 m/s
47. a. Two; upward normal force and inward   b. 0.24 N
49. a. 5.0 N   b. 30 rpm
51. 5.4 m/s
53. 22 m/s
55. a. 1.7 m/s², upward
    b.   c. 12 mN, upward   d. 9.8 mN, upward

57. 54 N
59. 2,400 m
61. a. 3.0×10^{24} kg   b. 0.89 m/s²
63. a. 3.77 m/s²   b. 1.6 m/s
65. (12 cm, 0 cm)
67. 6.5×10^{23} kg
69. 0.48 m/s
71. b. $v = 19.8$ m/s
73. b. $r = 1.00 \times 10^8$ m
75. C
77. A

Chapter 7

Answers to odd-numbered multiple-choice questions
17. C
19. A
21. A
23. C

Answers to odd-numbered problems
1. 11 m/s
3. a. 160 rad/s²   b. 50 rev
5. $\tau_1 < \tau_2 = \tau_3 < \tau_4$
7. −20 N·m

9. 5.7 N
11. a. 0.0363 N · m   b. 104 N · m
13. 5.5 N · m
15. a. 1.1 m   b. 1.2 m
17. 12 N · m
19. −2.1 N · m
21. a. 34 N · m   b. 24 N · m
23. a. 1.70 m   b. 833 N · m
25. 7.2×10^{-7} kg · m^2
27. 120 kg · m^2
29. 1.8 kg
31. a. 6.9 kg · m^2 b. 0.75 rad/s^2
33. 1.6 kg · m^2
35. 0.047 N · m
37. 17 rad/s^2
39. 0.50 s
41. 2.2 m/s^2
43. 17 m/s
45.

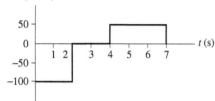

47. 55 rotations
49. −0.94 N · m
51. 7.5 cm
53. a. x_{cg} = 6.0 cm, y_{cg} = 8.2 cm   c. 54°
55. 0.018 kg · m^2
57. a. 1.4 kg · m^2 b. Increase
59. 3.5 rad/s^2
61. −0.28 N · m
63. 1.1 s
65. 9.9 N
67. B
69. B

Chapter 8

Answers to odd-numbered multiple-choice questions
15. A
17. B
19. B
21. B
23. D

Answers to odd-numbered problems
1. Right 470 N; left 160 N
3. 15 cm
5. 140 N
7. No, there is a net torque
9. 590 N
11. 1:1
13. 8.9°
15. 15.0 cm
17. 830 N/m
19. a. 13 cm   b. 8 cm
21. 18 cm
23. 1.5 m/s^2
25. a. 2.0 mm   b. 0.25 mm
27. 7900 N
29. a. 4000 N   b. 4.0 mm

31. 15 cm
33. 0.0078%
35. F_1 = 750 N F_2 = 1000 N
37. 860 N
39. a. 2000 N   b. 2200 N
41. 350 N
43. 1.0 m
45. a. 49 N   b. 1500 N/m   c. 3.4 cm
47. 17.4 N
49. a. 1.0 cm   b. 4.5 N to the left
51. 31 cm
53. a. 8.2 m/s to the right   b. 30 N
55. 81 cm
57. 2.5×10^{-5}
59. a. 4.8×10^{-2} m^2 b. 70000 kg   c. 14%
61. B
63. B

Part I Problems

Answers to odd-numbered problems
1. A
3. A
5. C
7. B
9. D
11. A
13. B
15. D
17. B
19. A
21. b. 3.4 N

Chapter 9

Answers to odd-numbered multiple-choice questions
19. D
21. D
23. D
25. C
27. B

Answers to odd-numbered problems
1. 75 m/s
3. 6.0 N
5. 80 N · s
7. a. 1.5 m/s to the right   b. 0.5 m/s to the right
9. −110 N
11. a. 19 kN   b. 300 kN
13. 0.205 m/s
15. 0.31 m/s
17. 1.43 m/s
19. 0.048 m/s
21. 4.8 m/s
23. 2.3 m/s
25. 1.0 kg
27. (−2 kg · m/s, 4 kg · m/s)
29. 14 m/s, 45° north of east
31. 510 kg · m^2/s
33. 0.025 kg · m^2/s
35. 1.3 rev/s
37. 0.2 s
39. 930 N
41. 3.9 m/s
43. 13 N · s; left, 15° above the horizontal

45. 7.5×10^{-10} N $\cdot$ s
47. a. 6.4 m/s   b. 360 N
49. 3.6 m/s
51. 1.1 m/s
53. 2.0 m/s
55. a. 6.7×10^{-8} m/s   b. $2.2 \times 10^{-10}\%$
57. 13 s
59. 440 m/s
61. -20.0 m/s
63. 196 m/s
65. Forward, 1.5×10^7 m/s
67. 0.85 m/s, $-72°$
69. 4.5 rpm
71. a. 2.8 m/s   b. 2.2 m/s, 25 cm
73. -0.90 rad/s
75. 18 rev/s, clockwise
77. B
79. C

Chapter 10

Answers to odd-numbered multiple-choice questions
23. C
25. C.
27. C.

Answers to odd-numbered problems
1. 0.0 J
3. $W_{\dot{w}} = 12.5$ kJ, $W_{\bar{T}_1} = -7.92$ kJ, $W_{\bar{T}_2} = -4.58$ kJ
5. a. 0 J   b. 2.6 kJ   c. -2.6 kJ
7. The bullet
9. a. 14 m/s   b. Factor of 4
11. 0.0 J
13. 1.8 kg $\cdot$ m^2
15. a. 6.8×10^5 J   b. 46 m   c. No
17. 63 kJ
19. 0.63 m
21. 9.7 J
23. 470 J
25. 1.0×10^2 N
27. a. 13 m/s   b. 14 m/s
29. 31 m/s
31. 3.0 m/s
33. 17 m/s
35. a. The child's gravitational potential energy will be changing into kinetic energy and thermal energy.   b. 550 J
37. 0.86 m/s   and   2.9 m/s
39. 1/2
41. a. 1.8×10^2 J   b. 59 W
43. 45 kW
45. a. 30 N   b. 45 W
47. 2.0×10^4 W
49. a. 7.7 m/s   b. 6.6 m/s
51. 2.3 m/s
53. a. 0.20 kJ   b. 98 N   c. 2.0 m   d. 0.20 kJ
55. 15 m/s
57. 51 cm
59. 3.8 m, not dependent on mass
61. a. $\sqrt{\dfrac{(m - M)kd^2}{m^2}}$ b. 2.0×10^2 m/s
    c. 99.8% kinetic energy transformed to thermal energy
63. 1.6 m/s
65. 8.0 m/s
67. 0.49 m
69. a. $0.048v_i$ b. 95%

71. a. 100 N   b. 0.20 kW   c. 1.2 kW
73. 5.5×10^4 L
75. B
77. C
79. A
81. B
83. C

Chapter 11

Answers to odd-numbered multiple-choice questions
29. C
31. B
33. D
35. C

Answers to odd-numbered problems
1. 1.7 MJ
3. 3.3%
5. 4.2 MJ
7. 230,000 J = 54,000 cal = 54 Cal
9. 1.4 km
11. 710 m or 260 flights
13. a. 200 J   b. 16,000 J/day   c. 0.0094 donuts
15. 313°C
17. 4.8°C
19. -700 J
21. -150 J
23. a. 15 kJ   b. 27%
25. 25%
27. a. 7°C   b. -4°C
29. 460°C
31. 1.5
33. a. 200 J   b. 250 J
35. a. (b) only   b. (a) only
37. 13%
39. 0.80 burritos
41. a. 1.4 MJ   b. 1.4 MJ   c. Cycling
43. a. 190 kJ   b. 750 kJ   c. 180 Cal   d. 130 Cal   e. 1200 W
45. 490 W
47. a. 300 W   b. 1.1 MJ = 260 Cal
49. a. 10000 Cal   b. 490 W; 390 W more
51. a. 2600 Cal   b. 1.1 kg
53. 7.2×10^{22} atoms
55. a. 40%   b. 220°C
57. 230 K
59. a. 60 J   b. -23°C
61. 95,000
63. a. 47%   b. 35%
65. a. 880 N   b. 4.4 kW   c. 18%
67. 8.0%
69. C
71. A
73. C

Part II Problems

Answers to odd-numbered problems
1. B
3. B
5. D
7. C
9. A
11. C
13. D

15. B
17. C
19. A
21. D
23. 0.22 m/s to the west
25. a. 3.0 m/s   b. 480 N   c. 60 J

Chapter 12

Answers to odd-numbered multiple-choice questions
27. D
29. D
31. A
33. E
35. B

Answers to odd-numbered problems
1. Carbon
3. 3.5×10^{24}
5. $0.024\ m^3 = 24\ L$
7. 49.7 psi
9. 1.1 N
11. a. $-140°C$ b. 2.7×10^{-21} J
13. 1900 kPa
15. 17 L
17. a. $T_f = T_i$ b. $p_f = \frac{1}{2}p_i$
19. a. 98 cm^3
21. a. Isochoric   b. 910 K, 300 K
23. a. Isobaric   b. 120°C   c. 0.0094 mol
25. 16°C
27. 0.30 atm
29. 4.7 m
31. 0.83%
33. 6.9 kJ
35. 2300 W
37. 250 Cal/day, 12 W
39. 260 kJ
41. 0.218 kg
43. Iron
45. 91 g
47. a. 31 J   b. 60°C
49. 0.080 K
51. 41 J
53. 830 W
55. 24 W
57. 6.0 W
59. 4.7 cm^2
61. a. 50 L   b. 1.3 atm
63. a. 5.4×10^{23} b. 3.6 g
65. a. 140 J   b. 0.4 L
67. 35 psi
69. 174°C
71. a. 0.73 atm   b. 0.52 atm
73. 60 J
75. a. 0.51 atm   b. 160 K
77. 8.7 h
79. 56 J
81. 2.4×10^6 kg/min
83. 60 K
85. 0.023 K, no
87. a. 83 J/kg·K   b. 200 kJ/kg
89. 970 g
91. 60 g
93. a. 3.1 atm   b. 9.8 L
95. a. 150 J   b. -91 J
97. 0.026 W/m·K
99. 2
101. A
103. C

Chapter 13

Answers to odd-numbered multiple-choice questions
31. A
33. D
35. B
37. B
39. A

Answers to odd-numbered problems
1. 1200 kg/m^3
3. 11 kg/m^3
5. a. 810 kg/m^3 b. 840 kg/m^3
7. 8.0%
9. a. 6.3 m^3 b. 1.2×10^5 Pa
11. 210 N
13. 3.2 km
15. a. 2.9×10^4 N   b. 30 football players
17. a. 1.1×10^5 Pa   b. 4400 Pa for both A–B and A–C
19. 3.68 mm
21. 89 mm
23. 0.82 m
25. 1.9 N
27. 46 kg
29. 1.0 m/s
31. 97 min
33. 110 kPa
35. 3.0 m/s
37. 260 Pa
39. 2.17 cm
41. 4.8×10^{23} atoms
43. 27 cm
45. a. 5800 N   b. 6000 N
47. 1.8 cm
49. 750 kg/m^3
51. 44 N
53. a. 0.38 N   b. 20 m/s
55. 2×10^{-3} m/s
57. a. p_{atmos} b. 4.6 m
59. 4.4 cm
61. $-28°C$
63. 13 mm Hg
65. B
67. A

Part III Problems

Answers to odd-numbered problems
1. A
3. B
5. D
7. B
9. C
11. A
13. B
15. D
17. A
19. 300 N
21. a. 0.071 mol   b. 6.7×10^{-4} m^3 c. 0.019 mol

Chapter 14

Answers to odd-numbered multiple-choice questions
23. a. B b. C c. B d. B e. B
25. B
27. B

Answers to odd-numbered problems
1. 2.3 ms
3. 0.80 s, 1.3 Hz
5. 40 N
7. a. 13 cm b. 9.0 cm
9. a. 20 cm b. 0.25 Hz
11. a. 0.30 m b. 2.3 m/s c. 17 m/s^2
13. a. 3.0 mm b. 0.024 m/s
15. a. $U = 1/4E$ $K = 3/4E$ b. 0.707A
17. a. 2.83 s b. 1.41 s c. 2.00 s d. 1.41 s
19. a. 2.0 cm b. 0.63 s c. 5.0 N/m d. 20 cm/s e. 1.0×10^{-3} J
    f. 15 cm/s
21. a. 1.00 s b. 0.628 m/s c. 0.100 J
23. a. 4.00 s b. 5.66 s c. 2.83 s d. 4.00 s
25. a. 0.10 rad b. 0.80 Hz c. 0.39 m d. $-$0.084 rad
27. 33.1 cm
29. 1.6 s
31. a. 0.124 rad b. 2.00 s c. 1.49 m
33. 1.3 s
35. 10.0 s
37. a. 6.2 s b. 3.4 cm
39. 2.8 s
41. 250 N/m
43. 1.1 m/s
45. a. 0.169 kg b. 0.565 m/s
47. 5.86 m/s^2
49. a. 0.25 Hz, 3.0 s b. 6.0 s, 1.5 s c. 2.25
51. a. 6.40 cm b. 28.3 cm/s
53. a. 47,000 N/m b. 1.8 Hz
55. 11 cm, 1.7 s
57. 0.64 Hz
59. 8.1 N/m
61. a. 2.00709 s b. 2.00721 s c. 4.6 h
63. a.

	f (Hz)	T (s)
24.8 cm rod	1.00	1.00
38.8 cm rod	0.800	1.25

    b. 5.00 s c. 0.200 Hz
65. a. 9.5 N/m b. 0.50 m/s c. 2.9 s
67. 73 cm
69. 236 oscillations
71. 2.4 J
73. A
75. C

Chapter 15

Answers to odd-numbered multiple-choice questions
21. D
23. D
25. D

Answers to odd-numbered problems
1. 280 m/s
3. 140 m/s
5. 6000 m/s

7.

9.

Snapshot graph at $t = 1.0$ s

11. 10 m/s
13. a. 8.6 mm b. 15 ms
15. a. 11 Hz b. 1.1 m c. 13 m/s
17. $A = 4$ cm; $\lambda = 12$ m; $f = 2.0$ Hz
19. 11 s
21. 14.8 mm
23. a. 1700 Hz b. 1.5 GHz c. 990 nm
25. a. 10 GHz b. 170 μs
27. 55 pJ
29. 600 kJ
31. 11 W
33. a. 6.7×10^4 W b. 8.5×10^{10} W/m^2
35. 25 pW/m^2, 14 dB
37. a. 3.2×10^{-3} W/m^2 b. 95 dB
39. 100 dB
41. a. 650 Hz b. 560 Hz
43. 16 m/s away
45. 4.5 m/s
47. 86 m
49. 790 m
51. 50 cm/s, 13 m/s^2
53. 890 g
55. $L_1 = 2.3$ m, $L_2 = 1.7$ m
57. a. 3.0037 m b. 11 μs c. 1.1×10^{-2}
59. 0.069°C
61. a. 3 s b. 9 m/s
63. $y(x, t) = (5.0 \text{ cm}) \cos\left[2\pi \left(\dfrac{x}{50 \text{ cm}} + \dfrac{t}{0.125 \text{ s}} \right) \right]$
65. b. 33 m/s to the right
67. 6.8 cm/s
69. 20 μW/m^2
71. a. 50 MW b. 5.0 W c. 6.4×10^{17} W/m^2 d 5.8×10^{14}
73. a. 110 dB b. 16 km
75. a. 1.9 W/m^2 b. 123 dB c. 71 m
77. 620 Hz, 580 Hz
79. 110 m/s
81. D
83. B

Chapter 16

Answers to odd-numbered multiple-choice questions
21. A
23. D
25. A
27. D

Answers to odd-numbered problems

1.

3. 4 s
5. 5.0 s
7. 60 Hz
9. 53 m/s
11. a. 4.80 m, 2.40 m, and 1.60 m   b. 75.0 Hz
13. a. 700 Hz   b. 56 N
15. 2180 N
17. a. 16 Hz   b. 3.18 m
19. a. 2.42 m, 1.21 m, and 0.807 m   b. 4.84 m, 1.61m, and 0.968 m
21. 510 Hz
23. a. 5.67 Hz   b. 3.5 Hz   c. The frequency will decrease.
25. 6700 Hz
27. 580 Hz and 4900 Hz
29. a. 40 cm   b. 60 cm
33. 203 Hz
35. 880 m/s
37. 1.2 m
39. 65 Hz
41. 270 N

43. 12 kg
45. 8.2 m/s^2
47. 19 kN
49. 18 cm
51. b. 10.5, 13.5, 16.5, and 19.5 GHz
53. a. 0.530 m   b. 2.83 × 10^8 Hz   c. 2.83 × 10^8 round trips
55. 1210 Hz
57. 18 cm
59. 1400 Hz
61. a. 3.00 m   b. Strong   c. Weak
63. 20
65. a. 2 Hz   b. 658 Hz
67. 0.81 s
69. 1750 Hz
71. 0.40 m/s
73. B
75. B

Part IV Problems

Answers to odd-numbered problems

1. $v_{\text{light}} > v_{\text{earthquake}} > v_{\text{sound}} > v_{\text{tsunami}}$
3. D
5. B
7. D
9. C
11. B
13. C
15. C
17. C
19. C
21. 500

Chapter 17

Answers to odd-numbered multiple-choice questions

19. B
21. C
23. B
25. D

Answers to odd-numbered problems

1. a. 1.5 × 20^{-11} s   b. 3.4 mm
3. 0.40 ns
5. 670 ns
7. 0.020 rad, 1.1°
9. 0.050 rad
11. 0.40 mm
13. 2.3 μm
15. 3.2°, 6.3°
17. 221 lines/mm
19. a. 1.3 m   b. 7
21. 216 nm
23. 85.9 nm
25. 121 nm
27. 97.8 nm
29. 94 μm
31. 610 nm
33. 4.9 mm
35. 78 cm
37. 6.4 cm
39. 500 nm
41. 450 nm

43.
Grating   Screen y

$y_1 = 0.58$ m $m = 1$

$\theta_1 = 0.53$ rad
$\theta_1 = 0.53$ rad
$y_0 = 0$ m $m = 0$

$y_1 = 0.58$ m $m = 1$

1.0 m

45. I_1
47. 43.2°
49. 43 cm
51. 500 nm
53. 25 cm
55. 1.8 μm
57. 500 nm
59. 667.8 nm
61. 410 nm, 690 nm, purple
63. 2.8°
65. 7.6 m
67. 0.10 mm
69. a. Double   b. 0.15 mm
71. 0.1 mm
73. a. Diffraction   b. 0.044°   c. 4.6 mm   d. 1.5 m
75. D
77. A

11. 1.37
13. 4.0 m
15. 76.7°
17. 23 cm
19. $s' = 15$ cm, inverted and real
21. $s' = -6.7$ cm, upright and virtual
23. $s' = -40$ cm, upright and virtual, $h' = 10$ cm
25. $s = 18$ cm
27. $s' = -1.3$ m, upright and virtual
29. $s' = 40$ cm, $h' = 2.0$ cm
31. $s' = -60$ cm, $h' = 8.0$ cm
33. $s' = -8.6$ cm, $h' = 1.1$ cm
35. $s' = -9.4$ cm, $h' = 1.9$ cm
37. $s' = -38$ cm, $h' = 7.5$ cm
39. 1.0 m
41. 42.0°
43. 60°
45. a. The angle of the beam is 32.1° from the normal.   b. No
47. 82.8°
51. 35°
53. a. $\beta = \sin^{-1}\left(n \sin \dfrac{\alpha}{2}\right)$ b. 1.58
55. 42°
57. 5.7 m
59. 1.52
63. $2f$
65. $s' = 20$ cm, $h' = 1.0$ cm
67. $s' = -4.3$ cm, $h' = 0.57$ cm
69. $s' = -50$ cm, $h' = 40$ cm
71. $f = 44$ cm, 67 cm
73. a. 5.9 cm   b. 6.0 cm
75. A
77. B

Chapter 18

Answers to odd-numbered multiple-choice questions
17. D
19. B
21. E
23. A
25. B
27. A

Answers to odd-numbered problems
1. 11 ft
3. 8.00 cm
5. B and C
7. 433 cm
9. a. 3   b. B = (4 m, 1 m), C = (2 m, 5 m), D = (4 m, 5 m)
   c.

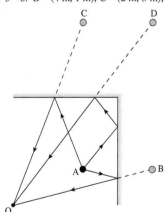

Chapter 19

Answers to odd-numbered multiple-choice questions
17. B
19. C
21. C
23. C

Answers to odd-numbered problems
1. a. −5.8 mm   b. The object must be getting closer.
3. 0.30 m
5. 1/30 s
7. 22 mm, 2.8 mm
9. 2.0 D
11. 3
13. a. Farsighted   b. ∞
15. 2.1 m
17. 5.0 cm
19. a. 1.20 cm   b. 1.67 cm
21. 11 mm
25. $s' = -6.4$ cm to the left of the diverging lens, $h' = 1.0$ cm, same orientation as the object
27. a. 0.058 D   b. 17 mm
29. a. 14°   b. 6.4 mm
31. 0.28 mm, violet
33. 55 km
35. 2.7 mm
39. 0.70 cm
41. b. $s'' = -20$ cm, $h'' = 2.0$ cm

43. 5.0 mm
45. 250
47. −4
49. a. Objective: + 3.0 D; eyepiece: + 4.5 D   b. $M = -1.5$ c. 0.56 m
51. 24 cm
53. 2.8×10^{-7} rad
55. 15 km
57. No
59. A
61. B

Part V Problems

Answers to odd-numbered problems

1. C
3. A
5. A
7. B
9. D
11. A
13. A
15. Aberrations are reduced.
17. 7.2 mm, 0.069 W/m^2

Chapter 20

Answers to odd-numbered multiple-choice questions

23. a. B   b. C   c. B   d. C
25. B
27. C
29. A

Answers to odd-numbered problems

1. a. Electrons are removed.   b. 3.1×10^{10}
3. 1.5×10^6 C
5. a. Electrons from sphere to rod   b. 2.5×10^{10}
7. A has −160 nC; B has 0 C
9. a. 9.0 mN   b. 9.0 mm/s^2
11. 2.6 cm
13. −10 nC
15. 8.0 nC
17. a. 1.7×10^{14} m/s^2, away from bead   b. 3.2×10^{17} m/s^2, toward bead
19. 1.4×10^5 N/C, away from bead
21. a. 1.4×10^{-3} N/C, away from proton   b. 1.4×10^{-3} N/C, toward electron
23. a. 3.6×10^4 N/C, 1.8×10^4 N/C, 1.8×10^4 N/C
    b.

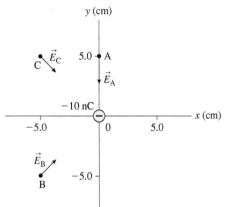

25. 2500 N/C downward
27. a. 1.0×10^{-7} N/C, upward   b. 5.6×10^{-11} N/C, downward
29. a. 2   b. ¼   c. 1
31. 1.9 cm
35. 7.2×10^{-15} N
37. a. 0   b. 5.6×10^{-27} N · m
39. 1.4×10^5 C
41. a. 500 N   b. 3.0×10^{29} m/s^2
43. a. 0.45 N   b. $q_A = 1.0 \times 10^{-6}$ C $q_B = 0.50 \times 10^{-6}$ C
45. 4000 N/C, 9.3° above the horizontal
47. 3.1×10^{-4} N, upward
49. 0
51. 1.1×10^{-5} N, upward
53. 0.68 nC
55. b. $(2 - \sqrt{2}) \dfrac{KQq}{L^2}$
57. 6.6×10^{15} rev/s
59. (−6.0 cm, 3.0 cm)
61. 5.9×10^5 N/C
63. 33 nC
65. 180 nC
67. 150 nC
69. 1.3 cm
71. b. 22 nC
73. D
75. A

Chapter 21

Answers to odd-numbered multiple-choice questions

21. A
23. A
25. C
27. A
29. C

Answers to odd-numbered problems

1. -3.0μC
3. 530 V
5. a. 3000 V   b. 75 μJ
7. a. 1000 eV   b. 1.6×10^{-16} J   c. 438 km/s
9. a. Lower   b. −0.712 V   c. 0.712 eV
11. 400 V
13. a. $E = 200$ kV/m, $\Delta V_C = 200$ V   b. $E = 200$ kV/m, $\Delta V_C = 400$ V
15. a. 23 cm, 11 cm, 7.5 cm, 5.6 cm
17. −5.8 kV
19. a. 1.5 V   b. 8.3 pC
21. −352 V,
23. 10 kV/m, left
25. a. Positive   b. Negative   c. Positive
27. a. 7.1 pF   b. 710 pC
29. 4.8 cm
31. 24 V
33. 15 μC
35. 13 nF
37. a. $Q = 5.0 \times 10^{-10}$ C, $\Delta V_C = 9.0$ V, $E = 9.0 \times 10^4$ V/m
    b. $Q = 2.5 \times 10^{-10}$ C, $\Delta V_C = 9.0$ V, $E = 9.0 \times 10^4$ V/m
39. 1.4 kV
41. 1/2
43. 1.2 kV/m
45. 32 μJ
47. a. 1.0×10^{-6} J   b. −20 V
49. -2.2×10^{-19} J
51. 1.4 mN

53. ± 12 cm
55. a. 103 V   b. 5.39 × 10⁴ N/C, along the +x-axis
57. a. 27 V   b. −4.3 × 10⁻¹⁸ J
59. a. 3100 V   b. 5.0 × 10⁻¹⁶ J
61. 10 kV/m
63. 0.070 eV, increase
65. 140 km/s
67. 71 km/s
69. $\Delta V = 47$ V
71. 10 nC
73. 4.0 × 10⁷ m/s
75. a. 2.1 nC, 3.0 kV/m, 15 V   b. 1.0 nC, 1.5 kV/m, 15 V
77. a. Smaller   b. Smaller   c. 550 V/m, to the right
79. a. 0.80 mm   b. 1.6 mm
81. 22 μF
83. b. 1.7 × 10⁶ m/s
85. b. 0.022 mm
87. A
89. D

Chapter 22

Answers to odd-numbered multiple-choice questions

23. C
25. C
27. D
29. C

Answers to odd-numbered problems

1. 3000 C, 1.9 × 10²²
3. 1.9 × 10²⁰ electrons
5. 9.4 × 10¹³ electrons
7. 13 A
9. 120 C
11. $I_B = 5$ A, $I_C = -2$ A
13. 9.4 × 10¹⁸ ions
15. 12 V
17. 32
19. a. 6.0 V, 6.0 A   b. 6.0 V, 3.0 A   c. 6.0 V, 2.0 A
21. 0.040 Ω
23. a. 0.087 Ω   b. 0.0097 Ω
25. 4100 Ω
27. 13 mV
29. a. 50 m   b. 1.0 A
31. 50 Ω
33. 3.0 mV
35. a.

b.

Battery
Connecting wire
Bulb 1
Connecting wire
Bulb 2
Connecting wire

37. Yes; the hair dryer will draw 14 A.
39. a. 0.38 A   b. 320 Ω
41. 15 kJ
43. 23 mA
45. 28 min
47. 20%
49. 42 GΩ
51. 33 h
53. 1.4 Ω · m
55. 1.9 V
57. a. 3.1 × 10¹⁴   b. 9.1 × 10⁵ N/C   c. 0.23 W
59. 0.62 mm
61. 28 cm
63. 8.4 × 10⁻⁸ Ω
65. a. 14 C   b. 27 J
67. a. 0.24 mA, no   b. 120 mA, yes
69. D
71. A

Chapter 23

Answers to odd-numbered multiple-choice questions

31. B
33. A
35. B
37. B

Answers to odd-numbered problems

1.

3.

5. a. $\Delta V_{12} = -2.0$ V, $\Delta V_{23} = -1.0$ V, $\Delta V_{34} = 0$ V
 b. $\Delta V_{12} = 0$ V, $\Delta V_{23} = -3.0$ V, $\Delta V_{34} = 0$ V
7. a. 0.17 A, left
11. a. 1.0 Ω b. 1.0 Ω c. 0.5 Ω
13. Four in parallel
15. The three 6.0 Ω resistors in parallel with each other, and then that combination in series with the 3.0 Ω resistor
17. 24 Ω
19. 300 Ω
21. a. 2.0 A b. 5.0 A
23. 20 Ω, 60 V
25. Numbering the resistors from left to right:

R	I (A)	ΔV (V)
R_1	1.5	7.5
R_2	0.50	2.5
R_3	0.50	2.5
R_4	0.50	2.5

27.

R	I (A)	ΔV (V)
6.0 Ω (left)	2.0	12
15 Ω	0.8	12
6.0 Ω (top)	1.2	7.2
4.0 Ω	1.2	4.8

29.

R	I (A)	ΔV (V)
3 Ω	2.0	6.0
4 Ω	1.5	6.0
48 Ω	0.13	6.0
16 Ω	0.38	6.0

31. a.

 b. 2.6 mA, 6.4 V
33. 3.0 μF
35. 150 μF in series
37. 8.9 μF
39. a. 0.57 μF b. 6.9 μC
41. 2.0 ms
43. 6.9 ms
45. 7.8 MV/m, 4.4 MV/m
47. 0.73 pF
49. a. 60 m/s b. It neglects the time between the stimulus and the peak of the action potential.
51. 1.3 W, 1.7 W
53. 93 W
55. a. $R_{0.25\,\Omega} = 0.36$ W b. $R_{0.50\,\Omega} = 0.50$ W c. $R_{1.0\,\Omega} = 0.56$ W
 d. $R_{2.0\,\Omega} = 0.50$ W e. $R_{4.0\,\Omega} = 0.36$ W
57. 1.2 A
59. 500 Ω

61. a.

 b.

 c.

 d.

63. Put three resistors in series and then the potential difference across any one would be 3.0 V.
65. a. 0.505 Ω b. 0.500 Ω
69. $Q_1 = Q_2 = Q_3 = 750$ μC $\Delta V_1 = 50$ V $\Delta V_2 = 25$ V
 $\Delta V_3 = 25$ V
71. 870 Ω
73. 18 μF
75. a. 80 μC
 b. 0.23 ms
77. 6100
79. a. 4.8 pC b. 3.0×10^7
81. C
83. B
85. A
87. B

Chapter 24

Answers to odd-numbered multiple-choice questions
33. A
35. A
37. D
39. C

Answers to odd-numbered problems
1. $I_{earthsurface} = 2.5$ A; $I_{refrigerator} = 250$ A;
 $I_{laboratory} = 5000$ A $-$ 50000 A; $I_{magnet} = 500{,}000$ A.
3. a. 20 A b. 1.6 mm
5. $\vec{B}_1 = (6.7 \times 10^{-5}$ T, out of page); $\vec{B}_2 = (2.0 \times 10^{-4}$ T, into page);
 $\vec{B}_3 = (6.7 \times 10^{-5}$ T, out of page)
7. a. 2 μT; 4% b. The fields from adjacent wires nearly cancel because the contributions will be in opposite directions.
9. 750 A
11. 1.6 kA
13. 3.8×10^{-7} A
15. 4.1×10^{-4} T
17. 8.6 μA
19. 13 T
21. a. $(8.0 \times 10^{-13}$ N, $-z$-direction) b. $(8.0 \times 10^{-13}$ N, 45° clockwise from $+z$-axis in yz plane)
23. a. 11 cm b. 10 m
25. 0.086 T
27. He$^+$
29. a. 3.2×10^7 m/s b. 3.7×10^{18} m/s^2 or $3.8 \times 10^{17}g$ c. 0.28 mm
 d. The force is always perpendicular to the velocity, so magnetic fields can't change the speed, only the direction.

31. $\vec{F}_{\text{on 1}} = (2.5 \times 10^{-4}\,\text{N, up})$; $\vec{F}_{\text{on 2}} = \vec{0}\,\text{N}$;
    $\vec{F}_{\text{on 3}} = (2.5 \times 10^{-4}\,\text{N, down})$
33. (56 N, into page)
35. a. 3.3 A   b. 2.0 N   c. 170 m/s^2
37. $7.5 \times 10^{-4}\,\text{N} \cdot \text{m}$
39. $1.1 \times 10^{10}\,\text{A}$
41. 0.036 mm
43. a. $1.0 \times 10^{-4}\,\text{T}$; twice the earth's   b. Immediately twists left, then deflection decreases as capacitor discharges.
45. $3.0\,\Omega$
47. (2.0 mT, into page)
49. a. 1400 A   b. 170 N, right   c. 64 m/s
51. a. $6.0 \times 10^{-21}\,\text{N}$ b. 38 mN/C   c. 110 μV
53. 0.20 A, axis of coil north-south
55. Rapid switching doesn't allow the moments to align.
57. 1.0 T
59. 8.6 mT
61. a.

    b. Attractive   c. To the left, toward the solenoid
63 B
65. C
67. B
69. D

Chapter 25

Answers to odd-numbered multiple-choice questions
27. A
29. B
31. C
33. D
35. D

Answers to odd-numbered problems
1. 0.10 T, out of the page
3. a. 4.0 m/s   b. 2.2 T
5. 9500 m/s
7. For $\theta = 0°$, 3.9×10^{-4} Wb; for $\theta = 30°$, 3.4×10^{-4} Wb; for $\theta = 60°$, 2.0×10^{-4} Wb; for $\theta = 90°$, 0 Wb
9. a. 6.3×10^{-5} Wb   b. 6.3×10^{-5} Wb
11. a. 8.7×10^{-4} Wb   b. Clockwise
13. $|\mathcal{E}_{\text{E}}| > |\mathcal{E}_{\text{B}}| > |\mathcal{E}_{\text{D}}| > |\mathcal{E}_{\text{A}}| > |\mathcal{E}_{\text{C}}|$.
15. 3.1 V
17. 0.44 A
19. 6.0×10^5 V/m
21. $E_0 = 1.4 \times 10^3$ V/m and $B_0 = 4.6 \times 10^{-6}$ T
23. $E_0 = 9.8 \times 10^5$ V/m and $B_0 = 3.3 \times 10^{-3}$ T
25. a. 10.0 nm   b. 3.00×10^{16} Hz   c. 6.67×10^{-8} T
27. a. 2.2×10^{11} V/m   b. $E_0/E = 0.43$
29. a. 0.25 m   b. 2500 m
31. 60°
33. 67%
35. 1200 eV

37. a. 250 keV   b. 1.0×10^6 bonds
39. 1.2×10^5 J
41. 4.68×10^{21} photon/s
43. 2100 °C
45. $\lambda_{\text{dental}} = 50$ pm and $\lambda_{\text{microtomography}} = 20$ pm
47. $\Phi = Bab$
49. 1.2 V
51. 0.11 V
53. 42 mV
55. 31mA
57. 8.7 T/s
59. a. 0.20 A   b. 4.0×10^{-3} N   c. 11°C
61. a. 6.3×10^{-4} N   b. 3.1×10^{-4} W   c. 1.3×10^{-2} A, counterclockwise   d. 3.1×10^{-4} W
63. $E = 550$ V/m and $B = 1.8 \times 10^{-4}$ T
65. a. 8.3×10^{-26} W/m^2 b. 7.9×10^{-12} V/m
67. $\sqrt{2}$
69. $I_0/8$
71. $f = 4.8 \times 10^{27}$ Hz and $\lambda = 6.2 \times 10^{-20}$ m
73. a. 3.4×10^{-19} J   b. 1.8×10^{13} photons
75. 4.5×10^{-2} cm
77. C
79. C

Chapter 26

Answers to odd-numbered multiple-choice questions
23. D
25. A
27. A

Answers to odd-numbered problems
1. a. 50 mA   b. 50 mA
3. 22.4 V
5. a. 9.0 Ω b. 19 A   c. 3200 W
7. 530 A
9. 0.50 A
11. 17 mA
13. a. 47 turns   b. 32 mA
15. a. 12 A   b. 10 Ω
17. Yes
19. $0.15
21. 0.18 mA, no, no
23. 1000 V AC, 3000 V DC, 100000 V AC, 500000 V DC
25. 0.28 mV
27. a. 1.9 mA   b. 1.9 A
29. a. 20.0 mA   b. 20.0 mA   c. 10.0 mA
31. 81 nF
33. 100 V
35. a. 5.00 mA   b. 20.0 mA   c. 40.0 mA
37. 1.4 mH
39. 7.8 min
41. 250 kHz to 360 kHz
43. 0.13 pF
45. 1/4
47. 10 mH
49. a. 200 kHz   b. 200 kHz
51. 320 mA
53. 5.8 mm
55. a. −7.5 V   b. 83 Ω c. 1.4 A
57. 0.63 ms
59. a. 500 Hz   b. 1.0 A
61. a. 35 mH   b. 4.6 A
63. A
65. B

Part VI Problems

Answers to odd-numbered problems
1. B
3. C
5. C
7. A
9. B
11. C
13. C
15. D
17. B
19. C
21. 2.0 A, clockwise

Chapter 27

Answers to odd-numbered multiple-choice questions
21. B
23. E
25. C

Answers to odd-numbered problems
1. $v_{sound} = 345$ m/s, $v_{sprinter} = 15$ m/s
3. a. 15 m/s   b. 5 m/s
5. 30 s
7. 3.00×10^8 m/s
9. 3.00×10^8 m/s
11. $t_1 = 1.0\ \mu s$, $t_2 = 2.0\ \mu s$
13. She sees flash 2 40 μs after flash 1.
15. Barn 1.0 μs before tree.
17. 350 μs
19. a. 5.0 yr   b. 2.2 yr   c. 9.5 yr
21. $0.80c$
23. 1.5 km
25. a. $(1 - 5 \times 10^{-11})c = 0.99999999995c$ b. 100,000 yr
27. $0.357c$
29. $0.36c$
31. $0.80c$
33. $\dfrac{\sqrt{2}}{2}c$
35. a. 1.8×10^{16} J   b. 9.0×10^9
37. $\dfrac{2\sqrt{2}}{3}c$
39. $0.60c$
41. a. 90 m   b. $0.44c$
43. a. 23 μs b. 6.2 km
45. 670 ps
47. a. Less   b. 14 ns
49. In the muon's frame, the atmosphere is only 1.5 km thick.
51. 1400 s
53. a. $0.99973c$ b. 7.6×10^{22} J   c. 760 times
55. $0.71c$
57. 9.00 nm/s
59. a. $0.52c$ b. 1 h, 40 min
61. a. $v = (1 - 4.9 \times 10^{-24})c$ b. 46 nm
63. $0.31c$
65. 6.3×10^{-19} kg · m/s
67. a. 6660 MeV   b. 3.63 MeV
69. $0.786c$
71. a. 5.12×10^{-3} MeV   b. 9.39 MeV
73. a. 1.3×10^{17} kg   b. 6.7×10^{-12} %   c. 1.5×10^{13} yr
75. a. 3.6×10^{-12} J   b. 0.6%

77. D
79. D

Chapter 28

Answers to odd-numbered multiple-choice questions
27. B
29. A
31. B
33. D
35. A

Answers to odd-numbered problems
1. 42°
3. 69.3°
5. 4
7. 3.20 eV
9. 1.8 eV
11. a. 290 nm   b. 3.7×10^5 m/s
13. a. 6.63×10^5 m/s   b. 2.30 eV
15. 8.0×10^{-16} J
17. For $\lambda = 437$ nm, $E = 2.84$ eV; for $\lambda = 533$ nm, $E = 2.33$ eV; for $\lambda = 564$ nm, $E = 2.20$ eV
19. 0.57
21. 8.7×10^{31}
23. a. 2.3 eV   b. 3×10^{18}
25. 9.5×10^{-7} W
27. a. 1.1×10^{-34} m   b. 1.7×10^{-23} m/s
29. 1.5 eV
31. 8.2 MeV
33. 6.0×10^{-6} V
35. 0.43 nm
37. $E_1 = 1.3 \times 10^{-12}$ J; $E_2 = 5.3 \times 10^{-12}$ J; $E_3 = 1.2 \times 10^{-11}$ J
39. $\lambda = 830$ nm for the $n = 2$ to $n = 1$ transition
    $\lambda = 500$ nm for the $n = 3$ to $n = 2$ transition
    $\lambda = 310$ nm for the $n = 3$ to $n = 1$ transition
41. 4
43. 5.8 μm
45. No, somewhere in the interval -6 m/s $\leq v_x \leq 6$ m/s
47. 0.15 nm
49. a. 2.3 eV   b. 240 nm
51. 4.1 eV
53. a. 250 eV, x-ray region;   b. 0.060 eV
55. 1.4
57. 4.3×10^{15} photon/s
59. a. 1.7×10^{18} b. 1.7×10^{26} photons/s
61. 3.5×10^{28} photons
63. 12%
65. 0.97 mm
67. a. 3.88×10^{-12} m   b. 3.71×10^{-12} m
69. a. 2.0×10^{-63} J   b. 1.2×10^{-30} m/s
71. 1.4 nm
73. 1.09×10^{-9} m
75. a. $E_{min} = h^2/4mL^2$
    b. E_{min} for $n = 1$ and $\ell = 1$; $(5/2)E_{min}$ for $n = 1$, $\ell = 2$, and $n = 2$, $\ell = 1$; $4E_{min}$ for $n = 2$, $\ell = 2$; $5E_{min}$ for $n = 1$, $\ell = 3$, and $n = 3$, $\ell = 1$; $(13/2)E_{min}$ for $n = 2$, $\ell = 3$, and $n = 3$, $\ell = 2$
77. 18 fm
79. 19 T
81. C
83. B

Chapter 29

Answers to odd-numbered multiple-choice questions

23. B
25. C
27. C
29. D

Answers to odd-numbered problems

1. a.

Wavelength (nm)	m	n
656.6	2	3
486.3	2	4
434.2	2	5
410.3	2	6

   b. 397.1 nm
3. 1876 nm, 1282 nm, 1094 nm, infrared
5. a. 3 electrons, 4 protons, 5 neutrons
   b. 6 electrons, 6 protons, 6 neutrons
   c. 4 electrons, 7 protons, 8 neutrons
7. a. ^{8}Li   b. ^{14}C$^+$
9. a. Yes   b. 0.50 eV
11. 6.7×10^5 m/s, 1.1×10^6 m/s
13. 3
15. a. $a_B = \dfrac{4\pi\epsilon_0\hbar^2}{me^2}$ b. $E_1 = \dfrac{-e^2}{4\pi\epsilon_0(2a_B)}$
17. a. 0.332 nm, 0.665 nm, 0.997 nm   b. 0.332 nm = $(2\pi(0.053 \text{ nm}))/1$
   0.665 nm = $(2\pi(0.212 \text{ nm}))/2$ 0.997 nm = $(2\pi(0.476 \text{ nm}))/3$
   c.

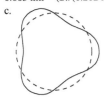

19. 97.26 nm, 486.3 nm, 1876 nm
21. $n = 1$: $\left(1, 0, 0, \pm\frac{1}{2}\right)$ $n = 2$: $\left(2, 0, 0, \pm\frac{1}{2}\right)$, $\left(2, 1, -1, \pm\frac{1}{2}\right)$,
   $\left(2, 1, 0, \pm\frac{1}{2}\right)$, $\left(2, 1, 1, \pm\frac{1}{2}\right)$ $n = 3$: $\left(3, 0, 0, \pm\frac{1}{2}\right)$, $\left(3, 1, -1, \pm\frac{1}{2}\right)$,
   $\left(3, 1, 0, \pm\frac{1}{2}\right)$, $\left(3, 1, 1, \pm\frac{1}{2}\right)$, $\left(3, 2, -2, \pm\frac{1}{2}\right)$, $\left(3, 2, -1, \pm\frac{1}{2}\right)$,
   $\left(3, 2, 0, \pm\frac{1}{2}\right)$, $\left(3, 2, 1, \pm\frac{1}{2}\right)$, $\left(3, 2, 2, \pm\frac{1}{2}\right)$
23. a. f b. -0.850 eV
25. -0.544 eV
27. $1s^2 2s^2 2p^6 3s^2 3p^2$, $1s^2 2s^2 2p^6 3s^2 3p^6 4s^2 3d^{10} 4p^2$,
   $1s^2 2s^2 2p^6 3s^2 3p^6 4s^2 3d^{10} 4p^6 5s^2 4d^{10} 5p^6 6s^2 4f^{14} 5d^{10} 6p^2$
29. a. Magnesium   b. Technetium
31. a. Can't have 8 electrons in a p state   b. Can't have 3 electrons in an s state
33. 4.86×10^6 m/s
35. 330 nm
37. a. Yes, 2180 nm   b. No, violates $\Delta l = 1$
39. 690 nm
41. 3.18×10^{15}
43. a. 1.7×10^{18} b. 1.7×10^{26} photons/s
45. a. 102.6 nm: $n = 3$, $m = 1$, 1876 nm: $n = 4$, $m = 3$
   b. Ultraviolet, infrared
47. a. 79, 79, 118,   b. 2.29×10^{17} kg/m^3 c. 2.01×10^{13}
49. 0.000000000058%, 99.999999999942%
51. a. 58 N   b. 4.7×10^{-35} N, no
53. 1.8×10^7 m/s
55. b. $\lambda_{41} = 200$ nm $\lambda_{31} = 300$ nm $\lambda_{21} = 500$ nm $\lambda_{42} = 333$ nm
   $\lambda_{43} = 600$ nm $\lambda_{32} = 750$ nm
57. 10
59. 91.18 nm
61. 1876 nm
63. 44200 m/s
65. $\sqrt{6}\hbar$
67. a. $6s - 5p$, $6s - 4p$, $6s - 3p$ b. 7290 nm, 1650 nm, 515 nm
69. 1.13×10^6 m/s
71.

Transition	a. Wavelength	b. Type	c. Absorption
$2p \to 2s$	670 nm	VIS	Yes
$3s \to 2p$	816 nm	IR	No
$3p \to 2s$	324 nm	UV	Yes
$3p \to 3s$	2696 nm	IR	No
$3d \to 2p$	611 nm	VIS	No
$3d \to 3p$	25 μm	IR	No
$4s \to 2p$	498 nm	VIS	No
$4s \to 3p$	2430 nm	IR	No

73. 2×10^{23} W/m^2
75. A
77. C

Chapter 30

Answers to odd-numbered multiple-choice questions

29. C
31. A
33. B
35. C

Answers to odd-numbered problems

1. a. 1 proton, 2 neutrons   b. 18 protons, 22 neutrons
   c. 20 protons, 20 neutrons   d. 94 protons, 145 neutrons
3. 6.94 u
5. a. ^{3}H: total is 8.48 MeV, per nucleon is 2.83 MeV
   b. ^{3}He: total is 7.72 MeV, per nucleon is 2.57 MeV
7. ^{3}He: 2.57 MeV, ^{4}He: 7.07 MeV, ^{4}He
9. a. ^{14}N: 7.48 MeV   b. ^{56}Fe: 8.79 MeV   c. ^{207}Pb: 7.87 MeV
11. ^{240}Pu: 7.56 MeV, ^{133}Xe: 8.41 MeV
13. ^{10}B is stable
15. ^{4}He, ^{12}C, ^{16}O
17. ^{234}U
19. a. ^{228}Th   b. ^{207}Tl   c. ^{7}Li   d. ^{60}Ni
21. 5.52 MeV
23. 1.50×10^{-4} u
25. a. 8.8×10^9 b. 2.7×10^9 c. 1.8×10^4
27. a. 3.3   b. 6.6
29. 17,000 yr
31. 80 d
33. 6.3 mCi
35. 4.0 mSv
37. 600 rad
39. 450 h
41. 2.0 Gy
43. 0.51 MeV
45. 0.391 MeV
47. ^{1}H: 99.985%, ^{2}H: 0.015%
49. 200 MeV
51. a. ^{17}N, ^{17}O   b. ^{17}O   c. ^{17}N decays by beta-minus decay to ^{17}O.
53. 2.7×10^{17}
55. a. 157 min   b. 29.5 h
57. 4.6×10^9
59. 210 million years
61. 5.9 billion years
63. 0.47 mSv
65. a. 4.5 kJ   b. 110 W   c. 1.4 K
67. 3.33×10^5 Gy

69. a. 2.6×10^{10} b. 24 mBq   c. 1.9×10^8 mSv   d. 64 million times greater than background level
71. A
73. C

Part VII Problems

Answers to odd-numbered problems

1. C
3. A
5. D
7. A
9. D
11. A
13. B
15. a. 1.1×10^{15} photons   b. 0.093 Sv
17. 0.00018

Credits

bottom right Shutterstock; **p. 545** Steve Horrell/Photo Researchers, Inc.; **p. 546 top** Todd Gipstein/Getty Images; **center and bottom** Richard Megna/Fundamental Photographs; **p. 547 top** Sciencephotos/Alamy; **bottom** David Parker/Photo Researchers, Inc.; **p. 551** Stuart Field; **p. 556 top** Andrew Syred/Photo Researchers; **bottom** Stuart Field; **p. 558 top** Andrew Bargery/Alamy; **bottom** Eric Schrader–Pearson Science; **p. 559 top** The Picture Source/Terry Oakley; **bottom** Edmund Optics; **p. 560 top** Sinclair Stammers/Photo Researchers, Inc.; **bottom** Richard Megna/Fundamental Photographs; **p. 562** Sabian Zigman; **p. 563** Ken Fay/Fundamental Photographs; **p. 566** NASA; **p. 571** Kim Taylor/Nature Picture Library; **p. 573 top** Tom Zagwodzki/Goddard Space Flight Center/NASA; **bottom left, right** Pete Vukusic, University of Exeter.

CHAPTER 18 **P. 574 top** Michael Kappeler/AFP/Getty Images; **center left to right** iStockphoto; Sciencephotos/Alamy; Leslie Garland Picture Library/Alamy; Shutterstock; Anya Levinson; **second from bottom right** David Maitland/Getty Images; **bottom left to right** Shutterstock; Piluhin/Alamy; Christopher O Driscoll/iStockphoto; **p. 576 top left** Onpoint Lasers, Inc.; **top middle left** Dynamic Graphics Group/IT Stock Free/Alamy; **top middle right** Mike Stone/Alamy; **top right** Paul Rapson/Alamy; **bottom** Stuart Field; **p. 577** Stuart Field; **p. 578 top** NASA; **bottom** Sylvester Allred/Fundamental Photographs; **p. 580** The Exploratorium; **p. 581** Creative Digital Visions; **p. 583 top** Canon; **bottom** Richard Megna/Fundamental Photographs; **p. 585 top** Pete Atkinson/Getty Images; **bottom** Custom Medical Stock Photography; **p. 586** Creative Digital Visions; **p. 587 both** Richard Megna/Fundamental Photographs; **p. 589** Creative Digital Visions; **p. 591** Photodisc Blue/Getty Images; **p. 594** Dr. Tamara Frank/Harbor Branch Oceanographic Institute at Florida Atlantic University; **p. 595** M.C. Escher's "Hand with Reflecting Sphere" ©2006 The M.C. Escher Company-Holland. All rights reserved. www.mcescher.com; **p. 596** Paul Silverman/Fundamental Photographs; **p. 601** Bajande/Photo Researchers, Inc.; **p. 603 top** AKG-Images; **bottom** Erich Lessing/Art Resource, NY; **p. 605 top** VStock/Alamy; **bottom** Nano Calvo/Alamy; **p. 607** Jason Horowitz/Corbis; **p. 608** David Hancock/Alamy.

CHAPTER 19 **P. 609 top** Juniors Bildarchiv/Alamy; **center left to right** Shutterstock; Judy Barranco/iStockphoto; Shutterstock; Richard Wainscoat/Alamy; **second from bottom middle** David Parker/SPL/Photo Researchers, Inc.; **bottom left to right** JupiterImages/Comstock Images/Alamy; Shutterstock; Springer-Verlag GmbH & Co KG; Sciencephotos/Alamy; **p. 610** Doug Perrine/Nature Photo Library; **p. 611 top** GardenWorld Images/Alamy; **bottom** NASA; **p. 612 top** Adam Black; **bottom** Richard Megna/Fundamental Photographs; **p. 614 top** Dynamic Graphics Group/IT Stock Free/Alamy; **bottom** Tetra Images/Alamy; **p. 617** Stuart Field; **p. 618** Stuart Field; **p. 619** Tetra Images/Alamy; **p. 620** Biophoto Associates/Photo Researchers, Inc.; **p. 621** NASA; **p. 625** NASA; **p. 626** Springer-Verlag GmbH & Co KG; **p. 627 left** James Cavallini/Photo Researchers, Inc.; **right** STEVE GSCHMEISSNER/Science Photo Library/Alamy; **p. 629** Shutterstock; **p. 631 top** Stuart Field; **bottom** Sam Ogden/Photo Researchers, Inc.; **p. 633** NASA; **p. 634** Alfred Pasieka/Photo Researchers, Inc.; **p. 635** NASA; **p. 637** Michael W. Davidson at Molecular Expressions; **p. 639** Jessica Riser.

PART VI **P. 640** Nonoy Tan/Alamy.

CHAPTER 20 **P. 642 top** Pacific Northwest National Laboratory; **center left** Andrew Lambert Photography/Photo Researchers, Inc.; **center middle** Eric Schrader–Pearson Science; **center right** Luminant Corporation; **bottom right** Susuma Nishinaga/Photo Researchers, Inc.; **p. 643** Creative Digital Visions; **p. 645** Creative Digital Visions; **p. 646** Allan Lee; **p. 648 top** Charles D. Winters/Photo Researchers, Inc.; **bottom** Steve Hopkin/Getty Images; **p. 652** Science Pictures Limited/Photo Researchers; **p. 655** Richard Megna/Fundamental Photographs; **p. 663 top** Brian Jones; **bottom** Reinhard H/Photolibrary; **p. 669** David Lassman/The Image Works.

CHAPTER 21 **P. 675 top** Image courtesy of the Scientific Computing and Imaging (SCI) Institute, University of Utah; **center left** MvH/iStockphoto; **center middle** Shutterstock; **center right** Photo Researchers, Inc.; **bottom left** Shutterstock; **p. 679 top** Aaron Horowitz/Corbis; **bottom** Ingram Publishing/Alamy; **p. 680 left** Stuart Field; **right** Jurg Streit/University of Bern; **p. 682** Creative Digital Visions; **p. 683** Varian Medical Systems; **p. 692** Jonathan Bird/Peter Arnold/Alamy; **p. 693** Paul Silverman/Fundamental Photographs; **p. 695 top** Lester Lefkowitz/Corbis; **bottom** Creative Digital Visions; **p. 697** Helmut Foll; **p. 699** Andrew Lambert/Alamy; **p. 700 top** Dimitri Vervits/Getty Images; **bottom** SPL/Photo Researchers, Inc.; **p. 702** NASA.

CHAPTER 22 **P. 712 top** May/Photo Researchers, Inc.; **center left** Creative Digital Visions; **center right** Creative Digital Visions; **bottom left** Fotolia; **bottom middle** iStockphoto; **bottom right** Fotolia; **p. 714** FLIR Systems, Inc. **p. 718** Brian Jones; **p. 719** Peter Scoones/Nature Picture Library; **p. 722** Dennia O'Clair/Getty Images; **p. 723** Dr. Jennifer L. Mueller; **p. 725 left** Charles Bowman/Alamy; **middle** Igor Sinicin/iStockphoto; **right** Brian Jones; **right, inset** Shutterstock; **p. 728** Brian Jones; **p. 735** Oxford Scientific/Photolibrary.

CHAPTER 23 **P. 739 top** Amazon Images/Alamy; **center left** Krzysztof Zmij/iStockphoto; **center middle** Franc Podgor˘sek/iStockphoto; **center right** Photos.com; **bottom left** Ace Stock Limited/Alamy; **bottom right** CNRI/Photo Researchers, Inc.; **p. 745** Dynamic Graphics Group/IT Stock Free/Alamy; **p. 747** Abelstock/Alamy; **p. 749 top** Cn Boon/Alamy; **bottom** Simon Fraser/Photo Researchers, Inc.; **p. 751** Bill Nicholson/Alamy; **p. 755** Creative Digital Visions; **p. 757** Eric Schrader–Pearson Science; **p. 758 top** SPL/Photo Researchers, Inc.; **bottom** Don W. Fawcett/Photo Researchers, Inc.; **p. 762** Stephane De Sakutin/AFP/Getty Images; **p. 763** STEVE GSCHMEISSNER/Science Photo Library/Alamy; **p. 764** SPL/Photo Researchers, Inc.

CHAPTER 24 **P. 776 top** Thierry Berrod/Mona Lisa Production/SPL/Photo Researchers, Inc.; **center left** Daniel Dempster Photography/Alamy; **center middle** Roman Krochuk/iStockphoto; **center right** Shutterstock; **bottom left** John Eisele; **bottom middle left** Urban Zone/Alamy; **bottom middle right** Pete Saloutos/Corbis RF/Alamy; **bottom right** Photos.com; **p. 779** John Eisele, Colorado State University Photography; **p. 780 top and bottom right** John Eisele, Colorado State University Photography; **bottom left** Brian Jones; **p. 781** IBM Corporation; **p. 782** John Eisele; **p. 787** Kathleen Gustafson, Ph.D., Hoglund Brain Imaging Center, University of Kansas, VSM Medtech, Ltd.; **p. 789** Charles Thatcher/Getty Images; **p. 793** Chris Madeley/Photo Researchers, Inc.; **p. 795 top** Marsh-McBirney/Hach Company; **bottom** Stuart Field; **p. 798** Prof. Brian James/Wikipedia.org; **p. 802** UHB Trust/Getty Images; **p. 804** Atsushi Arakaki et al., "Formation of magnetite by bacteria and its application," *J R Soc Interface*. 2008 September 6; 5(26): 977–999; **p. 805 top** John Eisele; **bottom** Andrew Lambert Photography/Photo Researchers, Inc.; **p. 809** 1m gradiometer results were obtained using the Bartington Grad601-2 gradiometer, courtesy of Bartington Instruments Ltd.

CHAPTER 25 **P. 816 top** Andrew Davidhazy; **center left** Richard Wheeler/Wikipedia.org; **center middle** Shutterstock; **center right** Palm, Inc.; **bottom left** Photo Researchers, Inc.; **bottom middle left** iStockphoto; **bottom middle right** Fotolia; **bottom right** iStockphoto; **p. 817** Scott McAlpine/British Columbia Institute of Technology; **p. 818** NASA; **p. 819** James Watt/Alamy; **p. 821** Eric Schrader–Pearson Science; **p. 826** James Leynse/CORBIS; **p. 828 left** Brian Jones; **right** Creative Digital Visions; **p. 830** SSPL/The Image Works; **p. 832** Tony Craddock/Photo Researchers, Inc.; **p. 833** Richard Megna/Fundamental Photographs; **p. 834 top** Innerspace Imaging/Photo Researchers, Inc.; **bottom** Brian Jones; **p. 835** Eugene Hecht, Optics 2e, p. 11, Addison Wesley; **p. 837** Brian Jones; **p. 838** Brian Jones; **p. 839 top** Ashok Captain/Alamy; **bottom** Edward Kinsman/Photo Researchers, Inc.; **p. 841 top left** NASA/JPL-Caltech/J. Keene (SSC/Caltech); **top right** NOAA; **bottom left** NASA; **bottom right** Jack O. Burns (University of Missouri) & David Clarke (St. Mary's University, Nova Scotia); **p. 845** Brian Jones; **p. 846** Dennis Nett/The Image Works.

CHAPTER 26 **P. 852 top** Duncan Usher/Alamy; **center left** Photo Researchers, Inc.; **center right** Shutterstock; **second from bottom left** Christoforos Giatzakis/Alamy; **bottom left** iStockphoto; **bottom middle** Photos.com; **bottom right** Johnny Greig RFSL/Alamy; **p. 853** Creative Digital Visions; **p. 855** iStockphoto; **p. 856 top** Eric Schrader–Pearson Science; **bottom** Creative Digital Visions; **p. 860 top** Pearson Education/PH College; **bottom** Brian Jones; **p. 861 top** Shutterstock; **bottom** Paul A. Souders/Corbis; **p. 862** Creative Digital Visions; **p. 863** Phil Degginger/Alamy; **p. 864** ViennaPhoto/Alamy; **p. 866** Eric Schrader–Pearson Science; **p. 867** Shutterstock; **p. 868** Kevin Eldredge; **p. 870** Pacific Northwest National Laboratory; **p. 879** Steve Sant/Alamy.

Index

Astronomical Data

Planetary body	Mean distance from sun (m)	Period (years)	Mass (kg)	Mean radius (m)
Sun	—	—	1.99×10^{30}	6.96×10^8
Moon	3.84×10^8*	27.3 days	7.36×10^{22}	1.74×10^6
Mercury	5.79×10^{10}	0.241	3.18×10^{23}	2.43×10^6
Venus	1.08×10^{11}	0.615	4.88×10^{24}	6.06×10^6
Earth	1.50×10^{11}	1.00	5.98×10^{24}	6.37×10^6
Mars	2.28×10^{11}	1.88	6.42×10^{23}	3.37×10^6
Jupiter	7.78×10^{11}	11.9	1.90×10^{27}	6.99×10^7
Saturn	1.43×10^{12}	29.5	5.68×10^{26}	5.85×10^7
Uranus	2.87×10^{12}	84.0	8.68×10^{25}	2.33×10^7
Neptune	4.50×10^{12}	165	1.03×10^{26}	2.21×10^7

*Distance from earth

Typical Coefficients of Friction

Material	Static μ_s	Kinetic μ_k	Rolling μ_r
Rubber on concrete	1.00	0.80	0.02
Steel on steel (dry)	0.80	0.60	0.002
Steel on steel (lubricated)	0.10	0.05	
Wood on wood	0.50	0.20	
Wood on snow	0.12	0.06	
Ice on ice	0.10	0.03	

Melting/Boiling Temperatures, Heats of Transformation

Substance	T_m (°C)	L_f (J/kg)	T_b (°C)	L_v (J/kg)
Water	0	3.33×10^5	100	22.6×10^5
Nitrogen (N_2)	−210	0.26×10^5	−196	1.99×10^5
Ethyl alcohol	−114	1.09×10^5	78	8.79×10^5
Mercury	−39	0.11×10^5	357	2.96×10^5
Lead	328	0.25×10^5	1750	8.58×10^5

Properties of Materials

Substance	ρ (kg/m³)	c (J/kg · K)	v_{sound} (m/s)
Helium gas (1 atm, 20°C)	0.166		1010
Air (1 atm, 0°C)	1.28		331
Air (1 atm, 20°C)	1.20		343
Ethyl alcohol	790	2400	1170
Gasoline	680		
Glycerin	1260		
Mercury	13,600	140	1450
Oil (typical)	900		
Water ice	920	2090	3500
Liquid water	1000	4190	1480
Seawater	1030		1500
Blood	1060		
Muscle	1040	3600	
Fat	920	3000	
Mammalian body	1005	3400	1540
Granite	2750	790	6000
Aluminum	2700	900	5100
Copper	8920	385	
Gold	19,300	129	
Iron	7870	449	
Lead	11,300	128	1200
Diamond	3520	510	12,000
Osmium	22,610		